Pearson New International Edition

Earth
An Introduction to Physical Geology
E.J. Tarbuck   F.K. Lutgens   D.G. Tasa
Eleventh Edition

PEARSON®

Pearson Education Limited
Edinburgh Gate
Harlow
Essex CM20 2JE
England and Associated Companies throughout the world

Visit us on the World Wide Web at: www.pearsoned.co.uk

© Pearson Education Limited 2014

 ISBN 10: 1-292-02094-6
ISBN 13: 978-1-292-02094-5

British Library Cataloguing-in-Publication Data
A catalogue record for this book is available from the British Library

ARP impression 98

Printed in Great Britain by Ashford Colour Press Ltd.

Table of Contents

An Introduction to Geology

From Chapter 1 of *Earth: An Introduction to Physical Geology*, Eleventh Edition. Edward J. Tarbuck, Frederick K. Lutgens, Dennis Tasa.

An Introduction to Geology

Rafting the Colorado River in Arizona's Marble Canyon.
(Photo by Michael Collier)

Each statement represents the primary learning objective for the corresponding major heading within the chapter. After you complete the chapter you should be able to:

1 Distinguish between physical and historical geology and describe the connections between people and geology.

2 Summarize early and modern views on how change occurs on Earth and relate them to the prevailing ideas about the age of Earth.

3 Discuss the nature of scientific inquiry, including the construction of hypotheses and the development of theories.

4 List and describe Earth's four major spheres.

5 Define *system* and explain why Earth is considered to be a system.

6 Outline the stages in the formation of our solar system.

7 Describe Earth's internal structure.

8 Sketch, label, and explain the rock cycle.

9 List and describe the major features of the continents and ocean basins.

Bryce Canyon in southern Utah. Rocks contain information about the processes that produce them. (Photo by Michael Collier)

The spectacular eruption of a volcano, the terror brought by an earthquake, the magnificent scenery of a mountain range, and the destruction created by a landslide or flood are all subjects for the geologist. The study of geology deals with many fascinating and practical questions about our physical environment. What forces produce mountains? Will there soon be a major earthquake in California? What was the Ice Age like, and will there be another? How were ore deposits formed? Where should we look for water? Will plentiful oil be found if a well is drilled in a particular location? Geologists seek to answer these and many other questions about Earth, its history, and its resources.

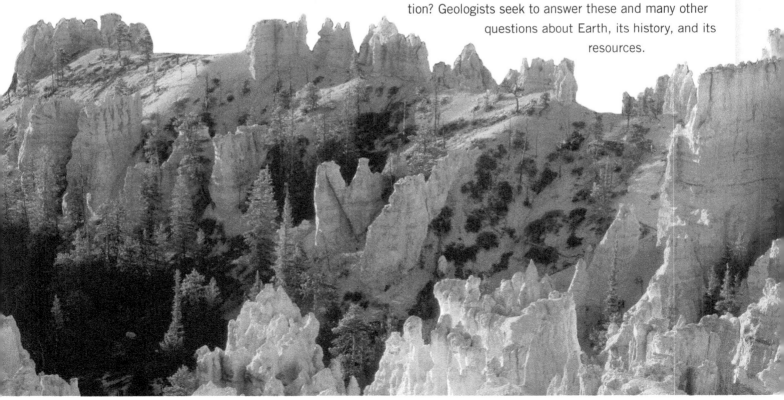

1 Geology: The Science of Earth

The subject of this text is **geology**, from the Greek *geo* (Earth) and *logos* (discourse). Geology is the science that pursues an understanding of planet Earth. Understanding Earth is challenging because our planet is a dynamic body with many interacting parts and a complex history. Throughout its long existence, Earth has been changing. In fact, it is changing as you read this page and will continue to do so into the foreseeable future. Sometimes the changes are rapid and violent, as when landslides or volcanic eruptions occur. Just as often, change takes place so slowly that it goes unnoticed during a lifetime. Scales of size and space also vary greatly among the phenomena that geologists study. Sometimes geologists must focus on phenomena that are submicroscopic, and at other times they must deal with features that are continental or global in scale.

Physical and Historical Geology

Geology is traditionally divided into two broad areas—physical and historical. **Physical geology**, which is the primary focus of this text, examines the materials composing Earth and seeks to understand the many processes that operate beneath and upon its surface (FIGURE 1). The aim of **historical geology**, on the other hand, is to understand the origin of Earth and its development through time. Thus, it strives to establish an orderly chronological arrangement of the multitude of physical and biological changes that have occurred in the geologic past. The study of physical geology logically precedes the study of Earth history because we must first understand how Earth works before we attempt to unravel its past. It should also be pointed out that physical and historical geology are divided into many areas of specialization.

Geology is perceived as a science that is done outdoors—and rightly so. A great deal of geology is based on observations, measurements, and experiments conducted in the field. But geology is also done in the laboratory where, for example, the analysis of minerals and rocks provides insights into many basic processes and the microscopic study of fossils unlocks clues to past environments (FIGURE 2). Frequently, geology requires an understanding and application of knowledge and principles from physics, chemistry, and biology. Geology is a science that seeks to expand our knowledge of the natural world and our place in it.

Geology, People, and the Environment

The primary focus of this text is to develop an understanding of basic geologic principles, but along the way we will explore numerous important relationships between people

Internal processes are those that occur beneath Earth's surface. Sometimes they lead to the formation of major features at the surface.

A.

External processes, such as landslides, rivers, and glaciers, erode and sculpt surface features. This glacier is shaping mountains in Alaska.

B.

FIGURE 1 Internal and external processes
The processes that operate beneath and upon Earth's surface are an important focus of physical geology. (Volcano photo by Lucas Jackson/Reuters; glacier photo by Michael Collier)

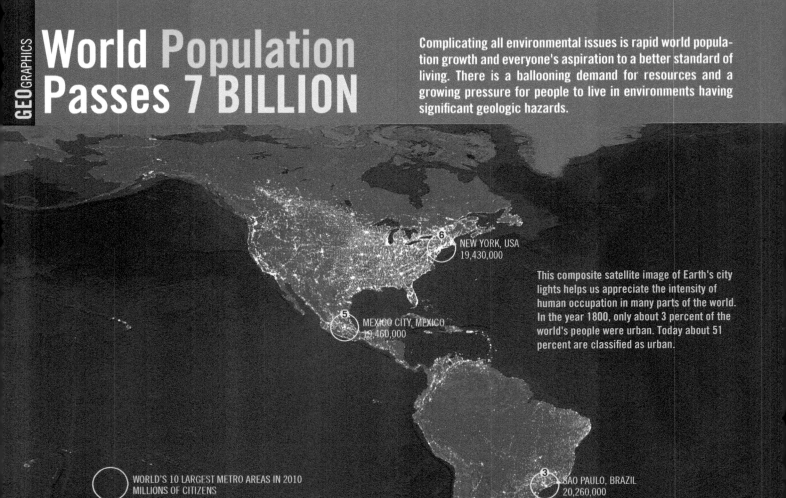

World Population Passes 7 BILLION

Complicating all environmental issues is rapid world population growth and everyone's aspiration to a better standard of living. There is a ballooning demand for resources and a growing pressure for people to live in environments having significant geologic hazards.

6 NEW YORK, USA
19,430,000

This composite satellite image of Earth's city lights helps us appreciate the intensity of human occupation in many parts of the world. In the year 1800, only about 3 percent of the world's people were urban. Today about 51 percent are classified as urban.

5 MEXICO CITY, MEXICO
19,460,000

WORLD'S 10 LARGEST METRO AREAS IN 2010
MILLIONS OF CITIZENS

3 SAO PAULO, BRAZIL
20,260,000

FIGURE 2 In the field and in the lab
Geology not only involves outdoor fieldwork but work in the laboratory as well.
(Photo by British Antarctic Survey/ Photo Researchers, Inc.)

This paleontologist is collecting fossils in Antarctica. Later, a detailed analysis will occur in the lab.

and the natural environment. Many of the problems and issues addressed by geology are of practical value to people.

Natural hazards are a part of living on Earth. Every day they adversely affect millions of people worldwide and are responsible for staggering damages (FIGURE 3). Among the hazardous Earth processes that geologists study are volcanoes, floods, tsunamis, earthquakes, and landslides. Of course, geologic hazards are *natural* processes. They become hazards only when people try to live where these processes occur.

According to the United Nations, in 2008, for the first

WORLD POPULATION MILESTONES
Growth of population 1800-2011 and projected to 2025

– – *projection

WORLD POPULATION IN BILLIONS

1800
1 BILLION

1927
2 BILLION

1960
3 BILLION

1974
4 BILLION

1987
5 BILLION

1999
6 BILLION

2011
7 BILLION

2025*
8 BILLION

1800   1850   1900   1950   2000   YEAR

KARACHI, PAKISTAN
13,120,000

DELHI, INDIA
22,160,000

SHANGHAI, CHINA
16,580,000

TOKYO, JAPAN
36,670,000

MUMBAI, INDIA
20,400,000

DHAKA, BANGLADESH
14,650,000

KOLKATA, INDIA
15,550,000

It took until about the year 1800 for world population to reach 1 billion people. By 1927, the number doubled to 2 billion. According to U.N. estimates, world population reached 7 billion in late October 2011. We are currently adding 80 million people per year to the planet.

NASA

time, more people lived in cities than in rural areas. This global trend toward urbanization concentrates millions of people into megacities, many of which are vulnerable to natural hazards. Coastal sites are becoming more vulnerable because development often destroys natural defenses such as wetlands and sand dunes. In addition, there is a growing threat associated with human influences on the Earth system; one example is sea-level rise that is linked to global climate change. Some megacities are exposed to seismic (earthquake) and volcanic hazards where inappropriate land use and poor construction

A massive earthquake in March 2011, created a tsunami that devastated a portion of coastal Japan.

FIGURE 3 Earthquake destruction
Geologic hazards are natural processes. They only become hazards when people try to live where these processes occur.
(Photo by Yasuyoshi Chiba/AFP/ Getty Images/Newscom)

7

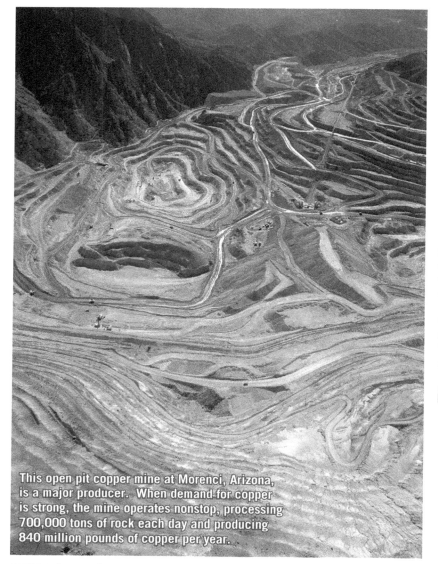

This open pit copper mine at Morenci, Arizona, is a major producer. When demand for copper is strong, the mine operates nonstop, processing 700,000 tons of rock each day and producing 840 million pounds of copper per year.

FIGURE 4 Copper mine
Resources represent an important link between people and geology. (Photo by Michael Collier)

practices, coupled with rapid population growth, are increasing vulnerability.

Resources represent another important focus of geology that is of great practical value to people. They include water and soil, a great variety of metallic and nonmetallic minerals, and energy (FIGURE 4). Together they form the very foundation of modern civilization. Geology deals not only with the formation and occurrence of these vital resources but also with maintaining supplies and with the environmental impact of their extraction and use.

Geologic processes clearly have an impact on people. In addition, we humans can dramatically influence geologic processes. For example, river flooding is natural, but the magnitude and frequency of flooding can be changed significantly by human activities such as clearing forests, building cities, and constructing dams. Unfortunately, natural systems do not always adjust to artificial changes in ways that we can anticipate. Thus, an alteration to the environment that was intended to benefit society often has the opposite effect.

At appropriate places throughout this text, you will have an opportunity to examine different aspects of our relationship with the physical environment. This includes natural hazards, environmental issues, or resources.

1 CONCEPT CHECKS

1. Name and distinguish between the two broad subdivisions of geology.
2. List at least three different geologic hazards.
3. Aside from geologic hazards, describe another important connection between people and geology.

2 The Development of Geology

The nature of our Earth—its materials and processes—has been a focus of study for centuries. Writings about such topics as fossils, gems, earthquakes, and volcanoes date back to the early Greeks, more than 2300 years ago.

Certainly the most influential Greek philosopher was Aristotle. Unfortunately, Aristotle's explanations about the natural world were not based on keen observations and experiments. Instead, they were arbitrary pronouncements. He believed that rocks were created under the "influence" of the stars and that earthquakes occurred when air crowded into the ground, was heated by central fires, and escaped explosively. When confronted with a fossil fish, he explained that "a great many fishes live in the earth motionless and are found when excavations are made." Although Aristotle's explanations may have been adequate for his day, they unfortunately continued to be viewed as authoritative for many centuries, thus inhibiting the acceptance of more up-to-date ideas. After the Renaissance of the 1500s, however, more people became interested in finding answers to questions about Earth.

Catastrophism

In the mid-1600s, James Ussher, Anglican Archbishop of Armagh, Primate of all Ireland, published a major work that had immediate and profound influences. A respected scholar of the Bible, Ussher constructed a chronology of human and Earth history in which he calculated that Earth was only a few thousand years old, having been created in 4004 B.C. Ussher's treatise earned widespread acceptance among Europe's scientific and religious leaders, and his chronology was soon printed in the margins of the Bible itself.

During the seventeenth and eighteenth centuries, Western thought about Earth's features and processes was strongly influenced by Ussher's calculation. The result was a guiding doctrine called **catastrophism**. Catastrophists believed that Earth's landscapes were shaped primarily by great catastrophes. Features such as mountains and canyons, which today we know take great spans of time to form, were explained as having been produced by sudden and often worldwide disasters produced by unknowable causes that no longer operate. This philosophy was an attempt to fit the rates of Earth processes to the then-current ideas on the age of Earth.

The Birth of Modern Geology

Against the backdrop of Aristotle's views and an Earth created in 4004 B.C., a Scottish physician and gentleman farmer named James Hutton published *Theory of the Earth* in 1795. In this work, Hutton put forth a fundamental principle that is a pillar of geology today: **uniformitarianism**. It states that the *physical, chemical, and biological laws that operate today have also operated in the geologic past.* This means that the forces and processes that we observe presently shaping our planet have been at work for a very long time. Thus, to understand ancient rocks, we must first understand present-day processes and their results. This idea is commonly stated as *the present is the key to the past.*

Prior to Hutton's *Theory of the Earth*, no one had effectively demonstrated that geologic processes occur over extremely long periods of time. However, Hutton persuasively argued that forces that appear small can, over long spans of time, produce effects that are just as great as those resulting from sudden catastrophic events. Unlike his predecessors, Hutton carefully cited verifiable observations to support his ideas.

For example, when Hutton argued that mountains are sculpted and ultimately destroyed by weathering and the work of running water and that their wastes are carried to the oceans by processes that can be observed, Hutton said, "We have a chain of facts which clearly demonstrate . . . that the materials of the wasted mountains have traveled through the rivers"; and further, "There is not one step in all this progress . . . that is not to be actually perceived." He then went on to summarize this thought by asking a question and immediately providing the answer: "What more can we require? Nothing but time."

Geology Today

Today the basic tenets of uniformitarianism are just as viable as in Hutton's day. Indeed, today we realize more strongly than ever before that the present gives us insight into the past and that the physical, chemical, and biological laws that govern geologic processes remain unchanging through time. However, we also understand that the doctrine should not be taken too literally. To say that geologic processes in the past were the same as those occurring today is not to suggest that they always had the same relative importance or that they operated at precisely the same rate. Moreover, some important geologic processes are not currently observable, but evidence that they occur is well established. For example, we know that Earth has experienced impacts from large

FIGURE 5 Earth history—written in the rocks
The Grand Canyon of the Colorado River in northern Arizona. (Photo by Dennis Tasa)

Grand Canyon rocks span about 1.5 billion years of Earth history.

The uppermost layer, the Kaibab Formation, is about 250 million years old.

Rocks at the bottom are nearly 2 billion years old.

EYE on Earth

These rock layers consist of sediments such as sand, mud, and gravel that were deposited by rivers, waves, wind, and glaciers. The material was buried and eventually compacted and cemented into solid rock. Later, erosion uncovered the layers. (Photo by David Carriere/AGE Fotostock)

Question 1 Can you establish a relative time scale for these rocks? That is, can you determine which one of the layers shown here is likely oldest and which is probably youngest?

Question 2 Explain the logic you used.

meteorites even though we have no human witness accounts of those impacts. Nevertheless, such events have altered Earth's crust, modified its climate, and strongly influenced life on the planet.

The acceptance of uniformitarianism meant the acceptance of a very long history for Earth. Although Earth processes vary in intensity, they still take a very long time to create or destroy major landscape features. The Grand Canyon provides a good example (FIGURE 5).

The rock record contains evidence which shows that Earth has experienced many cycles of mountain building and erosion. Concerning the ever-changing nature of Earth through great expanses of geologic time, Hutton made a statement that was to become his most famous. In concluding his classic 1788 paper published in the *Transactions of the Royal Society of Edinburgh*, he stated, "The results, therefore, of our present enquiry is, that we find no vestige of a beginning—no prospect of an end."

It is important to remember that, although many features of our physical landscape may seem to be unchanging over the decades we observe them, they are nevertheless changing—but on time scales of hundreds, thousands, or even many millions of years.

The Magnitude of Geologic Time

Among geology's important contributions to human knowledge is the discovery that Earth has a very long and complex history. Although Hutton and others

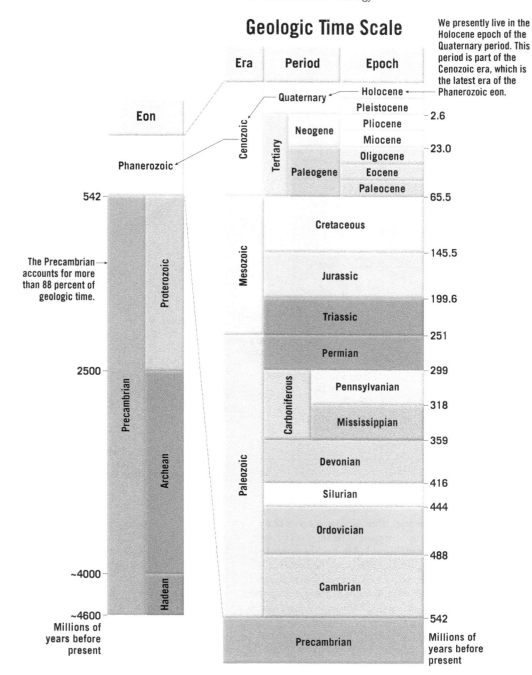

Geologic Time Scale

We presently live in the Holocene epoch of the Quaternary period. This period is part of the Cenozoic era, which is the latest era of the Phanerozoic eon.

Era	Period	Epoch	
	Quaternary	Holocene	
		Pleistocene	
	Neogene	Pliocene	2.6
Cenozoic		Miocene	
		Oligocene	23.0
	Paleogene	Eocene	
		Paleocene	
			65.5
Mesozoic	Cretaceous		
			145.5
	Jurassic		
			199.6
	Triassic		
			251
	Permian		
			299
Paleozoic	Carboniferous	Pennsylvanian	
			318
		Mississippian	
			359
	Devonian		
			416
	Silurian		444
	Ordovician		
			488
	Cambrian		
			542
	Precambrian		

Eon

Phanerozoic

542

The Precambrian accounts for more than 88 percent of geologic time.

Proterozoic

2500

Precambrian

Archean

~4000

Hadean

~4600

Millions of years before present

Millions of years before present

FIGURE 6 Geologic time scale: a basic reference The geologic time scale divides the vast 4.6-billion-year history of Earth into eons, eras, periods, and epochs. Numbers on the time scale represent time in millions of years before the present.

recognized that geologic time is exceedingly long, they had no methods to accurately determine the age of Earth. Early time scales simply placed the events of Earth history in the proper sequence or order, without knowledge of how long ago in years they occurred.

Today our understanding of radioactivity allows us to accurately determine numerical dates for rocks that represent important events in Earth's distant past (FIGURE 6). For example, we know that the dinosaurs died out about 65 million years ago. Today the age of Earth is put at about 4.6 billion years.

SMARTFIGURE 7
Magnitude of geologic time

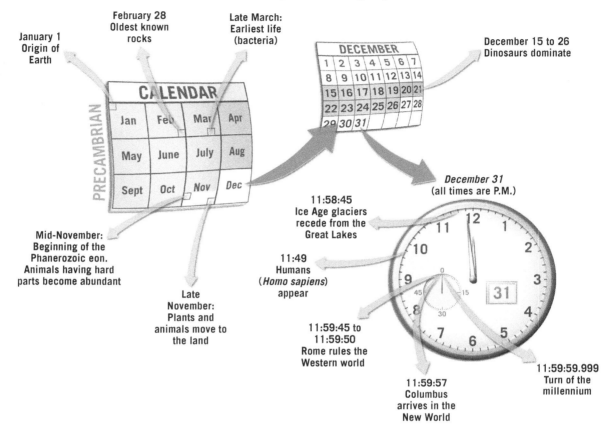

What if we compress the 4.6 billion years of Earth history into a single year?

SMARTFIGURE 7
Magnitude of geologic time

Figure 7 Magnitude of geologic time

The concept of geologic time is new to many non-geologists. People are accustomed to dealing with increments of time that are measured in hours, days, weeks, and years. Our history books often examine events over spans of centuries, but even a century is difficult to appreciate fully. For most of us, someone or something that is 90 years old is *very old*, and a 1000-year-old artifact is *ancient.*

By contrast, those who study geology must routinely deal with vast time periods—millions or billions (thousands of millions) of years. When viewed in the context of Earth's 4.6-billion-year history, a geologic event that occurred 100 million years ago may be characterized as "recent" by a geologist, and a rock sample that has been dated at 10 million years may be called "young." An appreciation for the magnitude of geologic time is important in the study of geology because many processes are so gradual that vast spans of time are needed before significant changes occur. How long is 4.6 billion years? If you were to begin counting at the rate of one number per

second and continued 24 hours a day, 7 days a week and never stopped, it would take about two lifetimes (150 years) to reach 4.6 billion! FIGURE 7 provides another interesting way of viewing the expanse of geologic time.

The foregoing is just one of many analogies that have been conceived in an attempt to convey the magnitude of geologic time. Although helpful, all of them, no matter how clever, only begin to help us comprehend the vast expanse of Earth history.

2 CONCEPT CHECKS

1. Describe Aristotle's influence on geology.
2. Contrast catastrophism and uniformitarianism. How did each view the age of Earth?
3. How old is Earth?
4. Why is an understanding of the magnitude of geologic time important for a geologist?

3 The Nature of Scientific Inquiry

As members of a modern society, we are constantly reminded of the benefits derived from science. But what exactly is the nature of scientific inquiry? Science is a process of producing knowledge. The process depends both on making careful observations and on creating explanations that make sense of the observations. Developing an understanding of how science is done and how scientists work is an important theme that appears throughout this text. You will explore the difficulties in gathering data and some of the ingenious methods that have been developed to overcome these difficulties. You will also see many examples of how hypotheses are formulated and tested, as well as learn about the evolution and development of some major scientific theories.

All science is based on the assumption that the natural world behaves in a consistent and predictable manner that is comprehensible through careful, systematic study. The overall goal of science is to discover the underlying patterns in nature and then to use this knowledge to make predictions about what should or should not be expected, given certain facts or circumstances. For example, by knowing how oil deposits form, geologists are able to predict the most favorable sites for exploration and, perhaps as importantly, how to avoid regions that have little or no potential.

The development of new scientific knowledge involves some basic logical processes that are universally accepted. To determine what is occurring in the natural world, scientists collect scientific facts through observation and measurement (FIGURE 8). The facts that are collected often seek to answer well-defined questions about the natural world. Because some error is inevitable, the accuracy of a particular measurement or observation is always open to question. Nevertheless, these data are essential to science and serve as a springboard for the development of scientific theories.

Hypothesis

Once facts have been gathered and principles have been formulated to describe a natural phenomenon, investigators try to explain how or why things happen in the manner observed. They often do this by constructing a tentative (or untested) explanation, which is called a scientific **hypothesis**. It is best if an investigator can formulate more than one hypothesis to explain a given set of observations. If an individual scientist is unable to devise multiple hypotheses, others in the scientific community will almost always develop alternative explanations. A spirited debate frequently ensues. As a result, extensive research is conducted by proponents of opposing hypotheses, and the results are made available to the wider scientific community in scientific journals.

Before a hypothesis can become an accepted part of scientific knowledge, it must pass objective testing and analysis. If a hypothesis cannot be tested, it is not scientifically useful, no matter how interesting it might seem. The

verification process requires that *predictions* be made, based on the hypothesis being considered, and that the predictions be tested through comparison against objective observations of nature. Put another way, hypotheses must fit observations other than those used to formulate them in the first place. Hypotheses that fail rigorous testing are ultimately discarded. The history of science is littered with discarded hypotheses. One of the best known is the Earth-centered model of the universe—a proposal that was supported by the apparent daily motion of the Sun, Moon, and

FIGURE 8 Observation and measurement
Scientific facts are gathered in many ways. (Satellite image by NASA)

Instruments aboard satellites provide detailed information about the movement of Antarctica's Lambert Glacier. Such data are basic to understanding glacier behavior.

Ice Velocity (m/year)
0   200   400   600   800   1000   1200

Paleontologists study ancient life. These scientists are excavating the remains of *Albertosaurus*, a large carnivorous dinosaur.
Richard T. Nowitz/Science Source

stars around Earth. As the mathematician Jacob Bronowski so ably stated, "Science is a great many things, but in the end they all return to this: Science is the acceptance of what works and the rejection of what does not."

Theory

When a hypothesis has survived extensive scrutiny and when competing hypotheses have been eliminated, a hypothesis may be elevated to the status of a scientific **theory**. In everyday language, we may say, "That's only a theory." But a scientific theory is a well-tested and widely accepted view that the scientific community agrees best explains certain observable facts. Some theories that are extensively documented and extremely well supported are comprehensive in scope. For example, the theory of plate tectonics provides a framework for understanding the origin of mountains, earthquakes, and volcanic activity. In addition, plate tectonics explains the evolution of the continents and the ocean basins through time.

Scientific Methods

The process just described, in which researchers gather facts through observations and formulate scientific hypotheses and theories, is called the *scientific method*. Contrary to popular belief, the scientific method is not a standard recipe that scientists apply in a routine manner to unravel the secrets of our natural world. Rather, it is an endeavor that involves creativity and insight. Rutherford and Ahlgren put it this way: "Inventing hypotheses or theories to imagine how the world works and then figuring out how they can be put to the test of reality is as creative as writing poetry, composing music, or designing skyscrapers."*

There is not a fixed path that scientists always follow that leads unerringly to scientific knowledge. However, many scientific investigations involve the following:

- A question is raised about the natural world.
- Scientific data that relate to the question are collected.
- Questions that relate to the data are posed, and one or more working hypotheses are developed that may answer these questions.
- Observations and experiments are developed to test the hypotheses.
- The hypotheses are accepted, modified, or rejected, based on extensive testing.
- Data and results are shared with the scientific community for critical examination and further testing.

Some scientific discoveries result from purely theoretical ideas that stand up to extensive examination. Some researchers use high-speed computers to create models that simulate what is happening in the "real"

world. These models are useful when dealing with natural processes that occur on very long time scales or that take place in extreme or inaccessible locations. Still other scientific advancements are made when a totally unexpected happening occurs during an experiment. These serendipitous discoveries are more than pure luck, for as Louis Pasteur said, "In the field of observation, chance favors only the prepared mind."

Scientific knowledge is acquired through several avenues, so it might be best to describe the nature of scientific inquiry as the methods of science rather than as the scientific method. In addition, it should always be remembered that even the most compelling scientific theories are still simplified explanations of the natural world.

Plate Tectonics and Scientific Inquiry

There are many opportunities in the pages of this text to develop and reinforce your understanding of how science works and, in particular, how the science of geology works. You will learn about the methods involved in gathering data and develop a sense of the observational techniques and reasoning processes used by geologists.

During the past several decades, a great deal has been learned about the workings of our dynamic planet. This period has seen an unequaled revolution in our understanding of Earth. The revolution began in the early part of the twentieth century, with the radical proposal of *continental drift*—the idea that the continents moved about the face of the planet. This hypothesis contradicted the established view that the continents and ocean basins are permanent and stationary features on the face of Earth. For that reason, the notion of drifting continents was received with great skepticism and even ridicule. More than 50 years passed before enough data were gathered to transform this controversial hypothesis into a sound theory that wove together the basic processes known to operate on Earth. The theory that finally emerged, called the *theory of plate tectonics*, provided geologists with the first comprehensive model of Earth's internal workings.

3 CONCEPT CHECKS

1. How is a scientific hypothesis different from a scientific theory?
2. Summarize the basic steps followed in many scientific investigations.
3. What explains the fact that continental drift is considered a hypothesis but plate tectonics is considered a theory?

---

*F. James Rutherford and Andrew Ahlgren, *Science for All Americans* (New York: Oxford University Press, 1990), p. 7.

4 Earth's Spheres

The images in FIGURE 9 are considered to be classics because they let humanity see Earth differently than ever before. These early views profoundly altered our conceptualizations of Earth and remain powerful images decades after they were first viewed. Seen from space, Earth is breathtaking in its beauty and startling in its solitude. The photos remind us that our home is, after all, a planet—small, self-contained, and in some ways even fragile.

FIGURE 9 Two classic views
Earth from space. (NASA)

View called "Earthrise" that greeted *Apollo 8* astronauts as their spacecraft emerged from behind the Moon in December 1968. This classic image let people see Earth differently than ever before.

This image taken from *Apollo 17* in December 1972 is perhaps the first to be called "The Blue Marble". The dark blue ocean and swirling cloud patterns remind us of the importance of the oceans and atmosphere.

As we look closely at our planet from space, it becomes apparent that Earth is much more than rock and soil. In fact, perhaps the most conspicuous features in Figure 9 are swirling clouds suspended above the surface of the vast global ocean. These features emphasize the importance of water on our planet.

The closer view of Earth from space shown in Figure 9 helps us appreciate why the physical environment is traditionally divided into three major parts: the water portion of our planet, the *hydrosphere*; Earth's gaseous envelope, the *atmosphere*; and, of course, the solid Earth, or *geosphere*. It needs to be emphasized that our environment is highly integrated and not dominated by rock, water, or air alone. Rather, it is characterized by continuous interactions as air comes in contact with rock, rock with water, and water with air. Moreover, the *biosphere*, which is the totality of all plant and animal life on our planet, interacts with each of the three physical realms and is an equally integral part of the planet. Thus, Earth can be thought of as consisting of four major spheres: the hydrosphere, atmosphere, geosphere, and biosphere.

The interactions among Earth's four spheres are incalculable. FIGURE 10 provides us with one easy-to-visualize example. The shoreline is an obvious meeting place for rock, water, and air. In this scene, ocean waves that were created by the drag of air moving across the

FIGURE 10 An interface in the earth system
The shoreline is one obvious interface—a common boundary where different parts of a system interact. In this scene, ocean waves (hydrosphere) that were created by the force of moving air (atmosphere) break against a rocky shore (geosphere). The force of the water can be powerful, and the erosional work that is accomplished can be great. (Photo by Radius images/ photolibrary.com)

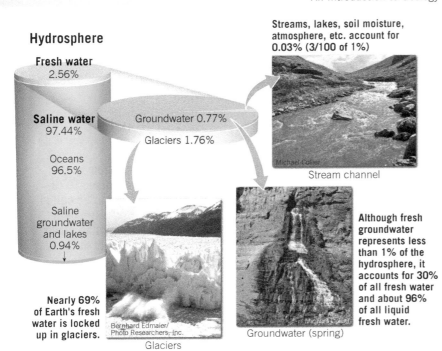

Hydrosphere

Fresh water
2.56%

Saline water
97.44%

Oceans
96.5%

Saline
groundwater
and lakes
0.94%
↓

**Nearly 69%
of Earth's fresh
water is locked
up in glaciers.**

Groundwater 0.77%

Glaciers 1.76%

Streams, lakes, soil moisture,
atmosphere, etc. account for
0.03% (3/100 of 1%)

Stream channel

**Although fresh
groundwater
represents less
than 1% of the
hydrosphere, it
accounts for 30%
of all fresh water
and about 96%
of all liquid
fresh water.**

Groundwater (spring)

Glaciers

Bernhard Edmaier/
Photo Researchers, Inc.

**FIGURE 11 The water
planet**
Distribution of water in the
hydrosphere.

water are breaking against the rocky shore. The force of
the water can be powerful, and the erosional work that is
accomplished can be great.

Hydrosphere

Earth is sometimes called the *blue* planet. Water, more
than anything else, makes Earth unique. The **hydrosphere** is a dynamic mass of water that is continually on
the move, evaporating from the oceans to the atmosphere,

precipitating to the land, and running back to the ocean
again. The global ocean is certainly the most prominent
feature of the hydrosphere, blanketing nearly 71 percent
of Earth's surface to an average depth of about 3800
meters (12,500 feet). It accounts for about 97 percent
of Earth's water (FIGURE 11). However, the hydrosphere
also includes the freshwater found underground and in
streams, lakes, and glaciers. Moreover, water is an important component of all living things.

Although these latter sources constitute just a tiny
fraction of the total, they are much more important
than their meager percentage indicates. In addition to
providing the freshwater that is so vital to life on land,
streams, glaciers, and groundwater are responsible
for sculpting and creating many of our planet's varied
landforms.

Atmosphere

Earth is surrounded by a life-giving gaseous envelope
called the **atmosphere** (FIGURE 12). When we watch
a high-flying jet plane cross the sky, it seems that the
atmosphere extends upward for a great distance. However, when compared to the thickness (radius) of the
solid Earth (about 6400 kilometers [4000 miles]), the
atmosphere is a very shallow layer. Despite its modest
dimensions, this thin blanket of air is an integral part of
the planet. It not only provides the air that we breathe
but also protects us from the Sun's intense heat and
dangerous ultraviolet radiation. The energy exchanges
that continually occur between the atmosphere and
Earth's surface and between the atmosphere and space
produce the effects we call *weather* and *climate*. Climate has a strong influence on the nature and intensity
of Earth's external processes. When climate changes,
these processes respond.

EYE on Earth

This jet is cruising at an altitude of 10
kilometers (6.2 miles). (Photo by interlight/
Shutterstock)

Question 1 Refer to the graph in Figure 12.
What is the approximate air pressure at the
altitude where the jet is flying?

Question 2 About what percentage of the
atmosphere is below the jet (assuming
that the pressure at the surface is 1000
millibars)?

FIGURE 12 **A shallow layer** The atmosphere is an integral part of the planet. (NASA)

Image of the atmosphere taken from the space shuttle. The thin streaks, called noctilucent clouds, are 80 km (50 mi) high. It is in the dense troposphere that practically all weather phenomena occur.

90% of the atmosphere is below 16 km (10 mi)

The air pressure atop Mt. Everest is about one-third that at sea level.

Average sea-level pressure is slightly more than 1000 millibars (about 14.7 lbs/sq. in)

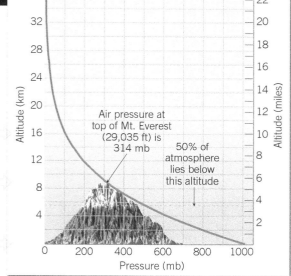

If, like the Moon, Earth had no atmosphere, our planet would be lifeless, and many of the processes and interactions that make the surface such a dynamic place could not operate. Without weathering and erosion, the face of our planet might more closely resemble the lunar surface, which has not changed appreciably in nearly 3 billion years.

Biosphere

The **biosphere** includes all life on Earth (FIGURE 13). Ocean life is concentrated in the sunlit surface waters of the sea. Most life on land is also concentrated near the surface, with tree roots and burrowing animals reaching a few meters underground and flying insects and birds reaching a kilometer or so into the

atmosphere. A surprising variety of life-forms are also adapted to extreme environments. For example, on the ocean floor, where pressures are extreme and no light penetrates, there are places where vents spew hot, mineral-rich fluids that support communities of exotic life-forms. On land, some bacteria thrive in rocks as deep as 4 kilometers (2.5 miles) and in boiling hot springs. Moreover, air currents can carry microorganisms many kilometers into the atmosphere. But even when we consider these extremes, life still must be thought of as being confined to a narrow band very near Earth's surface.

Plants and animals depend on the physical environment for the basics of life. However, organisms do not just respond to their physical environment. Through countless interactions, life-forms help maintain and alter the physical

FIGURE 13 The biosphere
The biosphere, one of
Earth's four spheres, in-
cludes all life. (Coral reef
photo by Darryl Leniuk/AGE Fotostock; rain forest photo by AGE
Fotostock/SuperStock)

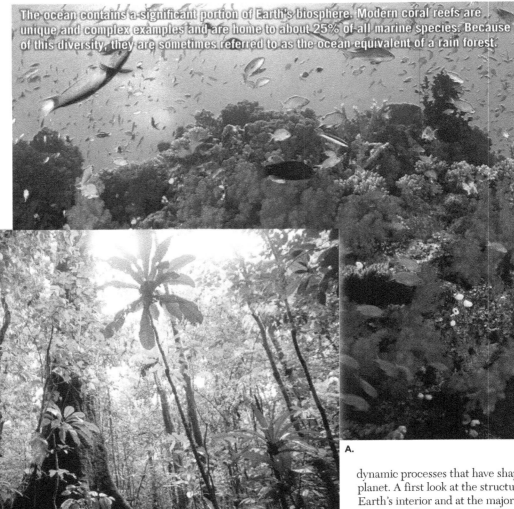

The ocean contains a significant portion of Earth's biosphere. Modern coral reefs are unique and complex examples and are home to about 25% of all marine species. Because of this diversity, they are sometimes referred to as the ocean equivalent of a rain forest.

A.

Tropical rain forests are characterized by hundreds of different species per square kilometer.

B.

environment. Without life, the makeup and nature of the geosphere, hydrosphere, and atmosphere would be very different.

Geosphere

Lying beneath the atmosphere and the oceans is the solid Earth, or **geosphere**. The geosphere extends from the surface to the center of the planet, a depth of nearly 6400 kilometers (nearly 4000 miles), making it by far the largest of Earth's four spheres. Much of our study of the solid Earth focuses on the more accessible surface features. Fortunately, many of these features represent the outward expression of the dynamic behavior of Earth's interior. By examining the most prominent surface features and their global extent, we can obtain clues to the dynamic processes that have shaped our planet. A first look at the structure of Earth's interior and at the major surface features of the geosphere will come later in the chapter.

Soil, the thin veneer of material at Earth's surface that supports the growth of plants, may be thought of as part of all four spheres. The solid portion is a mixture of weathered rock debris (geosphere) and organic matter from decayed plant and animal life (biosphere). The decomposed and disintegrated rock debris is the product of weathering processes that require air (atmosphere) and water (hydrosphere). Air and water also occupy the open spaces between the solid particles.

4 CONCEPT CHECKS

1. List and describe Earth's four spheres.
2. Compare the height of the atmosphere to the thickness of the geosphere.
3. How much of Earth's surface do oceans cover? What percentage of Earth's total water supply do oceans represent?
4. To which sphere does soil belong?

5 Earth as a System

Anyone who studies Earth soon learns that our planet is a dynamic body with many separate but interacting parts, or *spheres*. The hydrosphere, atmosphere, biosphere, and geosphere and all of their components can be studied separately. However, the parts are *not* isolated. Each is related in some way to the others, producing a complex and continuously interacting whole that we call the *Earth system*.

Earth System Science

A simple example of the interactions among different parts of the Earth system occurs every winter, as moisture evaporates from the Pacific Ocean and subsequently falls as rain in the hills and mountains of southern California, triggering destructive debris flows. The processes that move water from the hydrosphere to the atmosphere and then to the solid Earth have a profound impact on the plants and animals (including humans) that inhabit the affected regions. FIGURE 14 provides another example of how processes involving the atmosphere and hydrosphere can impact the geosphere.

Scientists have recognized that in order to more fully understand our planet, they must learn how its individual components (land, water, air, and life-forms) are interconnected. This endeavor, called *Earth system science*, aims to study Earth as a *system* composed of numerous interacting parts, or *subsystems*. Rather than looking through the limited lens of only one of the traditional sciences—geology, atmospheric science, chemistry, biology, and so on—Earth system science attempts to integrate the knowledge of several academic fields. Using an interdisciplinary approach, those engaged in Earth system science attempt to achieve the level of understanding necessary to comprehend and solve many of our global environmental problems.

A **system** is a group of interacting, or interdependent, parts that form a complex whole. Most of us hear and use the term *system* frequently. We may service our car's cooling *system*, make use of the city's transportation *system*, and be a participant in the political *system*. A news report might inform us of an approaching weather *system*. Further, we know that Earth is just a small part of a larger system known as the *solar system*, which in turn is a subsystem of an even larger system called the Milky Way Galaxy.

The Earth System

The Earth system has a nearly endless array of subsystems in which matter is recycled over and over. One subsystem traces the movements of carbon among Earth's four spheres. It shows us, for example, that the carbon dioxide in the air and the carbon in living things and in certain sedimentary rocks is all part of a subsystem described by the *carbon cycle*. A more familiar loop or subsystem is the *hydrologic cycle*. It represents the unending circulation of Earth's water among the hydrosphere, atmosphere, biosphere, and geosphere. Water enters the atmosphere through evaporation from Earth's surface and transpiration from plants. Water vapor condenses in the atmosphere to form clouds, which in turn produce precipitation that falls back to Earth's surface. Some of the rain that falls onto the land sinks in to be taken up by plants or become groundwater, and some flows across the surface toward the ocean.

Viewed over long time spans, the rocks of the geosphere are constantly forming, changing, and re-forming. The loop that involves the processes by which one rock changes to another is called the *rock cycle* and will be discussed at some length later in the chapter. The cycles of the Earth system are not independent of one another. To the contrary, there are many places where the cycles come in contact and interact.

The parts of the Earth system are linked so that a change in one part can produce changes in any or all of the other parts. For example, when a volcano erupts, lava from Earth's interior may flow out at the surface and block a nearby valley. This new obstruction influences the region's drainage system by creating a lake or causing streams to change course. The large quantities of volcanic ash and gases that can be emitted during an eruption might be blown high into the atmosphere and influence the amount of solar energy that can reach Earth's surface. The result could be a drop in air temperatures over the entire hemisphere.

FIGURE 14 The spheres interact
Aftermath of a natural disaster in northwestern China. (NASA)

On August 8, 2010, unusually intense rains triggered devastating debris flows (popularly called mudslides) that buried some densely populated parts of Zhouqu, a city tucked between steep mountain slopes and the Bailong River. The death toll exceeded 1500.

FIGURE 15 Change is a geologic constant When Mount St. Helens erupted in May 1980, the area shown here was buried by a volcanic mudflow. Now plants are reestablished and new soil is forming. (Photo by Terry Donnelly/Alamy Images)

Where the surface is covered by lava flows or a thick layer of volcanic ash, existing soils are buried. This causes the soil-forming processes to begin anew to transform the new surface material into soil (FIGURE 15). The soil that eventually forms will reflect the interactions among many parts of the Earth system—the volcanic parent material, the climate, and the impact of biological activity. Of course, there would also be significant changes in the biosphere. Some organisms and their habitats would be eliminated by the lava and ash, whereas new settings for life, such as a lake formed by a lava dam, would be created. The potential climate change could also impact sensitive life-forms.

The Earth system is characterized by processes that vary on spatial scales from fractions of millimeters to thousands of kilometers. Time scales for Earth's processes range from milliseconds to billions of years. As we learn about Earth, it becomes increasingly clear that despite significant separations in distance or time, many processes are connected, and a change in one component can influence the entire system.

The Earth system is powered by energy from two sources. The Sun drives external processes that occur in the atmosphere, in the hydrosphere, and at Earth's surface. Weather and climate, ocean circulation, and erosional processes are driven by energy from the Sun. Earth's interior is the second source of energy. Heat remaining from when our planet formed and heat that is continuously generated by radioactive decay power the internal processes that produce volcanoes, earthquakes, and mountains.

Humans are *part of* the Earth system, a system in which the living and nonliving components are entwined and interconnected. Therefore, our actions produce changes in all of the other parts. When we burn gasoline and coal, dispose of our wastes, and clear the land, we cause other parts of the system to respond, often in unforeseen ways. Throughout this text you will learn about many of Earth's subsystems, including the hydrologic system, the tectonic (mountain-building) system, the rock cycle, and the climate system. Remember that these components *and we humans* are all part of the complex interacting whole we call the Earth system.

EYE on Earth

This scene is in Mount Robson Provincial Park, British Columbia, Canada. (Photo by Michael Wheatley/AGE Fotostock)

Question 1 List as many examples as possible of features in this photo associated with each of Earth's four spheres.

Question 2 To which sphere does the glacier belong?

5 CONCEPT CHECKS

1. What is a system? List three examples.
2. What are the two sources of energy for the Earth system?
3. Predict how a change in the hydrologic cycle, such as increased rainfall in an area, might influence the biosphere and geosphere in that area.

6 Early Evolution of Earth

Recent earthquakes caused by displacements of Earth's crust, along with lavas spewed from active volcanoes, represent only the latest in a long line of events by which our planet has attained its present form and structure. The geologic processes operating in Earth's interior can be best understood when viewed in the context of much earlier events in Earth history.

Origin of Planet Earth

This section describes the most widely accepted views on the origin of our solar system. The theory described here represents the most consistent set of ideas we have to explain what we know about our solar system today.

The Universe Begins Our scenario begins about 13.7 billion years ago with the *Big Bang*, an incomprehensibly large explosion that sent all matter of the universe flying outward at incredible speeds. In time, the debris from this explosion, which was almost entirely hydrogen and helium, began to cool and condense into the first stars and galaxies. It was in one of these galaxies, the Milky Way, that our solar system and planet Earth took form.

The Solar System Forms Earth is one of eight planets that, along with several dozen moons and numerous

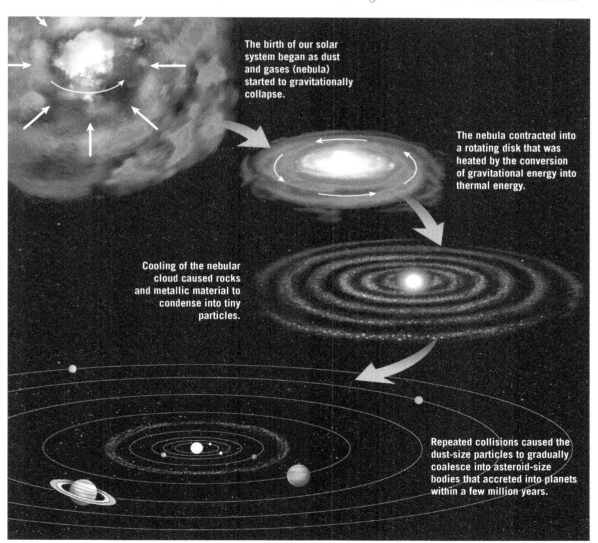

The birth of our solar system began as dust and gases (nebula) started to gravitationally collapse.

The nebula contracted into a rotating disk that was heated by the conversion of gravitational energy into thermal energy.

Cooling of the nebular cloud caused rocks and metallic material to condense into tiny particles.

Repeated collisions caused the dust-size particles to gradually coalesce into asteroid-size bodies that accreted into planets within a few million years.

SMARTFIGURE 16
Nebular theory
Formation of the solar system according to the nebular theory.

smaller bodies, revolve around the Sun. The orderly nature of our solar system leads most researchers to conclude that Earth and the other planets formed at essentially the same time and from the same primordial material as the Sun. The **nebular theory** proposes that the bodies of our solar system evolved from an enormous rotating cloud called the **solar nebula** (FIGURE 16). Besides the hydrogen and helium atoms generated during the Big Bang, the solar nebula consisted of microscopic dust grains and the ejected matter of long-dead stars. (Nuclear fusion in stars converts hydrogen and helium into the other elements found in the universe.)

Nearly 5 billion years ago, this huge cloud of gases and minute grains of heavier elements began to slowly contract due to the gravitational interactions among its particles. Some external influence, such as a shock wave traveling from a catastrophic explosion (*supernova*), may have triggered the collapse. As this slowly spiraling nebula contracted, it rotated faster and faster for the same reason ice skaters do when they draw their arms toward their bodies. Eventually the inward pull of gravity came into balance with the outward force caused by the rotational motion of the nebula (see Figure 16). By this time, the once vast cloud had assumed a flat disk shape with a large concentration of material at its center called the *protosun* (pre-Sun). (Astronomers are fairly confident that the nebular cloud formed a disk because similar structures have been detected around other stars.)

During the collapse, gravitational energy was converted to thermal energy (heat), causing the temperature of the inner portion of the nebula to dramatically rise. At these high temperatures, the dust grains broke up into molecules and extremely energetic atomic particles. However, at distances beyond the orbit of Mars, the temperatures probably remained quite low. At –200° C, the tiny particles in the outer portion of the nebula were likely covered with a thick layer of ices made of frozen water, carbon dioxide, ammonia, and methane. (Some of this material still resides in the outermost reaches of the solar system, in a region called the *Oort cloud*.) The disk-shaped cloud also contained appreciable amounts of the lighter gases hydrogen and helium.

The Inner Planets Form The formation of the Sun marked the end of the period of contraction and thus the end of gravitational heating. Temperatures in the region where the inner planets now reside began to decline. The decrease in temperature caused those substances with high melting points to condense into tiny particles that began to coalesce (join together). Materials such as iron and nickel and the elements of which the rock-forming minerals are composed—silicon, calcium, sodium, and so forth—formed metallic and rocky clumps that orbited the Sun (see Figure 16). Repeated collisions caused these masses to coalesce into larger asteroid-size bodies, called *planetesimals*, which in a few tens of millions of years accreted into the four inner planets we call Mercury, Venus, Earth, and Mars (FIGURE 17). Not all of these clumps of matter were incorporated into the planetesimals. Those rocky and metallic pieces that remained in orbit are called *meteorites* when they survive an impact with Earth.

As more and more material was swept up by the planets, the high-velocity impact of nebular debris caused the temperature of these bodies to rise. Because of their relatively high temperatures and weak gravitational fields, the inner planets were unable to accumulate much of the lighter components of the nebular cloud. The lightest of these, hydrogen and helium, were eventually whisked from the inner solar system by the solar wind.

The Outer Planets Develop At the same time that the inner planets were forming, the larger, outer planets (Jupiter, Saturn, Uranus, and Neptune), along with their extensive satellite systems, were also developing. Because of low temperatures far from the Sun, the material from which these planets formed contained a high percentage of ices—water, carbon

FIGURE 17 **A remnant planetesimal** This image of Asteroid 21 Lutetia was obtained by special cameras aboard the Rosetta spacecraft on July 10, 2010. Spacecraft instruments showed that Lutetia is a primitive body (planetesimal) left over from when the solar system formed. (Image courtesy of European Space Agency)

GEO GRAPHICS

Solar System: Size and Scale

The Sun is the center of a revolving system trillions of miles across, consisting of 8 planets, their satellites, and numerous dwarf planets, asteroids, comets, and meteoroids.

1
- The circumference of Earth is slightly more than 40,000 km (nearly 25,000 mi). It would take a jet plane traveling at 1000 km/hr (620 mi/hr) 40 hours (1.7 days) to circle the planet.

2
- The Sun contains 99.86 percent of the mass of the solar system.
- The circumference of the Sun is 109 times that of Earth.
- A jet plane traveling at 1000 km/hr would require nearly 182 days to circle the Sun.

3
- The average distance between Earth and Sun is 150 million km (93 million mi). This distance is referred to as 1 astronomical unit (AU).

- A jet plane traveling from Earth at 1000 km/hr would require about 17 years to reach the Sun!

Asia

EQUATOR

40,000 Km (nearly 25,000 miles)

Africa

Australia

NASA

Earth Sun

Mercury
Venus
Earth
Mars

Neptune   Uranus   Saturn   Jupiter

30   25   20   15   10   5   0

Distance in astronomical units (AU)

23

dioxide, ammonia, and methane—as well as rocky and metallic debris. The accumulation of ices accounts, in part, for the large size and low density of the outer planets. The two most massive planets, Jupiter and Saturn, had a surface gravity sufficient to attract and hold large quantities of even the lightest elements—hydrogen and helium.

Formation of Earth's Layered Structure

As material accumulated to form Earth (and for a short period afterward), the high-velocity impact of nebular debris and the decay of radioactive elements caused the temperature of our planet to steadily increase. During this time of intense heating, Earth became hot enough that iron and nickel began to melt. Melting produced liquid blobs of dense metal that sank toward the center of the planet. This process occurred rapidly on the scale of geologic time and produced Earth's dense iron-rich core.

Chemical Differentiation and Earth's Layers The early period of heating resulted in another process of chemical differentiation, whereby melting formed buoyant masses of molten rock that rose toward the surface, where they solidified to produce a primitive crust. These rocky materials were enriched in oxygen and "oxygen-seeking" elements, particularly silicon and aluminum, along with lesser amounts of calcium, sodium, potassium, iron, and magnesium. In addition, some heavy metals such as gold, lead, and uranium, which have low melting points or were highly soluble in the ascending molten masses, were scavenged from Earth's interior and concentrated in the developing crust. This early period of chemical differentiation established the three basic divisions of Earth's interior—the iron-rich *core*; the thin *primitive crust*; and Earth's largest layer, called the *mantle*, which is located between the core and crust.

An Atmosphere Develops An important consequence of the early period of chemical differentiation is that large quantities of gaseous materials were allowed to escape from Earth's interior, as happens today during volcanic eruptions. By this process, a primitive atmosphere gradually evolved. It is on this planet, with this atmosphere, that life as we know it came into existence.

Continents and Ocean Basins Evolve Following the events that established Earth's basic structure, the primitive crust was lost to erosion and other geologic processes, so we have no direct record of its makeup. When and exactly how the continental crust—and thus Earth's first landmasses—came into existence is a matter of ongoing research. Nevertheless, there is general agreement that the continental crust formed gradually over the past 4 billion years. (The oldest rocks yet discovered are isolated fragments found in the Northwest Territories of Canada that have radiometric dates of about 4 billion years.) In addition, Earth is an evolving planet whose continents and ocean basins have continually changed shape and even location during much of this period.

6 CONCEPT CHECKS

1. Name and briefly outline the theory that describes the formation of our solar system.
2. List the inner planets and outer planets. Describe basic differences in size and composition.
3. Explain why density and buoyancy were important in the development of Earth's layered structure.

The solar system is cluttered with meteoroids and other objects that occasionally strike Earth with explosive force. (Photo by Michael Collier)

7 Earth's Internal Structure

In the preceding section, you learned that the differentiation of material that began early in Earth's history resulted in the formation of three major layers defined by their chemical composition—the crust, mantle, and core. In addition to these compositionally distinct layers, Earth is divided into layers based on physical properties. The physical properties used to define such zones include whether the layer is solid or liquid and how weak or strong it is. Important examples include the lithosphere, asthenosphere, outer core, and inner core. Knowledge of both types of layers is important to our understanding of many geologic processes, including volcanism, earthquakes, and mountain building. FIGURE 18 shows different views of Earth's layered structure.

How did we learn about the composition and structure of Earth's interior? We have never sampled the mantle or core directly. The nature of Earth's interior is determined by analyzing seismic waves from earthquakes. As these waves of energy penetrate the planet, they change speed and are bent and reflected as they move through zones that have different properties. Monitoring stations around the world detect and record this energy.

With the aid of computers, these data are analyzed and used to build a detailed picture of Earth's interior.

Earth's Crust

The **crust**, Earth's relatively thin, rocky outer skin, is of two different types—continental crust and oceanic crust. Both share the word *crust*, but the similarity ends there.

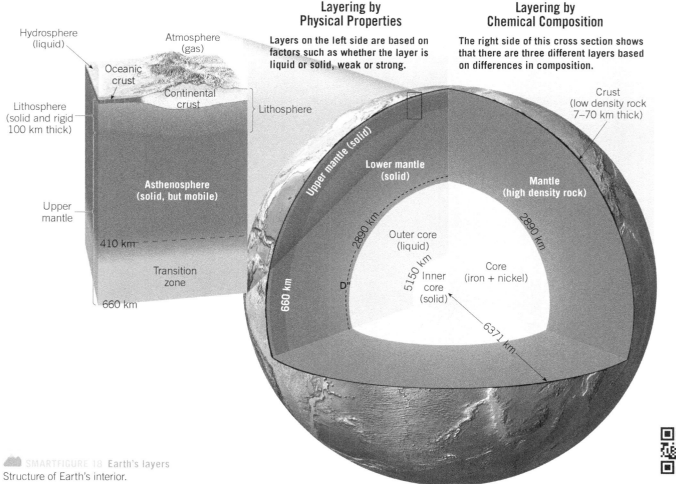

Layering by Physical Properties

Layers on the left side are based on factors such as whether the layer is liquid or solid, weak or strong.

Layering by Chemical Composition

The right side of this cross section shows that there are three different layers based on differences in composition.

Hydrosphere (liquid)

Atmosphere (gas)

Oceanic crust

Continental crust

Lithosphere (solid and rigid 100 km thick)

Lithosphere

Upper mantle (solid)

Lower mantle (solid)

Crust (low density rock 7–70 km thick)

Asthenosphere (solid, but mobile)

Upper mantle

410 km

Transition zone

660 km

660 km

2890 km

D"

5150 km

Outer core (liquid)

Inner core (solid)

Mantle (high density rock)

2890 km

Core (iron + nickel)

6371 km

SMARTFIGURE 18 Earth's layers
Structure of Earth's interior.

The oceanic crust is roughly 7 kilometers (5 miles) thick and composed of the dark igneous rock *basalt*. By contrast, the continental crust averages about 35 kilometers (22 miles) thick but may exceed 70 kilometers (40 miles) in some mountainous regions such as the Rockies and Himalayas. Unlike the oceanic crust, which has a relatively homogeneous chemical composition, the continental crust consists of many rock types. Although the upper crust has an average composition of a *granitic rock* called *granodiorite*, it varies considerably from place to place.

Continental rocks have an average density of about 2.7 g/cm^3, and some have been discovered that are more than 4 billion years old. The rocks of the oceanic crust are younger (180 million years or less) and denser (about 3.0 g/cm^3) than continental rocks. For comparison, liquid water has a density of 1 g/cm^3; therefore, the density of basalt, the primary rock composing oceanic crust, is three times that of water.

Earth's Mantle

More than 82 percent of Earth's volume is contained in the **mantle**, a solid, rocky shell that extends to a depth of about 2900 kilometers (1800 miles). The boundary between the crust and mantle represents a marked change in chemical composition. The dominant rock type in the uppermost mantle is *peridotite*, which is richer in the metals magnesium and iron than the minerals found in either the continental or oceanic crust.

The Upper Mantle   The upper mantle extends from the crust–mantle boundary down to a depth of about 660 kilometers (410 miles). The upper mantle can be divided into three different parts. The top portion of the upper mantle is part of the stronger *lithosphere*, and beneath that is the weaker *asthenosphere*. The bottom part of the upper mantle is called the *transition zone.*

The **lithosphere** (sphere of rock) consists of the entire crust plus the uppermost mantle and forms Earth's relatively cool, rigid outer shell (Figure 18). Averaging about 100 kilometers in thickness, the lithosphere is more than 250 kilometers thick below the oldest portions of the continents. Beneath this stiff layer to a depth of about 410 kilometers lies a soft, comparatively weak layer known as the **asthenosphere** ("weak sphere"). The top portion of the asthenosphere has a temperature/pressure regime that results in a small amount of melting. Within this very weak zone, the lithosphere is mechanically detached from the layer below. The result is that the lithosphere is able to move independently of the asthenosphere.

It is important to emphasize that the strength of various Earth materials is a function of both their composition and of the temperature and pressure of their environment. You should not get the idea that the entire lithosphere behaves like a rigid or brittle solid similar to rocks found on the surface. Rather, the rocks of the lithosphere get progressively hotter and weaker (more easily deformed) with increasing depth. At the depth of the uppermost asthenosphere, the rocks are close enough to their melting temperature (some melting may actually occur) that they are very easily deformed. Thus, the uppermost asthenosphere is weak because it is near its melting point, just as hot wax is weaker than cold wax.

From about 410 kilometers to about 660 kilometers in depth is the part of the upper mantle called the **transition zone**. The top of the transition zone is identified by a sudden increase in density from about 3.5 to 3.7 g/cm^3. This change occurs because minerals in the rock peridotite respond to the increase in pressure by forming new minerals with closely packed atomic structures.

The Lower Mantle   From a depth of 660 kilometers to the top of the core, at a depth of 2900 kilometers (1800 miles), is the **lower mantle**. Because of an increase in pressure (caused by the weight of the rock above), the mantle gradually strengthens with depth. Despite their strength, however, the rocks within the lower mantle are very hot and capable of extremely gradual flow.

In the bottom few hundred kilometers of the mantle is a highly variable and unusual layer called the D″ layer (pronounced "dee double-prime").

Earth's Core

The **core** is thought to be composed of an iron–nickel alloy with minor amounts of oxygen, silicon, and sulfur—elements that readily form compounds with iron. At the extreme pressure found in the core, this iron-rich material has an average density of nearly 11 g/cm^3 and approaches 14 times the density of water at Earth's center.

The core is divided into two regions that exhibit very different mechanical strengths. The **outer core** is a *liquid layer* 2270 kilometers (1410 miles) thick. It is the movement of metallic iron within this zone that generates Earth's magnetic field. The **inner core** is a sphere that has a radius of 1216 kilometers (754 miles). Despite its higher temperature, the iron in the inner core is *solid* due to the immense pressures that exist in the center of the planet.

7 CONCEPT CHECKS

1. List and describe the three major layers defined by their chemical composition.
2. Contrast the lithosphere and asthenosphere.
3. Distinguish between the outer core and the inner core.

8 Rocks and the Rock Cycle

Rock is the most common and abundant material on Earth. To a curious traveler, the variety seems nearly endless. When a rock is examined closely, we find that it usually consists of smaller crystals called minerals. *Minerals* are chemical compounds (or sometimes single elements), each with its own composition and physical properties. The grains or crystals may be microscopically small or easily seen with the unaided eye.

The nature and appearance of a rock is strongly influenced by the minerals that compose it. In addition, a rock's *texture*—the size, shape, and/or arrangement of its constituent minerals—also has a significant effect on its appearance. A rock's mineral composition and texture, in turn, are a reflection of the geologic processes that created it (FIGURE 19). Such analyses are critical to an understanding of our planet. This understanding has many practical applications, as in the search for energy and mineral resources and the solution of environmental problems.

Geologists divide rocks into three major groups: igneous, sedimentary, and metamorphic. FIGURE 20 provides some examples. As you will learn, each group is linked to the others by the processes that act upon and within the planet.

Earlier in this chapter you learned that Earth is a system. This means that our planet consists of many interacting parts that form a complex whole. Nowhere is this idea better illustrated than when we examine the rock cycle (FIGURE 21). The **rock cycle** allows us to view many of the interrelationships among different parts of the Earth system. It helps us understand the origin of igneous, sedimentary, and metamorphic rocks and to see that each type is linked to the others by processes that act upon and within the planet. Consider the rock cycle to be a simplified but useful overview of physical geology. Learn the rock cycle well; you will be examining its interrelationships in greater detail throughout this text.

The Basic Cycle

We will begin with magma, molten rock that forms deep beneath Earth's surface. Over time, magma cools and solidifies. This process, called *crystallization*, may occur either beneath the surface or, following a volcanic eruption, at the surface. In either situation, the resulting rocks are called **igneous rocks.**

If igneous rocks are exposed at the surface, they will undergo *weathering*, in which the day-in and day-out influences of the atmosphere slowly disintegrate and decompose rocks. The materials that result are often moved downslope by gravity before being picked up and transported by any of a number of erosional agents, such as running water, glaciers, wind, or waves. Eventually these particles and dissolved substances, called **sediment**, are deposited. Although most sediment ultimately comes to rest in the ocean, other sites of deposition include river floodplains, desert basins, swamps, and sand dunes.

Next, the sediments undergo *lithification*, a term meaning "conversion into rock." Sediment is usually

The large crystals of light-colored minerals in granite result from the slow cooling of molten rock deep beneath the surface. Granite is abundant in the continental crust.

FIGURE 19 Two basic rock characteristics
Texture and mineral composition are basic rock features. Both rock samples are about golf-ball size (Basalt photo by Tyler Boyes/Shutterstock; granite photo by geoz/Alamy Images)

Basalt is rich in dark minerals. Rapid cooling of molten rock at Earth's surface is responsible for the rock's microscopically small crystals. Oceanic crust is composed mainly of basalt.

Michael Collier

Igneous rocks form when molten rock solidifies at the surface (extrusive) or beneath the surface (intrusive). The lava flow in the foreground is the fine-grained rock basalt and came from SP Crater in northern Arizona.

Sedimentary rocks consist of particles derived from the weathering of other rocks. This layer consists of durable sand-size grains of the glassy mineral quartz that are cemented into a solid rock. The grains were once a part of extensive dunes. This rock layer, called the Navajo Sandstone, is prominent in southern Utah.

Dennis Tasa

Dennis Tasa

The metamorphic rock pictured here, known as the Vishnu Schist, is exposed in the inner gorge of the Grand Canyon. Its formation is associated with environments deep below Earth's surface where temperatures and pressures are high and with the forces associated with ancient mountain-building processes that occurred in Precambrian time.

FIGURE 20 Three rock groups
Geologists divide rocks into three groups—igneous, sedimentary, and metamorphic.

lithified into **sedimentary rock** when compacted by the weight of overlying layers or when cemented as percolating groundwater fills the pores with mineral matter.

If the resulting sedimentary rock is buried deep within Earth and involved in the dynamics of mountain building or intruded by a mass of magma, it will be subjected to great pressures and/or intense heat. The sedimentary rock will react to the changing environment and turn into the third rock type, **metamorphic rock**. When metamorphic rock is subjected to additional pressure changes or to still higher temperatures, it will melt, creat-

ing magma, which will eventually crystallize into igneous rock starting the cycle all over again.

Where does the energy that drives Earth's rock cycle come from? Processes driven by heat from Earth's interior are responsible for creating igneous and metamorphic rocks. Weathering and erosion, external processes powered by energy from the Sun, produce the sediment from which sedimentary rocks form.

Alternative Paths

The paths shown in the basic cycle are not the only ones that are possible. To the contrary, other paths are just as likely to be followed as those described in the preceding section. These alternatives are indicated by the light blue arrows in Figure 21.

Igneous rocks, rather than being exposed to weathering and erosion at Earth's surface, may remain deeply buried. Eventually these masses may be subjected to the strong compressional forces and high temperatures associated with mountain building. When this occurs, they are transformed directly into metamorphic rocks.

Metamorphic and sedimentary rocks, as well as sediment, do not always remain buried. Rather, overlying layers may be stripped away, exposing the once-buried rock. When this happens, the material is attacked by weathering processes and turned into new raw materials for sedimentary rocks.

Although rocks may seem to be unchanging masses, the rock cycle shows that they are not. The changes, however, take time—great amounts of time. We can observe different parts of the cycle operating all over the world. Today new magma is forming beneath the island of Hawaii. When it erupts at the surface, the lava flows add to the size of the island. Meanwhile, the Colorado Rockies are gradually being worn down by weathering and erosion. Some of this weathered debris will eventually be carried to the Gulf of Mexico, where it will add to the already substantial mass of sediment that has accumulated there.

8 CONCEPT CHECKS

1. List two rock characteristics that are used to determine the processes that created a rock.
2. Sketch and label a basic rock cycle. Make sure to include alternate paths.
3. Use the rock cycle to explain the statement "One rock is the raw material for another."

ROCK CYCLE

Viewed over long time spans,
rocks are constantly forming,
changing, and reforming.

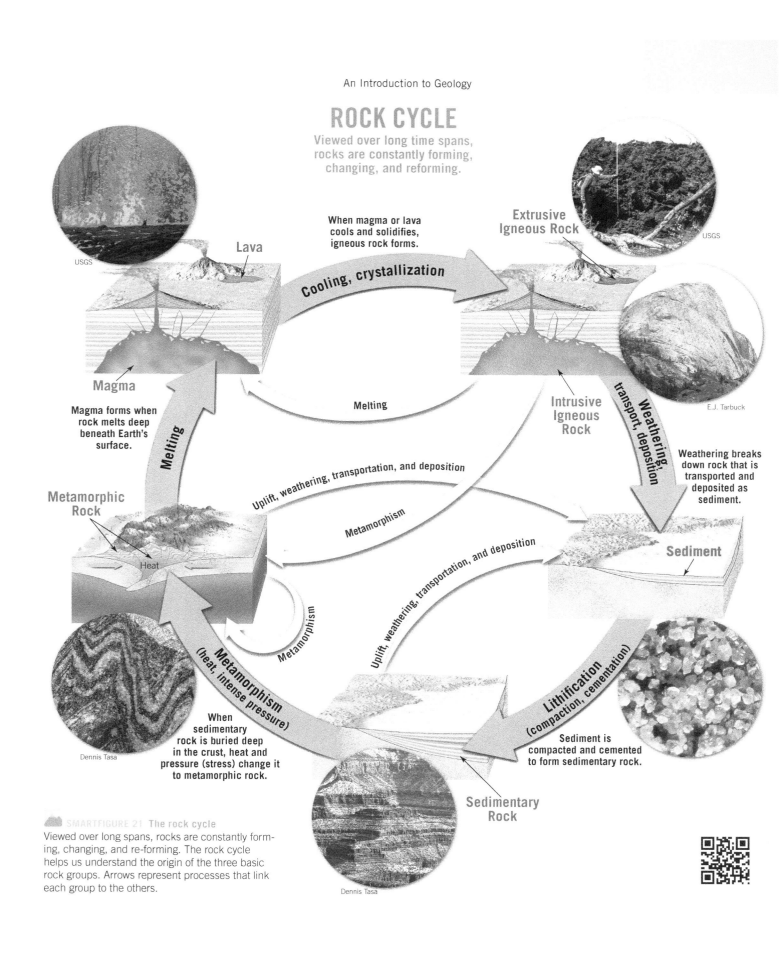

When magma or lava
cools and solidifies,
igneous rock forms.

**Extrusive
Igneous Rock**

USGS

Lava

Cooling, crystallization

USGS

Magma

Melting

Melting

Magma forms when
rock melts deep
beneath Earth's
surface.

**Intrusive
Igneous
Rock**

E.J. Tarbuck

**Weathering,
transport, deposition**

Weathering breaks
down rock that is
transported and
deposited as
sediment.

Uplift, weathering, transportation, and deposition

**Metamorphic
Rock**

Metamorphism

Heat

Sediment

Metamorphism

Uplift, weathering, transportation, and deposition

**Lithification
(compaction, cementation)**

Dennis Tasa

**Metamorphism
(heat, intense pressure)**

When
sedimentary
rock is buried deep
in the crust, heat and
pressure (stress) change it
to metamorphic rock.

Sediment is
compacted and cemented
to form sedimentary rock.

**Sedimentary
Rock**

Dennis Tasa

SMARTFIGURE 21 **The rock cycle**
Viewed over long spans, rocks are constantly forming, changing, and re-forming. The rock cycle
helps us understand the origin of the three basic
rock groups. Arrows represent processes that link
each group to the others.

9 The Face of Earth

The two principal divisions of Earth's surface are the **continents** and the **ocean basins** (FIGURE 22). A significant difference between these two areas is their relative levels. The elevation difference between the continents and ocean basins is primarily a result of differences in their respective densities and thicknesses:

FIGURE 22 The face of Earth
Major surface features of the geosphere.

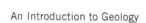

- **Continents.** The continents are remarkably flat features that have the appearance of plateaus protruding above sea level. With an average elevation of about 0.8 kilometer (0.5 mile), continental blocks lie close to sea level, except for limited areas of mountainous terrain. Recall that the continents average about 35 kilometers (22 miles) in thickness and are composed of granitic rocks that have a density of about 2.7 g/cm^3.

- **Ocean basins.** The average depth of the ocean floor is about 3.8 kilometers (2.4 miles) below sea level, or about 4.5 kilometers (2.8 miles) lower than the average elevation of the continents. The basaltic rocks that comprise the oceanic crust average only

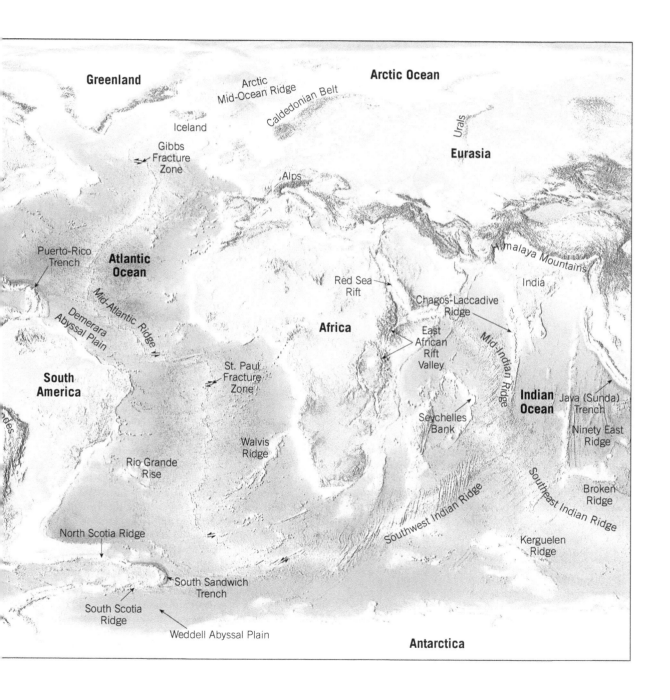

The Canadian shield is an expansive region of ancient Precambrian rocks, some more than 4 billion years old. It was recently scoured by Ice Age glaciers.

The Appalachians are old mountains. Mountain building began about 480 million years ago and continued for more than 200 million years. Erosion has lowered these once lofty peaks.

The rugged Himalayas are the highest mountains on Earth and are geologically young. They began forming about 50 million years ago and uplift continues today.

Key
- Young mountain belts (less than 100 million years old)
- Old mountain belts
- Shields
- Stable platforms (shields covered by sedimentary rock)

SMARTFIGURE 23 The continents
Distribution of mountain belts, stable platforms, and shields.

7 kilometers (5 miles) thick and have an average density of about 3.0 g/cm³.

Thus, the thicker and less dense continental crust is more buoyant than the oceanic crust. As a result, continental crust floats on top of the deformable rocks of the mantle at a higher level than oceanic crust for the same reason that a large, empty (less dense) cargo ship rides higher than a small, loaded (denser) one.

Major Features of the Continents

The major features of the continents can be grouped into two distinct categories: uplifted regions of deformed rocks that make up present-day mountain belts and extensive flat, stable areas that have eroded nearly to sea level. Notice in FIGURE 23 that the young mountain belts tend to be long, narrow features at the margins of continents and that the flat, stable areas are typically located in the interior of the continents.

Mountain Belts   The most prominent features of the continents are mountains. Although the distribution of mountains appears to be random, this is not the case. The youngest mountains (those less than 100 million years old) are located principally in two major zones. The circum-Pacific belt (the region surrounding the Pacific Ocean) includes the mountains of the western Americas and continues into the western Pacific, in the form of volcanic island arcs (see Figure 22). Island arcs are active mountainous regions composed largely of volcanic rocks and deformed sedimentary rocks. Examples include the Aleutian Islands, Japan, the Philippines, and New Guinea.

The other major **mountain belt** extends eastward from the Alps through Iran and the Himalayas and then dips southward into Indonesia. Careful examination of mountainous terrains reveals that most are places where thick sequences of rocks have been squeezed and highly deformed, as if placed in a gigantic vise. Older mountains are also found on the continents. Examples include the Appalachians in the eastern United States and the Urals in Russia. Their once lofty peaks are now worn low, as a result of millions of years of weathering and erosion.

The Stable Interior Unlike the young mountain belts, which have formed within the past 100 million years, the interiors of the continents, called **cratons**, have been relatively stable (undisturbed) for the past 600 million years or even longer. Typically these regions were involved in mountain-building episodes much earlier in Earth's history.

Within the stable interiors are areas known as **shields**, which are expansive, flat regions composed largely of deformed igneous and metamorphic rocks. Notice in Figure 23 that the Canadian Shield is exposed in much of the northeastern part of North America. Radiometric dating of various shields has revealed that they are truly ancient regions. All contain Precambrian-age rocks that are more than 1 billion years old, with some samples approaching 4 billion years in age. Even these oldest-known rocks exhibit evidence of enormous forces that have folded, faulted, and metamorphosed them. Thus, we conclude that these rocks were once part of an ancient mountain system that has since been eroded away to produce these expansive, flat regions.

Other flat areas of the craton exist, in which highly deformed rocks, like those found in the shields, are covered by a relatively thin veneer of sedimentary rocks. These areas are called **stable platforms**. The sedimentary rocks in stable platforms are nearly horizontal, except where they have been warped to form large basins or domes. In North America a major portion of the stable platform is located between the Canadian Shield and the Rocky Mountains.

Major Features of the Ocean Floor

If all water were drained from the ocean basins, a great variety of features would be seen, including chains of volcanoes, deep canyons, plateaus, and large expanses of monotonously flat plains. In fact, the scenery would be nearly as diverse as that on the continents (see Figure 22).

During the past 65 years, oceanographers have used modern depth-sounding equipment and satellite technology to map significant portions of the ocean floor. These studies have led them to identify three major regions: *continental margins, deep-ocean basins,* and *oceanic (mid-ocean) ridges.*

Continental Margins The **continental margin** is the portion of the seafloor adjacent to major landmasses. It may include the *continental shelf,* the *continental slope,* and the *continental rise.*

Although land and sea meet at the shoreline, this is *not* the boundary between the continents and the ocean basins. Rather, along most coasts, a gently sloping platform of material, called the **continental shelf**, extends seaward from the shore. Because it is underlain by continental crust, it is clearly a flooded extension of the continents. A glance at Figure 22 shows that the width of the continental shelf is variable. For example, it is broad along the east and Gulf coasts of the United States but relatively narrow along the Pacific margin of the continent.

The boundary between the continents and the deep-ocean basins lies along the **continental slope**, which is a relatively steep dropoff that extends from the outer edge of the continental shelf to the floor of the deep ocean (see Figure 22). Using this as the dividing line, we find that about 60 percent of Earth's surface is represented by ocean basins and the remaining 40 percent by continents.

In regions where trenches do not exist, the steep continental slope merges into a more gradual incline known as the **continental rise**. The continental rise consists of a thick wedge of sediment that moved downslope from the continental shelf and accumulated on the deep-ocean floor.

Deep-Ocean Basins Between the continental margins and oceanic ridges lie the **deep-ocean basins**. Parts of these regions consist of incredibly flat features called **abyssal plains**. The ocean floor also contains extremely deep depressions that are occasionally more than 11,000 meters (36,000 feet) deep. Although these **deep-ocean trenches** are relatively narrow and represent only a small fraction of the ocean floor, they are nevertheless very significant features. Some trenches are located adjacent to young mountains that flank the continents. For example, in Figure 22 the Peru–Chile trench off the west coast of South America parallels the Andes Mountains. Other trenches parallel island chains called *volcanic island arcs.*

Dotting the ocean floor are submerged volcanic structures called **seamounts**, which sometimes form long narrow chains. Volcanic activity has also produced several large *lava plateaus,* such as the Ontong Java Plateau located northeast of New Guinea. In addition, some submerged plateaus are composed of continental-type crust. Examples include the Campbell Plateau southeast of New Zealand and the Seychelles Bank northeast of Madagascar.

Oceanic Ridges The most prominent feature on the ocean floor is the **oceanic ridge**, or **mid-ocean ridge**. As shown in Figure 22, the Mid-Atlantic Ridge and the East Pacific Rise are parts of this system. This broad elevated feature forms a continuous belt that winds for more than 70,000 kilometers (43,000 miles) around the globe, in a manner similar to the seam of a baseball. Rather than consisting of highly deformed rock, such as most of the mountains on the continents, the oceanic ridge system consists of layer upon layer of igneous rock that has been fractured and uplifted.

Being familiar with the topographic features that comprise the face of Earth is essential to understanding the mechanisms that have shaped our planet. What is the significance of the enormous ridge system that extends through all the world's oceans? What is the connection, if any, between young, active mountain belts and oceanic trenches? What forces crumple rocks to produce majestic mountain ranges? These are a few of the questions that need to be addressed when investigating the dynamic processes that shaped our planet in the geologic past and continue to shape it in the future.

9 CONCEPT CHECKS

1. Compare and contrast continents and ocean basins.
2. Describe the general distribution of Earth's youngest mountains.
3. What is the difference between shields and stable platforms?
4. What are the three major regions of the ocean floor, and what are some features associated with each?

The position of the shoreline does not mark the outer edge of a continent. Rather the boundary between a continent and ocean basin lies along the continental slope. (Photo by Michael Collier)

CONCEPTS IN REVIEW: AN INTRODUCTION TO GEOLOGY

1 Geology: The science of Earth

Distinguish between physical and historical geology and describe the connections between people and geology.

KEY WORDS geology, physical geology, historical geology

- Geologists study Earth. Physical geologists focus on the processes by which Earth operates and the materials that result from those processes. Historical geologists apply an understanding of Earth materials and processes to reconstruct the history of our planet.

- People have a relationship with planet Earth that can be positive and negative. Earth processes and products sustain us every day, and on a bad day they could harm us. Similarly, people have the ability to alter or harm natural systems, including those that sustain civilization.

GET A JOB Consider the question of when a given volcano is likely to erupt, and also the question of whether volcanic eruptions caused the extinction of the dinosaurs. Which is an issue that a physical geologist would address? Which question would a historical geologist focus on?

2 The development of geology

Summarize early and modern views on how change occurs on Earth and relate them to the prevailing ideas about the age of Earth.

KEY WORDS catastrophism, uniformitarianism

- Early ideas about the nature of Earth were based on religious traditions and notions of great catastrophes. In 1795, James Hutton emphasized that the same slow processes have acted over great spans of time and are responsible for Earth's rocks, mountains, and landforms. This similarity of process over vast spans of time led to this principle being dubbed "uniformitarianism."

- Based on the rate of radioactive decay of certain elements, the age of Earth has been calculated to be about 4,600,000,000 (4.6 billion) years. That is an incredibly vast amount of time.

GET PERSPECTIVE The Washington Monument in Washington, DC, is a little less than 169.294 meters (555.5 feet) tall. A sheet of paper is about 0.7 millimeter thick. If you divide 0.7 millimeter by 169,294 millimeters, the result is about 0.0004 percent of the total.

Dinosaurs — Human history (a sheet of paper draped on top)

First fossils of animal bodies

Condensation of the solar system

Shutterstock

3 The nature of scientific inquiry

Discuss the nature of scientific inquiry, including the construction of hypotheses and the development of theories.

KEY WORDS hypothesis, theory

- Geologists make observations, construct tentative explanations for those observations (hypotheses), and then test those hypotheses with field investigations and laboratory work. In science, a theory is a well-tested and widely accepted view that the scientific community agrees best explains certain observable facts.

- As flawed hypotheses are discarded, scientific knowledge moves closer to a correct understanding, but we can never be fully confident that we know all the answers. Scientists must always be open to new information that forces a change in our model of the world.

EXPLAIN Describe the approach that geoscientists take in learning about Earth. List two major insights that result from a scientific examination of Earth processes.

4 Earth's spheres

List and describe Earth's four major spheres.

KEY WORDS hydrosphere, atmosphere, biosphere, geosphere

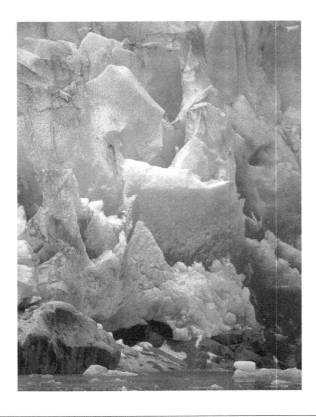

- The atmosphere, hydrosphere, geosphere, and biosphere all trade matter and energy on a daily basis. Carbon atoms that were once part of a rock could be washed into the sea, evaporated into the atmosphere, captured by a plant, and finally eaten by a person.
- Imagine that a volcano (part of the geosphere) erupted 10 years ago, emitting water vapor into the atmosphere. Later the water vapor condensed to form cloud droplets, which combined to become raindrops. The rain soaked into the ground and very slowly migrated toward a lake. Then, last Tuesday, some of the lake water was pumped out, treated, and funneled into your house. As you take a break from studying geology to have a sip of water, your living body (part of the biosphere) absorbs some of this water, and you realize that over time its component molecules have been part of each of Earth's four spheres.
- Life on Earth (the biosphere) is concentrated in a relatively thin zone that extends a few kilometers down into the hydrosphere and geosphere and a few kilometers up into the atmosphere. For comparison, the radius of the geosphere (6400 kilometers [4000 miles]) is about 1000 times thicker than that.
- Of all the water on Earth, 97 percent is in the oceans, which cover about 71 percent of the surface of the planet.

DEBATE IT Is glacial ice part of the geosphere or the hydrosphere? Justify your answer.

5 Earth as a system

Define *system* and explain why Earth is considered to be a system.

KEY WORD system

- Earth is a complex system of interacting matter and energy. Some of the energy initially comes from the Sun, while other energy is released from Earth's interior. Changes in one part of the system can have effects in distant areas. The changes may manifest quickly or may play out over long periods of time.
- Humans are part of the Earth system. Our actions are one of the many factors that influence it.

GIVE AND TAKE Give a specific example of how humans are affected by the Earth system and another example of how humans affect the Earth system.

6 Early evolution of Earth

Outline the stages in the formation of our solar system.

KEY WORDS nebular theory, solar nebula

- The scientific understanding of the formation of our planet is closely tied to the formation of the rest of our solar system. A large cloud of gas and dust called a nebula condensed to form the Sun, the planets, asteroids, and comets.
- The inner planets are made of denser matter and are "rocky" as a result. Beyond the asteroid belt, the outer planets are made of less dense ices and gases.
- Planet Earth has differentiated into layers of different densities: most dense in the center (core), medium densities in between (mantle and crust), and least dense on the outside (atmosphere).

EXTRAPOLATE If all the planets formed about the same time, according to the nebular theory, and the Earth is 4.6 billion years old, then how old would you expect Mars to be? Jupiter? The Sun?

7 Earth's internal structure

Describe Earth's internal structure.

KEY WORDS crust, mantle, lithosphere, asthenosphere, transition zone, lower mantle, core, outer core, inner core

- Compositionally, the solid Earth has three layers: core, mantle, and crust. The core is most dense, and the crust is least dense (and, of course, the ocean water and atmosphere overlie the crust because they are even less dense).
- Earth's interior can also be divided into layers based on physical properties. The crust and upper mantle make a two-part layer called the lithosphere, which is broken into the plates of plate tectonics. Beneath that is the "weak" asthenosphere. The lower mantle is stronger than the asthenosphere and overlies the molten outer core. This liquid is made of the same iron–nickel alloy as the inner core, but the extremely high pressure of Earth's center compacts the inner core into a solid form.

DRAW IT Without looking at this text, draw two cross sections of Earth from memory. In one, divide Earth into compositional layers. In the second, identify different layers based on physical properties.

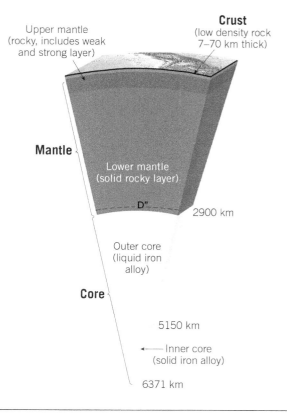

Upper mantle (rocky, includes weak and strong layer)

Crust (low density rock 7–70 km thick)

Mantle

Lower mantle (solid rocky layer)

D"

2900 km

Outer core (liquid iron alloy)

Core

5150 km

Inner core (solid iron alloy)

6371 km

8 Rocks and the rock cycle

Sketch, label, and explain the rock cycle.

KEY WORDS rock cycle, igneous rock, sediment, sedimentary rock, metamorphic rock

- The concept of the rock cycle is a good way to think about the transformation of rocks due to myriad Earth processes. All igneous rocks are made from molten rock. All sedimentary rocks are made from weathered products of other rocks. All metamorphic rocks are transformed when preexisting rocks are cooked or squeezed at high temperatures or pressures. Given the right ingredients and conditions, any kind of rock could be transformed into any other kind of rock.

TELL A STORY Add to the diagram here to tell a story of possible changes that could occur to the igneous rock.

Shutterstock   Dennis Tasa   USGS   Dennis Tasa

Sediment turns to **sedimentary rock**, which melts to produce **magma**, which then crystallizes into **igneous rock.**

9 The Face of Earth

List and describe the major features of the continents and ocean basins.

KEY WORDS continent, ocean basin, mountain belt, craton, shield, stable platform, continental margin, continental shelf, continental slope, continental rise, deep-ocean basin, abyssal plain, deep-ocean trench, seamount, oceanic ridge (mid-ocean ridge)

- In addition to regional variation, there are broad patterns to the structure of Earth's continents and ocean basins.
- Continents consist of relatively flat, stable areas called cratons. Where a craton is blanketed by a relatively thin layer of sediment or sedimentary rock, it is called a stable platform. Where a craton is exposed at the surface, it is known as a shield. Wrapping around the edges of some cratons are mountain belts, linear swaths of intense deformation and metamorphism. If the deformation is recent, the mountain belts are actually mountainous; you could climb them and get a good view of the land down below. As mountain belts age, they are torn down by gravity and weathering. Eventually, they can be worn flat as table tops, but the twisted and smashed rocks within are evidence of the mountains that used to stand in those spots.
- There are shallow portions of the oceans that are essentially flooded margins of the continents, and there are deeper portions that include vast abyssal plains and deep ocean trenches. Interrupting the abyssal plain may be seamounts and lava plateaus.

ARRANGE IT Put these features of the ocean floor in order from deepest to shallowest--continental slope, deep-ocean trench, continental shelf, abyssal plain, and continental shelf.

GIVE IT SOME THOUGHT

1. The length of recorded history for humankind is about 5000 years. Clearly, most people view this span as being very long. How does it compare to the length of geologic time? Calculate the percentage or fraction of geologic time that is represented by recorded history. To make calculations easier, round the age of Earth to the nearest billion.

2. After entering a dark room, you turn on a wall switch, but the light does not come on. Suggest at least three hypotheses that might explain this observation. Once you have formulated your hypotheses, what is the next logical step?

3. Making accurate measurements and observations is a basic part of scientific inquiry. The accompanying photo provides one example. Identify three other images in this chapter that illustrate ways in which scientific data are gathered. Suggest advantages that might be associated with each example.

4. Refer to the graph in Figure 12 to answer the following questions.
   a. If you were to climb to the top of Mount Everest, how many breaths of air would you have to take at that altitude to equal one breath at sea level?
   b. If you are flying in a commercial jet at an altitude of 12 kilometers (about 39,000 feet), about what percentage of the atmosphere's mass is below you?

5. Look at the accompanying concept map that links the four spheres of the Earth system. All of the spheres are linked by arrows representing processes by which the spheres interact and influence each other. For each arrow, describe at least one process.

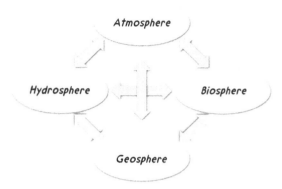

6. Jupiter, the largest planet in our solar system, is 5.2 astronomical units (AU) from the Sun. How long would it take to go from Earth to Jupiter if you traveled as fast as a jet (1000 kilometers/hour)? Do the same calculation for Neptune, which is 30 AU from the Sun. Referring to the GEOgraphics feature "Solar System Facts (Earth vs Sun)"

AP Photo/Pat Roque

7. The accompanying photo provides an example of interactions among different parts of the Earth system. It is a view of a mudflow that was triggered by extraordinary rains. Which of Earth's four "spheres" were involved in this natural disaster that buried a small town on the Philippine island of Leyte? Describe how each contributed to or was influenced by the event.

8. Refer to Figure 21. How does the rock cycle diagram, particularly the process arrows, support the fact that sedimentary rock is the most abundant rock type on the surface of Earth?

Glossary

Abyssal plain A very level area of the deep-ocean floor, usually lying at the foot of the continental rise.

Asthenosphere A subdivision of the mantle situated below the lithosphere. This zone of weak material exists below a depth of about 100 kilometers (60 miles) and in some regions extends as deep as 700 kilometers (430 miles). The rock within this zone is easily deformed.

Atmosphere The gaseous portion of a planet, the planet's envelope of air. One of the traditional subdivisions of Earth's physical environment.

Biosphere The totality of life-forms on Earth.

Catastrophism The concept that Earth was shaped by catastrophic events of a short-term nature.

Continental margin The portion of the seafloor that is adjacent to the continents. It may include the continental shelf, continental slope, and continental rise.

Continental rise The gently sloping surface at the base of the continental slope.

Continental shelf The gently sloping submerged portion of the continental margin, extending from the shoreline to the continental slope.

Continental slope The steep gradient that leads to the deep-ocean floor and marks the seaward edge of the continental shelf.

Core The innermost layer of Earth. It is thought to be largely an iron–nickel alloy, with minor amounts of oxygen, silicon, and sulfur.

Craton The part of the continental crust that has attained stability; that is, it has not been affected by significant tectonic activity during the Phanerozoic eon. It consists of the shield and the stable platform.

Crust The *very* thin, outermost layer of Earth.

Deep-ocean basin The portion of seafloor that lies between the continental margin and the oceanic ridge system. This region comprises almost 30 percent of Earth's surface.

Deep-ocean trench A narrow, elongated depression of the seafloor.

Geology The science that examines Earth, its form and composition, and the changes that it has undergone and is undergoing.

Geosphere The solid Earth; one of Earth's four basic spheres.

Historical geology A major division of geology that deals with the origin of Earth and its development through time. Usually involves the study of fossils and their sequence in rock beds.

Hydrosphere The water portion of our planet; one of the traditional subdivisions of Earth's physical environment.

Hypothesis A tentative explanation that is then tested to determine if it is valid.

Igneous rock Rock formed from the crystallization of magma.

Inner core The solid innermost layer of Earth, about 1216 kilometers (754 miles) in radius.

Lithosphere The rigid outer layer of Earth, including the crust and upper mantle.

Lower mantle See Mesosphere.

Magma A body of molten rock found at depth, including any dissolved gases and crystals.

Mantle One of Earth's compositional layers. The solid rocky shell that extends from the base of the crust to a depth of 2900 kilometers (1800 miles).

Metamorphic rock Rock formed by the alteration of preexisting rock deep within Earth (but still in the solid state) by heat, pressure, and/or chemically active fluids.

Mid-ocean ridge A continuous mountainous ridge on the floor of all the major ocean basins and varying in width from 500 to 5000 kilometers (300 to 3000 miles). The rifts at the crests of these ridges represent divergent plate boundaries.

Nebular theory A model for the origin of the solar system that supposes a rotating nebula of dust and gases that contracted to form the Sun and planets.

Oceanic ridge See Mid-ocean ridge.

Outer core A layer beneath the mantle about 2270 kilometers (1410 miles) thick, which has the properties of a liquid.

Physical geology A major division of geology that examines the materials of Earth and seeks to understand the processes and forces acting beneath and upon Earth's surface.

Rock cycle A model that illustrates the origin of the three basic rock types and the interrelatedness of Earth materials and processes.

Seamount An isolated volcanic peak that rises at least 1000 meters (3300 feet) above the deep-ocean floor.

Sediment Unconsolidated particles created by the weathering and erosion of rock by chemical precipitation from solution in water, or from the secretions of organisms, and transported by water, wind, or glaciers.

Sedimentary rock Rock formed from the weathered products of preexisting rocks that have been transported, deposited, and lithified.

Shield A large, relatively flat expanse of ancient igneous and metamorphic rocks within the craton.

Solar nebula The cloud of interstellar gas and/or dust from which the bodies of our solar system formed.

Stable platform That part of a carton that is mantled by relatively undeformed sedimentary rocks and underlain by a basement complex of igneous and metamorphic rocks.

System A group of interacting or interdependent parts that form a complex whole.

Theory A well-tested and widely accepted view that explains certain observable facts.

Uniformitarianism The concept that the processes that have shaped Earth in the geologic past are essentially the same as those operating today.

Plate Tectonics: A Scientific Revolution Unfolds

From Chapter 2 of *Earth: An Introduction to Physical Geology*, Eleventh Edition. Edward J. Tarbuck, Frederick K. Lutgens, Dennis Tasa.

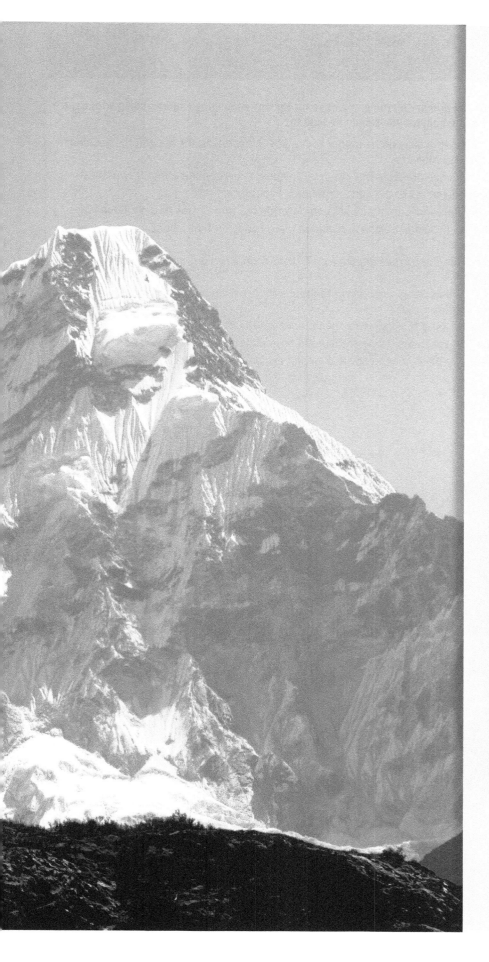

Plate Tectonics: A Scientific Revolution Unfolds

The collision of tectonic plates was responsible for creating the Alps and many other mountains around the world. (Photo by Doug Berry/Corbis/Glow Images)

43

Each statement represents the primary learning objective for the corresponding major heading within the chapter. After you complete the chapter you should be able to:

1 Discuss the view that most geologists held prior to the 1960s regarding the geographic positions of the ocean basins and continents.

2 List and explain the evidence presented by Wegener to support his continental drift hypothesis.

3 Discuss the two main objections to the continental drift hypothesis.

4 Identify Earth's major plates on a map and list and describe the three types of plate boundaries.

5 Sketch and describe the movement along a divergent plate boundary that results in the formation of new oceanic lithosphere.

6 Compare and contrast the three types of convergent plate boundaries and name a location where each type can be found.

7 Describe the relative motion along a transform fault boundary and be able to locate several examples on a plate boundary map.

8 Summarize the evidence used to support the plate tectonics theory.

9 Describe two methods researchers use to measure relative plate motion.

10 Discuss what is meant by plate–mantle convection and explain two of the primary driving forces for plate motion.

Volcanism is driven mainly by interactions between tectonic plates. (Photo by Stocktrek Images/Martin Rietze/ Glow Images)

P late tectonics is the first theory to provide a comprehensive view of the processes that produced Earth's major surface features, including the continents and ocean basins. Within the framework of this theory, geologists have found explanations for the basic causes and distribution of earthquakes, volcanoes, and mountain belts. Further, we are now better able to explain the distribution of plants and animals in the geologic past, as well as the distribution of economically significant mineral deposits.

1 From Continental Drift to Plate Tectonics

Prior to the late 1960s most geologists held the view that the ocean basins and continents had fixed geographic positions and were of great antiquity. Researchers came to realize that Earth's continents are not static; instead, they gradually migrate across the globe. Because of these movements, blocks of continental material collide, deforming the intervening crust, thereby creating Earth's great mountain chains (FIGURE 1). Furthermore, landmasses occasionally split apart. As continental blocks separate, a new ocean basin emerges between them. Meanwhile, other portions of the seafloor plunge into the mantle. In short, a dramatically different model of Earth's tectonic processes emerged. Tectonic processes are those that deform Earth's crust to create major structural features, such as mountains, continents, and ocean basins.

This profound reversal in scientific thought has been appropriately described as a *scientific revolution.* The revolution began early in the twentieth century as a relatively straightforward proposal called *continental drift.* For more than 50 years, most of the scientific establishment categorically rejected the idea that continents were capable of movement. Continental drift was particularly distasteful to North American geologists, perhaps because much of the supporting evidence had been gathered from the continents of Africa, South America, and Australia, with which most North American geologists were unfamiliar.

Following World War II, modern instruments replaced rock hammers as the tools of choice for many researchers. Armed with more advanced tools, geologists and a new breed of researchers, including *geophysicists* and *geochemists*, made several surprising discoveries that began to rekindle interest in the drift hypothesis. By 1968 these developments had led to the unfolding of a far more encompassing explanation known as the *theory of plate tectonics.*

In this chapter, we will examine the events that led to this dramatic reversal of scientific opinion. We will also briefly trace the development of the *continental drift hypothesis*, examine why it was initially rejected, and consider the evidence that finally led to the acceptance of its direct descendant—the theory of plate tectonics.

1 CONCEPT CHECKS

1. Briefly describe the view held by most geologists prior to the 1960s regarding the ocean basins and continents.
2. What group of geologists were the least receptive to the continental drift hypothesis? Explain.

FIGURE 1 The French Alps
This rock pinnacle is near Mount Blanc. The Alps were created by the collision of the African and Eurasian plates. (Photo by Bildagentur Waldhaeus/AGE Fotostock)

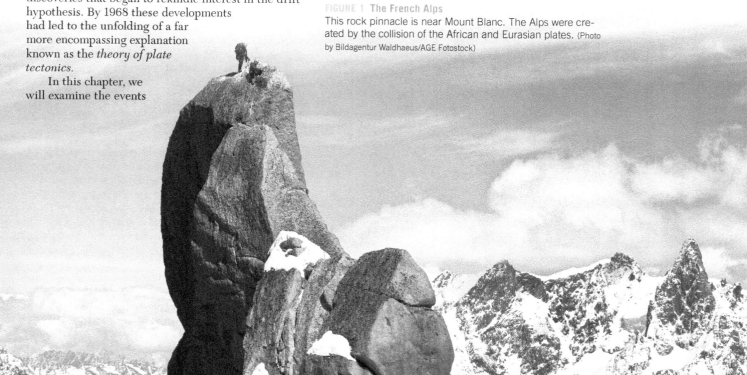

2 Continental Drift: An Idea Before Its Time

The idea that continents, particularly South America and Africa, fit together like pieces of a jigsaw puzzle came about during the 1600s, as better world maps became available. However, little significance was given to this notion until 1915, when Alfred Wegener (1880–1930), a German meteorologist and geophysicist, wrote *The Origin of Continents and Oceans*. This book set forth the basic outline of Wegener's hypothesis called **continental drift**, which dared to challenge the long-held assumption that the continents and ocean basins had fixed geographic positions.

Wegener suggested that a single **supercontinent** consisting of all Earth's landmasses once existed.* He named this giant landmass **Pangaea** (pronounced "Pan-jee-ah," meaning "all lands") (FIGURE 2). Wegener further hypothesized that during the early part of the Mesozoic era, this supercontinent began to fragment into smaller landmasses. These continental blocks then "drifted" to their present positions over a span of millions of years.

Wegener and others who advocated the continental drift hypothesis collected substantial evidence to support their point of view. The fit of South America and Africa and the geographic distribution of fossils and ancient climates all seemed to buttress the idea that these now separate landmasses were once joined. Let us examine some of this evidence.

*Wegener was not the first person to conceive of a long-vanished supercontinent. Edward Suess (1831–1914), a distinguished nineteenth-century geologist, pieced together evidence for a giant landmass consisting of the continents of South America, Africa, India, and Australia.

Evidence: The Continental Jigsaw Puzzle

Like a few others before him, Wegener suspected that the continents might once have been joined when he noticed the remarkable similarity between the coastlines on opposite sides of the Atlantic Ocean. However, Wegener's use of present-day shorelines to fit these continents together was challenged immediately by other Earth scientists. These opponents correctly argued that shorelines are continually modified by wave erosion and depositional processes. Even if continental displacement had taken place, a good fit today would be unlikely. Because Wegener's original jigsaw fit of the continents was crude, it is assumed that he was aware of this problem (Figure 2).

Scientists later determined that a much better approximation of the outer boundary of a continent is the seaward edge of its continental shelf, which lies submerged a few hundred meters below sea level. In the early 1960s, Sir Edward Bullard and two associates constructed a map that pieced together the edges of the continental shelves of South America and Africa at a depth of about 900 meters (3000 feet) (FIGURE 3). The remarkable fit that was obtained was more precise than even these researchers had expected.

Evidence: Fossils Match Across the Seas

Although the seed for Wegener's hypothesis came from the remarkable similarities of the continental margins on opposite sides of the Atlantic, it was when he learned that identical fossil organisms had been discovered in rocks from both South America and Africa that his pursuit of continental drift became more focused. Through a review of the literature, Wegener learned that most paleontologists (scientists who study the fossilized remains of ancient organisms) were in agreement that some type of land connection was

SMARTFIGURE 2
Reconstructions of Pangaea
Pangaea, as it is thought to have appeared 200 million years ago.

Modern reconstruction of Pangaea

Wegener's Pangaea, redrawn from his book published in 1912.

Drawing that shows the best fit of South America and Africa along the continental slope at a depth of 500 fathoms (about 900 meters).

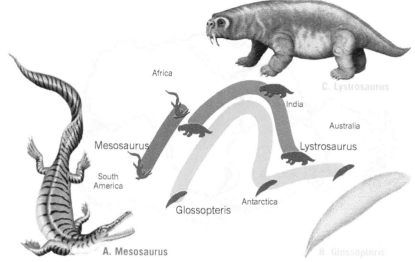

FIGURE 4 **Fossil evidence supporting continental drift**
Fossils of identical organisms have been discovered in rocks of similar age in Australia, Africa, South America, Antarctica, and India—continents that are currently widely separated by ocean barriers. Wegener accounted for these occurrences by placing these continents in their pre-drift locations.

needed to explain the existence of similar Mesozoic age life-forms on widely separated landmasses. Just as modern life-forms native to North America are quite different from those of Africa and Australia, during the Mesozoic era, organisms on widely separated continents should have been distinctly different.

Mesosaurus　To add credibility to his argument, Wegener documented cases of several fossil organisms found on different landmasses, despite the unlikely possibility that their living forms could have crossed the vast ocean presently separating them (FIGURE 4). A classic example is *Mesosaurus*, a small aquatic freshwater reptile whose fossil remains are limited to black shales of the Permian period (about 260 million years ago) in eastern South America and southwestern Africa. If *Mesosaurus* had been able to make the long journey across the South Atlantic, its remains would likely be more widely distributed. As this is not the case, Wegener asserted that South America and Africa must have been joined during that period of Earth history.

How did opponents of continental drift explain the existence of identical fossil organisms in places separated by thousands of kilometers of open ocean? Rafting, trans-oceanic land bridges (isthmian links), and island stepping stones were the most widely invoked explanations for these migrations (FIGURE 5). We know, for example, that during the Ice Age that ended about 8,000 years ago, the lowering of sea level allowed mammals (including humans) to cross the narrow Bering Strait that separates Russia and Alaska. Was it possible that land bridges once connected

Africa and South America but later subsided below sea level? Modern maps of the seafloor substantiate Wegener's contention that land bridges connecting these continents never existed.

FIGURE 5 **How do land animals cross vast oceans?**
These sketches by John Holden illustrate various explanations for the occurrence of similar species on landmasses that are presently separated by vast oceans. (Copyright John C. Holden)

Glossopteris Wegener also cited the distribution of the fossil "seed fern" *Glossopteris* as evidence for the existence of Pangaea (see Figure 4). This plant, identified by its tongue-shaped leaves and seeds that were too large to be carried by the wind, was known to be widely dispersed among Africa, Australia, India, and South America. Later, fossil remains of *Glossopteris* were also discovered in Antarctica.* Wegener also learned that these seed ferns and associated flora grew only in cool climates—similar to central Alaska. Therefore, he concluded that when these landmasses were joined, they were located much closer to the South Pole.

Evidence: Rock Types and Geologic Features

Anyone who has worked a jigsaw puzzle knows that its successful completion requires that you fit the pieces together while maintaining the continuity of the picture. The "picture" that must match in the "continental drift puzzle" is one of rock types and geologic features such as mountain belts. If the continents were together, the rocks found in a particular region on one continent should closely match in age and type those found in adjacent positions on the once adjoining continent. Wegener found evidence of highly deformed

---

*In 1912 Captain Robert Scott and two companions froze to death lying beside 35 pounds of rock on their return from a failed attempt to be the first to reach the South Pole. These samples, collected on the moraines of Beardmore Glacier, contained fossil remains of *Glossopteris*.

igneous rocks in Brazil that closely resembled similar rocks in Africa.

Similar evidence can be found in mountain belts that terminate at one coastline and reappear on landmasses across the ocean. For instance, the mountain belt that includes the Appalachians trends northeastward through the eastern United States and disappears off the coast of Newfoundland (FIGURE 6A). Mountains of comparable age and structure are found in the British Isles and Scandinavia. When these landmasses are positioned as they were about 200 million years ago, as shown in FIGURE 6B, the mountain chains form a nearly continuous belt.

Wegener described how the similarities in geologic features on both sides of the Atlantic linked these landmasses when he said, "It is just as if we were to refit the torn pieces of a newspaper by matching their edges and then check whether the lines of print run smoothly across. If they do, there is nothing left but to conclude that the pieces were in fact joined in this way."†

Evidence: Ancient Climates

Because Alfred Wegener was a student of world climates, he suspected that paleoclimatic (*paleo* = ancient, *climatic* = climate) data might also support the idea of mobile continents. His assertion was bolstered when he learned that evidence for a glacial

---

†Alfred Wegener, *The Origin of Continents and Oceans*, translated from the 4th revised German ed. of 1929 by J. Birman (London: Methuen, 1966).

FIGURE 6 Matching mountain ranges across the North Atlantic

A.

B.

period that dated to the late Paleozoic had been discovered in southern Africa, South America, Australia, and India. This meant that about 300 million years ago, vast ice sheets covered extensive portions of the Southern Hemisphere as well as India. Much of the land area that contains evidence of this period of Paleozoic glaciation presently lies within 30 degrees of the equator in subtropical or tropical climates.

How could extensive ice sheets form near the equator? One proposal suggested that our planet experienced a period of extreme global cooling. Wegener rejected this explanation because during the same span of geologic time, large tropical swamps existed in several locations in the Northern Hemisphere. The lush vegetation in these swamps was eventually buried and converted to coal (FIGURE 7A). Today these deposits comprise major coal fields in the eastern United States and Northern Europe. Many of the fossils found in these coal-bearing rocks were produced by tree ferns that possessed large fronds—a fact consistent with warm, moist climates.** The existence of these large tropical swamps, Wegener argued, was inconsistent with the proposals that extreme global cooling caused glaciers to form in what are currently tropical areas.

Wegener suggested that a more plausible explanation for the late Paleozoic glaciation was provided by the super-continent of Pangaea. In this configuration, the southern continents are joined together and located near the South Pole (FIGURE 7B). This would account for the conditions necessary to generate extensive expanses of glacial ice over much of these landmasses. At the same time, this geography would place today's northern continents nearer the equator and account for the tropical swamps that generated the vast coal deposits.

How does a glacier develop in hot, arid central Australia? How do land animals migrate across wide expanses of the ocean? As compelling as this evidence may have been, 50 years passed before most of the scientific community accepted the concept of continental drift and the logical conclusions to which it led.

** It is important to note that coal can form in a variety of climates, provided that large quantities of plant life are buried before decaying.

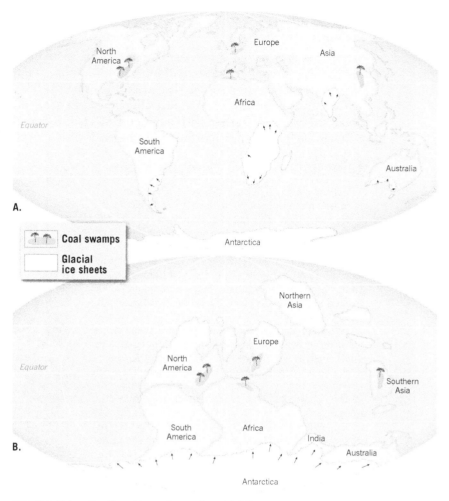

FIGURE 7 Paleoclimatic evidence for continental drift

2 CONCEPT CHECKS

1. What was the first line of evidence that led early investigators to suspect that the continents were once connected?
2. Explain why the discovery of the fossil remains of *Mesosaurus* in both South America and Africa, but nowhere else, supports the continental drift hypothesis.
3. Early in the twentieth century, what was the prevailing view of how land animals migrated across vast expanses of open ocean?
4. How did Wegener account for the existence of glaciers in the southern landmasses at a time when areas in North America, Europe, and Asia supported lush tropical swamps?

3 | The Great Debate

Wegener's proposal did not attract much open criticism until 1924, when his book was translated into English, French, Spanish, and Russian. From that point until his death in 1930, the drift hypothesis encountered a great deal of hostile criticism. The respected American geologist R. T. Chamberlain stated, "Wegener's hypothesis in general is of the foot-loose type, in that it takes considerable liberty with our globe, and is less bound by restrictions or tied down by awkward, ugly facts than most of its rival theories."

Rejection of the Drift Hypothesis

One of the main objections to Wegener's hypothesis stemmed from his inability to identify a credible mechanism for continental drift. Wegener proposed that gravitational forces of the Moon and Sun that produce Earth's tides were also capable of gradually moving the continents across the globe. However, the prominent physicist Harold Jeffreys correctly countered that tidal forces strong enough to move Earth's continents would have resulted in halting our planet's rotation, which, of course, has not happened.

Wegener also incorrectly suggested that the larger and sturdier continents broke through thinner oceanic crust, much as ice breakers cut through ice. However, no evidence existed to suggest that the ocean floor was weak enough to permit passage of the continents without the continents being appreciably deformed in the process.

In 1930 Wegener made his fourth and final trip to the Greenland Ice Sheet (FIGURE 8). Although the primary focus of this expedition was to study this great ice cap and its climate, Wegener continued to test his continental drift hypothesis. While returning from Eismitte, an experimental station located in the center of Greenland, Wegener perished along with his Greenland companion. His intriguing idea, however, did not die.

FIGURE 8 Alfred Wegener (Photo courtesy of Archive of Alfred Wegener Institute)

Alfred Wegener shown waiting out the 1912–1913 Arctic winter during an expedition to Greenland, where he made a 1200-kilometer traverse across the widest part of the island's ice sheet.

FIGURE 9 Plate movement causes destructive earthquakes Pisco, Peru, following a powerful earthquake on August 16, 2007. (Sergio Urday/EPA/Newscom)

Why was Wegener unable to overturn the established scientific views of his day? Foremost was the fact that, although the central theme of Wegener's drift hypothesis was correct, it contained some incorrect details. For example, continents do not break through the ocean floor, and tidal energy is much too weak to cause continents to be displaced. Moreover, in order for any comprehensive scientific theory to gain wide acceptance, it must withstand critical testing from all areas of science. Despite Wegener's great contribution to our understanding of Earth, not *all* of the evidence supported the continental drift hypothesis as he had proposed it.

Although many of Wegener's contemporaries opposed his views, even to the point of open ridicule, some considered his ideas plausible. For those geologists who continued the search, the exciting concept of continents adrift held their interest. Others viewed continental drift as a solution to previously unexplainable observations (FIGURE 9). Nevertheless, most of the scientific community, particularly in North America, either categorically rejected continental drift or treated it with considerable skepticism.

3 CONCEPT CHECK

1. What two aspects of Wegener's continental drift hypothesis were objectionable to most Earth scientists?

GEOGRAPHICS

The Breakup of Pangaea

Geologists have used paleoclimatic and paleomagnetic studies to re-create the steps in the breakup of Pangaea—an event that began about 180 million years ago.

Pangaea as it appeared 200 million years ago in the late Triassic Period.

200 Million Years Ago

The first major event during the breakup of Pangaea was the separation of North America and Africa, which marked the opening of the North Atlantic.

150 Million Years Ago

By 90 million years ago, the South Atlantic had opened. Continued breakup in the Southern Hemisphere led to the separation of Africa, India, and Antarctica.

90 Million Years Ago

? During the breakup of Pangaea, which modern continent grew significantly in size?

About 50 million years ago, Southeast Asia had docked with Eurasia, while India continued its northward journey.

50 Million Years Ago

During the past 20 million years of Earth history, Arabia has rifted from Africa creating the Red Sea, while Baja, California, has separated from Mexico to form the Gulf of California.

20 Million Years Ago

Present

By 20 million years ago India had begun its ongoing collision with Eurasia to create the Himalayas and the Tibetan Highlands.

4 The Theory of Plate Tectonics

Following World War II, oceanographers equipped with new marine tools and ample funding from the U.S. Office of Naval Research embarked on an unprecedented period of oceanographic exploration. Over the next two decades, a much better picture of large expanses of the seafloor slowly and painstakingly began to emerge. From this work came the discovery of a global **oceanic ridge system** that winds through all the major oceans in a manner similar to the seams on a baseball.

In other parts of the ocean, more new discoveries were being made. Studies conducted in the western Pacific demonstrated that earthquakes were occurring at great depths beneath deep-ocean trenches. Of equal importance was the fact that dredging of the seafloor did not bring up any oceanic crust that was older than 180 million years. Further, sediment accumulations in the deep-ocean basins were found to be thin, not the thousands of meters that were predicted. By 1968 these developments, among others, had led to the unfolding of a far more encompassing theory than continental drift, known as the **theory of plate tectonics** (*tekto* = to build).

Rigid Lithosphere Overlies Weak Asthenosphere

According to the plate tectonics model, the crust and the uppermost, and therefore coolest, part of the mantle constitute Earth's strong outer layer, known as the **lithosphere** (*lithos* = stone, *sphere* = ball). The lithosphere varies in both thickness and density, depending on whether it is oceanic lithosphere or continental lithosphere (FIGURE 10). Oceanic lithosphere is about 100 kilometers (60 miles) thick in the deep-ocean basins, but is considerably thinner along the crest of the oceanic ridge system—a topic we will consider later. By contrast, continental lithosphere averages about 150 kilometers thick but may extend to depths of 200 kilometers or more beneath the stable interiors of the continents. Further, the composition of both the oceanic and continental crusts affects their respective densities. Oceanic crust is composed of rocks that are rich in iron and magnesium, and therefore oceanic lithosphere has a greater density than continental lithosphere. Continental crust is composed largely of less dense rocks, making continental lithosphere less dense than its oceanic counterpart.

The **asthenosphere** (*asthenos* = weak, *sphere* = ball) is a hotter, weaker region in the mantle that lies below the lithosphere (Figure 10). The temperatures and pressures in the upper asthenosphere (100 to 200 kilometers in depth) are such that rocks at this depth are very near their melting temperatures and, hence, respond to forces by *flowing*. By contrast, the relatively cool and rigid lithosphere tends to respond to forces acting on it by *bending or breaking but not flowing*. Because of these differences, Earth's rigid outer shell is effectively detached from the asthenosphere, which allows these layers to move independently.

Earth's Major Plates

The lithosphere is broken into about two dozen segments of irregular size and shape called **lithospheric plates**, or simply **plates**, that are in constant motion with respect to one another (FIGURE 11). Seven major lithospheric plates are recognized and account for 94 percent of Earth's surface area. These include the *North American, South American, Pacific, African, Eurasian, Australian-Indian,* and *Antarctic plates.* The largest is the Pacific plate, which encompasses a significant portion of the Pacific basin. The six other large plates include an entire continent plus a significant amount of ocean floor. Notice in FIGURE 11 that the South American plate encompasses almost all of South America and about one-half of the floor of the South Atlantic. This is a major departure from Wegener's

SMARTFIGURE 10
Rigid lithosphere overlies the weak asthenosphere

Earth's Major Plates

Divergent boundary ⤢
Convergent boundary ⤐
Transform fault boundary ⟋

FIGURE 11 Earth's major lithospheric plates

continental drift hypothesis, which proposed that the continents move through the ocean floor, not with it. Note also that none of the plates are defined entirely by the margins of a single continent.

Intermediate-sized plates include the *Caribbean, Nazca, Philippine, Arabian, Cocos, Scotia,* and *Juan de Fuca plates.* These plates, with the exception of the Arabian plate, are composed mostly of oceanic lithosphere. In addition, several smaller plates (*microplates*) have been identified but are not shown in Figure 11.

Plate Boundaries

One of the main tenets of the plate tectonics theory is that plates move as somewhat rigid units relative to all other plates. As plates move, the distance between two locations on different plates, such as New York and London, gradually changes, whereas the distance between sites on the same plate—New York and Denver,

for example—remains relatively constant. However, parts of some plates are comparatively "soft," such as southern China, which is literally being squeezed as the Indian subcontinent rams into Asia proper.

Because plates are in constant motion relative to each other, most major interactions among them (and, therefore, most deformation) occur along their *boundaries.* In fact, plate boundaries were first established by plotting the locations of earthquakes and volcanoes. Plates are bounded by three distinct types of boundaries, which are differentiated by the type of movement they exhibit. These boundaries are depicted in FIGURE 12 and are briefly described here:

1. Divergent plate boundaries (*constructive margins*)— where two plates move apart, resulting in upwelling of hot material from the mantle to create new sea-floor (Figure 12A).
2. Convergent plate boundaries (*destructive margins*)— where two plates move together, resulting either in

A. Divergent boundary ——

B. Convergent boundary ——

C. Transform fault boundary ——

FIGURE 12 Divergent, convergent, and transform plate boundaries

oceanic lithosphere descending beneath an overriding plate, eventually to be reabsorbed into the mantle or possibly in the collision of two continental blocks to create a mountain belt (Figure 12B).

3. Transform plate boundaries (*conservative margins*)—where two plates grind past each other without the production or destruction of lithosphere (Figure 12C).

Divergent and convergent plate boundaries each account for about 40 percent of all plate boundaries. Transform faults account for the remaining 20 percent. In the

following sections we will summarize the nature of the three types of plate boundaries.

4 CONCEPT CHECKS

1. What major ocean floor feature did oceanographers discover after World War II?
2. Compare and contrast the lithosphere and the asthenosphere.
3. List the seven largest lithospheric plates.
4. List the three types of plate boundaries and describe the relative motion at each of them.

5 | Divergent Plate Boundaries and Seafloor Spreading

Most **divergent plate boundaries** (*di* = apart, *vergere* = to move) are located along the crests of oceanic ridges and can be thought of as *constructive plate margins* because this is where new ocean floor is generated (FIGURE 13). Here, two adjacent plates move away from each other, producing long, narrow fractures in the ocean crust. As a result, hot rock from the mantle below migrates upward to fill the voids left as the crust is being ripped apart. This molten material gradually cools to produce new slivers of seafloor. In a slow yet unending manner, adjacent plates spread apart, and new oceanic lithosphere forms between them.

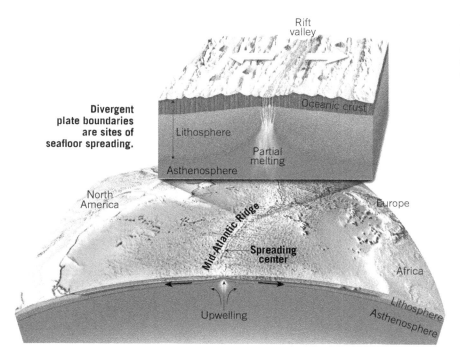

FIGURE 13 Seafloor spreading Most divergent plate boundaries are situated along the crests of oceanic ridges—the sites of seafloor spreading.

Oceanic Ridges and Seafloor Spreading

The majority of, but not all, divergent plate boundaries are associated with *oceanic ridges*: elevated areas of the seafloor characterized by high heat flow and volcanism. The global ridge system is the longest topographic feature on Earth's surface, exceeding 70,000 kilometers (43,000 miles) in length. As shown in Figure 12, various segments of the global ridge system have been named, including the Mid-Atlantic Ridge, East Pacific Rise, and Mid-Indian Ridge.

Representing 20 percent of Earth's surface, the oceanic ridge system winds through all major ocean basins like the seams on a baseball. Although the crest of the oceanic ridge is commonly 2 to 3 kilometers higher than the adjacent ocean basins, the term *ridge* may be misleading because it implies "narrow" when, in fact, ridges vary in width from 1000 to more than 4000 kilometers. Further, along the crest of some ridge segments is a deep canyonlike structure called a **rift valley** (FIGURE 14). This structure is evidence that tensional forces are actively pulling the ocean crust apart at the ridge crest.

The mechanism that operates along the oceanic ridge system to create new seafloor is appropriately called **seafloor spreading**. Typical rates of spreading average around 5 centimeters (2 inches) per year, roughly the same rate at which human fingernails grow. Comparatively slow spreading rates of 2 centimeters per year are found along the Mid-Atlantic Ridge, whereas spreading rates exceeding 15 centimeters (6 inches) per year have been measured along sections of the East Pacific Rise. Although these rates of seafloor production are slow on a human time scale, they are nevertheless rapid enough to have generated all of Earth's ocean basins within the past 200 million years.

FIGURE 14 Rift valley
Thingvellir National Park, Iceland is located on the western margin of a rift valley that is roughly 30 kilometers wide in this region. This rift valley is connected to a similar feature that extends along the crest of the Mid-Atlantic Ridge. The cliff in the left half of the image approximates the eastern edge of the North American plate.
(Photo by Ragnar Sigurdsson/ Arctic/Alamy)

The primary reason for the elevated position of the oceanic ridge is that newly created oceanic lithosphere is hot, making it less dense than cooler rocks found away from the ridge axis. (Geologists use the term *axis* to refer to a line that follows the general trend of the ridge crest.) As soon as new lithosphere forms, it is slowly yet continually displaced away from the zone of upwelling. Thus, it begins to cool and contract, thereby increasing in density. This thermal contraction accounts for the increase in ocean depths away from the ridge crest. It takes about 80 million years for the temperature of oceanic lithosphere to stabilize and contraction to cease. By this time, rock that was once part of the elevated oceanic ridge system is located in the deep-ocean basin, where it may be buried by substantial accumulations of sediment.

In addition, as the plate moves away from the ridge, cooling of the underlying asthenosphere causes it to become increasingly more rigid. Thus, oceanic lithosphere is generated by cooling of the asthenosphere from the top down. Stated another way, the thickness of oceanic lithosphere is age dependent. The older (cooler) it is, the greater its thickness. Oceanic lithosphere that exceeds 80 million years in age is about 100 kilometers thick—approximately its maximum thickness.

Continental Rifting

Divergent boundaries can develop within a continent, in which case the landmass may split into two or more smaller segments separated by an ocean basin. Continental rifting begins when plate motions produce opposing (tensional) forces that pull and stretch the lithosphere. Stretching, in turn, thins the lithosphere, which promotes mantle upwelling and broad upwarping of the overlying lithosphere (FIGURE 15A). During this process, the lithosphere is thinned, while the brittle crustal rocks break into large blocks. As the tectonic forces continue to pull apart the crust, the broken crustal fragments drop, generating an elongated depression called a **continental rift** (FIGURE 15B).

A modern example of an active continental rift is the East African Rift (see Figure 12). Whether this rift will eventually result in the breakup of Africa is a topic of continued research. Nevertheless, the East African Rift is an excellent model of the initial stage in the breakup of a continent. Here, tensional forces have stretched and thinned the lithosphere, allowing molten rock to ascend from the mantle. Evidence for recent volcanic activity includes several large volcanic mountains, including Mount Kilimanjaro and Mount Kenya, the tallest peaks in Africa. Research suggests that if rifting continues, the rift valley will lengthen and deepen (FIGURE 15C). At some point, the rift valley will become a narrow sea with an outlet to the ocean (FIGURE 15D). The Red Sea, which formed when the Arabian Peninsula split from Africa, is a modern example of such a feature and provides us with a view of how the Atlantic Ocean may have looked in its infancy.

Continental rifting occurs where plate motions produce tensional forces that thin the lithosphere and promote upwelling in the mantle.

Stretching causes the brittle crust to break into large blocks that sink, generating a rift valley.

Continued spreading generates a long narrow sea similar to the present-day Red Sea.

Eventually, an expansive deep-ocean basin containing a centrally located oceanic ridge is formed by continued seafloor spreading.

SMARTFIGURE 15 Continental rifting: formation of new ocean basins

5 CONCEPT CHECKS

1. Sketch or describe how two plates move in relation to each other along divergent plate boundaries.
2. What is the average rate of seafloor spreading in modern oceans?
3. List four facts that characterize the oceanic ridge system.
4. Briefly describe the process of continental rifting. Where is it occurring today?

6 Convergent Plate Boundaries and Subduction

New lithosphere is constantly being produced at the oceanic ridges. However, our planet is not growing larger; its total surface area remains constant. A balance is maintained because older, denser portions of oceanic lithosphere descend into the mantle at a rate equal to seafloor production. This activity occurs along **convergent plate boundaries**, where two plates move toward each other and the leading edge of one is bent downward, as it slides beneath the other (**FIGURE 16**).

SMARTFIGURE 16
Three types of convergent plate boundaries

A. Convergent plate boundary where oceanic lithosphere is subducting beneath continental lithosphere.

B. Convergent plate boundary involving two slabs of oceanic lithosphere.

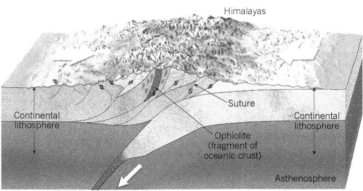

C. Continental collisions occur along convergent plate boundaries when both plates are capped with continental crust.

Convergent boundaries are also called **subduction zones** because they are sites where lithosphere is descending (being subducted) into the mantle. Subduction occurs because the density of the descending lithospheric plate is greater than the density of the underlying asthenosphere. In general, old oceanic lithosphere is about 2 percent more dense than the underlying asthenosphere, which causes it to subduct. Continental lithosphere, in contrast, is less dense and resists subduction. As a consequence, only oceanic lithosphere will subduct to great depths.

Deep-ocean trenches are the surface manifestations produced as oceanic lithosphere descends into the mantle. These large linear depressions are remarkably long and deep. The Peru–Chile trench along the west coast of South America is more than 4500 kilometers (3000 miles) long, and its base is as much as 8 kilometers (5 miles) below sea level. The trenches in the western Pacific, including the Mariana and Tonga trenches, tend to be even deeper than those of the eastern Pacific.

Slabs of oceanic lithosphere descend into the mantle at angles that vary from a few degrees to nearly vertical (90 degrees). The angle at which oceanic lithosphere subducts depends largely on its age and therefore its density. For example, when seafloor spreading occurs near a subduction zone, as is the case along the coast of Chile, the subducting lithosphere is young and buoyant, which results in a low angle of descent. As the two plates converge, the overriding plate scrapes over the top of the subducting plate below—a type of forced subduction. Consequently, the region around the Peru–Chile trench experiences great earthquakes, including the 2010 Chilean earthquake—one of the 10 largest on record.

As oceanic lithosphere ages (gets farther from the spreading center), it gradually cools, which causes it to thicken and increase in density. In parts of the western Pacific, some oceanic lithosphere is 180 million years old—the thickest and densest in today's oceans. The very dense slabs in this region typically plunge into the mantle at angles approaching 90 degrees. This largely explains the fact that most trenches in the western Pacific are deeper than trenches in the eastern Pacific.

Although all convergent zones have the same basic characteristics, they may vary considerably, based on the type of crustal material involved and the tectonic setting. Convergent boundaries can form between *two oceanic plates, one oceanic plate and one continental plate,* or *two continental plates.*

Oceanic–Continental Convergence

When the leading edge of a plate capped with continental crust converges with a slab of oceanic lithosphere, the buoyant continental block remains "floating," while the denser oceanic slab sinks into the mantle (Figure 16A). When a descending oceanic slab reaches a depth of about 100 kilometers (60 miles), melting is triggered within the wedge of hot asthenosphere that lies above it. But how does the subduction of a cool slab of oceanic lithosphere cause mantle rock to melt? The answer lies in the fact that water contained in the descending plates acts the way salt does to melt ice. That is, "wet" rock in a high-pressure environment melts at substantially lower temperatures than does "dry" rock of the same composition.

Sediments and oceanic crust contain large amounts of water, which is carried to great depths by a subducting plate. As the plate plunges downward, heat and pressure drive water from the voids in the rock. At a depth of roughly 100 kilometers (60 miles), the wedge of mantle rock is sufficiently hot that the introduction of water from the slab below leads to some melting. This process, called **partial melting**, is thought to generate some molten material, which is mixed with unmelted mantle rock. Being less dense than the surrounding mantle, this hot mobile material gradually rises toward the surface. Depending on the environment, these mantle-derived masses of molten rock may ascend through the crust and give rise to a volcanic eruption. However, much of this material

never reaches the surface; rather, it solidifies at depth—a process that thickens the crust.

The volcanoes of the towering Andes are the product of molten rock generated by the subduction of the Nazca plate beneath the South American continent (see Figure 12). Mountain systems, such as the Andes, which are produced in part by volcanic activity associated with the subduction of oceanic lithosphere, are called **continental volcanic arcs**. The Cascade Range in Washington, Oregon, and California is another mountain system that consists of several well-known volcanic mountains, including Mount Rainier, Mount Shasta, and Mount St. Helens (FIGURE 17). This active volcanic arc also extends into Canada, where it includes Mount Garibaldi, Mount Silverthrone, and others.

Mt. Hood, Oregon

FIGURE 17 Oceanic–continental convergent plate boundary
Mount Hood, Oregon, is one of more than a dozen large composite volcanoes in the Cascade Range.

When an oceanic plate descends into the asthenosphere, water driven from the subducting slab lowers the melting temperature of mantle rock sufficiently to generate magma. The Cascade Range is a continental volcanic arc formed by the subduction of the Juan de Fuca plate under the North American plate.

Island arcs are generally located 100 to 300 kilometers (60 to 200 miles) from a deep-ocean trench. Located adjacent to the island arcs just mentioned are the Aleutian trench, the Mariana trench, and the Tonga trench.

Most volcanic island arcs are located in the western Pacific. Only two are located in the Atlantic—the Lesser Antilles arc, on the eastern margin of the Caribbean Sea, and the Sandwich Islands, located off the tip of South America. The Lesser Antilles are a product of the subduction of the Atlantic seafloor beneath the Caribbean plate. Located within this volcanic arc are the Virgin Islands of the United States and Britain as well as the island of Martinique, where Mount Pelée erupted in 1902, destroying the town of St. Pierre and killing an estimated 28,000 people. This chain of islands also includes Montserrat, where there has been recent volcanic activity.

Island arcs are typically simple structures made of numerous volcanic cones underlain by oceanic crust that is generally less than 20 kilometers (12 miles) thick. By contrast, some island arcs are more complex and are underlain by highly deformed crust that may reach 35 kilometers (22 miles) in thickness. Examples include Japan, Indonesia, and the Alaskan Peninsula. These island arcs are built on material generated by earlier episodes of subduction or on small slivers of continental crust that have rafted away from the mainland.

FIGURE 18 Volcanoes of the Aleutian Islands The Aleutian Islands are a volcanic island arc produced by the subduction of the Pacific plate beneath the North American plate.

Oceanic–Oceanic Convergence

An *oceanic–oceanic convergent boundary* has many features in common with oceanic–continental plate margins. Where two oceanic slabs converge, one descends beneath the other, initiating volcanic activity by the same mechanism that operates at all subduction zones (see Figure 12). Water squeezed from the subducting slab of oceanic lithosphere triggers melting in the hot wedge of mantle rock above. In this setting, volcanoes grow up from the ocean floor rather than upon a continental platform. When subduction is sustained, it will eventually build a chain of volcanic structures large enough to emerge as islands. The newly formed land consisting of an arc-shaped chain of volcanic islands is called a **volcanic island arc**, or simply an **island arc** (FIGURE 18).

The Aleutian, Mariana, and Tonga islands are examples of relatively young volcanic island arcs.

Continental–Continental Convergence

The third type of convergent boundary results when one landmass moves toward the margin of another because of subduction of the intervening seafloor (FIGURE 19A). Whereas oceanic lithosphere tends to be dense and sink into the mantle, the thick buoyant continental lithosphere inhibits it from being subducted. Consequently, a collision between two converging continental fragments ensues (FIGURE 19B). This event folds and deforms the accumulation of sediments and sedimentary rocks along the continental margins as if they had been placed in a gigantic vise. The result is the formation of a new mountain belt composed of deformed sedimentary and metamorphic rocks that often contain slivers of oceanic crust (FIGURE 20).

FIGURE 19 Collision of India and Eurasia

The ongoing collision of the subcontinent of India with Eurasia began about 50 million years ago—producing the majestic Himalayas.

Continental volcanic arc

Eurasia

Ocean basin

Continental shelf deposits

Melting

India

Subducting oceanic lithosphere

Asthenosphere

N

A.

India today

10 million years ago

38 million years ago

55 million years ago

71 million years ago

N | B.

Ganges Plain

Himalayas

Tibetan Plateau

India

Indian plate

N

Lithosphere

Asthenosphere

C.

FIGURE 20 A continental collision produced the Alps (Photo by Gareth McCormack/ Alamy)

The Alps were created by the collision of the African and Eurasian plates.

Such a collision began about 50 million years ago, when the subcontinent of India "rammed" into Asia, producing the Himalayas—the most spectacular mountain range on Earth (Figure 19C). During this collision, the continental crust buckled and fractured and was generally shortened horizontally and thickened vertically. In addition to the Himalayas, several other major mountain systems, including the Alps, Appalachians, and Urals, formed as continental fragments collided.

6 CONCEPT CHECKS

1. Explain why the rate of lithosphere production roughly balances with the rate at which it is destroyed.
2. Compare a continental volcanic arc and a volcanic island arc.
3. Describe the process that leads to the formation of deep-ocean trenches.
4. Why does oceanic lithosphere subduct, while continental lithosphere does not?
5. Briefly describe how mountain belts such as the Himalayas form.

EYE on Earth

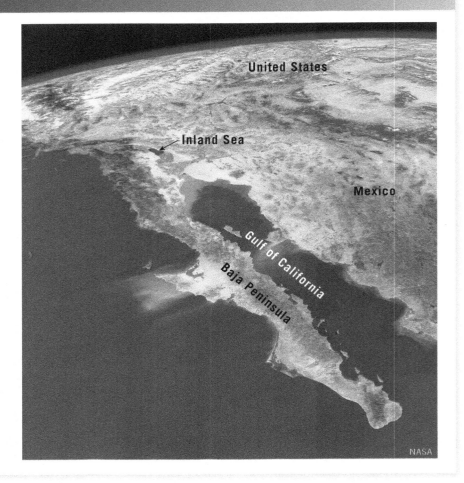

Baja, California, is separated from mainland Mexico by a long narrow sea called the Gulf of California (also known to local residents as the Sea of Cortez). The Gulf of California contains many islands that were created by volcanic activity.

Question 1 What type of plate boundary is responsible for opening the Gulf of California?

Question 2 What major U.S. river originates in the Colorado Rockies and created a large delta at the northern end of the Gulf of California?

Question 3 If the material carried by the river in Question 2 had *not* been deposited, the Gulf of California would extend northward to include the inland sea shown in this satellite image. What is the name of this inland sea?

7 Transform Plate Boundaries

Along a **transform plate boundary**, also called a **transform fault**, plates slide horizontally past one another without the production or destruction of lithosphere. The nature of transform faults was discovered in 1965 by Canadian geologist J. Tuzo Wilson, who proposed that these large faults connected two spreading centers (divergent boundaries) or, less commonly, two trenches (convergent boundaries). Most transform faults are found on the ocean floor, where they offset segments of the oceanic ridge system, producing a steplike plate margin (FIGURE 21). Notice that the zigzag shape of the Mid-Atlantic Ridge in Figure 12 roughly reflects the shape of the original rifting that caused the breakup of the supercontinent of Pangaea. (Compare the shapes of the continental margins of the landmasses on both sides of the Atlantic with the shape of the Mid-Atlantic Ridge.)

SMARTFIGURE 21
Transform plate boundaries

Most transform faults are part of prominent linear breaks in the seafloor known as **fracture zones**, which include both active transform faults as well as their inactive extensions into the plate interior (FIGURE 21B). Active transform faults lie *only between* the two offset ridge segments and are generally defined by weak, shallow earthquakes. Here seafloor produced at one ridge axis moves in the opposite direction of seafloor produced at an opposing ridge segment. Thus, between the ridge segments, these adjacent slabs of oceanic crust are grinding past each other along a transform fault. Beyond the ridge crests are inactive zones, where the fractures are preserved as linear topographic depressions. The trend of these fracture zones roughly parallels the direction of plate motion at the time of their formation. Thus, these structures are useful in mapping the direction of plate motion in the geologic past.

In another role, transform faults provide the means by which the oceanic crust created at ridge crests can be transported to a site of destruction—the deep-ocean trenches. FIGURE 22 illustrates this situation. Notice that the Juan de Fuca plate moves in a southeasterly direction, eventually being subducted under the west coast of the United States and Canada. The southern end of this plate is bounded by a transform fault called the Mendocino fault. This transform boundary connects the Juan de Fuca Ridge to the Cascadia subduction zone. Therefore, it facilitates the movement of the crustal material created at the Juan de Fuca Ridge to its destination beneath the North American continent.

Like the Mendocino fault, most other transform fault boundaries are located within the ocean basins; however, a few cut through continental crust. Two examples are the earthquake-prone San Andreas fault of California

Fracture zones are long, narrow scar-like features in the seafloor that are roughly perpendicular to the offset ridge segments. They include both the active transform fault and its "fossilized" trace.

Fracture zone

Inactive zone | Transform fault (active) | Inactive zone

Oceanic crust

B.

Most transform faults offset segments of a spreading center, producing a step-like plate margin.

Mid-Atlantic Ridge

South America

Africa

KEY
Spreading centers
Fracture zones
Transform faults

A. The Mid-Atlantic Ridge, with its zigzag pattern, roughly reflects the shape of the rifting zone which resulted in the break-up of Pangaea.

and New Zealand's Alpine fault. Notice in Figure 22 that the San Andreas fault connects a spreading center located in the Gulf of California to the Cascadia subduction zone and the Mendocino fault located along the northwest coast of the United States. Along the San Andreas fault, the Pacific plate is moving toward the

FIGURE 22 **Transform faults facilitate plate motion**
Seafloor generated along the Juan de Fuca Ridge
moves southeastward, past the Pacific plate. Eventually it subducts beneath the North American
plate. Thus, this transform fault connects a spreading center (divergent boundary) to a subduction
zone (convergent boundary). Also shown is the San
Andreas fault, a transform fault that connects two
spreading centers: the Juan de Fuca Ridge and a
spreading center located in the Gulf of California.

The Mendocino transform fault facilitates
the movement of seafloor generated at the
Juan de Fuca ridge by allowing it to slip
southeastward past the Pacific plate to its
site of destruction beneath the North
American plate.

FIGURE 23 **Movement along
the San Andreas Fault**
This aerial view shows the
offset in the dry channel of
Wallace Creek near Taft,
California. (Photo by Michael
Collier)

northwest, past the North American plate (FIGURE 23). If
this movement continues, the part of California west of
the fault zone, including the Baja Peninsula of Mexico,
will become an island off the West Coast of the United
States and Canada—with the potential to eventually
reach Alaska. However, a more immediate concern is
the earthquake activity triggered by movements along
this fault system.

7 CONCEPT CHECKS

1. Sketch or describe how two plates move in relation to
each other along a transform plate boundary.
2. Differentiate between transform faults and the two other
types of plate boundaries.

8 Testing the Plate Tectonics Model

Some of the evidence supporting continental drift has already been presented. With the development of the theory of plate tectonics, researchers began testing this new model of how Earth works. Although new supporting data were obtained, it has often been new interpretations of already existing data that have swayed the tide of opinion.

Evidence: Ocean Drilling

Some of the most convincing evidence for seafloor spreading came from the Deep Sea Drilling Project, which operated from 1968 until 1983. One of the early goals of the project was to gather samples of the ocean floor in order to establish its age. To accomplish this, the *Glomar Challenger*, a drilling ship capable of working in water thousands of meters deep, was built. Hundreds of holes were drilled through the layers of sediments that blanket the ocean crust, as well as into the basaltic rocks below. Rather than radiometrically dating the crustal rocks, researchers used the fossil remains of microorganisms found in the sediments resting directly on the crust to date the seafloor at each site.*

When the oldest sediment from each drill site was plotted against its distance from the ridge crest, the plot showed that the sediments increased in age with increasing distance from the ridge (FIGURE 24). This finding supported the seafloor-spreading hypothesis, which predicted that the youngest oceanic crust would be found at the ridge crest, the site of seafloor production, and the oldest oceanic crust would be located adjacent to the continents.

The thickness of ocean-floor sediments provided additional verification of seafloor spreading. Drill cores from the *Glomar Challenger* revealed that sediments are almost entirely absent on the ridge crest and that sediment thickness increases with increasing distance from the ridge (Figure 24). This pattern of sediment distribution should be expected if the seafloor-spreading hypothesis is correct.

The data collected by the Deep Sea Drilling Project also reinforced the idea that the ocean basins are geologically young because no seafloor with an age in excess of 180 million years was found. By comparison, most continental crust exceeds several hundred million years in age, and some has been located that exceeds 4 billion years in age.

In October 2003, the *JOIDES Resolution*, a replacement for the *Glomar Challenger*, became part of a new program, the Integrated Ocean Drilling Program (IODP). This new international effort uses multiple vessels for exploration, including the massive 210-meter-long (nearly 770-foot-long) *Chikyu* (meaning "planet Earth" in Japanese), which began operations in 2007 (Figure 24). One of the goals of the IODP is to recover a complete section of the ocean crust, from top to bottom.

_____

*Radiometric dates of the ocean crust itself are unreliable because of the alteration of basalt by seawater.

Core samples show that the thickness of sediments increase with distance from the ridge crest.

Age of seafloor
Older   Younger   Older

Drilling ship collects core samples of seafloor sediments and basaltic crust

Ocean crust (basalt)

Chikyu is a state-of-the-art drilling ship designed to drill up to 7,000 meters (more than 4 miles) below the seafloor.

AP/Wide World

FIGURE 24 Deep-sea drilling
Data collected through deep-sea drilling have shown that the ocean floor is indeed youngest at the ridge axis.

Evidence: Mantle Plumes and Hot Spots

Mapping volcanic islands and seamounts (submarine volcanoes) in the Pacific Ocean revealed several linear chains of volcanic structures. One of the most-studied chains consists of at least 129 volcanoes that extend from the Hawaiian Islands to Midway Island and continue northwestward toward the Aleutian trench (FIGURE 25A). Radiometric dating of this linear structure, called the *Hawaiian Island–Emperor Seamount chain*, showed that the volcanoes increase in age with increasing distance from the Big Island of Hawaii. The youngest volcanic island in the chain (Hawaii) rose from the ocean floor less than 1 million years ago, whereas Midway Island is 27 million years old, and Detroit Seamount, near the Aleutian trench, is about 80 million years old (Figure 25A).

Most researchers agree that a cylindrically shaped upwelling of hot rock, called a **mantle plume**, is located beneath the island of Hawaii. As the hot, rocky plume

FIGURE 25 Hot spots and hot-spot tracks
A. Radiometric dating of the Hawaiian islands shows that volcanic activity increases in age moving away from the Big Island of Hawaii. **B.** Locations of some well-documented hot spots and hot-spot tracks.

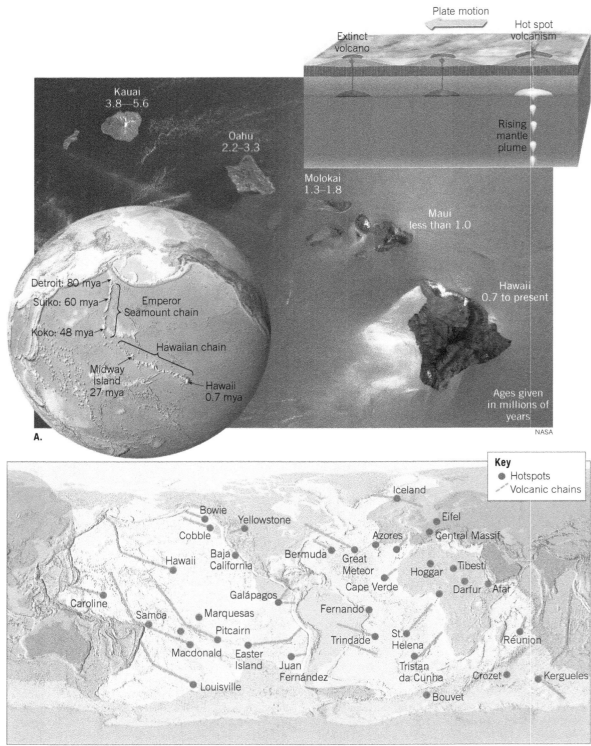

A.

NASA

B.

ascends through the mantle, the confining pressure drops, which triggers partial melting. This process is called *decompression melting*. The surface manifestation of this activity is a **hot spot**, an area of volcanism, high heat flow, and crustal uplifting that is a few hundred kilometers across. As the Pacific plate moved over a hot spot, a chain of volcanic structures known as a **hot-spot track** was built. As shown in Figure 25A, the age of each volcano indicates how much time has elapsed since it was situated over the mantle plume.

A closer look at the five largest Hawaiian islands reveals a similar pattern of ages, from the volcanically active island of Hawaii to the inactive volcanoes that make up the oldest island, Kauai (Figure 25). Five million years ago, when Kauai was positioned over the hot spot, it was the *only* modern Hawaiian island in existence. Visible evidence of the age of Kauai can be seen by examining its extinct volcanoes, which have been eroded into jagged peaks and vast canyons. By contrast, the relatively young island of Hawaii exhibits many fresh lava flows, and one of its five major volcanoes, Kilauea, remains active today.

Research suggests that at least some mantle plumes originate at great depth, perhaps at the core–mantle boundary. Others, however, may have a more shallow origin. For example, the mantle plume located beneath Iceland is thought to originate at a rather shallow depth of perhaps just 450 kilometers. Of the 40 or so hot spots that have been identified worldwide, most, but not all have hot-spot tracks (FIGURE 25B).

Evidence: Paleomagnetism

Anyone who has used a compass to find direction knows that Earth's magnetic field has north and south magnetic poles. Today these magnetic poles roughly align with the geographic poles. (The geographic poles are located where Earth's rotational axis intersects the surface.) Earth's magnetic field is similar to that produced by a simple bar magnet. Invisible lines of force pass through the planet and extend from one magnetic pole to the other (FIGURE 26). A compass needle, itself a small magnet free to rotate on an axis, becomes aligned with the magnetic lines of force and points to the magnetic poles.

Earth's magnetic field is less obvious than the pull of gravity because humans cannot feel it. Movement of a compass needle, however, confirms its presence. In addition, some naturally occurring minerals are magnetic and are influenced by Earth's magnetic field. One of the most common is the iron-rich mineral *magnetite*, which is abundant in lava flows of basaltic composition.* Basaltic lavas erupt at the surface at temperatures greater than 1000 °C, exceeding a threshold temperature for magnetism known as the **Curie point** (about 585 °C).

---
*Some sediments and sedimentary rocks also contain enough iron-bearing mineral grains to acquire a measurable amount of magnetization.

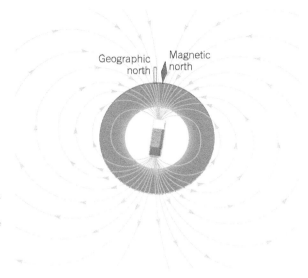

FIGURE 26 Earth's magnetic field Earth's magnetic field consists of lines of force much like those a giant bar magnet would produce if placed at the center of Earth.

Consequently, the magnetite grains in molten lava are nonmagnetic. However, as the lava cools, these iron-rich grains become magnetized and align themselves in the direction of the existing magnetic lines of force. Once the minerals solidify, the magnetism they possess usually remains "frozen" in this position. Thus, they act like a compass needle because they "point" toward the position of the magnetic poles at the time of their formation. Rocks that formed thousands or millions of years ago and contain a "record" of the direction of the magnetic poles at the time of their formation are said to possess **paleomagnetism**, or **fossil magnetism**.

Apparent Polar Wandering A study of paleomagnetism in ancient lava flows throughout Europe led to an interesting discovery. The magnetic alignment of iron-rich minerals in lava flows of different ages indicated that the position of the paleomagnetic poles had changed through time. A plot of the location of the magnetic north pole, as measured from Europe, revealed that during the past 500 million years, the pole had gradually wandered from a location near Hawaii northeastward to its present location over the Arctic Ocean (FIGURE 27). This was strong evidence that either the magnetic north pole had migrated, an idea known as *polar wandering*, or that the poles had remained in place and the continents had drifted beneath them—in other words, Europe had drifted in relation to the magnetic north pole.

Although the magnetic poles are known to move in a somewhat erratic path, studies of paleomagnetism from numerous locations show that the positions of the magnetic poles, averaged over thousands of years, correspond closely to the positions of the geographic poles. Therefore, a more acceptable explanation for

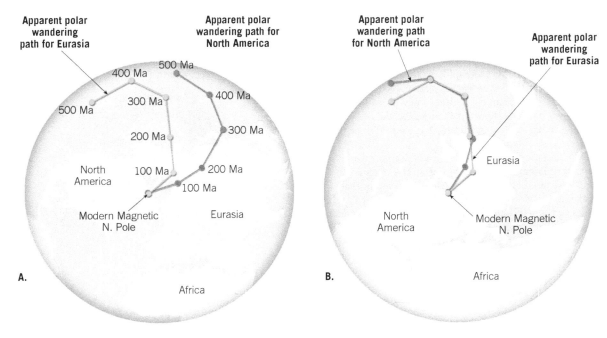

FIGURE 27 Apparent polar-wandering paths

the apparent polar wandering paths was provided by Wegener's hypothesis: If the magnetic poles remain stationary, their *apparent movement* is produced by continental drift.

Further evidence for continental drift came a few years later, when a polar-wandering path was constructed for North America (Figure 27A). For the first 300 million years or so, the paths for North America and Europe were found to be similar in direction—but separated by about 5000 kilometers (3000 miles). Then, during the middle of the Mesozoic era (180 million years ago), they began to converge on the present North Pole. The explanation for these curves is that North America and Europe were joined until the Mesozoic, when the Atlantic began to open. From this time forward, these continents continuously moved apart. When North America and Europe are moved back to their pre-drift positions, as shown in Figure 27B, these apparent wandering paths coincide. This is evidence that North America and Europe were once joined and moved relative to the poles as part of the same continent.

Magnetic Reversals and Seafloor Spreading

Another discovery came when geophysicists learned that over periods of hundreds of thousands of years, Earth's magnetic field periodically reverses polarity. During a **magnetic reversal**, the magnetic north pole becomes the magnetic south pole and vice versa. Lava solidifying during a period of reverse polarity will be magnetized with the polarity opposite that of volcanic rocks being formed today. When rocks exhibit the same magnetism as the present magnetic field, they are said to possess **normal polarity**, whereas rocks exhibiting the opposite magnetism are said to have **reverse polarity**.

Once the concept of magnetic reversals was confirmed, researchers set out to establish a time scale for these occurrences. The task was to measure the magnetic polarity of hundreds of lava flows and use radiometric dating techniques to establish the age of each flow. FIGURE 28 shows the **magnetic time scale** established using this technique for the past few million years. The major divisions of the magnetic time scale are called *chrons* and last for roughly 1 million years. As more measurements became available, researchers realized that several short-lived reversals (less than 200,000 years long) often occurred during a single chron.

Meanwhile, oceanographers had begun to do magnetic surveys of the ocean floor in conjunction with their efforts to construct detailed maps of seafloor topography. These magnetic surveys were accomplished by towing very sensitive instruments, called **magnetometers**, behind research vessels (FIGURE 29A). The goal of these geophysical surveys was to map variations in the strength of Earth's magnetic field that arise from differences in the magnetic properties of the underlying crustal rocks.

The first comprehensive study of this type was carried out off the Pacific Coast of North America and had an unexpected outcome. Researchers discovered

Magnetic Time Scale

SMARTFIGURE 28
Time scale of magnetic reversals
A. Time scale of Earth's magnetic reversals for the past 4 million years. **B.** This time scale was developed by establishing the magnetic polarity for lava flows of known age. (Data from Allen Cox and G. B. Dalrymple)

A.

Brunhes normal chron

Jaramillo normal subchron

Matuyama reversed chron

Olduvai normal subchron

Gauss normal chron

Mammoth reversed subchron

Gilbert reversed chron

Age Millions of years

Normal polarity 0.4 mya
Reversed polarity 1.2 mya
Normal polarity 2.6 mya

B.

FIGURE 29 Ocean floor as a magnetic recorder
A. Magnetic intensities are recorded when a magnetometer is towed across a segment of the oceanic floor. **B.** Notice the symmetrical stripes of low- and high-intensity magnetism that parallel the axis of the Juan de Fuca Ridge. Vine and Matthews suggested that the stripes of high-intensity magnetism occur where normally magnetized oceanic rocks enhanced the existing magnetic field. Conversely, the low-intensity stripes are regions where the crust is polarized in the reverse direction, which weakens the existing magnetic field.

Research vessel towing magnetometer across ridge crest

Ridge axis

Magnetometer record

Stronger magnetism

Weaker magnetism

A.

CANADA

Axis of Juan de Fuca Ridge

Normal polarity

Reverse polarity

Symmetrical strips of low- and high-intensity magnetism parallel the axis of the Juan de Fuca Ridge

UNITED STATES

B.

69

FIGURE 30 Magnetic reversals and seafloor spreading

When new basaltic rocks form at mid-ocean ridges, they magnetize according to Earth's existing magnetic field. Hence, oceanic crust provides a permanent record of each reversal of our planet's magnetic field over the past 200 million years.

A. Normal polarity

Magma

B. Reversed polarity

Magma

C. Normal polarity

Magma

TIME

alternating stripes of high- and low-intensity magnetism, as shown in FIGURE 29B. This relatively simple pattern of magnetic variation defied explanation until 1963, when Fred Vine and D. H. Matthews demonstrated that the high- and low-intensity stripes supported the concept of seafloor spreading. Vine and Matthews suggested that the stripes of high-intensity magnetism are regions where the paleomagnetism of the ocean crust exhibits normal polarity (Figure 29A). Consequently, these rocks *enhance* (reinforce) Earth's magnetic field. Conversely, the low-intensity stripes are regions where the ocean crust is polarized in the reverse direction and therefore *weaken* the existing magnetic field. But how do parallel stripes of normally and reversely magnetized rock become distributed across the ocean floor?

Vine and Matthews reasoned that as magma solidifies along narrow rifts at the crest of an oceanic ridge, it is magnetized with the polarity of the existing magnetic field (FIGURE 30). Because of seafloor spreading, this strip of magnetized crust would gradually increase in width. When Earth's magnetic field reverses polarity, any newly formed seafloor having the opposite polarity would form in the middle of the old strip. Gradually, the two halves of the old strip would be carried in opposite directions, away from the ridge crest. Subsequent reversals would

build a pattern of normal and reverse magnetic stripes, as shown in Figure 30. Because new rock is added in equal amounts to both trailing edges of the spreading ocean floor, we should expect the pattern of stripes (size and polarity) found on one side of an oceanic ridge to be a mirror image of those on the other side. In fact, a survey across the Mid-Atlantic Ridge just south of Iceland reveals a pattern of magnetic stripes exhibiting a remarkable degree of symmetry in relation to the ridge axis (FIGURE 30).

8 CONCEPT CHECKS

1. What is the age of the oldest sediments recovered using deep-ocean drilling? How do the ages of these sediments compare to the ages of the oldest continental rocks?
2. Assuming that hot spots remain fixed, in what direction was the Pacific plate moving while the Hawaiian islands were forming? When Suiko Seamount was forming?
3. How do sedimentary cores from the ocean floor support the concept of seafloor spreading?
4. Describe how Fred Vine and D. H. Matthews related the seafloor-spreading hypothesis to magnetic reversals.

9 How Is Plate Motion Measured?

A number of methods are used to establish the direction and rate of plate motion. Some of these techniques not only confirm that lithospheric plates move but allow us to trace those movements back in geologic time.

Geologic Evidence for Plate Motion

Using ocean-drilling ships, researchers have obtained radiometric dates for hundreds of locations on the ocean floor. By knowing the age of a sample and its distance from the ridge axis where it was generated, an average rate of plate motion can be calculated.

Scientists have used these data, combined with paleomagnetism stored in hardened lavas on the ocean floor, as well as extensive mapping of the seafloor, to create maps like the one in FIGURE 31. Examining this map, we can see that the reddish-orange colored band running along the East Pacific Rise is more than three times wider than the same-color band along the Mid-Atlantic Ridge. Therefore, we can conclude that the rate of seafloor spreading in the Pacific basin must be more than three times greater than in the Atlantic.

Maps of this type also provide clues to the current direction of plate movement. Notice the offsets in the ridges; these are transform faults that connect the spreading centers. Recall that transform faults are aligned parallel to the direction of spreading. Therefore,

when measured carefully, transform faults yield the direction of plate movement.

One way geologists can establish the direction of plate motion in the past is by examining the long fracture zones that extend for hundreds or even thousands of kilometers from ridge crests. Fracture zones are inactive extensions of transform faults and therefore preserve a record of past directions of plate motion. Unfortunately, most of the ocean floor is less than 180 million years old, so to look deeper into the past, researchers must rely on paleomagnetic evidence provided by continental rocks.

Measuring Plate Motion from Space

You are likely familiar with the Global Positioning System (GPS), which is part of the navigation system used to locate one's position in order to provide directions to some other location. The Global Positioning System employs satellites that send radio signals that are intercepted by GPS receivers located at Earth's surface. The exact position of a site is determined by simultaneously establishing the distance from the receiver to four or more

FIGURE 31 Age of the ocean floor

Age of Oceanic Lithosphere

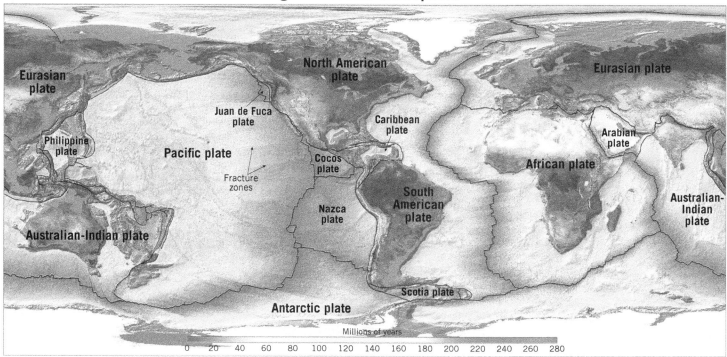

FIGURE 32 Rates of plate motion
The red arrows show plate motion at selected locations based on GPS data. The small black arrows and labels show seafloor spreading velocities based mainly on paleomagnetic data. (Seafloor data from DeMets and others; GPS data from Jet Propulsion Laboratory)

Directions and rates of plate motions measured in centimeters per year

satellites. Researchers use specifically designed equipment to locate the position of a point on Earth to within a few millimeters (about the diameter of a small pea). To establish plate motions, GPS data are collected at numerous sites repeatedly over a number of years.

Data obtained from these and other techniques are shown in FIGURE 32. Calculations show that Hawaii is moving in a northwesterly direction and approaching Japan at 8.3 centimeters per year. A location in Maryland is retreating from a location in England at a speed of 1.7 centimeters per year—a value that is close to the 2.0-centimeters-per-year spreading rate established from paleomagnetic evidence obtained for the North Atlantic. Techniques involving GPS devices have also been useful in establishing small-scale crustal movements such as those that occur along faults in regions known to be tectonically active—for example, the San Andreas fault.

How Does Plate Motion Affect Plate Boundaries?

Although the total surface area of Earth does not change, because of plate motion, the size and shape of individual plates are constantly changing. For example, the African plate, which is mainly bounded by divergent boundaries (the Mid-Atlantic Ridge on the west and Mid-Indian and Southwest Indian ridges on the east) is continually growing in size as new lithosphere is added to its margins. By contrast, the Pacific plate, which is

being consumed into the mantle along its northern and western flanks much faster than it is growing along the East Pacific Rise, is diminishing in size.

Another consequence of plate motion is that boundaries also migrate. For example, the relative position of the African continent to the ridges that surround it continually changes. The addition of new seafloor along the ridges requires that the ridges move outward relative to Africa.

Plate boundaries can also be created or destroyed in response to changes in the forces acting on the lithosphere. Recall that the Red Sea is the site of a relatively new spreading center. It came into existence less than 20 million years ago, when the Arabian Peninsula began to split from Africa. At other locations, plates carrying continental crust are presently moving toward one another. Eventually these continental fragments may collide, eliminating the convergent plate boundary that once separated them. A collision of this type occurred about 250 to 300 million years ago, when the western edge of the landmass that today we call Siberia collided with Europe to generate the Ural Mountains.

9 CONCEPT CHECKS

1. What do transform faults that connect spreading centers indicate about plate motion?
2. Refer to Figure 32 and determine which three plates appear to exhibit the highest rates of motion.

10 What Drives Plate Motions?

Researchers are in general agreement that some type of **convection**—where hot mantle rocks rise and cold, dense oceanic lithosphere sinks—is the ultimate driver of plate tectonics. Many of the details of this convective flow, however, remain topics of debate in the scientific community.

Forces That Drive Plate Motion

From geophysical evidence, we have learned that although the mantle consists almost entirely of solid rock, it is hot and weak enough to exhibit a slow, fluid-like convective flow. The simplest type of convection is analogous to heating a pot of water on a stove (FIGURE 33). Heating the base of a pot causes the water to become less dense (more buoyant), causing it to rise in relatively thin sheets or blobs that spread out at the surface. As the surface layer cools, its density increases, and the cooler water sinks back to the bottom of the pot, where it is reheated until it achieves enough buoyancy to rise again. Mantle convection is similar to, but considerably more complex than, the model just described.

There is general agreement that subduction of cold, dense slabs of oceanic lithosphere is a major driving force of plate motion (FIGURE 34). This phenomenon, called **slab pull**, occurs because cold slabs of oceanic lithosphere are more dense than the underlying warm asthenosphere and hence "sink like a rock."

The average density of the upper asthenosphere is about 3.25 g/cm^3, while 100-million-year-old oceanic lithosphere has an overall density that is slightly greater—about 3.28 g/cm^3. (Although this difference may seem insignificant, remember that most humans are roughly the same density as water and will sink if they expel the excess air from their lungs.) However, oceanic lithosphere that is less than 15 million years old and is still warm has a density less than that of the asthenosphere and therefore resists subduction, a topic we will consider later.

Cooler water sinks

Warm water rises

Convection is a type of heat transfer that involves the actual movement of a substance.

FIGURE 33 Convection in a cooking pot
As a stove warms the water in the bottom of a cooking pot, the heated water expands, becomes less dense (more buoyant), and rises. Simultaneously, the cooler, denser water near the top sinks.

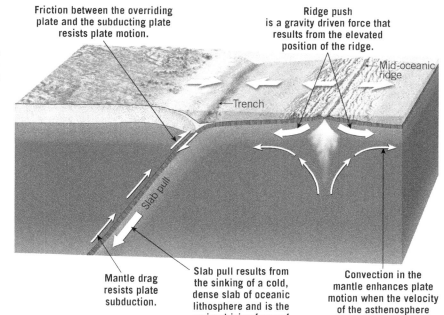

Friction between the overriding plate and the subducting plate resists plate motion.

Ridge push is a gravity driven force that results from the elevated position of the ridge.

Mid-oceanic ridge

Trench

Slab pull

Mantle drag resists plate subduction.

Slab pull results from the sinking of a cold, dense slab of oceanic lithosphere and is the major driving force of plate motion.

Convection in the mantle enhances plate motion when the velocity of the asthenosphere exceeds that of the overlying plate.

FIGURE 34 Forces that act on lithospheric plates

Another important driving force is **ridge push** (Figure 34). This gravity-driven mechanism results from the elevated position of the oceanic ridge, which causes slabs of lithosphere to "slide" down the flanks of the ridge. Ridge push appears to contribute far less to plate motions than slab pull. The primary evidence for this is that fastest-moving plates—the Pacific, Nazca, and Cocos plates—have extensive subduction zones along their margins. By contrast, the spreading rate in the North Atlantic basin, which is nearly devoid of subduction zones, is one of the lowest, at about 2.5 centimeters (1 inch) per year (see Figure 31).

Although the subduction of cold, dense lithospheric plates appears to be the dominant force acting on plates, other factors are at work as well. Flow in the mantle, perhaps best described as "mantle drag," is also thought to affect plate motion (Figure 34). When flow in the asthenosphere is moving at a velocity that exceeds that of the plate, mantle drag enhances plate motion. However, if the asthenosphere is moving more slowly than the plate, or if it is moving in the opposite direction, this force tends to resist plate motion. Another type of resistance to plate motion occurs along some subduction zones, where

FIGURE 35 Models of mantle convection
A. In the whole-mantle convection model, cold oceanic lithosphere descends into the lowermost mantle, while two types of hot mantle plumes transport heat toward the surface. **B.** The layer cake model consists of two convection layers—an upper dynamic convective layer overlying a sluggish layer below.

A. In the "whole mantle model", sinking slabs of cold oceanic lithosphere are the downward limbs of convection cells, while rising mantle plumes carry hot material from the core-mantle boundary toward the surface.

B. The "layer cake model" has two largely disconnected convective layers. A dynamic upper layer driven by descending slabs of cold oceanic lithosphere and a sluggish lower layer that carries heat upward without appreciably mixing with the layer above.

friction between the overriding plate and the descending slab generates significant earthquake activity.

Models of Plate–Mantle Convection

Although **convection** in the mantle has yet to be fully understood, researchers generally agree on the following:

1. Convective flow in the rocky 2900-kilometer-thick mantle—in which warm, buoyant rock rises and cooler, denser material sinks—is the underlying driving force for plate movement.
2. Mantle convection and plate tectonics are part of the same system. Subducting oceanic plates drive the cold downward-moving portion of convective flow, while shallow upwelling of hot rock along the oceanic ridge and buoyant mantle plumes are the upward-flowing arms of the convective mechanism.

3. Convective flow in the mantle is a major mechanism for transporting heat away from Earth's interior to the surface, where it is eventually radiated into space.

What is not known with certainty is the exact structure of this convective flow. Two models that have been proposed for plate–mantle convection are presented next.

Whole-Mantle Convection Most researchers favor some type of *whole-mantle convection* model, also called the *plume model*, in which cold oceanic lithosphere sinks to great depths and stirs the entire mantle (FIGURE 35A). The whole-mantle model suggests that the ultimate burial ground for subducting slabs is the core–mantle boundary. This downward flow is balanced by buoyantly rising mantle plumes that transport hot material toward the surface (Figure 35A).

EYE on Earth

In December 2011 a new volcanic island formed near the southern end of the Red Sea. People fishing in the area witnessed lava fountains reaching up to 30 meters (100 feet). This volcanic activity occurred off the west coast of Yemen, along the Red Sea Rift, among a collection of small islands in the Zubair Group.

Question 1 What type of plate boundary produced this new volcanic island?

Question 2 What two plates border the Red Sea Rift?

Question 3 Are these two plates moving *toward* or *away* from each other?

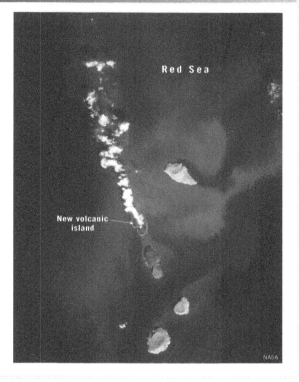

Red Sea

New volcanic island

NASA

Two kinds of plumes have been proposed—narrow tubes and giant upwellings. The long, narrow plumes that extend from the core–mantle boundary are thought to produce hot-spot volcanism of the type associated with the Hawaiian islands, Iceland, and Yellowstone. Areas of large upwelling, as shown in Figure 32A, are thought to occur beneath the Pacific basin and southern Africa. The latter structure is thought to account for the fact that southern Africa has an elevation that is much higher than would be predicted for a stable continental landmass. Heat for both types of plumes is thought to arise mainly from the core, while the deep mantle provides a source for chemically distinct magmas.

Layer Cake Model Some researchers argue that the mantle resembles a "layer cake" divided at a depth of perhaps 660 kilometers but no deeper than 1000 kilometers. As shown in FIGURE 35B, this layered model has two zones of convection—a thin, dynamic layer in the upper mantle and a thick, larger, sluggish one located below. As with the whole-mantle model, the downward convective flow is driven by the subduction of cold, dense oceanic lithosphere. However, rather than reach the lower mantle, these subducting slabs penetrate to depths of no more than 1000 kilometers (620 miles). Notice in Figure 35B

that the upper layer in the layer cake model is littered with recycled oceanic lithosphere of various ages. Melting of these fragments is thought to be the source of magma for some of the volcanism that occurs away from plate boundaries, as in the volcanoes of Hawaii.

In contrast to the active upper mantle, the lower mantle is sluggish and does not provide material to support volcanism at the surface. However, very slow convection within this layer likely carries heat upward, but very little mixing between these two layers is thought to occur.

Although the layer cake model has limited support among geologists, it is gaining in popularity. Perhaps a hypothesis that combines features from the layer cake model and the whole-mantle convection model will emerge.

10 CONCEPT CHECKS

1. Describe slab pull and ridge push. Which of these forces appears to contribute more to plate motion?
2. What role are mantle plumes thought to play in the convective flow in the mantle?
3. Briefly describe the two models proposed for mantle–plate convection.

CONCEPTS IN REVIEW: PLATE TECTONICS: A SCIENTIFIC REVOLUTION UNFOLDS

1 From continental drift to plate tectonics

Discuss the view that most geologists held prior to the 1960s regarding the geographic positions of the ocean basins and continents.

• Fifty years ago, most geologists thought that ocean basins were very old and that continents were fixed in place. Those ideas were discarded with a scientific revolution that revitalized geology: the theory of plate tectonics. Supported by multiple kinds of evidence, plate tectonics is the foundation of modern Earth science.

PARADIGM SHIFT   Today, we know that the early twentieth-century scientists who rejected the idea of continental drift were wrong. Were they therefore bad scientists? Why or why not?

2 Continental drift: An idea before its time

List and explain the evidence presented by Wegener to support his continental drift hypothesis.

KEY WORDS continental drift, supercontinent, Pangaea

• German meteorologist Alfred Wegener formulated the idea of continental drift in 1915. He suggested that Earth's continents were not fixed in place but moved slowly over geologic time.
• Wegener reconstructed a supercontinent called Pangaea that existed during the late Paleozoic and early Mesozoic. He presented several kinds of data to show that Pangaea once existed but later broke into pieces that drifted apart.
• Wegener's evidence included (1) the shape of the continents, (2) continental fossil organisms that matched across oceans, (3) modern mountain belts and ancient rocks, and (4) sedimentary rocks that recorded ancient climates, including glaciers on the southern portion of Pangaea.

CRITTERS   Why did Wegener choose organisms such as *Glossopteris* and *Mesosaurus* as evidence for continental drift, as opposed to other fossil organisms such as sharks or jellyfish?

John Cancalosi/AGE Fotostock

3 The great debate

Discuss the two main objections to the continental drift hypothesis.

• Wegener's bold hypothesis suffered from two flaws: It proposed tidal forces as the mechanism for the motion of continents, and it implied that the continents would have plowed their way through weaker oceanic crust, like a boat cutting through a thin layer of sea ice. Geologists rejected the idea of continental drift when Wegener proposed it, and it wasn't resurrected for another 50 years.

TEACH THE CONTROVERSY   Like Galileo before him, Wegener had scientific ideas that were rejected by his contemporaries. Many years later, Wegener was vindicated, when his ideas were shown to be correct. Does this imply that all minority viewpoints in science are correct and all consensus viewpoints suppress dissent?

4 The theory of plate tectonics

List the major differences between Earth's lithosphere and asthenosphere and explain the importance of each in the plate tectonics theory.

KEY WORDS ocean ridge system, theory of plate tectonics, lithosphere, asthenosphere, lithospheric plate (plate)

- Research conducted during World War II led to new insights that helped revive Wegener's hypothesis of continental drift. Exploration of the seafloor revealed previously unknown features, including an extremely long mid-ocean ridge system. Sampling of the oceanic crust revealed that it was quite young relative to the continents. Integrating these data with Wegener's evidence for continental drift led to the modern theory of plate tectonics.
- The lithosphere is Earth's outermost rocky layer. It is broken into the plates of plate tectonics. It is relatively stiff and deforms by breaking or bending. Beneath the lithosphere is the asthenosphere, a relatively weak layer that deforms by flowing. The lithosphere consists both of crust (either oceanic or continental) and underlying upper mantle. Plates are usually a combination of both continental and oceanic lithosphere.
- There are seven large plates, another seven intermediate-size plates, and numerous relatively small microplates. Plates meet along boundaries that may either be divergent (moving apart from each other), convergent (moving toward each other), or transform (moving laterally past each other).

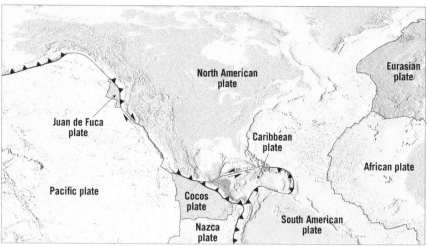

A SENSE OF WHERE YOU ARE On which plate do you live? How far are you from the nearest plate boundary? How far are you from the coastline? How far are you from the nearest oceanic lithosphere? Are these numbers the same or different? Why?

5 Divergent plate boundaries and seafloor spreading

Sketch and describe the movement along a divergent plate boundary that results in the formation of new oceanic lithosphere.

KEY WORDS divergent plate boundary, rift valley, seafloor spreading, continental rift

- Seafloor spreading leads to the generation of new oceanic lithosphere at mid-ocean ridge systems. As two plates move apart from one another, tensional forces open cracks in the "wake" of the plate. As a fracture opens, magma wells up to seal it shut with a new seam of igneous rock. This process generates new oceanic lithosphere at a rate of 2 to 15 centimeters each year.

- As it ages, oceanic lithosphere cools and becomes denser. As it is transported away from the mid-ocean ridge, it therefore subsides. At the same time, new material is added to its underside, and it grows thicker.
- Divergent boundaries are not limited to the seafloor. Continents can break apart, too, starting with a continental rift (like modern-day east Africa) and then separating into several fragments, with a new ocean basin opening between them.

GOING THE DISTANCE Seafloor spreading along the Mid-Atlantic Ridge has been measured to be about 2 centimeters per year. How much further away will Europe be from North America by the time you retire?

6 Convergent plate boundaries and subduction

Compare and contrast the three types of convergent plate boundaries and name a location where each type can be found.

KEY WORDS convergent plate boundary, subduction zones, deep-ocean trenches, partial melting, continental volcanic arcs, volcanic island arc (island arc)

- When plates move toward one another, oceanic lithosphere is recycled into the mantle by being subducted. Subduction manifests itself on the ocean floor as a deep linear trench. The subducting slab of oceanic lithosphere can descend at a variety of angles, from nearly horizontal to nearly vertical.
- Aided by the presence of water, the subducted oceanic lithosphere triggers melting in the mantle, which produces magma. The magma is less dense than the surrounding rock and will rise. It may cool at depth, thickening the crust, or it may make it all the way to Earth's surface, where it erupts as a volcano.
- A line of volcanoes that emerge through continental crust is termed a continental volcanic arc, while a line of volcanoes that emerge through an overriding plate of oceanic lithosphere is a volcanic island arc. Plate tectonics explains why these volcanoes are arranged in arcs.
- Continental crust resists subduction due to its relatively low density, and so when an intervening ocean basin is completely destroyed through subduction, the continents on either side collide, generating a new mountain range.

DRAW IT Sketch a typical continental volcanic arc and label the key parts. Then repeat the drawing with an overriding plate made of oceanic lithosphere.

7 Transform plate boundaries

Describe the relative motion along a transform fault boundary
and be able to locate several examples on a plate boundary map.

KEY WORDS transform plate boundary (transform fault), fracture
zone

* At a transform boundary, lithospheric plates slide horizontally
past one another. No new lithosphere is generated, and no old
lithosphere is consumed. Relatively weak, shallow earthquakes
signal the movement of these slabs of rock as they grind past their
neighbors.
* The San Andreas fault in California is an example of a transform
boundary in continental crust, while the fracture zones between
segments of the Mid-Atlantic Ridge are an example of oceanic crust.

HAITI'S FAULT   On the accompanying tectonic map of the
Caribbean, find the Enriquillo fault. (The location
of the 2010 Haiti earthquake is shown as a yellow star.) What kind of
plate boundary is shown here? Are there any other faults in the area that
show the same type of motion?

---

8 Testing the plate tectonics model

Summarize the evidence used to support the plate tectonics theory.

KEY WORDS mantle plume, hot spot, hot-spot track, Curie point, paleomagnetism (fossil magnetism), magnetic reversal, normal polarity,
reverse polarity, magnetic time scale, magnetometer

Magnetic Time Scale

Age
Millions
of years

Brunhes normal chron	—0—
Jaramillo normal subchron →	—1—
Matuyama reversed chron	
Olduvai normal subchron →	—2—
Gauss normal chron	—3—
Mammoth reversed subchron /	
Gilbert reversed chron	—4—

* The plate tectonics model has
been verified by multiple lines
of evidence. For instance, the
Deep Sea Drilling Project
found that the age of the
seafloor increases with distance
from a mid-ocean ridge. The
thickness of sediment atop this
seafloor is also proportional to
distance from the ridge: Older
lithosphere has had more time
to accumulate sediment.
* Overall, oceanic lithosphere is
quite young, with none older

than about 180 million years. We could view it as a short-lived addition
to the edge of continents. Oceanic lithosphere forms in the wake of
diverging continents and is destroyed at subduction zones as continents
converge.
* Stationary sites of magma production called hot spots provide another
test of plate tectonics. The volcanic rocks erupted by these hot spots
through the overriding plate provide a method of quantifying both the
direction and rate of plate movement over time.
* Magnetic minerals such as magnetite align themselves with Earth's
magnetic field as rock forms. These fossil magnets act as recorders
of the ancient orientation of Earth's magnetic field. This is useful to
geologists in two ways: (1) It allows a given stack of rock layers to be
interpreted in terms of changing position relative to the magnetic poles
through time, and (2) reversals in the orientation of the magnetic field
are preserved as "stripes" of normal and reversed polarity in the oceanic
crust. Magnetometers reveal this signature of seafloor spreading as a
symmetrical pattern of magnetic stripes parallel to the axis of the mid-
ocean ridge.

PATTERN RECOGNITION   Use the magnetic time scale in the accompanying figure to determine when continents
A and B began to diverge.

9   How is plate motion measured?

Describe two methods researchers use to measure relative plate motion.

- Data collected from the ocean floor has established the direction and rate of motion of lithospheric plates. Transform faults point in the direction the plate is moving. Sediments with diagnostic fossils and radiometric dates of igneous rocks both help to calibrate the rate of motion.

- GPS satellites can be used to accurately measure the motion of special receivers to within a few millimeters. These "real-time" data back up the inferences made from seafloor observations. Plates move at about the same rate your fingernails grow: an average of about 5 centimeters per year.

RATE THE RATE   The rate of seafloor spreading at the East Pacific Rise is about three times as rapid as at the Mid-Atlantic Ridge. However, the Atlantic is getting wider over time, while the Pacific is getting smaller. Explain this apparent conundrum.

10   What drives plate motions?

Discuss what is meant by plate–mantle convection and explain two of the primary driving forces for plate motion.

KEY WORDS slab pull, ridge push, convection

- Some kind of convection (upward movement of less dense material and downward movement of more dense material) appears to drive the motion of plates.
- Slabs of oceanic lithosphere sink at subduction zones because the subducted slab is denser than the underlying asthenosphere. This generates a force called slab pull that tugs at the rest of the plate. As lithosphere slides down the mid-ocean ridge, it exerts a small additional force, the outward-directed ridge push. Frictional drag exerted on the underside of plates by flowing mantle is another force that acts on plates and influences their direction and rate of movement.
- The exact patterns of mantle convection are not fully understood. Convection may occur throughout the entire mantle, as suggested by the plume model. Or it may occur in multiple layers stacked within the mantle. Or perhaps it may be even more complicated than that: a messy three-dimensional network of slowly moving rock. The actual shape of the convective flow in the mantle is a matter of current scientific investigation and is debated by geologists.

COMPARE AND CONTRAST   How does the operation of a lava lamp compare to mantle convection? List how they are similar and also list their many differences.

Steve Bower/Shutterstock

GIVE IT SOME THOUGHT

1. Answer the following:
   a. What observation led Alfred Wegener to develop his continental drift hypothesis?
   b. Why was the continental drift hypothesis rejected by the majority of the scientific community?
   c. Do you think Wegener followed the basic principles of scientific inquiry? Support your answer.

2. Referring to the accompanying diagrams that illustrate the three types of convergent plate boundaries, complete the following:

A.

B.

C.

   a. Identify each type of convergent boundary.
   b. Volcanic island arcs develop on what type of crust?
   c. Why are volcanoes largely absent where two continental blocks collide?
   d. Describe two ways that oceanic–oceanic convergent boundaries are different from oceanic–continental boundaries? How are they similar?

3. Some predict that California will sink into the ocean. Is this idea consistent with the theory of plate tectonics? Explain.

4. Refer to the accompanying hypothetical plate map to answer the following questions:

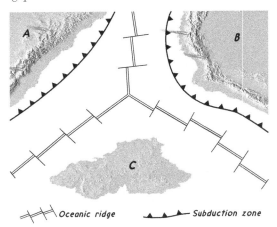

   a. How many portions of plates are shown?
   b. Are continents A, B, and C moving toward or away from each other? How did you determine your answer?
   c. Explain why active volcanoes are more likely to be found on continents A and B than on continent C.
   d. Provide at least one scenario in which volcanic activity might be triggered on continent C.

5. Volcanoes, such as the Hawaiian chain, that form over mantle plumes are some of the largest shield volcanoes on Earth. However, several shield volcanoes on Mars are gigantic compared to those on Earth. What does this difference tell us about the role of plate motion in shaping the Martian surface?

6. Imagine that you are studying seafloor spreading along two different oceanic ridges. Using data from a magnetometer, you produced the two accompanying maps. From these maps, what can you determine about the relative rates of seafloor spreading along these two ridges? Explain.

Spreading Center A

Spreading Center B

7. Australian marsupials (kangaroos, koala bears, etc.) have direct fossil links to marsupial opossums found in the Americas. Yet the modern marsupials in Australia are markedly different from their American relatives. How does the breakup of Pangaea help to explain these differences?

8. Density is a key component in the behavior of Earth materials and is especially important in understanding key aspects of plate tectonics. Describe three different ways that density and/or density differences play a role in plate tectonics.

9. Refer to the accompanying map and the city combinations given below to complete the following:

(Boston, Denver), (London, Boston), (Honolulu, Beijing)

a. List the cities (in pairs) that are moving apart as a result of plate motion.

b. List the cities (in pairs) that are moving closer as a result of plate motion.

c. List the cities (in pairs) that are presently not moving relative to each other.

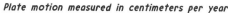

Plate motion measured in centimeters per year

MasteringGeology™

Looking for additional review and test prep materials? Visit the Study Area in MasteringGeology to enhance your understanding of this chapter's content by accessing a variety of resources, including **Self-Study Quizzes,** **Geoscience Animations, GEODe Tutorials, RSS feeds, flashcards, web links, self-study quizzes,** and an optional **Pearson eText.**

Glossary

Asthenosphere A subdivision of the mantle situated below the lithosphere. This zone of weak material exists below a depth of about 100 kilometers (60 miles) and in some regions extends as deep as 700 kilometers (430 miles). The rock within this zone is easily deformed.

Continental drift A hypothesis, credited largely to Alfred Wegener, which suggested that all present continents once existed as a single supercontinent. Further, beginning about 200 million years ago, the supercontinent began breaking into smaller continents, which then "drifted" to their present positions.

Continental rift A linear zone along which continental lithosphere stretches and pulls apart. Its creation may mark the beginning of a new ocean basin.

Continental volcanic arc Mountains formed in part by igneous activity associated with the subduction of oceanic lithosphere beneath a continent. Examples include the Andes and the Cascades.

Convection The transfer of heat by the mass movement or circulation of a substance.

Convergent plate boundary A boundary in which two plates move together, resulting in oceanic lithosphere being thrust beneath an overriding plate, eventually to be reabsorbed into the mantle. It can also involve the collision of two continental plates to create a mountain system.

Curie point The temperature above which a material loses its magnetization.

Deep-ocean trench A narrow, elongated depression of the seafloor.

Divergent plate boundary A boundary in which two plates move apart, resulting in upwelling of material from the mantle to create new seafloor.

Fossil magnetism See Paleomagnetism.

Fracture zone A linear zone of irregular topography on the deep-ocean floor that follows transform faults and their inactive *extensions*.

Hot spot A concentration of heat in the mantle, capable of producing magma that, in turn, extrudes onto Earth's surface. The intraplate volcanism that produced the Hawaiian Islands is one example.

Hot spot tracks   A chain of volcanic structures produced as a lithospheric plate moves over a mantle plume.

Island arc   *See Volcanic island* arc.

Lithosphere   The rigid outer layer of Earth, including the crust and upper mantle.

Lithospheric plate   A coherent unit of Earth's rigid outer layer that includes the crust and upper unit.

Magnetic reversal   A change in Earth's magnetic field from normal to reverse or vice versa.

Magnetometer   A sensitive instrument used to measure the intensity of Earth's magnetic field at various points.

Mantle plume   A mass of hotter-than-typical mantle material that ascends toward the surface, where it may lead to igneous activity. These plumes of solid yet mobile material may originate as deep as the core–mantle boundary.

Normal polarity   A magnetic field the same as that which presently exists.

Oceanic ridge   See Mid-ocean ridge.

Paleomagnetism   The natural remnant magnetism in rock bodies. The permanent magnetization acquired by rock that can be used to determine the location of the magnetic poles and the latitude of the rock at the time it became magnetized.

Pangaea   The proposed supercontinent that 200 million years ago began to break apart and form the present landmasses.

Partial melting   The process by which most igneous rocks melt. Since individual minerals have different melting points, most igneous rocks melt over a temperature range of a few hundred degrees. If the liquid is squeezed out after some melting has occurred, a melt with a higher silica content results.

Plate   See Lithospheric plate.

Reverse polarity   A magnetic field opposite that which presently exists.

Ridge push   A mechanism that may contribute to plate motion. It involves the oceanic lithosphere sliding down the oceanic ridge under the pull of gravity.

Rift valley   A long, narrow trough bounded by normal faults. It represents a region where divergence is taking place.

Seafloor spreading   A hypothesis, first proposed in the 1960s by Harry Hess, which suggested that new oceanic crust is produced at the crests of mid-ocean ridges, which are the sites of divergence.

Slab pull   A mechanism that contributes to plate motion in which cool, dense oceanic crust sinks into the mantle and "pulls" the trailing lithosphere along.

Subduction zone   A long, narrow zone where one lithospheric plate descends beneath another.

Supercontinent   A large landmass that contains all, or nearly all, of the existing continents.

Transform fault   A major strike-slip fault that cuts through the lithosphere and accommodates motion between two plates.

Transform fault boundary   A boundary in which two plates slide past one another without creating or destroying lithosphere.

Volcanic island arc   A chain of volcanic islands generally located a few hundred kilometers from a trench where there is active subduction of one oceanic plate beneath another.

Matter and Minerals

From Chapter 3 of *Earth: An Introduction to Physical Geology*, Eleventh Edition. Edward J. Tarbuck, Frederick K. Lutgens, Dennis Tasa.

Matter and Minerals

The Cave of Crystals, Chihuahua, Mexico, contains giant gypsum crystals, some of the largest natural crystals ever found. (Photo by Carsten Peter/Speleoresearch & Films/ Getty Images USA, Inc.)

Each statement represents the primary learning objective for the corresponding major heading within the chapter. After you complete the chapter you should be able to:

1. List the main characteristics that an Earth material must possess to be considered a mineral and describe each.
2. Compare and contrast the three primary particles contained in atoms.
3. Distinguish among ionic bonds, covalent bonds, and metallic bonds.
4. Describe three mechanisms that generate minerals and rocks.
5. List the properties that are used in mineral identification and briefly describe each.
6. Distinguish between compositional and structural variations in minerals and give examples.
7. Explain how minerals are classified and name the most abundant mineral group in Earth's crust.
8. Sketch the silicon–oxygen tetrahedron and explain how these fundamental building blocks join together to form other silicate structures.
9. Compare and contrast the light (nonferromagnesian) silicates with the dark (ferromagnesian) silicates and list four common minerals from each group.
10. List the common nonsilicate minerals and explain why each is important.

Crystals of elbaite, a colorful member of the tourmaline group. The white mineral albite is a member of the plagioclase feldspar group. (Photo by Jeff Scovil)

Earth's crust and oceans are home to a wide variety of useful and essential minerals. Most people are familiar with the common uses of many basic metals, including aluminum in beverage cans, copper in electrical wiring, and gold and silver in jewelry. But some people are not aware that pencil "lead" contains the greasy-feeling mineral graphite and that bath powders and many cosmetics contain the mineral talc. Moreover, many do not know that dentists use drill bits impregnated with diamonds to drill through tooth enamel, or that the common mineral quartz is the source of silicon for computer chips. In fact, practically every manufactured product contains materials obtained from minerals.

In addition to rocks and minerals having economic uses, all the processes that geologists study are in some way dependent on the properties of these basic Earth materials. Events such as volcanic eruptions, mountain building, weathering and erosion, and even earthquakes involve rocks and minerals. Consequently, a basic knowledge of Earth materials is essential to understanding all geologic phenomena.

1 Minerals: Building Blocks of Rocks

We begin our discussion of Earth materials with an overview of **mineralogy** (*mineral* = mineral, *ology* = study of) because minerals are the building blocks of rocks. In addition, humans have used minerals for both practical and decorative purposes for thousands of years (FIGURE 1). The first minerals mined were flint and chert, which people fashioned into weapons and cutting tools. As early as 3700 B.C., Egyptians began mining gold, silver, and copper; and by 2200 B.C. humans had discovered how to combine copper with tin to make bronze, a strong, hard alloy. Later, humans developed a process to extract iron from minerals such as hematite—a discovery that marked the decline of the Bronze Age. During the Middle Ages, mining of a variety of minerals became common, and the impetus for the formal study of minerals was in place.

FIGURE 1 Quartz crystals
A collection of well-developed quartz crystals found near Hot Springs, Arkansas. (Photo by Jeff Scovil)

The term *mineral* is used in several different ways. For example, those concerned with health and fitness extol the benefits of vitamins and minerals. The mining industry typically uses the word when referring to anything taken out of the ground, such as coal, iron ore, or sand and gravel. The guessing game known as *Twenty Questions* usually begins with the question, *Is it animal, vegetable, or mineral?* What criteria do geologists use to determine whether something is a mineral?

Defining a Mineral

Geologists define **mineral** as *any naturally occurring inorganic solid that possesses an orderly crystalline structure and a definite chemical composition that allows for some variation.* Thus, Earth materials that are classified as minerals exhibit the following characteristics:

1. **Naturally occurring.** Minerals form by natural geologic processes. Synthetic materials, meaning those produced in a laboratory or by human intervention, are not considered minerals.
2. **Generally inorganic.** Inorganic crystalline solids, such as ordinary table salt (halite), that are found naturally in the ground are considered minerals. (Organic compounds, on the other hand, are generally not. Sugar, a crystalline solid like salt but that comes from sugarcane or sugar beets, is a common example of such an organic compound.) Many marine animals secrete inorganic compounds, such as calcium carbonate (calcite), in the form of shells and coral reefs. If these materials are buried and become part of the rock record, geologists consider them minerals.
3. **Solid substance.** Only solid crystalline substances are considered minerals. Ice (frozen water) fits this criterion and is considered a mineral, whereas liquid water and water vapor do not. The exception is mercury, which is found in its liquid form in nature.
4. **Orderly crystalline structure.** Minerals are crystalline substances, which means their atoms are arranged in an orderly, repetitive manner (FIGURE 2). This orderly packing of atoms is reflected in the regularly shaped objects called crystals. Some naturally occurring solids, such as volcanic glass (obsidian), lack a repetitive atomic structure and are not considered minerals.
5. **Definite chemical composition that allows for some variation.** Most minerals are chemical compounds having compositions that can be expressed by a chemical formula. For example, the common mineral quartz has the formula SiO_2, which indicates that quartz consists of silicon (Si) and oxygen (O) atoms in a ratio of one-to-two. This proportion of silicon to oxygen is true for any sample of pure quartz, regardless of its origin. However, the compositions of some minerals vary *within specific, well-defined limits.* This occurs because certain elements can substitute for others of similar size without changing the mineral's internal structure. We will return to this topic later in the chapter.

A.   **B.**

FIGURE 2 Ordered versus unordered arrangement of atoms
Minerals have a repetitive, orderly arrangement of atoms, whereas substances such a glass have an unordered atomic structure.

SMARTFIGURE 3
Most rocks are aggregates of minerals
Shown here is a hand sample of the igneous rock granite and three of its major constituent minerals.
(Photos by E. J. Tarbuck)

Granite
(Rock)

Quartz
(Mineral)

Hornblende
(Mineral)

Feldspar
(Mineral)

the mineral constituents of granite can be easily identified. However, some rocks are composed almost entirely of one mineral. A common example is the sedimentary rock *limestone*, which is an impure mass of the mineral calcite.

In addition, some rocks are composed of nonmineral matter. These include the volcanic rocks *obsidian* and *pumice*, which are noncrystalline glassy substances, and *coal*, which consists of solid organic debris.

Although this chapter deals primarily with the nature of minerals, keep in mind that most rocks are simply aggregates of minerals. Because the properties of rocks are determined largely by the chemical composition and crystalline structure of the minerals contained within them, we will first consider these Earth materials.

What Is a Rock?

In contrast to minerals, rocks are more loosely defined. Simply, a **rock** is any solid mass of mineral, or mineral-like, matter that occurs naturally as part of our planet. Most rocks, like the sample of granite shown in FIGURE 3, occur as aggregates of several different minerals. The term *aggregate* implies that the minerals are joined in such a way that their individual properties are retained. Note that

1 CONCEPT CHECKS

1. List five characteristics an Earth material must have in order to be considered a mineral.
2. Based on the definition of a mineral, which of the following materials are not classified as minerals, and why: gold, water, synthetic diamonds, ice, and wood.
3. Define the term *rock*. How do rocks differ from minerals?

EYE on Earth

The accompanying image is of the world's largest open pit gold mine, located near Kalgoorlie, Australia. Known as the Super Pit, it originally consisted of a number of small underground mines that were consolidated into a single, open pit mine. Each year, about 28 metric tons of gold are extracted from the 15 million tons of rock shattered by blasting and then transported to the surface.

Question 1 What is one environmental advantage that underground mining has over open pit mining?

Question 2 If you had been employed at this mine, what change in working conditions would have occurred as it evolved from an underground mine to an open pit mine?

McPHOTO/AGE Fotostock

2 | Atoms: Building Blocks of Minerals

When minerals are carefully examined, even under optical microscopes, the innumerable tiny particles of their internal structures are not discernible. Nevertheless, scientists have discovered that all matter, including minerals, is composed of minute building blocks called **atoms**—the smallest particles that cannot be chemically split. Atoms, in turn, contain even smaller particles—*protons* and *neutrons* located in a central **nucleus** that is surrounded by *electrons* (FIGURE 4).

Properties of Protons, Neutrons, and Electrons

Protons and **neutrons** are very dense particles with almost identical masses. By contrast, **electrons** have a negligible mass, about 1/2000 that of a proton. For

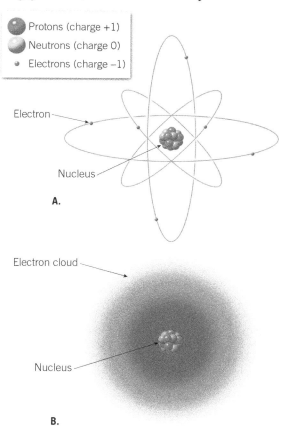

comparison, if a proton or a neutron had the mass of a baseball, an electron would have the mass of a single grain of rice.

Both protons and electrons share a fundamental property called *electrical charge*. Protons have an electrical charge of +1, and electrons have a charge of −1. Neutrons, as the name suggests, have no charge. The charges of protons and electrons are equal in magnitude but opposite in polarity, so when these two particles are paired, the charges cancel each other out. Since matter typically contains equal numbers of positively charged protons and negatively charged electrons, most substances are electrically neutral.

In illustrations, electrons are sometimes shown orbiting the nucleus in a manner that resembles the planets of our solar system orbiting the Sun (Figure 4A). However, electrons do not actually behave this way. A more realistic depiction shows electrons as a cloud of negative charges surrounding the nucleus (Figure 4B). Studies of the arrangements of electrons show that they move about the nucleus in regions called *principal shells*, each with an associated energy level. In addition, each shell can hold a specific number of electrons, with the outermost shell containing **valence electrons** that interact with other atoms to form chemical bonds.

Most of the atoms in the universe (except hydrogen and helium) were created inside massive stars by nuclear fusion and released into interstellar space during hot, fiery supernova explosions. As this ejected material cooled, the newly formed nuclei attracted electrons to complete their atomic structure. At the temperatures found at Earth's surface, all free atoms (those not bonded to other atoms) have a full complement of electrons—one for each proton in the nucleus.

Elements: Defined by Their Number of Protons

The simplest atoms have only 1 proton in their nuclei, whereas others have more than 100. The number of protons in the nucleus of an atom, called the **atomic number**, determines its chemical nature. All atoms with the same number of protons have the same chemical and physical properties. Together, a group of the same kind of atoms is called an **element**. There are about 90 naturally occurring elements and several more that have been

FIGURE 4 Two models of an atom
A. A very simplified view of an atom. The central nucleus consists of protons and neutrons encircled by high-speed electrons. **B.** This model of an atom shows spherically shaped electron clouds (shells) surrounding a central nucleus. The nucleus contains virtually all of the mass of the atom. The remainder of the atom is the space occupied by negatively charged electrons. (The relative sizes of the nuclei shown are greatly exaggerated.)

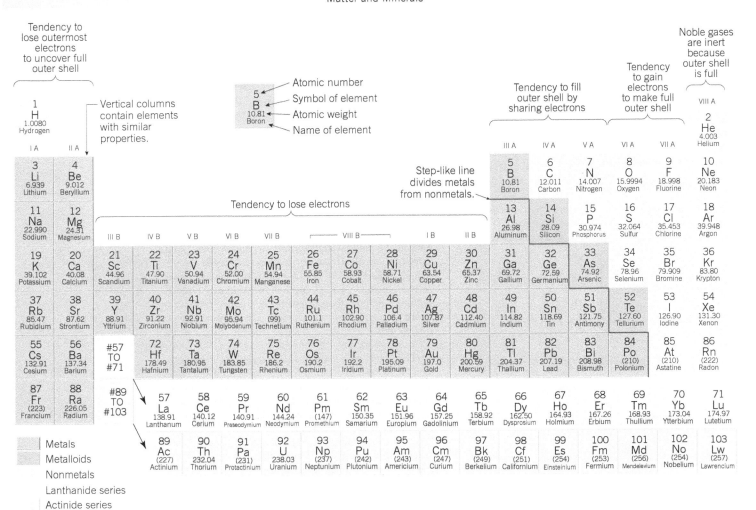

FIGURE 5 Periodic table of the elements

Metals
Metalloids
Nonmetals
Lanthanide series
Actinide series

FIGURE 6 Minerals composed of a single element

(Photos by Dennis Tasa)

A. Gold on quartz

B. Sulfur

C. Copper

synthesized in the laboratory. You are probably familiar with the names of many elements, including carbon, nitrogen, and oxygen. All carbon atoms have six protons, whereas all nitrogen atoms have seven protons, and all oxygen atoms have eight.

Elements are organized so that those with similar properties line up in columns. This arrangement, called the **periodic table**, is shown in FIGURE 5. Each element

has been assigned a one- or two-letter symbol. The atomic numbers and masses are also included for each element.

Atoms of the naturally occurring elements are the basic building blocks of Earth's minerals. A few minerals, such as native copper, diamonds, sulfur, and gold, are made entirely of atoms of only one element (FIGURE 6). However, most elements tend to join with atoms of other elements to form **chemical compounds**. Most minerals are chemical compounds composed of atoms of two or more elements.

2 CONCEPT CHECKS

1. List the three main particles of an atom and explain how they differ from one another.
2. Make a simple sketch of an atom and label its three main particles.
3. What is the significance of valence electrons?

3 Why Atoms Bond

Except for a group of elements known as the noble gases, atoms bond to one another under the conditions (temperatures and pressures) that occur on Earth. Some atoms bond to form *ionic compounds*, some form *molecules*, and still others form *metallic substances*. Why does this happen? Experiments show that electrical forces hold atoms together and bond them to each other. These electrical attractions lower the total energy of the bonded atoms, which, in turn, generally makes them more stable. Consequently, atoms that are bonded in compounds tend to be more stable than atoms that are free (not bonded).

FIGURE 7 Dot diagrams for certain elements
Each dot represents a valence electron found in the outermost principal shell.

The Octet Rule and Chemical Bonds

As was noted earlier, valence (outer shell) electrons are generally involved in chemical bonding. FIGURE 7 shows a shorthand way of representing the number of valence electrons. Notice that the elements in Group I have one valence electron, those in Group II have two valence electrons, and so on, up to eight valence electrons in Group VIII.

The noble gases (except helium) have very stable electron arrangements with eight valence electrons and, therefore, tend to lack chemical reactivity. Many other atoms gain, lose, or share electrons during chemical reactions, ending up with electron arrangements of the noble gases. This observation led to a chemical guideline known as the **octet rule**: *Atoms tend to gain, lose, or share electrons until they are surrounded by eight valence electrons.* Although there are exceptions to the octet rule, it is a useful *rule of thumb* for understanding chemical bonding.

When an atom's outer shell does not contain eight electrons, it is likely to chemically bond to other atoms to fill its shell. A **chemical bond** is the transfer or sharing of electrons that allows each atom to attain a full valence shell of electrons. Some atoms do this by transferring all their valence electrons to other atoms so that an inner shell becomes the full valence shell.

When the valence electrons are transferred between the elements to form ions, the bond is an *ionic bond*. When the electrons are shared between the atoms, the bond is a *covalent bond*. When the valence electrons are shared among all the atoms in a substance, the bonding is *metallic*.

Ionic Bonds: Electrons Transferred

Perhaps the easiest type of bond to visualize is the *ionic bond*, in which atoms of one element give up one or more of their valence electrons to atoms of another element to form **ions**—*positively and negatively charged atoms.* The atom that loses electrons becomes a positive ion, and the atom that gains electrons becomes a negative ion. Oppositely charged ions are strongly attracted to one another and join to form ionic compounds.

Consider the ionic bonding that occurs between sodium (Na) and chlorine (Cl) to produce the solid ionic compound sodium chloride—the mineral halite (common table salt). Notice in FIGURE 8 that a sodium atom gives up its single valence electron to chlorine and, as a result, becomes a positively charged sodium ion. Chlorine, on the other hand, gains one electron and becomes a negatively charged chloride ion. We know that ions having unlike charges attract. Thus, an **ionic bond** is the attraction of oppositely charged ions to one another, producing an electrically neutral ionic compound.

Figure 8 illustrates the arrangement of sodium and chlorine ions in ordinary table salt. Notice that salt consists of alternating sodium and chlorine ions, positioned in such a manner that each positive ion is attracted to and surrounded on all sides by negative ions and vice versa. This arrangement maximizes the attraction between ions with opposite charges while minimizing the repulsion between ions with identical charges. Thus, ionic compounds consist of an orderly arrangement of oppositely charged ions assembled in a definite ratio that provides overall electrical neutrality.

The properties of a chemical compound are dramatically different from the properties of the various elements comprising it. For example, sodium is a soft silvery metal that is extremely reactive and poisonous. If you were to consume even a small amount of elemental sodium, you would need immediate medical attention. Chlorine, a green poisonous gas, is so toxic that it was used as a chemical weapon during World War I. Together, however, these elements produce sodium chloride, a harmless flavor enhancer that we call table salt. Thus, when elements combine to form compounds, their properties change significantly.

Covalent Bonds: Electron Sharing

Sometimes the forces that hold atoms together cannot be understood on the basis of the attraction of oppositely charged ions. One example is the hydrogen molecule (H_2), in which the two hydrogen atoms are held together tightly and no ions are present. The

Electron Dot Diagrams for Some Representative Elements

I	II	III	IV	V	VI	VII	VIII
H							He
Li	Be	B	C	N	O	F	Ne
Na	Mg	Al	Si	P	S	Cl	Ar
K	Ca	Ga	Ge	As	Se	Br	Kr

The transfer of an electron from a sodium (Na) to a chlorine (Cl) atom leads to the formation of a Na⁺ ion and a Cl⁻ ion.

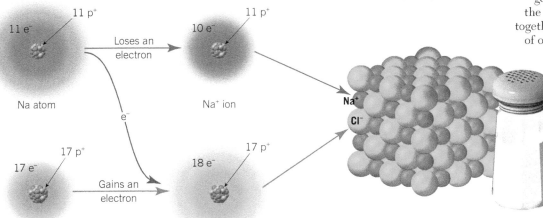

The arrangement of the Na⁺ and Cl⁻ in solid ionic compound sodium chloride (NaCl), table salt.

Na atom → Loses an electron → Na⁺ ion

Cl atom → Gains an electron → Cl⁻ ion

FIGURE 8 Formation of the ionic compound sodium chloride

FIGURE 9 Formation of a covalent bond
Covalent bonding of two hydrogen atoms (H) to form a hydrogen molecule (H_2). When hydrogen atoms bond, the negatively charged electrons are shared by both hydrogen atoms and attracted simultaneously by the positive charge of the proton in the nucleus of each atom.

strong attractive force that holds two hydrogen atoms together results from a **covalent bond**, *a chemical bond formed by the sharing of one or more valence electrons between a pair of atoms.*

Imagine two hydrogen atoms (each with one proton and one electron) approaching one another as shown in FIGURE 9. Once they meet, the electron configuration will change so that both electrons will primarily occupy the space between the atoms. In other words, the two electrons are shared by both hydrogen atoms and are attracted simultaneously by the positive charge of

Two hydrogen atoms combine to form a hydrogen molecule, held together by the attraction of oppositely charged particles—positively charged protons in each nuclei and negatively charged electrons that surround these nuclei.

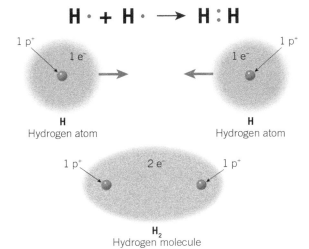

the proton in the nucleus of each atom. Although hydrogen atoms do not form ions, the force that holds these atoms together arises from the attraction of oppositely charged particles—positively charged protons in the nuclei and negatively charged electrons that surround these nuclei.

Metallic Bonds: Electrons Free to Move

In **metallic bonds**, the valence electrons are free to move from one atom to another so that all atoms share the available valence electrons. This type of bonding is found in metals such as copper, gold, aluminum, and silver, and in alloys such as brass and bronze. Metallic bonding accounts for the high electrical conductivity of metals, the ease with which metals are shaped, and numerous other special properties.

Hybrid Bonds

We have described the extremes in chemical bonding—complete transfer of electrons and perfect sharing of electrons. As you may suspect, many chemical bonds are actually hybrids that exhibit some degree of electron sharing and some degree of electron transfer. Bonds can be found with almost every possible combination of covalent and ionic character. For example, silicate minerals are composed of silicon and oxygen atoms that are joined together with other elements by bonds that display characteristics of both ionic and covalent bonds.

3 CONCEPT CHECKS

1. What is the difference between an atom and an ion?
2. What occurs in an atom to produce a positive ion? A negative ion?
3. Briefly distinguish between ionic and covalent bonding and the role that electrons play in each type of bond.

4 How Do Minerals Form?

Minerals form through a wide variety of processes and in many different environments whereby atoms chemically bond to form an orderly internal structure. Because most rocks are aggregates of minerals, they also form by these same processes. We will examine three ways minerals can form: precipitation of mineral matter from a solution, crystallization of molten rock by cooling, and mineral matter deposition as a result of biological processes.

Precipitation of Mineral Matter

Perhaps the most familiar way in which minerals grow is from an aqueous (water) solution containing dissolved material matter (ions). As long as the solution is not saturated, the motion of the dissolved ions keeps them from joining together. Two factors—a drop in temperature and water lost through evaporation—cause the solution to become closer to reaching saturation. Once saturation is reached, the ions begin to bond, forming solid crystalline solids (called salts) that precipitate from (settle out of) the solution.

The Great Salt Lake in Utah and Bolivia's great salt flat Salar de Uyuni provide good examples of this process at work (FIGURE 10). Because they are located in arid regions with high evaporation rates, these water bodies regularly precipitate the minerals halite, sylvite, and gypsum, as well as other soluble salts. Worldwide, extensive salt deposits, some exceeding hundreds of meters in thickness, provide

Geodes like this one form when silica dissolved in groundwater precipitates to form quartz crystals that grow within cavities in rocks.

Groundwater containing dissolved silica

Silica (SiO₂)

Purple quartz crystals

Geologist's Sketch

Geodes form in cavities in rocks, such as limestone and volcanic rocks. Slowly moving groundwater deposits dissolved mineral matter in these voids. (Photo by Jeff Scovil)

Mining salt in Bolivia's Solar de Uyuni, the largest known reserve of lithium chloride in the world. Lithium is in great demand because it is used to manufacture batteries for cell phones, computers, and electric and hybrid automobiles.

FIGURE 10 Salt being mined in Bolivia's Salar de Uyuni
The Salar de Uyuni is a salt flat that overlies a lake of brine up to 20 meters (66 feet) deep. It is the world's largest salt flat—25 times larger than the Bonneville Salt Flats in Utah. This region is completely surrounded by mountains and is quite arid, so water that enters the valley leaves via evaporation—which results in deposition of salts, including sodium chloride, magnesium chloride, and lithium chloride. (Photo by imagebrocker.net/SuperStock)

evidence of ancient seas that have long since evaporated (see Figure 42).

Minerals can also precipitate from slowly moving groundwater filling in fractures and voids in rocks and sediments. One interesting example, called a *geode*, is a somewhat spherically shaped object with inward-projecting crystals that were gradually deposited by groundwater (FIGURE 11). Geodes sometimes contain spectacular crystals of quartz, calcite, or other less common minerals.

Crystallization of Molten Rock

The crystallization of minerals from molten rock, although more complicated, is similar to water freezing (FIGURE 12). When magma is hot, the atoms are very mobile; but as the molten material cools, the atoms slow and begin to chemically combine. Crystallization of a molten mass generates igneous rocks that consist of a mosaic of intergrown crystals that tend to lack well-developed faces (see Figure 3).

FIGURE 12 Minerals form when molten rock solidifies
FIGURE 12 Minerals form when molten rock solidifies (Photo by Martin Rietze/ AGE Fotostock)

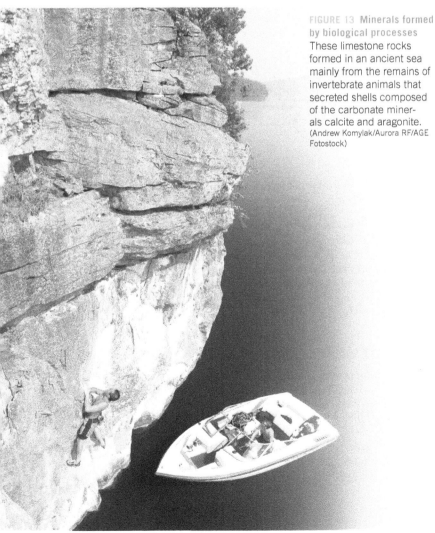

FIGURE 13 Minerals formed by biological processes These limestone rocks formed in an ancient sea mainly from the remains of invertebrate animals that secreted shells composed of the carbonate minerals calcite and aragonite. (Andrew Komylak/Aurora RF/AGE Fotostock)

Deposition as a Result of Biological Processes

Water-dwelling organisms are also responsible for transforming substantial quantities of dissolved material into mineral matter. For example, corals are organisms capable of creating large quantities of marine limestones, rocks composed of the mineral calcite. These relatively simple invertebrate animals use calcium (Ca) ions from seawater and in turn secrete external skeletons composed of calcium carbonate ($CaCO_3$). Over time, these small organisms are capable of creating massive limestone structures called reefs.

Mollusks (such as clams) and other marine invertebrates also secrete shells composed of the carbonate minerals calcite and aragonite. When the remains of these shells are buried, they become the major component of the sedimentary rock limestone. Limestone is a very common rock at Earth's surface and is visible across the entire United States (**FIGURE 13**).

Although most water-dwelling organisms produce hard parts made of calcium carbonate, some, such as diatoms and radiolarians, produce glasslike silica skeletons. During burial, this material forms microscopic silicon dioxide (quartz) crystals that are the main constituents of rocks such as chert and flint.

4 CONCEPT CHECKS

1. List three ways minerals and rocks can form.
2. Crystallization of molten rock produces which one of the three types of rock?
3. What is the chemical composition of the mineral matter secreted by most organisms? What is the name a mineral and a rock that results from this process?

5 | Physical Properties of Minerals

Minerals have definite crystalline structures and chemical compositions that give them unique sets of physical and chemical properties shared by all samples of that mineral. For example, all specimens of halite have the same hardness, have the same density, and break in a similar manner. Because a mineral's internal structure and chemical composition are difficult to determine without the aid of sophisticated tests and equipment, the more easily recognized physical properties are frequently used in identification.

Optical Properties

Of the many optical properties of minerals, their luster, their ability to transmit light, their color, and their streak are most frequently used for mineral identification.

Luster   The appearance or quality of light reflected from the surface of a mineral is known as **luster**. Minerals that have the appearance of metals, regardless of color, are said to have a *metallic luster* (FIGURE 14). Some metallic minerals, such as native copper and galena, develop a dull coating or tarnish when exposed to the atmosphere. Because they are not as shiny as samples with freshly broken surfaces, these samples are often said to exhibit a *submetallic luster*.

Most minerals have a *nonmetallic luster* and are described using various adjectives such as *vitreous* or *glassy*. Other nonmetallic minerals are described as having a *dull*, or *earthy*, *luster* (a dull appearance like soil) or a *pearly luster* (such as a pearl or the inside of a clamshell). Still others exhibit a *silky luster* (like satin cloth) or a *greasy luster* (as though coated in oil).

Ability to Transmit Light   Another optical property used in the identification of minerals is the ability to transmit light. When no light is transmitted, the mineral is described as *opaque*; when light, but not an image, is transmitted through a mineral sample, the mineral is said to be *translucent*. When both light and an image are visible through the sample, the mineral is described as *transparent*.

Color   Although **color** is generally the most conspicuous characteristic of any mineral, it is considered a diagnostic property of only a few minerals. Slight impurities in the common mineral quartz, for example, give it a variety of tints, including pink, purple, yellow, white, gray, and even black (FIGURE 15). Other minerals, such as tourmaline, also exhibit a variety of hues, with multiple colors sometimes occurring in the same sample. Thus, the use of color as a means of identification is often ambiguous or even misleading.

Streak   The color of a mineral in powdered form, called **streak**, is often useful in identification. A mineral's streak is obtained by rubbing it across a *streak plate* (a piece of unglazed porcelain) and observing the color of the mark it leaves (FIGURE 16). Although the color of a mineral may vary from sample to sample, its streak is usually consistent in color.

Streak can also help distinguish between minerals with metallic luster and those with nonmetallic luster. Metallic minerals generally have a dense, dark streak, whereas minerals with nonmetallic luster typically have a light-colored streak.

It should be noted that not all minerals produce a streak when rubbed across a streak plate. For example, the mineral quartz is harder than a porcelain streak plate. Therefore, no streak is observed using this method.

A. Fluorite

B. Quarctz

SMARTFIGURE 15
Color variations in minerals
Some minerals, such as fluorite and quartz, occur in a variety of colors. (Photo A by Dennis Tasa; photo B by E. J. Tarbuck)

The freshly broken sample of galena (right) displays a metallic luster, while the sample on the left is tarnished and has a submetallic luster.

FIGURE 14 Metallic versus submetallic luster
(Photo courtesy of E. J. Tarbuck)

Although the color of a mineral is not always helpful in identification, the streak, which is the color of the powdered mineral, can be very useful.

FIGURE 16 Streak

Crystal Shape, or Habit

Mineralogists use the term **crystal shape**, or **habit**, to refer to the common or characteristic shape of a crystal or aggregate of crystals. A few minerals exhibit somewhat regular polygons that are helpful in their identification. For example, magnetite crystals sometimes occur as octahedrons, garnets often form dodecahedrons, and halite and fluorite crystals tend to grow as cubes or near cubes. While most minerals have only one common habit, a few have two or more characteristic crystal shapes, such as the pyrite sample shown in FIGURE 17.

Although most minerals exhibit only one common crystal shape, some, such as pyrite, have two or more characteristic habits.

Dennis Tasa

FIGURE 17 Common crystal shapes of pyrite

By contrast, some minerals rarely develop perfect geometric forms. Many of these, however, develop other characteristic shapes that are useful for identification. Some minerals tend to grow equally in all three dimensions, whereas others tend to be elongated in one direction or flattened if growth in one dimension is suppressed. Terms commonly used to describe these and other crystal habits include *equant* (equidimensional), *bladed*, *fibrous*, *tabular*, *prismatic*, *platy*, and *blocky*. Some of these habits are pictured in FIGURE 18.

Mineral Strength

How easily minerals break or deform under stress is determined by the type and strength of the chemical bonds that hold the crystals together. Mineralogists use terms including *tenacity*, *hardness*, *cleavage*, and *fracture* to describe mineral strength and how minerals break when stress is applied.

E.J. Tarbuck

A. Fibrous

Dennis Tasa

B. Bladed

SMARTFIGURE 18
Some common crystal habits
A. Thin, rounded crystals that break into fibers.
B. Elongated crystals that are flattened in one direction. **C.** Minerals that have stripes or bands of different color or texture.
D. Groups of crystals that are shaped like cubes.

Dennis Tasa

C. Banded

Dennis Tasa

D. Cubic crystals

A. Mohs scale (Relative hardness)

INDEX MINERALS		COMMON OBJECTS
Diamond	10	
Corundum	9	
Topaz	8	
Quartz	7	
Orthoclase	6	Streak plate (6.5)
Apatite	5	Glass & knife blade (5.5)
Fluorite	4	Wire nail (4.5)
Calcite	3	Copper penny (3.5)
Gypsum	2	Fingernail (2.5)
Talc	1	

B. Comparison of Mohs scale and an absolute scale

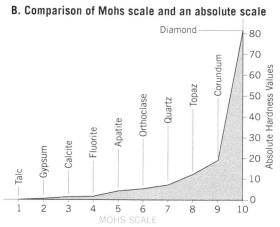

SMARTFIGURE 19
Hardness scales
A. The Mohs scale of hardness, with the hardnesses of some common objects.
B. Relationship between the Mohs relative hardness scale and an absolute hardness scale.

Tenacity The term **tenacity** describes a mineral's toughness, or its resistance to breaking or deforming. Minerals that are ionically bonded, such as fluorite and halite, tend to be *brittle* and shatter into small pieces when struck. By contrast, minerals with metallic bonds, such as native copper, are *malleable*, or easily hammered into different shapes. Minerals, including gypsum and talc, that can be cut into thin shavings are described as *sectile*. Still others, notably the micas, are *elastic* and will bend and snap back to their original shape after stress is released.

Hardness One of the most useful diagnostic properties is **hardness**, a measure of the resistance of a mineral to abrasion or scratching. This property is determined by rubbing a mineral of unknown hardness against one of known hardness or vice versa. A numerical value of hardness can be obtained by using the **Mohs scale** of hardness, which consists of 10 minerals arranged in order from 1 (softest) to 10 (hardest), as shown in FIGURE 19A. It should be noted that the Mohs scale is a relative ranking, and it does not imply that mineral number 2, gypsum, is twice as hard as mineral 1, talc. In fact, gypsum is only slightly harder than talc, as FIGURE 19B indicates.

In the laboratory, other common objects can be used to determine the hardness of a mineral. These include a human fingernail, which has a hardness of about 2.5, a copper penny (3.5), and a piece of glass (5.5). The mineral gypsum, which has a hardness of 2, can be easily scratched with a fingernail. On the other hand, the mineral calcite, which has a hardness of 3, will scratch a fingernail but will not scratch glass. Quartz, one of the hardest common minerals, will easily scratch glass. Diamonds, hardest of all, scratch anything, including other diamonds.

Cleavage In the crystal structure of many minerals, some atomic bonds are weaker than others. It is along these weak bonds that minerals tend to break when they are stressed. **Cleavage** (*kleiben* = carve) is the tendency of a mineral to break (cleave) along planes of weak bonding. Not all minerals have cleavage, but those that do can be identified by the relatively smooth, flat surfaces that are produced when the mineral is broken.

The simplest type of cleavage is exhibited by the micas (FIGURE 20). Because these minerals have very weak bonds in one direction, they cleave to form thin, flat sheets. Some minerals have excellent cleavage in one, two, three, or more directions, whereas others exhibit fair or poor cleavage, and still others have no cleavage at all. When minerals break evenly in more than one direction, cleavage is described by *the number of cleavage directions, the angle(s) at which they meet, and the quality of the cleavage.* (FIGURE 21).

FIGURE 20 **Micas exhibit perfect cleavage**
The thin sheets shown here exhibit one plane of cleavage.
(Photo by Chip Clark)

A. Cleavage in one direction.
Example: Muscovite

B. Cleavage in two directions at 90° angles.
Example: Feldspar

C. Cleavage in two directions not at 90° angles.
Example: Hornblende

D. Cleavage in three directions at 90° angles.
Example: Halite

E. Cleavage in three directions not at 90° angles.
Example: Calcite

F. Cleavage in four directions.
Example: Fluorite

SMARTFIGURE 21
Cleavage directions
exhibited by minerals
(Photos by E. J. Tarbuck and
Dennis Tasa)

Each cleavage surface that has a different orientation is counted as a different direction of cleavage. For example, some minerals cleave to form six-sided cubes. Because cubes are defined by three different sets of parallel planes that intersect at 90-degree angles, cleavage is described as *three directions of cleavage that meet at 90 degrees.*

Do not confuse cleavage with crystal shape. When a mineral exhibits cleavage, it will break into pieces that all have the same geometry. By contrast, the smooth-sided quartz crystals shown in Figure 1 do not have cleavage. If broken, they fracture into shapes that do not resemble one another or the original crystals.

Fracture   Minerals that have chemical bonds that are equally, or nearly equally, strong in all directions exhibit a property called **fracture**. When minerals fracture, most produce uneven surfaces and are described as exhibiting

irregular fracture. However, some minerals, such as quartz, break into smooth, curved surfaces resembling broken glass. Such breaks are called *conchoidal fractures* (FIGURE 22). Still other minerals exhibit fractures that produce splinters or fibers that are referred to as *splintery fracture* and *fibrous fracture*, respectively.

Density and Specific Gravity

Density, an important property of matter, is defined as mass per unit volume. Mineralogists often use a related measure called **specific gravity** to describe the density of minerals. Specific gravity is a dimensionless number representing the ratio of a mineral's weight to the weight of an equal volume of water.

Most common minerals have a specific gravity between 2 and 3. For example, quartz has a specific gravity of 2.65. By contrast, some metallic minerals, such as pyrite, native copper, and magnetite, are more than twice as dense and thus have more than twice the specific gravity of quartz. Galena, an ore of lead, has a specific gravity of roughly 7.5, whereas the specific gravity of 24-karat gold is approximately 20.

With a little practice, you can estimate the specific gravity of a mineral by hefting it in your hand. Does this mineral feel about as "heavy" as similar sized rocks you have handled? If the answer is "yes," the specific gravity of the sample will likely be between 2.5 and 3.

FIGURE 22 Irregular versus
conchoidal fracture
(Photos by E. J. Tarbuck)

A. Irregular fracture

B. Conchoidal fracture

FIGURE 23 Double refraction
This sample of calcite exhibits double refraction. (Photo by Chip Clark)

Other Properties of Minerals

In addition to the properties discussed thus far, some minerals can be recognized by other distinctive properties. For example, halite is ordinary salt, so it can be quickly identified through taste. Talc and graphite both have distinctive feels: Talc feels soapy, and graphite feels greasy. Further, the streaks of many sulfur-bearing minerals smell like rotten eggs. A few minerals, such as magnetite, have a high iron content and can be picked up

with a magnet, while some varieties (such as lodestone) are natural magnets and will pick up small iron-based objects such as pins and paper clips (see Figure 41F).

Moreover, some minerals exhibit special optical properties. For example, when a transparent piece of calcite is placed over printed text, the letters appear twice. This optical property is known as *double refraction* (FIGURE 23).

One very simple chemical test involves placing a drop of dilute hydrochloric acid from a dropper bottle onto a freshly broken mineral surface. Using this technique, certain minerals, called carbonates, will effervesce (fizz) as carbon dioxide gas is released (FIGURE 24). This test is especially useful in identifying the common carbonate mineral calcite.

FIGURE 24 Calcite reacting with a weak acid
(Photo by Chip Clark)

5 CONCEPT CHECKS

1. Define *luster*.
2. Why is color not always a useful property in mineral identification? Give an example of a mineral that supports your answer.
3. What do we mean when we refer to a mineral's *tenacity*? List three types of tenacity.
4. What differentiates cleavage from fracture?
5. What simple chemical test is useful in the identification of the mineral calcite?

Crystal shape or habit is a basic mineral property.
(Photo by Jeffrey Scovil)

GEOGRAPHICS

Gold

Gold has been treasured since long before recorded history for its beauty. Even today, its most common use is in jewelry.

How valuable is gold?

In early 2012, the value of one troy ounce of gold was about US$1,677. Based on that value, a 1000-gram (32-ounce) bar of gold, like the one shown, was worth $53,664. In 1970, the price of gold was less than $40 per troy ounce!

$53,664

Where is the world's gold produced?

China
355

Russia
200

United States
237

Canada
110

Uzbekistan
90

Australia
270

Mexico
85

Peru
150

Ghana
100

South Africa
190

Indonesia
100

Papua New Guinea
70

Brazil
55

Chile
45

Total for Other Countries
630

(Data from USGS)

Native gold

Because gold does not easily react with other elements, it often occurs as a native element in nuggets found in stream deposits or as grains in igneous rocks.

Shutterstock

Shutterstock

Shutterstock

What are the uses of gold?

About 50% of gold is used in jewelry. Another 40% is used for currency and investment, and about 10% is used in industry, including electronic devices such as cell phones and televisions. Gold is also used in gourmet foods and cocktails as a decorative ingredient. Because metallic gold is one of the least reactive materials, it has no taste, provides no nutritional value, and leaves the human body unaltered.

Shutterstock

How much gold has been mined?

It has been estimated that, as of 2009, 165,000 metric tons of gold has been extracted from Earth's crust throughout human history. This is equivalent to a solid cube measuring 20.4 meters (67 feet) per side.

20.4 meters

20.4 meters

20.4 meters

What is the chemical symbol for gold? ?

6 Mineral Structures and Compositions

Many people associate the word *crystal* with delicate wine goblets or glassy objects with smooth sides and gem-like shapes. In geology, the term **crystal** or **crystalline** refers to *any natural solid with an orderly, repeating internal structure*. Therefore, all mineral samples are crystals or crystalline solids, even if they lack smooth-sided faces. The specimen shown in Figure 1, for example, exhibits the characteristic crystal form associated with the mineral quartz—a six-sided prismatic shape with pyramidal ends. However, the quartz crystals in the sample of granite shown in Figure 3 do not display well-defined faces. Both quartz samples are nonetheless crystalline.

FIGURE 25 Relative sizes and charges of selected ions
Ionic radii are usually expressed in angstroms (1 angstrom equals 10^{-8} cm).

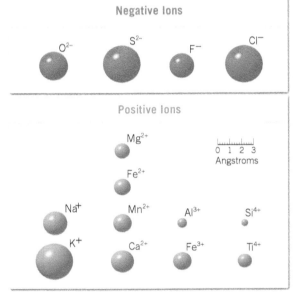

FIGURE 26 Arrangement of sodium and chloride ions in the mineral halite
The arrangement of atoms into basic building blocks that have a cubic shape results in regularly shaped cubic crystals. (Photo by Dennis Tasa)

A. Sodium and chlorine ions.

B. Basic building block of the mineral halite.

C. Collection of basic building blocks (crystal).

D. Crystals of the mineral halite.

Mineral Structures

The smooth faces and symmetry possessed by well-developed crystals are surface manifestations of the orderly packing of the atoms or ions that constitute a mineral's internal structure. This highly ordered atomic arrangement within minerals can be illustrated by using spherically shaped atoms held together by ionic, covalent, or metallic bonds. The simplest crystal structures are those of native metals, such as gold and silver, that are composed of only one element. These materials consist of atoms that are packed together in a rather simple three-dimensional network that minimizes voids. Imagine a group of cannon balls stacked in layers such that the spheres in one layer nestle in the hollows between spheres in the adjacent layers.

The atomic structure of most minerals consists of at least two different ions (often of very different sizes). FIGURE 25 illustrates the relative sizes of some of the most common ions found in minerals. Notice that the negative ions, which are atoms that gained electrons, tend to be larger than the positive ions, which lost electrons.

Crystal structures can be considered three-dimensional stacks of larger spheres (negative ions) with smaller spheres (positive ions) located in the spaces between them, so that the positive and negative charges cancel each other out. Consider the mineral halite (NaCl), which has a relatively simple framework composed of an equal number of positively charged sodium ions and negatively charged chlorine ions. Because ions of similar charge repel, they are spaced as far apart from each other as possible. Consequently, in the mineral halite, each sodium ion (Na^+) is surrounded on all sides by chlorine ions and vice versa (FIGURE 26). This particular

A. Cube (fluorite)

B. Octahedron (magnetite)

C. Dodecahedron (garnet)

FIGURE 27 Cubic unit cells These cells stack together in different ways to produce crystals that exhibit different shapes. Fluorite (**A**) tends to display cubic crystals, whereas magnetite crystals (**B**) are typically octahedrons, and garnets (**C**) usually occur as dodecahedrons. (Photos by Dennis Tasa)

arrangement results in basic building blocks, called **unit cells**, that have cubic shapes. As shown in Figure 26C, these cubic unit cells combine to form cubic-shaped halite crystals, including the ones that come out of salt shakers.

The shape and symmetry of these building blocks relate to the shape and symmetry of the entire crystal. It is important to note, however, that two minerals can be constructed of geometrically similar building blocks yet exhibit different external forms. For example, the minerals fluorite, magnetite, and garnet are all constructed of cubic unit cells. However, cubic cells can join to produce crystals of many shapes. Typically, fluorite crystals are cubes, whereas magnetite crystals are octahedrons, and garnets form dodecahedrons built up of many small cubes, as shown in FIGURE 27. Because the building blocks are so small, the resulting crystal faces are smooth and flat.

Despite the fact that natural crystals are rarely perfect, the angles between equivalent crystal faces of the same mineral are remarkably consistent. This observation was first made by Nicolas Steno in 1669. Steno found that the angles between adjacent prism faces of quartz crystals are 120 degrees, regardless of sample size, the size of the crystal faces, or where the crystals were collected (FIGURE 28). This observation is commonly called **Steno's Law**, or the **Law of Constancy of Interfacial Angles**, because it applies to all minerals. Because Steno's Law holds for all minerals, crystal shape is frequently a valuable tool in mineral identification.

Compositional Variations in Minerals

Mineralogists have determined that the chemical composition of some minerals varies substantially from sample to sample. These compositional variations are possible because ions of similar size can readily

Goniometer

120°

120°

120°

120°

Cross section

Quartz crystal

FIGURE 28 Steno's law Because some faces of a crystal may grow larger than others, two crystals of the same mineral may *not* have identical shapes. Nevertheless, the angles between equivalent faces are remarkably consistent.

substitute for one another without disrupting a mineral's internal framework. This is analogous to a wall made of bricks of different colors and materials. As long as the bricks are roughly the same size, the shape of the wall is unaffected; only its composition changes.

Consider the mineral olivine as an example of chemical variability. The chemical formula for olivine is $(Mg,Fe)_2SiO_4$—which has the variable components magnesium and iron in parentheses. Magnesium (Mg^{2+}) and iron (Fe^{2+}) readily substitute for one another because they are nearly the same size and have the same electrical charge. At one extreme, olivine may contain magnesium without any iron, or vice versa. Most samples of olivine, however, have some of both of these ions in their structure. Consequently, olivine can be thought of as having a range of combinations from a variety called fosterite $(MgSiO_4)$ at one end to fayalite (Fe_2SiO_4) at the other. Nevertheless, all specimens of olivine have the same internal structure and exhibit very similar, but not identical, properties. For example, iron-rich olivines have a higher density than magnesium-rich specimens, a reflection of the greater atomic weight of iron as compared to magnesium.

FIGURE 29 Diamond versus graphite
Both diamond and graphite are natural substances with the same chemical composition—carbon atoms. Nevertheless, their internal structures and physical properties reflect the fact that each formed in a very different environment.

(Photo A by Dane Pendland, courtesy of Smithsonian Institution; photo B by E. J. Tarbuck)

The carbon atoms in diamonds are covalently bonded into a compact, three-dimensional framework, which accounts for the extreme hardness of the mineral.

Strong bonds

Carbon atoms

A. Diamond

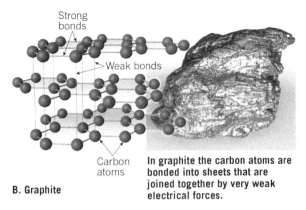

Strong bonds

Weak bonds

Carbon atoms

B. Graphite

In graphite the carbon atoms are bonded into sheets that are joined together by very weak electrical forces.

Graphite is the soft gray mineral from which pencil "lead" is made, whereas diamond is the hardest-known mineral. The differences between these minerals can be attributed to the conditions under which they form. Diamonds form at depths that may exceed 200 kilometers (nearly 125 miles), where extreme pressures and temperatures produce the compact structure shown in FIGURE 29A. Graphite, on the other hand, forms under comparatively low pressures and consists of sheets of carbon atoms that are widely spaced and weakly bonded (FIGURE 29B). Because the carbon sheets in graphite easily slide past one another, graphite has a greasy feel and makes an excellent lubricant.

Scientists have learned that by heating graphite under high confining pressures, they can generate synthetic diamonds. Because "man-made" diamonds often contain flaws, they are generally not gem quality, but due to their hardness, they have many industrial uses. Further, because diamonds form in environments of extreme pressure and temperature, they are somewhat unstable at Earth's surface. Fortunately for jewelers, "diamonds are forever" because the rate at which diamonds change to their more stable form, graphite, is infinitesimally slow.

The transformation of one polymorph to another is called a *phase change*. In nature, certain minerals go through phase changes as they move from one environment to another. For example, when a slab of ocean crust composed of olivine-rich basalt is carried to great depths by a subducting plate, olivine changes to a more compact, denser polymorph with the same structure as the mineral *spinel*.

Recall that oceanic lithosphere sinks because it is colder and more dense than the underlying mantle. It follows, therefore, that during subduction, the transformation of olivine from its low- to high-density form would contribute to plate subduction. Stated another way, this phase change causes an increase in the overall density of the slab, thereby enhancing its rate of descent.

In contrast to olivine, minerals such as quartz (SiO_2) and fluorite (CaF_2) tend to have chemical compositions that differ very little from their chemical formulas. However, even these minerals often contain tiny amounts of other less common elements, referred to as *trace elements*. Although trace elements have little effect on most mineral properties, they can significantly influence a mineral's color.

Structural Variations in Minerals

It is possible for two minerals with exactly the same chemical composition to have different internal structures and, hence, different external forms. Minerals of this type are called **polymorphs** (*poly* = many, *morph* = form). Graphite and diamond are particularly good examples of polymorphism because, when pure, they are both made up exclusively of carbon atoms.

---

6 CONCEPT CHECKS

1. State *Steno's Law* in your own words.
2. Name a mineral other than olivine that contains two elements that readily substitute for one another. What are these two elements? (Hint: Examine the chemical formulas in Figure 34.)
3. Define *polymorph* and give an example.

7 How Minerals Are Classified

More than 4000 minerals have been named, and several new ones are identified each year. Fortunately, for students who are beginning to study minerals, no more than a few dozen are abundant. Collectively, these few make up most of the rocks of Earth's crust and, as such, are often referred to as the **rock-forming minerals**.

Although less abundant, many other minerals are used extensively in the manufacture of products and are called **economic minerals**. However, rock-forming minerals and economic minerals are not mutually exclusive groups. When found in large deposits, some rock-forming minerals are economically significant. One example is the mineral calcite, which is the primary component of the sedimentary rock limestone and has many uses, including being a main ingredient in concrete.

Classifying Minerals

Minerals are placed into categories in much the same way that plants and animals are classified. Mineralogists use the term *mineral species* for a collection of specimens that exhibit similar internal structures and chemical compositions. Some common mineral species are quartz, calcite, galena, and pyrite. However, just as individual plants and animals within a species differ somewhat from one another, so do most specimens of the same mineral.

Some mineral species are further subdivided into mineral varieties. For example, pure quartz (SiO_2) is colorless and transparent. However, when small amounts of aluminum are incorporated into its atomic structure, quartz appears quite dark, in a variety called *smoky quartz*. *Amethyst*, another variety of quartz, owes its violet color to the presence of trace amounts of iron.

Mineral species are assigned to mineral classes. Some of the important mineral classes are the silicates, (SiO_4^{4-}), carbonates (CO_3^{2-}), halides (Cl^{1-}, F^{1-}, Br^{1-}), and sulfates (SO_4^{2-}). Minerals within each class tend to have similar internal structures and, hence, similar properties. For example, minerals that belong to the carbonate class react chemically with acid—albeit to varying degrees—and many exhibit similar cleavage. Furthermore, minerals within the same class are often found together in the same rock. For example, halite (NaCl) and silvite (KCl) belong to the halide class and commonly occur together in evaporite deposits.

Silicate Versus Nonsilicate Minerals

Only *eight elements* make up the vast majority of the rock-forming minerals and represent more than 98 percent (by weight) of the continental crust (FIGURE 30). These elements, in order of abundance, are oxygen (O),

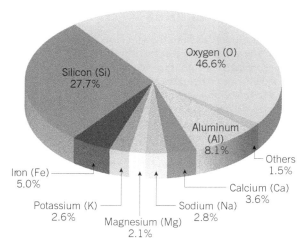

FIGURE 30 The eight most abundant elements in the continental crust

silicon (Si), aluminum (Al), iron (Fe), calcium (Ca), sodium (Na), potassium (K), and magnesium (Mg). As shown in Figure 30, silicon and oxygen are by far the most common elements in Earth's crust. Furthermore, these two elements readily combine to form the basic "building block" for the most common mineral group, the **silicates**. More than 800 silicate minerals are known, and they account for more than 90 percent of Earth's crust.

Because other mineral groups are far less abundant in Earth's crust than the silicates, they are often grouped together under the heading **nonsilicates**. Although not as common as silicates, some nonsilicate minerals are very important economically. They provide us with iron and aluminum to build automobiles, gypsum for plaster and drywall for home construction, and copper wire that carries electricity and connects us to the Internet. Some common nonsilicate mineral groups include the carbonates, sulfates, and halides. In addition to their economic importance, these mineral groups include members that are major constituents of sediments and sedimentary rocks.

7 CONCEPT CHECKS

1. Distinguish between *rock-forming minerals* and *economic minerals*.
2. List the eight most common elements in Earth's crust.
3. Distinguish between a mineral *species* and a *variety*.

8 The Silicates

Every silicate mineral contains the two most abundant elements in Earth's crust, oxygen and silicon. Further, most contain one or more of the other common elements. Together, these elements give rise to hundreds of silicate minerals with a wide variety of properties, including hard quartz, soft talc, sheet-like mica, fibrous asbestos, green olivine, and blood-red garnet.

Silicate Structures

All silicate minerals have the same fundamental building block, the **silicon–oxygen tetrahedron** (SiO_4^{4-}). This structure consists of four oxygen ions that are covalently bonded to one comparatively small silicon ion, forming a *tetrahedron*—a pyramid shape with four identical faces (FIGURE 31). These tetrahedra are not chemical compounds but rather complex ions (SiO_4^{4-}) having a net charge of -4. To become electrically balanced, these complex ions bond to positively charged metal ions. Specifically, each O^{2-} has one of its valence electrons bonding with the Si^{4+} located at the center of the tetrahedron. The remaining 1^- charge on each oxygen is available to bond with another positive ion or with the silicon ion in an adjacent tetrahedron.

Minerals with Independent Tetrahedra   One of the simplest silicate structures consists of independent tetrahedra that have their four oxygen ions bonded to positive ions, such as Mg^{2+}, Fe^{2+}, and Ca^{2+}. The mineral olivine, with the formula $(MgFe)_2SiO_4$, is a good example. In olivine, magnesium (Mg^{2+}) and/or iron (Fe^{2+}) ions pack between comparatively large independent SiO_4 tetrahedra, forming a dense three-dimensional structure (FIGURE 32). Garnet, another common silicate, is also composed of

independent tetrahedra ionically bonded by positive ions. Both olivine and garnet form dense, hard, equidimensional crystals that lack cleavage.

Minerals with Chain or Sheet Structures   One reason for the great variety of silicate minerals is the ability of SiO_4 tetrahedra to link to one another in a variety of configurations. This important phenomenon, called **polymerization**, is achieved by the sharing of one, two, three, or all four of the oxygen atoms with adjacent tetrahedra. Vast numbers of tetrahedra join together to form single chains, double chains, sheet structures, or three-dimensional frameworks, as shown in FIGURE 33.

To see how oxygen atoms are shared between adjacent tetrahedra, select one of the silicon ions (small blue spheres) near the middle of the single-chain shown in Figure 33B. Notice that this silicon ion is completely surrounded by four larger oxygen ions. Also notice that, of the four oxygen atoms, half are bonded to two silicon atoms, whereas the other two are not shared in this manner. It is the linkage across the shared oxygen ions that join the tetrahedra into a chain structure. Now examine a silicon ion near the middle of the sheet structure (Figure 33D) and count the number of shared and unshared oxygen ions surrounding it. As you likely observed, the sheet structure is the result of three of the four oxygen atoms being shared by adjacent tetrahedra.

Minerals with Three-Dimensional Frameworks   In the most common silicate structure, all four oxygen ions are shared, producing a complex three-dimensional framework (Figure 33E). Quartz and the most common mineral group, the feldspars, have structures in which all of the oxygens are shared.

The ratio of oxygen ions to silicon ions differs in each type of silicate structure. In independent tetrahedra (SiO_4) there are four oxygen ions for every silicon ion. In single chains, the oxygen-to-silicon ratio is 3:1 (SiO_3), and in three-dimensional frameworks, as found in quartz, the ratio is 2:1 (SiO_2). As more oxygen ions are shared, the percentage of silicon in the structure increases. Silicate minerals are, therefore, described as having a low or high silicon content, based on their ratio of oxygen to silicon. Silicate minerals with three-dimensional structures have the highest silicon content, while those composed of independent tetrahedra have the lowest.

A. Silicon-oxygen tetrahedron

B. Expanded view of silicon-oxygen tetrahedron

FIGURE 32 How independent tetrahedra bond with metallic ions The internal structure of the mineral olivine, which is composed of independent tetrahedra that are bonded together, with metallic ions (iron and magnesium) shown in green. This is an expanded view that does not show the bonds between the metallic ions and the tetrahedra.

Independent tetrahedra, which have an overall negative charge, form bonds (not shown) with positively charged metallic ions (green) to form a stable chemical compound.

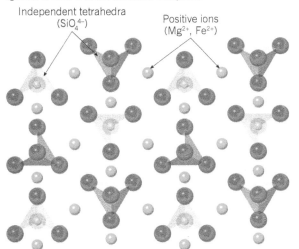

Independent tetrahedra (SiO_4^{4-})

Positive ions (Mg^{2+}, Fe^{2+})

A. Independent tetrahedra
Top view
Bottom view

B. Single chain
Top view
End view

C. Double chain
Top view
End view

D. Sheet structure
Top view
End view

E. Three-dimensional framework

SMARTFIGURE 33
Five basic silicate structures
A. Independent tetrahedra. **B.** Single chains. **C.** Double chains. **D.** Sheet structures. **E.** Three-dimensional framework.

Joining Silicate Structures

Except for quartz (SiO_2), the basic structure (chains, sheets, or three-dimensional frameworks) of most silicate minerals has a net negative charge. Therefore, metal ions are required to bring the overall charge into balance and to serve as the "mortar" that holds these structures together. The positive ions that most often link silicate structures are iron (Fe^{2+}), magnesium (Mg^{2+}), potassium (K^{1+}), sodium (Na^{1+}), aluminum (Al^{3+}), and calcium (Ca^{2+}). These positively charged ions bond with the unshared oxygen ions that occupy the corners of the silicate tetrahedra.

As a general rule, the hybrid covalent bonds between silicon and oxygen are stronger than the ionic bonds that hold one silicate structure to the next. Consequently, properties such as cleavage and, to some extent, hardness are controlled by the nature of the silicate framework. Quartz (SiO_2), which has only silicon–oxygen bonds, has great hardness and lacks cleavage, mainly because it has equally strong bonds in all directions. By contrast, the mineral talc (the source of talcum powder), has a sheet structure. Magnesium ions occur between the sheets and weakly join them together. The slippery feel of talcum powder is due to the silicate sheets sliding relative to one another, in much the same way that sheets of carbon atoms slide in graphite, giving it its lubricating properties.

Recall that atoms of similar size can substitute freely for one another without altering a mineral's structure. For example, in the mineral olivine, iron (Fe^{2+}) and magnesium (Mg^{2+}) substitute for each other. This also holds true for the third-most-common element in Earth's crust, aluminum (Al^{3+}), which often substitutes for silicon (Si) in the center of silicon–oxygen tetrahedra.

Because most silicate structures will readily accommodate two or more different positive ions at a given bonding site, individual specimens of a particular mineral may contain varying amounts of certain elements. As a result, many silicate minerals form a *mineral group* that exhibits a range of compositions between two end members. Examples include the olivines, pyroxenes, amphiboles, micas, and feldspars.

8 CONCEPT CHECKS

1. Explain the difference between the terms *silicon, silica,* and *silicate.*
2. Draw a sketch of the silicon–oxygen tetrahedron.
3. Explain the following statement: Silicate minerals with three-dimensional structures have the highest silicon content, while those composed of independent tetrahedra have the lowest.
4. What differences in their silicate structures account for the different properties of quartz and talc?

9 Common Silicate Minerals

The major groups of silicate minerals and common examples are given in FIGURE 34. The feldspars are, by far, the most plentiful silicate group, comprising more than 50 percent of Earth's crust. Quartz, the second-most-abundant mineral in the continental crust, is the only common mineral made completely of silicon and oxygen.

FIGURE 34 Common silicate minerals Note that the complexity of the silicate structure increases from top to bottom. (Photos by a: Marcel Clemens / Shutterstock; b: E. J. Tarbuck; c-g: Dennis Tasa

Mineral/Formula	Cleavage	Silicate Structure	Example
Olivine group $(Mg, Fe)_2SiO_4$	None	Single tetrahedra	Olivine
Pyroxene group (Augite) $(Mg,Fe)SiO_3$	Two planes at 90°	Single chains	Augite
Amphibole group (Hornblende) $Ca_2(Fe,Mg)_5Si8O_{22}(OH)_2$	Two planes at 60° and 120°	Double chains	Hornblende
Micas — **Biotite** $K(Mg,Fe)_3AlSi_3O_{10}(OH)_2$	One plane	Sheets	Biotite
Micas — **Muscovite** $KAl_2(AlSi_3O_{10})(OH)_2$	One plane	Sheets	Muscovite
Feldspars — **Potassium feldspar (Orthoclase)** $KAlSi_3O_8$	Two planes at 90°	Three-dimensional networks	Potassium feldspar
Feldspars — **Plagioclase** $(Ca,Na)AlSi_3O_8$	Two planes at 90°	Three-dimensional networks	
Quartz SiO_2	None		Quartz

Most silicate minerals form when molten rock cools and crystallizes. Cooling can occur at or near Earth's surface (low temperature and pressure) or at great depths (high temperature and pressure). The environment during crystallization and the chemical composition of the molten rock determine, to a large degree, which minerals are produced. For example, the silicate mineral olivine crystallizes early, whereas quartz forms much later in the crystallization process.

In addition, some silicate minerals form at Earth's surface from the weathered products of other silicate minerals. Still others are formed under the extreme pressures associated with mountain building. Each silicate mineral, therefore, has a structure and a chemical composition that *indicate the conditions under which it formed.* By carefully examining the mineral constituents of rocks, geologists can usually determine the circumstances under which the rocks formed.

We will now examine some of the most common silicate minerals, which we divide into two major groups on the basis of their chemical makeup: the light silicates and the dark silicates.

The Light Silicates

The **light** (or **nonferromagnesian**) **silicates** are generally light in color and have a specific gravity of about 2.7, less than that of the dark (ferromagnesian) silicates. These differences are mainly attributable to the presence or absence of iron and magnesium, which are "heavy." The light silicates contain varying amounts of aluminum, potassium, calcium, and sodium rather than iron and magnesium.

Feldspar Group
Feldspar minerals, which form the most common mineral group, can form under a wide range of temperatures and pressures, which partially accounts for their abundance (FIGURE 35). Two different feldspar structures exist. One group of feldspar minerals contains potassium ions in its structure and is therefore referred to as *potassium feldspar.* (*Orthoclase* and *microcline* are common members of the potassium feldspar group.) The other group, called *plagioclase feldspar,* contains both sodium and calcium ions that freely substitute for one another, depending on the environment during crystallization. Despite these differences, all feldspar minerals have similar physical properties. They have two planes of cleavage meeting at or near 90-degree angles, are relatively hard (6 on the Mohs scale), and have a luster that ranges from glassy to pearly. As a component in igneous rocks, feldspar crystals can be identified by their rectangular shape and rather smooth, shiny faces (FIGURE 36).

Potassium feldspar is usually light cream, salmon pink, or occasionally blue-green in color. The plagioclase feldspars, on the other hand, range in color from white to medium gray. However, color should not be used to

Potassium Feldspar

A. Potassium feldspar crystal (orthoclase) **B. Potassium feldspar showing cleavage (orthoclase)**

Plagioclase Feldspar

C. Sodium-rich plagioclase feldspar (albite) **D. Plagioclase feldspar showing striations (labradorite)**

FIGURE 35 Feldspar minerals
A. Characteristic crystal form of potassium feldspar. **B.** Like this sample, most pink feldspar belongs to the potassium feldspar subgroup. **C.** Most sodium-rich plagioclase feldspar is light colored and has a porcelain luster. **D.** Calcium-rich plagioclase feldspar tends to be gray, blue-gray, or black in color. Labradorite, the variety shown here, exhibits striations on one of its crystal faces. (Photos by Dennis Tasa and E. J. Tarbuck)

distinguish these groups. The only way to distinguish the feldspars physically is to look for a multitude of fine parallel lines, called *striations.* Striations are found on some cleavage planes of plagioclase feldspar but are not present on potassium feldspar (see Figure 35).

Quartz
Quartz (SiO_2) is the only common silicate mineral that consists entirely of silicon and oxygen. As such, the term *silica* is applied to quartz. Because quartz contains a ratio of two oxygen ions (O^{2-}) for every silicon ion (Si^{4+}), no other positive ions are needed to attain neutrality.

In quartz, a three-dimensional framework is developed through the complete sharing of oxygen by adjacent silicon atoms. Thus, all the bonds in quartz are of the strong silicon–oxygen type. Consequently, quartz is hard, is resistant to weathering, and does not have cleavage. When broken, quartz generally exhibits conchoidal fracture. When pure, quartz is clear and, if allowed to grow without interference, will develop hexagonal crystals that develop pyramid-shaped ends. However, like most other clear minerals, quartz is often colored by inclusions of various ions (impurities) and forms without developing good crystal faces. The most common varieties of quartz are milky (white), smoky (gray), rose (pink), amethyst (purple), and rock crystal (clear) (see Figure 15).

Muscovite
Muscovite is a common member of the mica family. It is light in color and has a pearly luster (see Figure 20). Like other micas, muscovite has excellent cleavage in one direction. In thin sheets, muscovite is clear, a property that accounts for its use as window "glass" during the Middle Ages. Because

A. Potassium feldspar

B. Plagioclase feldspar

FIGURE 36 Feldspar crystals in igneous rocks When found in igneous rocks, feldspar crystals tend to be rectangular in shape and exhibit smooth, shiny faces. (Photos by E. J. Tarbuck) muscovite is very shiny, it can often be identified by the sparkle it gives a rock. If you have ever looked closely at beach sand, you may have seen the glimmering brilliance of the mica flakes scattered among the other sand grains.

Clay Minerals   *Clay* is a term used to describe a category of complex minerals that, like the micas, have a sheet structure. Unlike other common silicates, most clay minerals originate as products of the chemical breakdown (chemical weathering) of other silicate minerals. Thus, clay minerals make up a large percentage of the surface material we call soil. Because of the importance of soil in agriculture, and because of its role as a supporting material for buildings, clay minerals are extremely important to humans. In addition, clays account for nearly half the volume of sedimentary rocks. Clay minerals are generally very fine grained, which makes identification difficult, unless they are studied microscopically. Their layered structure and weak bonding between layers give them a characteristic feel when wet. Clays are common in shales, mudstones, and other sedimentary rocks.

One of the most common clay minerals is *kaolinite* (FIGURE 37), which is used in the manufacture of fine china and as a coating for *high-gloss paper*, such as that used in this text. Further, some clay minerals absorb large amounts of water, which allows them to swell to several times their normal size. These clays have been used commercially in a variety of ingenious ways, including as an additive to thicken milkshakes in fast-food restaurants.

The Dark Silicates

The **dark** (or **ferromagnesian**) **silicates** are minerals containing ions of iron (iron = *ferro*) and/or magnesium in their structure. Because of their iron content, ferromagnesian silicates are dark in color and have a greater specific gravity, between 3.2 and 3.6, than nonferromagnesian silicates. The most common dark silicate minerals

FIGURE 37 Kaolinite
Kaolinite is a common clay mineral formed by weathering of feldspar minerals.

Kaolinite

Dennis Tasa

FIGURE 38 Olivine
Commonly black to olive green in color, olivine has a glassy luster and is commonly found in the igneous rocks basalt and peridotite.

Olivine-rich peridotite (variety dunite)

Dennis Tasa

are olivine, the pyroxenes, the amphiboles, dark mica (biotite), and garnet.

Olivine Group   *Olivine* is a family of high-temperature silicate minerals that are black to olive green in color and have a glassy luster and a conchoidal fracture (see Figure 34). Transparent olivine is occasionally used as a gemstone called peridot. Rather than developing large crystals, olivine commonly forms small, rounded crystals that give olivine-rich rocks a granular appearance (FIGURE 38). Olivine and related forms are common in the igneous rock basalt and are thought to constitute up to 50 percent of Earth's upper mantle.

Pyroxene Group   The *pyroxenes* are a group of diverse minerals that are important components in dark colored igneous rocks. The most common member, *augite*, is a black, opaque mineral with two directions of cleavage that meet at nearly a 90-degree angle. Augite is one of the dominant minerals in basalt, a common igneous rock of the oceanic crust and volcanic areas on the continents (FIGURE 39A).

Amphibole Group   *Hornblende* is the most common member of a chemically complex group of minerals called *amphiboles* (FIGURE 39B). Hornblende is usually dark green to black in color, and except for its cleavage

FIGURE 39 Augite and hornblende
These dark-colored silicate minerals are common constituents of a variety of igneous rocks. (Photos courtesy of E. J. Tarbuck)

A. Augite

B. Hornblende

angles, which are about 60 degrees and 120 degrees, it is very similar in appearance to augite. In a rock, hornblende often forms elongated crystals. This helps distinguish it from pyroxene, which forms rather blocky crystals. Hornblende is found in igneous rocks, where it often makes up the dark portion of an otherwise light-colored rock (see Figure 3).

Biotite *Biotite* is a dark, iron-rich member of the mica family (see Figure 34). Like other micas, biotite possesses a sheet structure that gives it excellent cleavage in one direction. Biotite also has a shiny black appearance that helps distinguish it from the other dark ferromagnesian minerals. Like hornblende, biotite is a common constituent of igneous rocks, including the rock granite.

Garnet *Garnet* is similar to olivine in that its structure is composed of individual tetrahedra linked by metallic ions. Also like olivine, garnet has a glassy luster, lacks cleavage, and exhibits conchoidal fracture. Although the colors of garnet are varied, this mineral is most often brown to deep red. Well developed, garnet crystals have 12 diamond-shaped faces and are most commonly found in metamorphic rocks (FIGURE 40). When transparent, garnets are prized as semiprecious gemstones.

← 2 cm →

FIGURE 40 **Well-formed garnet crystal**
Garnets come in a variety of colors and are commonly found in mica-rich metamorphic rocks.

9 CONCEPT CHECKS

1. How do most silicate minerals form?
2. Apart from their difference in color, what is one main distinction between light and dark silicates? What accounts for this difference?
3. Based on the chart in Figure 34, what do muscovite and biotite have in common? How do they differ?
4. Is color a good way to distinguish between orthoclase and plagioclase feldspar? If not, what is a more effective means of distinguishing them?

EYE on Earth

Glass bottles, like most other manufactured products, contain substances obtained from minerals extracted from Earth's crust and oceans. The primary ingredient in commercially produced glass bottles is the mineral quartz. Glass also contains lesser amounts of the mineral calcite. (Photo by Chris Brignell/Shutterstock)

Question 1 In what mineral group does quartz belong?

Question 2 Glass beer bottles are usually clear, green, or brown. Based on what you know about how the mineral quartz is colored, what do glass manufacturers do to get green and brown bottles?

Question 3 Why did some brewers start using brown bottles, rather than green bottles which were popular until the 1930s.

10 Important Nonsilicate Minerals

Nonsilicate minerals are typically divided into groups, based on the negatively charged ion or complex ion that the members have in common (TABLE 1). For example, the *oxides* contain the negative oxygen ions (O^{2-}), which are bonded to one or more kinds of positive ions. Thus, within each mineral group, the basic structure and type of bonding is similar. As a result, the minerals in each group have similar physical properties that are useful in mineral identification.

Although the nonsilicates make up only about 8 percent of Earth's crust, some minerals, such as gypsum, calcite, and halite, occur as constituents in sedimentary rocks in significant amounts. Furthermore, many others are important economically. Table 1 lists some of the nonsilicate mineral groups and a few examples of each. A brief discussion of a few of the most common nonsilicate minerals follows.

Some of the most common nonsilicate minerals belong to one of three classes of minerals: the carbonates (CO_3^{2-}), the sulfates (SO_4^{2-}), and the halides (Cl^{1-}, F^{1-}, Br^{1-}). The carbonate minerals are much simpler structurally than the silicates. This mineral group is composed of the carbonate ion (CO_3^{2-}) and one or more kinds of positive ions. FIGURE 41A,B shows the two most common carbonate minerals: *calcite*, $CaCO_3$ (calcium carbonate) and *dolomite*, $CaMg(CO_3)_2$ (calcium/magnesium carbonate). Calcite and dolomite are usually found together as the primary constituents in the sedimentary rocks limestone

and dolostone. When calcite is the dominant mineral, the rock is called *limestone*, whereas *dolostone* results from a predominance of dolomite. Limestone has many uses, including as road aggregate, as building stone, and as the main ingredient in Portland cement.

Two other nonsilicate minerals frequently found in sedimentary rocks are *halite* and *gypsum* (Figure 41C,D). Both minerals are commonly found in thick layers that are the last vestiges of ancient seas that have long since evaporated (FIGURE 42). Like limestone, both halite and gypsum are important nonmetallic resources. Halite is the mineral name for common table salt (NaCl). Gypsum ($CaSO_4 \cdot 2 H_2O$), which is calcium sulfate with water bound into the structure, is the mineral of which plaster and other similar building materials are composed.

Most nonsilicate mineral classes contain members that are prized for their economic value. This includes the oxides, whose members hematite and magnetite are important ores of iron (Figure 41E,F). Also significant

Mineral Groups [key ion(s) or element(s)]	Mineral Name	Chemical Formula	Economic Use
Carbonates (CO_3^{2-})	Calcite	$CaCO_3$	Portland cement, lime
	Dolomite	$CaMg(CO_3)_2$	Portland cement, lime
Halides (Cl^{1-}, F^{1-}, Br^{1-})	Halite	NaCl	Common salt
	Fluorite	CaF_2	Used in steelmaking
	Sylvite	KCl	Fertilizer
Oxides (O^{2-})	Hematite	Fe_2O_3	Ore of iron, pigment
	Magnetite	Fe_3O_4	Ore of iron
	Corundum	Al_2O_3	Gemstone, abrasive
	Ice	H_2O	Solid form of water
Sulfides (S^{2-})	Galena	PbS	Ore of lead
	Sphalerite	ZnS	Ore of zinc
	Pyrite	FeS_2	Sulfuric acid production
	Chalcopyrite	$CuFeS_2$	Ore of copper
	Cinnabar	HgS	Ore of mercury
Sulfates (SO_4^{2-})	Gypsum	$CaSO_4 \cdot 2H_2O$	Plaster
	Anhydrite	$CaSO_4$	Plaster
	Barite	$BaSO_4$	Drilling mud
Native elements (single elements)	Gold	Au	Trade, jewelry
	Copper	Cu	Electrical conductor
	Diamond	C	Gemstone, abrasive
	Sulfur	S	Sulfa drugs, chemicals
	Graphite	C	Pencil lead, dry lubricant
	Silver	Ag	Jewelry, photography
	Platinum	Pt	Catalyst

TABLE 1 Common Nonsilicate Mineral Groups

FIGURE 41 Important nonsilicate minerals (Photos by Dennis Tasa and E. J. Tarbuck)

A. Calcite

B. Dolomite

C. Halite

D. Gypsum

E. Hematite

F. Magnetite

G. Galena

H. Chalcopyrite

I. Fluorite

are the sulfides, which are basically compounds of sulfur (S) and one or more metals. Examples of important sulfide minerals include galena (lead), sphalerite (zinc), and chalcopyrite (copper). In addition, native elements—including gold, silver, and carbon (diamonds)—plus a host of other nonsilicate minerals—fluorite (flux in making steel), corundum (gemstone, abrasive), and uraninite (a uranium source)—are important economically.

10 CONCEPT CHECKS

1. List six common nonsilicate mineral groups. What key ion(s) or element(s) define each group?
2. What simple test can be used to distinguish calcite from dolomite?
3. What does a deposit of halite or gypsum indicate about the past environment at that location?
4. Refer to Table 1. List one mineral from each nonsilicate class and the mineral's economic use.

FIGURE 42 Thick bed of halite exposed in an underground mine Halite (salt) mine in Grand Saline, Texas. Note the person for scale. (Photo by Tom Bochsler)

Gemstones

Precious stones have been prized since antiquity. Although most gemstones are varieties of a particular mineral, misinformation abounds regarding gems and their mineral makeup.

Important Gemstones

Gemstones are classified in one of two categories: precious or semiprecious. Precious gems are rare and generally have hardnesses that exceed 9 on the Mohs scale. Therefore, they are more valuable and thus more expensive than semiprecious gems.

GEM	MINERAL NAME	PRIZED HUES
PRECIOUS		
Diamond	Diamond	Colorless, pinks, blues
Emerald	Beryl	Greens
Ruby	Corundum	Reds
Sapphire	Corundum	Blues
Opal	Opal	Brilliant hues
SEMIPRECIOUS		
Alexandrite	Chrysoberyl	Variable
Amethyst	Quartz	Purples
Cat's-eye	Chrysoberyl	Yellows
Chalcedony	Quartz (agate)	Banded
Citrine	Quartz	Yellows
Garnet	Garnet	Red, greens
Jade	Jadeite or nephrite	Greens
Moonstone	Feldspar	Transparent blues
Peridot	Olivine	Olive greens
Smoky quartz	Quartz	Browns
Spinel	Spinel	Reds
Topaz	Topaz	Purples, reds
Tourmaline	Tourmaline	Reds, blue-greens
Turquoise	Turquoise	Blues
Zircon	Zircon	Reds

Reuters

The Famous Hope Diamond

The deep-blue Hope Diamond is a 45.52-carat gem that is thought to have been cut from a much larger 115-carat stone discovered in India in the mid-1600s. The original 115-carat stone was cut into a smaller gem that became part of the crown jewels of France and was in the possession of King Louis XVI and Marie Antoinette before they attempted to escape France. Stolen during the French Revolution in 1792, the gem is thought to have been recut to its present size and shape. In the 1800s, it became part of the collection of Henry Hope (hence its name) and is on display at the Smithsonian in Washington, DC.

What Constitutes a Gemstone?

When found in their natural state, most gemstones are dull and would be passed over by most people as "just another rock." Gems must be cut and polished by experienced professionals before their true beauty is displayed. Cutting and polishing is accomplished using abrasive material, most often tiny fragments of diamonds that are embedded in a metal disk.

Shutterstock

? Why are diamonds used as an abrasive material to cut and polish gemstones?

Charles D. Winters/ Photo Researchers, Inc.

Naming Gemstones

Most precious stones are given names that differ from their parent mineral. For example, sapphire is one of two gems that are varieties of the same mineral, corundum. Trace elements can produce vivid sapphires of nearly every color. Tiny amounts of titanium and iron in corundum produce the most prized blue sapphires. When the mineral corundum contains a sufficient quantity of chromium, it exhibits a brilliant red color. This variety of corundum is called ruby.

Rubies, like sapphires, are varieties of the mineral corundum

Sapphires, showing variations of colors

Dorling Kindersley

Greg C. Grace/ Alamy

CONCEPTS IN REVIEW: MATTER AND MINERALS

1 Minerals: Building blocks of rocks

List the main characteristics that an Earth material must possess to be considered a mineral and describe each.

KEY WORDS mineralogy, mineral, rock

- In Earth science, the word *mineral* refers to naturally occurring inorganic solids that possess an orderly crystalline structure and a characteristic chemical composition. The study of minerals is *mineralogy*.

- Minerals are the building blocks of rocks. Rocks are naturally occurring masses of minerals or mineral-like matter, such as glass or organic debris.

DRAW IT Make a sketch that shows how elements, minerals, and rocks relate to one another.

2 Atoms: Building blocks of minerals

Compare and contrast the three primary particles contained in atoms.

KEY WORDS atom, nucleus, proton, neutron, electron, valence electron, atomic number, element, periodic table, chemical compound

- Minerals are composed of atoms of one or more elements. The atoms of any element consist of the same three basic ingredients: protons, neutrons, and electrons.
- The atomic number is the number of protons in an atom. For example, an oxygen atom has eight protons, so its atomic number is eight. Nitrogen has one less; fluorine has one more. Protons and neutrons are approximately the same size and mass, but while protons are positively charged, neutrons have no charge.

- Electrons are much smaller than both protons and neutrons, and they weigh about 2000 times less. However, each electron has a full negative charge, equal in magnitude to the positive charge of a proton. Electrons swarm around an atom's nucleus at a distance, generally in several distinctive energy levels called *principal shells*. The electrons in the outermost principal shell are called *valence electrons*: They are important when the atom is bonding with other atoms to form chemical compounds.
- Elements with similar numbers of valence electrons tend to behave in similar ways. The periodic table displays these similarities in its graphical arrangement of the elements.

IT'S ELEMENTARY Use the periodic table (Figure 5) to identify these geologically important elements by their number of protons: (A) 14, (B) 6, (C) 13, (D) 17, and (E) 26.

3 Why atoms bond

Distinguish between ionic bonds, covalent bonds, and metallic bonds.

KEY WORDS octet rule, chemical bond, ion, ionic bond, covalent bond, metallic bond

- When atoms are attracted to other atoms, they can form bonds, which generally involves the transfer or sharing of valence electrons. For most atoms, the most stable arrangement is to have eight electrons in the outermost principal shell. This idea is called the *octet rule*.

- There are several kinds of bonds. Ionic bonds involve atoms of one element giving up electrons to atoms of another element, forming positively and negatively charged atoms called *ions*. Positively charged ions bond with negative ions to form ionic bonds.
- Covalent bonds involve the sharing of electrons between two adjacent atoms. In metallic bonds, the sharing is more extensive: Electrons can freely move from one atom to the next throughout the entire mass.

EYE ON IONS Which of the situations in the diagram shows ionic bonding? What are its distinguishing characteristics? How does ionic bonding happen?

4 How do minerals form?

Describe three mechanisms that generate minerals and rocks.

- Mineral crystals can form in several ways. When elements are dissolved in solutions of water, precipitation of minerals may be triggered by a drop in temperature or when loss of water by evaporation causes the concentration of ions to become greater.
- In molten rock, free-moving atoms form bonds with other atoms as the liquid cools, and that "nucleus" of a mineral crystal will add additional atoms on its outer edges, growing larger as more atoms enter the lower-energy solid state.
- Marine organisms can extract ions from the surrounding seawater and then biochemically secrete skeletal material made of either calcium carbonate or silica.

SNOW ME THE ANSWER   When snowflakes form in clouds, crystals of ice grow in the air. Which of the methods of mineral formation does this most resemble? Why?

1. Crystallization from an aqueous solution   Dennis Tasa

2. Crystallization by living organisms   Givaga/Shutterstock

3. Crystallization of molten rock   Dennis Tasa

5 Physical properties of minerals

List the properties that are used in mineral identification and briefly describe each.

KEY WORDS luster, color, streak, crystal shape (habit), tenacity, hardness, Mohs scale, cleavage, fracture, density, specific gravity

- The composition and structure of a mineral's crystal lattice give it specific physical properties. These properties can be used to tell minerals apart from one another and make certain minerals useful for specific human tasks.
- Luster is a mineral's ability to reflect light. The degree to which a mineral can transmit light may be described as transparent, translucent, or opaque. Color is an unreliable characteristic for identification, as slight impurities can "stain" minerals into misleading colors. More trustworthy is streak, the color of the powder generated by scraping a mineral against a porcelain streak plate.
- The shape a crystal assumes as it grows is often very useful for identifying it. We call this its *habit.*
- Minerals vary in the strength of the bonds that hold their atoms together. Variation in these bonds gives minerals properties such as tenacity (whether a mineral breaks in a brittle fashion or bends when stressed), cleavage, fracture, and hardness (resistance to being scratched). Cleavage, the preferential breakage of a mineral along planes of weakly bonded atoms, is very useful in identifying minerals.
- The amount of matter packed into a given volume determines a mineral's density. Mineralogists find it simplest to measure a similar quantity, specific gravity, which is the ratio between a mineral's density and the density of water.
- A suite of other properties are diagnostic for certain minerals but rare in most others. Smell, taste, feel, reaction to hydrochloric acid, magnetism, and double refraction are examples.

Quartz   Dennis Tasa   Calcite   Dennis Tasa

CRITICAL CRITERIA   Research the minerals quartz and calcite. List five physical characteristics that may be used to distinguish one from the other.

6 Mineral structures and compositions

Distinguish between compositional and structural variations in minerals and give examples.

KEY WORDS crystal, crystalline, unit cell, Steno's Law (Law of Constancy of Interfacial Angles), polymorph

- Crystals are naturally occurring solids with orderly, repeating internal structures. All minerals occur in crystal form, even if those crystals aren't stereotypical large, perfectly formed prisms. The atoms that make up a mineral are packed together in some geometrically regular fashion. The smallest expression of that arrangement is called a *unit cell;* many unit cells repeating in three dimensions yield a mineral crystal.
- Steno's Law, or the Law of Constancy of Interfacial Angles, says that no matter how big a crystal of a given mineral may be, the angles between its faces will always be the same.
- The composition of minerals may vary within certain parameters. Certain portions of the chemical formula of a mineral may be fixed and

invariable, while other parts have flexibility in terms of which atoms are present. Generally, atoms of similar size and charge can "swap out" for one another.

- The same chemical compound can grow into different mineral crystals, with different arrangements of atoms. Calcite and aragonite are an example of this "polymorph" relationship: Though different minerals, they both are $CaCO_3$.

CONSTANT COMMENT

A crystal of the mineral corundum measuring 1 millimeter long has an angle between two crystal faces that measures 60°. Assume the crystal continued to grow until it had tripled in size. What is the angle between the crystal faces now?

The crystal lattice of fluorite (CaF_2) is typical of minerals in its regular, repetitive geometry.

7 How minerals are classified

Explain how minerals are classified and name the most abundant mineral group in Earth's crust.

KEY WORDS rock-forming mineral, economic mineral, silicate, nonsilicate

- Several thousand different minerals have been identified, but only a few dozen are especially common in the crust: These are the rock-forming minerals. Other minerals have economic value.
- Minerals are placed into classes on the basis of similar crystal structures and compositions. Minerals of the same class tend to have similar properties and are found in similar geologic settings.
- Silicon and oxygen are the most common elements in Earth's crust, and so the most common minerals in the crust are silicate minerals, with crystal structures dominated by those two elements. For comparison, nonsilicate minerals make up only about 8 percent of the crust.

QUARTZ OF A DIFFERENT COLOR A geologist finds a mineral deposit with crystals of amethyst and smoky quartz. Why are these two minerals, which look so different, classified as the same type of mineral?

8 The silicates

Sketch the silicon–oxygen tetrahedron and explain how these fundamental building blocks join together to form other silicate structures.

KEY WORDS silicon–oxygen tetrahedron, polymerization

- Silicate minerals have a basic building block in common: a small pyramid-shaped structure that consists of one silicon atom surrounded by four oxygen atoms. Because this structure has four sides, it is called the *silicon-oxygen tetrahedron*. Individual tetrahedra can be bonded to other elements, such as aluminum, iron, or potassium. Neighboring tetrahedra can share some of their oxygen atoms, causing them to develop long chains. This is the process of polymerization.
- Polymerization can produce silicate mineral structures with high or low degrees of oxygen sharing. The more sharing there is, the higher the ratio of silicon to oxygen will be. Polymerization can produce unit cells that are single "chains" of tetrahedra, double chains, sheets of shared tetrahedra, or even complicated three-dimensional networks of tetrahedra that share all the oxygen atoms in the mineral.
- Mineral groups are suites of minerals with similar properties because they have similar structures. Minerals within a group are differentiated mainly by slight variations in the proportions of elements involved.

Minerals like muscovite (in the mica mineral group) are built on a sheet-like sharing of silicon-oxygen tetrahedra.

COMPARE AND CONTRAST The chapter discusses several different arrangements for bonding silicon–oxygen tetrahedra together. List each arrangement and give an example of a mineral for each.

9 Common silicate minerals

Compare and contrast the light (nonferromagnesian) silicates with the dark (ferromagnesian) silicates and list four common minerals from each group.

KEY WORDS light (nonferromagnesian) silicate, dark (ferromagnesian) silicate

- Silicate minerals make up the most common mineral class on Earth. They are subdivided into minerals that contain iron and/or magnesium and those that do not. Respectively, these are the ferromagnesian and nonferromagnesian minerals. The circumstances of mineral formation (elements available, temperature, and so on) determine whether ferromagnesian or nonferromagnesian minerals will form.
- Nonferromagnesian minerals are generally light in color and generally of relatively low specific gravity. Feldspar, quartz, muscovite, and clays are all examples.
- Ferromagnesian minerals are generally dark in color and relatively dense. Olivine, pyroxene, amphibole, biotite, and garnet are all examples.

Dennis Tasa

Smoky quartz

EXCEPTION TO THE RULE   In general, nonferromagnesian minerals are light in color: shades of peach, tan, clear, or white. What could account for the fact that some nonferromagnesian minerals are dark colored like the smoky quartz in this photo.

---

10 Important nonsilicate minerals

List the common nonsilicate minerals and explain why each is important.

- Nonsilicate mineral groups don't have the silicon–oxygen tetrahedron as the fundamental unit of their structures. Instead, these minerals are made of other elements in other chemical arrangements.
- Oxides are dominated by the bonding of other elements (usually metals) to oxygen ions. Carbonates have CO_3 as a critical part of their crystal structure. Sulfates have SO_4 as their basic building block. Halides have a nonmetal ion such as chlorine, bromine, or fluorine bonded to a metal ion such as sodium or calcium.
- Nonsilicate minerals are often economic minerals. Hematite is an important source of industrial iron, for instance. Calcite is a critical component of cement. Halite makes popcorn taste good.

POSSIBLE PLANET   Reconsider Figure 30. What would be the most abundant elements on a planet that instead of being dominated by silicate minerals had mostly halides? What about a carbonate planet?

GIVE IT SOME THOUGHT

1. Using the geologic definition of *mineral* as your guide, determine which of the items on this list are minerals and which are not. If not a mineral, explain.

   a. Gold nugget
   b. Seawater
   c. Quartz
   d. Cubic zirconia
   e. Obsidian
   f. Ruby
   g. Glacial ice
   h. Amber

   Refer to the periodic table of the elements (Figure 5) to help you answer Questions 2, 3, and 4.

2. Assume that the number of protons in a neutral atom is 92 and its mass number is 238.

   a. What is the name of the element?
   b. How many electrons does it have?
   c. How many neutrons does it have?

3. Which of the following elements is more likely to form chemical bonds: xenon (Xe) or sodium (Na)? Explain why.

4. Referring to the accompanying photos of five minerals, determine which of these specimens exhibit a metallic luster and which have a nonmetallic luster. (Photos by Dennis Tasa)

5. Gold has a specific gravity of almost 20. A 5-gallon bucket of water weighs 40 pounds. How much would a 5-gallon bucket of gold weigh?

6. Examine the accompanying photo of a mineral that has several smooth, flat surfaces that resulted when the specimen was broken.

   a. How many flat surfaces are present on this specimen?
   b. How many different directions of cleavage does this specimen have?
   c. Do the cleavage directions meet at 90-degree angles?

Cleaved sample

7. Each of the following statements describes a silicate mineral or mineral group. In each case, provide the appropriate name:

   a. The most common member of the amphibole group
   b. The most common nonferromagnesian member of the mica family

   c. The only common silicate mineral made entirely of silicon and oxygen
   d. A high-temperature silicate with a name that is based on its color
   e. A silicate mineral that is characterized by striations
   f. A silicate mineral that originates as a product of chemical weathering

8. The continents have an average elevation of about 1 kilometer *above* sea level, whereas the ocean basins have an average elevation of about 4 kilometers *below* sea level. Based on what you know about minerals and their properties, name two minerals that are likely abundant in the continental crust and two minerals that may be abundant in the oceanic crust. Explain why you chose those minerals. (*Hint:* Earth's crust is composed mainly of silicate minerals.)

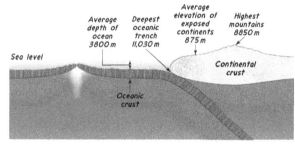

9. What mineral property is illustrated in the accompanying photo?

10. Do an Internet search to determine what mineral or minerals are extracted from the ground during the manufacturing of the following products.

    a. Stainless steel utensils
    b. Cat litter
    c. Tums brand antacid tablets
    d. Lithium batteries
    e. Aluminum beverage cans

11. Most states have designated a state mineral, rock, or gemstone to promote interest in the state's natural resources. Describe your state mineral, rock, or gemstone and explain why it was selected. If your state does not have a state mineral, rock, or gemstone, complete the exercise by selecting one from a state adjacent to yours.

MasteringGeology™

Looking for additional review and test prep materials? Visit the Study Area in MasteringGeology to enhance your understanding of this chapter's content by accessing a variety of resources, including **Self-Study Quizzes,** **Geoscience Animations, GEODe Tutorials, RSS feeds, flashcards, web links, self-study quizzes,** and an optional **Pearson eText.**

Glossary

Atom The smallest particle that exists as an element.

Atomic number The number of protons in the nucleus of an atom.

Chemical bond A strong attractive force that exists between atoms in a substance. It involves the transfer or sharing of electrons that allows each atom to attain a full valence shell.

Cleavage The tendency of a mineral to break along planes of weak bonding.

Color A phenomenon of light by which otherwise identical objects may be differentiated.

Covalent bond A chemical bond produced by the sharing of electrons.

Crystal Any natural solid with an ordered, repetitive atomic structure.

Crystalline See *Crystal*.

Crystal shape See Habit.

Dark silicate A silicate mineral that contains ions of iron and/or magnesium in its structure. Dark silicates are dark in color and have a higher specific gravity than nonferromagnesian silicates.

Density A property of matter defined as mass per unit volume.

Electron A negatively charged subatomic particle that has a negligible mass and is found outside an atom's nucleus.

Element A substance that cannot be decomposed into simpler substances by ordinary chemical or physical means.

Ferromagnesian silicate See Dark silicate.

Fracture Any break or rupture in rock along which no appreciable movement has taken place.

Habit Refers to the common or characteristic shape of a crystal or an aggregate of crystals.

Hardness A mineral's resistance to scratching and abrasion.

Ionic bond A chemical bond between two oppositely charged ions that is formed by the transfer of valence electrons from one atom to the other.

Law of Constancy of Interfacial Angles A law which states that the angle between equivalent faces of the same mineral is always the same.

Light silicate A silicate mineral that lacks iron and/or magnesium. Light silicates are generally lighter in color and have lower specific gravities than dark silicates.

Luster The appearance *or quality of light* reflected from the surface of a mineral.

Metallic bond A chemical bond that is present in all metals that may be characterized as an extreme type of electron sharing in which the electrons move freely from atom to atom.

Mineral A naturally occurring, inorganic crystalline material with a unique chemical structure.

Mineralogy The study of minerals.

Mohs scale A series of 10 minerals used as a standard in determining hardness.

Neutron A subatomic particle found in the nucleus of an atom. The neutron is electrically neutral, with a mass approximately equal to that of a proton.

Nucleus The small, heavy core of an atom that contains all of its positive charge and most of its mass.

Nonferromagnesian silicate See Light silicate.

Octet rule A rule which states that atoms combine in order that each may have the electron arrangement of a noble gas (that is, the outer energy level contains eight neutrons).

Periodic table An arrangement of the elements in which atomic number increases from the left to right and elements with similar properties appear in columns called families or groups.

Polymorphs Two or more minerals having the same chemical composition but different crystalline structures. Exemplified by the diamond and graphite forms of carbon.

Proton A positively charged subatomic particle found in the nucleus of an atom.

Rock A consolidated mixture of minerals.

Rock-forming minerals The relatively few minerals that make up most of the rocks in Earth's crust.

Silicon-oxygen tetrahedron A structure composed of four oxygen atoms surrounding a silicon atom that constitutes the basic building block of silicate minerals.

Specific gravity The ratio of a substance's weight to the weight of an equal volume of water.

Steno's Law See Law of Constancy of Interfacial Angles.

Streak The color of a mineral in powdered form.

Tenacity Describes a mineral's toughness or resistance to breaking or deforming.

Unit cell The smallest group of atoms, ions, or molecules that form the building block of a crystal.

Valence electron The electrons involved in the bonding process; the electrons occupying the highest principal *energy level* of an atom.

Magma, Igneous Rocks, and Intrusive Activity

From Chapter 4 of *Earth: An Introduction to Physical Geology*, Eleventh Edition. Edward J. Tarbuck, Frederick K. Lutgens, Dennis Tasa.

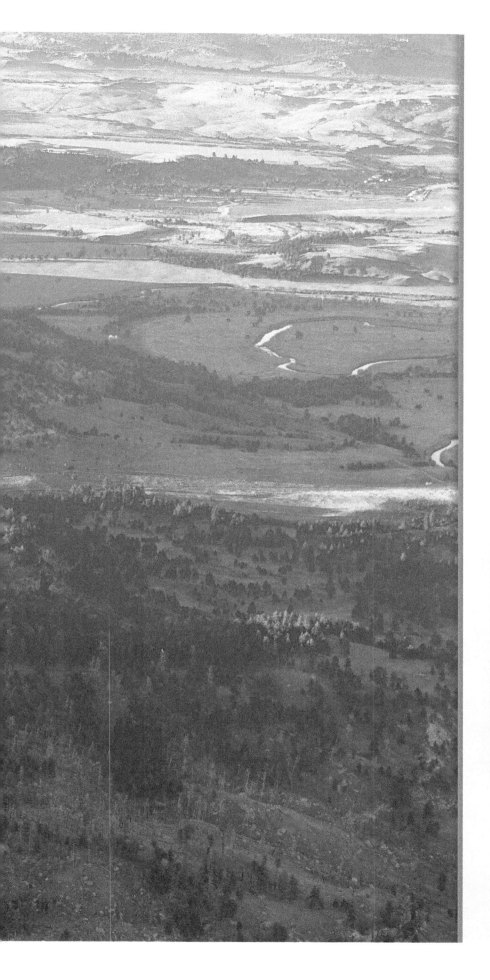

Magma, Igneous Rocks, and Intrusive Activity

Devil's Tower, composed of intrusive igneous rock, is located in northeastern Wyoming. (Photo by Michael Collier.)

Each statement represents the primary learning objective for the corresponding major heading within the chapter. After you complete the chapter you should be able to:

1 List and describe the three major components of magma.
2 Compare and contrast the four basic igneous compositions: basaltic (mafic), granitic (felsic), andesitic (intermediate), and ultramafic.
3 Identify and describe the six major igneous textures.
4 Distinguish among the common igneous rocks based on texture and mineral composition.
5 Summarize the major processes that generate magma from solid rock.
6 Write a statement describing how magmatic differentiation can result in the formation of one or more secondary magmas from a single parent magma.
7 Describe how partial melting of the mantle rock peridotite generates basaltic (mafic) magma.
8 Compare and contrast these intrusive igneous structures: dikes, sills, batholiths, stocks, and laccoliths.

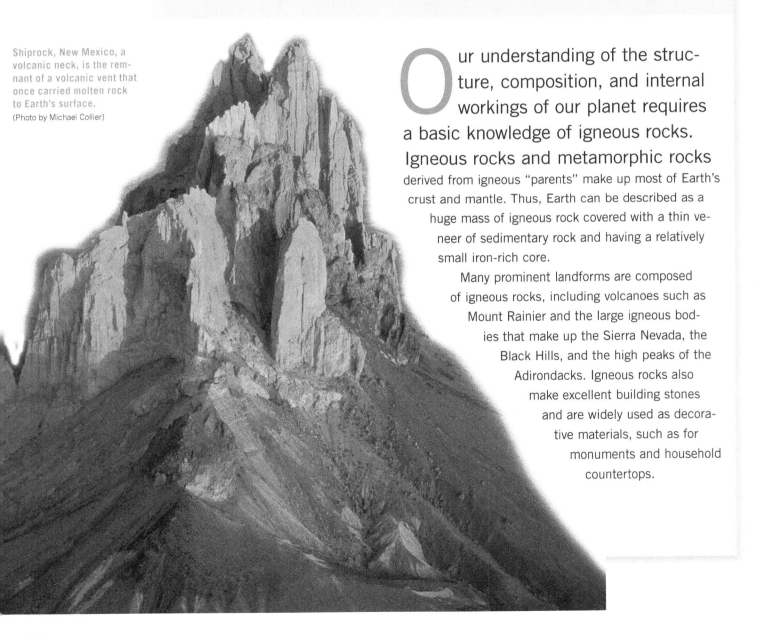

Shiprock, New Mexico, a volcanic neck, is the remnant of a volcanic vent that once carried molten rock to Earth's surface. (Photo by Michael Collier)

Our understanding of the structure, composition, and internal workings of our planet requires a basic knowledge of igneous rocks. Igneous rocks and metamorphic rocks derived from igneous "parents" make up most of Earth's crust and mantle. Thus, Earth can be described as a huge mass of igneous rock covered with a thin veneer of sedimentary rock and having a relatively small iron-rich core.

Many prominent landforms are composed of igneous rocks, including volcanoes such as Mount Rainier and the large igneous bodies that make up the Sierra Nevada, the Black Hills, and the high peaks of the Adirondacks. Igneous rocks also make excellent building stones and are widely used as decorative materials, such as for monuments and household countertops.

1 Magma: Parent Material of Igneous Rock

In our discussion of the rock cycle, it was noted that **igneous rocks** (*ignis* = fire) form as molten rock cools and solidifies. Considerable evidence supports the idea that the parent material for igneous rocks, called **magma**, is formed by partial melting that occurs at various levels within Earth's crust and upper mantle to depths of about 250 kilometers (about 150 miles).

Once formed, a magma body buoyantly rises toward the surface because it is less dense than the surrounding rocks. (When rock melts, it takes up more space and, hence, it becomes less dense than the surrounding solid rock.) Occasionally, molten rock reaches Earth's surface, where it is called **lava** (FIGURE 1). Sometimes lava is emitted as fountains that are produced when escaping gasses propel it from a magma chamber. On other occasions, lava is explosively ejected, producing dramatic steam and ash eruptions.

However, not all eruptions are violent; many volcanoes emit quiet outpourings of fluid lava.

The Nature of Magma

Magma is completely or partly molten rock, which when cooled solidifies to form igneous rocks composed of silicate minerals. Most magmas consist of three materials: a *liquid component*, a *solid component*, and a *gaseous component*.

The liquid portion, called **melt**, is composed mainly of mobile ions of the eight most common elements found in Earth's crust—silicon and oxygen, along with lesser amounts of aluminum, potassium, calcium, sodium, iron, and magnesium.

The solid components (if any) in magma are crystals of silicate minerals. As a magma body cools, the size and number of crystals increase. During the last stage of cooling, a magma body is like a "crystalline mush" (resembling a bowl of very thick oatmeal) that contains only small amounts of melt.

FIGURE 1 Fluid lava emitted from Hawaii's Kilauea Volcano Kilauea, on Hawaii's Big Island, is one of the most active volcanoes on the planet.

USG

125

Potassium feldspar (pink)

Amphibole (black)

Quartz (gray, glassy)

Plagioclase feldspar (white)

Dennis Tasa

FIGURE 2 Igneous rock composed of interlocking crystals
The largest crystals are about 1 centimeter in length.

The gaseous components of magma, called **volatiles**, are materials that vaporize (form a gas) at surface pressures. The most common volatiles found in magma are water vapor (H_2O), carbon dioxide (CO_2), and sulfur dioxide (SO_2), which are confined by the immense pressure exerted by the overlying rocks. These gases tend to separate from the melt as it moves toward the surface (from a high- to a low-pressure environment). As the gases build up, they may eventually propel magma from the vent. When deeply buried magma bodies crystallize, the remaining volatiles collect as hot, water-rich fluids that migrate through the surrounding rocks. These hot fluids play an important role in metamorphism.

From Magma to Crystalline Rock

To better understand how magma crystallizes, let us consider how a simple crystalline solid melts. Recall that, in any crystalline solid, the ions are arranged in a closely packed regular pattern. However, they are not without some motion; they exhibit a restricted vibration about fixed points. As temperature rises, ions vibrate more rapidly and consequently collide with ever-increasing vigor with their neighbors. Thus, heating causes the ions to occupy more space, which in turn causes the solid to

expand. When the ions are vibrating rapidly enough to overcome the force of their chemical bonds, melting occurs. At this stage, the ions are able to slide past one another, and the orderly crystalline structure disintegrates. Thus, melting converts a solid consisting of tight, uniformly packed ions into a liquid composed of unordered ions moving randomly about.

In the process called **crystallization**, cooling reverses the events of melting. As the temperature of the liquid drops, ions pack more closely together as their rate of movement slows. When they are cooled sufficiently, the forces of the chemical bonds will again confine the ions to an orderly crystalline arrangement.

When magma cools, it is generally the silicon and oxygen atoms that link together first to form silicon–oxygen tetrahedra, the basic building blocks of the silicate minerals. As magma continues to lose heat to its surroundings, the tetrahedra join with each other and with other ions to form embryonic crystal nuclei. Slowly each nucleus grows as ions lose their mobility and join the crystalline network.

The earliest formed minerals have space to grow and tend to have better-developed crystal faces than do the ones that form later and occupy the remaining spaces. Eventually all of the melt is transformed into a solid mass of interlocking silicate minerals that we call an *igneous rock* (FIGURE 2).

Igneous Processes

Igneous rocks form in two basic settings. Molten rock may crystallize at depth, or it may solidify at Earth's surface (FIGURE 3).

When magma crystallizes at depth, it forms **intrusive igneous rocks**, also known as **plutonic**

A. Molten rock may crystallize at depth or at Earth's surface.

Lava flow

Magma chamber

Extrusive igneous rocks

Intrusive igneous rocks

B. When magma crystallizes at depth intrusive igneous rocks form. When it solidifies on Earth's surface extrusive igneous rocks form.

SMARTFIGURE 3
Intrusive versus extrusive igneous rocks

FIGURE 4 Mount Rushmore National Memorial
This memorial, located in the Black Hills of South Dakota, is carved from intrusive igneous rocks. (Photo by Barbara A. Harvey/Shutterstock)

rocks—after Pluto, the god of the lower world in classical mythology. These rocks are observed at the surface in locations where uplifting and erosion have stripped away the overlying rocks. Exposures of intrusive igneous rocks occur in many places, including the White Mountains, New Hampshire; Stone Mountain, Georgia; the Black Hills of South Dakota; and Yosemite National Park, California (FIGURE 4).

Igneous rocks that form when molten rock solidifies *at the surface* are classified as **extrusive igneous rocks**. They are also called **volcanic rocks**—after Vulcan, the Roman fire god. Extrusive igneous rocks form when lava solidifies or when volcanic debris falls to Earth's surface. Extrusive igneous rocks are abundant in western portions of the Americas, where they make up the volcanic peaks of the Cascade Range and the Andes Mountains. In addition, many oceanic islands, including the Hawaiian chain and Alaska's Aleutian Islands, are composed almost entirely of extrusive igneous rocks.

1 CONCEPT CHECKS

1. What is magma? How does magma differ from lava?
2. List and describe the three components of magma.
3. Describe the process of crystallization.
4. Compare and contrast extrusive and intrusive igneous rocks.

Lava fountains from a volcanic eruption on Iceland in 2012. The rocks that formed when this molten material solidified are called extrusive or volcanic igneous rocks. (Photo by Ragnar Th. Sigurdsson/AGE Fotostock)

2 Igneous Compositions

Igneous rocks are composed mainly of silicate minerals. Chemical analyses show that silicon and oxygen are by far the most abundant constituents of igneous rocks. These two elements, plus ions of aluminum (Al), calcium (Ca), sodium (Na), potassium (K), magnesium (Mg), and iron (Fe), make up roughly 98 percent, by weight, of most magmas. In addition, magma contains small amounts of many other elements, including titanium and manganese, and trace amounts of much rarer elements, such as gold, silver, and uranium.

As magma cools and solidifies, these elements combine to form two major groups of silicate minerals (FIGURE 5). The *dark* (or *ferromagnesian*) *silicates* are rich in iron and/or magnesium and comparatively low in silica. *Olivine, pyroxene, amphibole,* and *biotite mica* are the common dark silicate minerals of Earth's crust. By contrast, the *light* (or *nonferromagnesian*) *silicates* contain greater amounts of potassium, sodium, and calcium rather than iron and magnesium. The light silicate minerals, including *quartz, muscovite mica,* and the most abundant mineral group, the *feldspars,* are richer in silica than the dark silicates.

Granitic (Felsic) versus Basaltic (Mafic) Compositions

Despite their great compositional diversity, igneous rocks (and the magmas from which they form) can be divided into broad groups according to their proportions of light and dark minerals (Figure 5). Near one end of the continuum are rocks composed almost entirely of light-colored silicates—quartz and potassium feldspar. Igneous rocks in which these are the dominant minerals have a **granitic composition** (FIGURE 6A). Geologists also refer to granitic rocks as being **felsic**, a term

SMARTFIGURE 5
Mineralogy of common igneous rocks
(After Dietrich, Daily, and Larsen)

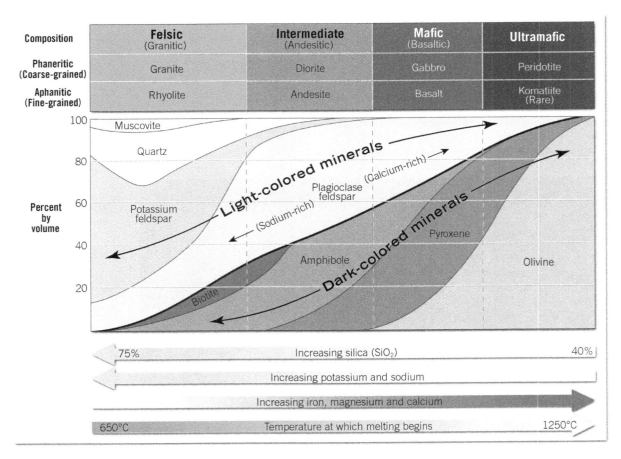

derived from *feld*spar and *si*lica (quartz). In addition to quartz and feldspar, most granitic rocks contain about 10 percent dark silicate minerals, usually biotite mica and amphibole. Granitic rocks are rich in silica (about 70 percent) and are major constituents of the continental crust.

Rocks that contain at least 45 percent dark silicate minerals and calcium-rich plagioclase feldspar (but no quartz) are said to have a **basaltic composition** (FIGURE 6B). Basaltic rocks contain a high percentage of ferromagnesian minerals, so geologists also refer to them as **mafic** (from *ma*gnesium and *fer*rum, the Latin name for iron). Because of their iron content, mafic rocks are typically darker and denser than granitic rocks. Basaltic rocks make up the ocean floor as well as many of the volcanic islands located within the ocean basins. Basalt also forms extensive lava flows on the continents.

Other Compositional Groups

As you can see in Figure 5, rocks with a composition between granitic and basaltic rocks are said to have an **andesitic composition**, or **intermediate composition**, after the common volcanic rock *andesite*. Intermediate rocks contain at least 25 percent dark silicate minerals, mainly amphibole, pyroxene, and biotite mica, with the other dominant mineral being plagioclase feldspar. This important category of igneous rocks is associated with volcanic activity that is typically confined to the seaward margins of the continents and on volcanic island arcs such as the Aleutian Chain.

Another important igneous rock, *peridotite*, contains mostly olivine and pyroxene and thus falls on the opposite side of the compositional spectrum from granitic rocks (see Figure 5). Because peridotite is composed almost entirely of ferromagnesian minerals, its chemical composition is referred to as **ultramafic**. Although ultramafic rocks are rare at Earth's surface, peridotite is the main constituent of the upper mantle.

Silica Content as an Indicator of Composition

An important aspect of the chemical composition of igneous rocks is silica (SiO_2) content. Typically, the silica content of crustal rocks ranges from a low of about 40 percent in ultramafic rocks to a high of more than 70 percent in felsic rocks (see Figure 5). The percentage of silica in igneous rocks varies in a systematic manner that parallels the abundance of other elements. For example, rocks that are relatively low in silica contain large

A. Granite is a felsic, coarse-grained igneous rock composed of light-colored silicates—quartz and potassium feldspar.

B. Basalt is a fine-grained mafic igneous rock containing substantial amounts of dark colored silicates and plagioclase feldspar.

FIGURE 6 Granitic (felsic) versus basaltic (mafic) compositions
Inset images are photomicrographs that show the interlocking crystals that make up granite and basalt respectively.

amounts of iron, magnesium, and calcium. By contrast, rocks high in silica contain very little iron, magnesium, or calcium but are enriched with sodium and potassium. Consequently, the chemical makeup of an igneous rock can be inferred directly from its silica content.

Further, the amount of silica present in magma strongly influences its behavior. Granitic magma, which has a high silica content, is quite viscous ("thick") and may erupt at temperatures as low as 650° C (1200° F). On the other hand, basaltic magmas are low in silica and are generally more fluid. Basaltic magmas also erupt at higher temperatures than granitic magmas—usually at temperatures between 1050° and 1250° C (1920° and 2280° F).

2 CONCEPT CHECKS

1. Igneous rocks are composed mainly of which group of minerals?
2. How do light-colored igneous rocks differ in composition from dark-colored igneous rocks?
3. Distinguish among the four basic compositional groups of igneous rocks.
4. How does silica content vary with the abundance of other elements and how does it affect the behavior of magma?

3 Igneous Textures: What Can They Tell Us?

The term **texture** is used to describe the overall appearance of a rock based on the size, shape, and arrangement of its mineral grains—not how it feels to touch. Texture is an important property because it reveals a great deal about the environment in which the rock formed (FIGURE 7). Geologists can make inferences about a rock's origin based on careful observations of grain size and other characteristics of the rock.

A. Glassy texture
Composed of unordered atoms and resembles dark manufactured glass. (Obsidian is a natural glass that usually forms when highly silica-rich magmas solidify.)

B. Porphyritic texture
Composed of two distinctly different crystal sizes.

C. Phaneritic (coarse-grained) texture
Composed of mineral grains that are large enough to be identified without a microscope.

D. Vesicular texture
Extrusive rock containing voids left by gas bubbles that escape as lava solidifies. (Pumice is a frothy volcanic glass that displays a vesicular texture.)

E. Pyroclastic (fragmental) texture
Produced by the consolidation of fragments that may include ash, once molten blobs, or large angular blocks that were ejected during an explosive volcanic eruption.

F. Aphanitic (fine-grained) texture
Composed of crystals that are too small for the individual minerals to be identified without a microscope.

 SMARTFIGURE 7 Igneous rock textures

Three factors influence the textures of igneous rocks: *the rate at which molten rock cools*, *the amount of silica present*, and *the amount of dissolved gases in the magma*. Among these, the rate of cooling tends to be the dominant factor.

A very large magma body located many kilometers beneath Earth's surface will cool over a period of perhaps tens of thousands to millions of years. Initially, relatively few crystal nuclei form. Slow cooling permits ions to migrate freely until they eventually join one of the existing crystals. Consequently, slow cooling promotes the growth of fewer but larger crystals.

On the other hand, when cooling occurs rapidly—for example, in a thin lava flow—the ions quickly lose their mobility and readily combine to form crystals. This results in the development of numerous embryonic nuclei, all of which compete for the available ions. The result is a solid mass of tiny intergrown crystals.

Types of Igneous Textures

The effect of cooling on rock textures is fairly straightforward: Slow cooling promotes the growth of large crystals, whereas rapid cooling tends to generate small crystals. However, a magma body may migrate to a new location or erupt at the surface before it is completely solidified. As a result, several types of igneous textures exist, including anphanitic (fine grained), phaneritic (course grained), vesicular, porphyritic, glassy, pyroclastic (fragmented), and pegmatitic.

Aphanitic (Fine-Grained) Texture   Igneous rocks that form at the surface or as small intrusive masses within the upper crust where cooling is relatively rapid exhibit a **fine-grained texture** termed **aphanitic** (*a* = not, *phaner* = visible). By definition, the crystals that make up aphanitic rocks are so small that individual minerals can only be distinguished with the aid of a polarizing microscope or other sophisticated techniques (see Figure 6B). Therefore, we commonly characterize fine-grained rocks as being light, intermediate, or dark in color. Using this system of grouping, light-colored aphanitic rocks are those containing primarily light-colored nonferromagnesian silicate minerals.

Phaneritic (Coarse-Grained) Texture   When large masses of magma slowly crystallize at great depth, they form igneous rocks that exhibit a **coarse-grained texture** described as **phaneritic** (*phaner* = visible). Coarse-grained rocks consist of a mass of intergrown crystals that are roughly equal in size and large enough so that the individual minerals can be identified without the aid of a microscope (see Figure 6A). Geologists often use a small magnifying lens to aid in identifying minerals in a phaneritic rock.

Porphyritic Texture   A large mass of magma may require thousands or even millions of years to solidify. Because different minerals crystallize under different environmental conditions (temperatures and pressure), it is possible for crystals of one mineral to become quite large before others even begin to form. If molten rock containing some large crystals moves to a different environment—for example, by erupting at the surface—the remaining liquid portion of the lava cools more quickly. The resulting rock, which has large crystals embedded in a matrix of smaller crystals, is said to have a **porphyritic texture** (FIGURE 8). The large crystals in porphyritic rocks are referred to as **phenocrysts** (*pheno* = show, *cryst* = crystal), whereas the matrix of smaller crystals is called **groundmass**. A rock with a *porphyritic* texture is termed a **porphyry**.

Vesicular Texture   Common features of many extrusive rocks are the voids left by gas bubbles that escape as lava solidifies. These nearly spherical openings are called *vesicles*, and the rocks that contain them are said to have a **vesicular texture**. Rocks that exhibit a vesicular texture often form in the upper zone of a lava flow, where cooling occurs rapidly enough to preserve

FIGURE 8   Porphyritic texture
The large crystals in porphyritic rocks are called *phenocrysts*, and the matrix of smaller crystals is called *groundmass*.

Groundmass

Phenocryst

1 cm

the openings produced by the expanding gas bubbles (FIGURE 9). Another common vesicular rock, called *pumice*, forms when silica-rich lava is ejected during an explosive eruption (see Figure 7D).

Glassy Texture During some volcanic eruptions, molten rock is ejected into the atmosphere, where it is quenched and cools quickly to become a solid. Rapid cooling of this type may generate rocks having a **glassy texture**. Glass results when unordered ions are "frozen in place" before they are able to unite into an orderly crystalline structure.

Obsidian, a common type of natural glass, is similar in appearance to dark chunks of manufactured glass. Because of its excellent conchoidal fracture and ability to hold a sharp, hard edge, obsidian was a prized material from which Native Americans chipped arrowheads and cutting tools (FIGURE 10).

Obsidian flows, typically a few hundred feet thick, provide evidence that rapid cooling is not the only mechanism that produces a glassy texture (FIGURE 11). Magmas with a high silica content tend to form long, chainlike structures (polymers) before crystallization is complete. These structures, in turn, impede ionic transport and increase the magma's viscosity. (*Viscosity* is a measure of a fluid's resistance to flow.) So, granitic magma, which is rich in silica, may be extruded as an extremely viscous mass that eventually solidifies to form obsidian.

By contrast, basaltic magma, which is low in silica, forms very fluid lavas that, upon cooling, usually generate fine-grained crystalline rocks. However, when a basaltic lava flow enters the ocean, its surface is quenched rapidly enough to form a thin, glassy skin.

Pyroclastic (Fragmental) Texture Another group of igneous rocks is formed from the consolidation of individual rock fragments ejected during explosive volcanic eruptions. The ejected particles might be very fine ash, molten blobs, or large angular blocks torn from the walls of a vent during an eruption (FIGURE 12). Igneous rocks composed of these rock fragments are said to have a **pyroclastic texture**, or **fragmental texture** (see Figure 7E).

FIGURE 9 **Vesicular texture**
The larger image shows a lava flow on Hawaii's Kilauea Volcano. The inset photo is a close-up showing the vesicular texture of hardened lava. Vesicles are small holes left by escaping gas bubbles.

FIGURE 11 **Obsidian, a dark-colored, glassy rock formed from silica-rich lava**
The leading edge of an obsidian flow located south of Mono Lake, California.
(Photo by E. J. Tarbuck)

FIGURE 10 **Obsidian arrowhead**
This natural glass was used by Native Americans for making arrowheads and cutting tools. (Photo by Jeffrey Scovil)

B. Hand sample of obsidian.

A. Obsidian flow.

FIGURE 12 **Pyroclastic rocks are the product of explosive eruptions**
Notice the ash fall behind the plume. These fragments may eventually consolidate to become rocks displaying a pyroclastic texture. (Photo by Jorge Santos/AGE Fotostock)

A common type of pyroclastic rock, called *welded tuff*, is composed of fine fragments of glass that remained hot enough to fuse together. Other pyroclastic rocks are composed of fragments that solidified before impact and became cemented together at some later time. Because pyroclastic rocks are made of individual particles or fragments rather than interlocking crystals, their textures often resemble those exhibited by sedimentary rocks rather than those associated with igneous rocks.

Magma, Igneous Rocks, and Intrusive Activity

Pegmatitic Texture   Under special conditions, exceptionally coarse-grained igneous rocks, called **pegmatites**, may form. Rocks of this type, in which most of the crystals are larger than 1 centimeter in diameter, are described as having a **pegmatitic texture** (FIGURE 13). Most pegmatites occur as small masses or thin veins within or around the margins of large intrusive igneous bodies.

Pegmatites form late in the crystallization of a magma, when water and other materials, such as carbon dioxide, chlorine, and fluorine, make up an unusually high percentage of the melt. Because ion migration is enhanced in these fluid-rich environments, the crystals that form are abnormally large. Thus, the large crystals in pegmatites do not result from inordinately long cooling histories; rather, they are the consequence of a fluid-rich environment that enhances crystallization.

The composition of most pegmatites is similar to that of granite. Thus, pegmatites contain large crystals of quartz, feldspar, and muscovite. However, some contain significant quantities of relatively rare and hence valuable elements—gold, tungsten, beryllium, and the rare earth elements that are used in modern technological devices, including cell phones and hybrid autos.

FIGURE 13 **Pegmatitic texture**
This granite pegmatite is composed mainly of quartz and feldspar.

Feldspar

Quartz

Muscovite

Dennis Tasa

3 CONCEPT CHECKS

1. Define *texture*.
2. How does the rate of cooling influence crystal size? What other factors influence the texture of igneous rocks?
3. List the six major igneous rock textures.
4. Explain how the crystals in pegmatites are able to grow so large.
5. What does a porphyritic texture indicate about the cooling history of an igneous rock?

133

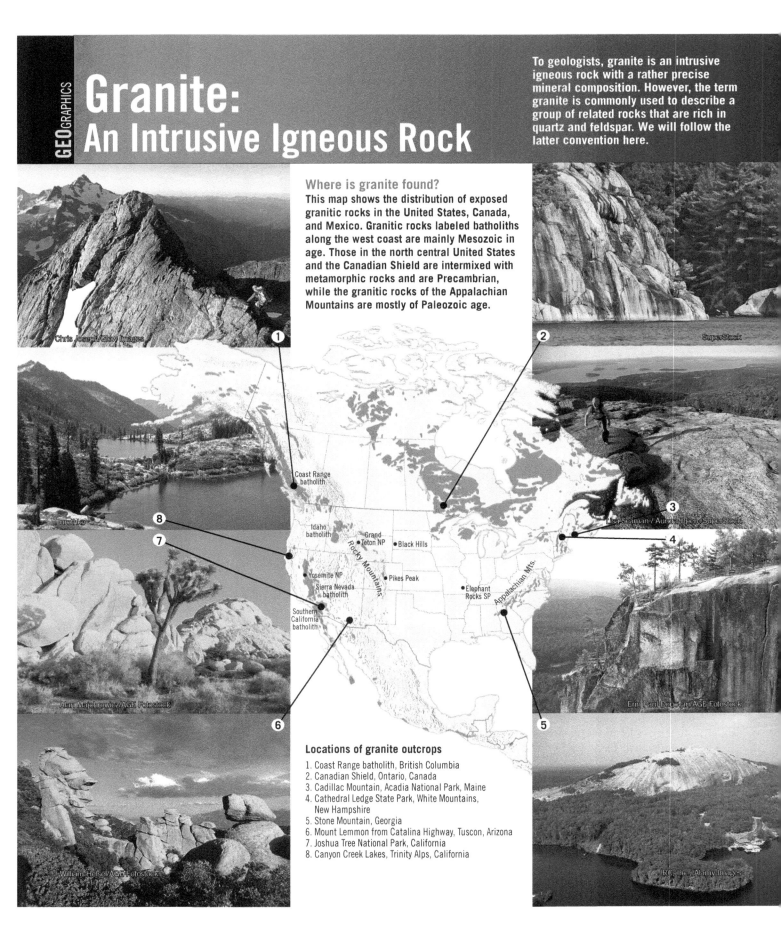

Granite:
An Intrusive Igneous Rock

To geologists, granite is an intrusive igneous rock with a rather precise mineral composition. However, the term granite is commonly used to describe a group of related rocks that are rich in quartz and feldspar. We will follow the latter convention here.

Where is granite found?

This map shows the distribution of exposed granitic rocks in the United States, Canada, and Mexico. Granitic rocks labeled batholiths along the west coast are mainly Mesozoic in age. Those in the north central United States and the Canadian Shield are intermixed with metamorphic rocks and are Precambrian, while the granitic rocks of the Appalachian Mountains are mostly of Paleozoic age.

Coast Range batholith

Idaho batholith

Grand Teton NP

Black Hills

Rocky Mountains

Yosemite NP

Pikes Peak

Sierra Nevada batholith

Elephant Rocks SP

Southern California batholith

Appalachian Mts.

Locations of granite outcrops

1. Coast Range batholith, British Columbia
2. Canadian Shield, Ontario, Canada
3. Cadillac Mountain, Acadia National Park, Maine
4. Cathedral Ledge State Park, White Mountains, New Hampshire
5. Stone Mountain, Georgia
6. Mount Lemmon from Catalina Highway, Tuscon, Arizona
7. Joshua Tree National Park, California
8. Canyon Creek Lakes, Trinity Alps, California

Chris Joseph/Glow Images

SuperStock

Lisa Seaman / Aurora Open/SuperStock

imtmphoto

Alan Majchrowicz/AGE Fotostock

William Helsel/AGE Fotostock

Erin Paul Donovan/AGE Fotostock

JRC, Inc. /Alamy Images

What are the uses of granite?
Granite is widely used as a building material for countertops, floor tiles, building stones, and memorials.

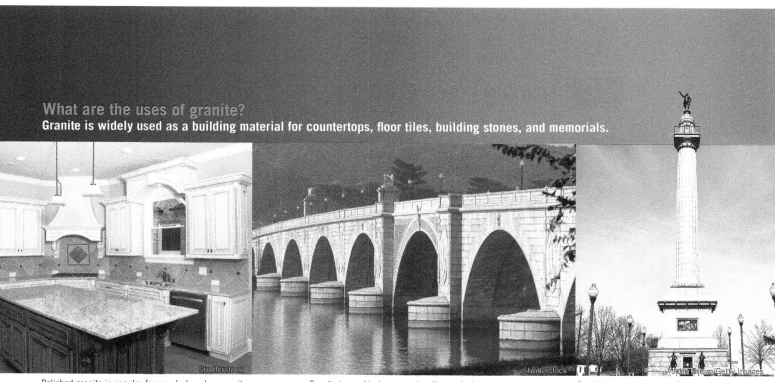

Polished granite is popular for countertops because it is durable as well as aesthetically pleasing. However, in the stone trade the name "granite" is applied to almost every coarse-grained igneous rock. "Black granite", for example, is usually the rock gabbro.

Granite is used in large construction projects as a structural element and decorative facing or veneer. The Arlington Memorial Bridge, constructed mainly of concrete, is covered by a decorative granite veneer.

Granite is commonly used for memorials and gravestones because of its resistance to chemical weathering. The Trenton Battle Monument commemorates the December 26, 1776 battle in which the Continental Army defeated the British forces in Trenton, New Jersey.

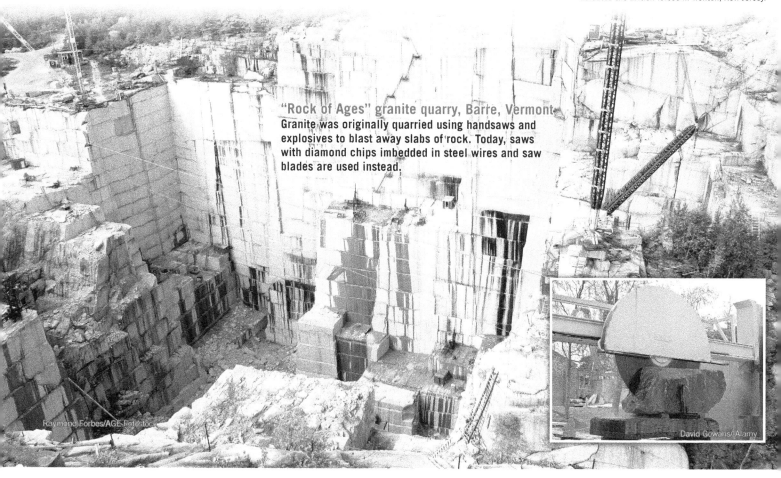

"Rock of Ages" granite quarry, Barre, Vermont
Granite was originally quarried using handsaws and explosives to blast away slabs of rock. Today, saws with diamond chips imbedded in steel wires and saw blades are used instead.

4 Naming Igneous Rocks

Igneous rocks are classified on the basis of their texture and mineral composition (FIGURE 14). The various igneous textures result mainly from different cooling histories, whereas the mineralogy of an igneous rock depends on the chemical makeup of its parent magma. Because igneous rocks are classified on the basis of both mineral composition and texture, some rocks having similar mineral constituents but exhibiting different textures are given different names.

**SMARTFIGURE 14
Classification of igneous rocks**
The classification of igneous rocks is based on mineral composition and texture. (Photos by Dennis Tasa and E. J. Tarbuck)

IGNEOUS ROCK CLASSIFICATION CHART

MINERAL COMPOSITION			
Felsic (Granitic)	**Intermediate** (Andesitic)	**Mafic** (Basaltic)	**Ultramafic**
Dominant Minerals: Quartz, Potassium feldspar	Amphibole, Plagioclase feldspar	Pyroxene, Plagioclase feldspar	Olivine, Pyroxene
Accessory Minerals: Plagioclase feldspar, Amphibole, Muscovite, Biotite	Pyroxene, Biotite	Amphibole, Olivine	Plagioclase feldspar

TEXTURE:
- **Phaneritic** (coarse-grained): Granite, Diorite, Gabbro, Peridotite
- **Aphanitic** (fine-grained): Rhyolite, Andesite, Basalt, Komatiite (rare)
- **Porphyritic** (two distinct grain sizes): Granite porphyry, Andesite porphyry, Basalt porphyry, Uncommon
- **Glassy**: Obsidian, Less common, Less common, Uncommon
- **Vesicular** (contains voids): Pumice (also glassy), Scoria, Uncommon
- **Pyroclastic** (fragmental): Tuff or welded tuff (Most fragments < 4mm), Volcanic breccia (Most fragments > 4mm), Uncommon

Rock Color (based on % of dark minerals): 0% to 25% | 25% to 45% | 45% to 85% | 85% to 100%

136

Granitic (Felsic) Igneous Rocks

Granite   **Granite** is perhaps the best known of all igneous rocks (see Figure 2). This is because of its natural beauty, which is enhanced when it is polished, and its abundance in the continental crust. Slabs of polished granite are commonly used for tombstones and monuments and as building stones. Well-known areas in the United States where granite is quarried include Barre, Vermont; Mount Airy, North Carolina; and St. Cloud, Minnesota.

Granite is a coarse-grained rock composed of about 10 to 20 percent quartz and roughly 50 percent potassium feldspar. When examining granite close-up, the quartz grains appear somewhat rounded in shape, glassy, and clear to gray in color. By contrast, feldspar crystals are generally white, gray, or salmon pink in color, and they are blocky or rectangular in shape. Other minor constituents of granite include small amounts of dark silicates, particularly biotite and amphibole, and sometimes muscovite. Although the dark components generally make up less than 10 percent of most granites, dark minerals appear to be more prominent than their percentage indicates.

At a distance, most granites appear gray in color (**FIGURE 15**). However, when composed of dark pink feldspar grains, granite can exhibit a reddish color. In addition, some granites have a porphyritic texture. These specimens contain elongated feldspar crystals a few centimeters in length that are scattered among smaller crystals of quartz and amphibole (see Figure 14).

Rhyolite   **Rhyolite** is the fine-grained equivalent of granite and, like granite, is composed essentially of the light-colored silicates (see Figure 14). This fact accounts for its color, which is usually buff to pink or occasionally light gray. Rhyolite is fine grained and frequently contains glass fragments and voids, indicating that it cooled rapidly in a surface, or near surface, environment. In contrast to granite, which is widely distributed as large intrusive masses, rhyolite deposits are less common and generally less voluminous. The thick rhyolite lava flows and extensive ash deposits in and around Yellowstone National Park are well-known exceptions to this generalization.

Obsidian   **Obsidian** is a dark-colored glassy rock that usually forms when highly silica-rich lava cools quickly at Earth's surface (see Figure 14). In contrast to the orderly arrangement of ions characteristic of minerals, the arrangement of ions in glass is unordered. Consequently, glassy rocks such as obsidian are not composed of minerals in the same sense as most other rocks.

Although usually black or reddish-brown in color, obsidian has a chemical composition that is roughly equivalent to that of the light-colored igneous rock granite, not like dark rocks such as basalt. Obsidian's dark color results from small amounts of metallic ions in an otherwise relatively clear, glassy substance. If you examine a thin edge, obsidian will appear nearly transparent (see Figure 7).

FIGURE 15 Rocks contain information about the processes that produced them
This massive granitic monolith (El Capitan) located in Yosemite National Park, California, was once a molten mass deep within Earth.

Corey Rich/Getty Images

Henrik Lehnerer/Glow Images

Granite

←— 2 cm —→

FIGURE 16 Pumice, a vesicular (and also glassy) igneous rock
Most samples of pumice will float in water because they contain numerous vesicles. (Inset photo by Chip Clark)

Pumice

Pumice Pumice is a volcanic rock with a glassy texture that forms when large amounts of gas escape through silica-rich lava to generate a gray, frothy mass. In some samples, the voids are quite noticeable, whereas in others the pumice resembles fine shards of intertwined glass. Because of the large percentage of voids, many samples of pumice will float when placed in water (FIGURE 16). Oftentimes, flow lines are visible in pumice, indicating that some movement occurred before solidification was complete. Moreover, pumice and obsidian can often be found in the same rock mass, where they exist in alternating layers (see Figure 11).

Andesitic (Intermediate) Igneous Rocks

Andesite Andesite is a medium-gray, fine-grained rock typically of volcanic origin. Its name comes from South America's Andes Mountains, where numerous volcanoes are composed of this rock type. In addition, the volcanoes of the Cascade Range and many of the volcanic structures occupying the continental margins that surround the Pacific Ocean are of andesitic composition. Andesite commonly exhibits a porphyritic texture (see Figure 14). When this is the case, the phenocrysts are often light, rectangular crystals of plagioclase feldspar or black, elongated amphibole crystals. Andesite may also resemble rhyolite, so its identification usually requires microscopic examination to verify mineral makeup.

Diorite Diorite is the intrusive equivalent of andesite. It is a coarse-grained rock that looks somewhat like gray granite. However, it can be distinguished from granite because it contains little or no visible quartz crystals and has a higher percentage of dark silicate minerals. The mineral makeup of diorite is primarily plagioclase feldspar and amphibole. Because the light-colored feldspar grains and dark amphibole crystals appear to be roughly equal in abundance, diorite has a salt-and-pepper appearance (see Figure 14).

Basaltic (Mafic) Igneous Rocks

Basalt Basalt is a very dark green to black, fine-grained rock composed primarily of pyroxene and calcium-rich plagioclase feldspar, with lesser amounts of olivine and amphibole (see Figure 14). When it is porphyritic, basalt commonly contains small light-colored feldspar phenocrysts or green, glassy-appearing olivine grains embedded in a dark groundmass.

Basalt is the most common extrusive igneous rock. Many volcanic islands, such as the Hawaiian Islands and Iceland, are composed mainly of basalt. Further, the upper layers of the oceanic crust consist of basalt. In the United States, large portions of central Oregon and Washington were the sites of extensive basaltic outpourings (FIGURE 17). At some locations, these once-fluid basaltic flows have accumulated to thicknesses approaching 3 kilometers.

Gabbro Gabbro is the intrusive equivalent of basalt (see Figure 14). Like basalt, it tends to be dark green to black in color and composed primarily of pyroxene and calcium-rich plagioclase feldspar. Although gabbro is uncommon in the continental crust, it makes up a significant percentage of oceanic crust.

Pyroclastic Rocks

Pyroclastic rocks are composed of fragments ejected during a volcanic eruption. One of the most common pyroclastic rocks, called *tuff*, is composed mainly of tiny, ash-size fragments that were later cemented together. In situations where the ash particles remained hot enough to fuse, the rock is called *welded tuff*. Although welded tuff consists mostly of tiny glass shards, it may contain walnut-size pieces of pumice and other rock fragments.

FIGURE 17 Columbia River basalts
At some locations, these once-fluid lava flows are more than 3 kilometers thick. (Photo by Mark Herren)

Welded tuff deposits cover vast portions of previously volcanically active areas of the western United States (FIGURE 18). Some of these tuff deposits are hundreds of feet thick and extend for more than 100 kilometers (60 miles) from their source. Most formed millions of years ago, as volcanic ash spewed from large volcanic structures (calderas) sometimes spreading laterally at speeds approaching 100 kilometers per hour. Early investigators of these deposits incorrectly

FIGURE 18 Welded tuff, a pyroclastic igneous rock
Outcrop of welded tuff from Valles Caldera near Los Alamos, New Mexico. Tuff is composed mainly of ash-sized particles and may contain larger fragments of pumice or other volcanic rocks. (Photo by Marli Miller)

classified them as rhyolite lava flows. Today, we know that silica-rich lava is too viscous (thick) to flow more than a few miles from a vent.

Pyroclastic rocks composed mainly of particles larger than ash are called *volcanic breccia*. The particles in volcanic breccia may consist of streamlined lava blobs that solidified in air, blocks broken from the walls of the vent, ash, and glass fragments.

Unlike most igneous rock names, such as granite and basalt, the terms *tuff* and *volcanic breccia* do not imply mineral composition. Instead, they are frequently identified with a modifier; for example, *rhyolite tuff* indicates a rock composed of ash-size particles having a felsic composition

4 CONCEPT CHECKS

1. The classification of igneous rocks is based largely on two criteria. Name these criteria.
2. How are granite and rhyolite different? In what way are they similar?
3. Classify each of the following as felsic, intermediate, or mafic: gabbro, obsidian, granite, and andesite.
4. Describe each of the following in terms of composition and texture: diorite, rhyolite, and basalt porphyry.
5. How do tuff and volcanic breccia differ from igneous rocks such as granite and basalt?

EYE on Earth

These two types of hardened lava, called Pele's hair and Pele's tears, are commonly generated during lava fountaining that occurs at Kilauea Volcano. They are named after Pele, the Hawaiian goddess of fire and volcanoes. Pele's hair consists of goldish strands that are created when tiny blobs of lava are stretched by strong winds. When lava droplets cool quickly, they form Pele's tears, which are sometimes connected to strands of Pele's hair.

Question 1 What is the texture of Pele's hair and Pele's tears?

Question 2 What is the igneous rock name for Pele's tears?

1. Pele's hair   Marli Miller

2. Pele's tears   USGS

5 Origin of Magma

Based on evidence from the study of earthquake waves, we know that *Earth's crust and mantle are composed primarily of solid, not molten, rock.* Although the outer core is fluid, this iron-rich material is very dense and remains deep within Earth. So where does magma come from?

Most magma originates in Earth's uppermost mantle. The greatest quantities are produced at divergent plate boundaries, in association with seafloor spreading, with lesser amounts forming at subduction zones, where oceanic lithosphere descends into the mantle. In addition, magma can be generated when crustal rocks are heated sufficiently to melt.

Generating Magma from Solid Rock

Workers in underground mines know that temperatures increase as they descend deeper below Earth's surface. Although the rate of temperature change varies considerably from place to place, it *averages* about 25° C (75° F) per kilometer in the *upper* crust. This increase in temperature with depth is known as the **geothermal gradient**. As shown in FIGURE 19, when a typical geothermal gradient is compared to the melting point curve for the mantle rock peridotite, the temperature at which peridotite melts is higher than the geothermal

gradient. Thus, under normal conditions, the mantle is solid. However, tectonic processes trigger melting though various processes including reducing the melting point (temperature) of mantle rock.

Decrease in Pressure: Decompression Melting

If temperature were the only factor that determined whether rock melts, our planet would be a molten ball covered with a thin, solid outer shell. This is not the case because pressure, which also increases with depth, influences the melting temperatures of rocks.

Melting, which is accompanied by an increase in volume, *occurs at progressively higher temperatures with increased depth.* This is the result of the steady increase in confining pressure exerted by the weight of overlying rocks. Conversely, reducing confining pressure lowers a rock's melting temperature. When confining pressure drops sufficiently, **decompression melting** is triggered.

Decompression melting occurs where hot, solid mantle rock ascends in zones of convective upwelling,

FIGURE 19 **Why the mantle is mainly solid**
This diagram shows the geothermal gradient (increase in temperature with depth) for the crust and upper mantle. Also illustrated is the melting point curve for the mantle rock peridotite.

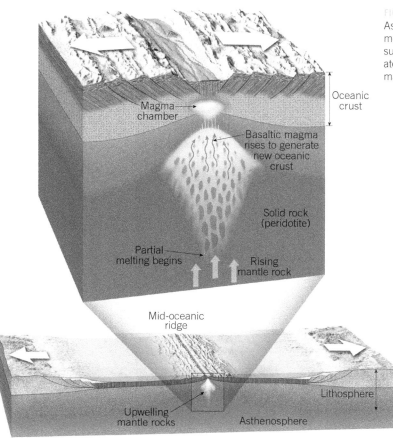

FIGURE 20 Decompression melting
FIGURE 20 Decompression melting
As hot mantle rock ascends, it continually moves into zones of lower and lower pressure. This drop in confining pressure initiates *decompression melting*, in the upper mantle.

thereby moving into regions of lower pressure. This process is responsible for generating magma along divergent plate boundaries (oceanic ridges) where plates are rifting apart (FIGURE 20). Below the ridge crest, hot mantle rock rises and melts, replacing the material that shifted horizontally away from the ridge axis. Decompression melting also occurs when ascending mantle plumes reach the uppermost mantle.

Addition of Water
Another important factor affecting the melting temperature of rock is its water content. Water and other volatiles act as salt does to melt ice. That is, water causes rock to melt at lower temperatures, just as putting rock salt on an icy sidewalk induces melting.

The introduction of water to generate magma occurs mainly at convergent plate boundaries, where cool slabs of oceanic lithosphere descend into the mantle (FIGURE 21). As an oceanic plate sinks, heat and pressure drive water from the subducting oceanic crust and overlying sediments. These fluids migrate into the wedge of hot mantle that lies directly above. At a depth of about 100 kilometers the wedge of mantle rock is sufficiently hot that the addition of water leads to some melting.

Partial melting of the mantle rock peridotite generates hot basaltic magma whose temperatures may exceed 1250° C (nearly 2300° F).

Temperature Increase: Melting Crustal Rocks
When enough mantle-derived basaltic magma forms, it will buoyantly rise toward the surface. In continental settings, basaltic magma often "ponds" beneath crustal rocks, which have a lower density and are already near their melting temperature. The hot basaltic magma may heat the overlying crustal rocks sufficiently to generate a secondary, silica-rich magma. If these low-density silica-rich magmas reach the surface, they tend to produce explosive eruptions that we associate with convergent plate boundaries.

Crustal rocks can also melt during continental collisions that result in the formation of a large mountain belt. During these events, the crust is greatly thickened, and some crustal rocks are buried to depths where the temperatures are elevated sufficiently to cause partial melting. The felsic (granitic) magmas produced in this manner usually solidify before reaching the surface, so volcanism is not typically associated with these collision-type mountain belts.

FIGURE 21 Water lowers the melting temperature of hot mantle rock to trigger partial melting

As an oceanic plate descends into the mantle, water and other volatiles are driven from the subducting crustal rocks into the mantle above.

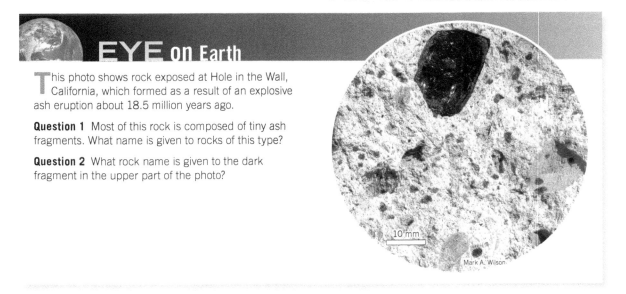

In summary, magma can be generated three ways: (1) *a decrease in pressure* (without an increase in temperature) can result in *decompression melting*; (2) the *introduction of water*, can lower the melting temperature of hot mantle rock sufficiently to generate magma; and (3) heating of crustal rocks above their melting temperature produces magma.

5 CONCEPT CHECKS

1. What is the geothermal gradient? Describe how the geothermal gradient compares with the melting temperatures of the mantle rock peridotite at various depths.
2. Explain the process of decompression melting.
3. What role do water and other volatiles play in the formation of magma?
4. Name two plate tectonic settings in which you would expect magma to be generated.

EYE on Earth

This photo shows rock exposed at Hole in the Wall, California, which formed as a result of an explosive ash eruption about 18.5 million years ago.

Question 1 Most of this rock is composed of tiny ash fragments. What name is given to rocks of this type?

Question 2 What rock name is given to the dark fragment in the upper part of the photo?

6 How Magmas Evolve

Geologists have observed that, over time, a volcano may extrude lavas that vary in composition. Data of this type led them to examine the possibility that magma might change (evolve), and thus one magma body could become the parent to a variety of igneous rocks. To explore this idea, N. L. Bowen carried out a pioneering investigation into the crystallization of magma early in the twentieth century.

Bowen's Reaction Series and the Composition of Igneous Rocks

Recall that ice freezes at a specific temperature, whereas basaltic magma crystallizes over a range of at least 200° C of cooling—about 1200° to 1000° C). In a laboratory setting, Bowen and his coworkers demonstrated that as a basaltic magma cools, minerals tend to crystallize in a systematic fashion, based on their melting temperatures. As shown in FIGURE 22, the first mineral to crystallize is the ferromagnesian mineral olivine. Further cooling generates calcium-rich plagioclase feldspar as well as pyroxene, and so forth down the diagram.

During the crystallization process, the composition of the remaining liquid portion of the magma also continually changes. For example, at the stage when about one-third of the magma has solidified, the remaining molten material will be nearly depleted in iron, magnesium, and calcium because these elements are major constituents of the minerals that form earliest in the process.

The absence of these elements causes the melt to become enriched in sodium and potassium. Further, because the original basaltic magma contained about 50 percent silica (SiO_2), the crystallization of the earliest-formed mineral, olivine, which is only about 40 percent silica, leaves the remaining melt richer in SiO_2. Thus, the silica component of the remaining melt becomes enriched as the magma evolves.

Bowen also demonstrated that if the solid components of a magma remain in contact with the remaining melt, they will chemically react and change mineralogy, as shown in Figure 22. For this reason, this arrangement of minerals became known as **Bowen's reaction series**. However, in nature, the earliest-formed minerals can separate from the melt, thus halting any further chemical reaction.

The diagram of Bowen's reaction series in Figure 22 depicts the sequence in which minerals crystallize from a magma of basaltic composition under laboratory conditions. Evidence that this highly idealized crystallization model approximates what can happen in

BOWEN'S REACTION SERIES

Temperature Regimes	Composition (rock types)	Sequence in which minerals crystallize from magma
High temperatures (~1200°C)	Ultramafic (peridotite/ komatiite)	Olivine ... Calcium-rich
	Mafic (gabbro/basalt)	Pyroxene ... Amphibole
	Intermediate (diorite/andesite)	Biotite mica
Low temperatures (~750°C)	Felsic (granite/rhyolite)	Sodium-rich — Potassium feldspar + Muscovite mica + Quartz

Cooling magma

Discontinuous Series of Crystallization

Plagioclase feldspar — Continuous Series of Crystallization

FIGURE 22 Bowen's reaction series
This diagram shows the sequence in which minerals crystallize from a mafic magma. Compare this figure to the mineral composition of the rock groups in Figure 14. Note that each rock group consists of minerals that crystallize in the same temperature range.

nature comes from analysis of igneous rocks. In particular, scientists know that minerals that form in the same general temperature regime depicted in Bowen's reaction series are found together in the same igneous rocks. For example, notice in Figure 22 that the minerals quartz, potassium feldspar, and muscovite, which are located in the same region of Bowen's diagram, are typically found together as major constituents of the intrusive igneous rock granite.

Magmatic Differentiation and Crystal Settling

Bowen demonstrated that minerals crystallize from magma in a systematic fashion. But how do Bowen's findings account for the great diversity of igneous rocks? It has been shown that, at one or more stages during the crystallization of magma, a separation of various components can occur. One mechanism that allows this to happen is called **crystal settling**. This process occurs when the earlier-formed minerals are denser (heavier) than the liquid portion and sink toward the bottom of the magma chamber, as shown in FIGURE 23. (Crystallization can also occur along the cool margins of magma bodies.) When the remaining melt solidifies—either in place or in another location, if it migrates into fractures in the surrounding rocks—it will form a rock with a mineralogy much different from the parent magma (Figure 23). The formation of one or more secondary magmas from a single parent magma is called **magmatic differentiation**.

A classic example of magmatic differentiation is found in the Palisades Sill, which is a 300-meter-thick (1000-foot-thick) slab of dark igneous rock exposed along the west bank of the lower Hudson River across from New York City. Because of its great thickness and subsequent slow rate of solidification, crystals of olivine (the first mineral to form) sank and make up about 25 percent of the lower portion of the Palisades Sill. By contrast, near the top of this igneous body, where the last melt crystallized, olivine represents only 1 percent of the rock mass.*

Assimilation and Magma Mixing

Bowen successfully demonstrated that through magmatic differentiation, a parent magma can generate several mineralogically different igneous rocks. However, more recent work indicates that magmatic differentiation involving crystal settling cannot, by itself, account for the entire compositional spectrum of igneous rocks.

Once a magma body forms, its composition can also change through the incorporation of foreign material. For example, as magma migrates through the crust, it may incorporate some of the surrounding rock, in a process called **assimilation** (FIGURE 24). In a near-surface environment where rocks are brittle, as the

*Recent studies indicate that this igneous body was produced by multiple injections of magma and represents more than just a simple case of crystal settling.

FIGURE 23 Crystal settling results in a change in the composition of the remaining melt Illustration of how a magma evolves as the earliest-formed minerals (those richer in iron, magnesium, and calcium) crystallize and settle to the bottom of the magma chamber, leaving the remaining melt richer in sodium, potassium, and silica (SiO_2)

A. A magma having a mafic (basaltic) composition erupts fluid basaltic lavas.

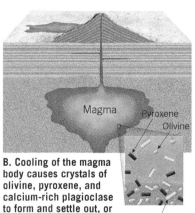

B. Cooling of the magma body causes crystals of olivine, pyroxene, and calcium-rich plagioclase to form and settle out, or crystallize along the magma body's cool margins.

C. The remaining melt will be enriched with silica, and should a subsequent eruption occur, the rocks generated will be more silica-rich and closer to the felsic (granitic) end of the compositional range than the initial magma.

Fractures

Host rock

Rising magma

As magma rises through Earth's brittle upper crust, it may dislodge and incorporate the surrounding host rocks. Melting of these blocks, a process called *assimilation*, changes the overall composition of the rising magma body.

FIGURE 24 Assimilation
The composition of magma changes when the molten mass incorporates pieces of surrounding host rock, a process called assimilation.

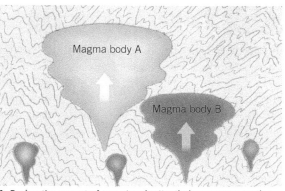

A. During the ascent of two chemically distinct magma bodies, the more buoyant mass may overtake the slower rising body.

Magma body A

Magma body B

B. Once joined, convective flow will mix the two magmas, generating a mass that is a blend of the two magma bodies.

Mixing

FIGURE 25 Magma mixing
This is one way the composition of a magma body can change.

magma pushes upward, it causes numerous fractures in the overlying rock. The force of the injected magma is often sufficient to dislodge blocks of "foreign" rock, which melt and are incorporated into the magma body.

Another means by which the composition of magma can be altered is called **magma mixing**. Magma mixing may occur during the ascent of two chemically distinct magma bodies as the more buoyant mass overtakes the more slowly rising body (FIGURE 25). Once they are joined, convective flow stirs the two magmas, generating a single mass that has an intermediate composition.

6 CONCEPT CHECKS

1. In general, how does the crystallization of minerals in a body of magma affect the composition of the magma that remains?
2. Define *Bowen's reaction series*.
3. Describe the process of crystal settling and how it results in magmatic differentiation.
4. Compare the processes of assimilation and magma mixing.

7 Partial Melting and Magma Composition

Recall that igneous rocks are composed of a mixture of minerals and, therefore, tend to melt over a temperature range of at least 200° C. As rock begins to melt, the minerals with the lowest melting temperatures are the first to melt. If melting continues, minerals with higher melting points begin to melt, and the composition of the melt steadily approaches the overall composition of the rock from which it was derived. Most often, however, melting is not complete. The incomplete melting of rocks is known as **partial melting**, a process that produces most magma.

Recall from Bowen's reaction series that rocks with a granitic composition are composed of minerals with the lowest melting (crystallization) temperatures—namely, quartz and potassium feldspar (see Figure 22). Also note that as we move up Bowen's reaction series, the minerals have progressively higher melting temperatures and that olivine, which is found at the top, has the highest melting point. When a rock undergoes partial melting, it will form a melt that is enriched in ions from minerals with the lowest melting temperatures, while the unmelted portion will be composed of minerals with higher melting temperatures (FIGURE 26). Separation of these two fractions yields a melt with a chemical composition that is richer in silica and nearer the felsic (granitic) end of the spectrum than the rock from which it formed. Specifically, partial melting of *ultramafic* rocks yields *mafic (basaltic) magmas*, partial melting of *mafic* rocks yields *intermediate (andesitic) magmas*, and partial melting of *intermediate* rocks yields *felsic (granitic) magmas.*

Formation of Basaltic Magma

Most magma that erupts at Earth's surface is basaltic in composition and has a temperature of 1000° to 1250° C. Experiments show that under the high-pressure conditions calculated for the upper mantle, partial melting of the ultramafic rock peridotite will yield a magma of basaltic composition. Further evidence for a mantle source are inclusions of the rock *peridotite*, which basaltic magmas often carry up to the surface from the mantle.

Basaltic (mafic) magmas that originate from partial melting of mantle rocks are called *primary* or *primitive* magmas because they have not yet evolved. Recall that partial melting that produces mantle-derived magmas may be triggered by a reduction in confining pressure during the process of decompression melting. This can occur, for example, where hot mantle rock ascends as part of slow-moving convective flow at mid-ocean ridges (see Figure 20). Basaltic magmas are also generated at subduction zones, where water driven from the descending slab of oceanic crust promotes partial melting of the mantle rocks that lie above (see Figure 21).

Formation of Andesitic and Granitic Magmas

If partial melting of mantle rocks generates most basaltic magmas, what is the source of the magma that crystallizes to form andesitic (intermediate) and granitic (felsic) rocks? Recall that silica-rich magmas erupt mainly along the continental margins. This is strong evidence that continental crust, which is thicker and has a lower density than oceanic crust, must play a role in generating these more highly evolved magmas.

One way andesitic magma can form is when a rising mantle-derived basaltic magma undergoes magmatic differentiation as it slowly makes its way through the continental crust. Recall from our discussion of Bowen's reaction series that as basaltic magma solidifies, the silica-poor ferromagnesian minerals crystallize first. If these iron-rich components are separated from the liquid by crystal settling, the remaining melt will have an andesitic composition (see Figure 23). These evolved (changed) magmas are termed *secondary magmas.*

SMARTFIGURE 26

Partial melting

Partial melting generates a magma that is nearer the felsic (granitic) end of the compositional spectrum than the parent rock from which it was derived.

Partial melting of a hypothetical rock composed of the minerals on Bowen's reaction series yields two products.

A melt having an intermediate to felsic composition.

An unmelted residue having a mafic composition.

Key
- Olivine
- Quartz
- Plagioclase feldspar
- Potassium feldspar
- Pyroxene
- Amphibole

Andesitic magmas can also form when rising basaltic magmas assimilate crustal rocks that tend to be silica rich. Partial melting of basaltic rocks is yet another way in which at least some andesitic magmas are produced.

Although granitic magmas can arise through magmatic differentiation of andesitic magmas, most granitic magmas probably form when hot basaltic magma ponds below continental crust (FIGURE 27). Recall that heat from the hot basaltic magma can partially melt the overlying crustal rocks, which are silica rich and have a much lower melting temperature, thereby producing large quantities of granitic magmas. This process is thought to have been responsible for the volcanic activity in and around Yellowstone National Park in the distant past.

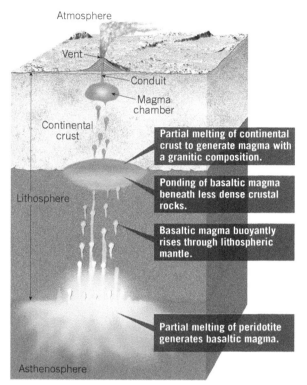

FIGURE 27 Formation of granitic magma
Granitic magmas are generated by the partial melting of continental crust.

Atmosphere
Vent
Conduit
Magma chamber
Continental crust
Lithosphere
Asthenosphere

Partial melting of continental crust to generate magma with a granitic composition.

Ponding of basaltic magma beneath less dense crustal rocks.

Basaltic magma buoyantly rises through lithospheric mantle.

Partial melting of peridotite generates basaltic magma.

7 CONCEPT CHECKS

1. Describe what occurs during partial melting.
2. How do most basaltic magmas form?
3. What is the difference between primitive magmas and secondary magmas?
4. What is the process that generates most granitic magmas?

EYE on Earth

The Palisades form impressive cliffs along the west side of the Hudson River for more than 80 kilometers (50 miles). This structure, which is visible from Manhattan, formed when magma was injected between layers of sandstone and shale.

Question 1 What type of geologic structure constitutes the Palisades?

Question 2 Is this feature tabular or massive?

June Marie Sobrito / Shutterstock

147

8 | Intrusive Igneous Activity

Although volcanic eruptions can be violent and spectacular events, most magma is emplaced and crystallizes at depth, without fanfare. Therefore, understanding the igneous processes that occur deep underground is as important to geologists as studying volcanic events.

FIGURE 28 Intrusive igneous structures

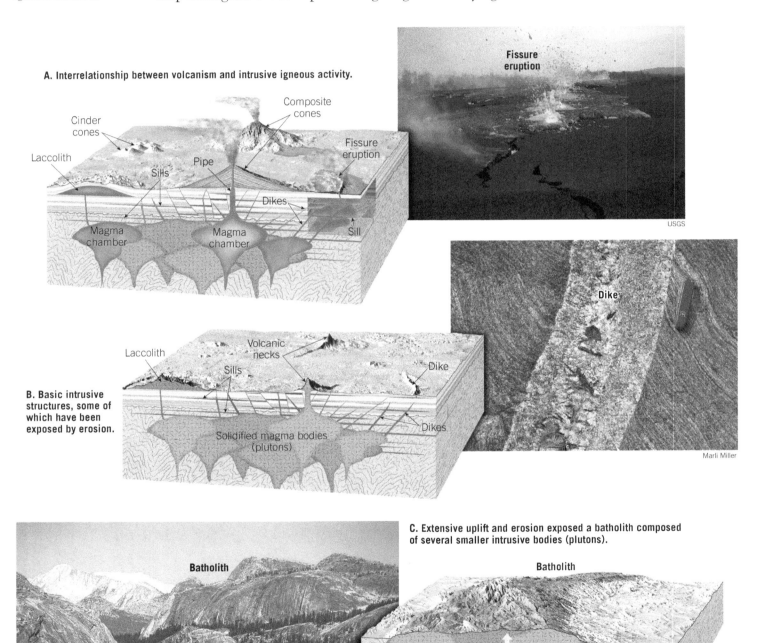

A. Interrelationship between volcanism and intrusive igneous activity.

Cinder cones
Composite cones
Laccolith
Pipe
Sills
Fissure eruption
Dikes
Magma chamber
Magma chamber
Sill

Fissure eruption

USGS

B. Basic intrusive structures, some of which have been exposed by erosion.

Laccolith
Volcanic necks
Sills
Dike
Dikes
Solidified magma bodies (plutons)

Dike

Marli Miller

Batholith

Belinda Images/SuperStock

C. Extensive uplift and erosion exposed a batholith composed of several smaller intrusive bodies (plutons).

Batholith
Plutons

Nature of Intrusive Bodies

When magma rises through the crust, it forcefully displaces preexisting crustal rocks referred to as *host* or *country rock*. The structures that result from the emplacement of magma into preexisting rocks are called **intrusions** or **plutons**. Because all intrusions form far below Earth's surface, they are studied primarily after uplifting and erosion have exposed them. The challenge lies in reconstructing the events that generated these structures millions of years ago and in vastly different conditions deep underground.

Intrusions are known to occur in a great variety of sizes and shapes. Some of the most common types are illustrated in FIGURE 28. Notice that some plutons have a tabular (tablet) shape, whereas others are best described as massive (blob shaped). Also, observe that some of these bodies cut across existing structures, such as sedimentary strata, whereas others form when magma is injected between sedimentary layers. Because of these differences, intrusive igneous bodies are generally classified according to their shape as either **tabular** (*tabula* = table) or **massive** and by their orientation with respect to the host rock. Igneous bodies are said to be **discordant** (*discordare* = to disagree) if they cut across existing structures and **concordant** (*concordare* = to agree) if they inject parallel to features such as sedimentary strata.

Tabular Intrusive Bodies: Dikes and Sills

Tabular intrusive bodies are produced when magma is forcibly injected into a fracture or zone of weakness, such as a bedding surface (see Figure 28). **Dikes** are discordant bodies that cut across bedding surfaces or other structures in the country rock. By contrast, **sills** are nearly horizontal, concordant bodies that form when magma exploits weaknesses between sedimentary beds or other structures (FIGURE 29). In general, dikes serve as tabular conduits that transport magma, whereas sills tend to accumulate magma and increase in thickness.

Dikes and sills are typically shallow features, occurring where the country rocks are sufficiently brittle to fracture. They can range in thickness from less than 1 millimeter to more than 1 kilometer.

While dikes and sills can occur as solitary bodies, dikes tend to form in roughly parallel groups called *dike swarms.* These multiple structures reflect the tendency for fractures to form in sets when tensional forces stretch brittle country rock. Dikes can also radiate from an eroded volcanic neck, like spokes on a wheel. In these situations, the active ascent of magma generated fissures in the volcanic cone out of which lava flowed. Dikes frequently weather more slowly than the surrounding rock. Consequently, when exposed by erosion, dikes tend to have a wall-like appearance, as shown in FIGURE 30.

FIGURE 29 **Sill exposed in Salt River Canyon, Arizona** The dark, essentially horizontal band is a sill of basaltic composition that intruded horizontal layers of sedimentary rock.

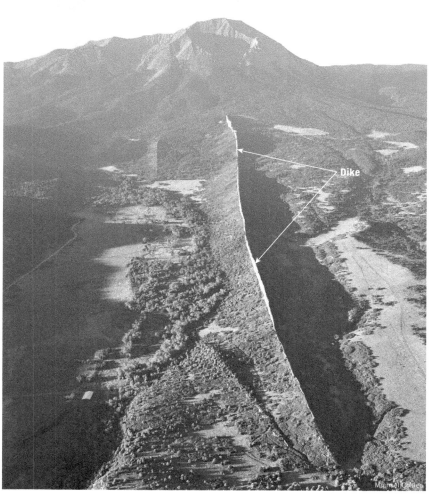

FIGURE 30 **Dike Exposed in the Spanish Peaks, Colorado** This wall-like dike is composed of igneous rock that is more resistant to weathering than the surrounding material.

FIGURE 31 Columnar jointing
Giant's Causeway in Northern Ireland is an excellent example of columnar jointing. (Photo by John Lawrence/Getty Images)

Columnar jointing

Rapid cooling from the outside causes shrinkage cracks

Columnar jointing tends to produce 6-sided columns

Geologist's Sketch

FIGURE 32 Granitic batholiths along the western margin of North America
These gigantic, elongated bodies consist of numerous plutons that were emplaced beginning about 150 million years ago.

Coast Range batholith

Pacific

Ocean

Idaho batholith

Sierra Nevada batholith

Southern California batholith

Because dikes and sills are relatively uniform in thickness and can extend for many kilometers, they are assumed to be the product of very fluid, and therefore mobile, magmas. One of the largest and most studied of all sills in the United States is the Palisades Sill. Exposed for 80 kilometers (50 miles) along the west bank of the Hudson River in southeastern New York and northeastern New Jersey, this sill is about 300 meters (1000 feet) thick. Because it is resistant to erosion, the Palisades Sill forms an imposing cliff that can be easily seen from the opposite side of the Hudson.

In many respects, sills closely resemble buried lava flows. Both are tabular and can have a wide aerial extent, and both may exhibit columnar jointing. **Columnar jointing** occurs when igneous rocks cool and develop shrinkage fractures that produce elongated, pillar-like columns that most often have six sides (FIGURE 31). Further, because sills and dikes generally form in near-surface environments and may be only a few meters thick, the emplaced magma often cools quickly enough to generate a fine-grained texture. (Recall that most intrusive igneous bodies have a coarse-grained texture.)

Massive Intrusive Bodies: Batholiths, Stocks, and Laccoliths

By far the largest intrusive igneous bodies are **batholiths** (*bathos* = depth, *lithos* = stone). Batholiths occur as mammoth linear structures several hundred kilometers long and up to 100 kilometers wide (FIGURE 32). The Sierra Nevada batholith, for example, is a continuous granitic structure that forms much of the Sierra Nevada in California. An even larger batholith extends for over 1800 kilometers (1100 miles) along the Coast Mountains of western Canada and into southern Alaska. Although batholiths can cover a large area, recent gravitational studies indicate that most are less than 10 kilometers (6 miles) thick. Some are even thinner; the Coastal batholith of Peru, for example, is essentially a flat slab with an average thickness of only 2 to 3 kilometers (1 to 2 miles).

Batholiths are typically composed of felsic and intermediate rock types and are often referred to as "granite batholiths." Large granite batholiths consist of hundreds of plutons that intimately crowd against or penetrate one another. These bulbous masses were emplaced over spans of millions of years. The intrusive activity that created the Sierra Nevada batholith, for example, occurred nearly continuously over a 130-million-year period that ended about 80 million years ago (see Figure 32).

By definition, a plutonic body must have a surface exposure greater than 100 square kilometers (40 square miles) to be considered a batholith. Smaller plutons are termed **stocks**. However, many stocks appear to be portions of much larger intrusive bodies that would be classified batholiths if they were fully exposed.

Emplacement of Batholiths   How did massive granitic batholiths come to reside within sedimentary and metamorphic rocks that are only moderately deformed? What happened to the rock that was displaced by these huge igneous masses? (Geologists call this the "room problem.") How do magma bodies make their way through several kilometers of solid rock? Geologists continue to study and debate these questions.

We know that magma rises because it is less dense than the surrounding rock, much as a cork held at the bottom of a container of water will rise when it is released. In the upper mantle and lower crust, where temperatures and pressures are high, rock is ductile (able to flow). In this setting, buoyant magma bodies are assumed to rise in the form of *diapirs*, inverted-teardrop-shaped masses with rounded heads and tapered tails. However, in the upper crust, large dike-like structures may provide conduits for the ascent of magma.

Depending on the tectonic environment, several mechanisms have been proposed to solve the room problem. At great depths, where rock is ductile, a mass of buoyant, rising magma can forcibly make room for itself by pushing aside the overlying rock—a process called *shouldering*. As the magma continues

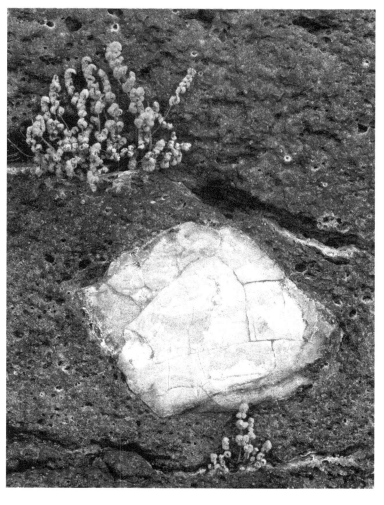

FIGURE 33 Xenoliths
Xenoliths are inclusions of host rock contained within igneous bodies. This xenolith is a chunk of the Kaibab Limestone that was carried to Earth's surface by basaltic magma. The lava flow is near Flagstaff, Arizona. (Photo by Michael Collier)

to move upward, some of the host rock that was displaced will fill in the space left by the magma body as it passes.*

As a magma body nears the surface, it encounters relatively cool, brittle country rock that is not easily pushed aside. Further upward movement may be accomplished by a process called *stoping*, in which blocks of the roof overlying a hot, rising mass become dislodged and sink through the magma (see Figure 24). Evidence supporting stoping is found in plutons that contain suspended blocks of country rock called **xenoliths** (*xenos* = a stranger, *lithos* = stone) (FIGURE 33).

Magma may also *melt* and *assimilate* some of the overlying host rock. However, this process is greatly limited by the available thermal energy contained in the magma body. When plutons are emplaced near the

---

*An analogous situation occurs when a can of oil-based paint is left in storage. The oily component of the paint is less dense than the pigments used for coloration; thus, oil collects into drops that slowly migrate upward, while the heavier pigments settle to the bottom.

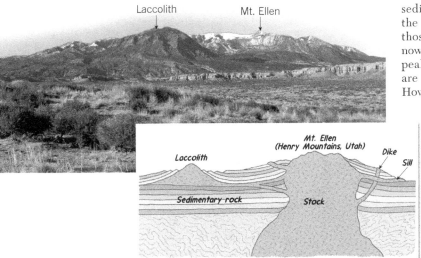

FIGURE 34 Laccoliths
Mount Ellen in Utah's Henry Mountains is one of five peaks that make up this small mountain range. Although the main intrusions in the Henry Mountains are stocks, numerous laccoliths formed as offshoots of these structures. (Photo by Michael DeFreitas North America/Alamy)

Geologist's Sketch

surface, the room problem may be solved by "lifting the roof" that overlies the intrusive body.

Laccoliths A nineteenth-century study by G. K. Gilbert of the U.S. Geological Survey in the Henry Mountains of Utah produced the first clear evidence that igneous intrusions can lift the sedimentary strata they penetrate. Gilbert named the igneous intrusions he observed **laccoliths**, which he envisioned as igneous rock forcibly injected between sedimentary strata, so as to arch the beds above while leaving those below relatively flat. It is now known that the five major peaks of the Henry Mountains are not laccoliths but stocks. However, these central magma bodies are the source material for branching offshoots that are true laccoliths, as Gilbert defined them (FIGURE 34).

Numerous other granitic laccoliths have since been identified in Utah. The largest is a part of the Pine Valley Mountains located north of St. George, Utah. Others are found in the La Sal Mountains near Arches National Park and in the Abajo Mountains directly to the south.

8 CONCEPT CHECKS

1. What is meant by the term *country rock*?
2. Describe *dike* and *sill*, using the appropriate terms from the following list: massive, discordant, tabular, and concordant.
3. Compare and contrast batholiths, stocks, and laccoliths in terms of size and shape.

EYE on Earth

Shiprock, New Mexico, is an igneous structure that rises more than 420 meters (1,380 feet) above the surrounding desert in northwestern New Mexico. It consists of rock that accumulated in the vent of a volcano that has since been eliminated by erosion.

Question 1 What type of landform is Shiprock?

Question 2 What type of structure is the long, narrow ridge extending away from Shiprock?

CONCEPTS IN REVIEW: MAGMA, IGNEOUS ROCKS, AND INTRUSIVE ACTIVITY

1 Magma: Parent Material of Igneous Rock

List and describe the three major components of magma.

KEY WORDS igneous rock, magma, lava, melt, volatile, crystallization, intrusive igneous rock (plutonic rock), extrusive igneous rock (volcanic rock)

• Completely or partly molten rock is called magma if it is below Earth's surface and lava if it has erupted onto the surface. It consists of a liquid melt with possible additions of solids (mineral crystals) and gases (volatiles), such as water vapor or carbon dioxide.

• As magma cools, silicate minerals begin to form from the cocktail of mobile ions in the melt. These tiny crystals grow by the addition of ions to their outer surface. As cooling proceeds, crystallization gradually transforms the magma into a solid mass of interlocking crystals—an igneous rock.

• Magmas that cool at below the surface produce intrusive igneous rocks, whereas those that erupt onto Earth's surface produce extrusive igneous rocks.

COMPARE & CONTRAST   How is the solidification of a magma like the freezing of water? How do the two processes differ?

2 Igneous Compositions

Compare and contrast the four basic igneous compositions: basaltic (mafic), granitic (felsic), andesitic (intermediate), and ultramafic.

KEY WORDS granitic (felsic) composition, basaltic (mafic) composition, andesitic (intermediate) composition, ultramafic

• Igneous rocks are composed mostly of silicate minerals. If a given igneous rock is mostly composed of nonferromagnesian minerals, it is described as felsic. If the rock has a greater proportion of ferromagnesian minerals, it may be classified as mafic. Mafic rocks are generally darker in color and of greater density than their felsic counterparts. Broadly, continental crust is felsic in composition, and oceanic crust is mafic.

COMMON COMPOSITIONS   • Intermediate rocks in which plagioclase feldspar predominates are compositionally between felsic and mafic. They are typical of continental volcanic arcs. Ultramafic rocks, which are rich in the minerals olivine and pyroxene, dominate in the upper mantle.

• The amount of silica (SiO_2) in an igneous rock is an indication of its overall composition. Rocks that contain a lot of silica (up to 70 percent) are felsic, while rocks that are poor in silica (as low as 40 percent) fall on the ultramafic end of the spectrum. The amount of silica present in a magma determines both its viscosity and its crystallization temperature.

Describe the composition of igneous rocks at positions A and B. Compare and contrast the compositions of C and D. Would you ever expect to find quartz and olivine in the same rock? Why or why not?

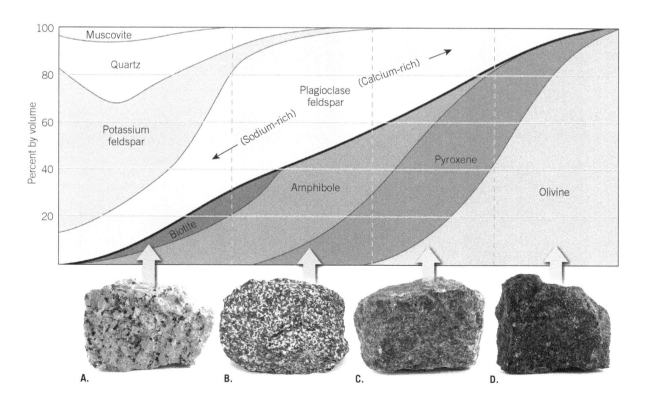

3 Igneous Textures: **What Can They Tell Us?**

List and describe the six major igneous textures.

KEY WORDS texture, aphanitic (fine-grained texture), phaneritic (coarse-grained texture), porphyritic texture, phenocryst, groundmass, porphyry, vesicular texture, glassy texture, pyroclastic (fragmental) texture, pegmatite, pegmatitic texture

- To geologists, "texture" is a description of the size, shape, and arrangement of mineral grains in a rock. Careful observation of the texture of igneous rocks can lead to insights about the conditions under which they formed. The rate at which magma or lava cools is an important factor in the rock's final texture.
- The cooling rate is quick for lava at or close to the surface, so crystallization is rapid and results in a large number of very small crystals. The result is a fine-grained texture. When magma cools at depth, the surrounding rock insulates it, and heat is lost more slowly. This allows sufficient time for the magma's ions to be organized into larger crystals, resulting in a rock with a coarse-grained texture. If crystals begin to form at depth and then the magma moves to a shallow depth or erupts at the surface, it will have a two-stage cooling history. The result is a rock with a porphyritic texture.
- Volcanic rocks may exhibit additional textures: vesicular if they had a high gas content, glassy if they were high in silica, pyroclastic if they erupted explosively. The large crystals that characterize pegmatitic textures result from the crystallization of exceptionally "wet" magmas (magmas with high water content).

SAMPLE IT Do these two igneous rocks have different textures? Why or why not?

Shutterstock

Dirk Wiersma/ Photo Researchers, Inc.

Shutterstock

Dirk Wiersma/ Photo Researchers, Inc.

4 Naming Igneous Rocks

Distinguish between the common igneous rocks based on texture and mineral composition.

KEY WORDS granite, rhyolite, obsidian, pumice, andesite, diorite, basalt, gabbro

- Igneous rocks are classified on the basis of their textures and their compositions. Figure 14 summarizes the naming system based on

these two criteria. Two magmas with the same composition can cool at different rates, resulting in different final textures. On the other hand, two magmas that have different compositions may attain similar textures if they cool under similar circumstances.

PLAUSIBLE PERMUTATIONS Could a granite ever be transformed into a rhyolite? If so, what processes would have to be involved? Could a granite ever be transformed into a gabbro? If so, what processes would have to be involved?

5 Origin of Magma

Summarize the major processes that generate magma from solid rock.

KEY WORDS geothermal gradient, decompression melting

- Solid rock may melt under three geologic circumstances: when heat is added to the rock, raising its temperature; when already

hot rock experiences lower pressures (decompression, as seen at mid-ocean ridges); and when water is added (as occurs at subduction zones).

TECTONIC TRIGGERS Different processes produce magma in different tectonic settings. Consider situations A, B, and C in the diagram and describe the processes that would be most likely to trigger melting in each.

6 How Magmas Evolve

Write a statement describing how magmatic differentiation can result in the formation of one or more secondary magmas from a single parent magma.

KEY WORDS Bowen's reaction series, crystal settling, magmatic differentiation, assimilation, magma mixing

- Pioneering experimentation by N. L. Bowen revealed that in a cooling magma, minerals crystallize in a specific order. Ferromagnesian silicates such as olivine crystallize first, at the highest temperatures (1250° C), and nonferromagnesian silicates such as quartz crystallize last, at the lowest temperatures (650° C). Bowen found that in between these temperatures, chemical reactions take place between the crystallized silicates and the melt, resulting in compositional changes to each and the formation of new minerals.
- Various physical processes can cause changes in the composition of magma. For instance, if crystallized silicates are denser than the remaining magma, they will sink to the bottom of the magma chamber. Because these early-formed minerals are likely to be ferromagnesians, the magma has now differentiated toward a more felsic composition.
- As they migrate, magmas may react with their "host" rocks or with other magma bodies. Assimilation of host rock or magma mixing will alter the magma's composition.

OBSERVATION & INTERPRETATION Consider the diagram, which shows a cross-sectional view of a hypothetical pluton. Using your understanding of Bowen's reaction series and magma evolution, interpret the layered structure by explaining how crystallization occurred.

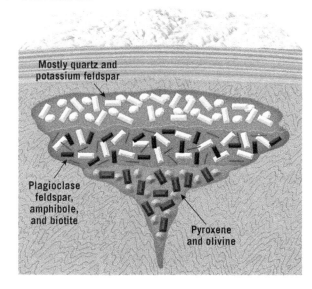

Mostly quartz and potassium feldspar

Plagioclase feldspar, amphibole, and biotite

Pyroxene and olivine

7 Partial Melting and Magma Composition

Describe how partial melting of the mantle rock peridotite generates basaltic (mafic) magma.

KEY WORD partial melting

- In most circumstances, when rocks melt, they do not melt completely. Different minerals have different temperatures at which they change state from solid to liquid (or liquid to solid). In a warming rock, the minerals that melt at the lowest temperatures are most likely to melt.
- Partial melting of the ultramafic mantle yields mafic oceanic crust. Partial melting of the lower continental crust at subduction zones produces secondary magmas that have intermediate or felsic compositions.

CONSIDER THE IMPLICATIONS If all silicate minerals melted at exactly the same temperature, would magmas of different compositions even exist? How is partial melting important for generating the different kinds of rocks on Earth?

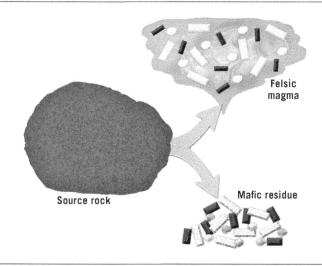

Felsic magma

Source rock

Mafic residue

8 Intrusive Igneous Activity

Compare and contrast these intrusive igneous structures: dikes, sills, batholiths, stocks, and laccoliths.

KEY WORDS intrusion, pluton, tabular, massive, discordant, concordant, dike, sill, columnar jointing, batholith, stock, xenolith, laccolith

- When magma intrudes other rocks, it may cool and crystallize before reaching the surface to produce intrusions called plutons. Plutons come in many shapes. They may cut across the host rocks without regard for preexisting structures, or the magma may flow along weak zones in the host rock, such as between the horizontal layers of sedimentary bedding.

- Tabular intrusions may be concordant (sills) or discordant (dikes). Massive plutons may be small (stocks) or very large (batholiths). Blister-like intrusions also exist (laccoliths). As solid igneous rock cools, its volume decreases. Contraction can produce columnar jointing, a distinctive pattern of fractures exemplified by Devils Tower, Wyoming.
- Several processes contribute to magma's intrusion into host rocks. Rising diapirs are one possibility, and another is shouldering aside of host rocks. Stoping of xenoliths from the host rock can open up more room, or the magma can melt and assimilate some of the host rock.

DRAW IT Create a sketch, including labels, showing a series of igneous intrusions into sedimentary rocks. Include a dike, a sill, a stock, a batholith, a laccolith, some xenoliths, and a diapir.

GIVE IT SOME THOUGHT

1. Would you expect all the crystals in an intrusive igneous rock to be the same size? Explain why or why not.

2. Apply your understanding of igneous rock textures to describe the cooling history of each of the igneous rocks pictured here.

A.

B.

C.

D.

3. Is it possible for two igneous rocks to have the same mineral composition but be different rocks? Use an example to support your answer.

4. Use Figure 5 to classify the following igneous rocks:
   a. An aphanitic rock containing about 30 percent calcium-rich plagioclase feldspar, 55 percent pyroxene, and 15 percent olivine
   b. A phaneritic rock containing about 20 percent quartz, 40 percent potassium feldspar, 20 percent sodium-rich plagioclase feldspar, a few percent muscovite, and the remainder dark-colored silicate
   c. An aphanitic rock containing about 50 percent plagioclase feldspar, 35 percent amphibole, 10 percent pyroxene, and minor amounts of other light-colored silicates
   d. A phaneritic rock made mainly of olivine and pyroxene, with lesser amounts of calcium-rich plagioclase feldspar

5. The statements that follow relate to terms used to describe igneous rock textures. For each statement, identify the appropriate term.
   a. Openings produced by escaping gases
   b. The texture of obsidian
   c. A matrix of fine crystals surrounding phenocrysts
   d. Consists of crystals that are too small to be seen without a microscope
   e. A texture characterized by two distinctly different crystal sizes
   f. Coarse grained, with crystals of roughly equal size
   g. Exceptionally large crystals, most exceeding 1 centimeter in diameter

6. During a hike, you pick up the igneous rock shown in the accompanying photo.

Siim Sepp

   a. What is the mineral name of the small, rounded, glassy green crystals?
   b. Did the magma from which this rock formed likely originate in the mantle or in the crust? Explain.
   c. Was the magma likely a high-temperature magma or a low-temperature magma? Explain.
   d. Describe the texture of this rock.

7. A common misconception about Earth's upper mantle is that it is a thick shell of molten rock. Explain why Earth's mantle is actually solid under most conditions.

8. Describe two mechanisms by which mantle rock can melt without an increase in temperature. How do these magma-generating mechanisms relate to plate tectonics?

9. Use your understanding of Bowen's reaction series (Figure 22) to explain how partial melting can generate magmas that have different compositions.

10. During a field trip with your geology class, you visit an exposure of rock layers similar to the one sketched here. A fellow student suggests that the layer of basalt is a sill. You disagree. Why do you think the other student is incorrect? What is a more likely explanation for the basalt layer?

Shale

Basalt

Vesicles

Sandstone

Shale

Limestone

11. Each statement describes how an intrusive feature appears when exposed at Earth's surface due to erosion. Name the feature.
    a. A dome-shaped mountainous structure flanked by upturned layers of sedimentary rocks
    b. A vertical wall-like feature a few meters wide and hundreds of meters long
    c. A huge expanse of granitic rock forming a mountainous terrain tens of kilometers wide
    d. A relatively thin layer of basalt sandwiched between horizontal layers of sedimentary rocks exposed along the walls of a river valley

12. Mount Whitney, the highest summit (4421 meters or 14,505 feet]) in the contiguous United States, is located in the Sierra Nevada batholith. Based on its location, is Mount Whitney likely composed of granitic, andesitic, or basaltic rocks?

Don Smith/Getty Images

MasteringGeology™

Looking for additional review and test prep materials? Visit the Study Area in MasteringGeology to enhance your understanding of this chapter's content by accessing a variety of resources, including **Self-Study Quizzes,** **Geoscience Animations, GEODe Tutorials, RSS feeds, flashcards, web links, self-study quizzes,** and an optional **Pearson eText.**

Glossary

Andesitic composition See Intermediate composition.

Aphanitic texture A texture of igneous rocks in which the crystals are too small for individual minerals to be distinguished without the aid of a microscope.

Assimilation In igneous activity, the process of incorporating country rock into a magma body.

Basalt A fine-grained igneous rock of mafic composition.

Basaltic composition A compositional group of igneous rocks indicating that the rock contains substantial dark silicate minerals and calcium-rich plagioclase feldspar.

Batholith A large mass of igneous rock that formed when magma was emplaced at depth, crystallized, and subsequently exposed by erosion.

Bowen's reaction series A concept proposed by N. L. Bowen that illustrates the relationships between magma and the minerals crystallizing from it during the formation of igneous rocks.

Coarse-grained See Phaneritic texture.

Columnar joints A pattern of cracks that forms during cooling of molten rock to generate columns.

Concordant A term used to describe intrusive igneous masses that form parallel to the bedding of the surrounding rock.

Crystallization The formation and growth of a crystalline solid from a liquid or gas.

Crystal settling A process that occurs during the crystallization of magma, in which the earlier-formed minerals are denser than the liquid portion and settle to the bottom of the magma chamber.

Decompression melting Melting that occurs as rock ascends due to a drop in confining pressure.

Dike A tabular-shaped intrusive igneous feature that cuts through the surrounding rock.

Discordant A term used to describe plutons that cut across existing rock structures, such as bedding planes.

Extrusive Igneous activity that occurs at Earth's surface.

Felsic composition See Granitic composition.

Fine-grained See Aphanitic texture.

Fragmental texture See Pyroclastic texture.

Geothermal gradient The gradual increase in temperature with depth in the crust. The average is 30° C per kilometer in the upper crust.

Glassy A term used to describe the texture of certain igneous rocks, such as obsidian, that contain no crystals.

Granitic composition A compositional group of igneous rocks indicating the rock is composed almost entirely of light-colored silicates.

Groundmass The matrix of smaller crystals within an igneous rock that has porphyritic texture.

Igneous rock Rock formed from the crystallization of magma.

Intermediate composition A compositional group of igneous rocks that contains at least 25 percent dark silicate minerals. The other dominant mineral is plagioclase feldspar.

Intrusion See *Pluton*.

Intrusive rock Igneous rock that formed below Earth's surface.

Laccolith A massive igneous body intruded between preexisting strata.

Lava Magma that reaches Earth's surface.

Mafic composition See *Basaltic composition*.

Magma mixing The process of altering the composition of a magma through the mixing of material from another magma body.

Magmatic differentiation The process of generating more than one rock type from a single magma.

Massive An igneous pluton that is not tabular in shape.

Melt The liquid portion of magma excluding the solid crystals.

Partial melting The process by which most igneous rocks melt. Since individual minerals have different melting points, most igneous rocks melt over a temperature range of a few hundred degrees. If the liquid is squeezed out after some melting has occurred, a melt with a higher silica content results.

Pegmatite A very coarse-grained igneous rock (typically granite) commonly found as a dike associated with a large mass of plutonic rock that has smaller crystals. Crystallization in a water-rich environment is believed to be responsible for the very large crystals.

Pegmatitic texture A texture of igneous rocks in which the interlocking crystals are all larger than one centimeter in diameter.

Phaneritic texture An igneous rock texture in which the crystals are roughly equal in size and large enough so the individual minerals can be identified without the aid of a microscope.

Phenocryst A conspicuously large crystal embedded in a matrix of finer-grained crystals.

Pluton A structure that results from the emplacement and crystallization of magma beneath the surface of Earth.

Plutonic rock Igneous rocks that form at depth. Named after Pluto, the god of the lower world in classical mythology.

Porphyritic texture An igneous rock texture characterized by two distinctively different crystal sizes. The larger crystals are called phenocrysts, whereas the matrix of smaller crystals is termed the groundmass.

Porphyry An igneous rock that has a porphyritic texture.

Pumice A light-colored, glassy vesicular rock commonly having a granitic composition.

Pyroclastic texture An igneous rock texture resulting from the consolidation of individual rock fragments that are ejected during a violent volcanic eruption.

Sill A tabular igneous body that was intruded parallel to the layering of preexisting rock.

Stock A pluton similar to but smaller than a batholith.

Tabular Describing a feature such as an igneous pluton that has two dimensions that are much longer than the third.

Texture The size, shape, and distribution of the particles that collectively constitute a rock.

Ultramafic composition A compositional group of igneous rocks containing mostly olivine and pyroxene.

Vesicular texture A term applied to aphanitic igneous rocks that contain many small cavities called vesicles.

Volatiles Gaseous components of magma dissolved in the melt. Volatiles will readily vaporize (form a gas) at surface pressures.

Volcanic Pertaining to the activities, structures, or rock types of a volcano.

Xenolith An inclusion of unmelted country rock in an igneous pluton.

Volcanoes and Volcanic Hazards

From Chapter 5 of *Earth: An Introduction to Physical Geology*, Eleventh Edition. Edward J. Tarbuck, Frederick K. Lutgens, Dennis Tasa.

Volcanoes and Volcanic Hazards

A recent eruption of Italy's Mount Etna.
(Stocktrek Images/SuperStock)

Each statement represents the primary learning objective for the corresponding major heading within the chapter. After you complete the chapter you should be able to:

1 Explain why some volcanic eruptions are explosive and others are quiescent.
2 List and describe the three categories of materials extruded during volcanic eruptions.
3 Label a diagram that illustrates the basic features of a typical volcanic cone.
4 Summarize the characteristics of shield volcanoes and provide one example.
5 Describe the formation, size, and composition of cinder cones.
6 Discuss the formation, distribution, and characteristics of composite volcanoes.
7 Discuss the major geologic hazards associated with volcanoes.
8 List and describe volcanic landforms other than shield, cinder, and composite volcanoes.
9 Relate the types and distribution of volcanic activity to plate tectonics.
10 List and describe the techniques used to monitor potentially dangerous volcanoes.

On Sunday, May 18, 1980, the most destructive volcanic eruption to occur in North America in recorded history transformed Mount St. Helens, once a picturesque volcano, into a decapitated remnant. The blast blew out the entire north flank of the volcano. Almost instantaneously, a 400-square-kilometer area was devastated, and ash was propelled 18,000 meters into the stratosphere.

Not all volcanic eruptions are as violent as the 1980 Mount St. Helens event. Some volcanoes, such as Hawaii's Kilauea volcano, typically generate relatively quiet outpourings of fluid lavas. These quiescent eruptions are not without some fiery displays; occasionally fountains of incandescent lava spray hundreds of meters into the air. During Kilauea's most recent active phase, which began in 1983, more than 180 homes and a national park visitor center have been destroyed.

Why do some volcanoes, like Mount St. Helens, erupt explosively, whereas others, like Kilauea, are relatively quiescent? Why do volcanoes occur in chains like those that compose the Aleutian Islands and the Cascade Range in the Pacific Northwest? Why do some volcanoes form in the deep ocean basins, while others occur along margins of the continents? This chapter will deal with these and other questions, as we explore the nature and movement of magma and lava.

Eruption of Mount Etna, Sicily.
(Photo by Martin Rietze/ AGE Fotostock)

1 The Nature of Volcanic Eruptions

Volcanic activity is commonly perceived as a process that produces a picturesque, cone-shaped structure that periodically erupts in a violent manner (FIGURE 1). However, many eruptions are not explosive. What determines the manner in which volcanoes erupt?

Factors Affecting Viscosity

All eruptions involve **magma**, molten rock that usually contains some crystals and varying amounts of dissolved gas. Erupted magma is called **lava**. The primary factors that affect the behavior of magma are its *temperature* and *composition* and, to a lesser extent, the amount of *dissolved gases* it contains. To varying degrees, these factors determine a magma's mobility, or **viscosity** (*viscos* = sticky). The more viscous the material, the greater its resistance to flow. For example, syrup is more viscous, and thus more resistant to flow, than water.

Temperature   The effect of temperature on viscosity is easily seen. Just as heating syrup makes it more fluid (less viscous), temperature also strongly influences the mobility of lava. As lava cools and begins to congeal, its viscosity increases, and eventually the flow halts.

Composition   Another significant factor influencing volcanic behavior is the chemical composition of the magma. Recall that a major difference among various igneous rocks is their silica (SiO_2) content (TABLE 1). Basaltic (mafic) magmas contain about 50 percent silica and

produce mafic rocks such as basalt. Andesitic (intermediate) magmas contain about 60 percent silica and form rocks such as andesite and diorite. Rhyolitic (felsic) magmas contain more than 70 percent silica and produce rocks such as granite and its extrusive equivalent, rhyolite.

The viscosity of magma is directly related to its silica content: *The more silica in magma, the greater its viscosity.* Silica impedes the flow of magma because early in the crystallization process, silicate structures (tetrahedra) start to link together into long chains. Consequently, andesitic and rhyolitic lavas, which have a high silica content, are quite viscous and tend to form comparatively short, thick flows (FIGURE 2). By contrast, basaltic lavas, which are lower in silica, are relatively fluid and have been known to travel 150 kilometers (90 miles) or more before congealing.

Dissolved Gases   The gaseous components in magma, mainly dissolved water, also affect its mobility. Other factors being equal, water dissolved in magma tends to increase fluidity because it reduces formation of long silicate chains by breaking silicon–oxygen bonds. It follows, therefore, that the loss of gases renders magma (lava) more viscous. Gases also give magmas their explosive character.

FIGURE 1 Eruption of Iceland's Eyjafjallaökull volcano
This eruption occurred in the spring of 2010 and disrupted air traffic in Europe for several weeks. (Photo by Ragnar Sigurdsson/AGE Fotostock)

TABLE 1   Different Compositions of Magmas Cause Properties to Vary

Composition	Silica Content	Gas Content	Eruptive Temperatures	Viscosity	Tendency to Form Pyroclastics	Volcanic Landform
Basaltic (mafic)	Least (~50%)	Least (1–2%)	1000–1250°C	Least	Least	Shield volcanoes, basalt plateaus, cinder cones
Andesitic (intermediate)	Intermediate (~60%)	Intermediate (3–4%)	800–1050°C	Intermediate	Intermediate	Composite cones
Rhyolitic (felsic)	Most (~70%)	Most (4–6%)	650–900°C	Greatest	Greatest	Pyroclastic flows, lava domes

Silica-rich magmas, which are highly viscous, tend to form comparatively short, thick lava flows like the one shown that traveled down the steep slopes of Mt. Eldon, Arizona.

Fluid basaltic lavas, which have comparatively low silica content, can form lava rivers capable of travelling many miles.

Michael Collier

USGS

FIGURE 2 Viscous versus fluid lavas
Silica-rich magmas, which are highly viscous, tend to form comparatively short, thick lava flows, whereas fluid basaltic lavas can form lava rivers that may travel many miles.

Quiescent versus Explosive Eruptions

Most magma is generated by partial melting of the rock peridotite in the upper mantle to form magma with a basaltic composition. Once formed, the newly formed magma, which is less dense than the surrounding rock, slowly rises toward the surface. In some settings, high-temperature basaltic magmas reach Earth's surface, where they produce highly fluid lavas. This most commonly occurs on the ocean floor, in association with seafloor spreading. In continental settings, however, the density of crustal rocks is less than that of the ascending material, causing the magma to pond at the crust–mantle boundary. Heat from the hot magma is often sufficient to partially melt the overlying crustal rocks, generating a less dense, silica-rich magma, which continues the journey toward Earth's surface.

Quiescent Hawaiian-Type Eruptions Eruptions that involve very fluid basaltic lavas, such as the eruptions of Kilauea on Hawaii's Big Island, are often triggered by the arrival of a new batch of molten rock into a near-surface magma chamber. This event can usually be detected because the summit of the volcano begins to inflate and rise months or even years before an eruption. The injection of a fresh supply of hot molten rock heats and remobilizes the semi-liquid magma chamber. In addition, swelling of the magma chamber fractures the rock above allowing the fluid magma to move upward along the newly formed openings, often generating outpourings of lava for weeks, months, or possibly years. The eruption of Kilauea that began in 1983 has been ongoing ever since.

Explosive Eruptions All magmas contain some water vapor and other gases that are kept in solution by the immense pressure of the overlying rock. As magma rises (or the rocks confining the magma fail), a reduction in pressure occurs, and the dissolved gases begin to separate from the melt, forming tiny bubbles. This is analogous to opening a can of soda and allowing the carbon dioxide bubbles to escape.

When fluid basaltic magmas erupt, the pressurized gases readily escape. At temperatures that often exceed 1100° C, these gases can quickly expand to occupy hundreds of times their original volumes. Occasionally, these expanding gases propel incandescent lava hundreds of meters into the air, producing lava fountains (FIGURE 3). Although spectacular, these

FIGURE 3 Lava fountain
Fluid basaltic lava erupting from Mount Etna, Italy.
(Photo by D. Szczepanski terras/AGE Fotostock)

Gases readily escape hot fluid basaltic flows, producing lava fountains. Although often spectacular, these features generally do not cause great loss of life or property.

fountains are usually harmless and generally not associated with major explosive events that cause great loss of life and property.

At the other extreme, highly viscous magmas expel particles of fragmented lava and gases at nearly supersonic speeds that evolve into buoyant plumes called **eruption columns**. Eruption columns can rise perhaps 40 kilometers (25 miles) into the atmosphere (FIGURE 4). Because silica-rich magmas are sticky (viscous), a significant portion of the gaseous materials remain dissolved until the magma nears Earth's surface, at which time tiny bubbles begin to form and grow. When the pressure of the expanding magma body exceeds the strength of the overlying rock, fracturing occurs. As magma moves up the fractures, a further drop in confining pressure causes more gas bubbles to form and grow. This chain reaction may generate an explosive event in which magma is literally blown into fragments (ash and pumice) that are carried to great heights by the hot gases. (As exemplified by the 1980 erup St. Helens, the collapse of a volcano's flank can result in a reduction in pressure on the magma below, triggering an explosive eruption.)

When magma in the uppermost portion of the magma chamber is forcefully ejected by the escaping gases, the confining pressure on the molten rock directly below drops suddenly. Thus, rather than a single "bang," volcanic eruptions are really a series of explosions. Following explosive eruptions, degassed lava may slowly ooze out of the vent to form short obsidian or rhyolitic flows or dome-shaped lava bodies that grow over the vent.

Eruptions of highly viscous lavas may produce explosive clouds of hot ash and gases called eruption columns.

FIGURE 4 Eruption column
Steam and ash eruption column from Mount Augustine, Cook Inlet, Alaska. (Photo by Steve Kaufman/Getty Images)

1 CONCEPT CHECKS

1. Define viscosity and list three factors that influence the viscosity of magma.
2. Explain how the viscosity of magma influences the explosiveness of a volcano.
3. List these three magmas—basaltic magma, rhyolitic magma, andesitic magma—in order, from the *most* silica-rich to the *least* silica-rich.

Eruption of Mount St. Helens

On Sunday, May 18, 1980, the most destructive volcanic eruption to occur in North America in recorded history transformed a picturesque volcano into a decapitated remnant. Despite the fact that most residents of the area heeded evacuation warnings the event claimed 57 human lives.

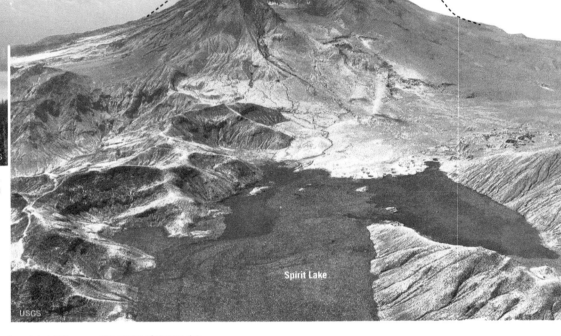

Sears Tower 1450 feet

1350 feet

Spirit Lake

Spirit Lake

USGS

The blast blew out the entire north flank of Mount St. Helen's, leaving a gaping hole. In a brief moment, a prominent volcano was lowered by 1350 feet.

The initial eruption devastated 400 square kilometers of timber-rich land. Trees lay flattened and intertwined, stripped of their branches, and looking like toothpicks strewn about. (Inset image by John Burnley/Photo Researchers, Inc.)

USGS

Mt. St. Helens Eruption Stages

1

Accumulation of magma over several months caused a large bulge to form on the volcano's north flank.

2

An earthquake caused the collapse of the north flank of the volcano, which triggered a lateral blast that destroyed a 400 square-kilometer area.

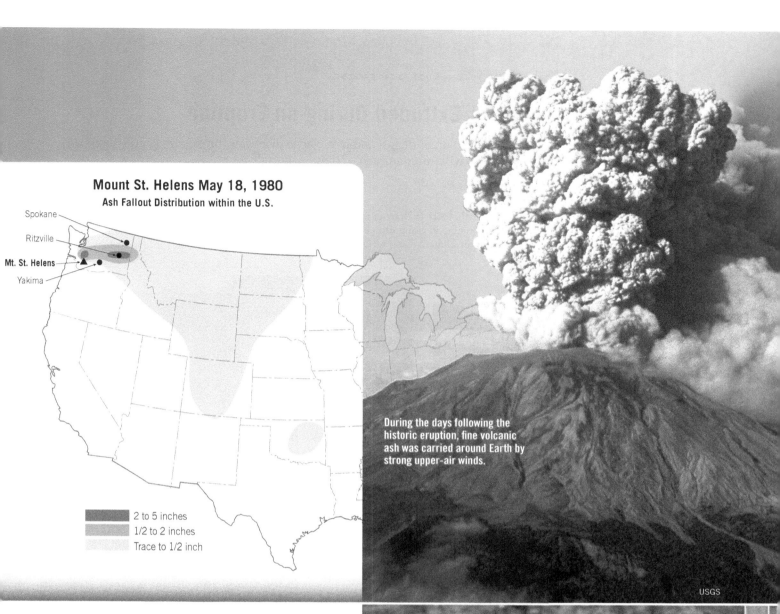

Mount St. Helens May 18, 1980
Ash Fallout Distribution within the U.S.

Spokane
Ritzville
Mt. St. Helens
Yakima

2 to 5 inches
1/2 to 2 inches
Trace to 1/2 inch

During the days following the historic eruption, fine volcanic ash was carried around Earth by strong upper-air winds.

USGS

Within seconds of the lateral blast, an enormous vertical eruption sent a column of volcanic ash to an altitude of 18 kilometers (11 miles).

3

Volcanologist David Johnston, monitoring the volcano from 6 miles away on the morning of May 18, 1980, transmitted the message "Vancouver! Vancouver! This is it!" before being killed by the blast. In commemoration, the USGS office in Vancouver, Washington, was renamed the David A. Johnson Cascades Volcano Observatory.

USGS

2 Materials Extruded During an Eruption

Volcanoes erupt lava, large volumes of gas, and pyroclastic materials (broken rock, lava "bombs," and ash). In this section we will examine each of these materials.

Lava Flows

FIGURE 5 Types of lava flows

The vast majority of lava on Earth, more than 90 percent of the total volume, is basaltic (mafic) in composition. Andesitic lavas, which are of intermediate composition, account for less than 10 percent, while rhyolitic (felsic) flows make up as little as 1 percent of the total.

Hot basaltic lavas, which are usually very fluid, generally flow in thin, broad sheets or stream-like ribbons. On the island of Hawaii, these lavas have been

A. Aa flow, from the flanks of Kilauea volcano, moves toward the subdivision of Royal Gardens.

B. Aerial view of a pahoehoe flow. Note the ropy appearance of the pahoehoe flow shown in the inset image.

C. This block lava flow consists of chunks of obsidian (dark colored) and rhyolite (light colored).

D. Pillow lavas that formed off the coast of Hawaii. They form elongated shapes, like toothpaste coming out of a tube.

clocked at 30 kilometers (19 miles) per hour down steep slopes. By contrast, the movement of silica-rich, rhyolitic lava may be too slow to perceive. Furthermore, most rhyolitic lavas seldom travel more than a few kilometers from their vents. As you might expect, andesitic lavas, which are intermediate in composition, exhibit characteristics that are between these extremes.

Aa and Pahoehoe Flows

Fluid basaltic magmas tend to generate two types of lava flows known by Hawaiian names. One of these, called **aa** (pronounced "ah-ah") flows, have surfaces of rough jagged blocks with dangerously sharp edges and spiny projections (FIGURE 5A). Crossing a hardened aa flow can be a trying and miserable experience. The second type, **pahoehoe** (pronounced "pah-hoy-hoy") flows, exhibit smooth surfaces that sometimes resemble the twisted braids of ropes (FIGURE 5B). Pahoehoe means "on which one can walk."

Although both lava types can erupt from the same volcano, pahoehoe lavas are hotter and more fluid than aa flows. In addition, pahoehoe lavas can change into aa lava flows, although the reverse (aa to pahoehoe) does not occur.

Cooling that occurs as the flow moves away from the vent is one factor that facilitates the change from pahoehoe to aa. The reduction in temperature increases viscosity and promotes bubble formation. Escaping gas bubbles produce numerous voids (vesicles) and sharp spines in the surface of the congealing lava. As the molten interior advances, the outer crust is broken, transforming a relatively smooth surface of a pahoehoe flow into an aa flow made up of an advancing mass of rough, sharp, broken lava blocks.

Pahoehoe flows often develop cave-like tunnels called **lava tubes** that were previously conduits for carrying lava from an active vent to the flow's leading edge (FIGURE 6). Lava tubes form in the interior of a lava flow, where the temperature remains high long after the surface cools and hardens. Because they serve as insulated pathways that facilitate the advance of lava great distances from its source, lava tubes are important features of fluid lava flows.

Block Lavas

In contrast to fluid basaltic magmas that can travel many kilometers, viscous andesitic and rhyolitic magmas tend to generate relatively short thick flows—a few hundred meters to a few kilometers long. Their upper surface consists largely of massive, detached blocks—hence the name **block lava** (FIGURE 5C). Although similar to aa flows, these lavas consist of blocks with slightly curved, smooth surfaces rather than the rough, sharp, spiny surfaces typical of aa flows.

Lava tubes. These cave-like tunnels were once conduits carrying lava from an active vent to the flow's leading edge.

Valentine cave, a lava tube at Lava Beds National Monument, California.

A.

Skylights develop where the roofs of lava tubes collapse and reveal the hot lava flowing through the tube.

B.

Pillow Lavas

Recall that much of Earth's volcanic output occurs along oceanic ridges (divergent plate boundaries). When outpourings of lava occur on the ocean floor, the flow's outer skin quickly freezes to form obsidian. However, the interior lava is able to move forward by breaking through the hardened surface. This process occurs over and over, as molten basalt is extruded—like toothpaste from a tightly squeezed tube. The result is a lava flow composed of numerous tube-like structures called **pillow lavas**, stacked one atop the other (FIGURE 5D). Pillow lavas are useful in the reconstruction of geologic history because their presence indicates that the lava flow formed below the surface of a water body.

FIGURE 6 Lava tubes
Pahoehoe lava flows often develop a solid upper crust, while the molten lava below continues to advance in conduits called *lava tubes*. Some lava tubes exhibit extraordinary dimensions. One such structure, Kazumura Cave, located on the southeast slope of Hawaii's Mauna Loa volcano, extends for more than 60 kilometers (40 miles). (Photo A. by Dave Bunnell and Photo B. by Michael Collier)

Gases

Magmas contain varying amounts of dissolved gases held in the molten rock by confining pressure, just as carbon dioxide is held in cans and bottles of soft drinks. As with soft drinks, as soon as the pressure is reduced, the gases begin to escape. Obtaining gas samples from an erupting volcano is difficult and dangerous, requiring geologists to indirectly measure the amount of gas originally contained within the magma.

FIGURE 7 Types of pyroclastic materials Pyroclastic materials are also commonly referred to as tephra.

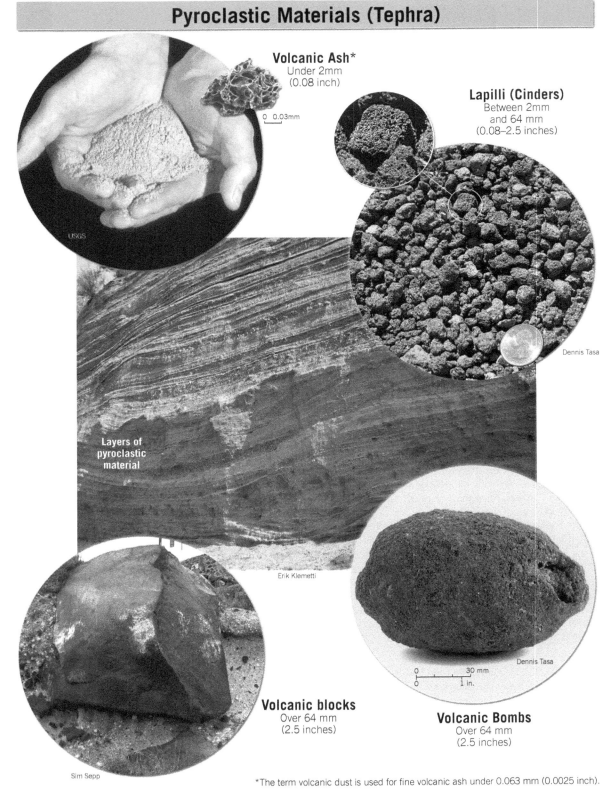

Pyroclastic Materials (Tephra)

Volcanic Ash*
Under 2mm
(0.08 inch)

0   0.03mm

USGS

Lapilli (Cinders)
Between 2mm
and 64 mm
(0.08–2.5 inches)

Dennis Tasa

Layers of
pyroclastic
material

Erik Klemetti

Volcanic blocks
Over 64 mm
(2.5 inches)

Sim Sepp

Dennis Tasa

0   30 mm
0   1 in.

Volcanic Bombs
Over 64 mm
(2.5 inches)

*The term volcanic dust is used for fine volcanic ash under 0.063 mm (0.0025 inch).

170

The gaseous portion of most magmas makes up from 1 to 6 percent (most in the form of water vapor) of its total weight. Although the percentage may be small, the actual quantity of emitted gas can exceed thousands of tons per day. Occasionally, eruptions emit colossal amounts of volcanic gases that rise high into the atmosphere, where they may reside for several years. Some of these eruptions have had an impact on Earth's climate.

Analyses of samples taken during Hawaiian eruptions indicate that the gas component is more than 70 percent water vapor and 15 percent carbon dioxide, with lesser amounts of sulfur, chlorine, and fluorine gases. The relative proportion of each gas varies significantly from one volcanic region to another. Sulfur compounds are easily recognized by their pungent odor. Volcanoes are also natural sources of air pollution—some emit large quantities of sulfur dioxide, which readily combines with atmospheric gases to form sulfuric acid and other sulfate compounds.

A.

Scoria is a vesicular rock commonly having a basaltic or andesitic composition. Pea-to-basketball size scoria fragments make up a large portion of most cinder cones (also called *scoria cones*).

B.

Pumice is a low density vesicular rock that forms during explosive eruptions of viscous magma having an andesitic to rhyolitic composition.

FIGURE 8 Common vesicular rocks Scoria and pumice are volcanic rocks that exhibit a vesicular texture. Vesicles are small holes left by escaping gas bubbles.(Photos by E.J. Tarbuck)

Pyroclastic Materials

When volcanoes erupt energetically, they eject **pyroclastic materials**—pulverized rock and lava fragments—from the vent. This volcanic material is referred to as pyroclastic (*pyro* = fire, *clast* = fragment) materials, also known as **tephra** and ranges in size from very fine dust and sand-sized volcanic ash (less than 2 millimeters) to pieces that weigh several tons.

Volcanic *ash* is produced when gas-rich viscous magma erupts explosively (FIGURE 7). As magma moves up in the vent, the gases rapidly expand, so that the magma resembles the froth that flows from a bottle of Champagne. As the hot gases expand explosively, the froth is blown into very fine glassy fragments (Figure 7). When the hot ash falls, the glassy shards often compact and fuse together to form a rock called *welded tuff.* Sheets of welded tuff, as well as ash deposits that later consolidate, cover vast portions of the western United States.

Somewhat larger pyroclasts that range in size from 2 to 64 millimeters (small beads to walnuts) are known as *lapilli* ("little stones"). These ejected materials are also referred to as *cinders*. Particles larger than 64 millimeters (2.5 inches) in diameter are called *blocks* when they are made of fragments of already-hardened lava and *bombs* when they are ejected as incandescent lava (see Figure 3). Because bombs are semi-molten upon ejection, they often take on a streamlined shape as they hurtle through the air (Figure 7). Because of their size, bombs and blocks usually fall near the vent; however, they are occasionally propelled great distances. For instance, bombs as large as trucks and

weighing about 200 tons were blown 600 meters (2000 feet) from the vent during an eruption of the Japanese volcano Asama.

Thus far we have distinguished various pyroclastic materials based primarily on the size of the fragments. Some pyroclastic materials, however, are identified by their texture and composition. One example is *scoria*, a volcanic rock containing many holes or voids called *vesicles* (FIGURE 8A). Vesicles form when the gases that were dissolved in the magma escape as it erupts, creating voids in the rock as it cools and solidifies. Typically scoria is black to reddish-brown in color and basaltic or andesitic in composition.

When magmas with andesitic or rhyolitic compositions erupt explosively, they usually emit ash and the vesicular rock *pumice* (FIGURE 8B). Pumice is lighter in color and less dense than scoria. Pumice fragments typically have so many vesicles that they are light enough to float on water.

2 CONCEPT CHECKS

1. Describe aa and pahoehoe lava flows. What do they have in common?
2. Contrast block and aa lavas.
3. Where do pillow lavas form?
4. List the main gases released during a volcanic eruption. What roles do gases play in an eruption?
5. What are pyroclastic materials (tephra)? List and describe at least three examples.
6. How is scoria different from pumice?

3 Anatomy of a Volcano

The popular image of a volcano is that of a solitary, graceful, snowcapped cone, such as Mount Hood in Oregon or Japan's Fujiyama. These picturesque, conical mountains are produced by volcanic activity that occurred intermittently over thousands, or even hundreds of thousands, of years. However, many volcanoes do not fit this image. Cinder cones are quite small and form during a single eruptive phase that lasts a few days to a few years. Alaska's Valley of Ten Thousand Smokes is a flat-topped deposit consisting of 15 cubic kilometers (3.6 cubic miles) of ash, more than 20 times the volume of the 1980 Mount St. Helen's eruption, that formed in less than 60 hours and blanketed a river valley to a depth of 200 meters (600 feet).

Volcanic landforms come in a wide variety of shapes and sizes, and each volcano has a unique eruptive history. Nevertheless, volcanologists have been able to classify volcanic landforms and determine their eruptive patterns. In this section we will consider the general anatomy of an idealized volcanic cone. We will follow this discussion by exploring the three major types of volcanic cones—shield volcanoes, cinder cones, and composite volcanoes—as well as their associated hazards. The remainder of the chapter will consider other volcanic landforms that do not fall into these categories.

Volcanic activity frequently begins when a **fissure** (crack) develops in Earth's crust as magma moves forcefully toward the surface. As the gas-rich magma moves up through a fissure, its path is usually localized into a circular **conduit** that terminates at a surface opening called a **vent** (FIGURE 9). The cone-shaped structure we call a **volcanic cone** is often created by successive eruptions of lava, pyroclastic material, or frequently a combination of both, often separated by long periods of inactivity.

Located at the summit of most volcanic cones is a somewhat funnel-shaped depression, called a **crater** (*crater* = a bowl). Volcanoes built primarily of pyroclastic materials typically have craters that form by gradual accumulation of volcanic debris on the surrounding rim. Other craters form during explosive eruptions, as the rapidly ejected particles erode the crater walls. Craters also form when the summit area of a volcano collapses following an eruption. Some volcanoes have very large circular depressions called *calderas* that have diameters greater than 1 kilometer and in rare cases can exceed 50 kilometers. We will consider the formation of various types of calderas later in this chapter.

During early stages of growth, most volcanic discharges come from a central summit vent. As a volcano matures, material also tends to be emitted from fissures that develop along the flanks or at the base of the volcano. Continued activity from a flank eruption may produce one or more small **parasitic cones** (*parasitus* = one who eats at the table of another). Italy's Mount Etna, for example, has more than 200 secondary vents, some of which have built parasitic cones. Many of these vents, however, emit only gases and are appropriately called **fumaroles** (*fumus* = smoke).

Bombs

Lava

Crater

Vent

Parasitic cone

Pyroclastic material

Conduit

Magma chamber

SMARTFIGURE 9
Anatomy of a volcano
Compare the structure of a "typical" composite cone to that of a shield volcano (Figure 10) and a cinder cone (Figure 11).

3 CONCEPT CHECKS

1. How is a crater different from a caldera?
2. Distinguish among a conduit, a vent, and a crater.
3. What is a parasitic cone, and where does it form?
4. What is emitted from a fumarole?

Comparison of Three Types of Volcanic Cones

These images and drawings compare the relative sizes and shapes of three different volcanic edifices. Note the size comparison between a large shield volcano and a large composite volcano.

1 Mauna Loa, Hawaii, the largest shield volcano on Earth, is composed of roughly 200 times more volcanic material than a large composite volcano such as Mount Hood, Oregon.

Greg Vaughn/Alamy

1 Shield volcano

2 Composite volcano
(Stratovolcano)

3 Cinder cone
(Scoria cone)

Lava flow

2 Aerial view of Mount Shasta, California, a large composite cone in the Cascade Range.

3 SP Crater, a cinder cone located in the San Francisco Peaks volcanic field north of Flagstaff, Arizona.

Michael Collier

Michael Collier

4 Shield Volcanoes

A **shield volcano** is produced by the accumulation of fluid basaltic lavas and exhibits the shape of a broad, slightly domed structure that resembles a warrior's shield (FIGURE 10). Most shield volcanoes begin on the ocean floor as seamounts, a few of which grow large enough to form volcanic islands. In fact, with the exception of the volcanic islands that form above subduction zones, most other small oceanic islands are either a single shield volcano or, more often, the coalescence of two or more shields built upon massive amounts of pillow lavas. Examples include the Canary Islands, the Hawaiian Islands, the Galapagos, and Easter Island. In addition, some shield volcanoes form on continental crust. Included in this group are Nyamuragira, Africa's most active volcano, and Newberry Volcano in Oregon.

Mauna Loa: Earth's Largest Shield Volcano

Extensive study of the Hawaiian Islands has revealed that they are constructed of a myriad of thin basaltic lava flows averaging a few meters thick intermixed with relatively minor amounts of pyroclastic ejected material. Mauna Loa is one of five overlapping shield volcanoes that comprise the Big Island of Hawaii (Figure 10). From its base on the floor of the Pacific Ocean to its summit,

Mauna Loa is over 9 kilometers (6 miles) high, exceeding the elevation of Mount Everest. Comparatively, the volume of material composing Mauna Loa is roughly 200 times greater than that of a large composite cone such as Mount Rainier that was extruded over a span of about 1 million years.

The flanks of Mauna Loa have gentle slopes of only a few degrees. This low angle results because of very hot, fluid lava that travelled fast and far from the vent. In addition, most of the lava (perhaps 80 percent)

FIGURE 10 Mauna Loa: Earth's largest volcano
Mauna Loa is one of five shield volcanoes that collectively make up the Big Island of Hawaii. Shield volcanoes are built primarily of fluid basaltic lava flows and contain only a small percentage of pyroclastic materials.

Mauna Loa's summit caldera, which measures about 3 by 5 kilometers, is thought to have collapsed between 600–750 years ago.

Smaller pit craters also formed by collapse.

USGS

Kohala

Mauna Kea

Hualalai

Mauna Loa

HAWAII

Kilauea

Flank eruption

Summit caldera

Fluid lava flow

Shallow magma chamber

flowed through a well-developed system of lava tubes. Another feature common to many active shield volcanoes is a large, steep-walled caldera that occupies the summit (Figure 10). Calderas on large shield volcanoes form when the roof above the magma chamber has collapsed. This usually occurs as the magma reservoir empties following a large eruption or as magma migrates to the flank of a volcano to feed a fissure eruption.

In the final stage of growth, shield volcanoes behave more sporadically, and pyroclastic ejections are more common. Further, lavas increase in viscosity, resulting in thicker, shorter flows. These eruptions tend to steepen the slope of the summit area, which often becomes capped with clusters of cinder cones. This may explain why Mauna Kea, which is a more mature volcano that has not erupted in historic times, has a steeper summit than Mauna Loa, which erupted as recently as 1984. Astronomers are so certain that Mauna Kea is "over the hill" that they built an elaborate astronomical observatory on its summit to house some of the world's most advanced and expensive telescopes.

Evolution of Volcanic Islands

Although Mauna Loa is commonly regarded as a typical shield volcano, other ocean island volcanoes exhibit significant differences. The basaltic shields that comprise the Canary Islands, for example, have been active for as long as 20 million years and tend to eject more pyroclastic material than typical Hawaiian eruptions.

Despite these differences, most large oceanic shields have similar origins. They form above a long-lived, rising plume of hot rock anchored in Earth's mantle. Partial melting results in volcanic activity on the ocean floor producing piles of pillow lavas that evolve into a *seamount* (*submarine volcano*). Eventually, a few of these structures grow large enough to emerge as volcanic islands.

A volcanic island will continue to grow as long as it is located over a magma source. However, as the lithospheric plate moves away from the zone of melting, volcanic activity ceases. As the lithosphere cools and contracts, the island gradually subsides. Many small basaltic islands ultimately sink below sea level.

4 CONCEPT CHECKS

1. Describe the composition and viscosity of the lava associated with shield volcanoes.
2. Are pyroclastic materials a significant component of shield volcanoes?
3. Where do most shield volcanoes form—on the ocean floor or on the continents?
4. Relate lava tubes to the extent of lava flows associated with shield volcanoes.
5. Where are the best-known shield volcanoes in the United States? Name some examples in other parts of the world.

Fluid basaltic lava flowing down the slopes of Hawaii's Kilauea Volcano.

Michael Collier

Kilauea's East Rift Zone Eruption

Kilauea, one of the most active volcanoes in the world, is located on the island of Hawaii in the shadow of Mauna Loa. Most of the recent activity on Kilauea has occurred along the flanks of the volcano in a region called the East Rift Zone. The longest and largest eruption ever recorded on Kilauea began in 1983, and continues with no signs of abating.

Greg Vaughn/Alamy

1 Kilauea's most recent eruptive phase began along a 6-kilometer (4 mile) fissure where a 100-meter (300-foot) high "curtain of fire" formed as red-hot basaltic lava was ejected skyward.

2 The activity became localized at a single vent and a series of 44 short-lived episodes of lava fountaining built a cinder and spatter cone—given the Hawaiian name *Puu Oo*.

3 One of many fluid pahoehoe flows that have moved down the flanks of Kilauea since 1983.

David Reggie/ Getty Images

4 By the summer of 1986 a new vent opened along the rift. Pahoehoe lava flowing from this vent cut off the coastal highway and destroyed more than 180 structures including the National Park Visitor Center.

Michael Collier

USGS

1983 to Present

Kilauea summit caldera

(11)

Halemaumau Crater

N

0 1 2 3 4 miles
0 3 6 kilometers

Pacific Ocean

Kupaianaha

Puu Oo

East rift zone

(130)

Royal Gardens

Kalapana

1983–1986

1986–1992

2007–2011

Royal Gardens

1992–2007

Kalapana

KEY

1983–1986

1986–1992

N

1992–2007

2007–2012

0 1 2 3 miles
0 1 2 3 kilometers

Other vents have since opened around Puu Oo and lava continues to flow toward the sea.

5

USGS

ERUPTION SUMMARY

January 3, 1983

Fissure eruption began along East Rift Zone in an area southeast of Kilauea's summit caldera.

1983-1986

Lava fountains built a cinder-and-spatter cone called Puu Oo and produced mainly aa flows that destroyed 16 homes in the sparsely populated Royal Gardens subdivision.

1986-1992

Eruption moved eastward and built a small shield volcano called Kupaianaha which contained an extensive lava lake. Lava flows buried most of the homes in the village of Kalapana under 15-25 meters (50-80 feet) of lava.

1992-2007

Activity returned to the flanks of Puu Oo. Lava tubes carried lava nearly continuously to the ocean.

2007-2012

Several new vents open, including a small vent within Kilauea's summit caldera.

5 Cinder Cones

As the name suggests, **cinder cones** (also called scoria cones) are built from ejected lava fragments that begin to harden in flight to produce the vesicular rock **scoria** (FIGURE 11). These pyroclastic fragments range in size from fine ash to bombs that may exceed 1 meter in diameter. However, most of the volume of a cinder cone consists of pea- to walnut-sized fragments that are markedly vesicular and have a black to reddish-brown color. In addition, this pyroclastic material tends to have basaltic composition.

Although cinder cones are composed mostly of loose scoria fragments, some produce extensive lava fields. These lava flows generally form in the final stages of the volcano's life span, when the magma body has lost most of its gas content. Because cinder cones are composed of loose fragments rather than solid rock, the lava usually flows out from the unconsolidated base of the cone rather than from the crater.

Cinder cones have very simple, distinct shapes determined by the slope that loose pyroclastic material maintains as it comes to rest (Figure 11). Because cinders have a high angle of repose (the steepest angle at which material remains stable), cinder cones are steep-sided, having slopes between 30 and 40 degrees.

In addition, a cinder cone has quite a large, deep crater in relation to the overall size of the structure. Although relatively symmetrical, some cinder cones are elongated and higher on the side that was downwind during the final eruptive phase.

Most cinder cones are produced by a single, short-lived eruptive event. One study found that half of all cinder cones examined were constructed in less than a month and that 95 percent formed in less than a year. Once the event ceases, the magma in the "plumbing" connecting the vent to the magma source solidifies, and the volcano usually does not erupt again. (One exception is Cerro Negro, a cinder cone in Nicaragua, which has erupted more than 20 times since it formed in 1850.)

A young (350 years old) cinder cone, located near Lassen Peak, California.

Ash

Lava flow

Michael Collier

Crater

Pyroclastic material

Central vent filled with rock fragments

FIGURE 11 Cinder cones
Cinder cones are built from ejected lava fragments (mostly cinders and bombs) and are relatively small—usually less than 300 meters (1000 feet)—in height. This cinder cone is located near Lasen Peak, California.

Parícutin, a cinder cone located in Mexico, erupted for nine years.

Lava flow

Photos by Michael Collier

An aa flow emanating from the base of the cone buried much of the village of San Juan Parangaricutiro, leaving only remnants of the village's church.

FIGURE 12 Parícutin, a large cinder cone The village of San Juan Parangaricutiro, engulfed by aa lava from Parícutin. Only the church steeple remains. (Photos by Michael Collier)

As a consequence of this typically short life span, cinder cones are small, usually between 30 and 300 meters (100 and 1000 feet) tall. A few rare examples exceed 700 meters (2100 feet) in height.

Cinder cones number in the thousands around the globe. Some occur in groups such as the volcanic field near Flagstaff, Arizona, which consists of about 600 cones. Others are parasitic cones that are found on the flanks or within the calderas of larger volcanic structures.

Parícutin: Life of a Garden-Variety Cinder Cone

One of the very few volcanoes studied by geologists from its very beginning is the cinder cone called Parícutin, located about 320 kilometers (200 miles) west of Mexico City. In 1943, its eruptive phase began in a cornfield owned by Dionisio Pulido, who witnessed the event as he was preparing the field for planting.

For 2 weeks prior to the first eruption, numerous Earth tremors caused apprehension in the nearby village of Parícutin. Then, on February 20, sulfurous gases began billowing from a small depression that had been in the cornfield for as long as local residents could remember. During the night, hot, glowing rock fragments were ejected from the vent, producing a spectacular fireworks display. Explosive discharges continued, throwing hot fragments and ash occasionally as high as 6000 meters (20,000 feet) into the air. Larger fragments fell near the crater, some remaining incandescent as they rolled down the slope. These built an aesthetically pleasing cone, while finer ash fell over a much larger area, burning and eventually covering the village of Parícutin. In the first day, the cone grew to 40 meters (130 feet), and by the fifth day it was more than 100 meters (330 feet) high.

The first lava flow came from a fissure that opened just north of the cone, but after a few months flows began to emerge from the base of the cone itself. In June 1944, an aa flow 10 meters (30 feet) thick moved over much of the village of San Juan Parangaricutiro, leaving only the church steeple exposed (FIGURE 12). After 9 years of intermittent pyroclastic explosions and nearly continuous discharge of lava from vents at its base, the activity ceased almost as quickly as it had begun. Today, Parícutin is just another one of the scores of cinder cones dotting the landscape in this region of Mexico. Like the others, it will not erupt again.

5 CONCEPT CHECKS

1. Describe the composition of a cinder cone.
2. How do the size and steepness of slopes of a cinder cone compare with those of a shield volcano?
3. Over what time span does a typical cinder cone form?

6 Composite Volcanoes

Earth's most picturesque yet potentially dangerous volcanoes are **composite volcanoes**, also known as **stratovolcanoes**. Most are located in a relatively narrow zone that rims the Pacific Ocean, appropriately called the *Ring of Fire* (see Figure 27). This active zone consists of a chain of continental volcanoes that are distributed along the west coast of the Americas, including the large cones of the Andes in South America and the Cascade Range of the western United States and Canada.

Classic composite cones are large, nearly symmetrical structures consisting of alternating layers of explosively erupted cinders and ash interbedded with lava flows. A few composite cones, notably Italy's Etna and Stromboli, display very persistent eruption activity, and molten lava has been observed in their summit craters for decades. Stromboli is so well known for eruptions that eject incandescent blobs of lava that it has been referred to as the "Lighthouse of the Mediterranean." Mount Etna, on the other hand, has erupted, on average, once every 2 years since 1979 (see the chapter-opening photo).

Just as shield volcanoes owe their shape to fluid basaltic lavas, composite cones reflect the viscous nature of the material from which they are made. In general, composite cones are the product of silica-rich magma that has an andesitic composition. However, many composite cones also emit various amounts of fluid basaltic lava and, occasionally, pyroclastic material that has a rhyolitic composition. The silica-rich magmas typical of composite cones generate thick, viscous lavas that travel less than a few kilometers. In addition, composite cones are noted for generating explosive eruptions that eject huge quantities of pyroclastic material.

A conical shape, with a steep summit area and more gradually sloping flanks, is typical of most large composite cones. This classic profile, which adorns calendars and postcards, is partially a consequence of the way viscous lavas and pyroclastic ejected material contribute to the growth of the cone. Coarse fragments ejected from the summit crater tend to accumulate near their source and contribute to the steep slopes of the summit area.

Finer ejected materials, on the other hand, are deposited as a thin layer over a large area that acts to flatten the flank of the cone. In addition, during the early stages of growth, lavas tend to be more abundant and flow greater distances from the vent than later in the volcano's history, which contributes to the cone's broad base. As a composite volcano matures, the shorter flows that come from the central vent serve to armor and strengthen the summit area. Consequently, steep slopes exceeding 40 degrees are possible. Two of the most perfect cones—Mount Mayon in the Philippines and Fujiyama in Japan—exhibit the classic form we expect of composite cones, with steep summits and gently sloping flanks (FIGURE 13).

Despite the symmetrical forms of many composite cones, most have complex histories. Many composite volcanoes have secondary vents that have produced cinder cones or even much larger volcanic structures on their flanks. Huge mounds of volcanic debris surrounding these structures provide evidence that large sections of these volcanoes slid down slope as massive landslides. Some develop amphitheater-shaped depressions at their summits as a result of explosive lateral eruptions—as occurred during the 1980 eruption of Mount St. Helens. Often, so much rebuilding has occurred since these eruptions that no trace of the amphitheater-shaped scars remain. Others, such as Crater Lake, have been truncated by the collapse of their summit (see Figure 18).

FIGURE 13 Fujiyama, a classic composite volcano Japan's Fujiyama exhibits the classic form of a composite cone—a steep summit and gently sloping flanks. (Photo by Koji Nakano/ Getty Images, Inc-Liaison)

6 CONCEPT CHECKS

1. What zone on Earth has the greatest concentration of composite volcanoes?
2. Describe the materials that compose composite volcanoes.
3. How does the composition and viscosity of lava flows differ between composite volcanoes and shield volcanoes?

7 Volcanic Hazards

Roughly 1500 of Earth's known volcanoes have erupted at least once, and some several times, in the past 10,000 years. Based on historical records and studies of active volcanoes, 70 volcanic eruptions can be expected each year, and one large-volume eruption can be expected every decade. As one might expect, these large-magnitude eruptions account for the vast majority of human fatalities. For example, the 1902 eruption of Mount Pelée on the island of Martinique killed 28,000 people, wiping out nearly the entire population of the nearby city of St. Pierre.

Today, an estimated 500 million people from Japan and Indonesia to Italy and Oregon live near active volcanoes. They face a number of volcanic hazards, such as pyroclastic flows, lahars, lava flows, falling volcanic ash, and volcanic gases.

Pyroclastic Flow: A Deadly Force of Nature

Some of the most destructive forces of nature are **pyroclastic flows**, which consist of hot gases infused with incandescent ash and larger lava fragments. Also referred to as **nuée ardentes** (*glowing avalanches*), these fiery flows are capable of racing down steep volcanic slopes at speeds that can exceed 100 kilometers (60 miles) per hour (FIGURE 14). A pyroclastic flow is composed of two parts—a low-density cloud of hot expanding gases containing fine ash particles and a ground-hugging portion that is often composed of pumice and other vesicular pyroclastic material.

Driven by Gravity Pyroclastic flows are propelled by the force of gravity and tend to move in a manner similar to snow avalanches. They are mobilized by expanding volcanic gases released from the lava fragments and by the expansion of heated air that is overtaken and trapped in the moving front. These gases reduce friction between ash and pumice fragments, which gravity propels downslope in a nearly frictionless environment. This explains why some pyroclastic flow deposits are found many miles from their source (Figure 14).

Occasionally, powerful hot blasts that carry small amounts of ash separate from the main body of a pyroclastic flow. These low-density clouds, called *surges*, can be deadly but seldom have sufficient force to destroy buildings in their paths. Nevertheless, in 1991, a hot ash cloud from Japan's Mount Unzen engulfed and burned hundreds of homes and moved cars as far as 80 meters (250 feet).

Pyroclastic flows may originate in a variety of volcanic settings. Some occur when a powerful eruption blasts pyroclastic material out of the side of a volcano. More frequently, however, pyroclastic flows are generated by the collapse of tall eruption columns during an explosive event. When gravity eventually overcomes the

Pyroclastic flow racing down the flanks of Mount St. Helens, August, 1980. Pyroclastic flows composed of ash and pumice typically move at speeds of 100 kilometers (60 miles) per hour and may exceed temperatures of 400° C (800° F).

FIGURE 14 **Pyroclastic flows** Pyroclastic flows are composed of hot ash and pumice and/or blocky lava fragments that race down the slopes of volcanoes.

Geologists examining pumice blocks deposited by a pyroclastic flow that occurred on May 18, 1980. Mount St. Helens is in the background shrouded in steam.

St. Pierre following the eruption of Mount Pelée.

are triggered when magma nears the surface of a glacially clad volcano, causing large volumes of ice and snow to melt. Others are generated when heavy rains saturate weathered volcanic deposits. Thus, lahars may occur even when a volcano is *not* erupting.

When Mount St. Helens erupted in 1980, several lahars were generated. These flows and accompanying floodwaters raced down nearby river valleys at speeds exceeding 30 kilometers (20 miles) per hour. These raging rivers of mud destroyed or severely damaged nearly all the homes and bridges along their paths (FIGURE 16). Fortunately, the area was not densely populated.

initial upward thrust provided by the escaping gases, the ejected materials begin to fall, sending massive amounts of incandescent blocks, ash, and pumice cascading down slope.

The Destruction of St. Pierre In 1902, an infamous pyroclastic flow and associated surge from Mount Pelée, a small volcano on the Caribbean island of Martinique, destroyed the port town of St. Pierre. Although the main pyroclastic flow was largely confined to the valley of Riviere Blanche, a low-density fiery surge spread south of the river and quickly engulfed the entire city. The destruction happened in moments and was so devastating that nearly all of St. Pierre's 28,000 inhabitants were killed. Only 1 person on the outskirts of town—a prisoner protected in a dungeon—and a few people on ships in the harbor were spared (FIGURE 15).

Within days of this calamitous eruption, scientists arrived on the scene. Although St. Pierre was mantled by only a thin layer of volcanic debris, they discovered that masonry walls nearly 1 meter thick were knocked over like dominoes; large trees were uprooted, and cannons were torn from their mounts.

Lahars: Mudflows on Active and Inactive Cones

In addition to having violent eruptions, large composite cones may generate a type of fluid mudflow referred to by its Indonesian name, **lahar**. These destructive flows occur when volcanic debris becomes saturated with water and rapidly moves down steep volcanic slopes, generally following stream valleys. Some lahars

FIGURE 16 Lahars
A. This lahar raced down the Toutle River, which flows westward from Mount St. Helens, following the May 18, 1980, eruption. **B.** Note the muddy consistency of lahar deposits.

In 1985, deadly lahars were produced during a small eruption of Nevado del Ruiz, a 5300-meter (17,400-foot) volcano in the Andes Mountains of Colombia. Hot pyroclastic material melted ice and snow that capped the mountain (*nevado* means *snow* in Spanish) and sent torrents of ash and debris down three major river valleys that flank the volcano. Reaching speeds of 100 kilometers (60 miles) per hour, these mudflows tragically claimed 25,000 lives.

Mount Rainier, Washington, is considered by many to be America's most dangerous volcano because, like Nevado del Ruiz, it has a thick, year-round mantle of snow and glacial ice. Adding to the risk is the fact that more than 100,000 people live in the valleys around Rainier, and many homes are built on deposits left by lahars that flowed down the volcano hundreds or thousands of years ago. A future eruption, or perhaps just a period of heavier-than-average rainfall, may produce lahars that could be similarly destructive.

What Are Other Volcanic Hazards?

Volcanoes can be hazardous to human health and property in other various ways. Ash and other pyroclastic material can collapse the roofs of buildings or can be drawn into the lungs of humans and other animals or into the engines of aircrafts (FIGURE 17). Volcanoes also emit gases, most notably sulfur dioxide that affects air quality and, when mixed with rainwater, may destroy vegetation and reduce the quality of groundwater. Despite the known risks, millions of people live in close proximity to active volcanoes.

FIGURE 17 **Volcanic hazards**
In addition to generating pyroclastic flows and lahars, volcanoes can be hazardous to human health and property, in many other ways.

Volcanic ash can destroy plant life and be drawn into the lungs of humans and other animals.

Ash and other pyroclastic materials can collapse roofs, or completely cover buildings.

Lava flows can destroy homes, roads, and other structures in their paths.

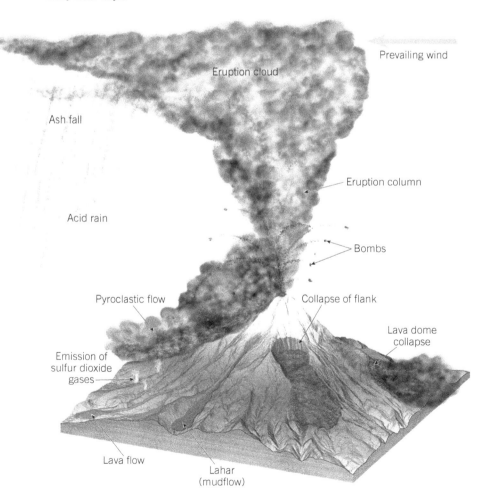

Prevailing wind

Eruption cloud

Ash fall

Eruption column

Acid rain

Bombs

Pyroclastic flow

Collapse of flank

Lava dome collapse

Emission of sulfur dioxide gases

Lava flow

Lahar (mudflow)

EYE on Earth

This image was obtained during the 1991 eruption of Mount Pinatubo in the Philippines. This was the largest eruption to affect a densely populated area in recent times. Timely forecasts of the event by scientists were credited with saving at least 5,000 lives. (Alberto Garcia/CORBIS)

Question 1 What name is given to the ash- and pumice-laden cloud that is racing toward the photographer?

Question 2 At what speeds can these fiery clouds move down steep mountain slopes?

Jeep   Alberto Garcia/Corbis

Volcano-Related Tsunamis   One not-so-familiar hazard associated with volcanoes is their ability to generate **tsunamis**. Although usually caused by strong earthquakes, these destructive sea waves are sometimes the result of powerful volcanic explosions or the sudden collapse of flanks of volcanoes into the ocean. In 1883, a volcanic eruption on the Indonesian island Krakatau literally tore the island apart and generated a tsunami that claimed an estimated 36,000 lives.

Volcanic Ash and Aviation   During the past few decades, at least 80 commercial jets have been damaged by inadvertently flying into clouds of volcanic ash. For example, in 1989, a Boeing 747 carrying more than 300 passengers encountered an ash cloud from Alaska's Redoubt Volcano. All four of the engines stalled when they became clogged with ash. Fortunately, the pilots were able to restart the engines and safely land the aircraft in Anchorage.

More recently, in 2010, the eruption of Iceland's Eyjafjallajökull Volcano sent ash high into the atmosphere. The thick plume of ash drifted over Europe, causing airlines to cancel thousands of flights, leaving hundreds of thousands of travelers stranded. Several weeks passed before air travel resumed its normal schedule.

Volcanic Gases and Respiratory Health   One of the most destructive volcanic events, called the Laki eruptions, began along a large fissure in southern Iceland in 1783. An estimated 14 cubic kilometers of fluid basaltic lavas, in addition to 130 million tons of **sulfur dioxide** and other poisonous gases, were released. When sulfur dioxide is inhaled, it reacts with moisture in the lungs to produce sulfuric acid. As a result, this eruption caused the death of more than 50 percent of Iceland's livestock, and the ensuing famine killed 25 percent of the island's human population.

In addition, this huge eruption endangered people and property all across Europe. Crop failure occurred in parts of Western Europe, and thousands of residents perished from lung-related diseases. A recent report estimated that a similar eruption today would cause more than 140,000 cardiopulmonary fatalities in Europe alone.

Effects of Volcanic Ash and Gases on Weather and Climate   Volcanic eruptions can eject dust-sized particles of volcanic ash and sulfur dioxide gas high into the atmosphere. The sulfur dioxide gas combines with water vapor to produce tiny sulfuric acid particles, which along with the ash, reflect sunlight back to space. This loss of solar energy to the climate system produces temporary cooling as long as the particles remain suspended in the atmosphere. In the case of the 1783 Laki eruption in Iceland, the atmospheric circulation across the globe appears to have been affected. Drought conditions prevailed in portions of Africa and India, while the winter of 1784 brought the longest period of below-zero temperatures in New England's history.

Other eruptions that have produced significant effects on climate worldwide include the eruption of Indonesia's Mount Tambora in 1815, which produced the "year without a summer" (1816), and more recently, Mexico's El Chichón and Mount Pinatubo in the Philippines which both caused measurable cooling of the lower atmosphere.

7 CONCEPT CHECKS

1. Describe pyroclastic flows and explain why they are capable of traveling great distances.
2. What is a lahar?
3. List at least three volcanic hazards besides pyroclastic flows and lahars.

Eruption of Mount Vesuvius, AD 79

One well-documented volcanic eruption of historic proportions was the AD 79 eruption of the Italian volcano we now call Mount Vesuvius. For centuries prior to this eruption, Vesuvius had been relatively quiescent and its slopes were adorned with vineyards. However, the tranquility abruptly ended, and in less than 24 hours the entire city of Pompeii and a few thousand of its residents were entombed beneath a layer of volcanic ash and pumice that fell like rain.

ITALY
CAMPANIA

Naples

Bay of Naples

Herculaneum

▲ Vesuvius

Pompeii

© Google Earth

Mount Vesuvius has had more than two dozen explosive eruptions since AD 79, the most recent occurring in 1944. Today, roughly 3 million people inhabit the area around Mount Vesuvius, making it potentially one of the most dangerous volcanoes in the world.

Olivier Goujon/Robert Harding

Ruins of Pompeii Nearly 17 centuries after the eruption, excavation of Pompeii gave archeologists a superb picture of Roman life. Most of the roofs in Pompeii collapsed under the weight of volcanic debris that fell at the rate of 5 to 6 inches per hour. Herculaneum, located closer to the modern city of Naples, was buried under 75 feet of ash and pumice.

Leonard von Matt/Photo Researchers, Inc.

Victims of the AD 79 eruption of Mount Vesuvius The remains of human victims were quickly buried by falling ash and subsequent rainfall caused the ash to harden. Over the centuries, the remains decomposed which created cavities discovered by nineteenth-century excavators. Casts were then produced by pouring plaster into the voids.

Jose Fuste Raga/Corbis/Glow Images

Mount Vesuvius today This image of Naples, Italy, with Vesuvius in the background, should prompt us to consider how volcanic crises might be managed in the future.

8 Other Volcanic Landforms

The most widely recognized volcanic structures are the cone-shaped edifices of composite volcanoes that dot Earth's surface. However, other distinctive and important landforms are also produced by volcanic activity on Earth.

Calderas

Calderas (*caldaria* = a cooking pot) are large steep-sided depressions with diameters that exceed one kilometer and have a somewhat circular form. (Those less than 1 kilometer across are called *collapse pits*, or *craters*.) Most calderas are formed by one of the following processes: (1) the collapse of the summit of a large composite volcano following an explosive eruption of silica-rich pumice and ash fragments (*Crater Lake–type calderas*); (2) the collapse of the top of a shield volcano caused by subterranean drainage from a central magma chamber (*Hawaiian-type calderas*); and (3) the collapse of a large area, caused by the discharge of colossal volumes of silica-rich pumice and ash along ring fractures (*Yellowstone-type calderas*).

Crater Lake–Type Calderas   Crater Lake, Oregon, is situated in a caldera approximately 10 kilometers (6 miles) wide and 1175 meters (more than 3800 feet) deep. This caldera formed about 7000 years ago, when a composite cone named Mount Mazama violently extruded 50 to 70 cubic kilometers of pyroclastic material (FIGURE 18). With the loss of support, 1500 meters (nearly a mile) of the summit of this once-prominent cone collapsed, producing a caldera that eventually filled with rainwater. Later, volcanic activity built a small cinder cone in the caldera. Today, this cone, called Wizard Island, provides a mute reminder of past activity (Figure 18).

Hawaiian-Type Calderas   Unlike Crater Lake–type calderas, many calderas form gradually because of the loss of lava from a shallow magma chamber underlying the volcano's summit. For example, Hawaii's active shield volcanoes, Mauna Loa and Kilauea, both have large calderas at their summits. Kilauea's measures 3.3 by 4.4 kilometers (about 2 by 3 miles) and is 150 meters (500 feet) deep (FIGURE 19). The walls of this caldera are almost vertical, and as a result, it looks like a vast, nearly flat-bottomed pit. Kilauea's caldera formed by gradual subsidence as magma slowly drained laterally from the underlying magma chamber, leaving the summit unsupported.

An explosive eruption partially empties a shallow magma chamber.

① Magma chamber

Summit of volcano collapses, enhancing the eruption.

②

Newly formed caldera fills with rain and groundwater.

③

Subsequent eruptions produce the cinder cone called Wizard Island.

④ Wizard Island

Crater Lake

Wizard Island

Michael Collier

Close-up view of Wizard Island.

USGS

FIGURE 18 Formation of Crater Lake–type calderas
About 7000 years ago, a violent eruption partly emptied the magma chamber of former Mount Mazama, causing its summit to collapse. Rainfall and groundwater contributed to form Crater Lake, the deepest lake in the United States—594 meters (1949 feet) deep—and the ninth deepest in the world. (Photo by Michael Collier)

Halemaʻumaʻu crater during a period of recent activity.

USGS

Kilauea's summit caldera.

USGS

Geologist's Sketch

Kilauea Caldera

Caldera rim

Hawaii Volcano Observatory

Halemaʻumaʻu

Keanakakaʻi Crater

Key
- 1800s
- 1919–21
- 1971–74
- 1982

FIGURE 19 Kilauea's Summit Caldera
Kilauea's caldera measures 3.3 by 4.4 kilometers (about 2 by 3 miles) and is 150 meters (500 feet) deep. More recent flows are dark, while the older flows are pale because the iron in the lava oxidizes into "rust." Halemáumáu, the pit crater in the southwestern part of the caldera, was active as recently as 2012.

EYE on Earth

This image shows the Buddhist monastery Taung Kalat, located in central Myanmar (Burma). The monastery sits high on a sheer-sided rock made mainly of magmas that solidified in the conduit of an ancient volcano. The volcano has since been worn away. (Photo by Dreamstime)

Question 1 Based on this information, what volcanic structure do you think is shown in this photo?

Question 2 Would this volcanic structure most likely have been associated with a composite volcano or cinder cone? Explain how you arrived at your answer.

Taolmor/Dreamstime

Formation of Yellowstone-type Calderas

① The emplacement of silica-rich magma causes the layers of rock above to bulge and crack, producing a set of *ring fractures*.

③ With loss of support, the roof of the magma chamber collapses forming a large caldera.

② Massive amounts of magma erupt, producing fiery clouds of ash and gases called *pyroclastic flows* that devastate the surrounding landscape.

④ Following the eruption, the caldera floor experiences a long period of slow upheaval that produces an elevated central region, called a *resurgent dome*.

 SMARTFIGURE 20
Formation of a Yellowstone-type caldera
Several Yellowstone-type calderas exist around the globe. These large volcanic structures are capable of rendering a large area of Earth's surface lifeless in perhaps only a few days, hence the name "supervolcanoes."

FIGURE 21 Pyroclastic flow deposits
Mesa Falls Tuff is the middle of three, mostly welded, pyroclastic flow deposits that were generated by eruptions in the Yellowstone area. Based on radiometric dating, we know that this extensive ash and pumice sheet was deposited by a massive eruption that occurred about 1.2 million years ago. In places, the Mesa Falls Tuff is more than 100 meters (300 feet) thick.
(Photo by Robert L. Christianson/ U.S. Geological Survey)

Geologist's Sketch

Yellowstone-Type Calderas Historic and destructive eruptions such as Mount St. Helens and Vesuvius pale in comparison to what happened 630,000 years ago, in the region now occupied by Yellowstone National Park, when approximately 1000 cubic kilometers of pyroclastic material erupted. This catastrophic eruption sent showers of ash as far as the Gulf of Mexico and resulted in the formation of a caldera 70 kilometers (43 miles) across. Vestiges of this event are the many hot springs and geysers in the Yellowstone region.

Based on the extraordinary volume of erupted material, researchers have determined that the magma chambers associated with Yellowstone-type calderas must be similarly monstrous. As more and more magma accumulates, the pressure within the magma chamber begins to exceed the pressure exerted by the weight of the overlying rocks (FIGURE 20). An eruption occurs when the gas-rich magma raises the overlying crust enough to create vertical fractures that extend to the surface. Magma surges upward along these cracks, forming a ring-shaped eruption. With a loss of support, the roof of the magma chamber collapses.

Caldera-forming eruptions are of colossal proportions, ejecting huge volumes of pyroclastic materials, mainly in the form of ash and pumice fragments. Typically, these materials form pyroclastic flows that sweep across the landscape, destroying most living things in their paths. Upon coming to rest, the hot fragments of ash and pumice fuse together, forming a welded tuff that closely resembles a solidified lava flow (FIGURE 21). Despite the immense size of these calderas, the eruptions that cause them are brief, lasting hours to perhaps a few days.

Large calderas tend to exhibit a complex eruptive history. In the Yellowstone region, for example, three caldera-forming episodes are known to have occurred over the past 2.1 million years. The most recent event (630,000 years ago) was followed by episodic outpourings of degassed rhyolitic and basaltic lavas. Geologic evidence suggests that a magma reservoir still exists beneath Yellowstone; thus, another caldera-forming eruption is likely—but not necessarily imminent.

A distinctive characteristic of large caldera-forming eruptions is a slow upheaval of the floor of the caldera that produce a central elevated region called a *resurgent dome* (Figure 20). Unlike calderas associated with shield volcanoes or composite cones, Yellowstone-type depressions are so large and poorly defined that many remained undetected until high-quality aerial and satellite images became available. Other examples of large calderas located in the United States are California's Long Valley Caldera; LaGarita Caldera, located in the San Juan Mountains of southern Colorado; and the Valles Caldera, west of Los Alamos, New Mexico. These and similar calderas found around the globe are among the largest volcanic structures on Earth—hence the name "supervolcanoes." Volcanologists have compared their destructive force with that of the impact of a small asteroid. Fortunately, no caldera-forming eruption has occurred in historic times.

Fissure Eruptions and Large Igneous Provinces

The greatest volume of volcanic material is extruded from fractures in Earth's crust called **fissures** (*fissura* = to split) Rather than building cones, these long, narrow cracks most often emit fluid basaltic lavas that blanket wide areas (FIGURE 22). Recall that the recent volcanic activity on Kilauea began along a series of fissures with the East Rift Zone.

In some locations, extraordinary amounts of lava have been extruded along fissures in a relatively short time, geographically speaking. These voluminous accumulations, called **large igneous provinces**, are also commonly referred to as *basalt plateaus* because most have a basaltic composition and tend to be

FIGURE 22 **Basaltic fissure eruptions** Lava fountaining from a fissure and formation of fluid lava flows called *flood basalts.* The lower photo shows flood basalt flows near Idaho Falls.

Basaltic lava flows

Lava fountaining

Fissure

Basaltic lava flows

rather flat and broad. The Columbia Plateau located in the northwestern United States, which consists of the Columbia River basalts, is the product of this type of activity (FIGURE 23). Numerous **fissure eruptions** have buried the landscape, creating a lava plateau nearly 1 mile thick. Some of the lava remained molten long enough to flow 150 kilometers (90 miles) from its source. The term **flood basalts** appropriately describe these extrusions.

Massive accumulations of basaltic lava, similar to those of the Columbia Plateau, occur elsewhere in the world. One of the largest is the Deccan Traps,

FIGURE 23 Columbia River basalts

A. The Columbia River basalts cover an area of nearly 164,000 square kilometers (63,000 square miles) that is commonly called the Columbia Plateau. Activity here began about 17 million years ago, as lava began to pour out of large fissures, eventually producing a basalt plateau with an average thickness of more than 1 kilometer. **B.** Basalt flows exposed in the Palouse River Canyon in southwestern Washington State. (Photo by Williamborg)

The Palouse River in Washington State has cut a canyon about 300 meters (1000 feet) deep into the flood basalts of the Columbia Plateau.

B.

A.

KEY

▨ Columbia River Basalts

▨ Other basaltic rocks

▲ Large Cascade volcanoes

FIGURE 24 Pancake-shaped lava dome

This lava dome was produced when viscous, degassed silica-rich lava erupted in the area between Mono Lake and Long Valley Caldera in eastern California. Note the trees for scale. (Photo by Michael Collier)

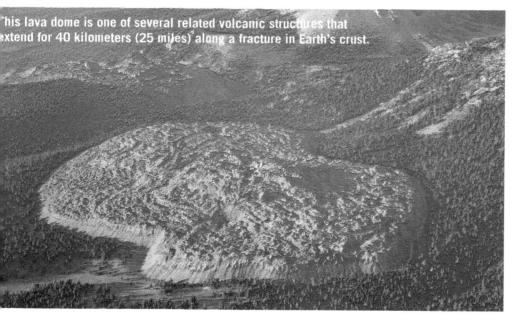

This lava dome is one of several related volcanic structures that extend for 40 kilometers (25 miles) along a fracture in Earth's crust.

a thick sequence of flat-lying basalt flows covering nearly 500,000 square kilometers (195,000 square miles) of west-central India. When the Deccan Traps formed about 66 million years ago, nearly 2 million cubic kilometers of lava were extruded over a period of approximately 1 million years. Several other huge deposits of flood basalts, including the Ontong Java Plateau, are found on the floor of the ocean (see Figure 30).

Lava Domes

In contrast to hot basaltic lavas, cool silica-rich rhyolitic lavas are so viscous that they hardly flow at all. As the thick lava is "squeezed" out of a vent, it often produces a dome-shaped mass called a lava dome. Lava domes are usually only a few tens of meters high, and come in a variety of shapes that range from pancake-like flows (FIGURE 24) to steep-sided plugs that were pushed upward like pistons. Most lava domes grow over a period of several years

Lava domes are produced when highly viscous magma slowly rises over a period of months or years.

When a growing lava dome becomes over-steepened, it may collapse producing a blocky pyroclastic flow.

Blocky pyroclastic flow

Decompression of the interior magma may produce an explosive eruption and pyroclastic flow.

Fiery pyroclastic flow

B.

A.

FIGURE 25 Lava domes can generate pyroclastic flows **A.** This lava dome began to develop in the vent of Mount St. Helen's following the May 1980 eruption. **B.** The collapse of a lava dome often results in a powerful pyroclastic flow. (Photo by Lyn Topinka/ U.S. Geological Survey)

following an explosive eruption of silica-rich magma. A recent example is the dome that began to grow in the crater of Mount St. Helens immediately following the 1980 eruption (FIGURE 25A).

The collapse of lava domes, particularly those that form on the summit or along the steep flanks of composite cones, often produce powerful pyroclastic flows (FIGURE 25B). These flows result from highly viscous magma slowly entering the dome, causing it to expand and steepen its flanks. Over time, the cooler outer layer of the dome may start to crumble, producing relatively small pyroclastic flows consisting of dense blocks of lava. Occasionally, the rapid removal of the outer layer causes a significant decrease in pressure on the hot gaseous magma in the interior of the dome. Explosive degassing of the interior magma triggers a fiery pyroclastic flow that races down the flanks of the volcano (Figure 25B).

Since 1995, pyroclastic flows generated by the collapse of several lava domes on Soufriére Hills Volcano have rendered more than half of the Caribbean island of Montserrat uninhabitable. The capital city, Plymouth, was destroyed, and two-thirds of the population has evacuated. A few years earlier, a collapsed lava dome at the summit of Japan's Mount Unzen produced a pyroclastic flow that claimed 42 lives. Many of the victims were journalists and film makers who ventured too close to the volcano in order to obtain photographs and document the event.

Volcanic Necks and Pipes

Most volcanic eruptions are fed lava through short conduits that connect shallow magma chambers to vents located at the surface. When a volcano becomes inactive, congealed magma often becomes preserved in the feeding conduit of the volcano as a crudely cylindrical mass. Over time, all volcanoes will succumb to forces of weathering and erosion. Over time, the rock occupying the volcanic conduit, which is highly resistant to weathering, may remain standing above the surrounding terrain long after the cone has been worn away. Shiprock, New Mexico, is a widely recognized and spectacular example of these structures, which geologists call **volcanic necks** (or plugs) (FIGURE 26). Higher than most skyscrapers, at 420 meters (1380 feet) high, Shiprock is one of many such landforms that protrude conspicuously from the red desert landscapes of the American Southwest.

One rare type of conduit, called a **pipe**, carries magma that originated in the mantle at depths that may exceed 150 kilometers (93 miles). The gas-laden magmas that migrate through pipes travel rapidly enough to undergo minimal alteration during their ascent.

The best-known volcanic pipes are the diamond-bearing kimberlite pipes of South Africa. The rocks filling these pipes originated at great depths, where pressure is sufficiently high to generate diamonds and

Geologist's Sketch

Conduit filled
with hardened
lava

Volcano

Shiprock
(volcanic neck)

Weathering
and erosion
eliminates
volcano

**Shiprock, New Mexico is
a volcanic neck composed
of igneous rock which
solidified in the conduit
of a now vanished
volcano.**

1380 ft

Dennis Tasa

 SMARTFIGURE 26

Volcanic neck

Shiprock, New Mexico, is a volcanic neck that stands over 420 meters (1380 feet) high. It consists of igneous rock that crystallized in the vent of a volcano that has long since been eroded.

other high-pressure minerals. The process of transporting essentially unaltered magma (along with diamond inclusions) through 150 kilometers of solid rock is exceptional—which accounts for the scarcity of natural diamonds. Geologists consider pipes to be "windows" into Earth that allow us to view rocks that normally form only at great depths.

8 CONCEPT CHECKS

1. Describe the formation of Crater Lake. Compare it to the caldera found on shield volcanoes such as Kilauea.
2. Pyroclastic flows are associated with what volcanic structure that is not a composite volcano?
3. How do the eruptions that created the Columbia Plateau differ from eruptions that create large composite volcanoes?
4. Contrast the composition of a typical lava dome and a typical fissure eruption.
5. What type of volcanic structure is Shiprock, New Mexico, and how did it form?

9 Plate Tectonics and Volcanic Activity

Geologists have known for decades that the global distribution of most of Earth's volcanoes is not random. Most active volcanoes on land are located along the margins of the ocean basins—notably within the circum-Pacific belt known as the **Ring of Fire** (FIGURE 27). These volcanoes consist mainly of composite cones that emit volatile-rich magma that has an andesitic (intermediate) composition and occasionally produce awe-inspiring eruptions.

Another group of volcanoes includes the innumerable seamounts that form along the crest of the mid-ocean ridges. At these depths (1 to 3 kilometers below sea level), the pressures are so intense that the gases emitted quickly dissolve in the seawater and never reach the surface.

There are some volcanic structures, however, that appear to be somewhat randomly distributed around the globe. These volcanic structures comprise most of the islands of the deep ocean basins, including the Hawaiian Islands, the Galapagos Islands, and Easter Island.

Prior to the development of the theory of plate tectonics geologists did not have an acceptable explanation for the distribution of Earth's volcanoes. Recall that most magma originates in rocks from Earth's upper mantle that is essentially solid, *not molten*. The basic connection between plate tectonics and volcanism is that *plate motions provide the mechanisms by which mantle rocks undergo partial melting to generate magma.*

Volcanism at Convergent Plate Boundaries

Recall that along certain convergent plate boundaries, two plates move toward each other, and a slab of oceanic lithosphere descends into the mantle, generating a deep-ocean trench. As the slab sinks deeper into the mantle, the increase in temperature and pressure drives water and carbon dioxide from the oceanic crust. At a depth of about 100 kilometers, the wedge of mantle rock that lies above the descending slab is sufficiently hot that the introduction of water leads to partial melting. (FIGURE 28A). Recall that the partial melting of mantle rock (peridotite) generates magma with a basaltic composition. After a sufficient quantity of the rock has melted, blobs of buoyant magma slowly migrate upward.

Volcanism at a convergent plate margin results in the development of a slightly curved chain of volcanoes called a *volcanic arc*. These volcanic chains develop roughly parallel to the associated trench—at distances of 200 to 300 kilometers (100 to 200 miles). Volcanic arcs can be constructed on oceanic as well as continental lithosphere. Those that develop within the ocean and grow large enough for their tops to rise above the surface are labeled *archipelagos* in most atlases. Geologists prefer the more descriptive term **volcanic island arcs**, or simply island arcs (Figure 28A). Several young volcanic island arcs border the western Pacific basin, including the Aleutians, the Tongas, and the Marianas.

Volcanism associated with convergent plate boundaries may also develop where slabs of oceanic

FIGURE 27 Earth's major volcanoes
Most of Earth's major volcanoes are located in a zone around the Pacific called the Ring of Fire. Another large group of active volcanoes lie undiscovered along the mid-ocean ridge system.

A. *Convergent Plate Volcanism* When an oceanic plate subducts, melting in the mantle produces magma that gives rise to a volcanic island arc on the overlying oceanic crust.

Mount Augustine, Alaska (NASA)

Volcanic island arc

Trench

Oceanic crust

Marginal sea

Continental crust

Mantle rock melts

Water driven from plate

Subducting oceanic lithosphere

Asthenosphere

C. *Intraplate Volcanism* When an oceanic plate moves over a hot spot, a chain of volcanic structures such as the Hawaiian Islands is created.

Oceanic crust

Hot spot

Hawaii

Decompression melting

Rising mantle plume

North America

Hawaii

So
Ame

Kilauea, Hawaii (USGS)

E. *Convergent Plate Volcanism* When oceanic lithosphere descends beneath a continent, magma generated in the mantle rises to form a continental volcanic arc.

Continental volcanic arc

Trench

Oceanic crust

Continental crust

Subducting oceanic lithosphere

Mantle rock melts

Water driven from plate

SMARTFIGURE 28
Earth's zones of volcanism

194

B. *Divergent Plate Volcanism* Along the oceanic ridge, where two plates are being pulled apart, upwelling of hot mantle rock creates new seafloor.

Oceanic crust

Magma chamber

Decompression melting

Asthenosphere

Iceland (Wedigo Ferchland/ Photoshot Holdings)

Mid-Atlantic Rift

Africa

Deccan Plateau

South America

East Africa Rift Valley

Hot spot

Flood basalts

Continental crust

Decompression melting

Rising mantle plume

D. *Intraplate Volcanism* When a large mantle plume ascends beneath continental crust, vast outpourings of fluid basaltic lava like those that formed the Deccan Plateau may be generated.

Rift valley

Continental crust

Decompression melting

Mount Kilimanjaro, Africa (Corbis/Photolibrary)

F. *Divergent Plate Volcanism* When plate motion pulls a continental block apart, stretching and thinning of the lithosphere causes molten rock to ascend from the mantle.

SMARTFIGURE 28
Earth's zones of volcanism *continued*

lithosphere are subducted under continental lithosphere to produce a **continental volcanic arc** (FIGURE 28E). The mechanisms that generate these mantle-derived magmas are essentially the same as those that create volcanic island arcs. The most significant difference is that continental crust is much thicker and is composed of rocks having higher silica content than oceanic crust. Hence, a mantle-derived magma changes chemically as it rises by assimilating silica-rich crustal rocks. At the same time, extensive magmatic differentiation occurs. (Recall that magmatic differentiation is the formation of secondary magmas from parent magma.) Stated another way, the magmas generated in the mantle may change from a fluid basaltic magma to a silica-rich andesitic or rhyolitic magma as it moves up through the continental crust.

Recall that the Ring of Fire, a belt of explosive volcanoes, surrounds the Pacific basin. The Ring of Fire exists because oceanic lithosphere is being subducted beneath most of the landmasses that surround the Pacific Ocean. The volcanoes of the Cascade Range in the northwestern United States, including Mount Hood, Mount Rainier, and Mount Shasta, are examples of volcanoes generated at a convergent plate boundary (FIGURE 29).

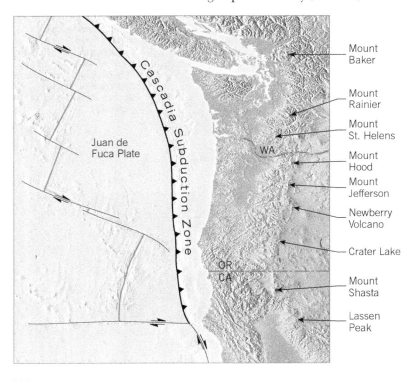

Mount Baker

Mount Rainier

Mount St. Helens

Mount Hood

Mount Jefferson

Newberry Volcano

Crater Lake

Mount Shasta

Lassen Peak

SMARTFIGURE 29
Subduction-produced Cascade Range volcanoes
Major volcanic structures of the Cascade Range formed along a convergent plate boundary (Cascadia subduction zone) off the Pacific coast of North America.

Volcanism at Divergent Plate Boundaries

The greatest volume of magma (perhaps 60 percent of Earth's total yearly output) is produced along the oceanic ridge system in association with seafloor spreading (see FIGURE 28B). Below the ridge axis where lithospheric plates are continually being pulled apart, the solid, yet mobile, mantle responds by ascending to fill the rift. Recall that as hot rock rises, it experiences a decrease in confining pressure and undergoes melting without the addition of heat. This process, called *decompression melting*, is the most common process by which mantle rocks melt.

Partial melting of mantle rock at spreading centers produces basaltic magma. Because this newly formed magma is less dense than the mantle rock from which it was derived, it rises and collects in reservoirs located just below the ridge crest. This activity continuously adds new basaltic rock to plate margins, temporarily welding them together, only to have them break again as spreading continues. Along some ridge segments, outpourings of pillow lavas build numerous volcanic structures, the largest of which is Iceland.

Although most spreading centers are located along the axis of an oceanic ridge, some are not. In particular, the East African Rift is a site where continental lithosphere is being pulled apart (see FIGURE 28F). Vast outpourings of fluid basaltic lavas as well as several active composite volcanoes are found in this region of the globe.

Intraplate Volcanism

We know why igneous activity is initiated along plate boundaries, but why do eruptions occur in the interiors of plates? Hawaii's Kilauea is considered the world's most active volcano, yet it is situated thousands of kilometers from the nearest plate boundary in the middle of the vast Pacific plate (see FIGURE 28C). Other sites of **intraplate volcanism** (meaning "within the plate") include the large outpourings of fluid basaltic lavas such as those that compose the Columbia River basalts, the Siberian Traps in Russia, India's Deccan Plateau, and several large oceanic plateaus, including the Ontong Java Plateau in the western Pacific (FIGURE 30). These massive structures are estimated to be 10 to 40 kilometers (6 to 25 miles) thick.

It is thought that most intraplate volcanism occurs where a mass of hotter-than-normal mantle material called a **mantle plume** ascends toward the surface (FIGURE 31).* Although the depth at which mantle plumes originate is a topic of debate, some appear to form deep within Earth, at the core–mantle boundary. These plumes of solid yet mobile rock rise toward the surface in a manner similar to the blobs that form within a lava lamp. (These are the trendy

---

*Recent research on the nature of mantle plumes has caused some geologists to question their role, if any, in the formation of at least some large basalt provinces.

North Atlantic basalts (56–61 mya)

Siberian Traps (250 mya)

Wrangellia (230–225 mya)

Caribbean (89 mya)

Deccan (65 mya)

Emeishan (259 mya)

Shatsky Rise (145 mya)

Columbia River basalts (16 mya)

Hawaiian

Afar (30 mya)

Galapagos

Parana (133 mya)

Etendeka (133 mya)

Karoo (183 mya)

Broken Ridge (118 mya)

Réunion

Ontong Java (122 mya)

Manihiki (120 mya)

Tristan

Louisville

Kerguelen Plateau (118 mya)

FIGURE 30 Large basalt provinces
Global distribution of large basalt provinces.

A rising mantle plume with a large bulbous head is thought to generate Earth's large basalt provinces.

A.

Rapid decompression melting of the plume head produces extensive outpourings of flood basalts over a relatively short time span.

B.

Because of plate movement, volcanic activity from the rising tail of the plume generates a linear chain of smaller volcanic structures.

C.

lamps that contain two immiscible liquids in a glass container. As the base of the lamp is heated, the denser liquid at the bottom becomes buoyant and forms blobs that rise to the top.) Like the blobs in a lava lamp, a mantle plume has a bulbous head that draws out a narrow stalk beneath it as it rises. Once the plume head nears the top of the mantle, decompression melting generates basaltic magma that triggers volcanism at the surface.

Large mantle plumes, dubbed *superplumes*, are thought to be responsible for the vast outpourings of basaltic lava that created the large basalt provinces. When the head of the plume reaches the base of the lithosphere, melting progresses rapidly. This causes the burst of volcanism that emits voluminous outpourings of lava to form a huge basalt province in a matter of 1 million or so years (Figure 31B). Due to the extreme nature of the eruptions required to produce the large basalt provinces, some researchers believe the eruptions were responsible for the extinction of many of Earth's life-forms.

The comparatively short initial eruptive phase is often followed by millions of years of less voluminous activity, as the plume tail slowly rises to the surface. Extending away from some large flood basalt provinces is a chain of volcanic structures, similar to the Hawaiian chain (Figure 31C).

9 CONCEPT CHECKS

1. Are volcanoes in the Ring of Fire generally described as quiescent or violent? Name an example that supports your answer.
2. How is magma generated along convergent plate boundaries?
3. Volcanism at divergent plate boundaries is most often associated with which rock type? What causes rocks to melt in these settings?
4. What is thought to be the source of magma for most intraplate volcanism?
5. At which of the three types of plate boundaries is the greatest quantity of magma generated?

FIGURE 31 Mantle plumes and large basalt provinces
Model of hot-spot volcanism thought to explain the formation of large basalt provinces and the chains of volcanic islands associated with these features.

10 Monitoring Volcanic Activity

Volcanologists utilize several volcano monitoring techniques, with most of the efforts aimed at detecting the movement of magma from a subterranean reservoir (typically several kilometers deep) toward the surface. The four most noticeable changes in a volcanic landscape caused by the migration of magma are (1) changes in the pattern of earthquakes produced by the movement of magma; (2) magma entering a near-surface magma chamber which leads to inflation of the volcano; (3) changes in the amount and/or composition of gases released from a volcano; and (4) an increase in ground temperature caused by the introduction of new magma.

Almost one-third of all volcanoes that have erupted in historic times are now monitored using seismographs, instruments that detect earthquake tremors. In general, a sharp increase in seismic unrest followed by a period of relative quiet has been shown to be a precursor for many volcanic eruptions. However, some large volcanic structures have exhibited lengthy periods of seismic unrest. For example, in 1981, a strong increase in seismicity was recorded for Rabaul Caldera in New Guinea. The activity lasted 13 years and culminated with an eruption in 1994. Occasionally, a large earthquake triggers a volcanic eruption, or at least disturbs the volcano's plumbing. Hawaii's Kilauea, for example, began to erupt after the strong Kalapana earthquake (magnitude 7.2) of 1975.

The development of remote-sensing devices has greatly enhanced our ability to monitor volcanoes. These instruments and techniques are particularly useful for monitoring eruptions in progress. Photographic images and infrared (heat) sensors can detect lava flows and volcanic columns rising from a volcano (FIGURE 32). Furthermore, satellites can detect ground deformation as well as monitor SO_2 emissions.

Because accessibility to many volcanoes is limited, remote-sensing devices, including lasers, Global Positioning System (GPS) devices, and Earth-orbiting satellites, are often used to determine potential swelling of a volcano (FIGURE 33A). For example, swelling occurs when the roof of a volcano rises as new magma accumulates in its interior—a phenomenon that precedes many volcanic

FIGURE 32 **Monitoring volcanoes using infrared cameras**
Remote-sensing cameras on satellites have greatly enhanced our ability to monitor volcanoes. Infrared (heat) sensors produce false-color images of volcanoes that show hot objects in warm colors and cold objects in cool colors. This image shows an eruption of Mount St. Augustine Volcano, Alaska, that occurred on March 27, 1986.

False color satellite image of Mount St. Augustine that shows the hottest material, the volcanic crater, as yellow. A recently erupted hot pyroclastic flow on the north flank of the volcano appears bright red, while the coldest snow covered areas of the cone appear bright blue. A small lava flow (orange) is shown on the east flank of the cone and several lahars (mudflows) are shown as dark lobes.

NASA

A.

Mount Adams

GPS devices are used to monitor the inflation or deflation of a volcano as magma moves within. Inflation often precedes an eruption phase by a few months, or longer.

FIGURE 33 Monitoring volcanoes
A. A high-precision Global Positioning System (GPS) antenna used to monitor horizontal and vertical ground motions on Mount St. Helens. **B.** Geologist monitoring gas emissions from a fumarole. The analysis of volcanic gases is used in the long-term study of volcanic systems. (Photos courtesy of U.S. Geological Society)

FIGURE 33 Monitoring volcanoes
A. A high-precision Global Positioning System (GPS) antenna used to monitor horizontal and vertical ground motions on Mount St. Helens. **B.** Geologist monitoring gas emissions from a fumarole. The analysis of volcanic gases is used in the long-term study of volcanic systems. (Photos courtesy of U.S. Geological Society)

An increase in sulfur dioxide (SO^2) gas emissions has been shown to precede an eruption.

B.

Each of the four multi-colored rings represents slightly more than one inch (2.8 cm) of elevation change, or a total of 4 inches of ground uplift. The most likely cause is magma accumulation in Earth's crust in the area directly southwest of the Three Sisters volcanic system.

North Sister
South Sister
Broken Top
Mt. Bacheler
Center maximum of uplift

Distance North (km)
30
20
10

Distance East (km)
10
20
30

0   2.8 cm (1 inch)
Elevation change

FIGURE 34 Magma movement detected by satellites
This radar image was produced using satellite data collected over 4 years. The pattern shows that the ground uplifted about 10 centimeters (4 inches), centered on an area directly southwest of Oregon's Three Sisters volcanic area. (Image courtesy of USGS)

composition of the gases being released (FIGURE 33B). Some volcanoes show an increase in sulfur dioxide (SO_2) emissions months or years prior to an eruption.

The overriding goal of all monitoring is to discover precursors that may warn of an impending or imminent eruption. This is accomplished by first diagnosing the current condition of a volcano and using this baseline data to predict its future behavior. Stated another way, a volcano must be observed over an extended period of time to recognize significant changes from its "resting state."

10 CONCEPT CHECKS

1. What four factors do volcanologists monitor in order to determine whether magma is migrating toward Earth's surface?

2. What is the overriding goal of volcano monitoring?

eruptions. The recent discovery of ground doming at Three Sisters Volcanoes in Oregon was first detected using images obtained from satellites (FIGURE 34).

Volcanologists also frequently monitor volcanoes in an effort to detect changes in the quantity and/or

CONCEPTS IN REVIEW: VOLCANOES AND VOLCANIC HAZARDS

1 The nature of volcanic eruptions

Explain why some volcanic eruptions are explosive and others are quiescent.

KEY WORDS viscosity, volatiles, eruption columns

- Volcanoes are places where liquid rock (lava) emerges at Earth's surface.
- Lava has some degree of viscosity (resistance to flow). In general, the more silica in the lava, the more viscous it is. The lower the silica content, the runnier the lava. Another factor that influences viscosity is temperature. Hot lavas are more runny, while cool lavas are more viscous.

- Viscous lavas clog the plumbing of a volcano, allowing great pressures to build up. High-silica, low-temperature lavas are most viscous and allow the greatest amount of pressure to build up before they "let go" in an eruption. In contrast, lavas that are low in silica and hot are most runny. Because basaltic lava is less viscous, much less pressure can build up, and it produces relatively gentle eruptions. Thus, volcanoes that erupt felsic lava (rhyolite) and intermediate lava (andesite) are more dangerous than those that erupt only mafic lava (basalt).

PONDER THE POSSIBILITIES Although Kilauea mostly erupts in a gentle manner, what would be the risks if you chose to live nearby?

2 Materials extruded during a volcanic eruption

List and describe the three categories of materials extruded during volcanic eruptions.

KEY WORDS aa, pahoehoe, lava tube, block lava, pillow lava, pyroclastic materials, tephra

- Volcanoes bring gases and solid chunks to the surface, as well as liquid lava.
- Because of their low viscosity, basaltic lava flows can extend great distances from a volcano. Sometimes they travel over the surface as pahoehoe or aa flows. Sometimes the surface congeals but lava continues to flow below, in tunnels called lava tubes. When lava erupts in water, the outer surface is chilled instantly to obsidian, while the inside continues to flow, producing tube-shaped structures called pillow lavas.
- The gases most commonly emitted by volcanoes are water vapor and carbon dioxide. When these gases reach the surface, their rapid expansion results in explosive power that helps a volcano to "clear its throat" and produces a mass of lava fragments called pyroclastic materials. These hot gases have low densities, so they rise, picking up ash and lapilli to produce spectacular eruption columns.

- If bubbles of gas in the lava don't pop before solidification, they are preserved as voids called vesicles. Especially frothy rhyolitic lava can cool to make pumice, which often floats in water. Mafic lava, with lots of bubbles, cools to make scoria.
- Pyroclastic materials come in several sizes. From smallest to largest, they are ash, lapilli, and blocks or bombs, depending on whether the material left the volcano as solid fragments or as liquid blobs.

Volcanoes erupt solids, liquids, and gases. Mineral crystals that formed during slower cooling underground are carried upward as solid particles, the liquid lava itself crystallizes rapidly into a fine-grained groundmass, and vesicles represent the release of gases that were dissolved in the lava before eruption.

Vesicles (gas)
Phenocrysts (solid)
Groundmass (former liquid)

3 Anatomy of a volcano

Label a diagram that illustrates the basic features of a typical volcanic cone.

KEY WORDS fissure, conduit, vent, volcanic cone, crater, parasitic cone, fumarole

- Volcanoes are varied in form but share a few common features. Most are roughly conical piles of extruded material that collect around a central vent. The vent is usually within a summit crater or caldera. On the flanks of the volcano, there may be smaller vents marked by small parasitic cones, or there may be fumaroles, spots where gas is expelled.

TAG IT Label the diagram: conduit, vent, crater, parasitic cone, fumarole

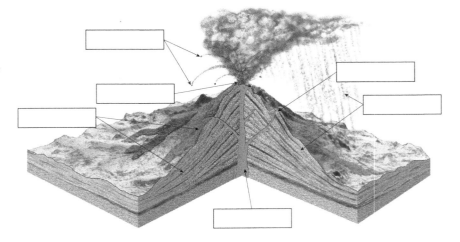

4 Shield volcanoes

Summarize the characteristics of shield volcanoes and provide one example.

KEY WORD shield volcano

• Shield volcanoes are built of many successive lava flows of low-viscosity basaltic lava. Typically, they emerge from oceanic crust and lack significant amounts of pyroclastic debris. Lava tubes help transport lava far from the main vent, resulting in very gentle, shield-like profiles.

• Most shield volcanoes are associated with hot-spot volcanism, and the volcanoes of Kilauea, Mauna Loa, and Mauna Kea in Hawaii are classic examples of the low, wide form.

QUANTIFY IT The formula for the volume of a cone is $V = 1/3\pi r^2 h$. If Mauna Loa is 9 km high and has a radius of roughly 85 km, what is its total volume?

5 Cinder cones

Describe the formation, size, and composition of cinder cones.

KEY WORDS cinder cone, scoria

• Cinder cones are steep-sided structures composed mainly of pyroclastic debris that typically have a basaltic composition. Lava flows are not a significant part of a cinder cone, but lava flows sometimes emerge from the bases of cinder cones.

• Cinder cones are small compared to the other major kinds of volcanoes, reflecting the fact that they form quickly, as single eruptive events. Because they are unconsolidated, cinder cones don't stand up well to weathering and erosion.

LASTING EFFECTS If you had a time machine and were going to move 4 million years into the future, would a shield volcano or a cinder volcano make a more reliable landmark, still around after all that time? Explain.

6 Composite volcanoes

Discuss the formation, distribution, and characteristics of composite volcanoes.

KEY WORDS composite volcano, stratovolcano

• Composite volcanoes are called "composite" because they consist of both pyroclastic material and lava flows. They typically erupt silica-rich lavas that cool to produce andesite or rhyolite. They are much larger than cinder cones and form from multiple eruptions over millions of years.

• Because the andesitic or rhyolitic lava erupted from composite volcanoes is more viscous than basaltic lava, it piles up to a steeper angle than does the lava from shield volcanoes. Over time, a composite volcano's combination of lava and cinders produces a towering volcano with a classic "Hershey's kiss" shape.

• Mount Rainier and the other volcanoes of the Cascade Range in the northwest United States are good examples of composite volcanoes, as are the other volcanoes of the Pacific Ocean's "Ring of Fire."

CRITICAL COMPARISON If your family had to live next to a shield volcano, a cinder cone, or a composite volcano, which one would you pick, and why?

7 Volcanic hazards

Discuss the major geologic hazards associated with volcanoes.

KEY WORDS pyroclastic flow, nuée ardente, lahar, tsunami, sulfur dioxide, aerosol

• The greatest volcanic hazard to human life is the pyroclastic flow, or nuée ardente. This dense mix of hot gas and pyroclastic fragments races downhill at great speed, like a snow avalanche. A pyroclastic flow can travel many miles from its source volcano, following the contours of the landscape. Because pyroclastic flows are hot, their deposits frequently "weld" together into a solid rock called welded tuff. Pyroclastic flows incinerate everything in their path.

• Lahars are volcanic mudflows. These rapidly moving slurries of ash and debris suspended in water can occur even when a volcano isn't actively erupting, and they can overwhelm people or villages in their path.

• Volcanic ash in the atmosphere can be a risk to air travel if it is sucked into airplane engines. Volcanoes at sea level can generate tsunamis when they erupt or when their flanks collapse into the ocean. Finally, volcanoes that spew large amounts of gas, such as sulfur dioxide, can cause human respiratory problems. If these gases reach the stratosphere, they screen out a portion of incoming solar radiation and can trigger short-term cooling at Earth's surface.

ACTION PLAN What do lahars and pyroclastic flows have in common? What's the best strategy for people to avoid the worst effects of lahars and pyroclastic flows?

8 Other volcanic landforms

List and describe volcanic landforms other than shield, cinder, and composite volcanoes.

KEY WORDS caldera, fissure, large igneous province, fissure eruption, flood basalt, lava dome, volcanic neck, pipe

- Calderas are among the largest volcanic structures. They form when the stiff, cold rock above a magma chamber cannot be supported and collapses, creating a broad, bowl-like depression. On shield volcanoes, calderas form slowly, as lava is drained from the magma chamber beneath the volcano. On a composite volcano, caldera collapse can be a catastrophic event.
- Lava domes are thick masses of high-viscosity, silica-rich lava that accumulate in the summit crater or caldera of a composite volcano. When they collapse, lava domes can produce extensive pyroclastic flows.

- Fissure eruptions produce massive floods of low-viscosity, silica-poor lava from large cracks in the crust. Layer upon layer of these flood basalts may build up to significant thicknesses, as in the Columbia Plateau or the Deccan Traps, but their defining feature is the broad areas they cover.
- A superb example of a volcanic neck is preserved at Shiprock, New Mexico. Because the lava in the "throat" of this ancient volcano crystallized to form a "plug" of solid rock, it has weathered more slowly than the conical volcano in which it formed. Now, after the mound of pyroclastic debris has been eroded away, the resistant neck stands up as a distinctive landform.

RISK RANK   If you were to rank volcanic landforms in terms of the risk they pose to humans, which would be the most risky landform to encounter, and which would be relatively safe?

9 Plate tectonics and volcanic activity

Relate the types and distribution of volcanic activity to plate tectonics.

KEY WORDS Ring of Fire, volcanic island arc, continental volcanic arc, intraplate volcanism, mantle plume

- Volcanoes occur at both convergent and divergent plate boundaries, and also in intraplate settings. Different mechanisms supply the magma for each.
- Convergent plate boundaries that involve the subduction of oceanic crust are the sites where the explosive volcanoes of the Pacific Ring of Fire form. Here, release of water from the subducted plate triggers melting in the adjacent mantle. The resulting magma interacts with the lower crust of the overlying plate during its ascent and results in the formation of a volcanic arc at the surface.
- At divergent boundaries, decompression melting is the dominant generator of magma. As warm rock rises, it can begin to melt without the addition of heat. The result will be a rift valley if the overlying crust is continental, or a mid-ocean ridge if it is oceanic.

- In an intraplate setting, the source of magma is a mantle plume: a column of warm, rising solid rock in the mantle.

EVIDENCE OF ABSENCE   Is there a plate tectonic setting where volcanoes are unlikely? If so, what is it?

10 Monitoring volcanic activity

List and describe the techniques used to monitor potentially dangerous volcanoes.

- Volcanoes give off physical signals, which volcanologists monitor for signs that a volcano is getting ready to erupt.
- Volcano monitoring involves observing changes in the shape of a volcano, earthquakes beneath a volcano that could signal magma movement, the composition and quantity of its gas output, and its temperature.

UH-OH   Which of the volcano-monitoring techniques would have been most obvious before the May 1980 eruption of Mount St. Helens?

GIVE IT SOME THOUGHT

1. Match each of the following volcanic landforms with the principle zone of volcanism (convergent plate boundaries, divergent plate boundaries, or intraplate volcanism) with which it is associated:
   a. Crater Lake
   b. Hawaii's Kilauea
   c. Mount St. Helens
   d. East African Rift
   e. Yellowstone
   f. Mount Pelée
   g. Deccan Plateau
   h. Fujiyama

2. Examine the accompanying photo and complete the following:
   a. What type of volcano is it? What features helped you classify it as such?
   b. What is the eruptive style of such volcanoes? Describe the likely composition and viscosity of its magma.
   c. Which of the three zones of volcanism is the likely setting for this volcano?
   d. Name a city that is vulnerable to the effects of a volcano of this type.

3. Divergent boundaries, such as the Mid-Atlantic Ridge, are characterized by outpourings of basaltic lava. Answer the following questions about divergent boundaries and their associated lavas:
   a. What is the source of these lavas?
   b. What causes the source rocks to melt?
   c. Describe a divergent boundary that would generate lavas with a large range of compositions.

4. For each of the accompanying four sketches, identify the geologic setting (zone of volcanism). Which of these settings will most likely generate explosive eruptions? Which will produce outpouring of fluid basaltic lavas?

5. Assume that you want to monitor a volcano that has erupted several times in the recent past but appears to be quiet now. How might you determine if magma were actually moving through the crust beneath the volcano? Suggest at least two phenomena you would observe or measure.

6. Examine the accompanying photo and identify the volcanic landform shown.

7. Imagine that you are a geologist charged with the task of choosing three sites (anywhere in the world) where state-of-the-art volcano-monitoring systems will be deployed. What criteria would you use to select these sites? List some potential choices and your reasons for considering them.

8. Explain why an eruption of Mount Rainier, similar to the one that occurred at Mount St. Helens in 1980, would be considerably more destructive.

9. The accompanying image shows a geologist at the end of a large flow consisting of dense lava blocks that traveled down the flank of Mount Augustine.
   a. What is this type of flow called?
   b. What do volcanologists call the structure composed of broken lava blocks (emitting steam) visible near the summit of this volcano?

MasteringGeology™

Glossary

Aa flow A type of lava flow that has a jagged, blocky surface.

Block lava Lava that has a surface of angular blocks associated with material having andesitic and rhyolitic compositions.

Caldera A large depression typically caused by collapse or ejection of the summit area of a volcano.

Cinder cone A rather small volcano built primarily of ejected lava fragments that consist mostly of pea- to walnut-size lapilli.

Composite cone A volcano composed of both lava flows and pyroclastic material.

Conduit A pipelike opening through which magma moves toward Earth's surface. It terminates at a surface opening called a vent.

Continental volcanic arc Mountains formed in part by igneous activity associated with the subduction of oceanic lithosphere beneath a continent. Examples include the Andes and the Cascades.

Crater The depression at the summit of a volcano or a depression that is produced by a meteorite impact.

Eruption column Buoyant plumes of hot, ash-laden gases that can extend thousands of meters into the atmosphere.

Fissure A crack in rock along which there is a distinct separation.

Fissure eruption An eruption in which lava is extruded from narrow fractures or cracks in the crust.

Flood basalts Flows of basaltic lava that issue from numerous cracks or fissures and commonly cover extensive areas to thicknesses of hundreds of meters.

Fumarole A vent in a volcanic area from which fumes or gases escape.

Intraplate volcanism Igneous activity that occurs within a tectonic plate, away from plate boundaries.

Lahar A debris flow on the slopes of a volcano that results when unstable layers of ash and debris become saturated and flow downslope, usually following stream channels.

Large igneous province Voluminous accumulations of lava extruded along fissures that produce broad, flat features that are also referred to as basalt plateaus.

Lava Magma that reaches Earth's surface.

Lava tube A tunnel in hardened lava that acts as a horizontal conduit for lava flowing from a volcanic vent. Lava tubes allow fluid lavas to advance great distances.

Magma A body of molten rock found at depth, including any dissolved gases and crystals.

Mantle plume A mass of hotter-than-typical mantle material that ascends toward the surface, where it may lead to igneous activity. These plumes of solid yet mobile material may originate as deep as the core–mantle boundary.

Nuée ardente Incandescent volcanic debris buoyed up by hot gases that moves downslope in an avalanche fashion.

Pahoehoe flow A lava flow with a smooth to ropy surface.

Parasitic cone A volcanic cone that forms on the flank of a larger volcano.

Pipe A vertical conduit through which magmatic materials have passed.

Pyroclastic flow A highly heated mixture, largely of ash and pumice fragments, that travels down the flanks of a volcano or along the surface of the ground.

Pyroclastic material The volcanic rock ejected during an eruption. Pyroclastics include ash, bombs, and blocks.

Ring of Fire The zone of active volcanoes surrounding the Pacific Ocean.

Scoria Vesicular ejecta that is the product of basaltic magma.

Shield volcano A broad, gently sloping volcano built from fluid basaltic lavas.

Stratovolcano See *Composite cone*.

Sulfur dioxide A gas with the chemical formula SO_2, that is associated naturally with volcanic activity, and as a waste gas (air pollutant) with the burning of fossil fuels and various industrial processes.

Tephra See *Pyroclastic materials*.

Tsunami The Japanese word for a seismic sea wave.

Vent The surface opening of a conduit or pipe.

Viscosity A measure of a fluid's resistance to flow.

Volcanic cone A cone-shaped structure built by successive eruptions of lava and/or pyroclastic materials.

Volcanic island arc A chain of volcanic islands generally located a few hundred kilometers from a trench where there is active subduction of one oceanic plate beneath another.

Volcanic neck An isolated, steep-sided, erosional remnant consisting of lava that once occupied the vent of a volcano.

Weathering
and Soil

From Chapter 6 of *Earth: An Introduction to Physical Geology*, Eleventh Edition. Edward J. Tarbuck, Frederick K. Lutgens, Dennis Tasa.

Weathering and Soil

Weathering shaped these rock formations in California's Mohave Desert.   (Photo by Bob Allen/Aurora Open/SuperStock)

Each statement represents the primary learning objective for the corresponding major heading within the chapter. After you complete the chapter you should be able to:

1   Define *weathering* and distinguish between the two main categories of weathering.
2   List and describe four examples of mechanical weathering.
3   Discuss the role of water in each of three chemical weathering processes.
4   Summarize the factors that influence the type and rate of rock weathering.
5   Define *soil* and explain why it is referred to as an *interface*.
6   List and briefly discuss five controls of soil formation.
7   Sketch, label, and describe an idealized soil profile.
8   Explain the need for classifying soils.
9   Discuss the detrimental impact of human activities on soil.

Earth's surface is constantly changing. Rock is disintegrated and decomposed, moved to lower elevations by gravity, and carried away by water, wind, or ice. In this manner Earth's physical landscape is sculpted. This chapter focuses on the first step of this never-ending process— weathering. What causes solid rock to crumble, and why do the type and rate of weathering vary from place to place? Soil, an important product of the weathering process and a vital resource, is also examined.

Weathered sandstone towers in the Sahara Desert. (Photo by Jimmy Chin/Aurora Photos/Alamy Images)

1 Weathering

Weathering involves the physical breakdown (disintegration) and chemical alteration (decomposition) of rock at or near Earth's surface. Weathering goes on all around us, but it seems like such a slow and subtle process that it is easy to underestimate its importance. Yet weathering is a basic part of the rock cycle and thus a key process in the Earth system. Weathering is also important to humans—even to those of us who are not studying geology. For example, many of the life-sustaining minerals and elements found in soil, and ultimately in the food we eat, were freed from solid rock by weathering processes. As the chapter-opening photo, FIGURE 1, and many other images in this text illustrate, weathering also contributes to the formation of some of Earth's most spectacular scenery. Of course these same processes are also responsible for causing the deterioration of many of the structures we build.

There are two basic categories of weathering. **Mechanical weathering** is accomplished by physical forces that break rock into smaller and smaller pieces without changing the rock's mineral composition. **Chemical weathering** involves a chemical transformation of rock into one or more new compounds. These two concepts can be illustrated with a large log. The log disintegrates when it is split into smaller and smaller pieces, whereas decomposition occurs when the log is set afire and burned.

Why does rock weather? Simply, weathering is the response of Earth materials to a changing environment. For instance, after millions of years of uplift and erosion, the rocks overlying a large, intrusive igneous body may be removed, exposing it at the surface. This mass of crystalline rock—formed deep below ground where temperatures and pressures are high—is now subjected to a very different and comparatively hostile surface environment. In response, this rock mass will gradually change. This transformation of rock is what we call weathering.

In the following sections we will examine the various types of mechanical and chemical weathering. Although we will consider these two categories separately, keep in mind that mechanical and chemical weathering processes usually work simultaneously in nature and reinforce each other.

1 CONCEPT CHECKS

1. What are the two basic categories of weathering?
2. How do the products of each category differ?

FIGURE 1 **Arches National Park**
Mechanical and chemical weathering contributed greatly to the formation of the arches and other rock formations in Utah's Arches National Park.
(Photo by Whit Richardson/Aurora Open/SuperStock)

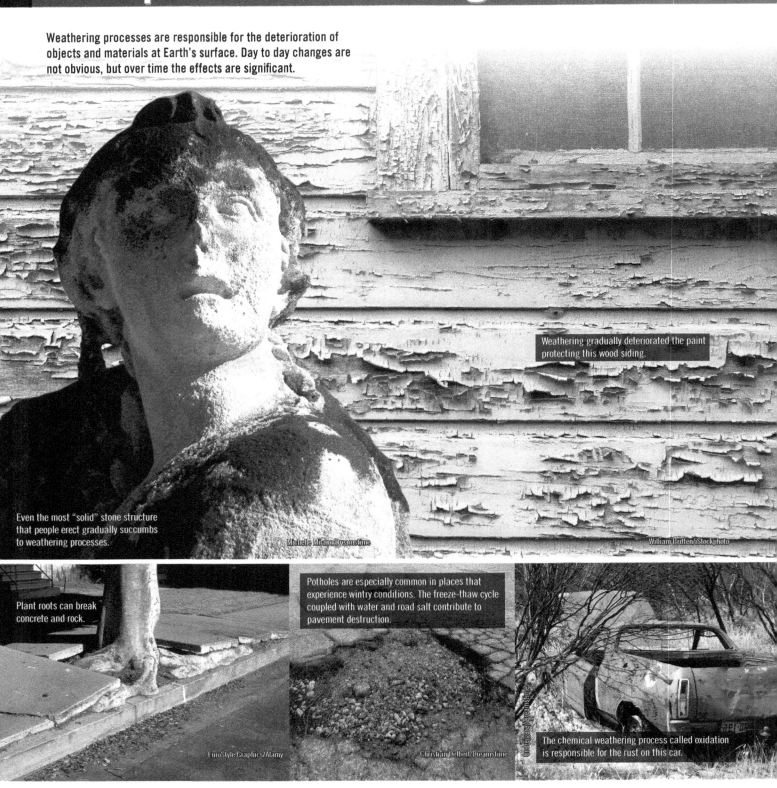

Some Everyday Examples of Weathering

Weathering processes are responsible for the deterioration of objects and materials at Earth's surface. Day to day changes are not obvious, but over time the effects are significant.

Weathering gradually deteriorated the paint protecting this wood siding.

William Britten/iStockphoto

Even the most "solid" stone structure that people erect gradually succumbs to weathering processes.

Michelle Milano/Dreamstime

Plant roots can break concrete and rock.

EuroStyle Graphics/Alamy

Potholes are especially common in places that experience wintry conditions. The freeze-thaw cycle coupled with water and road salt contribute to pavement destruction.

Christian Delbert/Dreamstime

The chemical weathering process called oxidation is responsible for the rust on this car.

2 | Mechanical Weathering

When a rock undergoes *mechanical weathering*, it is broken into smaller and smaller pieces, each retaining the characteristics of the original material. The end result is many small pieces from a single large one. FIGURE 2 shows that breaking a rock into smaller pieces increases the surface area available for chemical attack. An analogous situation occurs when sugar is added to a liquid. In this situation, a cube of sugar will dissolve much more slowly than an equal volume of sugar granules because the cube has much less surface area available for dissolution. Hence, by breaking rocks into smaller pieces, mechanical weathering increases the amount of surface area available for chemical weathering.

In nature, four important physical processes lead to the fragmentation of rock: frost wedging, salt crystal growth, expansion resulting from un- loading, and biological activ- ity. In addition, although the work of erosional agents such as wind, waves, glacial ice, and running water is usually considered separately from mechanical weathering, it is nevertheless related. As these mobile agents transport rock debris, particles continue to be broken and abraded.

As mechanical weathering breaks rock into smaller pieces, more surface area is exposed to chemical weathering.

4 square units × 6 sides × 1 cube = **24 square units**

1 square unit × 6 sides × 8 cubes = **48 square units**

.25 square unit × 6 sides × 64 cubes = **96 square units**

Increase in surface area

SMARTFIGURE 2
Mechanical weathering increases surface area
Mechanical weathering adds to the effectiveness of chemical weathering be- cause chemical weathering can occur only on exposed surfaces.

Frost Wedging

If you leave a glass bottle of water in the freezer a bit too long, you will find the bottle fractured, as in FIGURE 3. The bottle breaks because liquid water has the unique property of expanding about 9 percent upon freezing. This is also the reason that poorly insulated or exposed water pipes rupture during frigid weather. You might

also expect this same process to fracture rocks in nature. This is, in fact, the basis for the traditional explanation of **frost wedging**. After water works its way into the cracks in rock, the freezing water enlarges the cracks, and angu- lar fragments are eventually produced (FIGURE 4).

FIGURE 3 Ice breaks bottle
The bottle broke because water expands about 9 percent when it freezes. (Photo by Bill Aron/Photo Edit)

SMARTFIGURE 4 Ice breaks rock
In mountainous areas frost wedging creates angular rock fragments that ac- cumulate to form talus slopes. (Photo by Marli Miller)

Frost wedging

Slightly tilted sedimentary beds

Falling rock debris

Falling rock debris

Patches of snow

Talus slope composed of angular rock fragments

For many years, the conventional wisdom was that most frost wedging occurred in this way. Recently, however, research has shown that frost wedging can also occur in a different way.* It has long been known that when moist soils freeze, they expand, or *frost heave*, due to the growth of ice lenses. These masses of ice grow larger because they are supplied with water migrating from unfrozen areas as thin liquid films. As more water accumulates and freezes, the soil is heaved upward. A similar process occurs within the cracks and pore spaces of rocks. Lenses of ice grow larger as they attract liquid water from surrounding pores. The growth of these ice masses gradually weakens the rock, causing it to fracture.

Salt Crystal Growth

Another expansive force that can split rocks is created by the growth of salt crystals. Rocky shorelines and arid regions are common settings for this process. It begins when sea spray from breaking waves or salty groundwater penetrates crevices and pore spaces in rock. As this water evaporates, salt crystals form. As these crystals gradually grow larger, they weaken the rock by pushing apart the surrounding grains or enlarging tiny cracks.

*Bernard Hallet, "Why Do Freezing Rocks Break?" *Science* 314(17): 1092–1093, November 2006.

This same process can also contribute to crumbling roadways where salt is spread to melt snow and ice in winter. The salt dissolves in water and seeps into cracks that quite likely originated from frost action. When the water evaporates, the growth of salt crystals further breaks the pavement.

Sheeting

When large masses of igneous rock, particularly granite, are exposed by erosion, concentric slabs begin to break loose. The process that generates these onion-like layers is called **sheeting**. It takes place, at least in part, due to the great reduction in pressure that occurs as the overlying rock is eroded away, a process called *unloading*. FIGURE 5 illustrates what happens: As the overburden is removed, the outer parts of the granitic mass expand more than the rock below and separate from the rock body. Continued weathering eventually causes the slabs to separate and spall off, creating an **exfoliation dome** (*ex* = off, *folium* = leaf). Excellent examples of exfoliation domes are Stone Mountain, Georgia, and Half Dome and Liberty Cap in Yosemite National Park.

Other examples illustrate how rock behaves when the confining pressure is greatly reduced and thus support the process of unloading as the cause of sheeting. In deep mines, large rock slabs have been known to explode off the walls of newly cut tunnels. In quarries, fractures occur parallel to the floor when large blocks of rock are removed.

SMARTFIGURE 5
Unloading leads to sheeting
Sheeting leads to the formation of an exfoliation dome. (Photo by Gary Moon/AGE Fotostock America, Inc.)

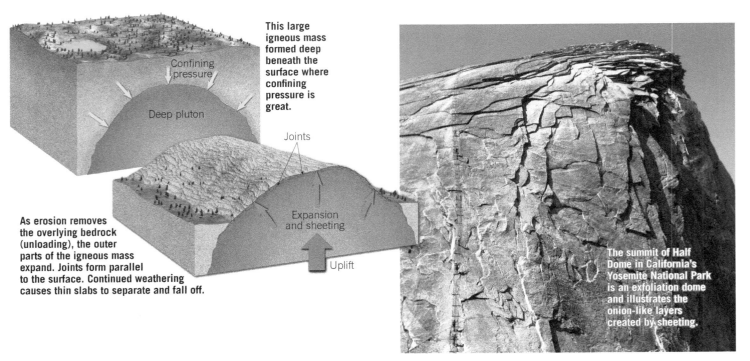

This large igneous mass formed deep beneath the surface where confining pressure is great.

As erosion removes the overlying bedrock (unloading), the outer parts of the igneous mass expand. Joints form parallel to the surface. Continued weathering causes thin slabs to separate and fall off.

Confining pressure · Deep pluton · Joints · Expansion and sheeting · Uplift

The summit of Half Dome in California's Yosemite National Park is an exfoliation dome and illustrates the onion-like layers created by sheeting.

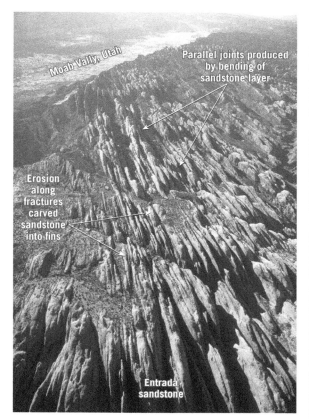

FIGURE 6 Joints aid weathering
Aerial view of nearly parallel joints near Moab, Utah. (Photo by Michael Collier)

Although many fractures are created by expansion, others are produced by contraction during the crystallization of magma, and still others are produced by tectonic forces during mountain building. Fractures produced by these activities generally form a definite pattern and are called *joints* (FIGURE 6). Joints are important rock structures that allow water to penetrate to depth and start the process of weathering long before the rock is exposed.

Biological Activity

Weathering can be accomplished by the activities of organisms, including plants, burrowing animals, and humans. Plant roots in search of nutrients and water grow into fractures, and as the roots grow, they wedge the rock apart (FIGURE 7). Burrowing animals further break down rock by moving fresh material to the surface, where physical and chemical processes can more effectively attack it. Decaying organisms also produce acids that contribute to chemical weathering. Where rock has been blasted in search of minerals or for road construction, the impact of humans is particularly noticeable.

FIGURE 7 Plants can break rock
Root wedging near Boulder, Colorado. (Photo by Kristin Piljay)

2 CONCEPT CHECKS

1. When a rock is mechanically weathered, how does its surface area change? How does this influence chemical weathering?
2. Explain how water can cause mechanical weathering.
3. How does an exfoliation dome form?
4. How do joints promote weathering?
5. How does biological activity contribute to weathering?

The Old Man of the Mountain

The Old Man of the Mountain in New Hampshire's Franconia State Park was one of the most famous rock faces. From forehead to chin his profile measured 12 meters (40 feet). On May 3, 2003, this iconic feature, weakened by weathering, collapsed.

The Old Man of the Mountain as it appeared **before** May 3, 2003. The state emblem featured the famous rock face.

The famous granite outcrop **after** it collapsed on May 3, 2003. The collapse ended decades of efforts to protect and reinforce the state symbol from the same natural processes that created it in the first place. Ultimately frost wedging and other weathering processes prevailed.

Jim Cole/AP Photo

Nina Shannon/iStockphoto

The New Hampshire quarter featured the state emblem with the Old Man.

Jim Cole/AP Photo

EYE on Earth

This is a close-up view of a massive granite feature in the Sierra Nevada of California. (Photo by Marli Miller)

Question 1 Relatively thin slabs of granite are separating from this rock mass. Describe the process that caused this to occur.

Question 2 What term is applied to this process? What term describes the dome-like feature that results?

3 Chemical Weathering

In the preceding discussion of mechanical weathering, you learned that breaking rock into smaller pieces aids chemical weathering by increasing the surface area available for chemical attack. It should also be pointed out that chemical weathering contributes to mechanical weathering. It does so by weakening the outer portions of some rocks, which, in turn, makes them more susceptible to being broken by mechanical weathering processes.

Chemical weathering involves the complex processes that break down rock components and internal structures of minerals. Such processes convert the constituents to new minerals or release them to the surrounding environment. During this transformation, the original rock decomposes into substances that are stable in the surface environment. Consequently, the products of chemical weathering will remain essentially unchanged as long as they remain in an environment similar to the one in which they formed.

Water is by far the most important agent of chemical weathering. Pure water alone is a good solvent, and small amounts of dissolved materials result in increased chemical activity for weathering solutions. The major processes of chemical weathering are dissolution, oxidation, and hydrolysis. Water plays a leading role in each.

Dissolution

Perhaps the easiest type of decomposition to envision is the process of **dissolution**. Just as sugar dissolves in water, so too do certain minerals. One of the most water-soluble minerals is halite (common salt), which, as you may recall, is composed of sodium and chloride ions. Halite readily dissolves in water because, although this compound maintains overall electrical neutrality, the individual ions retain their respective charges.

Moreover, the surrounding water molecules are polar—that is, the oxygen end of the molecule has a small residual negative charge; the hydrogen end has a small positive charge. As the water molecules come in contact with halite, their negative ends approach sodium ions and their positive ends cluster about chloride ions. This disrupts the attractive forces in the halite crystal and releases the ions to the water solution (FIGURE 8).

Although most minerals are, for all practical purposes, insoluble in pure water, the presence of even a small amount of acid dramatically increases the corrosive force of water—thus causing dissolution. (An acidic solution contains the reactive hydrogen ion, H^+.) In nature, acids are produced by a number of processes. For example, carbonic acid is created when carbon dioxide in the atmosphere dissolves in raindrops. As acidic rainwater soaks into the ground, carbon dioxide in the soil may increase the acidity of

Water molecules are polar because both hydrogen atoms bond to the same side of an oxygen atom. Thus, the hydrogen side of the molecule is slightly positive and the oxygen side is slightly negative.

Halite crystals consist of ions that are attracted to polar water molecules.

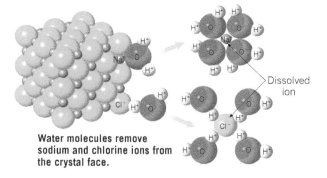

Water molecules remove sodium and chlorine ions from the crystal face.

Dissolved ion

FIGURE 8 Water can dissolve some rocks Dissolution is chemical weathering in which minerals dissolve in water. Halite readily dissolves in pure water. Other minerals, such as calcite, readily dissolve only in water that is acidic.

the weathering solution. Various organic acids are also released into the soil as organisms decay, and sulfuric acid is produced by the weathering of pyrite and other sulfide minerals.

Regardless of the source of the acid, this highly reactive substance readily decomposes most rocks and produces certain products that are water soluble. For example, the mineral calcite, $CaCO_3$, which composes the common building stones marble and limestone, is easily attacked by even a weakly acidic solution.

The overall reaction by which calcite dissolves in water containing carbon dioxide is:

$$CaCO_3 + (H^+ + HCO_3^-) \longrightarrow Ca^{2+} + 2\,HCO_3^-$$

calcite   carbonic acid   calcium ion   bicarbonate ion

During this process, the insoluble calcium carbonate is transformed into soluble products. In nature, over periods of thousands of years, large quantities of limestone are dissolved and carried away by underground water. This activity is largely responsible for the formation of limestone caverns (FIGURE 9). Monuments and buildings made of limestone or marble are also subjected to the corrosive work of acids, particularly in urban and industrial areas that have smoggy, polluted air.

The soluble ions from reactions of this type are retained in our underground water supply. It is these dissolved ions that are responsible for the so-called hard water found in many locales. Simply, hard water is undesirable because the active ions react with soap to produce an insoluble material that renders soap nearly useless in removing dirt. To solve this problem, a water softener can be used to remove these ions, generally by replacing them with others that do not chemically react with soap.

Oxidation

Everyone has seen iron and steel objects that have rusted when exposed to water. The same thing can happen to iron-rich minerals. The process of rusting occurs when oxygen combines with iron to form iron oxide, as follows:

$$4\,\underset{\text{iron}}{Fe} + 3\,\underset{\text{oxygen}}{O_2} \longrightarrow 2\,\underset{\text{iron oxide (hematite)}}{Fe_2O_3}$$

This type of chemical reaction, called **oxidation**,[*] occurs when electrons are lost from one element during the reaction. In this case, we say that iron was oxidized because it lost electrons to oxygen. Although the oxidation of iron progresses very slowly in a dry environment, the addition of water greatly speeds the reaction.

Oxidation is important in decomposing such ferromagnesian minerals as olivine, pyroxene, hornblende, and biotite. Oxygen readily combines with the iron in these minerals to form the reddish-brown iron oxide called *hematite* (Fe_2O_3) or in other cases a yellowish-colored rust called *limonite* [$FeO(OH)$]. These products are responsible for the rusty color on the surfaces of dark igneous rocks, such as basalt, as they begin to weather. Hematite and limonite are also important cementing and coloring agents in many sedimentary rocks (FIGURE 10). However, oxidation can occur only after iron is freed from the silicate structure by another process, called *hydrolysis*.

Another important oxidation reaction occurs when sulfide minerals such as pyrite decompose. Sulfide minerals are major constituents of many metallic ores, and pyrite is frequently associated with coal deposits

---

[*]Note that *oxidation* is a term that refers to any chemical reaction in which a compound or radical loses electrons. The element oxygen is not necessarily present.

FIGURE 10 Iron oxides add color
Many sedimentary rocks are very colorful. The most important "pigments" are small amounts of iron oxides. Hematite produces orange, red, and pink hues. These rocks are in Red Rock Country near Sedona, Arizona. (Photo by Prisma/SuperStock)

as well. In a moist environment, chemical weathering of pyrite (FeS_2) yields sulfuric acid (H_2SO_4) and iron oxide [$FeO(OH)$]. In many mining locales, this weathering process creates a serious environmental hazard, particularly in humid areas where abundant rainfall infiltrates spoil banks (waste material left after coal or other minerals are removed). This so-called acid mine drainage eventually makes its way to streams, killing aquatic organisms and degrading aquatic habitats (FIGURE 11).

Acid mine drainage

FIGURE 11 Acid mine drainage
The water seeping from an abandoned mine in Clarion County, Pennsylvania, is an example of *acid mine drainage.* Acid mine drainage is water with a high concentration of sulfuric acid (H_2SO_4) produced by the oxidation of sulfide minerals such as pyrite. When such acid-rich water migrates from its source, it may pollute surface waters and groundwater and cause significant ecological damage. (Photo by Joel Bosch.)

Hydrolysis

The most common mineral group, the silicates, is decomposed primarily by the process of **hydrolysis** (*hydro* = water, *lysis* = a loosening), which basically is the reaction of any substance with water. Ideally, the hydrolysis of a mineral could take place in pure water as some of the water molecules dissociate to form the very reactive hydrogen (H^+) and hydroxyl (OH^-) ions. It is the hydrogen ion that attacks and replaces other positive ions found in the crystal lattice. With the introduction of hydrogen ions into the crystalline structure, the original orderly arrangement of atoms is destroyed, and the mineral decomposes.

Hydrolysis in the Presence of Acids

In nature, water usually contains other substances that contribute additional hydrogen ions, thereby greatly accelerating hydrolysis. The most common of these substances is carbon dioxide, CO_2, which dissolves in water to form carbonic acid, H_2CO_3. Rain dissolves some carbon dioxide in the atmosphere, and additional amounts, released by decaying organic matter, are acquired as the water percolates through the soil.

In water, carbonic acid ionizes to form hydrogen ions (H^+) and bicarbonate ions (HCO_3^-). To illustrate how a rock undergoes hydrolysis in the presence of carbonic acid, let's examine the chemical weathering of granite, a common continental rock. Recall that granite consists mainly of quartz and potassium feldspar. The weathering of the potassium feldspar component of granite is as follows:

$$2\ \underset{\substack{\text{potassium}\\\text{feldspar}}}{KAlSi_3O_8} + 2\underset{\text{carbonic acid}}{(H^+ + HCO_3^-)} + \underset{\text{water}}{H_2O} \longrightarrow$$

$$\underset{\substack{\text{kaolinite}\\\text{(residual clay)}}}{Al_2Si_2O_5(OH)_4} + \underset{\substack{\text{potassium}\\\text{ion}}}{2\ K^+} + \underset{\substack{\text{bicarbonate}\\\text{ion}}}{2\ HCO_3^-} + \underset{\text{silica}}{4\ SiO_2}$$

in solution

In this reaction, the hydrogen ions (H^+) attack and replace potassium ions (K^+) in the feldspar structure, thereby disrupting the crystalline network. Once removed, the potassium is available as a nutrient for plants or becomes the soluble salt potassium bicarbonate ($KHCO_3$), which may be incorporated into other minerals or carried to the ocean.

Products of Silicate-Mineral Weathering

The most abundant product of the chemical breakdown of potassium feldspar is the clay mineral kaolinite. Clay minerals are the end products of weathering and are very stable under surface conditions. Consequently, clay minerals make up a high percentage of the inorganic material in soils. Moreover, the most abundant sedimentary rock, shale, contains a high proportion of clay minerals.

In addition to the formation of clay minerals during the weathering of potassium feldspar, some silica is removed from the feldspar structure and carried away by groundwater. This dissolved silica will eventually precipitate, producing nodules of chert or flint, or it will fill in the pore spaces between grains of sediment, or it will be carried to the ocean, where microscopic animals will remove it from the water to build hard silica shells.

To summarize, the weathering of potassium feldspar generates a residual clay mineral, a soluble salt (potassium bicarbonate), and some silica, which enters into solution.

Quartz, the other main component of granite, is very resistant to chemical weathering; it remains substantially unaltered when attacked by weak acidic solutions. As a result, when granite weathers, the feldspar crystals dull and slowly turn to clay, releasing the once interlocked quartz grains, which still retain their fresh, glassy appearance. Although some of the quartz remains in the soil, much is eventually transported to the sea or to other sites of deposition, where it becomes the main constituent of such features as sandy beaches and sand dunes.

EYE on Earth

This sample of granite is rich in potassium feldspar and quartz. There are minor quantities of biotite and hornblende.

Question 1 If this rock were to undergo chemical weathering, how would its minerals change? Describe the products you would expect to result from each of the minerals in the sample.

Question 2 Would all of the minerals decompose? If not, which mineral would likely be most resistant and remain relatively intact?

E.J. Tarbuck

TABLE 1	Products of Chemical Weathering	
Mineral	Residual Products	Material in Solution
Quartz	Quartz grains	Silica
Feldspars	Clay minerals	Silica, K^+, Na^+, Ca^{2+}
Amphibole (hornblende)	Clay minerals Limonite Hematite	Silica Ca^{2+}, Mg^{2+}
Olivine	Limonite Hematite	Silica Mg^{2+}

In time these quartz grains may be lithified to form the sedimentary rock sandstone.

TABLE 1 lists the weathered products of some of the most common silicate minerals. Remember that silicate minerals make up most of Earth's crust and that these minerals are essentially composed of only eight elements. When chemically weathered, the silicate minerals yield sodium, calcium, potassium, and magnesium ions that form soluble products, which may be removed from groundwater. The element iron combines with oxygen, producing relatively insoluble iron oxides, most notably hematite and limonite, which give soil a reddish-brown or yellowish color. Under most conditions, the three remaining elements—aluminum, silicon, and oxygen—join with water to produce residual clay minerals. However, even the highly insoluble clay minerals are very slowly removed by subsurface water.

Spheroidal Weathering

Many rock outcrops have a rounded appearance. This occurs because chemical weathering works inward from exposed surfaces. FIGURE 12 illustrates how angular masses of jointed rock change through time. The process is aptly called **spheroidal weathering**. Because weathering attacks edges from two sides and corners from three sides, these areas wear down faster than a single flat surface. Gradually, sharp edges and corners become smooth and rounded. Eventually an angular block may evolve into a nearly spherical boulder. Once this occurs, the boulder's shape does not change, but the spherical mass continues to get smaller.

3 CONCEPT CHECKS

1. How is carbonic acid formed in nature?
2. What occurs when carbonic acid reacts with calcite-rich rocks such as limestone?
3. What products result when carbonic acid reacts with potassium feldspar?
4. List several minerals that are especially susceptible to oxidation and list two common products of oxidation.
5. Explain why angular masses of rock often become spherical boulders.

SMARTFIGURE 12
The formation of rounded boulders
Spheroidal weathering of extensively jointed rock.
(Photo by E. J. Tarbuck)

Water penetrates extensively jointed rock

Chemical weathering decomposes minerals and enlarges joints

Rocks are attacked more on corners and edges and take on a spherical shape

Spheroidal weathering in Joshua Tree National Park, California

TIME

Weathering attacks an edge on two sides

Weathering attacks a corner on three sides

Weathering attacks a face on one side

4 Rates of Weathering

Several factors influence the type and rate of rock weathering. We have already seen how mechanical weathering affects the rate of weathering. By breaking rock into smaller pieces, the amount of surface area exposed to chemical weathering increases. Other important factors examined here include the roles of rock characteristics and climate.

Rock Characteristics

Rock characteristics encompass all of the chemical traits of rocks, including mineral composition and solubility. In addition, any physical features, such as joints, can be important because they influence the ability of water to penetrate rock.

The variations in weathering rates due to the mineral constituents can be demonstrated by comparing old headstones made from different rock types. Headstones of granite, which is composed of silicate minerals, are relatively resistant to chemical weathering. We can see this by examining the inscriptions on the headstones shown in FIGURE 13. In contrast, the marble headstone shows signs of extensive chemical alteration over a relatively short period. Marble is composed of calcite (calcium carbonate), which readily dissolves even in a weakly acidic solution.

The silicates, the most abundant mineral group, chemically weather in essentially the same order as their order of crystallization. By examining Bowen's Reaction Series, you can see that olivine crystallizes first and is therefore least resistant to chemical weathering, whereas quartz, which crystallizes last, is the most resistant.

Climate

Climatic factors, particularly temperature and moisture, are crucial to the rate of rock weathering. One important example from mechanical weathering is that the frequency of freeze–thaw cycles greatly affects the amount of frost wedging. Temperature and moisture also exert a strong influence on rates of chemical weathering and on the kind and amount of vegetation present. Regions with lush vegetation often have a thick mantle of soil rich in decayed organic matter from which chemically active fluids such as carbonic acid and humic acids are derived.

The optimum environment for chemical weathering is a combination of warm temperatures and abundant moisture. In polar regions, chemical weathering is ineffective because frigid temperatures keep the available moisture locked up as ice, whereas in arid regions there is insufficient moisture to foster rapid chemical weathering.

Human activities often produce pollutants that alter the composition of the atmosphere. Such changes can, in turn, influence the rate of chemical weathering. One well-known example is acid rain.

Differential Weathering

Masses of rock do not weather uniformly. A glance at Figure 1 shows an example of this phenomenon, called **differential weathering**. The results vary in scale from the rough, uneven surface of the marble headstone in Figure 13 to the boldly sculpted rock formations in Arizona's Monument Valley (FIGURE 14).

Many factors influence the rate of rock weathering. Among the most important are variations in the composition of the rock. More resistant rock protrudes as ridges or pinnacles, or as steeper cliffs on an irregular hillside. The number and spacing of joints can also be a significant factor (see Figures 6 and 12). Differential weathering and subsequent erosion are responsible for creating many unusual and sometimes spectacular rock formations and landforms.

SMARTFIGURE 13
Rock type influences weathering
An examination of headstones in the same cemetery shows that the rate of chemical weathering is influenced by rock type.
(Photos by E. J. Tarbuck)

This granite headstone was erected in 1868. The inscription is still fresh looking.

This monument is composed of marble, a calcite-rich metamorphic rock. The headstone was erected in 1872, four years after the granite stone. The inscription is nearly illegible.

4 CONCEPT CHECKS

1. Why did the headstones in Figure 13 weather so differently?
2. How does climate influence weathering?

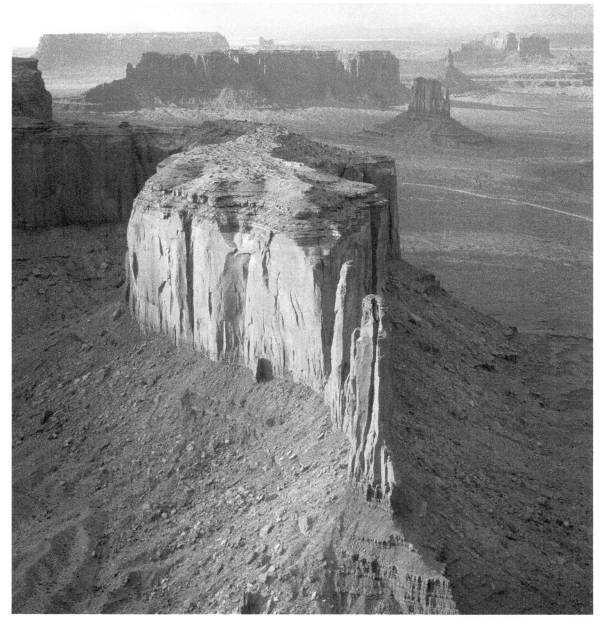

FIGURE 14 Monuments to weathering
Differential weathering in Arizona's Monument Valley. When weathering accentuates differences in rocks, spectacular landforms are sometimes created. (Photo by Michael Collier)

EYE on Earth

The rounded boulders in this image gradually formed in place from a rock mass that had many fractures. Initially the rocks had sharp corners and edges. (Photo by Mike Brine/Alamy Images)

Question 1 Explain the process that transformed angular blocks of bedrock into rounded boulders.

Question 2 What term is applied to this process?

Acid Precipitation
A Human Impact on the Earth System

As a consequence of burning large quantities of coal and petroleum, tens of millions of tons of sulfur dioxide and nitrogen oxides enter the atmosphere each year. Through a series of complex chemical reactions, these pollutants are converted into acids that eventually fall to Earth's surface. The map shows precipitation pH values for 2008.

The pH scale measures the degree of acidity or alkalinity of a solution. Each whole number indicates a tenfold difference. Unpolluted rain has a pH of about 5. In the United States, acid rain is most serious in the Northeast.

MORE STRONGLY ALKALINE

14
13 ← LYE
12 ← AMMONIA
11
10
9
8 ← BAKING SODA
7 ← DISTILLED WATER (NEUTRAL)
6
5
4
3 ← CARBONATED SOFT DRINK
2 ← LEMON JUICE
1 ← STOMACH ACID
0

MORE STRONGLY ACIDIC

LESS ACIDIC

pH VALUE

MORE ACIDIC

| >5.3 |
| 5.2 - 5.3 |
| 5.1 - 5.2 |
| 5.0 - 5.1 |
| 4.9 - 5.0 |
| 4.8 - 4.9 |
| 4.7 - 4.8 |
| 4.6 - 4.7 |
| 4.5 - 4.6 |
| 4.4 - 4.5 |
| 4.3 - 4.4 |
| <4.3 |

Damage to forests by acid precipitation is well documented in Europe and eastern North America. These trees in the Appalachian Mountains of North Carolina are one example. In addition, increased acidity in many lakes has had a detrimental impact on aquatic ecosystems.

Andre Jenny/Stock Connection Worldwide/Newscom

Although we expect rock to gradually decompose, many stone monuments have succumbed prematurely because of accelerated chemical weathering linked to acid precipitation.

Ryan McGinnis/Alamy

5 Soil

Weathering is a key process in the formation of soil. Along with air and water, soil is one of our most indispensable resources. Also like air and water, soil is often taken for granted. The following quote helps put this vital layer in perspective:

> Science, in recent years, has focused more and more on the Earth as a planet, one that for all we know is unique—where a thin blanket of air, a thinner film of water, and the thinnest veneer of soil combine to support a web of life of wondrous diversity in continuous change.*

Soil has accurately been called "the bridge between life and the inanimate world." All life—the entire biosphere—owes its existence to a dozen or so elements that must ultimately come from Earth's crust. Once weathering and other processes create soil, plants carry out the intermediary role of assimilating the necessary elements and making them available to animals, including humans.

An Interface in the Earth System

When Earth is viewed as a system, soil is referred to as an *interface*—a common boundary where different parts of a system interact. This is an appropriate designation because soil forms where the geosphere, the atmosphere, the hydrosphere, and the biosphere meet. Soil is a material that develops in response to complex environmental interactions among different parts of the Earth system. Over time, soil gradually evolves to a state of equilibrium or balance with the environment. Soil is dynamic and sensitive to almost every aspect of its surroundings. Thus, when environmental changes occur, such as climate, vegetative cover, and animal (including human) activity, the soil responds. Any such change produces a gradual alteration of soil characteristics until a new balance is reached. Although thinly distributed over the land surface, soil functions as a fundamental interface, providing an excellent example of the integration among many parts of the Earth system.

What Is Soil?

With few exceptions, Earth's land surface is covered by **regolith** (*rhegos* = blanket, *lithos* = stone), the layer of rock and mineral fragments produced by weathering. Some would call this material soil, but soil is more than an accumulation of weathered debris. **Soil** is a combination of mineral and organic matter, water, and air—the portion of the regolith that supports the growth of plants. Although the proportions of the major components in soil vary, the same four components are always present to some extent (FIGURE 15). About one-half of the total volume

25% air

45% mineral matter

25% water

5% organic matter

FIGURE 15 What is soil?
The composition (by volume) of a soil in good condition for plant growth. Although percentages vary, each soil is composed of mineral and organic matter, water, and air. (Photo by i love images/gardening/Alamy Images)

of good-quality surface soil is a mixture of disintegrated and decomposed rock (mineral matter) and **humus**, the decayed remains of animal and plant life (organic matter). The remaining half consists of pore spaces among the solid particles where air and water circulate.

Although the mineral portion of the soil is usually much greater than the organic portion, humus is an essential component. In addition to being an important source of plant nutrients, humus enhances the soil's ability to retain water. Because plants require air and water to live and grow, the portion of the soil consisting of pore spaces that allow for the circulation of these fluids is as vital as the solid soil constituents.

Soil water is far from "pure" water; instead, it is a complex solution that contains many soluble nutrients. Soil water not only provides the necessary moisture for the chemical reactions that sustain life, it also supplies plants with nutrients in a form they can use. The pore spaces not filled with water contain air. This air is the source of necessary oxygen and carbon dioxide for most microorganisms and plants that live in the soil.

5 CONCEPT CHECKS

1. Why is soil considered an interface in the Earth system?
2. How is regolith different from soil?

*Jack Eddy, "A Fragile Seam of Dark Blue Light," in *Proceedings of the Global Change Research Forum.* U.S. Geological Survey Circular 1086, 1993, p. 15.

6 Controls of Soil Formation

Soil is the product of the complex interplay of several factors, including parent material, time, climate, plants and animals, and topography. Although all these factors are interdependent, their roles will be examined separately.

Parent Material

The source of the weathered mineral matter from which soils develop is called the **parent material** and is a major factor influencing newly forming soil. Gradually it undergoes physical and chemical changes as the processes of soil formation progress. Parent material can either be the underlying bedrock or a layer of unconsolidated deposits. When the parent material is bedrock, the soils are termed *residual soils.* By contrast, those developed on unconsolidated sediment are called *transported soils* (FIGURE 16). It should be pointed out that transported soils form *in place* on parent materials that have been carried from elsewhere and deposited by gravity, water, wind, or ice.

The nature of the parent material influences soils in two ways. First, the type of parent material will affect the rate of weathering and thus the rate of soil formation. Also, because unconsolidated deposits are already partly weathered, soil development on such material will likely progress more rapidly than when bedrock is the parent material. Second, the chemical makeup of the parent material will affect the soil's fertility. This influences the character of the natural vegetation the soil can support.

At one time the parent material was thought to be the primary factor causing differences among soils. However, soil scientists have come to understand that other factors, especially climate, are more important. In fact, it has been found that similar soils often develop from different parent materials and that dissimilar soils can develop from the same parent material. Such discoveries reinforce the importance of other soil-forming factors.

Time

Time is an important component of *every* geological process, and soil formation is no exception. The nature of soil is strongly influenced by the length of time that processes have been operating. If weathering has been going on for a comparatively short time, the character of the parent material strongly influences the characteristics of the soil. As weathering processes continue, the influence of parent material on soil is overshadowed by other soil-forming factors, especially climate. The amount of time required for various soils to evolve cannot be listed because the soil-forming processes act at varying rates under different circumstances. However, as a rule, the longer a soil has been forming, the thicker it becomes and the less it resembles the parent material.

FIGURE 16 **Slopes and soil development**
The parent material for residual soils is the underlying bedrock. Transported soils form on unconsolidated deposits. Also note that as slopes become steeper, soil becomes thinner. (Left and center photos by E. J. Tarbuck; right photo by Lucarelli Temistocle/Shutterstock)

No soil development
because of very steep slope

Transported soil
developed on unconsolidated
stream deposits

Residual soil
is developed on bedrock

Thicker soil
develops on flat terrain

Bedrock

Unconsolidated deposits

Thinner soil
on steep slope
because of erosion

Climate

Climate is considered to be the most influential control of soil formation. Temperature and precipitation are the elements that exert the strongest impact. Variations in temperature and precipitation determine whether chemical or mechanical weathering will predominate and also greatly influence the rate and depth of weathering. For instance, a hot, wet climate may produce a thick layer of chemically weathered soil in the same amount of time that a cold, dry climate produces a thin mantle of mechanically weathered debris. Also, the amount of precipitation influences the degree to which various materials are removed from the soil by percolating waters (a process called *leaching*), thereby affecting soil fertility. Finally, climatic conditions are an important control on the type of plant and animal life present.

Plants and Animals

Plants and animals play a vital role in soil formation. The types and abundance of organisms present have a strong influence on the physical and chemical properties of a soil (FIGURE 17). In fact, for well-developed soils in many regions, the significance of natural vegetation in influencing soil type is frequently implied in the description used by soil scientists. Such phrases as *prairie soil*, *forest soil*, and *tundra soil* are common.

Plants and animals furnish organic matter to the soil. Certain bog soils are composed almost entirely of organic matter, whereas desert soils might contain as little as a small fraction of 1 percent. Although the quantity of organic matter varies substantially among soils, it is a rare soil that completely lacks it.

The primary source of organic matter in soil is plants, although animals and an infinite number of microorganisms also contribute. When organic matter is decomposed, important nutrients are supplied to plants, as well as to animals and microorganisms living in the soil. Consequently, soil fertility is in part related to the amount of organic matter present. Furthermore, the decay of plant and animal remains causes the formation of various organic acids. These complex acids hasten the weathering process. Organic matter also has a high water-holding ability and thus aids water retention in a soil.

Microorganisms, including fungi, bacteria, and single-celled protozoa, play an active role in the decay of plant and animal remains. The end product is humus, a material that no longer resembles the plants and animals from which it is formed. In addition, certain microorganisms aid soil fertility because they have the ability to convert atmospheric nitrogen into soil nitrogen.

Earthworms and other burrowing animals act to mix the mineral and organic portions of a soil. Earthworms, for example, feed on organic matter and thoroughly mix soils in which they live, often moving and enriching many tons per acre each year. Burrows and holes also aid the passage of water and air through the soil.

Meager desert rainfall means reduced rates of weathering and relatively meager vegetation. Desert soils are typically thin and lack much organic matter.

In the northern coniferous forest, the organic litter is high in acid resin which contributes to an accumulation of acid in the soil. As a result, acid leaching is an important soil-forming process.

Soils that develop in well-drained prairie regions typically have a humus-rich surface horizon that is rich in calcium and magnesium. Fertility is usually excellent.

FIGURE 17 Plants influence soil
The nature of the vegetation in an area can have a significant influence on soil formation. (Photos by Bill Brooks/Alamy Images; Nickolay Stanev/Shutterstock; and Elizabeth C. Doemer/Shutterstock)

Topography

The lay of the land can vary greatly over short distances. Variations in topography can lead to the development of a variety of localized soil types. Many of the differences exist because the length and steepness of slopes have a significant impact on the amount of erosion and the water content of soil.

On steep slopes, soils are often poorly developed. In such situations the quantity of water soaking in is slight; as a result, the moisture content of the soil may not be sufficient for vigorous plant growth. Further, because of accelerated erosion on steep slopes, the soils are thin or in some cases nonexistent (see Figure 16).

In contrast, poorly drained and waterlogged soils found in bottomlands have a much different character. Such soils are usually thick and dark. The dark color results from the large quantity of organic matter that accumulates because saturated conditions retard the decay of vegetation. The optimum terrain for soil development is a flat-to-undulating upland surface. Here we find good drainage, minimum erosion, and sufficient infiltration of water into the soil.

Slope orientation, or the direction a slope is facing, is another consideration. In the mid-latitudes of the Northern Hemisphere, a south-facing slope will receive a great deal more sunlight than a north-facing slope. In fact, a steep north-facing slope may receive no direct sunlight at all. The difference in the amount of solar radiation received will cause differences in soil temperature and moisture, which in turn influence the nature of the vegetation and the character of the soil.

Although this section dealt separately with each of the soil-forming factors, remember that all of them work together to form soil. No single factor is responsible for a soil's character; rather, it is the combined influence of parent material, time, climate, plants and animals, and topography that determines this character.

6 CONCEPT CHECKS

1. List the five basic controls of soil formation.
2. Which factor is most influential in soil formation?
3. How might the direction a slope is facing influence soil formation?

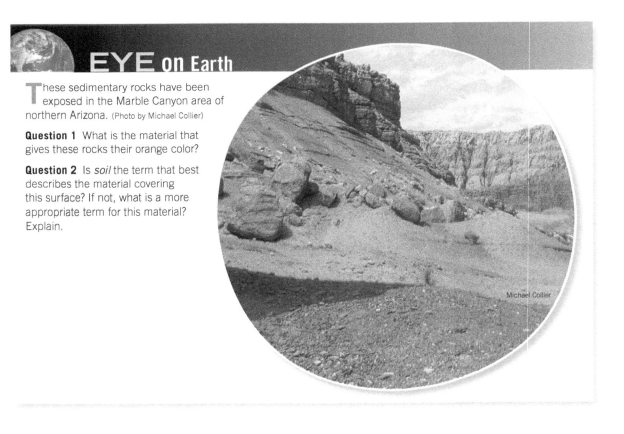

EYE on Earth

These sedimentary rocks have been exposed in the Marble Canyon area of northern Arizona. (Photo by Michael Collier)

Question 1 What is the material that gives these rocks their orange color?

Question 2 Is *soil* the term that best describes the material covering this surface? If not, what is a more appropriate term for this material? Explain.

Michael Collier

7 The Soil Profile

Because soil-forming processes operate from the surface downward, variations in composition, texture, structure, and color gradually evolve at varying depths. These vertical differences, which usually become more pronounced as time passes, divide the soil into zones or layers known as **horizons**. If you were to dig a trench in soil, you would see that its walls are layered. Such a vertical section through all of the soil horizons constitutes the **soil profile**.

FIGURE 18 presents an idealized view of a well-developed soil profile in which five horizons are identified. From the surface downward, they are designated as *O, A, E, B,* and *C*. These five horizons are common to soils in temperate regions. The characteristics and extent of development of horizons vary in different environments. Thus, different localities exhibit soil profiles that can contrast greatly with one another.

- *The O soil horizon* consists largely of organic material. This is in contrast to the layers beneath it, which consist mainly of mineral matter. The upper portion of the *O* horizon is primarily plant litter, such as loose leaves and other organic debris that are still recognizable. By contrast, the lower portion of the *O* horizon is made up of partly decomposed organic matter (humus) in which plant structures can no longer be identified. In addition to plants, the *O* horizon is teeming with microscopic life, including bacteria, fungi, algae, and insects. All of these organisms contribute oxygen, carbon dioxide, and organic acids to the developing soil.
- *The A horizon* is largely mineral matter, yet biological activity is high and humus is generally present—up to 30 percent in some instances. Together the *O* and *A* horizons make up what is commonly called the *topsoil.*
- *The E horizon* is a light-colored layer that contains little organic material. As water percolates downward through this zone, finer particles are carried away. This washing out of fine soil components is termed **eluviation** (*elu* = get away from, *via* = a way). Water percolating downward also dissolves soluble inorganic soil components and carries them to deeper zones. This depletion of soluble materials from the upper soil is termed **leaching**.
- *The B horizon,* or *subsoil,* is where much of the material removed from the *E* horizon by eluviation is deposited. Thus, the *B* horizon is often referred to as the *zone of accumulation.* The accumulation of the fine clay particles enhances water retention in the subsoil. In extreme cases clay accumulation can form a very compact and impermeable layer called *hardpan.*
- The *O, A, E,* and *B* horizons together constitute the **solum**, or "true soil." It is in the solum that the

soil-forming processes are active and that living roots and other plant and animal life are largely confined.
- *The C horizon* is characterized by partially altered parent material. Whereas the *O, A, E,* and *B* horizons bear little resemblance to the parent material, it is easily identifiable in the *C* horizon. Although this material is undergoing changes that will eventually transform it into soil, it has not yet crossed the threshold that separates regolith from soil.

The characteristics and extent of development can vary greatly among soils in different environments

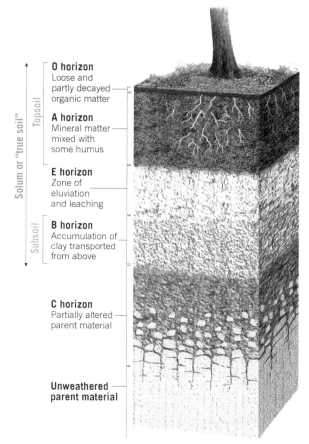

FIGURE 18 Soil horizons
Idealized soil profile from a humid climate in the middle latitudes.

Solum or "true soil"

Topsoil

O horizon
Loose and partly decayed organic matter

A horizon
Mineral matter mixed with some humus

E horizon
Zone of eluviation and leaching

Subsoil

B horizon
Accumulation of clay transported from above

C horizon
Partially altered parent material

Unweathered parent material

FIGURE 19 Contrasting soil profiles
Soil characteristics and development vary greatly in different environments. (Left photo by E. J. Tarbuck; right photo courtesy of Soil Science Society of America)

This profile shows a soil in southeastern South Dakota with well-developed horizons.

Horizons are indistinct in this soil in Puerto Rico, giving it a relatively uniform appearance.

(FIGURE 19). The boundaries between soil horizons may be sharp, or the horizons may blend gradually from one to another. Consequently, a well-developed soil profile indicates that environmental conditions have been relatively stable over an extended time span and that the soil is *mature*. By contrast, some soils lack horizons altogether. Such soils are called *immature* because soil building has been going on for only a short time. Immature soils are also characteristic of steep slopes, where erosion continually strips away the soil, preventing full development.

7 CONCEPT CHECKS

1. Sketch and label the main soil horizons in a well-developed soil profile.
2. Describe the following features or processes: eluviation, leaching, zone of accumulation, and hardpan.

Soil characteristics are very important when selecting a site for a vineyard. (Photo by Lynn Betts/Shutterstock)

8 | Classifying Soils

There are many variations from place to place and from time to time among the factors that control soil formation. These differences lead to a bewildering variety of soil types. To cope with such variety, it is essential to devise some means of classifying the vast array of data to be studied. Establishing groups consisting of items that have certain important characteristics in common introduces order and simplicity. Bringing order to large quantities of information not only aids comprehension and understanding but also facilitates analysis and explanation.

In the United States, soil scientists have devised a system for classifying soils known as the **Soil Taxonomy**. It emphasizes the physical and chemical properties of the soil profile and is organized on the basis of observable soil characteristics. There are six hierarchical categories of classification, ranging from *order*, the broadest category, to *series*, the most specific category. The system recognizes 12 soil orders and more than 19,000 soil series.

The names of the classification units are combinations of syllables, most of which are derived from Latin or Greek. The names are descriptive. For example, soils of the order aridosol (from the Latin *aridus* = dry and *solum* = soil) are characteristically dry soils in arid regions. Soils in the order inceptisol (from Latin *inceptum* = beginning and *solum* = soil) are soils with only the beginning or inception of profile development.

Brief descriptions of the 12 basic soil orders are provided in TABLE 2. FIGURE 20 shows the complex worldwide distribution pattern of the Soil Taxonomy's 12 soil orders. Like many other classification systems, the Soil

TABLE 2	Basic Soil Orders	
Soil Order	Description	Percentage*
Alfisol	Moderately weathered soils that form under boreal forests or broadleaf deciduous forests, rich in iron and aluminum. Clay particles accumulate in a subsurface layer in response to leaching in moist environments. Fertile, productive soils because they are neither too wet nor too dry.	9.65
Andisol	Young soils in which the parent material is volcanic ash and cinders, deposited by recent volcanic activity.	0.7
Aridosol	Soils that develop in dry places where there is insufficient water to remove soluble minerals; may have an accumulation of calcium carbonate, gypsum, or salt in subsoil; low organic content.	12.02
Entisol	Young soils having limited development and exhibiting properties of the parent material. Productivity ranges from very high for some formed on recent river deposits to very low for those forming on shifting sand or rocky slopes.	16.16
Gelisol	Young soils with little profile development that occur in regions with permafrost. Low temperatures and frozen conditions for much of the year; slow soil-forming processes.	8.61
Histosol	Organic soils with little or no climatic implications. Can be found in any climate where organic debris can accumulate to form a bog soil. Dark, partially decomposed organic material commonly referred to as *peat*.	1.17
Inceptisol	Weakly developed young soils in which the beginning (inception) of profile development is evident. Most common in humid climates, they exist from the arctic to the tropics. Native vegetation is most often forest.	9.81
Mollisol	Dark, soft soils that have developed under grass vegetation, generally found in prairie areas. Humus-rich surface horizon that is rich in calcium and magnesium. Soil fertility is excellent. Also found in hardwood forests with significant earthworm activity. Climatic range is boreal or alpine to tropical. Dry seasons are normal.	6.89
Oxisol	Soils that occur on old land surfaces unless parent materials were strongly weathered before they were deposited. Generally found in the tropics and subtropical regions. Rich in iron and aluminum oxides, oxisols are heavily leached and hence are poor soils for agricultural activity.	7.5
Spodosol	Soils found only in humid regions on sandy material. Common in northern coniferous forests and cool humid forests. Beneath the dark upper horizon of weathered organic material lies a light-colored horizon of leached material, the distinctive property of this soil.	2.56
Ultisol	Soils that represent the products of long periods of weathering. Water percolating through the soil concentrates clay particles in the lower horizons (argillic horizons). Restricted to humid climates in the temperate regions and the tropics, where the growing season is long. Abundant water and a long frost-free period contribute to extensive leaching, hence poorer soil quality.	8.45
Vertisol	Soils containing large amounts of clay, which shrink upon drying and swell with the addition of water. Found in subhumid to arid climates, provided that adequate supplies of water are available to saturate the soil after periods of drought. Soil expansion and contraction exert stresses on human structures.	2.24

*Percentages refer to the world's ice-free surface.

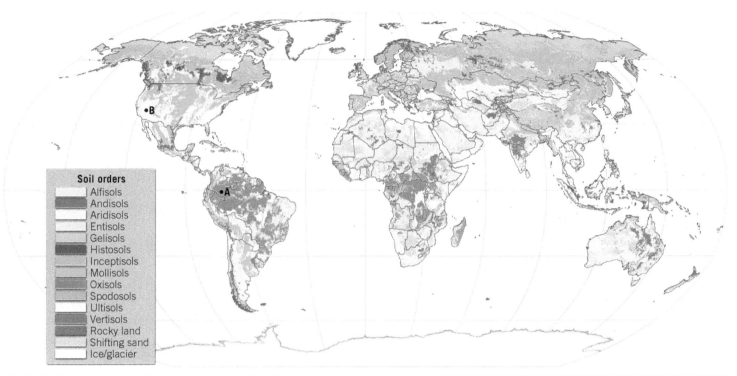

Soil orders
- Alfisols
- Andisols
- Aridisols
- Entisols
- Gelisols
- Histosols
- Inceptisols
- Mollisols
- Oxisols
- Spodosols
- Ultisols
- Vertisols
- Rocky land
- Shifting sand
- Ice/glacier

FIGURE 20 **Global soil regions**
Worldwide distribution of the Soil Taxonomy's 12 soil orders. Points A and B are references for a *Give It Some Thought* item at the end of the chapter. (Natural Resources Conservation Service/U.S.D.A.)

Taxonomy is not suitable for every purpose. It is especially useful for agricultural and related land-use purposes, but it is not a useful system for engineers who are preparing evaluations of potential construction sites.

8 CONCEPT CHECKS

1. Why are soils classified?
2. Refer to Figure 20 and identify three particularly extensive soil orders that occur in the contiguous 48 United States. Describe two soil orders in Alaska.

EYE on Earth

This thick red soil is exposed in one of the states in the United States and is either a gelisol, a molisol, or an oxisol. (Photo by Sandra A. Dunlap/Shutterstock)

Question 1 Refer to the descriptions in Table 2 and determine the likely soil order shown in this image. Explain your choice.

Question 2 Which one of these states is the most likely location of the soil—Alaska, Illinois, or Hawaii?

9 The Impact of Human Activities on Soil

Soils are just a tiny fraction of all Earth materials, yet they are vital. Soils are necessary for the growth of rooted plants and thus are a basic foundation of the human life-support system. Because soil forms very slowly, it must be thought of as a nonrenewable resource. Just as human ingenuity can increase the agricultural productivity of soils through fertilization and irrigation, soils can be damaged or destroyed by careless activities. Despite their role in providing food, fiber, and other basic materials, soils are among our most abused resources.

Clearing the Tropical Rain Forest—A Case Study of Human Impact on Soil

Over the past few decades, the destruction of tropical forests has become a serious environmental issue. Each year millions of acres are cleared for agriculture and logging (FIGURE 21). This clearing results in soil degradation, loss of biodiversity, and climate change.

Thick red-orange soils (oxisols) are common in the wet tropics and subtropics (see Figure 20). They are the end product of extreme chemical weathering. Because lush tropical rain forests are associated with these soils, many people assume that they are fertile and have great potential for agriculture. However, just the opposite is true: They are among the poorest soils for farming. How can this be?

Because rain forest soils develop under conditions of high temperature and heavy rainfall, they are severely leached. Not only does leaching remove the soluble materials such as calcium carbonate, but the great quantities of percolating rain water also remove much of the silica, and as a result, insoluble oxides of iron and aluminum become concentrated in the soil. Iron oxides give the soil its distinctive color. Because bacterial activity is high in the wet tropics, rain forest soils contain very little humus. Moreover, leaching destroys fertility because most plant nutrients are removed by the large volume of downward-percolating water. Therefore, even though the vegetation may be

This recent satellite image shows tropical deforestation in western Brazil. Intact forest is dark green, cleared areas (bare ground) are tan, and light green is crops and pasture.

Clearing the Amazon rain forest in Surinam. The thick soils (oxisols) are highly leached.

FIGURE 21 Tropical deforestation
Clearing the tropical rain forest is a serious environmental issue. (Photo by Wesley Bocxe/Photo Researchers; satellite image by NASA)

dense and luxuriant, the soil itself contains few available nutrients.

Most nutrients that support the rain forest are locked up in the trees themselves. As vegetation dies and decomposes, the roots of the rain forest trees quickly absorb the nutrients before they are leached from the soil. The nutrients are continuously recycled as trees die and decompose. Therefore, when forests are cleared to provide land for farming or to harvest timber, most of the nutrients are removed as well. What remains is a soil that contains little to nourish planted crops.

The clearing of rain forests not only removes plant nutrients but also accelerates soil erosion. When vegetation is present, roots anchor the soil, and leaves and branches provide a canopy that protects the ground by deflecting the full force of the frequent heavy rains. When the protective vegetation is gone, soil erosion increases.

The removal of vegetation also exposes the ground to strong direct sunlight. When baked by the Sun, these tropical soils can harden to a bricklike consistency and become practically impenetrable to water and crop roots. In just a few years, a freshly cleared area may no longer be cultivable.

Soil Erosion: Losing a Vital Resource

Many people do not realize that soil erosion is a serious environmental problem. Perhaps this is the case because a substantial amount of soil seems to remain even where soil erosion is serious. Nevertheless, although the loss of fertile topsoil may not be obvious to the untrained eye, it is a significant and growing problem as human activities expand and disturb more and more of Earth's surface.

Soil erosion is a natural process; it is part of the constant recycling of Earth materials that we call the *rock cycle.* Once soil forms, erosional forces, especially water and wind, move soil components from one place to another. Every time it rains, raindrops strike the land with surprising force (FIGURE 22). Each drop acts like a tiny bomb, blasting movable soil particles out of their positions in the soil mass. Then, water flowing across the surface carries away the dislodged soil particles. Because the soil is moved by thin sheets of water, this process is termed *sheet erosion.*

After flowing as a thin, unconfined sheet for a relatively short distance, threads of current typically develop, and tiny channels called *rills* begin to form. Still deeper cuts in the soil, known as *gullies,* are created as

Raindrops may strike the surface at velocities approaching 35 km per hour. When a drop strikes an exposed surface, soil particles may splash as high as one meter and land more than a meter away from the point of raindrop impact.

FIGURE 22 Raindrop impact
Soil dislodged by raindrop impact is more easily moved by sheet erosion.
(Photo courtesy U.S. Dept. of the Navy/Soil Conservation Service/USDA)

rills enlarge (FIGURE 23). When normal farm cultivation cannot eliminate the channels, we know the rills have grown large enough to be called gullies. Although most dislodged soil particles move only a short distance during each rainfall, substantial quantities eventually leave the fields and make their way downslope to a stream. Once in the stream channel, these soil particles, which can now be called *sediment,* are transported downstream and eventually deposited.

Rates of Erosion We know that soil erosion is the ultimate fate of practically all soils. In the past, erosion occurred at slower rates than it does today because more of the land surface was covered and protected by trees, shrubs, grasses, and other plants. However, human activities such as farming, logging, and construction, which remove or disrupt the natural vegetation, have greatly accelerated the rate of soil erosion. Without the stabilizing effect of plants, the soil is more easily swept away by the wind or carried downslope by sheet wash.

Natural rates of soil erosion vary greatly from one place to another and depend on soil characteristics as well as factors such as climate, slope, and type of vegetation. Over a broad area, erosion caused by surface runoff may be estimated by determining the sediment loads of the streams that drain the region. When studies of this kind were made on a global scale, they indicated that prior to the appearance of humans, sediment transport by rivers to the ocean amounted to just over 9 billion metric tons per year. In contrast, the amount of material currently transported to the sea by rivers is about 24 billion metric tons per year, or more than two and a half times the earlier rate.

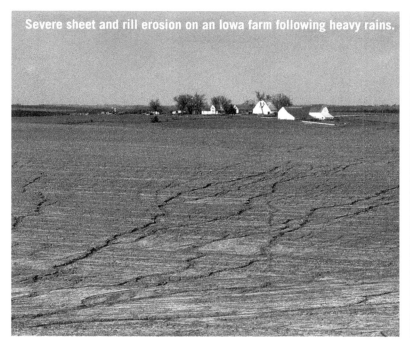

Severe sheet and rill erosion on an Iowa farm following heavy rains.

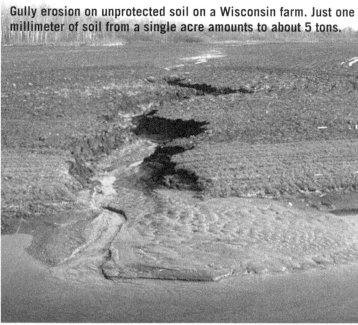

Gully erosion on unprotected soil on a Wisconsin farm. Just one millimeter of soil from a single acre amounts to about 5 tons.

FIGURE 23 **Soil erosion**
Sheetflow, rills, and gullies on unprotected soils.
(Photos by Lynn Betts /NRCS and D. P. Burnside/Photo Researchers, Inc.)

It is estimated that flowing water is responsible for about two-thirds of the soil erosion in the United States. Much of the remainder is caused by wind. When dry conditions prevail, strong winds can remove large quantities of soil from unprotected fields (FIGURE 24). At present, it is estimated that topsoil is eroding faster than it forms on more than one-third of the world's croplands. The results are lower productivity, poorer crop quality, reduced agricultural income, and an ominous future.

Controlling Soil Erosion   On every continent, unnecessary soil loss is occurring because appropriate conservation measures are not being used. Although it is a recognized fact that soil erosion can never be completely eliminated, soil conservation programs can substantially reduce the loss of this basic resource.

Steepness of slope is an important factor in soil erosion. The steeper the slope, the faster the water runs off and the greater the erosion. It is best to leave steep slopes

The man is pointing to where the ground surface was when the grasses began to grow. Wind erosion lowered the land surface to the level of his feet.

Clumps of anchored soil

Unanchored soil

Sand dune

1.2 meters

FIGURE 24 **Wind erosion**
When the land is dry and largely unprotected by anchoring vegetation, soil erosion by wind can be significant. (Photo courtesy Natural Resources Conservation Service/U.S.D.A.)

FIGURE 25 Soil conservation

Planting crops to decrease water erosion on a farm in northeastern Iowa. (Photo courtesy of Erwin C. Cole/USDA/NRCS)

FIGURE 26 Reducing erosion by water

Grassed waterway on a Pennsylvania farm. (Photo courtesy Bob Nichols/NRCS/USDA)

FIGURE 27 Reducing wind erosion

Windbreaks protecting wheat fields in North Dakota. (Photo courtesy Natural Resources Conservation Service/U.S.D.A)

undisturbed. When such slopes are farmed, terraces can be constructed. These nearly flat, step-like surfaces slow runoff and thus decrease soil loss while allowing more water to soak into the ground.

Soil erosion by water also occurs on gentle slopes. FIGURE 25 illustrates one conservation method in which crops are planted parallel to the contours of the slope. This pattern reduces soil loss by slowing runoff. Strips of grass or cover crops such as hay slow runoff even more and act to promote water infiltration and trap sediment.

Creating grassed waterways is another common practice (FIGURE 26). Natural drainageways are shaped to form smooth, shallow channels and then planted with grass. The grass prevents the formation of gullies and traps soil washed from cropland. Frequently crop residues are also left on fields. This debris protects the surface from both water and wind erosion. To protect fields from excessive wind erosion, rows of trees and shrubs are planted that act as windbreaks that slow the wind and deflect it upward (FIGURE 27).

9 CONCEPT CHECKS

1. Why are soils in tropical rain forests not well suited for farming?
2. Place these phenomena related to soil erosion in the proper sequence: sheet erosion, gullies, rain drop impact, rills, stream.
3. How have human activities affected the rate of soil erosion?
4. Briefly describe three ways that soil erosion is controlled.

The 1930s Dust Bowl
An Environmental Disaster

During a span of dry years in the 1930s, large dust storms plagued the Great Plains. Topsoil was stripped from millions of acres. Because of the size and severity of these storms, the region came to be called the Dust Bowl and the time period the Dirty Thirties.

In places, dust drifted like snow, covering farm buildings, fences, and fields. Crop failure and economic hardship resulted in many farms being abandoned.

Arthur Rothstein/ Library of Congress

HEART OF THE
DUST BOWL

OTHER AREAS SEVERELY
AFFECTED BY DUST STORMS

The southern Great Plains were most severely affected. ▶

WA
ND
MT
OR
WY
SD
MN
CA
NE
IA
NV
CO
KS
AZ
NM
OK
TX

Dust blackens the sky near Elkhart, Kansas, on May 21, 1937. The transformation of semiarid grasslands into farms during an unusually wet period set the stage for this disastrous period of soil erosion. When drought struck, the unprotected soils were vulnerable to the wind.

Library of Congress

LANDS

CONCEPTS IN REVIEW: WEATHERING AND SOIL

1 Weathering

Define *weathering* and distinguish between the two main categories of weathering.

KEY WORDS weathering, mechanical weathering, chemical weathering

- Weathering is the disintegration and decomposition of rocks on the surface of Earth. Rocks might break into many smaller pieces through physical processes called *mechanical weathering*. Rocks can also "rot" as minerals react with environmental agents such as oxygen and water to produce new substances that are stable at Earth's surface. This is called *chemical weathering*.

EVERYDAY ANALOGIES Would a shattered window be an example of mechanical weathering or chemical weathering? What about a rusty bicycle?

3 Chemical weathering

Discuss the role of water in each of three chemical weathering processes.

KEY WORDS dissolution, oxidation, hydrolysis, spheroidal weathering

- Water plays an important role in the chemical reactions that take place at the surface of Earth. It can liberate and transport ions from some minerals through dissolution. Water can also facilitate reactions such as rusting, an example of oxidation. Acid mine drainage is an environmental consequence of the oxidation of pyrite in old coal mines.
- Water may also directly react with exposed minerals, producing new minerals that are stable at Earth's surface. The hydrolysis of feldspar to form kaolinite clay is an example. Clays are stable minerals at Earth's surface conditions, and they are profusely generated by the hydrolysis of silicate minerals. As a result, clay is a common constituent of soil and sedimentary rocks.
- Spheroidal weathering is the result when sharp edges and corners of rocks are chemically weathered more rapidly than flat rock faces. The higher proportion of surface area for a given volume of rock at the edges and corners means there is more mineral material exposed to chemical "attack." Faster weathering at the corners produces weathered rocks that become increasingly sphere-shaped over time.

CHOOSE Which one of these minerals, potassium feldspar, halite, or pyrite, is most likely to chemically weather via dissolution? Oxidation? Hydrolysis?

4 Rates of weathering

Summarize the factors that influence the type and rate of rock weathering.

KEY WORD differential weathering

- Some types of rocks are more stable at Earth's surface than others, due to the minerals they contain. Different minerals break down at different rates under the same conditions. Quartz is the most stable silicate mineral, while minerals high in Bowen's Reaction Series such as olivine tend to decompose more rapidly.

2 Mechanical weathering

List and describe four examples of mechanical weathering.

KEY WORDS frost wedging, sheeting, exfoliation dome

- Mechanical weathering forces include the expansion of ice, the crystallization of salt, and the growth of plant roots. All work to pry apart grains and enlarge fractures.
- Rocks that form under lots of pressure deep in Earth will expand when they are exposed at the surface, and sometimes this expansion will be great enough to cause the rock to fracture into onion-like layers. This sheeting can generate broad dome-shaped exposures of rock called *exfoliation domes*.

COMPARE How do ice, salt, and trees act to induce mechanical weathering.

- Rock weathers most rapidly in an environment with lots of heat to drive reactions and water to facilitate those reactions. Consequently, rocks decompose relatively quickly in hot, wet climates and slowly in cold, dry conditions.
- The position of a rock mass matters in weathering: If a rock mass is protected from weathering by another, more resistant rock, then it will weather at a slower rate than a fully exposed equivalent rock. Differential weathering produces many of our most spectacular landforms.

THOUGHT EXPERIMENT Imagine if we broke a sample of granite into two equal pieces. We put one piece in the Dry Valleys of Antarctica and the other in Panama. Which one will weather more rapidly, and why?

Alamy Creativity/Alamy

Kevin Schafer/Alamy

Lynn Betts/NRCS/USDA

5 Soil

Define soil and explain why it is referred to as an interface.

KEY WORDS regolith, soil, humus

- Soils are vital combinations of organic and non-organic components found at the interface where the geosphere, atmosphere, hydrosphere, and biosphere meet. This dynamic zone is the overlap between different parts of the Earth system. It includes the regolith's rocky debris, mixed with humus, water, and air.

INGREDIENTS Label the four components of a soil on this pie chart.

7 The soil profile

Sketch, label, and describe an idealized soil profile.

KEY WORDS horizon, soil profile, eluviation, leaching, solum

- Despite the great diversity of soils around the world, there are some broad patterns to the vertical anatomy of soil layers. Organic material, called humus, is added at the top (*O* horizon), mainly from plant sources. There, it mixes with mineral matter (*A* horizon). At the bottom, bedrock breaks down and contributes mineral matter (*C* horizon). In between, some materials are leached out or eluviated from higher levels (*E* horizon) and transported to lower levels (*B* horizon), where they may form an impermeable layer called hardpan.

ANOTHER WORLD Sketch an imaginary soil profile for a planet where there were no surface organisms, but plenty of subterranean life. How does your sketch differ from Earth soils? On a planet without precipitation, would the *B* and *E* horizons ever develop? Why or why not?

8 Classifying soils

Explain the need for classifying soils.

KEY WORD Soil Taxonomy

- The need to bring order to huge quantities of data motivated the establishment of a classification scheme for the world's soils. This Soil Taxonomy features 12 broad orders.

6 Controls of soil formation

List and briefly discuss five controls of soil formation.

KEY WORD parent material

- Residual soils form in place due to the weathering of bedrock, whereas transported soils develop on unconsolidated sediment.
- It takes time to form soil. Soils that have developed for a longer period of time will have different characteristics than young soils. In addition, some minerals break down more readily than others. Soils produced from the weathering of different parent rocks will be produced at different rates.
- Soils formed in different climates will be different in part due to temperature and moisture differences but also due to the organisms that live in those different environments. These organisms can add organic matter or chemical compounds to the developing soil or can help mix the soil through their growth and movement.
- The steepness of the slope on which a soil is forming is a key variable, with shallow slopes retaining their soils and steeper slopes shedding them to accumulate elsewhere.

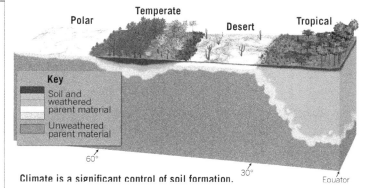

Climate is a significant control of soil formation.

CONNECTIONS How does the addition of acids from coniferous trees affect soil formation?

TAKE YOUR PICK Which soil order would likely contain a higher proportion of humus: inceptisol or histosol? Which soil order would be more likely found in Brazil: gelisol or oxisol?

9 The impact of human activities on soil

Discuss the detrimental impact of human activities on soil.

- Because soil supplies the biosphere with nutrients (and therefore feeds humans), its loss is a matter of concern. Because of human agricultural practices, soil erosion rates have increased over the past several hundred years. Natural soil production rates are constant, so there is a net loss of soil at a time when a record-breaking number of people live on the planet. Using windbreaks, terracing, installing grassed waterways, and plowing the land along horizontal contour lines are all practices that have been shown to reduce soil erosion.
- The clearing of tropical forests is an issue of particular concern. The soils in these regions are rich in clays and metal oxides but poor in silica and humus. Most of the nutrients in the tropical forest ecosystem are not in the soil but in the trees themselves. When the trees are removed, the nutrients are removed, and the soils become highly susceptible to erosion in tropical rainstorms. They may also be baked by the Sun into a bricklike consistency.

PERSPECTIVE By what factor have erosion rates increased in the industrial era (24 billion metric tons per year) relative to the pre-industrial state (9 billion metric tons per year)? Why is it an increasingly acute problem that soil is eroding at a rate faster than it forms on much of the world's agricultural lands?

NRCS/USDA

GIVE IT SOME THOUGHT

1. How are the two main categories of weathering represented in this image that shows human-made objects? (Photo by Michael Collier)

2. Describe how plants promote mechanical and chemical weathering yet inhibit erosion.

3. Granite and basalt are exposed at Earth's surface in a hot, wet region. Will mechanical or chemical weathering predominate? Which rock will weather most rapidly? Why?

4. The level of carbon dioxide (CO_2) in the atmosphere has been increasing for more than 150 years. Will this increase tend to accelerate or slow the rate of chemical weathering of Earth's surface rocks? Explain.

5. Feldspars are very common minerals in igneous rocks. However, in sedimentary rocks, feldspars are relatively rare. Applying what you have learned about chemical weathering, explain why this is true. Based on this explanation, what mineral might you expect to be common in sedimentary rocks that is not found in igneous rocks?

6. The accompanying photo shows Shiprock, a volcanic neck and well-known landmark in northwestern New Mexico. Extending toward the upper left is a wall-like dike. Explain why this once deeply buried intrusive feature now stands high above the surrounding terrain. What term in this chapter applies to this situation? (Photo by Michael Collier)

7. If a historic monument or building were particularly valuable to your community, how would you determine how rapidly the structure might deteriorate and whether it needed protection?

8. This satellite image shows sulfur dioxide (SO_2) levels for air trapped in the lower atmosphere over eastern China on an October day in 2010. Peak concentrations were 20 times the normal levels experienced in the United States. Such episodes are relatively frequent in this region. Discuss how such events might influence chemical weathering. (Satellite image by NASA)

9. The accompanying photo shows a footprint on the Moon left by an *Apollo* astronaut in material popularly called *lunar soil*. Does this material meet the definition we use for soil on Earth? Explain why or why not. You may want to refer to Figure 15. (NASA)

10. This soil sample is from a farm in the Midwest. From which horizon was the sample most likely taken—*A*, *E*, *B*, or *C*? Explain? (Photo by Lynn Betts/NRCS)

11. Using the map of global soil regions in Figure 20, identify the main soil order in the region adjacent to South America's Amazon River (point A on the map) and the predominant soil order in the American Southwest (point B). Briefly contrast these soils. Do they have anything in common? Referring to Table 2 might be helpful.

12. Explain this apparent contradiction: Lush tropical rain forests typically grow in infertile soils.

Glossary

Chemical weathering The processes by which the internal structure of a mineral is altered by the removal and/or addition of elements.

Differential weathering The variation in the rate and degree of weathering caused by such factors as mineral makeup, degree of jointing, and climate.

Dissolution A common form of chemical weathering, it is the process of dissolving into a homogeneous solution, as when an acidic solution dissolves limestone.

Eluviation The washing out of fine soil components from the *A* horizon by downward-percolating water.

Exfoliation dome A large, dome-shaped structure, usually composed of granite, that is formed by sheeting.

Frost wedging The mechanical breakup of rock caused by the expansion of freezing water in cracks and crevices.

Horizon A layer in a soil profile.

Humus Organic matter in soil that is produced by the decomposition of plants and animals.

Hydrolysis A chemical weathering process in which minerals are altered by chemically reacting with water and acids.

Leaching The depletion of soluble materials from the upper soil by downward-percolating water.

Mechanical weathering The physical disintegration of rock, resulting in smaller fragments.

Oxidation The removal of one or more electrons from an atom or ion. So named because elements commonly combine with oxygen.

Parent material The material on which a soil develops.

Regolith The layer of rock and mineral fragments that nearly everywhere covers Earth's land surface.

Sheeting A mechanical weathering process that is characterized by the splitting off of slablike sheets of rock.

Soil A combination of mineral and organic matter, water, and air; the portion of the regolith that supports plant growth.

Soil profile A vertical section through a soil, showing its succession of horizons and the underlying parent material.

Soil taxonomy A soil classification system that consists of six hierarchical categories, based on observable soil characteristics. The system recognizes 12 soil orders.

Solum The *O*, *A*, and *B* horizons in a soil profile. Living roots and other plant and animal life are largely confined to this zone.

Spheroidal weathering Any weathering process that tends to produce a spherical shape from an initially blocky shape.

Weathering The disintegration and decomposition of rock at or near the surface of Earth.

Sedimentary Rocks

From Chapter 7 of *Earth: An Introduction to Physical Geology*, Eleventh Edition. Edward J. Tarbuck, Frederick K. Lutgens, Dennis Tasa.

Sedimentary Rocks

These massive sandstone cliffs in Utah's Zion National Park are remnants of sand dunes from the Mesozoic Era (Photo by Michael Collier)

Each statement represents the primary learning objective for the corresponding major heading within the chapter. After you complete the chapter you should be able to:

1 Discuss the importance of sedimentary rocks to the study of geology and to the general public.

2 Summarize the part of the rock cycle that pertains to sediments and sedimentary rocks and distinguish among the three categories of sedimentary rocks.

3 Discuss the primary basis for distinguishing among detrital rocks and describe how the origin and history of such rocks might be determined.

4 Explain the processes involved in the formation of chemical sedimentary rocks and describe several examples.

5 Outline the successive stages in the formation of coal.

6 Describe the processes that convert sediment into sedimentary rock and other changes associated with burial.

7 Summarize the criteria used to classify sedimentary rocks.

8 Contrast the three broad categories of sedimentary environments and list specific examples of each.

9 List several sedimentary structures and explain why these features are useful to geologists.

10 Relate weathering processes and sedimentary rocks to the carbon cycle.

This exposure of sedimentary rocks is in New York's Shawangunk Mountains. (Photo by Colin D. Young/Shutterstock)

Recall that weathering of existing rocks begins the process. Next, gravity and agents of erosion such as running water, wind, and glacial ice remove the products of weathering and carry them to a new location, where they are deposited. Usually the particles are broken down further during this transport phase. Following deposition, this material, which is now called sediment, becomes lithified (turned to rock). It is from sedimentary rocks that geologists reconstruct many details of Earth's history. Because sediments are deposited in a variety of settings at the surface, the rock layers that they eventually form hold many clues to past surface environments. A layer may represent a desert sand dune, the muddy floor of a swamp, or a tropical coral reef. There are many possibilities. Many sedimentary rocks are associated with important energy and mineral resources and are therefore important economically as well.

1 The Importance of Sedimentary Rocks

Most of the solid Earth consists of igneous and metamorphic rocks. Geologists estimate these two categories represent 90 to 95 percent of the outer 16 kilometers (10 miles) of the crust. Nevertheless, most of Earth's solid surface consists of either sediment or sedimentary rock! About 75 percent of land areas are covered by sediments and sedimentary rocks. Across the ocean floor, which represents about 70 percent of Earth's solid surface, virtually everything is covered by sediment. Igneous rocks are exposed only at the crests of mid-ocean ridges and at some volcanic areas. Thus, while sediment and sedimentary rocks make up only a small percentage of Earth's crust, they are concentrated at or near the surface—the interface among the geosphere, hydrosphere, atmosphere, and biosphere. Because of this unique position, sediments and the rock layers that they eventually form contain evidence of past conditions and events at the surface. Furthermore, sedimentary rocks contain fossils, which are vital tools in the study of the geologic past. This group of rocks provides geologists with much of the basic information they need to reconstruct the details of Earth history (FIGURE 1).

Such study is not only of interest for its own sake but has practical value as well. Coal, which provides a significant portion of our electrical energy, is classified as a sedimentary rock. Moreover, other major energy sources—including oil, natural gas, and uranium—are derived from sedimentary rocks. So are major sources of iron, aluminum, manganese, and phosphate fertilizer, plus numerous materials essential to the construction industry, such as cement and aggregate. Sediments and sedimentary rocks are also the primary reservoir of groundwater. Thus, an understanding of this group of rocks and the processes that form and modify them is basic to locating additional supplies of many important resources.

1 CONCEPT CHECKS

1. How does the volume of sedimentary rocks in Earth's crust compare to the volume of igneous and metamorphic rocks?
2. List two ways in which sedimentary rocks are important.

FIGURE 1 Sedimentary rocks record change Because they contain fossils and other clues about the geologic past, sedimentary rocks are important in the study of Earth history. Vertical changes in rock types represent environmental changes through time. These strata are exposed at Dunraven Bay along the coast of Wales. (Photo by Adam Burton/Alamy Images)

2 Origins of Sedimentary Rock

SMARTFIGURE 2
The big picture
An outline of the portion of the rock cycle that pertains to the formation of sedimentary rocks.

Like other rocks, the **sedimentary rocks** that we see around us and use in so many different ways have their origin in the rock cycle. FIGURE 2 illustrates the portion of the rock cycle that occurs near Earth's surface—the part that pertains to sediments and sedimentary rocks. A brief overview of these processes provides a useful perspective:

- Weathering begins the process. It involves the physical disintegration and chemical decomposition of preexisting igneous, metamorphic, and sedimentary rocks. Weathering generates a variety of products, including various solid particles and ions in solution. These are the raw materials for sedimentary rocks.

- Soluble constituents are carried away by runoff and groundwater. Solid particles are frequently moved downslope by gravity, a process termed *mass wasting*, before running water, groundwater, wind, and glacial ice remove them. Transportation moves these materials from the sites where they originated to locations where they accumulate.

E.J.Tarbuck

Bob Gibbons/Alamy Images

Rivers, glaciers and wind transport sediment.

Wehrle/Premium Stock Photography GmbH/Alamy

Deposition of solid particles produces many different features—glacial ridges, dunes, floodplains, deltas. Ultimately much sediment reaches the ocean floor.

Gravity moves solid particles downslope.

Landslide

Glacier

Wind

Dunes

River

Ocean

Lake

Chemical and mechanical weathering decompose and disintegrate rock.

Soluble products of chemical weathering become dissolved in groundwater and streams.

Reef

When material dissolved in water precipitates, it is the source of such features as reefs and deposits rich in shells.

As sediments are buried, they become compacted and cemented into solid rock.

The transport of sediment is usually intermittent. For example, during a flood, a rapidly moving river moves large quantities of sand and gravel. As the floodwaters recede, particles are temporarily deposited, only to be moved again by a subsequent flood.

- Deposition of solid particles occurs when wind and water currents slow down and as glacial ice melts. The word *sedimentary* actually refers to this process. It is derived from the Latin *sedimentum*, which means "to settle," a reference to solid material settling out of a fluid (water or air). The mud on the floor of a lake, a delta at the mouth of a river, a gravel bar in a stream bed, the particles in a desert sand dune, and even household dust are examples.

- The deposition of material dissolved in water is not related to the strength of water currents. Rather, ions in solution are removed when chemical or temperature changes cause material to crystallize and precipitate or when organisms remove dissolved material to build shells.

- As deposition continues, older sediments are buried beneath younger layers and gradually converted to sedimentary rock (lithified) by compaction and cementation. This and other changes are referred to as *diagenesis* (*dia* = change; *genesis* = origin), a collective term for all the changes (short of metamorphism) that take place in texture, composition, and other physical properties after sediments are deposited.

Because there are a variety of ways that the products of weathering are transported, deposited, and transformed into solid rock, three categories of sedimentary rocks are recognized. As the overview reminds us, sediment has two principal sources. First, it may be an accumulation of material that originates and is transported as solid particles derived from both mechanical and chemical weathering. Deposits of this type are termed *detrital*, and the sedimentary rocks that they form are called **detrital sedimentary rocks**.

The second major source of sediment is soluble material produced largely by chemical weathering. When these ions in solution are precipitated by either inorganic or biological processes, the material is known as chemical sediment, and the rocks formed from it are called **chemical sedimentary rocks**.

The third category is **organic sedimentary rocks**, which form from the carbon-rich remains of organisms. The primary example is coal. This black combustible rock consists of organic carbon from the remains of plants that died and accumulated on the floor of a swamp. The bits and pieces of undecayed plant material that constitute the "sediments" in coal are quite unlike the weathering products that make up detrital and chemical sedimentary rocks.

2 CONCEPT CHECKS

1. Outline the steps that would transform an exposure of granite in the mountains into various sedimentary rocks.
2. List and briefly distinguish among the three basic sedimentary rock categories.

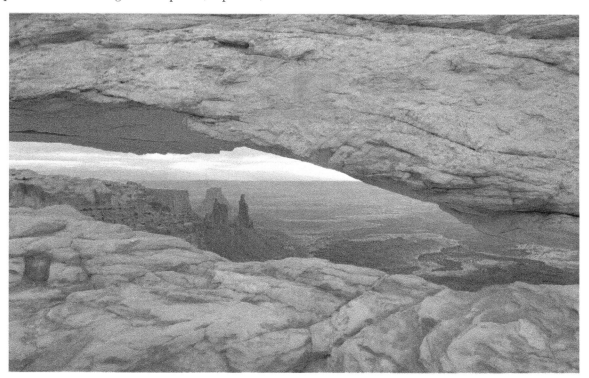

The arch, canyons, and rock formations in this photo are all sculpted from sedimentary rock. Canyonlands National Park, Utah. (Photo by S. Sailer/A. Sailer/AGE Fotostock)

3 Detrital Sedimentary Rocks

Though a wide variety of minerals and rock fragments (*clasts*) may be found in detrital rocks, clay minerals and quartz are the chief constituents of most sedimentary rocks in this category. Clay minerals are the most abundant product of the chemical weathering of silicate minerals, especially the feldspars. Clays are fine-grained minerals with sheetlike crystalline structures similar to the micas. The other common mineral, quartz, is abundant because it is extremely durable and very resistant to chemical weathering. Thus, when igneous rocks such as granite are attacked by weathering processes, individual quartz grains are freed.

Other common minerals in detrital rocks are feldspars and micas. Because chemical weathering rapidly transforms these minerals into new substances, their presence in sedimentary rocks indicates that erosion and deposition were fast enough to preserve some of the primary minerals from the source rock before they could be decomposed.

Particle size is the primary basis for distinguishing among various detrital sedimentary rocks. FIGURE 3

presents the size categories for particles making up detrital rocks. Particle size is not only a convenient method of dividing detrital rocks, the sizes of the component grains also provide useful information about environments of deposition. Currents of water or air sort the particles by size; the stronger the current, the larger the particle size carried. Gravels, for example, are moved by swiftly flowing rivers as well as by landslides and glaciers. Less energy is required to transport sand; thus, it is common to such features as windblown dunes and some river deposits and beaches. Very little energy is needed to transport clay, so it settles very slowly. Accumulation of these tiny particles is generally associated with the quiet water of a lake, lagoon, swamp, or certain marine environments.

In order of increasing particle size, common detrital sedimentary rocks include shale, sandstone, and conglomerate or breccia. We will now look at each type and how it forms.

Shale

Shale is a sedimentary rock consisting of silt- and clay-size particles (FIGURE 4). These fine-grained detrital rocks account for well over half of all sedimentary rocks. The particles in these rocks are so small that they cannot be readily identified without great magnification, and this makes shale more difficult to study and analyze than most other sedimentary rocks.

How Does Shale Form? Much of what can be learned about the process that forms shale is related to particle size. The tiny grains in shale indicate that deposition occurs as

FIGURE 3 Particle size categories Particle size is the primary basis for distinguishing among various detrital sedimentary rocks. (Photos by E. J. Tarbuck)

Size Range (millimeters)	Particle Name	Common Name	Detrital Rock
>256	Boulder	Gravel	Conglomerate / Breccia
64–256	Cobble		
4–64	Pebble		
2–4	Granule		
1/16–2	Sand	Sand	Sandstone
1/256–1/16	Silt	Mud	Shale / Mudstone or Siltstone
<1/256	Clay		

FIGURE 4 **Shale—The most abundant sedimentary rock**
Dark shale containing plant remains is relatively common.
(Photo by E. J. Tarbuck)

the result of gradual settling from relatively quiet, non-turbulent currents. Such environments include lakes, river floodplains, lagoons, and portions of the deep-ocean basins. Even in these "quiet" environments, there is usually enough turbulence to keep clay-size particles suspended almost indefinitely. Consequently, much of the clay is deposited only after the individual particles coalesce to form larger aggregates.

Sometimes the chemical composition of the rock provides additional information. One example is black shale, which is black because it contains abundant organic matter (carbon). When such a rock is found, it strongly implies that deposition occurred in an oxygen-poor environment such as a swamp, where organic materials do not readily oxidize and decay.

Thin Layers
As silt and clay accumulate, they tend to form thin layers, which are commonly referred to as *laminae (lamin = a thin sheet)*. Initially the particles in the laminae are oriented randomly. This disordered arrangement leaves a high percentage of open space (called *pore space*) that is filled with water. However, this situation usually changes with time, as additional layers of sediment pile up and compact the sediment below.

During this phase, the clay and silt particles take on a more nearly parallel alignment and become tightly packed. This rearrangement of grains reduces the size of the pore spaces and forces out much of the

water. Once the grains are pressed closely together, the tiny spaces between particles do not readily permit solutions containing cementing material to circulate. Therefore, shales are often described as being weak because they are poorly cemented and therefore not well lithified.

The inability of water to penetrate its microscopic pore spaces explains why shale often forms barriers to the subsurface movement of water and petroleum. Indeed, rock layers that contain groundwater are commonly underlain by shale beds that block further downward movement. The opposite is true for underground reservoirs of petroleum. They are often capped by shale beds that effectively prevent oil and gas from escaping to the surface.

Shale, Mudstone, or Siltstone? It is common to apply the term *shale* to all fine-grained sedimentary rocks, especially in a nontechnical context. However, be aware that there is a more restricted use of the term. In this narrower usage, shale must exhibit the ability to split into thin layers along well-developed, closely spaced planes. This property is termed **fissility** (*fissilis* = that which can be cleft or split). If the rock breaks into chunks or blocks, the name *mudstone* is applied. Another fine-grained sedimentary rock that, like mudstone, is often grouped with shale but lacks fissility is *siltstone* (see Figure 3). As its name implies, siltstone is composed largely of silt-size particles and contains less clay-size material than shale and mudstone.

Gentle Slopes Although shale is far more common than other sedimentary rocks, it does not usually attract as much notice as other, less abundant, members of this group. The reason is that shale does not form prominent outcrops, as sandstone and limestone often do. Rather, shale crumbles easily and usually forms a cover of soil that hides the unweathered rock below. This is illustrated nicely in the Grand Canyon, where the gentler slopes of weathered shale are quite inconspicuous and overgrown with vegetation, in sharp contrast with the bold cliffs produced by more durable rocks (**FIGURE 5**).

Although shale beds may not form striking cliffs and prominent outcrops, some deposits have economic value. Certain shales are quarried to obtain raw material for pottery, brick, tile, and china. Moreover, when mixed with limestone, shale is used to make cement. In the future, one type of shale, called oil shale, may become a valuable energy resource.

Beds of resistant sandstone and limestone produce bold cliffs. Weaker, poorly cemented shale produces gentler slopes of weathered debris. (Photo by LH Images/ Alamy)

Weak, poorly cemented shale crumbles and produces a gentler slope of weathered debris

Beds of resistant sandstone and limestone produce bold cliffs

Sandstone

Sandstone is the name given rocks in which sand-size grains predominate (FIGURE 6). After shale, sandstone is the most abundant sedimentary rock, accounting for approximately 20 percent of the entire group. Sandstones form in a variety of environments and often contain significant clues about their origin, including sorting, particle shape, and composition.

FIGURE 6 **Quartz sandstone**
After shale, sandstone is the most abundant sedimentary rock.

Dennis Tasa

Close up

Sorting All the particles in sandstone are not necessarily identical in size. **Sorting** refers to the degree of similarity in particle size in a sedimentary rock. For example, if all the grains in a sample of sandstone are about the same size, the sand is considered *well sorted*. Conversely, if the rock contains mixed large and small particles, the sand is said to be *poorly sorted* (FIGURE 7). By studying the degree of sorting, we can learn much about the depositing current. Deposits of wind-blown sand are usually better sorted than deposits sorted by wave activity (FIGURE 8). Particles washed by waves are commonly better sorted than materials deposited by streams. Sediment accumulations that exhibit poor sorting usually result when particles are transported for only a relatively short time and then rapidly deposited. For example, when a turbulent stream reaches the gentler slopes at the base of a steep mountain, its velocity is quickly reduced, and poorly sorted sands and gravels are deposited.

Particle Shape The shapes of sand grains can also help decipher the history of a sandstone (Figure 7). When streams, winds, or waves move sand and other larger sedimentary particles, the grains lose their sharp edges and corners and become more rounded as they collide with other particles during transport. Thus, rounded grains likely have been airborne or waterborne. Further, the degree of rounding indicates the distance or time involved in the transportation of sediment by currents of air or water. Highly rounded grains indicate that a great deal of abrasion and hence a great deal of transport has occurred.

Very angular grains, on the other hand, imply two things: that the materials were transported only a short distance before they were deposited or that some other medium may have transported them. For example, when glaciers move sediment, the particles are usually made more irregular by the crushing and grinding action of the ice.

Transport Affects Mineral Composition   In addition to affecting the degree of rounding and the amount of sorting that particles undergo, the length of transport by turbulent air and water currents also influences the mineral composition of a sedimentary deposit. Substantial weathering and long transport lead to the gradual destruction of weaker and less stable minerals, including the feldspars and ferromagnesians. Because quartz is very durable, it is usually the mineral that survives a long trip in a turbulent environment.

The preceding discussion has shown that the origin and history of sandstone can often be deduced by examining the sorting, roundness, and mineral composition of its constituent grains. Knowing this information allows us to infer that a well-sorted, quartz-rich sandstone consisting of highly rounded grains must be the result of a great deal of transport. Such a rock, in fact, may represent several cycles of weathering, transport, and deposition. We may also conclude that a sandstone containing significant amounts of feldspar and angular grains of ferromagnesian minerals underwent little chemical weathering and transport and was probably deposited close to the source area of the particles.

Varieties of Sandstone   Due to its durability, quartz is the predominant mineral in most sandstones. Such rock is often simply called *quartz sandstone*. When a sandstone contains appreciable quantities of feldspar (25 percent or more), the rock is called *arkose*. In addition to feldspar, arkose usually contains quartz and sparkling bits of mica. The mineral composition of arkose indicates that the grains were derived from granitic source rocks. The particles are generally poorly sorted and angular, which suggests short-distance transport, minimal

Sorting

| Very poorly sorted | Poorly sorted | Well sorted | Very well sorted |

Sediments are "very poorly sorted" when there is a wide range of different sizes.

Rocks with particles that are nearly all the same size are "well sorted."

Angularity and Sphericity

| Angular | Subangular | Subrounded | Rounded |

High sphericity

Low sphericity

Transportation reduces the size and angularity of particles but does not change their general shape.

SMARTFIGURE 7 Sorting and particle shape
Sorting refers to the range of particle sizes present in a rock. Geologists describe a particle's shape in terms of its *angularity* (degree to which edges and corners are rounded) and *sphericity* (how close the shape is to a sphere).

chemical weathering in a relatively dry climate, and rapid deposition and burial.

A third variety of sandstone is known as *graywacke*. Along with quartz and feldspar, this dark-colored rock contains abundant rock fragments and matrix. More than 15 percent of graywacke's volume is matrix. The poor sorting and angular grains characteristic of graywacke suggest that the particles were transported only a relatively short distance from their source area and then rapidly deposited. Before the sediment could be

FIGURE 8 Sand dunes are well sorted
Ancient and modern dunes. (Photo on left by Dennis Tasa; photo on right by George H.H. Huey/Alamy Images)

The orange and yellow cliffs of Utah's Zion National Park expose thousands of feet of Jurassic-age Navajo Sandstone.

The quartz grains composing the Navajo Sandstone were deposited by wind as dunes similar to these in Colorado's Great Sand Dunes National Park. The sand is well sorted because all of the particles are practically the same size.

FIGURE 9 **Conglomerate**
The gravel-size particles in this rock are rounded. (Photo by E. J. Tarbuck)

FIGURE 10 **Poorly sorted sediments**
Gravel deposits along Carbon Creek in Grand Canyon National Park are poorly sorted. (Photo by Michael Collier)

reworked and sorted further, it was buried by additional layers of material. Graywacke is frequently associated with submarine deposits made by dense sediment-choked torrents called *turbidity currents*.

Conglomerate and Breccia

Conglomerate consists largely of gravels (FIGURE 9). As Figure 3 indicates, these particles can range in size from large boulders to particles as small as peas (FIGURE 10). The particles are often large enough to be identified as distinctive rock types; thus, they can be valuable in identifying the source areas of sediments. More often than not, conglomerates are poorly sorted because the opening between the large gravel particles contains sand or mud.

Gravels accumulate in a variety of environments and usually indicate the existence of steep slopes or very turbulent currents. The coarse particles in a conglomerate may reflect the action of energetic mountain streams or result from strong wave activity along a rapidly eroding coast. Some glacial and landslide deposits also contain plentiful gravel.

If the large particles are angular rather than rounded, the rock is called *breccia* (FIGURE 11). Because large particles abrade and become rounded very rapidly during transport, the pebbles and cobbles in a breccia indicate that they did not travel far from their source area before they were deposited. Thus, as with many other sedimentary rocks, conglomerates and breccias contain

FIGURE 11 **Breccia**
The gravel-size sediments in this rock are sharp and angular. (Photo by E. J. Tarbuck)

clues to their history. Their particle sizes reveal the strength of the currents that transported them, whereas the degree of rounding indicates how far the particles traveled. The fragments within a sample identify the source rocks that supplied them.

EYE on Earth

This detrital rock consists of angular grains and is rich in potassium feldspar and quartz. (Photo by E. J. Tarbuck)

Question 1 What do the angular grains indicate about the distance the sediment was transported?

Question 2 The source of the sediment in this rock was an igneous mass. Name the likely rock type.

Question 3 Did the sediment in this sample undergo a great deal of chemical weathering? Explain.

3 CONCEPT CHECKS

1. What minerals are most abundant in detrital sedimentary rocks? In which rocks do these sediments predominate?
2. What is the primary basis for distinguishing among detrital rocks?
3. Describe how sediments become sorted.
4. Distinguish between conglomerate and breccia.

4 Chemical Sedimentary Rocks

FIGURE 13 Coquina
This variety of limestone consists of shell fragments; therefore, it has a biochemical origin. (Rock sample photo by E. J. Tarbuck; beach photo by Donald R. Frazier Photolibrary, Inc./Alamy Images)

In contrast to detrital rocks, which form from the solid products of weathering, chemical sediments derive from ions that are carried *in solution* to lakes and seas. This material does not remain dissolved in the water indefinitely, however. Some of it precipitates to form chemical sediments. These become rocks such as limestone, chert, and rock salt.

This precipitation of material occurs in two ways. *Inorganic* (*in* = not, *organicus* = life) processes such as evaporation and chemical activity can produce chemical sediments. *Organic* (life) processes of water-dwelling organisms also form chemical sediments, said to be of **biochemical** origin.

One example of a deposit resulting from inorganic chemical processes is the dripstone that decorates many caves (FIGURE 12). Another is the salt left behind as a body of seawater evaporates. In contrast, many water-dwelling animals and plants extract dissolved mineral matter to form shells and other hard parts. After the organisms die, their skeletons collect by the millions on the floor of a lake or ocean as biochemical sediment (FIGURE 13).

Delicate calcite crystals forming in a drop of water at the tip of soda straw stalactite. The formation of crystals is triggered when some carbon dioxide escapes from the water drop.

FIGURE 12 Cave deposits
An example of a chemical sedimentary rock with an inorganic origin. (Photo by Guillen Photography/Alamy Images; inset photo by Dante Fenolio/Photo Researchers, Inc.)

Limestone

Representing about 10 percent of the total volume of all sedimentary rocks, *limestone* is the most abundant chemical sedimentary rock. It is composed chiefly of the mineral calcite ($CaCO_3$) and forms either by inorganic means or as a result of biochemical processes. Regardless of its origin, the mineral composition of all limestone is similar, yet many different types exist. This is true because limestones are produced under a variety of conditions. Those forms having a marine biochemical origin are by far the most common.

Carbonate Reefs

Corals are one important example of organisms that are capable of creating large quantities of marine limestone. These relatively simple invertebrate animals secrete a calcareous (calcium carbonate) external skeleton. Although they are small, corals are capable of creating massive structures called *reefs* (FIGURE 14). Reefs consist of coral colonies made up of great numbers of individuals that live side by side on a calcite structure secreted by the animals. In addition, calcium carbonate–secreting algae live with the corals and help cement the entire structure into a solid mass. A wide variety of other organisms also live in and near the reefs.

Certainly the best-known modern reef is Australia's Great Barrier Reef, 2000 kilometers (1240 miles) long, but many lesser reefs also exist. They develop in the shallow, warm waters of the tropics and subtropics equatorward of about 30° latitude. Striking examples exist in the Bahamas, Hawaii, and the Florida Keys.

Modern corals were not the first reef builders. Earth's first reef-building organisms were photosynthesizing bacteria living during Precambrian time more than

Close up

253

FIGURE 14 Carbonate reefs
Large quantities of bio-
chemical limestone are
created by reef-building
organisms. (Photos by Ingo
Schulz/Photolibrary/Getty Images
and Michael Collier)

This image in Guadalupe Mountains National Park, Texas, shows a small portion of an ancient (Permian-age) reef complex that once formed a 600-kilometer loop around the margin of the Delaware Basin.

Aerial view showing a small portion of Australia's Great Barrier Reef. Located off the coast of Queensland, it extends for 2600 kilometers and consists of more than 2900 individual reefs.

FIGURE 15 The White Chalk
Cliffs
This prominent deposit
underlies large portions
of southern England as
well as parts of northern
France. (Photos by Science
Library/Alamy Images; satellite
image courtesy of NASA)

The massive White Chalk Cliffs. Chalk is a biochemical limestone made up almost entirely of the tiny hard parts of microscopic marine organisms.

View of a group of *coccolithophores* from a scanning electron microscope. Individual plates shaped like hubcaps are only three one-thousandths of a millimeter in diameter; so tiny they could pass through the eye of a needle.

Coccolithophores are one-celled marine plants (plankton) that live in large numbers throughout the upper layers of the ocean. The bright blue-green area in the satellite image is a "bloom" of these organisms off the coast of Tasmania. Their skeletons will settle to the ocean floor as biochemical sediment.

Plankton bloom

2 billion years ago. From fossil remains, it is known that a variety of organisms have constructed reefs, including bivalves (clams and oysters), bryozoans (coral-like animals), and sponges. Corals have been found in fossil reefs as old as 500 million years, but corals similar to the modern colonial varieties have constructed reefs only during the past 60 million years.

In the United States, reefs of Silurian age (416 to 444 million years ago) are prominent features in Wisconsin, Illinois, and Indiana. In western Texas and adjacent southeastern New Mexico, a massive reef complex that formed during the Permian period (251 to 299 million years ago) is strikingly exposed in Guadalupe Mountains National Park (see Figure 14).

Coquina and Chalk   Although a great deal of limestone is produced by biological processes, this origin is not always evident because shells and skeletons may undergo considerable change before becoming lithified into rock. However, one easily identified biochemical limestone is *coquina*, a coarse rock composed of poorly cemented shells and shell fragments (Figure 13). Another less obvious but nevertheless familiar example is *chalk*, a soft, porous rock made up almost entirely of the hard parts of microscopic marine organisms. Among the most famous chalk deposits are those exposed along the southeast coast of England (FIGURE 15).

Inorganic Limestones   Limestones having an inorganic origin form when chemical changes or high water temperatures increase the concentration of calcium carbonate to the point that it precipitates. *Travertine*, the type of limestone commonly seen in caves, is an example (see Figure 12). When travertine is deposited in caves, groundwater is the source of the calcium carbonate. As water droplets become exposed to the air in a cavern, some of the carbon dioxide dissolved in the water escapes, causing calcium carbonate to precipitate.

Another variety of inorganic limestone is *oolitic limestone*. It is a rock composed of small spherical grains called *ooids*. Ooids form in shallow marine waters as tiny "seed" particles (commonly small shell fragments) are moved back and forth by currents. As the grains are rolled about in the warm water, which is supersaturated with calcium carbonate, they become coated with layer upon layer of the chemical precipitate (FIGURE 16).

Dolostone

Closely related to limestone is *dolostone*, a rock composed of the calcium-magnesium carbonate mineral dolomite [$CaMg(CO_3)_2$]. Although dolostone and limestone sometimes closely resemble one another, they can be easily distinguished by observing their reaction to

FIGURE 16 Oolitic limestone
An inorganic limestone composed of ooids. Note the dime coin for scale.
(Photos by Marli Miller)

Small spherical grains called *ooids* are formed by chemical precipitation of calcium carbonate around a tiny nucleus and are the raw material for oolitic limestone.

dilute hydrochloric acid. When a drop of acid is placed on limestone, the reaction (fizzing) is obvious. However, unless dolostone is powdered, it will not visibly react to the acid.

The origin of dolostone is not altogether clear and remains a subject of discussion among geologists. No marine organisms produce hard parts of dolomite and the chemical precipitation of dolomite from seawater occurs only under conditions of unusual water chemistry in certain near-shore sites. Yet dolostone is abundant in many ancient sedimentary rock successions.

It appears that significant quantities of dolostone are produced when magnesium-rich waters circulate through limestone and convert calcite to dolomite by the replacement of some calcium ions with magnesium ions (a process called *dolomitization*). However, other dolostones lack evidence that they formed by such a process and their origin remains uncertain.

Chert

Chert is a name used for a number of very compact and hard rocks made of microcrystalline quartz (SiO_2). One well-known form is *flint*, whose dark color results from the organic matter it contains. *Jasper*, a red variety, gets its bright color from iron oxide. The banded form is

Agate

Flint

Jasper

Arrowhead

Petrified wood

called *agate* (FIGURE 17). Agate precipitates in concentric rings within voids in a rock. Its striped appearance is caused by variations in impurities that occur while precipitation is taking place. *Petrified wood* is chert that is made when silica-rich material such as volcanic ash buries trees. Groundwater rich in dissolved silica from

the ash penetrates the wood. As the dissolved silica precipitates, it gradually replaces the wood. The shape and structures such as growth rings are often preserved. Like glass, most chert has a conchoidal fracture. Its hardness, ease of chipping, and ability to hold a sharp edge made chert a favorite of Native Americans for fashioning points for spears and arrows. Because of chert's durability and extensive use, arrowheads are found in many parts of North America.

Chert deposits are commonly found in one of two situations: as layered deposits referred to as *bedded cherts* and as *nodules*, somewhat spherical masses varying in diameter from a few millimeters (pea size) to a few centimeters. Most water-dwelling organisms that produce hard parts make them of calcium carbonate. But some, such as diatoms and radiolarians, produce glasslike silica skeletons. These tiny organisms are able to extract silica even though seawater contains only tiny quantities. It is from their remains that most bedded cherts are believed to originate. Some bedded cherts occur in association with lava flows and layers of volcanic ash. For these occurrences it is probable that the silica was derived from the decomposition of the volcanic ash and not from biochemical sources. Chert nodules are sometimes referred to as *secondary cherts*, or *replacement cherts*, and they most often occur within beds of limestone. They form when silica, originally deposited in one place, dissolves, migrates, and then chemically precipitates elsewhere, replacing older material.

Evaporites

In the geologic past, many areas that are now dry land were basins, submerged under shallow arms of a sea that had only narrow connections to the open ocean. Under these conditions, seawater continually moved into the bay to replace water lost by evaporation. Eventually the waters of the bay became saturated and salt deposition began. Such deposits are called **evaporites**.

Minerals commonly precipitated in this fashion include halite (sodium chloride, NaCl), the chief component of *rock salt*, and gypsum (hydrous calcium sulfate, $CaSO_4 \cdot 2H_2O$), the main ingredient of *rock gypsum* (FIGURE 18). Both have significant importance. Halite is familiar to everyone as the common salt used in cooking and seasoning foods. Of course, it has many other uses, from melting ice on roads to making hydrochloric acid, and it has been considered important enough that people have sought, traded, and fought over it for much of human history. Gypsum is the basic ingredient in plaster of Paris. This material is used most extensively in the construction industry for wallboard and interior plaster.

When a body of seawater evaporates, the minerals that precipitate do so in a sequence that is determined by their solubility. Less soluble minerals precipitate first, and more soluble minerals precipitate later, as salinity increases. For example, gypsum precipitates

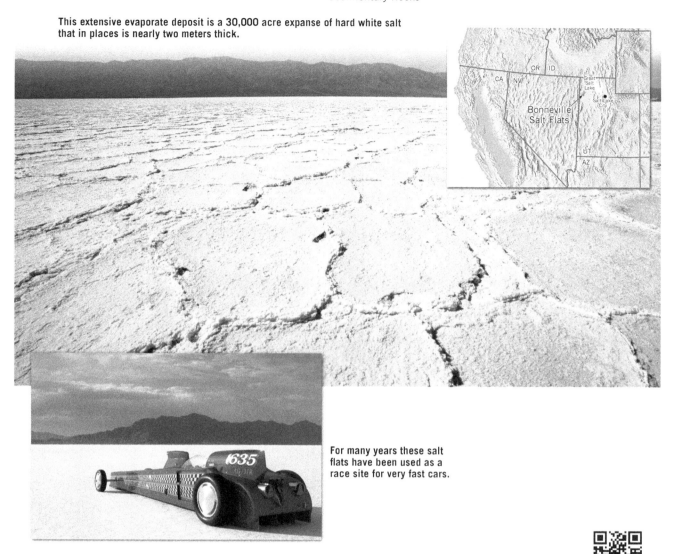

This extensive evaporate deposit is a 30,000 acre expanse of hard white salt that in places is nearly two meters thick.

For many years these salt flats have been used as a race site for very fast cars.

SMARTFIGURE 19 Bonneville salt flats
This well-known Utah site was once a large salt lake. (Photo by Creatas/Photolibrary; inset photo by Stock Connection/Glow Images)

when about 80 percent of the seawater has evaporated, and halite crystallizes when 90 percent of the water has been removed. During the last stages of this process, potassium and magnesium salts precipitate. One of these last-formed salts, the mineral *sylvite*, is mined as a significant source of potassium ("potash") for fertilizer.

On a smaller scale, evaporite deposits can be seen in such places as Death Valley, California. Here, following rains or periods of snowmelt in the mountains, streams flow from the surrounding mountains into an enclosed basin. As the water evaporates, **salt flats** form when

dissolved materials are precipitated as a white crust on the ground (FIGURE 19).

4 CONCEPT CHECKS

1. Explain how the formation of biochemical sediments differs from the formation of sediments formed by inorganic processes. Include examples as part of your explanation.
2. Distinguish among limestone, dolostone, and chert. Describe several varieties of each.
3. How do evaporites form? What are some examples?

Limestone
An Important and Versatile Commodity

Limestone, as defined by the minerals industry, refers to any rock composed mostly of the carbonate minerals calcite and dolomite. The U.S. Geological Survey characterizes limestone as an *"essential mineral commodity of national importance."*

Why is limestone important?

Limestone that has undergone metamorphism is called marble. It is used as floor tile, table and countertops, and as a building stone.

Purified limestone is added to bread and cereal as a source of calcium and is an ingredient in antacid tablets and calcium supplements. It is even used to neutralize acids in wine and beer making!

Limestone is used as a filler and white pigment in many products including paper, plastics, paint, and even toothpaste.

Limestone is a key ingredient in making Portland cement, an essential product to the building industry.

White roofing granules.

USGS

Huge quantities of limestone are crushed and used as aggregate—the solid base of many roads and an ingredient in concrete. It is the raw material for making lime (CaO), which is used to treat soils, purify water, and smelt copper among many uses.

Limestone has been used as a building stone for centuries—from Egypt's ancient pyramids and Europe's medieval castles, to modern buildings such as this.

Martin Bond/Photo Researchers, Inc. B. Christopher/Alamy Images

UNITED STATES

FEDERAL TRADE COMMISSIO BUILDING

5 | Coal: An Organic Sedimentary Rock

Coal is quite different from other rocks. Unlike limestone and chert, which are calcite and silica rich, coal is made of organic matter. Close examination of coal under a magnifying glass often reveals plant structures such as leaves, bark, and wood that have been chemically altered but are still identifiable. This supports the conclusion that coal is the end product of large amounts of plant material, buried for millions of years (FIGURE 20):

- **Accumulation of plant remains.** The initial stage in coal formation is the accumulation of large quantities of plant remains. Special conditions are required for such accumulations because dead plants readily decompose when exposed to the atmosphere or other oxygen-rich environments. One important environment that allows for the buildup of plant material is a swamp. Stagnant swamp water is oxygen deficient, so complete decay (oxidation) of the plant material is not possible. Instead, the plants are attacked by certain bacteria that partly decompose the organic material and liberate oxygen and hydrogen. As these elements escape, the percentage of carbon gradually increases. The bacteria are not able to finish the job of decomposition because their growth is impeded by acids liberated from the plants.

- **Formation of peat.** The partial decomposition of plant remains in an oxygen-poor swamp creates a layer of *peat*, a soft brown material in which plant structures are still easily recognized. With shallow burial, peat slowly changes to *lignite*, a soft brown coal. Burial increases the temperature of sediments as well as the pressure on them.

- **Formation of lignite and bituminous coal.** The higher temperatures bring about chemical reactions within the plant materials and yield water and organic gases (volatiles). As the load increases from more sediment on top of the developing coal, the water and volatiles are pressed out, and the proportion of *fixed carbon* (the remaining solid combustible material) increases. The greater the carbon content, the greater the coal's energy ranking as a fuel. During burial, the coal also becomes increasingly compact. For example, deeper burial transforms lignite into a harder, more compacted black rock called *bituminous* coal. Compared to the peat from which it

SWAMP ENVIRONMENT

Burial

Compaction

Greater burial

Compaction

Metamorphism

Stress

PEAT
(Partially altered plant material)

LIGNITE
(Soft, brown coal)

BITUMINOUS
(Soft, black coal)

ANTHRACITE
(Hard, black coal)

SMARTFIGURE 20
From plants to coal
Successive stages in the formation of coal. (Photos by E. J. Tarbuck)

formed, a bed of bituminous coal may be only 1/10 as thick.

- **Formation of anthracite coal.** Lignite and bituminous coals are sedimentary rocks. However, when sedimentary layers are subjected to the folding and deformation associated with mountain building, the heat and pressure cause a further loss of volatiles and water, thus increasing the concentration of fixed carbon. This metamorphoses bituminous coal into *anthracite*, a very hard, shiny, black *metamorphic* rock. Although anthracite is a clean-burning fuel, only a relatively small amount

is mined. Anthracite is not widespread and is more difficult and expensive to extract than the relatively flat-lying layers of bituminous coal.

5 CONCEPT CHECKS

1. What is the "raw material" for coal? Under what circumstances does it accumulate?
2. Outline the successive stages in the formation of coal.

EYE on Earth

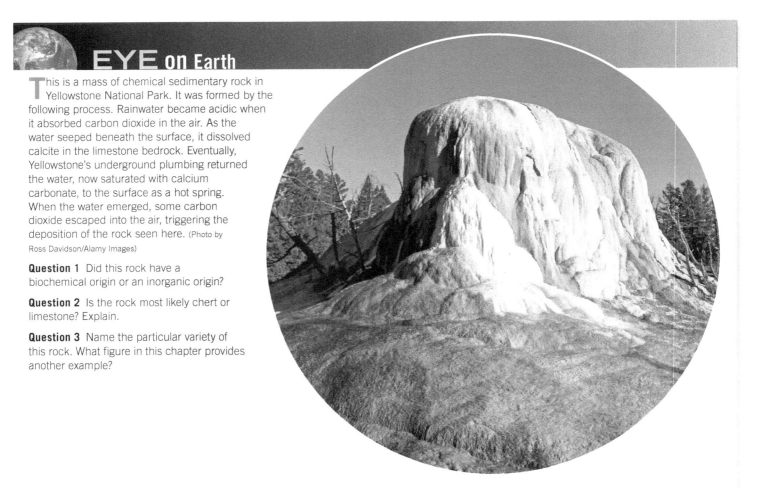

This is a mass of chemical sedimentary rock in Yellowstone National Park. It was formed by the following process. Rainwater became acidic when it absorbed carbon dioxide in the air. As the water seeped beneath the surface, it dissolved calcite in the limestone bedrock. Eventually, Yellowstone's underground plumbing returned the water, now saturated with calcium carbonate, to the surface as a hot spring. When the water emerged, some carbon dioxide escaped into the air, triggering the deposition of the rock seen here. (Photo by Ross Davidson/Alamy Images)

Question 1 Did this rock have a biochemical origin or an inorganic origin?

Question 2 Is the rock most likely chert or limestone? Explain.

Question 3 Name the particular variety of this rock. What figure in this chapter provides another example?

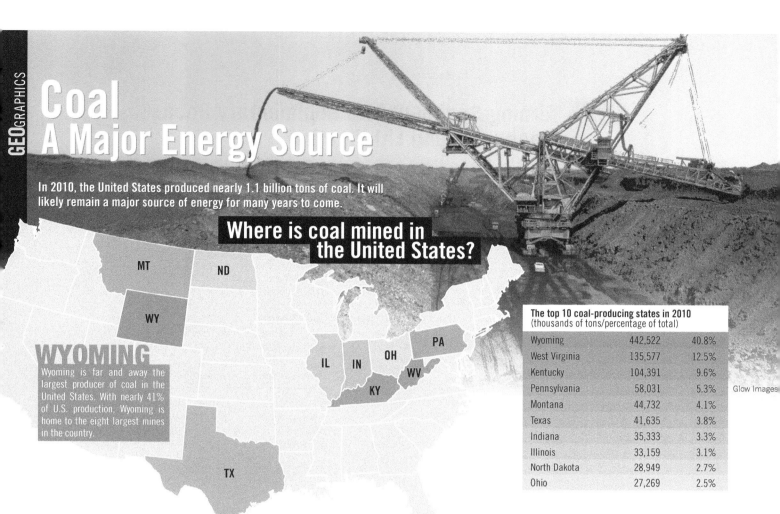

GEOGRAPHICS

Coal
A Major Energy Source

In 2010, the United States produced nearly 1.1 billion tons of coal. It will likely remain a major source of energy for many years to come.

Where is coal mined in the United States?

WYOMING

Wyoming is far and away the largest producer of coal in the United States. With nearly 41% of U.S. production, Wyoming is home to the eight largest mines in the country.

Glow Images

The top 10 coal-producing states in 2010 (thousands of tons/percentage of total)		
Wyoming	442,522	40.8%
West Virginia	135,577	12.5%
Kentucky	104,391	9.6%
Pennsylvania	58,031	5.3%
Montana	44,732	4.1%
Texas	41,635	3.8%
Indiana	35,333	3.3%
Illinois	33,159	3.1%
North Dakota	28,949	2.7%
Ohio	27,269	2.5%

What type of coal is mined?

Subbituminous coal is 35 to 45% carbon. Large quantities occur in thick beds near the surface, resulting in low mining costs. Wyoming is the major source of this type.

Bituminous coal Coal classified as bituminous has the widest range of carbon content—45 to 86%. West Virginia leads production, followed by Kentucky and Pennsylvania.

47%

45%

0.2%

7%

Anthracite coal has the highest carbon content—86 to 97%. It is relatively rare in the United States and is more difficult to mine. All of the mines are in northeastern Pennsylvania.

Lignite coal has a low carbon content of 25 to 35% and therefore the lowest energy content of the four types. Texas and North Dakota are the leading producers.

How important is coal as a source of energy?

In 2010 coal represented 21% of total U.S. energy production. The vast bulk was used to generate 45% of U.S. electricity. The U.S. Energy Information Administration projects that coal will be a very important energy source for decades to come.

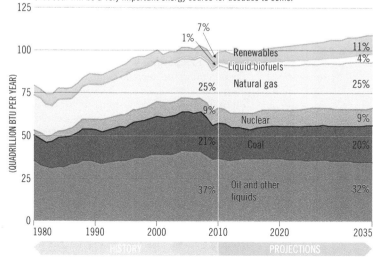

(QUADRILLION BTU PER YEAR)

125

100

75

50

25

0

1980   1990   2000   2010   2020   2035

1%   7%

Renewables   11%

Liquid biofuels   4%

25%   Natural gas   25%

9%   Nuclear   9%

21%   Coal   20%

37%   Oil and other liquids   32%

HISTORY   PROJECTIONS

261

Turning Sediment into Sedimentary Rock: Diagenesis and Lithification

A great deal of change can occur to sediment from the time it is deposited until it becomes a sedimentary rock and is subsequently subjected to the temperatures and pressures that convert it to metamorphic rock. The term **diagenesis** (*dia* = change, *genesis* = origin) is a collective term for all the chemical, physical, and biological changes that take place after sediments are deposited and during and after lithification.

Diagenesis

Burial promotes diagenesis because as sediments are buried, they are subjected to increasingly higher temperatures and pressures. Diagenesis occurs within the upper few kilometers of Earth's crust at temperatures that are generally less than 150° to 200°C (300° to 400°F). Beyond this somewhat arbitrary threshold, metamorphism is said to occur.

One example of diagenetic change is *recrystallization*, the development of more stable minerals from less stable ones. For example, the mineral aragonite is the less stable form of calcium carbonate ($CaCO_3$). Aragonite is secreted by many marine organisms to form shells and other hard parts, such as the skeletal structures produced by corals. In some environments, large quantities of these solid materials accumulate as sediment. As burial takes place, aragonite recrystallizes to the more stable form of calcium carbonate, calcite, the main constituent in the sedimentary rock limestone.

Another example of diagenesis is provided in the preceding discussion of coal. It involves the chemical alteration of organic matter in an oxygen-poor environment. Instead of completely decaying, as would occur in the presence of oxygen, the organic matter is slowly transformed into solid carbon.

Lithification

Diagenesis includes **lithification**, the processes by which unconsolidated sediments are transformed into solid sedimentary rocks (*lithos* = stone, *fic* = making). Basic lithification processes include compaction and cementation.

Compaction   The most common physical diagenetic change is **compaction**. As sediment accumulates, the weight of overlying material compresses the deeper sediments. The deeper a sediment is buried, the more it is compacted and the firmer it becomes. As the grains are pressed closer and closer, there is considerable reduction in pore space (the open space between particles). For example, when clays are buried beneath several thousand meters of material, the volume of the clay layer may be reduced by as much as 40 percent. As pore space decreases, much of the water that was trapped in the sediments is

driven out. Because sands and other coarse sediments are less compressible, compaction is most significant as a lithification process in fine-grained sedimentary rocks.

Cementation   The most important process by which sediments are converted to sedimentary rock is **cementation**. It is a change that involves the crystallization of minerals among the individual sediment grains. Groundwater carries ions in solution. Gradually, the crystallization of new minerals from these ions takes place in the pore spaces, cementing the clasts together. Just as the amount of pore space is reduced during compaction, the addition of cement into a sedimentary deposit reduces its porosity as well.

Calcite, silica, and iron oxide are the most common cements. It is often a relatively simple matter to identify the cementing material. Calcite cement will effervesce with dilute hydrochloric acid. Silica is the hardest cement and thus produces the hardest sedimentary rocks. An orange or dark-red color in a sedimentary rock means that iron oxide is present.

Most sedimentary rocks are lithified by means of compaction and cementation. However, some initially form as solid masses of intergrown crystals rather than beginning as accumulations of separate particles that later become solid. Other crystalline sedimentary rocks do not begin that way but are transformed into masses of interlocking crystals sometime after the sediment is deposited.

For example, with time and burial, loose sediment consisting of delicate calcium carbonate–rich skeletal debris may be recrystallized into a relatively dense crystalline limestone. Because crystals grow until they fill all the available space, pore spaces are frequently lacking in crystalline sedimentary rocks. Unless the rocks later develop joints and fractures, they will be relatively impermeable to fluids such as water and oil.

6 CONCEPT CHECKS

1. What is diagenesis?
2. Compaction is most important as a lithification process with which sediment size?
3. List three common cements. How might each be identified?

7 Classification of Sedimentary Rocks

The classification scheme in FIGURE 21 divides sedimentary rocks into major groups: detrital on the left side and chemical/organic on the right. Further, we can see that the main criterion for subdividing the detrital rocks is particle size, whereas the primary basis for distinguishing among different rocks in the chemical group is their mineral composition.

As is the case with many (perhaps most) classifications of natural phenomena, the categories presented in Figure 21 are more rigid than the actual state of nature. In reality, many of the sedimentary rocks classified into the chemical group also contain at least small quantities of detrital sediment. Many limestones, for example, contain varying amounts of mud or sand, giving them a "sandy" or "shaly" quality. Conversely, because practically all detrital rocks are cemented with material that was originally dissolved in water, they too are far from being "pure."

Texture is a part of sedimentary rock classification. There are two major textures used in the classification of sedimentary rocks: clastic and nonclastic. The term **clastic** is taken from a Greek word meaning "broken." Rocks that display a clastic texture consist of discrete fragments and particles that are cemented and compacted together. Although cement is present in the spaces between particles, these openings are rarely filled completely. All detrital rocks have a clastic texture. In addition, some chemical sedimentary rocks exhibit this texture. For example, coquina, the limestone composed of shells and shell fragments, is obviously as clastic as a conglomerate or sandstone. The same applies for some varieties of oolitic limestone.

Some chemical sedimentary rocks have a **nonclastic** or **crystalline** texture, in which the minerals form a pattern of interlocking crystals. The crystals may be microscopically small or large enough to

Detrital Sedimentary Rocks

Clastic Texture (particle size)		Sediment Name	Rock Name
Coarse (over 2 mm)		Gravel (Rounded particles)	Conglomerate
		Gravel (Angular particles)	Breccia
Medium (1/16 to 2 mm)		Sand	Sandstone (Arkose)*
Fine (1/16 to 1/256 mm)		Mud	Siltstone
Very fine (less than 1/256 mm)		Mud	Shale or Mudstone

*If abundant feldspar is present the rock is called Arkose.

Chemical and Organic Sedimentary Rocks

Composition	Texture	Rock Name	
Calcite, $CaCO_3$	Nonclastic: Fine to coarse crystalline	Crystalline Limestone	
		Travertine	
	Clastic: Visible shells and shell fragments loosely cemented	Coquina	Biochemical Limestone
	Clastic: Various size shells and shell fragments cemented with calcite cement	Fossiliferous Limestone	
	Clastic: Microscopic shells and clay	Chalk	
Quartz, SiO_2	Nonclastic: Very fine crystalline	Chert (light colored) Flint (dark colored) Jasper (red) Agate (banded)	
Gypsum $CaSO_4 \cdot 2H_2O$	Nonclastic: Fine to coarse crystalline	Rock Gypsum	
Halite, NaCl	Nonclastic: Fine to coarse crystalline	Rock Salt	
Altered plant fragments	Nonclastic: Fine-grained organic matter	Bituminous Coal	

FIGURE 21 Identification of sedimentary rocks
The main criterion for naming detrital rocks is particle size. The primary basis for naming chemical and organic sedimentary rocks is their composition.

Close up

actually have originated as detrital deposits. In these instances, the particles probably consisted of shell fragments and other hard parts rich in calcium carbonate or silica. The clastic nature of the grains was subsequently obliterated or obscured because the particles recrystallized when they were consolidated into limestone or chert.

Nonclastic rocks consist of intergrown crystals, and some may resemble igneous rocks, which are also crystalline. The two rock types are usually easy to distinguish because the minerals contained in nonclastic sedimentary rocks are quite unlike those found in most igneous rocks. For example, rock salt, rock gypsum, and some forms of limestone consist of intergrown crystals, but the minerals within these rocks (halite, gypsum, and calcite) are seldom associated with igneous rocks.

be visible without magnification. Common examples of rocks with nonclastic textures are those deposited when saline water evaporates (FIGURE 22). The materials that make up many other nonclastic rocks may

7 CONCEPT CHECKS

1. What is the primary basis for distinguishing (naming) different chemical sedimentary rocks? How is the naming of detrital rocks different?
2. Distinguish between clastic and nonclastic. Which texture is associated with all detrital rocks?

8 Sedimentary Rocks Represent Past Environments

Sedimentary rocks are important in the interpretation of Earth history. By understanding the conditions under which sedimentary rocks form, geologists can often deduce the history of a rock, including information about the origin of its component particles, the method of sediment transport, and the nature of the place where the grains eventually came to rest; that is, the environment of deposition.

An **environment of deposition**, or **sedimentary environment**, is a geographic setting where sediment is accumulating. Each site is characterized by a particular combination of geologic processes and environmental conditions. Some sediments, such as the chemical sediments that precipitate in water bodies, are solely the product of their sedimentary environment. That is, their component minerals originated and were deposited in the same place. Other sediments originate far from the site where they accumulate. These materials are transported great distances from their source by some combination of gravity, water, wind, and ice.

At any given time, the geographic setting and environmental conditions of a sedimentary environment determine the nature of the sediments that accumulate. Therefore, geologists carefully study the sediments in present-day depositional environments because the features they find can also be observed in ancient sedimentary rocks.

By applying a thorough knowledge of present-day conditions, geologists attempt to reconstruct the ancient environments and geographic relationships of an area at the time a particular set of sedimentary layers were deposited. Such analyses often lead to the creation of maps, which depict the geographic distribution of land and sea, mountains and river valleys, deserts and glaciers, and other environments of deposition. The foregoing description is an excellent example of the application of a fundamental principle of modern geology: "The present is the key to the past."

Types of Sedimentary Environments

Sedimentary environments are commonly placed into one of three broad categories: continental, marine, or transitional (shoreline). Each category includes many specific subenvironments. FIGURE 23 is an idealized diagram illustrating a number of important sedimentary environments associated with each category. Realize that this is just a sampling of the great diversity of depositional environments. The remainder of this section provides a brief overview of each category. Each of these three categories is an area where sediment accumulates and where organisms live and die. Each

produces a characteristic sedimentary rock or assemblage that reflects prevailing conditions.

Continental Environments   Continental environments are dominated by the erosion and deposition associated with streams. In some cold regions, moving masses of glacial ice replace running water as the dominant process. In arid regions (as well as some coastal settings) wind takes on greater importance. Clearly, the nature of the sediments deposited in continental environments is strongly influenced by climate.

Streams are the dominant agent of landscape alteration, eroding more land and transporting and depositing more sediment than any other process. In addition to channel deposits, large quantities of sediment are dropped when floodwaters periodically inundate broad, flat valley floors (called *floodplains*). Where rapid streams emerge from a mountainous area onto a flatter surface, a distinctive cone-shaped accumulation of sediment known as an *alluvial fan* forms.

In frigid, high-latitude or high-altitude settings, glaciers pick up and transport huge volumes of sediment. Materials deposited directly from ice are typically unsorted mixtures of particles that range in size from clay to boulders. Water from melting glaciers transports and redeposits some of the glacial sediment, creating stratified, sorted accumulations.

The work of wind and its resulting deposits are referred to as *eolian*, after Aeolus, the Greek god of wind. Unlike glacial deposits, eolian sediments are well sorted. Wind can lift fine dust high into the atmosphere and transport it great distances. Where winds are strong and the surface is not anchored by vegetation, sand is transported closer to the ground, where it accumulates in *dunes*. Deserts and coasts are common sites for this type of deposition.

In addition to being areas where dunes sometimes develop, desert basins are the sites where shallow *playa lakes* occasionally form following heavy rains or periods of snowmelt in adjacent mountains. They rapidly dry up, sometimes leaving behind evaporites and other characteristic deposits. In humid regions lakes are more enduring features, and their quiet waters are excellent sediment traps. Small deltas, beaches, and bars form along

FIGURE 23 Sedimentary environments

Each environment is characterized by certain physical, chemical, and biological conditions. Because sediments contain clues about the environment in which they were deposited, sedimentary rocks are important in the interpretation of Earth history. A number of important examples are represented in this idealized diagram.

Sand dunes consist of well-sorted sand grains deposited by the wind.

Caves that develop in limestone are sites where calcium carbonate is deposited as dripstone.

Beaches that form where wave activity is strong, consist mainly of pebbles and cobbles.

Beaches, bars, and **spits** along low-lying coasts and in sheltered coves are typically composed of well-sorted sand and/or shell fragments.

Salt flat

Lake

Estuary

Deep-sea fans

Tidal flats and **lagoons** are areas where fine clay particles or carbonate-rich muds accumulate.

Turbidity current

Deep marine environments adjacent to the continental slope often contain material that was transported by dense underwater currents of suspended sediment. Each layer has coarser particles at the bottom and finer material on top.

Shallow marine environments are sites where sand, clay, and carbonate-rich muds are often deposited. Ripple marks caused by wave activity may be present.

Inland seas and **lakes** in arid environments where evaporation exceeds precipitation, produce evaporite deposits such as rock salt and gypsum.

Alluvial fans consist of coarse sediments that are deposited when mountain streams reach flat lowlands.

Glacial deposits often consist of a poorly-sorted mixture of many different sediment sizes ranging from clay to boulders.

Salt flat

Alluvial fans

Inland lake

Swamp

Delta

Swamps and **bogs** are quiet-water environments where mud and decayed plant material accumulate.

Streams in mountainous areas erode and deposit a wide variety of sediment, while those in lowlands transport and deposit mostly mud (silt and clay) and sand.

Landslides produce an unsorted jumble of many sediment sizes.

Coral reefs are massive limestone structures that form in warm, shallow clear seas and consist of material secreted by corals and other marine life.

the lakeshore, with finer sediments coming to rest on the lake floor.

Marine Environments   Marine depositional environments are divided according to depth. The *shallow marine* environment reaches to depths of about 200 meters (nearly 700 feet) and extends from the shore to the outer edge of the continental shelf. The *deep marine* environment lies seaward of the continental shelf in waters deeper than 200 meters.

The shallow marine environment borders all of the world's continents. Its width varies greatly, from practically nonexistent in some places to broad expanses extending as far as 1500 kilometers (more than 900 miles) in other locations. On average this zone is about 80 kilometers (50 miles) wide. The kind of sediment deposited here depends on several factors, including distance from shore, the elevation of the adjacent land area, water depth, water temperature, and climate.

Due to the ongoing erosion of the adjacent continent, the shallow marine environment receives huge quantities of land-derived sediment. Where the influx of such sediment is small and the seas are relatively warm, carbonate-rich muds may be the predominant sediment. Most of this material consists of the skeletal debris of carbonate-secreting organisms mixed with inorganic precipitates. Coral reefs are also associated with warm, shallow marine environments. In hot regions where the sea occupies a basin with restricted circulation, evaporation triggers the precipitation of soluble materials and the formation of marine evaporite deposits.

Deep marine environments include all the floors of the deep ocean. Far from landmasses, tiny particles from many sources remain adrift for long spans. Gradually these small grains "rain" down on the ocean floor, where they accumulate very slowly. Significant exceptions are thick deposits of relatively coarse sediment that occur at the base of the continental slope. These materials move down from the continental shelf as turbidity currents—dense gravity-driven masses of sediment and water (see Figure 27).

Transitional Environments   The shoreline is the transition zone between marine and continental environments. Here we find the familiar deposits of sand or gravel called *beaches*. Mud-covered *tidal flats* are alternately covered with shallow sheets of water and then exposed to air as tides rise and fall. Along and near the shore, the work of waves and currents distributes sand, creating *spits*, *bars*, and *barrier islands*. Offshore bars

EYE on Earth

This is an aerial view of North Carolina's Hatteras Island (looking toward the south). To the left (east) of the island is the Atlantic Ocean. The sheltered waters of Pamlico Sound are on the right, the side of the island facing the mainland. Assume that the sediments accumulating in the area are primarily detrital.
(Photo by Michael Collier)

Question 1 If you were to sample the sediments at points A and B, which would likely have the coarser particles?

Question 2 Explain why the sediments at these two sites would probably be different.

Question 3 Which one of the three broad categories of sedimentary environments is represented in this image?

and reefs create *lagoons.* The quieter waters in these sheltered areas are another site of deposition in the transition zone.

Deltas are among the most significant deposits associated with transitional environments. The complex accumulations of sediment build outward into the sea when rivers experience an abrupt loss of velocity and drop their load of detrital debris.

Sedimentary Facies

When we study a series of sedimentary layers, we can see the successive changes in environmental conditions that occurred at a particular place with the passage of time. Changes in past environments may also be seen when a single layer of sedimentary rock is traced laterally. This is true because at any one time, many different depositional environments can exist over a broad area. For example, when sand is accumulating in a beach environment, finer muds are often being deposited in quieter offshore waters. Still farther out, perhaps in a zone where biological activity is high and land-derived sediments are scarce, the deposits consist largely of the calcite-rich remains of small organisms. In this example, different sediments are accumulating adjacent to one another at the same time. Different parts of each layer possess a distinctive set of characteristics that reflect the conditions in a particular environment. To describe such sets of sediments, the term **facies** is used. When a sedimentary layer is examined in cross section from one end to the other, each facies grades laterally into another that formed at the

 SMARTFIGURE 24 **Lateral change**
When a sedimentary layer is traced laterally, we may find that it is made up of several different rock types. This occurs because many sedimentary environments can exist at the same time over a broad area. The term *facies* is used to describe such sets of sedimentary rocks. Each facies grades laterally into another that formed at the same time but in a different environment.

same time but that exhibits different characteristics (FIGURE 24). The merging of adjacent facies tends to be a gradual transition rather than a sharp boundary, but abrupt changes do sometimes occur.

8 CONCEPT CHECKS

1. What are the three broad categories of sedimentary environments?
2. List specific examples associated with each category.
3. Why might a single layer exhibit different types of sedimentary rock? What term applies to the different parts of such a layer?

Los Osos Creek entering California's Morro Bay. The sediment being deposited in this transitional environment has created a delta.
(Photo by Michael Collier)

9 Sedimentary Structures

In addition to variations in grain size, mineral composition, and texture, sediments exhibit a variety of structures that are often preserved when they change to sedimentary rock. Some, such as graded beds, are created when sediments are accumulating and are a reflection of the transporting medium. Others, such as *mud cracks*, form after the materials have been deposited and result from processes occurring in the environment. When present, sedimentary structures provide additional information that can be useful in the interpretation of Earth history.

Sedimentary rocks form as layer upon layer of sediment accumulates in various depositional environments. These layers, called **strata**, or **beds**, are probably *the single most common and characteristic feature of sedimentary rocks.* Each stratum is unique. It may be a coarse sandstone, a fossil-rich limestone, a black shale, and so on. When you look at FIGURE 25, or look back at the chapter-opening photo and at Figures 1 and 5, you see many such layers, each different from the others. The variations in texture, composition, and thickness reflect the different conditions under which each layer was deposited.

The thickness of beds ranges from microscopically thin to tens of meters thick. Separating the strata are **bedding planes**, relatively flat surfaces along which rocks tend to separate or break. Changes in the grain size or in the composition of the sediment being deposited can create bedding planes. Pauses in deposition can also lead to layering because chances are slight that newly deposited material will be exactly the same as previously deposited sediment. Generally, each bedding plane marks the end of one episode of sedimentation and the beginning of another.

Because sediments usually accumulate as particles that settle from a fluid, most strata are originally deposited as horizontal layers. There are circumstances, however, when sediments do not accumulate in horizontal beds. Sometimes when a bed of sedimentary rock is examined, we see layers within it that are inclined to the horizontal. This is called **cross-bedding**, and it is most characteristic of sand dunes, river deltas, and certain stream channel deposits (FIGURE 26).

Graded beds represent another special type of bedding. In this case, the particles within a single

This outcrop of sedimentary strata illustrates the characteristic layering of this group of rocks. Karijini National Park, Western Australia. (Photo by S. Sailer/A. Sailer/AGE Fotostock)

The cutaway section of this sand dune shows the characteristic cross-bedding

The cross-bedding in this sandstone indicates it was once a sand dune

Weathered bedding planes within unit

Principal bedding surfaces

Cross-bedding unit

Steep truncated cross-beds

0 1 2 3 meters

John Shelton

John S. Shelton/University of Washington Libraries

FIGURE 26 Cross-bedding
Sand dunes typically exhibit thin layers inclined at an angle to the main bedding.

sedimentary layer gradually change from coarse at the bottom to fine at the top. Graded beds are most characteristic of rapid deposition from water containing sediment of varying sizes. When a current experiences a rapid energy loss, the largest particles settle first, followed by successively smaller grains. The deposition of a graded bed is most often associated with a turbidity current, a mass of sediment-choked water that is denser than clear water and that moves downslope along the bottom of a lake or an ocean (FIGURE 27).

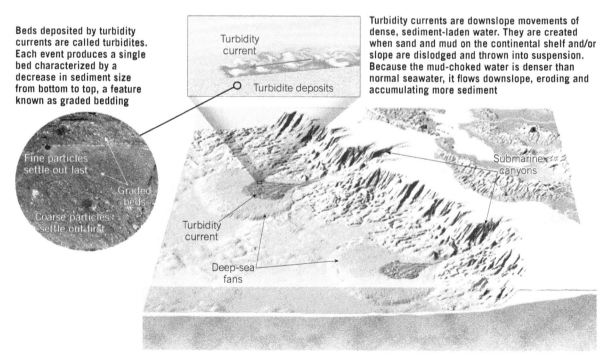

Beds deposited by turbidity currents are called turbidites. Each event produces a single bed characterized by a decrease in sediment size from bottom to top, a feature known as graded bedding

Turbidity current

Turbidite deposits

Fine particles settle out last

Graded beds

Coarse particles settle out first

Turbidity currents are downslope movements of dense, sediment-laden water. They are created when sand and mud on the continental shelf and/or slope are dislodged and thrown into suspension. Because the mud-choked water is denser than normal seawater, it flows downslope, eroding and accumulating more sediment

Turbidity current

Submarine canyons

Deep-sea fans

FIGURE 27 Graded bedding
A graded bed is characterized by a decrease in sediment size from bottom to top. Graded beds are associated with submarine currents known as *turbidity currents*. (Photo by Marli Miller)

271

As geologists examine sedimentary rocks, they can deduce quite a bit. A conglomerate, for example, may indicate a high-energy environment, such as a surf zone or rushing stream, where only coarse materials remain and finer particles are kept suspended (FIGURE 28). If the rock is arkose, it may signify a dry climate, where little chemical alteration of feldspar is possible. Carbonaceous shale is a sign of a low-energy, organic-rich environment, such as a swamp or lagoon.

Other features found in some sedimentary rocks also give clues to past environments. Ripple marks are such a feature. **Ripple marks** are small waves of sand that develop on the surface of a sediment layer by the action of moving water or air (FIGURE 29). The ridges form at right angles to the direction of motion. If the ripple marks were formed by air or water moving in essentially one direction, their form will be asymmetrical. These *current ripple marks* will have steeper sides in the downcurrent direction and more gradual slopes on the upcurrent side. Ripple marks produced by

FIGURE 28 Streams sort sediment
A rushing stream is a high-energy environment in which only large particles settle out. (Photo by Kharlamov Igor Viktorovich/Shutterstock)

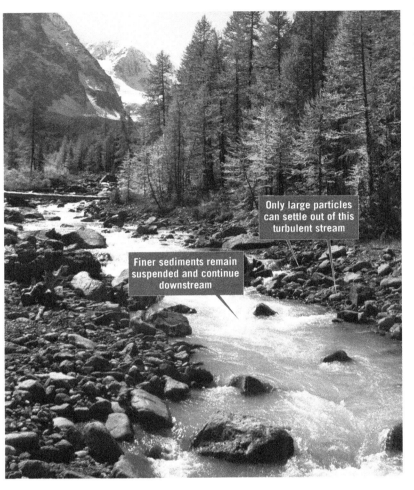

Only large particles can settle out of this turbulent stream

Finer sediments remain suspended and continue downstream

FIGURE 29 Frozen in stone
These current ripple marks formed in sandy sediment and are now preserved in rock. (Photo by Tim Graham/ Alamy Images)

FIGURE 31 Fossils—clues to the past
Fossils, the remains or traces of prehistoric life are primarily associated with sediments and sedimentary rocks. A great variety of trilobites are associated with the Paleozoic era. (Photo by Russell Shively/ Shutterstock) The impressions are dinosaur footprints (Photo by José Antonio Hernaiz/AGE Fotostock).

FIGURE 30 Mud cracks
When muddy sediments dry out, they shrink and create cracks. When the sediment is turned into rock, the cracks are preserved. (Photo by Marli Miller)

a stream flowing across a sandy channel and by wind blowing over a sand dune are two common examples of current ripples. When present in solid rock, they may be used to determine the direction of movement of ancient wind or water currents. Other ripple marks have a symmetrical form. These features, called *oscillation ripple marks*, result from the back-and-forth movement of surface waves in a shallow near-shore environment.

Mud cracks (FIGURE 30) indicate that the sediment in which they were formed was alternately wet and dry. When exposed to air, wet mud dries out and shrinks, producing cracks. Mud cracks are associated with such environments as tidal flats, shallow lakes, and desert basins.

Fossils, the remains or traces of prehistoric life, are important inclusions in sediment and sedimentary rocks (FIGURE 31). They are important tools for interpreting the geologic past. Knowing the nature of the life-forms that existed at a particular time helps researchers understand past environmental conditions. Further, fossils are im-

portant time indicators and play a key role in correlating rocks of similar ages that are from different places.

9 CONCEPT CHECKS

1. What is the single most characteristic feature of sedimentary rocks?
2. What is the difference between cross-bedding and graded bedding?
3. How might mud cracks and ripple marks be useful clues about the geologic past?

10 The Carbon Cycle and Sedimentary Rocks

To illustrate the movement of material and energy among the spheres of the Earth system, let us take a brief look at the *carbon cycle* (FIGURE 32). Most carbon is bonded chemically to other elements to form compounds such as carbon dioxide, calcium carbonate, and the hydrocarbons found in coal and petroleum. Carbon is also the basic building block of life, as it readily combines with hydrogen and oxygen to form the fundamental organic compounds that compose living things.

Certainly one of the most active parts of the carbon cycle is the movement of CO_2 from the atmosphere to the biosphere and back again. In the atmosphere, carbon is found mainly as carbon dioxide (CO_2). Atmospheric carbon dioxide is significant because it is a greenhouse gas, which means it is an efficient absorber of energy emitted by Earth and thus influences the heating of the atmosphere. Because many of the processes that operate on Earth involve carbon dioxide, this gas is constantly moving into and out of the atmosphere. Through the process of photosynthesis, plants absorb carbon dioxide from the atmosphere to produce the essential organic compounds needed for growth. Animals that consume these plants (or that consume other animals that eat plants) use these organic compounds as a source of energy and, through the process of respiration, return carbon dioxide to the atmosphere. (Plants also return some CO_2 to the atmosphere via respiration.) Further, when plants die and decay or are burned, this biomass is oxidized, and carbon dioxide is returned to the atmosphere.

Not all dead plant material decays immediately back to carbon dioxide. A small percentage is deposited as sediment. Over long spans of geologic time, considerable biomass is buried with sediment. Under the right conditions, some of these carbon-rich deposits are converted to fossil fuels—coal, petroleum, or natural gas. Eventually some of the fuels are recovered (mined or pumped from a well) and burned to generate electricity and fuel our transportation system. One result of fossil-fuel combustion is the release of huge quantities of CO_2 into the atmosphere. Carbon also moves from the geosphere and hydrosphere to the atmosphere and back again. For example, volcanic activity early in Earth's history is thought to be the source of much of the carbon dioxide found in the atmosphere. One way that carbon dioxide makes its way back to the hydrosphere and then to the solid Earth is by first combining with water to form carbonic acid (H_2CO_3), which then attacks the rocks that compose Earth's crust. One product of this chemical weathering of solid rock is the soluble bicarbonate ion (HCO_3^-) which is carried by groundwater and streams to the ocean. Water-dwelling organisms extract this dissolved material to produce hard parts of calcium carbonate ($CaCO_3$). When the organisms die, these skeletal remains settle to the ocean floor as biochemical sediment and become sedimentary rock. In fact, the crust is by far Earth's largest depository of carbon, where it is a constituent of a variety of rocks, the most abundant being limestone. Eventually the limestone may be exposed at Earth's surface, where chemical weathering will cause the carbon stored in the rock to be released to the atmosphere as CO_2.

In summary, carbon moves among all four of Earth's major spheres. It is essential to every living thing in the biosphere. In the atmosphere, carbon dioxide is an important greenhouse gas. In the hydrosphere, carbon dioxide is dissolved in lakes, rivers, and the ocean. In the geosphere, carbon is contained in carbonate sediments and sedimentary rocks and is stored as organic matter dispersed through sedimentary rocks and as deposits of coal and petroleum.

FIGURE 32 Carbon cycle
This simplified diagram emphasizes the flow of carbon between the atmosphere and the hydrosphere, geosphere, and biosphere. The arrows show whether the flow of carbon is into or out of the atmosphere.

10 CONCEPT CHECKS

1. Describe how chemical weathering and the formation of biochemical sediment remove carbon from the atmosphere and store it in the geosphere.
2. Provide an example by which carbon moves from the geosphere to the atmosphere.

CONCEPTS IN REVIEW: SEDIMENTARY ROCKS

1 The Importance of Sedimentary Rocks

Discuss the importance of sedimentary rocks to the study of geology and to the general public.

- Though igneous and metamorphic rocks make up most of the crust by volume, sediment and sedimentary rocks are concentrated near the surface. There, at the interface between Earth's four spheres, sediments and the rock layers that they eventually form make a record of past conditions and events at the surface. Sedimentary rocks contain fossils that show the evolution of life over time.
- Numerous geologic resources are restricted to sedimentary rocks, such as coal, oil, uranium, and several major ores of metals.

DIFFERENT STROKES

Why would a pale-ontologist care about sedimentary rocks? What about an exploration geologist working in the oil industry? What about an environmental activist?

Dennis Tasa

The organic sedimentary rock coal is an important geologic resource.

2 Origins of Sedimentary Rock

Summarize the part of the rock cycle that pertains to sediments and sedimentary rocks and distinguish among the three categories of sedimentary rocks.

KEY WORDS sedimentary rocks, detrital sedimentary rocks, chemical sedimentary rocks, organic sedimentary rocks

- Sediments are the raw materials from which sedimentary rocks are made. Sediments are produced from the weathering of preexisting rocks. Both solid particles of many sizes and chemical residues, including ions in solution, qualify as sediments.

- Once produced, sediments leave their source area and are transported by water currents, wind, or simply downhill movement under the influence of gravity. Eventually, they will be deposited at a new site. There, they will be compacted and/or cemented so that the individual sediments become bonded together into a sedimentary rock.
- There are three main varieties of sedimentary rocks: detrital, chemical, and organic.

CYCLES How could a sedimentary rock be transformed into another sedimentary rock? What processes would be necessary? In what order?

3 Detrital Sedimentary Rocks

Discuss the primary basis for distinguishing among detrital rocks and describe how the origin and history of such rocks might be determined.

KEY WORDS fissility, sorting

- Detrital sedimentary rocks are made of solid particles, mostly quartz grains and microscopic clay minerals. Quartz and clay dominate because unlike most other minerals, they are stable at Earth's surface. Feldspars and micas are conspicuous additions to certain detrital sediments, indicating a relatively short time in the chemical weathering environment; they were physically weathered, transported a relatively short distance, and deposited with minimal decomposition.
- Detrital sedimentary rocks are classified mainly based on the size of the sedimentary grains of which they are composed. Bigger particles indicate more powerful transporting currents. Finer grains can be deposited only where current energy is relatively low. So grain size is a clue about how energetic the environment of deposition was for a detrital sedimentary rock.
- Shale is made mostly of small grains of clay minerals. It accumulates in low-energy depositional environments such as the deep sea, lake bottoms, and floodplains adjacent to rivers. Shale is fissile due to the alignment of microscopic clay flakes parallel to bedding. Shale containing a lot of organic material accumulates in low-oxygen environments and is characterized by a black color.
- Sandstone is dominated by sand-sized grains. Sandstones may exhibit various degrees of sorting, in which similar-sized grains are deposited together. Sorting is a reflection of how abruptly or

gradually the sand was deposited as water or wind slowed down. Rounding of the individual sand grains is another important aspect of a sandstone's texture: The rounder the grains, the further they have been transported. Angular grains imply a shorter transport distance. Sandstones also vary in their composition: If minerals that are relatively unstable at the surface (like feldspar) are present, this implies that the sand was not subjected to much chemical weathering prior to its deposition and lithification. The greater the proportion of quartz, the more the source sediment was chemically weathered before deposition. There are three main varieties of sandstone worth knowing: quartz sandstone, arkose, and graywacke.

- Conglomerate and breccia are characterized by a high proportion of gravel-sized grains. If deposited by water, a conglomerate implies a very energetic current, one capable of moving gravel. Grains in a breccia are angular, indicating that the material was deposited closer to its source area. Conglomerate is made of rounded grains, implying a significant amount of transport before deposition.

MATCH THEM Examine these sketches of sediment particles. Which particle, A, B, or C has traveled farthest from its source? Explain your reasoning.

A.   B.   C.

4 Chemical Sedimentary Rocks

Explain the processes involved in the formation of chemical sedimentary rocks and describe several examples.

KEY WORDS biochemical, evaporites, salt flats

- Chemical sedimentary rocks are formed when ions dissolved in solution link together to form mineral crystals. Sometimes this happens inorganically (without life being involved), and other times living organisms biochemically extract the ions to precipitate mineral matter as bone or shell.
- Limestone is the most common chemical sedimentary rock. It forms mainly in shallow, warm ocean settings. Limestone is dominated by calcium carbonate. This is the material from which corals construct reefs. Coquina and chalk are also examples of biochemical limestone. Travertine and oolitic limestone are examples of inorganic limestone.
- Dolostone is a chemical sedimentary rock that is dominated by the mineral dolomite. Like calcite, dolomite is a carbonate mineral, but about half of its calcium ions have been replaced by magnesium ions.
- Chert is the general term for rocks made of microcrystalline silica. If the chert is red, it is called jasper. Black chert is flint. Agate is multicolored. When silica replaces plant matter to make petrified wood, often a variety of colors are present.

Dennis Tasa

Rock salt is a chemical sedimentary rock dominated by the mineral halite.

- Evaporite deposits form when minerals precipitate from an ever-more-concentrated solution of dissolved ions. This is how the vast salt flats of the American West formed. Digging into these deposits will reveal rock salt, rock gypsum, and the potassium salt sylvite.

BASICS How can the ocean be salty, but rivers leading to the ocean are "fresh"? Explain the role (and concentration) of dissolved ions in resolving this conundrum.

---

5 Coal: An Organic Sedimentary Rock

Outline the successive stages in the formation of coal.

- Coal forms from the burial of large amounts of plant matter in low-oxygen depositional environments such as swamps and bogs. Through compression, the peat becomes compressed into a low-grade form of coal called lignite. Lignite can be compressed further, driving out

volatile components and concentrating carbon to make higher-grade bituminous coal. Metamorphism accompanying mountain building can take this concentration process even further, producing the highest-grade coal, anthracite.

ANCIENT ORIGINS Considering that it comes from plants, what is the ultimate source of the energy in coal?

---

6 Turning Sediment into Sedimentary Rock: Diagenesis and Lithification

Describe the processes that convert sediment into sedimentary rock and other changes associated with burial.

KEY WORDS diagenesis, lithification, compaction, cementation

- When sediments are buried to relatively shallow depths (the upper few kilometers of the crust), they undergo a variety of processes collectively called diagenesis.
- The transformation of sediment into sedimentary rock is lithification. The two main processes that contribute to lithification are compaction (a reduction in pore space by packing grains more tightly together) and cementation (a reduction in pore space by adding new mineral material that acts as a "glue" to bind the grains to each other).

EDIBLE ANALOGY Would squeezing a handful of chocolate chips be more like cementation or compaction? What about holding chocolate chips together with cookie dough?

---

7 Classification of Sedimentary Rocks

Summarize the criteria used to classify sedimentary rocks.

KEY WORDS clastic, nonclastic, crystalline

- Sedimentary rocks are classified primarily based on whether they are detrital or chemical or organic. Detrital rocks are subdivided by grain size, while among the chemical rocks, mineral composition is the key distinguishing characteristic. An additional characteristic is whether the rocks exhibit a clastic or nonclastic (crystalline) texture.
- Crystalline texture is common to nonclastic sedimentary rocks and igneous rocks and is particularly apparent under magnification. However, the minerals involved are totally different and allow the two types of rock to be distinguished.

CLASSIFY IT Would a limestone made of fossil fragments be detrital or chemical? In addition, would it be clastic or crystalline (nonclastic)?

8 Sedimentary Rocks Represent Past Environments

Contrast the three broad categories of sedimentary environments and list specific examples of each.

KEY WORDS environment of deposition (sedimentary environment), facies

- Different combinations of tectonic, climatic, and biological conditions result in different types of sediment accumulating. The principle of uniformity suggests that the sedimentary record can be interpreted in light of modern depositional environments. Continental, marine, and transitional (shoreline) environments all have distinctive characteristics that allow geologists to identify sedimentary rocks formed in those environments.
- Sedimentary facies are lateral equivalents that represent different depositional conditions operating in adjacent areas at the same time. For instance, a beach may be depositing sand today, while a kilometer or two offshore, only mud is being deposited, and further beyond that, carbonate minerals may be precipitating. All are the same age, but they represent neighboring areas that are governed by different conditions.

ODD MAN OUT   Which of these sedimentary environments—alluvial fan, lagoon, playa lake, floodplain—is not continental, and where does it belong instead?

10 The Carbon Cycle and Sedimentary Rocks

Relate weathering processes and sedimentary rocks to the carbon cycle.

- Carbon is a vital component of the atmosphere, biosphere, geosphere, and hydrosphere. The same atom of carbon that is currently part of your nose may have entered your body in a piece of bread. Prior to that, it may once have been part of a plant, and before that it may have been a carbon dioxide molecule in the atmosphere. How did it get to the atmosphere? Perhaps it escaped into the air after originally being dissolved in the ocean, and perhaps it got to the ocean by being weathered from limestone and then washed down a stream. While the individual details vary, the key point is that carbon is a reactive element that is equally at home in rocks, water, the air, and living tissue.

TELL A STORY   Follow the history of a single carbon atom from one part of the Earth system to another. Include as many of the following components as possible: a cave, a river, a dinosaur, a coal-fired power plant, a volcanic eruption, a swamp, a can of beer, and the coral reef pictured here.

9 Sedimentary Structures

List several sedimentary structures and explain why these features are useful to geologists.

KEY WORDS strata (beds), bedding planes, cross-bedding, graded beds, ripple marks, mud cracks, fossils

- Sedimentary structures are patterns that form in sedimentary rock at the time of deposition (or shortly thereafter), before the sediments become lithified. They can provide powerful clues to the conditions under which the sediment accumulated.
- Beds (or strata) are sheets of sediment deposited in a more-or-less continuous layer. Sometimes cross-beds are preserved within bedding, allowing geologists to deduce the direction of the depositional current. Ripple marks, small waves that develop on the surface of a sediment layer by the action of moving water or wind, also provide useful clues. Graded beds indicate depositional currents that quickly lost their energy. Larger grains settled out first, and the smallest grains settled out last. Mud cracks form when mud contracts upon drying out, and they indicate the sediment was exposed to the air. Fossils are the remains or traces of ancient organisms, and they are not only interesting in their own right but serve as useful tools that allow geologists to read past environmental conditions from sedimentary rock.

INTERPRET THEM   Identify and describe each of the sedimentary structures shown here.

A.

B.

C.

GIVE IT SOME THOUGHT

1. Develop a geological "life history" of a sedimentary rock. Begin with a mass of igneous bedrock in a mountain area and end with your sedimentary rock being collected by a future geology student. Be as complete as possible.

2. This question was intentionally excluded from this edition.

3. One of the labeled sedimentary layers in the accompanying photo is sandstone and the other is mostly shale. How can you determine which one is which just by looking at the photo?

Dennis Tasa

4. If you hiked to a mountain peak and found limestone at the top, what would that indicate about the likely geologic history of the rock atop the mountain?

5. Why is it not necessary to indicate the texture of detrital rocks on the identification chart for sedimentary rocks (Figure 21)?

6. During a hike in Utah's Zion National Park, you pick up a sedimentary rock sample. When you examine the sample with your hand lens, you see that the rock consists mainly of rounded glassy particles that appear to be quartz. To be sure, you make two basic tests. When you check for hardness, the rock easily scratches glass, which is what quartz would do. However, when you place a drop of acid on the sample, it fizzes. Explain how a rock that appears to be rich in quartz could effervesce with acid.

7. Examine the accompanying sketch, which shows three sediment layers on the ocean floor. What term is applied to such layers? What process was responsible for creating these layers? Are these layers more likely part of an offshore lagoon or a deep-sea fan?

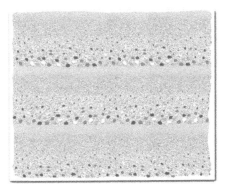

8. This image shows the surface of a sand dune. What term is applied to the wave-like ridges on the surface? Be as specific as possible. Is the prevailing wind direction most likely from the left or from the right? Explain.

Michael Collier

9. In which of the environments illustrated in Figure 23 would you expect to find:
   a. An evaporite deposit?
   b. A well-sorted sand deposit?
   c. A deposit that includes a high percentage of partially decomposed plant material?
   d. A jumbled mix of many sediment sizes?

10. While on a field trip with your geology class, you stop at an outcrop of sandstone. An examination with a hand lens shows that the sandstone is poorly sorted and rich in feldspar and quartz. Your instructor tells you that the sediment was derived from one of two sites in the area:

   Site #1: A nearby exposure of weathered basaltic lava flows.
   Site #2: An outcrop of granite at the previous field trip stop up the road.

   Select the most likely site and explain your choice. What name is given to this type of sandstone?

11. This rock sample consists of intergrown crystals. How would you determine whether the rock is sedimentary or igneous? If it is sedimentary, what term describes its texture?

E.J. Tarbuck

Glossary

Bed See *Strata*.

Bedding plane A nearly flat surface that separates two beds of sedimentary rock. Each bedding plane marks the end of one deposit and the beginning of another having different characteristics.

Biochemical A type of chemical sediment that forms when material dissolved in water is precipitated by water-dwelling organisms. Shells are common examples.

Cementation One way in which sedimentary rocks are lithified. As material precipitates from water that percolates through the sediment, open spaces are filled and particles are joined into a solid mass.

Chemical sedimentary rock Sedimentary rock consisting of material that was precipitated from water by either inorganic or organic means.

Clastic texture A sedimentary rock texture consisting of broken fragments of preexisting rock.

Compaction A type of lithification in which the weight of overlying material compresses more deeply buried sediment. It is most important in the fine-grained sedimentary rocks such as shale.

Cross-bedding A structure in which relatively thin layers are inclined at an angle to the main bedding. Cross-bedding is formed by currents of wind or water.

Crystalline See *Crystal*.

Detrital sedimentary rocks Rocks that form from the accumulation of materials that originate and are transported as solid particles derived from both mechanical and chemical weathering.

Environment of deposition A geographic setting where sediment accumulates. Each site is characterized by a particular combination of geologic processes and environmental conditions.

Evaporite A sedimentary rock formed of material deposited from solution by evaporation of the water.

Facies A portion of a rock unit that possesses a distinctive set of characteristics that distinguishes it from other parts of the same unit.

Fissility The property of splitting easily into thin layers along closely spaced, parallel surfaces, such as bedding planes in shale.

Fossil The remains or traces of organisms preserved from the geologic past.

Graded bed A sediment layer characterized by a decrease in sediment size from bottom to top.

Lithification The process, generally involving cementation and/or compaction, of converting sediments to solid rock.

Mud crack A feature in some sedimentary rocks that forms when wet mud dries out, shrinks, and cracks.

Nonclastic texture A term for the texture of sedimentary rocks in which the minerals form a pattern of interlocking crystals.

Organic sedimentary rock Sedimentary rock composed of organic carbon from the remains of plants that died and accumulated on the floor of a swamp. Coal is the primary example.

Ripple marks Small waves of sand that develop on the surface of a sediment layer by the action of moving water or air.

Salt flat A white crust on the ground that is produced when water evaporates and leaves behind its dissolved materials.

Sedimentary environment See *Environment of deposition*.

Sedimentary rock Rock formed from the weathered products of preexisting rocks that have been transported, deposited, and lithified.

Sorting The degree of similarity in particle size in sediment or sedimentary rock.

Strata Parallel layers of sedimentary rock.

Metamorphism and Metamorphic Rocks

From Chapter 8 of *Earth: An Introduction to Physical Geology*, Eleventh Edition. Edward J. Tarbuck, Frederick K. Lutgens, Dennis Tasa.

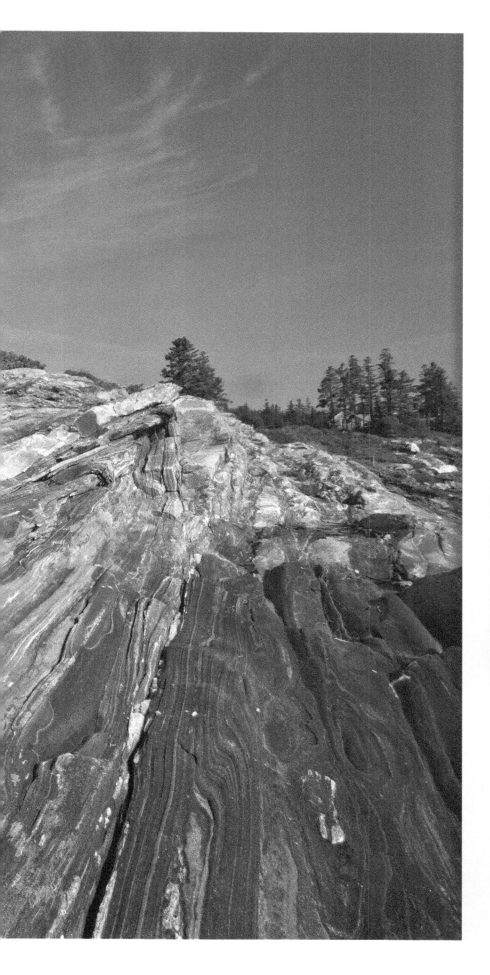

Metamorphism and Metamorphic Rocks

Metamorphic rocks of Permaquid Point, Bristol Maine.
(Photo by George Oze Photography/SuperStock)

Each statement represents the primary learning objective for the corresponding major heading within the chapter. After you complete the chapter you should be able to:

1. Compare and contrast the environments that produce metamorphic, sedimentary, and igneous rocks.
2. List and distinguish between the three agents that drive metamorphism.
3. Explain how foliated and nonfoliated textures develop.
4. List and describe the most common metamorphic rocks.
5. Write a statement that describes each of these metamorphic environments: contact metamorphism, hydrothermal metamorphism, subduction zone metamorphism, and regional metamorphism.
6. Explain how index minerals are used to establish the metamorphic grade of a rock body.
7. Describe the conditions of temperature and pressure that you would associate with the following metamorphic facies: blueschist facies, hornfels facies, and zeolite facies.

T he folded and metamorphosed rocks shown in the chapter opening photo were once flat-lying sedimentary strata. Compressional forces of unimaginable magnitude and temperatures hundreds of degrees above surface conditions prevailed for perhaps thousands or millions of years, to produce the deformation displayed by these rocks. Under such extreme conditions, solid rock responds by folding, fracturing, and often flowing. This chapter looks at the tectonic forces that forge metamorphic rocks and how these rocks change in appearance, mineralogy, and sometimes overall chemical composition.

Unlike some igneous and sedimentary processes that occur in surface or near-surface environments, metamorphism most often occurs deep within Earth, beyond our direct observation. Notwithstanding this significant obstacle, geologists have developed techniques that allow them to learn about the conditions under which metamorphic rocks form. In turn, the study of metamorphic rocks provides important insights into how tectonic processes operate to alter the structure and composition of Earth's crust.

Deformed and folded gneiss, Anza Borrego Desert State Park, California. (Photo by A. P. Trujillo/APT Photos)

1 What Is Metamorphism?

Metamorphism is the transformation of one rock type into another rock type. Metamorphic rocks are produced from preexisting sedimentary and igneous rocks, as well as from other metamorphic rocks. Thus, every metamorphic rock has a **parent rock**—the rock from which it was formed.

Metamorphism, which means to "change form," is a process that leads to changes in the **mineralogy**, texture, and sometimes chemical composition of the parent rock. The mineralogy (mineral constituents of a rock) changes because the rock is subjected to new conditions, usually elevated temperatures and pressures, which are significantly different from those in which it initially formed. For example, clay minerals, which are the most common minerals in sedimentary rocks, are stable only at Earth's surface. (Kaolinite is one example of a clay mineral.) When clay minerals are buried to a depth where temperatures exceed 200°C (nearly 400° F), they become the minerals chlorite and/or muscovite mica. (Chlorite is a mica-like mineral formed by the metamorphism of dark iron- and magnesium-rich silicate minerals.) Under more extreme conditions, chlorite becomes biotite mica.

Metamorphism also alters a rock's texture, producing larger crystals and sometimes distinct layering or a banded appearance.

The degree to which a parent rock changes during metamorphism is called its **metamorphic grade**, and it varies from low grade (low temperatures and pressures) to high grade (high temperatures and pressures). For example, in low-grade metamorphic environments, the common sedimentary rock shale becomes the more compact metamorphic rock slate. During this transformation, the clay minerals in shale are transformed into tiny chlorite and muscovite mica flakes. Hand samples of these rocks are sometimes difficult to distinguish, illustrating that the transition from sedimentary to metamorphic rock is often gradual and the change subtle (FIGURE 1A).

Parent rock (Shale) — Low-grade metamorphism — Low temperatures and pressures — **Metamorphic rock (Slate)**

A. Loosely packed clay minerals → Tightly packed chlorite and mica grains

Parent rock (Granodiorite) — High-grade metamorphism — Strong compressional forces, high temperatures and pressures — **Metamorphic rock (Folded gneiss)**

B. Randomly oriented mineral grain → Deformed layers of segregated grains

FIGURE 1 Metamorphic grade A. Low-grade metamorphism illustrated by the transformation of the common sedimentary rock shale to the more compact metamorphic rock slate. **B.** High-grade metamorphic environments obliterate the existing texture and often change the mineralogy of the parent rock. High-grade metamorphism occurs at temperatures that approach those at which rocks melt.
(Photos by Dennis Tasa)

FIGURE 2 Metamorphic environments
Metamorphism occurs over a range of temperatures that lie between those experienced in sedimentary environments to temperatures that approach those at which rocks melt. Pressure, which includes confining pressure and differential stress, also plays a major role in metamorphism.

Metamorphic Versus Sedimentary and Igneous Environments

Sedimentary environments	Metamorphic environments	Igneous environments

Surface conditions → 200°C ⟶ 700°C ⟶ 1200°C

Sediment converted to sedimentary rock

Increasing temperature and pressure

Partial melting

Complete melting

In environments where temperatures and pressures are more extreme, metamorphism causes a transformation so complete that the identity of the parent rock cannot be easily determined. In high-grade metamorphism, such features as bedding planes, fossils, and vesicles that existed in the parent rock are obliterated. Further, when rocks deep in the crust are subjected to compressional stress (like being placed in a giant vise), the entire mass may be deformed, usually by folding (FIGURE 1B).

In the most extreme metamorphic environments, the temperatures approach those at which rocks melt. However, *during metamorphism, the rock remains essentially solid*. If complete melting occurs, the rock has entered the realm of igneous activity. FIGURE 2 illustrates the relationships among metamorphic, sedimentary, and igneous environments.

---

1 CONCEPT CHECKS

1. *Metamorphism* means to "change form." Describe how a rock may change during metamorphism.
2. What is meant by the statement "Every metamorphic rock has a *parent rock*"?
3. Define *metamorphic grade*.

Metamorphic rocks that exhibit rock cleavage exposed along the coast of East Greenland. (Photo by M Lohmann/AGE Fotostock)

2 | What Drives Metamorphism?

The agents of metamorphism include *heat, pressure, directional stress,* and *chemically active fluids.* During metamorphism, rocks may be subjected to all four metamorphic agents simultaneously. However, the degree of metamorphism and the contribution of each agent vary greatly from one environment to another.

Heat as a Metamorphic Agent

The most important factor driving metamorphism is *heat* because it provides the energy needed to drive the chemical reactions that result in the recrystallization of existing minerals. An increase in temperature causes the atoms within a mineral to vibrate more rapidly. Even in a crystalline solid, where atoms are strongly bonded, this elevated level of activity allows individual atoms to migrate more freely between sites in the crystalline structure.

Changes Caused by Heat The formation of new mineral grains that tend to be larger than the original grains is called **recrystallization**. During this process, the mineralogy of the rock may or may not change. For example, when quartz sandstone is metamorphosed to form quartzite, the mineralogy does not change; the quartz grains remain quartz. By contrast, when shale is metamorphosed to slate, the clay minerals are recrystallized and become new minerals—usually chlorite and muscovite.

Although the mineralogy changes in the transition from shale to slate, the overall chemical composition remains essentially unchanged. What occurs instead is the rearrangement of the existing atoms into new crystalline structures that are more stable in the new environment. (In some environments, ions may actually migrate into or out of a rock, thereby changing its overall chemical composition.)

What Is the Source of Heat? There are two primary sources of heat within Earth. One is the increasing temperature that occurs as we travel deeper into Earth's interior. The second is heat being released to the surrounding rocks as a magma body cools.

Earth's interior is extremely hot, mainly because of heat released from the repeated collision of asteroid-size bodies during the formation of our planet as well as from energy being continually released by the decay of radioactive elements. The rate of increase in temperature with depth is known as the *geothermal gradient.* In the upper crust, this increase in temperature averages about 25° C (45° F) per kilometer (FIGURE 3). Thus, rocks that formed at Earth's surface will experience a gradual increase in temperature if they are transported to greater depths. When buried to a depth of about 8 kilometers (5 miles), where temperatures are about 200° C (400° F), clay minerals tend to become unstable and begin to recrystallize into new minerals, such as chlorite and muscovite, both of which are stable in this new environment. However, many silicate minerals, particularly those found in crystalline igneous rocks—such as quartz and feldspar—remain stable at these temperatures. Thus, metamorphic changes in quartz and feldspar generally occur at higher temperatures.

Environments where rocks may be carried to great depths and heated include convergent plate boundaries where slabs of sediment-laden oceanic crust are being subducted. Rocks may also become deeply buried in large basins where gradual subsidence results in thick accumulations of sediment (see Figure 3). These basins, exemplified by the Gulf of Mexico, are

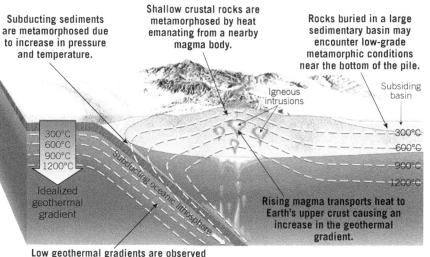

Subducting sediments are metamorphosed due to increase in pressure and temperature.

Shallow crustal rocks are metamorphosed by heat emanating from a nearby magma body.

Rocks buried in a large sedimentary basin may encounter low-grade metamorphic conditions near the bottom of the pile.

Igneous intrusions

Subsiding basin

300°C
600°C
900°C
1200°C

Idealized geothermal gradient

Subducting oceanic lithosphere

300°C
600°C
900°C
1200°C

Rising magma transports heat to Earth's upper crust causing an increase in the geothermal gradient.

Low geothermal gradients are observed in subduction zones because cold oceanic crust and overlying sediments are descending into the mantle.

SMARTFIGURE 3
Sources of heat for metamorphism
The two main sources of heat for metamorphism are the increasing temperature that occurs as we travel deeper into Earth's interior and heat being released to the surrounding rocks when a magma body cools.

known to develop low-grade metamorphic conditions near the base of the pile. In addition, continental collisions, which result in mountain building, cause some rocks to be uplifted while others are thrust downward, where elevated temperatures and pressures trigger metamorphism.

Heat may also be transported from the mantle into the shallowest layers of the crust. Rising mantle plumes, upwelling at mid-ocean ridges, and magma generated by partial melting of mantle rock at subduction zones are three such examples (see Figure 3). When magma intrudes rocks at shallow depths, the magma cools and releases heat, which "bakes" the surrounding host rock.

Confining Pressure

Pressure, like temperature, increases with depth because the thickness of the overlying rock increases. Buried rocks are subjected to **confining pressure**, which is analogous to water pressure, in which the forces are applied equally in all directions (FIGURE

4A). The deeper you go in the ocean, the greater the confining pressure. The same is true when rocks are buried. Confining pressure causes the spaces between mineral grains to close, producing more compact rocks that have greater densities. If the pressure becomes extreme enough, it can cause the atoms in a mineral to pack more closely together to produce a new, denser mineral. The transformation of one mineral (polymorph) to another is called a *phase change*. Confining pressure does *not*, however, fold or fracture rocks.

Differential Stress

In addition to confining pressure, rocks may be subjected to directed pressure. This occurs, for example, at convergent plate boundaries where slabs of lithosphere collide. Here the forces that deform rock are unequal in different directions and are referred to as **differential stress**. Unlike confining pressure, which "squeezes" rock equally in all directions, differential stresses are greater in one direction than in others.

Differential stress that squeezes a rock mass as if it were placed in a vise is termed **compressional stress**. As shown in FIGURE 4B, rocks subjected to compressional stress are shortened in the direction of greatest stress and elongated, or lengthened, in the direction perpendicular to that stress. Along convergent plate boundaries, the greatest differential stress is directed horizontally in the direction of plate motion. Consequently, in these settings, the crust is greatly shortened (horizontally) and thickened (vertically), resulting in mountainous topography.

SMARTFIGURE 4
Confining pressure and differential stress

In a depositional environment, as confining pressure increases, rocks deform by decreasing in volume.

Increasing confining pressure

High confining pressure

A.

During mountain building, rocks subjected to differential stress are shortened in the direction of maximum stress and lengthened in the direction of minimum stress.

B.

Differential stress — Maximum — Maximum

Also called stretched pebble conglomerate, this metaconglomerate is made of once nearly spherical pebbles that have been heated and flattened into elongated structures by differential stress. (Photo by E. J. Tarbuck)

Hot, chemically active fluids enhance metamorphism by dissolving and transporting ions from one site in the crystal structure to another, thereby facilitating the process of recrystallization. In increasingly hotter environments, these fluids become correspondingly more reactive.

In some metamorphic environments, hot fluids transport mineral matter over considerable distances. This occurs, for example, when hot, ion-rich fluids are expelled from a magma body as it cools and solidifies. If the rocks that surround the pluton differ markedly in chemical composition from the invading fluids, there may be an exchange of ions between the fluids and host rocks. In other words, these fluids bring in new atoms or take out atoms rather than simply reorganize what is already present. When this occurs, the overall chemical composition of the surrounding rock changes, in a process called *metasomatism*. One example of metasomatism is the formation of the mineral wollastonite ($CaSiO_3$) from calcite ($CaCO_2$), the primary ingredient in limestone. When a silica-rich hydrothermal solution invades limestone, calcite reacts with silica (SiO_2) to generate wollastonite, and the gas carbon dioxide (CO_2) is driven off.

In high-temperature, high-pressure environments, rocks are *ductile*. When rocks exhibit ductile behavior, their mineral grains tend to flatten (similar to stepping on a ball of silly putty) when subjected to differential stress (FIGURE 5). This accounts for their ability to deform by flowing, rather than fracturing, thereby generating intricate folds. By contrast, in surface environments where temperatures and pressure are comparatively low, rocks are *brittle* and tend to fracture when subjected to differential stress. Continued deformation grinds and pulverizes the mineral grains into small fragments.

Chemically Active Fluids

Water is abundant in Earth's crust. In the upper crust, water occurs as groundwater. At depth, hot water is released into the surrounding rocks when a magma body cools and solidifies. In addition, many minerals, including clays, micas, and amphiboles, are hydrated—which means they contain water in their crystalline structures. Elevated temperatures and pressures cause these minerals to dehydrate, expelling hot, mineral-laden water.

The Importance of Parent Rock

Most metamorphic rocks have the same overall chemical composition as the parent rocks from which they formed, except for the possible loss or acquisition of volatiles such as water (H_2O) and carbon dioxide (CO_2) Therefore, when we try to establish from what parent material metamorphic rocks were derived, the most important clue comes from their overall chemical composition.

Consider the large exposures of the metamorphic rock marble found high in the Alps of Southern Europe (FIGURE 6). Because marble and the common sedimentary rock limestone have the same mineralogy (calcite), it seems reasonable to conclude that limestone is the parent rock of marble. Furthermore, because limestone usually forms in warm, shallow marine environments, we can surmise that considerable deformation must have occurred to convert limy deposits in a shallow sea into marble crags in the lofty Alps.

The mineral makeup of the parent rock also largely determines the degree to which each metamorphic agent

FIGURE 6 Marble peaks in the Apuan Alps
These marble peaks, located in northwestern Tuscany, Italy, were once flat-lying limestone beds on the ocean floor. The collision of the African plate with the Eurasian plate has lifted them nearly 2000 meters (more than 6000 feet) above sea level. These mountains are home to the world-renowned Carrara marble. (Photo by Robert Harding Picture Library/SuperStock)

will cause change. For example, when magma forces its way into an existing body of rock, high temperatures and hot fluids may alter the host rock. If the host rock is composed of minerals that are comparatively nonreactive, such as quartz, any alterations that may occur will be confined to a narrow zone next to the igneous intrusion. However, when the host rock is limestone, which is highly reactive, the zone of metamorphism may extend far from the intrusion.

2 CONCEPT CHECKS

1. List four agents that drive metamorphism.
2. Why is heat considered the most important agent of metamorphism?
3. How is confining pressure different from differential stress?
4. What role do chemically active fluids play in metamorphism?
5. In what way does the parent rock determine the characteristics of the metamorphic rock that formed from it?

EYE on Earth

This metamorphic rock outcrop located in Purgatory Chasm in Newport, Rhode Island, is made of cobbles that are composed mainly of quartz.

Question 1 What name would you give to this metamorphic rock?

Question 2 Which set of arrows (red or black) best represents the direction of maximum directional stress?

Callan Bentley

3 Metamorphic Textures

The term **texture** is used to describe the size, shape, and arrangement of the mineral grains within a rock. Most igneous and many sedimentary rocks consist of mineral grains or crystals that have a random orientation and thus appear uniform when viewed from any direction. By contrast, metamorphic rocks that contain platy minerals (such as micas) and/or elongated minerals (such as amphiboles) typically display some kind of *preferred orientation* in which the mineral grains exhibit a parallel to subparallel alignment. Like a fistful of pencils, rocks containing elongated mineral grains that are oriented parallel to each other appear different when viewed from the side than when viewed head-on. A rock that exhibits a preferred orientation of its mineral constituents is said to possess *foliation*.

Foliation

The term **foliation** refers to any planar (nearly flat) arrangement of mineral grains or crystals within a rock. Although foliation may occur in some sedimentary and even a few types of igneous rocks, it is a fundamental characteristic of metamorphosed rocks that have been strongly deformed, mainly by folding. In metamorphic environments, foliation is ultimately driven by compressional stress that shortens rock units, causing mineral grains in preexisting rocks to develop parallel, or nearly parallel, alignments. Examples of foliation include *the parallel alignment of platy minerals*, *parallel alignment of flattened mineral grains or pebbles*, *compositional banding in which the separation of dark and light minerals generates a layered appearance*, and *rock cleavage where rocks can be easily split into tabular slabs*. These diverse types of foliation can form in many different ways.

Rotation of Platy Mineral Grains

The rotation of existing mineral grains is the easiest of the foliation mechanisms to envision. FIGURE 7 illustrates the mechanics by which platy or elongated mineral grains are rotated. Note that the new alignment is roughly perpendicular to the direction of maximum stress. Although physical rotation of platy minerals contributes to the development of foliation in low-grade metamorphism, other mechanisms dominate in more extreme environments.

Recrystallization That Produces New Minerals

Recall that recrystallization is the creation of new mineral grains from preexisting ones. When recrystallization occurs as rock is being subjected to differential stress, any elongated minerals (such as amphiboles) and platy minerals (such as micas) that form tend to recrystallize perpendicular to the direction of maximum stress. Thus, the newly formed mineral grains exhibit a distinct layering, and the metamorphic rocks containing them exhibit foliation.

Flattening Spherically Shaped Grains

Mechanisms that flatten existing mineral grains are important in the metamorphism of rocks that contain minerals such as quartz, calcite, and olivine. These minerals normally develop roughly spherical crystals and have a rather simple chemical composition.

A change in grain shape can occur as distinct units of a mineral's crystalline structure slide relative to one another along discrete planes, thereby distorting the grain, as shown in FIGURE 8. This type of gradual *solid-state flow* involves slippage that disrupts the crystal lattice as atoms shift positions by breaking existing chemical bonds and forming new ones.

The shape of a mineral may also be altered by a process where individual atoms move from a location along the margin of the grain that is highly stressed to a less-stressed position on the same grain (FIGURE 9). This mechanism, called *pressure solution*, is significantly aided by hot, ion-rich water. Mineral matter

FIGURE 8 Solid-state flow Mineral grains can be flattened by solid-state flow when units of a mineral's crystalline structure slide relative to each other. This mechanism involves breaking existing chemical bonds and forming new ones.

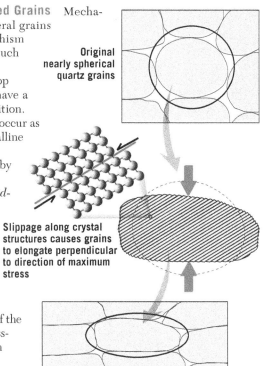

Original nearly spherical quartz grains

Slippage along crystal structures causes grains to elongate perpendicular to direction of maximum stress

Flattened rock containing elongated quartz grains

Before metamorphism (Confining pressure)

After metamorphism (Differential stress)

Metamorphism

Platy mineral grains having random orientation.

When differential stress causes rocks to flatten, the mineral grains rotate and align roughly perpendicular to the direction of maximum differential stress.

FIGURE 7 Mechanical rotation of platy mineral grains

FIGURE 9 Pressure

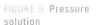

FIGURE 9 Pressure solution
This mechanism flattens mineral grains by dissolving ions from areas of high stress and depositing ions at sites of low stress. This mechanism, as well as the one shown in Figure 8, changes the shape of mineral grains but not their volume and mineralogy.

Original nearly spherical quartz grains

Mineral matter moves from areas of higher stress to areas of lower stress

Flattened rock containing elongated quartz grains

FIGURE 10 Excellent slaty cleavage
Slaty cleavage is exhibited by the rock in this slate quarry. Because slate breaks into flat slabs, it has many uses. (Photo by Fred Bruemmer/Photolibrary) The inset photo shows the use of slate for the roof of this house in Switzerland. (Photo by E. J. Tarbuck)

(ions) dissolves where grains are in contact with each other (areas of high stress) and is deposited in pore spaces (areas of low stress). As a result, the mineral grains tend to become shortened in the direction of maximum stress and elongated in the direction of minimum stress. While both of these mechanisms flatten mineral grains, the mineralogy remains the same.

Foliated Textures

Various types of foliation exist, depending largely upon the grade of metamorphism and the mineralogy of the parent rock. We will look at three: *rock, or slaty, cleavage; schistosity*; and *gneissic texture, or banding*.

Rock, or Slaty, Cleavage   Rocks that split into thin slabs when hit with a hammer exhibit **rock cleavage**. Rock cleavage develops in various metamorphic rocks but is best displayed in slates that exhibit an excellent splitting property called **slaty cleavage** (FIGURE 10). Because it splits easily, slate is used for building materials such as roof and floor tiles as well as billiard table surfaces.

In low-grade metamorphic environments, slaty cleavage is known to develop where beds of shale (and

related sedimentary rocks) are strongly folded and metamorphosed to form slate (FIGURE 11). The process begins when compressional stress begins to deform rock units, producing broad folds. With further deformation, the clay minerals in shale, which initially aligned roughly parallel to the bedding surfaces, begin to recrystallize into tiny flakes of chlorite and mica. However, these new platy mineral grains grow so they are aligned roughly perpendicular to the maximum directional stress, as shown in Figure 11B.

Because slate typically forms during the low-grade metamorphism of shale, evidence of the original sedimentary bedding planes is often preserved. However, as Figure 11C illustrates, the orientation of slate's cleavage usually develops at an angle to the sedimentary beds. Thus, unlike shale, which splits along bedding planes, slate often splits across bedding. Other metamorphic rocks, such as schists and gneisses, sometimes split along planar surfaces and exhibit rock cleavage.

Schistosity   At higher temperatures and pressures, the minute mica and chlorite flakes in slate begin to recrystallize into larger muscovite and biotite crystals. When these platy minerals are large enough to be discernible with the unaided eye, they exhibit planar or layered structures called **schistosity**. Rocks that have this type of foliation are referred to as *schist*. In addition to containing platy minerals, schist often contains deformed quartz and feldspar crystals that appear

A.

Sedimentary strata

Bedding

Sand grains

Clay minerals

B.

Differential stress

Slaty cleavage

Relict bedding surfaces

C.

Slaty cleavage

Relict bedding

Callan Bentley

FIGURE 11 Development of rock cleavage
When shale that is interbedded with sandstone is strongly folded and metamorphosed, the clay minerals begin to recrystallize into tiny flakes of chlorite and mica. These new platy minerals grow so they are aligned roughly perpendicular to the directed stress, which gives slate its foliation.

This outcrop of slate illustrates rock cleavage and its orientation to relict bedding surfaces.

flattened or lens shaped and are embedded among the mica grains.

Gneissic Texture, or Banding   During high-grade metamorphism, ion migration can result in the segregation of minerals, as shown in FIGURE 12. Notice that the dark biotite and amphibole crystals and light silicate minerals (quartz and feldspar) have separated, giving the rock a banded appearance called **gneissic texture**, or **gneissic banding**. Metamorphic rocks with this texture are called *gneiss* (pronounced "nice"). Although they are foliated, gneisses do not usually split as easily as slates and some schists.

Other Metamorphic Textures

Metamorphic rocks that *do not* exhibit foliated textures are referred to as **nonfoliated**. Nonfoliated metamorphic rocks typically develop in environments where deformation is minimal and the parent rocks are composed of minerals that exhibit equidimensional crystals, such as quartz or calcite. For example, when a fine-grained

limestone (made of calcite) is metamorphosed by the intrusion of a hot magma body, the small calcite grains recrystallize to form larger interlocking crystals. The resulting rock, *marble*, exhibits large, intergrown calcite crystals, similar in appearance to those in coarse-grained igneous rocks.

Metamorphic rocks may also contain some unusually large grains, called *porphyroblasts*, that are surrounded by a fine-grained matrix of other minerals. **Porphyroblastic textures** develop in a wide range of

FIGURE 12 Development of gneissic banding
Gneissic banding develops through the migration of ions that cause felsic and mafic minerals to grow in separate layers.

Parent rock with randomly oriented mineral grains.

Quartz
Amphibole
Biotite
Feldspar

Unmetamorphosed

Ion migration causes light and dark minerals to separate.

Differential stress

High-grade metamorphism

Dennis Tasa

Gneissic texture

Porphyroblasts

Close up of porphyroblast

FIGURE 13 Garnet–mica schist **FIGURE 13 Garnet–mica schist** The dark red garnet crystals (porphyroblasts) are embedded in a matrix of fine-grained micas. (Photo by E. J. Tarbuck)

rock types and metamorphic environments when minerals in the parent rock recrystallize to form new minerals. During recrystallization, certain metamorphic minerals, such as garnet, tend to develop *a small number of very large crystals*. By contrast, minerals such as muscovite and biotite typically form *a large number of smaller grains*. As a result, metamorphic rocks that contain large crystals (porphyroblasts) of, for example, garnet embedded in a finer-grained matrix of biotite and muscovite are relatively common (FIGURE 13).

3 CONCEPT CHECKS

1. Define *foliation*.
2. Distinguish among *slaty cleavage, schistosity,* and *gneissic textures.*
3. Briefly describe three ways in which the mineral grains in a rock develop a preferred orientation (that is, foliation).
4. What is meant by *nonfoliated texture*? Name one rock that exhibits this texture.

EYE on Earth

This metamorphic rock outcrop is found in the Southern Alps, located on the South Island of New Zealand. The continued growth of the Southern Alps is somewhat unique in that these mountains lie where the Pacific and Australian plates collide and simultaneously slide past one anther along a large transform fault called the Alpine Fault.

Question 1 Do the rocks in this outcrop display foliation? Explain.

Question 2 Do these rocks appear to have experienced high-grade or low-grade metamorphism? Explain.

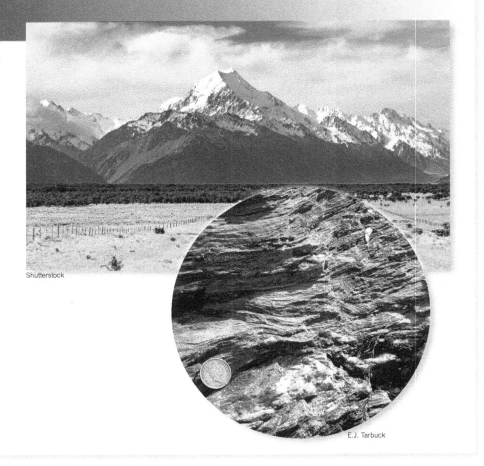

Shutterstock

E.J. Tarbuck

4 | Common Metamorphic Rocks

Most metamorphic rocks that we observe at Earth's surface were derived from the three most common sedimentary rocks—shale, limestone, and quartz sandstone. Shale is the most likely parent of most slate, phyllite, schist, and gneiss. This sequence of metamorphic rocks reflects an increase in grain size, a change in rock texture, and a change in mineralogy.

FIGURE 14 Classification of common metamorphic rocks
(Photos by E. J. Tarbuck)

Limestone, which is composed of the mineral calcite ($CaCO_3$), is the parent rock of marble, while quartz (SiO_2) sandstone is the parent of quartzite. Because calcite and quartz are simple chemical compounds compared to clay minerals, their mineralogy does not change during metamorphism—calcite usually remains calcite and quartz remains quartz. Rather, these minerals recrystallize to produce larger fused grains that are the main constituents of marble and quartzite, respectively.

The major characteristics of the most common metamorphic rocks are summarized in FIGURE 14. Notice that metamorphic rocks can be broadly classified by the type of foliation exhibited and, to a lesser extent, the chemical composition of the parent rock. It is worth noting that certain rock *names* (slate, schist, and gneiss) are also used to describe rock *texture*.

Foliated Rocks

Slate Slate is a very fine-grained (less than 0.5 millimeter) foliated rock composed mainly of minute chlorite and mica flakes that are too small to be visible. It may also contain tiny quartz and feldspar crystals. Thus, slate generally appears dull and closely resembles shale. A noteworthy characteristic of slate is its excellent rock cleavage, or tendency to break into flat slabs (FIGURE 15).

Slate is most often generated by the low-grade metamorphism of shale, mudstone, or siltstone. Less frequently it is produced when volcanic ash is metamorphosed. Slate's color depends on its mineral constituents: Black (carbonaceous) slate contains organic material, red slate gets its color from iron oxide, and green slate usually contains a lot of the mineral chlorite.

Phyllite Phyllite represents a degree of metamorphism between slate and schist. Its constituent platy minerals are larger than those in slate but not large enough to be readily identifiable with the unaided eye. Although phyllite appears similar to slate, it can be easily distinguished from slate by its glossy sheen and wavy surface (see Figure 14). Phyllite exhibits rock cleavage and is composed mainly of very fine crystals of mainly muscovite, chlorite, or both.

Schist Schists are medium- to coarse-grained metamorphic rocks in which platy minerals are dominant. These flat components commonly include muscovite

Metamorphic Rock	Texture	Comments	Parent Rock
Slate	Foliated	Composed of tiny chlorite and mica flakes, breaks in flat slabs called slaty cleavage, smooth dull surfaces	Shale, mudstone, or siltstone
Phyllite	Foliated	Fine-grained, glossy sheen, breaks along wavy surfaces	Shale, mudstone, or siltstone
Schist	Foliated	Medium- to coarse-grained, scaly foliation, micas dominate	Shale, mudstone, or siltstone
Gneiss	Foliated	Coarse-grained, compositional banding due to segregation of light and dark colored minerals	Shale, granite, or volcanic rocks
Marble	Nonfoliated	Medium- to coarse-grained, relatively soft (3 on the Mohs scale), interlocking calcite or dolomite grains	Limestone, dolostone
Quartzite	Nonfoliated	Medium- to coarse-grained, very hard, massive, fused quartz grains	Quartz sandstone
Hornfels	Nonfoliated	Very fine-grained, often exceedingly tough and durable, usually dark colored	Often shale, but can have any composition

and biotite that display parallel alignments that give the rock its foliated texture (FIGURE 16). In addition, schists contain smaller amounts of other minerals, often quartz and feldspar. Some schists are composed mostly of dark

295

SMARTFIGURE 15
Outcrop exhibiting slaty cleavage

Rock cleavage surfaces

E.J. Tarbuck

Gneiss *Gneiss* is the term applied to medium- to coarse-grained banded metamorphic rocks in which granular and elongated (as opposed to platy) minerals predominate. The most common minerals in gneiss are quartz, potassium feldspar, and plagioclase feldspar. Most gneisses also contain lesser amounts of biotite, muscovite, and amphibole. Some gneisses will split along the layers of platy minerals, but most break in an irregular fashion.

Recall that during high-grade metamorphism, the light and dark components separate, giving gneisses their characteristic banded or layered appearance. Thus, most gneisses consist of alternating bands of white or reddish feldspar-rich zones and layers of dark ferromagnesian minerals (see Figure 14). These banded gneisses often exhibit evidence of deformation, including folds and sometimes faults.

Gneisses having a felsic composition may be derived from granite or its fine-grained equivalent, rhyolite. However, most gneisses are generated through high-grade metamorphism of shale. Therefore, gneiss represents the highest-grade metamorphic rock in the sequence of shale, slate, phyllite, schist, and gneiss (FIGURE 17). Like schists, gneisses may also include large crystals of accessory minerals such as garnet and staurolite. Gneisses made up primarily of dark minerals also occur. For example, an amphibole-rich rock that exhibits a gneissic texture is called *amphibolite*.

minerals (such as amphiboles). As with slate, the parent rock of most schists is shale that has undergone medium- to high-grade metamorphism during a major mountain-building episode.

The term *schist* describes the texture of rocks, and as such it is used to name rocks that have a wide variety of chemical compositions. To indicate composition, mineral names are added. For example, schists composed primarily of muscovite and biotite are called *mica schist* (see Figure 16). Mica schists often contain *accessory minerals*, some of which are unique to metamorphic rocks. Some common accessory minerals that occur as porphyroblasts include *garnet, staurolite,* and *andalusite,* in which case the rock is called *garnet-mica schist, staurolite-mica schist,* or *andalusite-mica schist* (see Figure 13).

In addition, schists may be composed largely of the minerals chlorite or talc, in which case they are called *chlorite schist* and *talc schist,* respectively. Both chlorite and talc schists can form when rocks having basaltic compositions undergo metamorphism.

FIGURE 16 **Mica schist** This sample of schist is composed mostly of muscovite and biotite and exhibits foliation. (Photo by E. J. Tarbuck)

Mica schist

Parallel alignment of mineral grains

Nonfoliated Rocks

Marble Marble is a crystalline metamorphic rock whose parent is limestone or dolostone (see Figure 14). Pure marble is white and composed essentially of the mineral calcite. Because of its relative softness (3 on the Mohs scale), marble is easy to cut and shape. White marble is particularly prized as a stone from which monuments and statues are carved, such as the Lincoln Memorial in Washington, DC. Unfortunately, when exposed to acid rain, marble's composition (calcium carbonate) makes it susceptible to chemical weathering.

The parent rocks of most marbles contain impurities that color the stone. Thus, marble can be pink, gray, green, or even black and may contain a variety of accessory minerals (such as chlorite, mica, garnet, and wollastonite). When marble forms from limestone interbedded with shales, it appears banded and exhibits visible

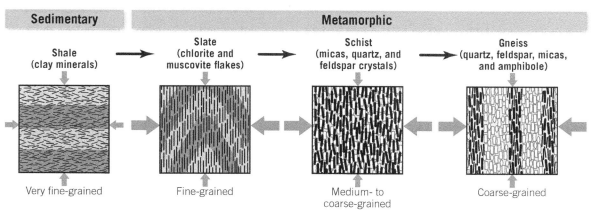

FIGURE 17 Increasing metamorphic grade This sequence of shale (sedimentary parent), slate, schist, and gneiss illustrates a change from low-grade (slate) to high-grade (gneiss) metamorphism.

foliation. When deformed, these banded marbles may develop highly contorted mica-rich folds that enhance the rocks' artistic appearance. These decorative marbles have been used as building stones since prehistoric times.

Quartzite Quartzite is a very hard metamorphic rock formed from quartz sandstone (FIGURE 18). Under moderate- to high-grade metamorphism, the quartz grains in sandstone fuse together (inset in Figure 18). The recrystallization is often so complete that, when broken, quartzite splits across the original quartz grains rather than along their boundaries. In some instances, sedimentary features such as cross-bedding are preserved and give the rock a banded appearance. Pure quartzite is white, but iron oxide may produce reddish or pinkish stains, while dark mineral grains may impart shades of green or gray.

Hornfels Hornfels is a fine-grained nonfoliated metamorphic rock, and unlike marble and quartzite, it has a variable mineral composition. The parent rock of most hornfels is shale or another clay-rich rock, which has been "baked" by a hot intruding magma body.

Hornfels tends to be gray to black in color and quite hard, and it may display conchoidal fracture.

4 CONCEPT CHECKS

1. Slate and phyllite resemble each other. How might you distinguish them from each other?
2. In the rock mica schist, what does *mica* indicate, and what does *schist* indicate?
3. Briefly describe the appearance of the metamorphic rock gneiss and explain how it forms.
4. Describe slate, phyllite, schist, and gneiss in terms of texture and grain size.
5. Compare and contrast marble and quartzite.

FIGURE 18 Quartzite Quartzite is a nonfoliated metamorphic rock formed from quartz sandstone. These close-up images show the interlocking quartz grains typical of quartzite as compared to the loosely bound grains in this quartz sandstone. (Photos by Dennis Tasa)

Marble

Marble is crystalline metamorphic rock whose parent rock was limestone or dolostone. Pure marble is white; however, most marble contains impurities such as iron oxide, chlorite, and organic debris which renders the marble pink, green, gray or sometimes black.

Pure white marbles are prized for sculpture

Statue of David carved by Michelangelo from pure Carrara marble between 1501 and 1504. The statue rises over 17 feet above the base.

Venus de Milo is an ancient Greek statue carved out of marble sometime between 130 and 100 B.C. This statue is on permanent display at the Louvre in Paris, France.

Carrara Marble quarries located in the mountains near Carrara, Italy have produced some of the finest marbles for thousands of years.

These marble quarries located near Carrara, Italy are so large they can be seen from space.

BL Images Ltd/Alamy Images

Ray Roberts/Alamy Images

Fotografiche/Shutterstock

NASA

Marble, because of its workability, is a widely used building stone

Taj Mahal Constructed primarily of marble, the Taj Mahal is considered one of the world's most spectacular buildings. Built by Mughal Emperor Shah Jahin in memory of his third wife, the structure is located in northcentral India. Construction began around 1632 and was completed in 1653.

Steve Vidler/Superstock

The white exterior of the Lincoln Memorial in Washington, DC is constructed mainly of marble that was quarried near the town of Marble, Colorado. Inside, pink Tennessee "marble" was used for the floors, Alabama marble for the ceilings, and Georgia marble for Lincoln's statue.

Marble is also widely used for floor tile and countertops. The marble in these floor tiles contains impurities that impart a variety of color and also show evidence of deformation.

Vilo Vad/Shutterstock

Orhan Cam/Shutterstock

5 Metamorphic Environments

There are many different environments in which metamorphism occurs. Most of these environments occur in the vicinity of plate margins, and several are associated with igneous activity. We will consider the basic metamorphic environments *contact* or *thermal metamorphism*, *hydrothermal metamorphism*, *burial and subduction zone metamorphism*, and *regional metamorphism*, as well as a few types of metamorphism that generate relatively small quantities of metamorphic rock.

As FIGURE 19 illustrates, each type of metamorphism occurs over a range of temperatures and pressures. On this graph, temperature, which increases from surface conditions to about 1000° C (1800° F), is displayed along the top, and pressure is shown along the vertical axis. Notice that hydrothermal metamorphism occurs in relatively low-temperature and low-pressure environments, whereas burial and subduction metamorphism occur under relatively low-temperature and high-pressure conditions. Although not shown on this graph, regional and subduction metamorphism involves directional stress, whereas hydrothermal and contact metamorphism do not.

Contact or Thermal Metamorphism

Contact metamorphism, or **thermal metamorphism**, occurs in Earth's upper crust (low pressure), when rocks immediately surrounding a molten igneous body are "baked" (high temperature). The altered rocks occur in a zone called a metamorphic **aureole** (FIGURE 20). The emplacement of small intrusions such as dikes and sills typically form aureoles only a few centimeters thick. By contrast, large molten bodies that cool to form batholiths can produce aureoles that extend outward for several kilometers. These large aureoles often consist of distinct *zones of metamorphism.* Near the magma body,

high-temperature minerals such as garnet may form, whereas farther away, low-grade minerals such as chlorite are produced.

Because contact metamorphism does not involve directional stress, rocks found within a metamorphic

A. Implacement of igneous body and metamorphism

Host rock
Magma chamber
Metamorphic aureole

B. Crystallization of pluton

Host rock
Igneous pluton

Roof pendant (metamorphic aureole)

Igneous pluton

C. Uplift and erosion expose pluton and metamorphic cap rock

FIGURE 20 Contact metamorphism
Contact metamorphism produces a zone of alteration called an *aureole* around an intrusive igneous body. In the photo, the dark layer, called a *roof pendant*, consists of metamorphosed host rocks that are in contact with the upper part of the light-colored igneous pluton. The term *roof pendant* implies that the rock was once the roof of a magma chamber. Sierra Nevada, near Bishop, California. (Photo by John S. Shelton)

FIGURE 19 Metamorphic environments
This graph illustrates the temperatures and pressures typically associated with the major types of metamorphic environments.

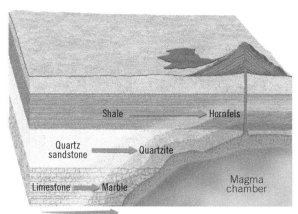

Shale → Hornfels

Quartz sandstone → Quartzite

Limestone → Marble

Magma chamber

Increasing metamorphic grade

SMARTFIGURE 21 **Rocks produced by contact metamorphism**
Contact metamorphism of shale yields hornfels, while contact metamorphism of quartz sandstone and limestone produces quartzite and marble, respectively.

aureole are not foliated. During contact metamorphism of mudstones and shales, the clay minerals are baked, much like clay is baked in a kiln to make pottery. The result is a very hard, fine-grained metamorphic rock called *hornfels* (FIGURE 21). Hornfels can also form from a variety of other materials, including volcanic ash and basaltic rocks.

Other metamorphic rocks that are produced by contact metamorphism are marble and quartzite (see Figure 21). Recall that limestone is the parent of marble and that the metamorphism of quartz sandstone produces quartzite.

Hydrothermal Metamorphism

When hot, ion-rich water circulates through pore spaces or fractures in rock, a chemical alteration called **hydrothermal metamorphism** may occur (FIGURE 22). Recall that hot mineral-laden fluids, called *hydrothermal solutions*, contribute to metamorphism by enhancing the recrystallization of existing minerals. In addition, hot iron-rich solutions facilitate the movement of mineral matter into and out of rock bodies, thereby changing their overall chemical composition.

The water for hydrothermal metamorphism can be groundwater that has percolated down from the surface, where it is heated and circulates upward. This type of

metamorphism tends to occur at low pressures (shallow depth) and relatively low to moderate temperature.

Water that drives hydrothermal metamorphism may also arise from igneous activity. As large magma bodies cool and solidify, ion-rich waters are driven into the surrounding host rocks. When the host rock is porous or highly fractured, mineral matter contained in these fluids may precipitate to form important deposits of copper, silver, and gold. These ion-rich fluids can also generate pegmatites—very coarse-grained granitic (felsic) igneous rocks.

As scientific understanding of plate tectonics developed, it became clear that the most widespread occurrence of hydrothermal metamorphism is along the axis of the mid-ocean ridge system. As plates move apart, upwelling magma from the mantle generates new seafloor. As seawater percolates through the young, hot oceanic crust, it is heated and chemically reacts with the newly formed basaltic rocks (FIGURE 23). The result is the conversion of mafic rocks of the oceanic crust and uppermost mantle into the hydrated rocks serpentinite and soapstone (FIGURE 24).

Hydrothermal solutions circulating through the seafloor also remove large amounts of metals, such as iron, cobalt, nickel, silver, gold, and copper, from the newly formed crust. These hot, metal-rich fluids eventually rise along fractures and gush from the seafloor

Hydrothermal metamorphism can occur at shallow crustal depths in regions where geysers and hot springs are active.

Hydrothermal vein deposits

E.J. Tarbuck

Geyser

Pegmatite deposits

Fault

Igneous body (pluton)

Magma chamber

FIGURE 22 **Hydrothermal metamorphism**
Illustration of the relationship between an igneous body and associated pegmatites and hydrothermal mineral deposits. (Photo by Pavel Svofoda/Fotolia)

FIGURE 23 Hydrothermal
metamorphism along a
mid-ocean ridge
(Photo by Fisheries and Oceans
Canada/Uvic-Verena Tunnicliffe/
Newscom)

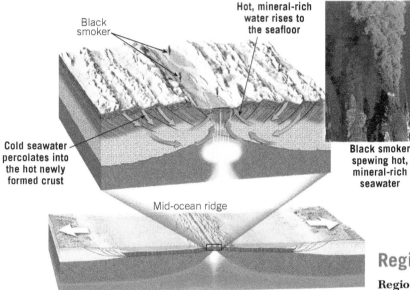

Black smoker

Hot, mineral-rich water rises to the seafloor

Cold seawater percolates into the hot newly formed crust

Mid-ocean ridge

Black smoker spewing hot, mineral-rich seawater

lithosphere is being subducted (see Figure 3). In this setting, cold, dense oceanic crust and sediments, which are poor conductors of heat, are subducting rapidly enough that pressure increases faster than temperature. This phenomenon, called **subduction zone metamorphism**, differs from burial metamorphism in that differential stress plays a major role in deforming rock as it is being metamorphosed.

at temperatures of about 350° C (360° F), generating particle-filled clouds called *black smokers*. Upon mixing with the cold seawater, sulfides and carbonate minerals containing these heavy metals precipitate to form metallic deposits. Geologists credit this process with the formation of the copper ores mined today on the Mediterranean island of Cyprus.

Burial and Subduction Zone Metamorphism

Burial metamorphism tends to occur where massive amounts of sedimentary or volcanic material accumulate in a subsiding basin such as the Gulf of Mexico (see Figure 3). Here, low-grade metamorphic conditions may be reached within the deepest layers. Confining pressure and heat drive the recrystallization of the constituent minerals, changing the texture and/or mineralogy of the rock without appreciable deformation.

Rocks and sediments can also be carried to great depths along convergent boundaries where oceanic

Regional Metamorphism

Regional metamorphism is a common, widespread type of metamorphism typically associated with mountain building, where large segments of Earth's crust are intensely deformed by the collision of two continental blocks (FIGURE 25). Sediments and crustal rocks that form the margins of the colliding continents are folded and faulted, causing them to shorten and thicken like a rumpled carpet. Continental collisions may also cause crystalline basement rocks, as well as slices of oceanic crust that once floored the intervening ocean basin, to be uplifted and deformed (FIGURE 26).

The general thickening of the crust that occurs during mountain building results in buoyant lifting, in which deformed rocks are elevated high above sea level. Crustal thickening also results in the deep burial of large quantities of rock as one crustal block is thrust beneath another. Deep in the roots of mountains, elevated temperatures caused by deep burial are responsible for the most intense metamorphic activity within a mountain belt.

In some settings, deeply buried rocks become heated beyond their melting points, producing magma. When these magma bodies grow large enough to buoyantly rise, they intrude the overlying metamorphic and sedimentary rocks (see Figure 25). Consequently, the cores of many mountain belts consist of folded and faulted metamorphic rocks, often intertwined with igneous bodies. Over time, these deformed rock masses are uplifted, and erosion removes the overlying material to expose the igneous and metamorphic core of the mountain range (see Figure 26).

Regional metamorphism produces some of the most common metamorphic rocks. In these setting, shale is metamorphosed to produce the sequences of rocks slate, phyllite, schist, and gneiss. In addition, quartz

FIGURE 24 Serpentinite and soapstone
These metamorphic rocks are produced by hydrothermal alteration of mafic rocks along the mid-ocean ridge system.
(Photos by Dennis Tasa)

Serpentinite

Soapstone

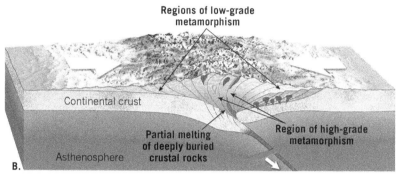

FIGURE 25 Regional metamorphism
Regional metamorphism is associated with a continental collision where rocks are squeezed between two converging plates, resulting in mountain building.

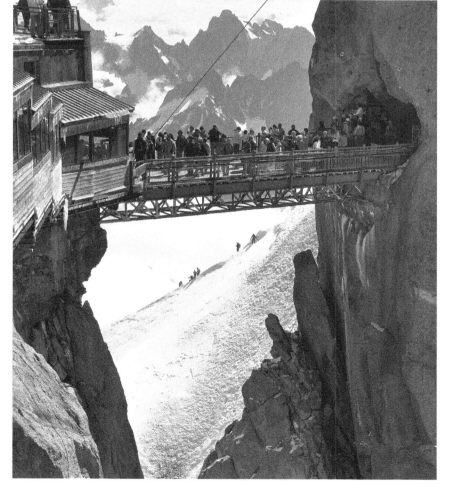

FIGURE 26 Crystalline core of the Alps
Metamorphic and igneous rocks that compose the crystalline core of the Alps near Mount Blanc, France, consist of older basement rocks uplifted during the continental collision of Africa and Eurasia. The crystalline cores of mountains, including the Appalachians, can also be produced by intense metamorphism of sedimentary rocks that once lay along the margins of colliding plates. Over time, these highly deformed rocks are uplifted, and erosion removes the rocks to expose the metamorphic and igneous core of the mountain. (Photo by Pablo Galan Cela/AGE Fotostock)

sandstone and limestone are metamorphosed into quartzite and marble.

Other Metamorphic Environments

Other, less-common types of metamorphism generate relatively small amounts of metamorphic rock that tends to be geographically localized.

Metamorphism Along Fault Zones Near Earth's surface, rock behaves like a brittle solid. Consequently, movement along a fault zone fractures and pulverizes rock (FIGURE 27A). The result is a loosely coherent rock called *fault breccia* that is composed of broken and crushed rock fragments (Figure 27A). Displacements along California's San Andreas Fault have created a zone of fault breccia and related rock types more than 1000 kilometers long and up to 3 kilometers wide.

Much of the deformation associated with fault zones occurs at great depth and thus at high temperatures. In this environment, preexisting minerals deform by ductile flow (FIGURE 27B). As large slabs of rock move in opposite directions, the minerals in the fault zone between them tend to form elongated grains that give the rock a foliated and/or lineated appearance. Rocks formed in these zones of intense ductile deformation are termed *mylonites* (*mylo* = a mill, *ite* = a stone).

Impact Metamorphism **Impact** (or **shock**) **metamorphism** occurs when high-speed projectiles called *meteorites* (fragments of comets or asteroids) strike Earth's surface. Upon impact, the energy of the once rapidly moving meteorite is transformed into heat energy and shock waves that pass through the surrounding rocks. The result is pulverized, shattered, and sometimes melted rock.

The products of these impacts, called *impactiles*, include mixtures of fused fragmented rock plus glass-rich ejecta that resemble volcanic bombs. In some cases, a very dense form of quartz (*coesite*) and minute *diamonds* are found. The existence of these high-pressure minerals provides convincing evidence that pressures and temperatures involved in impact metamorphism can be as great as those found in the upper mantle.

5 CONCEPT CHECKS

1. In which of the major types of metamorphism does compressional stress play a major role?
2. Name three rocks that are produced by contact metamorphism.
3. What is an aureole?
4. What is the agent of hydrothermal metamorphism?
5. Describe subduction metamorphism.
6. Which type of plate boundary is associated with regional metamorphism?
7. List the common metamorphic rocks generated by regional metamorphism.

SMARTFIGURE 27
Metamorphism along a fault zone
(Photo A by A. P. Trujillo; photo B by Ann Bykerk-Kauffman)

Zone of fault breccia and gouge

Brittle fracture

Offset drainage

Active fault zone

Ductile flow

Zone of mylonite

A. Near Earth's surface, where rocks behave like a brittle solid, fault breccia is generated along fault zones.

B. At depth, rocks deform by slow ductile flow to form rocks called mylonites.

Impact Metamorphism

Recently it became clear that comets and asteroids have collided with Earth far more frequently than was once assumed. The evidence: More than 100 giant impact structures have been identified to date.

Leigh Anne Del Ray-Crowell/Aerolite Meteorites LLC

One signature of impact craters is shock metamorphism

When high-velocity projectiles (comets, asteroids) impact Earth's surface, pressures are extreme and temperatures momentarily exceed 2000 °C. The result is pulverized and shattered rock that may form impact breccia.

Tektites: Products of impact metamorphism

Tektites are silica-rich glass beads no more than a few centimeters across that are jet black, dark green, or yellowish in color. Most researchers agree that tektites are the result of impacts of large projectiles that are capable of melting crustal rock. In Australia, millions of tektites are strewn over an area seven times the size of Texas. Several other tektite groupings (called strewnfields) have been identified worldwide, one stretching across China, Thailand, and Cambodia.

Tektites recovered from Nullarbor Plain, Australia.

Brian Mason/Smithsonian

Most meteorite impacts occurred millions of years ago.

Michael Collier

Meteor Crater, Arizona

Comparatively young impact craters, like Meteor Crater located west of Winslow, Arizona, appears fresh with rock fragments (ejecta) that ring the impact site.

6 Metamorphic Zones

In areas affected by metamorphism, there are usually systematic variations in the mineralogy and texture of the rocks that can be observed. These differences are clearly related to variations in the degree of metamorphism experienced in each metamorphic zone.

Textural Variations

Across areas where regional metamorphism has occurred, rock textures vary based on the intensity of metamorphism. If we begin with a clay-rich sedimentary rock such as shale or mudstone, a gradual increase in metamorphic intensity is accompanied by a general coarsening of the grain size. FIGURE 28 illustrates that as metamorphic intensity increases, shale changes to a fine-grained slate, which then forms phyllite, which, through continued recrystallization, generates a

medium-grained schist. Under more intense conditions, a gneissic texture that exhibits layers of dark and light minerals may develop. This systematic transition in metamorphic textures can be observed as we approach the Appalachian Mountains from the west. Beds of shale, which once extended over large areas of the eastern United States, still occur as nearly flat-lying strata in Ohio. However, in the broadly folded Appalachians of central Pennsylvania, the rocks that once formed flat-lying beds are folded and display a preferred

 SMARTFIGURE 28
Textural variations caused by regional metamorphism Idealized illustration of textural variations produced by regional metamorphism, progressing from low-grade metamorphism (slate) to high-grade metamorphism (gneiss). (Photos by E. J. Tarbuck)

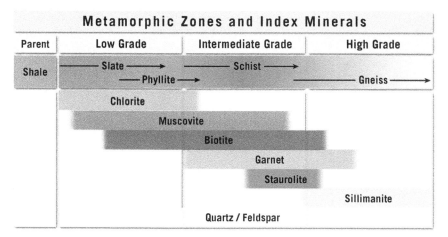

Metamorphic Zones and Index Minerals

Parent	Low Grade	Intermediate Grade	High Grade
Shale	Slate → Phyllite →	Schist →	Gneiss →

Chlorite

Muscovite

Biotite

Garnet

Staurolite

Sillimanite

Quartz / Feldspar

FIGURE 29 Metamorphic zones and index minerals
The typical transition of various index minerals associated with the progression from low-grade to high-grade metamorphism of the rock shale.

orientation of platy mineral grains, as exhibited by well-developed slaty cleavage. As we move farther eastward, into the intensely deformed crystalline Appalachians, we find large outcrops of schists. Some of the most intense zones of metamorphism are found in Vermont and New Hampshire, where gneissic rocks outcrop.

Index Minerals and Metamorphic Grade

In addition to textural changes, we encounter corresponding changes in mineralogy as we shift from regions of low-grade metamorphism to regions of high-grade metamorphism. An idealized transition in mineralogy that results from the regional metamorphism of shale is shown in FIGURE 29. The first new mineral to form as shale changes to slate is chlorite. At higher temperatures, flakes of muscovite and biotite begin to dominate. Under more extreme conditions, metamorphic rocks may contain garnet and staurolite crystals. At temperatures approaching the melting point of rock, sillimanite forms. Sillimanite is a high-temperature metamorphic mineral used to make porcelains used in extreme environments, such as for spark plugs.

Through the study of metamorphic rocks in their natural settings (called *field studies*) and through experimental studies, researchers have learned that certain minerals, such as those in Figure 28, are good indicators of the metamorphic environment in which they formed. Using these **index minerals**, geologists distinguish among different zones of regional metamorphism. For example, the mineral chlorite begins to form when temperatures are relatively low—less than 200° C (400° F; Figure 29). Thus, rocks that contain chlorite (usually slates) are referred to as *low grade*. By contrast, the mineral sillimanite forms only in extreme environments where temperatures exceed 600° C (1100° F), and rocks

containing it are considered *high grade*. By mapping the occurrences of index minerals, geologists can identify zones of varying metamorphic grades (FIGURE 30).

Migmatites In the most extreme environments, even the highest-grade metamorphic rocks undergo change. For example, gneissic rocks may be heated sufficiently to trigger melting. However, minerals melt at different temperatures. The light-colored silicates, usually quartz and potassium feldspar, have the lowest melting temperatures and begin to melt first, whereas the mafic silicates, such as amphibole and biotite, remain solid. When the partially melted rock cools, the light bands will be composed of igneous or igneous-appearing components, while the dark bands will consist of unmelted metamorphic material. Rocks of this type are called **migmatites**

FIGURE 30 Zones of metamorphic intensities in New England

Under high-grade metamorphism, light-colored (felsic) minerals in a gneiss may begin to melt. If this melt solidifies in place, the rock—called a migmatite—will contain light-colored igneous rock intermixed with metamorphic rock composed of dark-colored (mafic) minerals. (Photo by Harlan H. Roepke)

(*migma* = mixture, *ite* = a stone) (FIGURE 31). The bands in migmatites often form intricate folds and may contain tabular inclusions of the dark components. Migmatites serve to illustrate the fact that some rocks are transitional and do not fit neatly into any of the three basic rock groups.

6 CONCEPT CHECKS

1. Describe the different grades of metamorphism that might be encountered moving west to east from Ohio to the crystalline core of the Appalachians.
2. How do geologists use index minerals?
3. Why are migmatites difficult to place into any one of the three basic rock groups?

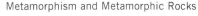

EYE on Earth

This rock outcrop, located in Joshua Tree National Park, consists of dark-colored metamorphic rocks that overlie light-colored igneous rocks.

Question 1 Name the type of metamorphism—contact, hydrothermal, burial, subduction zone, or regional metamorphism—that likely produced these metamorphic rocks.

Question 2 Write a brief statement that outlines the geologic history of this area, based on what you observe in this image.

E.J. Tarbuck

7 Interpreting Metamorphic Environments

About a century ago, geologists realized that groups of associated minerals could be used to determine the pressures and temperatures at which rocks undergo metamorphism. This discovery led Finnish geologist Pentti Eskola to propose the concept of metamorphic facies. Simply, metamorphic rocks containing the same assemblage of minerals belong to the same **metamorphic facies**—implying that they formed in very similar metamorphic environments. Using metamorphic facies to determine a metamorphic environment is analogous to using a group of plants to define a climatic zone, that experiences similar conditions of precipitation and temperature. For instance, forests consisting of scrawny spruce, fir, larch, and birch trees identify the subarctic or taiga climate zone.

Common Metamorphic Facies

Several of the common metamorphic facies are shown in FIGURE 32. These include the *hornfels, zeolite, greenschist, amphibolite, granulite, blueschist*, and *eclogite facies.* The name for each facies is based on the minerals that define them. For example, rocks of the amphibolite facies are characterized by the mineral hornblende (a common amphibole); the greenschist facies consists of schists in which the green minerals chlorite, epidote, and serpentine are prominent. Similar suites of minerals are found in rocks of all ages and in all parts of the world. Thus, the concept of metamorphic facies is useful in the interpretation of Earth history. Rocks that belong to the same metamorphic facies all formed under the same conditions of temperature and pressure, and therefore in similar tectonic settings, regardless of their location or age.

It should be noted that the name for each metamorphic facies refers to a metamorphic rock derived specifically from a basaltic parent. This occurs because Pentti Eskola concentrated his work on the metamorphism of basalts, and his basic terminology, although now slightly modified, remains. The names of Eskola's facies serve as convenient labels for particular combinations of temperatures and pressures, no matter what the mineral composition. In other words, even if a nonbasaltic parent rock produces different indicator minerals under a given set of metamorphic conditions, the facies names shown in Figure 32 are used for the purpose of denoting the temperature and pressure ranges embodied by that metamorphic rock. For example, mica

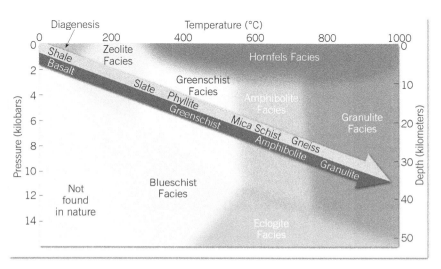

schist belongs to the amphibolite facies, despite the fact that mica schist was derived from shale—a nonbasaltic parent rock.

Metamorphic Facies and Plate Tectonics

FIGURE 33 shows how the concept of facies fits into the context of plate tectonics. Near deep-ocean trenches, slabs of relatively cool oceanic lithosphere and the overlying crust are subducted. As the lithosphere descends, sediments and crustal rocks are subjected to steadily increasing temperatures and pressures (Figure 33A). However, temperatures in the slab remain cooler than the surrounding mantle because rock is a poor conductor of heat and therefore warms slowly. The metamorphic facies associated with this type of high-pressure, low-temperature environment is called the *blueschist facies* because of the presence of the blue-colored variety of amphibole called *glaucophane* (FIGURE 34A). The rocks of the Coast Range of California belong to the blueschist facies. Highly deformed rocks that were once deeply

FIGURE 32 Metamorphic facies
Metamorphic facies and corresponding temperature and pressure conditions. Note the metamorphic rocks produced from regional metamorphism of basalt versus shale under similar conditions of temperature and pressure.

309

FIGURE 33 Metamorphic facies and plate tectonics These block diagrams show various metamorphic facies and the tectonic environments that generate them.

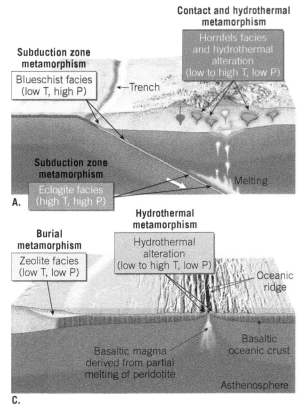

Subduction zone metamorphism
Blueschist facies (low T, high P)

—Trench

Subduction zone metamorphism
Eclogite facies (high T, high P)

A.

Melting

Contact and hydrothermal metamorphism
Hornfels facies and hydrothermal alteration (low to high T, low P)

Regional metamorphism
Low T, Low P
Zeolite facies
Greenschist facies
Amphibolite facies
Granulite facies
High T, High P

Continental crust

Partial melting of crust

Asthenosphere

B.

Burial metamorphism
Zeolite facies (low T, low P)

Hydrothermal metamorphism
Hydrothermal alteration (low to high T, low P)

Oceanic ridge

Basaltic oceanic crust

Basaltic magma derived from partial melting of peridotite

Asthenosphere

C.

buried have been uplifted because of a change in the plate boundary. In some areas, subduction carries rocks to even greater depths, producing the *eclogite facies* that is diagnostic of very high temperatures and pressures (FIGURE 34B).

Along some convergent zones, continental blocks collide to form extensive mountain belts (see Figure 33B). This activity results in large areas of regional metamorphism that often include zones of

contact and hydrothermal metamorphism. The increasing temperatures and pressures associated with regional metamorphism are recorded by the *zeolite–greenschist–amphibolite–granulite facies* sequence shown in Figure 33.

Mineral Stability and Metamorphic Environments

In most tectonic environments, such as along subduction zones, rocks experience an increase in *both* pressure and temperature simultaneously. An increase in pressure causes minerals to contract, which favors the formation of high-density minerals. However, increased temperature results in expansion, so mineral phases that occupy greater volume (are less dense) tend to be more stable at high temperatures. Thus, determining the conditions of temperature and pressure at which a mineral is stable (does not change) is not an easy task. To help in this endeavor, researchers have turned to the laboratory. Here materials of various composition are heated and placed under pressures that approximate conditions at various depths within Earth. From such experiments, we can determine what minerals are likely to form in various metamorphic environments.

Some minerals, such as quartz, are stable over a wide range of metamorphic settings and therefore are not useful in determining metamorphic environments. Fortunately, other suites of minerals do provide useful estimates of conditions during metamorphism. One of the most important of these groups

FIGURE 34 Rocks produced by subduction zone metamorphism
A. Blueschist, representing low-temperature, high-pressure conditions. Rocks that form in this environment have a blue hue because of the blue-colored amphibole called glaucophane. **B.** Eclogite, representing high-temperature, high-pressure conditions of the mantle. Note the reddish grains of garnet and green grains of pyroxene.

Rocks produced by subduction zone metamorphism.

Dennis Tasa

A. Blueschist forms in low-temperature, high-pressure environments

Dennis Tasa

B. Eclogite forms in high-temperature and extreme high-pressure environments includes the minerals *kyanite, andalusite,* and *silliman-ite.* These three minerals have identical chemical compositions (Al_2SiO_5) but different crystalline structures, which makes them *polymorphs.* FIGURE 35 is a *phase diagram* that shows the specific range of pressures and temperatures at which each of these aluminum-rich silicates is stable.

Because shales and mudstones, which are very common, contain the elements found in these minerals, metamorphic products of shale (slate, phyllite, schist, and gneiss) often contain varying amounts of either kyanite, andalusite, or sillimanite. For example, if shale were buried to a depth of about 35 kilometers (10 kbars), where the temperature was 550° C, the mineral kyanite would form (see the *x* in Figure 35).

In general, andalusite is produced by contact metamorphism in near-surface environments where temperatures are high but pressures are relatively low. Kyanite is the high-pressure polymorph that forms during the subduction and deep burial associated with mountain building. Sillimanite, on the other hand, forms only at high temperatures, as a result of contact with a very hot magma body and/or very deep burial. Knowing the ranges of temperatures and pressures a rock experienced during metamorphism provides geologists with valuable data needed to interpret past tectonic environments.

A. Andalusite   B. Kyanite   C. Sillimanite

FIGURE 35 Minerals used to predict metamorphic environments
Phase diagram illustration of the conditions of pressure and temperature at which the three polymorphs of Al_2SiO_5 are stable. (Photo A by Harry Taylor/ Dorling Kindersley Media Library; photo B by Dennis Tasa; photo C by Biophoto Associates/Photo Researchers, Inc.)

7   CONCEPT CHECKS

1. Define *metamorphic facies.*
2. What two physical conditions vary within Earth to produce different metamorphic environments?
3. The rocks of the Coast Range of California belong to the blueschist facies. What does this tell you about the environment in which these rocks formed?
4. Which process most likely leads to the formation of minerals belonging to the hornfels facies—contact metamorphism or regional metamorphism? Explain.

EYE on Earth

The Matterhorn, located on the border between Switzerland and Italy, is one of the highest peaks in the Alps. Except for its base, the Matterhorn is composed mainly of the metamorphic rock gneiss.

Question 1 To which metamorphic grade do the rocks of the upper Matterhorn belong?

Question 2 What type of plate boundary—divergent, convergent, or transform fault boundary—is associated with the formation of the Matterhorn and related mountainous structures of the Alps?

Question 3 Which type of metamorphism—contact, hydrothermal, burial, subduction zone, or regional metamorphism—likely produced the Matterhorn?

Vaclav Volrab/Shutterstock

CONCEPTS IN REVIEW: METAMORPHISM AND METAMORPHIC ROCKS

1 What Is Metamorphism?

Compare and contrast the environments that produce metamorphic, sedimentary, and igneous rocks.

KEY WORDS parent rock, metamorphism, mineralogy, metamorphic grade

- When rocks are subjected to elevated temperatures and pressures, they can react and "change form" to produce metamorphic rocks. Every metamorphic rock has a parent rock—the rock it used to be prior to metamorphism. When the minerals in parent rocks are subjected to extra heat and pressure, new minerals form. Metamorphic reactions tend to produce larger crystals and may generate layers of minerals aligned in a common direction.
- Metamorphic grade describes whether a rock is slightly or intensely metamorphosed. Low-grade metamorphic rocks strongly resemble their parent rock. High-grade metamorphism destroys textures of parent rocks and features such as fossils.

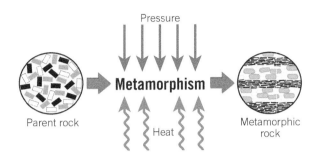

- Metamorphism takes place in the solid state and in most cases does not involve any melting.

PROCESSES and PRODUCTS   Compare the processes that produce metamorphic rocks to the processes that produce igneous or sedimentary rocks. Where do these processes fit into a diagram of the rock cycle?

2 What Drives Metamorphism?

List and distinguish between the three agents that drive metamorphism.

KEY WORDS recrystallization, confining pressure, differential stress, compressional stress

- Heat, pressure, directional stress, and chemically active fluids are four agents that drive metamorphic reactions. Any one alone may trigger metamorphism, or all four may exert influence simultaneously.
- The burial of rock or the intrusion of a nearby magma body will add heat to a rock. Heat provides energy that drives chemical reactions and recrystallization. Different minerals have different levels of susceptibility to recrystallization: Some crystals just grow larger, while others react to form new minerals. Quartz is stable across a wide range of temperatures, whereas clay minerals are stable only at low (surface) temperatures.
- Confining pressure results from burial. The pressure is of the same magnitude in every direction, like the pressure that a swimmer experiences when diving to the bottom of a swimming pool. An increase in confining pressure causes rocks and minerals to compact into more dense configurations.
- Differential stress results from tectonic forces. The pressure is greater in some directions and less in other directions. Rocks subjected to differential stress deep in the crust tend to shorten in the direction of greatest stress and elongate in the direction(s) of least stress, producing flattened or stretched grains. (Think of a heavy boot crushing a soda can.) If the same differential stress is applied to a rock in the shallow crust, it may deform in a brittle fashion instead, breaking into smaller pieces (like a boot crushing a champagne glass).
- Water is an important chemically active fluid in Earth's crust. Hot water can facilitate numerous chemical reactions and may transport dissolved mineral matter great distances to new sites of reaction. This may alter the composition of the metamorphosing rock by introducing or removing certain atoms.

SKETCH IT   Draw a picture illustrating the difference between confining pressure and differential stress.

3 Metamorphic Textures

Explain how foliated and nonfoliated textures develop.

KEY WORDS texture, foliation, rock cleavage, slaty cleavage, schistosity, gneissic texture (gneissic banding), nonfoliated, porphyroblastic texture

- Texture can reveal the orientation of stresses that helped to form a metamorphic rock. A common kind of texture is metamorphic foliation, the planar arrangement of mineral grains. Foliation forms perpendicular to the direction of maximum differential stress, through a combination of processes: rotation of stiff mineral grains, recrystallization and growth of new mineral grains, and flattening of grains by solid-state flow or pressure solution.
- Several arrangements of mineral grains can be classified as varieties of foliation. Varieties of foliation include slaty (rock) cleavage, schistosity, and gneissic banding.
- Nonfoliated metamorphic rocks recrystallize under confining pressure, so the mineral grains exhibit a random orientation. Marble, for instance, is produced when the calcite in a parent limestone grows into a crystalline mass.
- Porphyroblasts are large crystals of certain minerals, such as garnet, that form in some metamorphic rocks. They are larger than other grains in the same rock and are distributed through the rock with some space between them, like chocolate chips in a cookie.

Dennis Tasa

FORCING FOLIATION?   Examine the photograph. Based on whether this rock is foliated or nonfoliated, decide whether it formed under confining pressure or differential stress. Which of the pairs of arrows shows the direction of maximum stress?

4 Common Metamorphic Rocks

List and describe the most common metamorphic rocks.

- Common foliated metamorphic rocks include slate, phyllite, schist, and gneiss. The order listed here is the order of increasing metamorphic grade: Slate is least metamorphosed, and gneiss is the most metamorphosed.
- Common nonfoliated metamorphic rocks include quartzite, marble, and hornfels, the recrystallized rocks that form from quartz sandstone, limestone, and shale, respectively.

If you were on a field trip and found an outcrop of nonfoliated white rock, how would you determine whether it is quartzite or marble? How would you distinguish quartzite from quartz sandstone?

Dennis Tasa

5 Metamorphic Environments

Write a statement that describes each of these metamorphic environments: contact metamorphism, hydrothermal metamorphism, subduction zone metamorphism, and regional metamorphism.

KEY WORDS contact (thermal) metamorphism, aureole, hydrothermal metamorphism, burial metamorphism, subduction zone metamorphism, regional metamorphism, impact (shock) metamorphism

- The chemical reactions and physical reorganization of mineral crystals that we call *metamorphism* can be triggered by diverse geologic situations. Convergent and divergent plate boundaries are both sites of metamorphism, as are deep stacks of sediments on passive margins.
- Contact metamorphism occurs when heat is the dominant metamorphic variable. Typically, this heat emanates from a nearby body of magma that "bakes" the surrounding rock a short distance away.
- Hydrothermal metamorphism occurs in relatively limited areas, but water rather than conduction is the agent of heat transfer. The hot water readily dissolves a variety of ions, which may cause metamorphic reactions. Hydrothermal metamorphism produces economically important deposits of metal ore.
- Burial metamorphism occurs when rocks are buried beneath kilometers of overlying rock. Under confining pressure, elevated temperatures cause metamorphic reactions. Subduction zone metamorphism is similar, but with the added influence of differential stress.
- Areas of plate collision produce regional metamorphism. The rocks at these sites of crustal thickening are subjected to both high temperatures and differential pressure. The resulting belts of metamorphic rock (and associated igneous intrusions) mark the zones where continental blocks collided to produce mountains. Long after the mountains have worn away, the site of a former mountain range is marked by a deformed zone of regional metamorphic rocks such as slate, schist, marble, and gneiss.
- Other distinctive varieties of metamorphism are associated with faults and meteorite impact structures.

FIELD OF IMAGINATION Suppose that a helicopter dropped you off on two islands. Your job as an exploration geologist is to interpret the metamorphic rocks to see if the islands would be a good prospect for mining metals. Island #1 shows a circular ring of disturbed rock with coesite (a dense form of quartz), tiny diamonds, and glass, surrounded by ejecta. Island #2 is dominated by parallel bands of phyllite and garnet-mica schist. Is either island typical of hydrothermal metamorphism? What do you tell your boss?

6 Metamorphic Zones

Explain how index minerals are used to establish the metamorphic grade of a rock body.

KEY WORDS index mineral, migmatite

- Rocks change due to metamorphism, and the amount of change increases as the rocks are exposed to higher temperatures and pressures. As a piece of bread in a toaster gets darker the longer it cooks, metamorphic rocks reveal the degree of metamorphism through their textures and the minerals that formed.
- Grain size increases with higher levels of metamorphism. Under progressively higher temperatures and pressures, shale may transform first to slate, then to phyllite, to schist, and to gneiss.
- Certain minerals can act as indicators of the temperature/pressure conditions that a metamorphic rock experienced. Chlorite is a mineral associated with low-grade metamorphism, whereas sillimanite indicates a relatively high metamorphic grade. Garnet and staurolite are index minerals for intermediate metamorphic grades.
- At high temperatures, the minerals with the lowest melting points can turn to magma. Because these minerals are usually felsic in composition, rocks that exhibit evidence of partial melting typically show clots or bands of light-colored granite mixed with dark clots or bands of unmelted dark-colored metamorphic rock. These are migmatites.

BACK TO THE START A shale is exposed to high-grade metamorphic conditions over sufficient time to become a schist with porphyroblasts of sillimanite. Later, uplift and erosion expose this rock at the surface. Would you expect it to be more or less resistant to chemical weathering than a low-grade metamorphic rock such as chlorite-bearing phyllite? Why?

Does this sillimanite porphyroblast indicate low-, intermediate- or high-grade metamorphism?

Marli Miller

7 Interpreting Metamorphic Environments

Describe the conditions of temperature and pressure that you would associate with the following metamorphic facies: blueschist facies, hornfels facies, and zeolite facies.

KEY WORD metamorphic facies

- Similar metamorphic conditions encourage the growth of similar suites of metamorphic minerals. The assemblage of minerals in a metamorphic rock is evidence of the specific temperature/pressure conditions the rock reached during metamorphism.
- Blueschist and eclogite facies metamorphism is typical of subduction zones, where pressure is the dominant driver of change. The zeolite–greenschist–amphibolite–granulite sequence of metamorphic facies is typical of mountain-building activity at convergent plate boundaries, where both temperature

and pressure conditions are important. This regional metamorphism results in these facies grading into one another across the trend of a mountain belt. The hornfels facies is typical of metamorphic rocks that get "baked" at high temperatures but relatively low pressures.

INTERPRET IT In west-central Turkey, rocks such as the two

shown here crop out only a few kilometers apart. Which two metamorphic facies do they represent? (Compare them to images shown in the chapter.) Assume that we know that these rocks were heated to a maximum temperature of 500°C. Use Figure 32 to determine their approximate depth of burial. What tectonic setting produced these metamorphic rocks?

Sample A — Glaucophane porphyroblasts

Sample B — Garnet porphyroblasts

Photos by Callan Bentley

GIVE IT SOME THOUGHT

1. Each of the following statements describes one or more characteristics of a particular metamorphic rock. For each statement, identify the metamorphic rock that is being described:
   a. calcite rich and nonfoliated
   b. loosely coherent and composed of broken fragments that formed along a fault zone
   c. represents a grade of metamorphism between slate and schist
   d. composed of tiny chlorite and mica grains and displays excellent rock cleavage
   e. foliated and composed predominately of platy materials
   f. composed of alternating bands of light and dark silicate minerals
   g. hard and nonfoliated, often produced by contact metamorphism

2. One of the rock outcrops in the accompanying photos consists mainly of metamorphic rock. Which do you think it is? Explain why you ruled out the other rock bodies.

A.

B.

C.

3. Describe the textural changes that occur as shale goes from low- to high-metamorphic grade to form the rocks slate, schist, and gneiss.

4. Examine the accompanying photos that show the geology of the Grand Canyon. Notice that most of the canyon consists of layers of sedimentary rocks, but if you were to hike into the inner gorge, you would encounter the Vishnu schist, a metamorphic rock.
   a. What process might have been responsible for the formation of the Vishnu schist? How does this process differ from the processes that formed the sedimentary rocks that are atop the Vishnu schist?
   b. What does the Vishnu schist tell you about the history of the Grand Canyon prior to the formation of the canyon itself?
   c. Why is the Vishnu schist visible at Earth's surface?
   d. Is it likely that rocks similar to the Vishnu schist exist elsewhere but are not exposed at Earth's surface? Explain.

A. Inner gorge of the Grand Canyon

B. Close up of Vishnu Schist (dark color)

5. Examine the accompanying close-up images of a conglomerate and a metaconglomerate.
   a. Describe how the conglomerate is different from the metaconglomerate.
   b. Does this metaconglomerate appear to have been exposed to significant differential stress? Explain.

A. Conglomerate **B. Metaconglomerate** Photos by Dennis Tasa

6. Refer to the accompanying diagram and match each labeled area with the appropriate environment listed below:
   a. contact metamorphism
   b. subduction metamorphism
   c. regional metamorphism
   d. burial metamorphism
   e. hydrothermal metamorphism

7. Based on the information provided in Figure 30, complete the following:
   a. Describe how the metamorphic grade changes from west to east across New England along line A–B.
   b. How might these metamorphic rocks have formed?
   c. Are these zones of metamorphism consistent with the current tectonic setting of New England? Explain.

8. Examine the accompanying close-up images of six different rocks labeled A–F. Classify them as igneous, sedimentary, or metamorphic, based on texture. (*Hint:* There are two of each rock type.)

A. **B.**

C. **D.**

E. **F.** Photos by Dennis Tasa

9. The accompanying image shows folded and metamorphosed rock that displays slaty cleavage.
   a. Which colored dashed lines (red or black) represent the slaty cleavage, and which represent relic bedding surfaces?
   b. Was the maximum directional stress oriented horizontally or vertically?

Callan Bentley

MasteringGeology™

www.masteringgeology.com

Looking for additional review and test prep materials? Visit the Study Area in MasteringGeology to enhance your understanding of this chapter's content by accessing a variety of resources, including **Self-Study Quizzes,** **Geoscience Animations, GEODe Tutorials, RSS feeds, flashcards, web links, self-study quizzes,** and an optional **Pearson eText.**

Glossary

Aureole A zone or halo of contact metamorphism found in the country rock surrounding an igneous intrusion.

Burial metamorphism Low-grade metamorphism that occurs in the lowest layers of very thick accumulations of sedimentary strata.

Compressional stress Differential stress that shortens a rock body.

Confining pressure Stress that is applied uniformly in all directions.

Contact metamorphism Changes in rock caused by the heat from a nearby magma body.

Differential stress Forces that are unequal in different directions.

Foliation A term for a linear arrangement of textural features often exhibited by metamorphic rocks.

Gneissic texture A texture of metamorphic rocks in which dark and light silicate minerals are separated, giving the rock a banded appearance.

Hydrothermal metamorphism Chemical alterations that occur as hot, ion-rich water circulates through fractures in rock.

Impact metamorphism Metamorphism that occurs when meteorites strike Earth's surface.

Index mineral A mineral that is a good indicator of the metamorphic environment in which it formed. Used to distinguish different zones of regional metamorphism.

Metamorphic facies A group of associated minerals that are used to establish the pressures and temperatures at which rocks undergo metamorphism.

Metamorphic grade The degree to which a parent rock changes during metamorphism. It varies from low grade (low temperatures and pressures) to high grade (high temperatures and pressures).

Metamorphism The changes in mineral composition and texture of a rock subjected to high temperatures and pressures within Earth.

Migmatite A rock exhibiting both igneous and metamorphic rock characteristics. Such rocks may form when light-colored silicate minerals melt and then crystallize, while the dark silicate minerals remain solid.

Mineralogy The study of minerals.

Nonfoliated rocks Metamorphic rocks that do not exhibit foliation.

Parent rock The rock from which a metamorphic rock formed.

Porphyroblastic texture A texture of metamorphic rocks in which particularly large grains (porphyroblasts) are surrounded by a fine-grained matrix of other minerals.

Recrystallization The formation of new mineral crystals in a rock that tend to be larger than the original crystals.

Regional metamorphism Metamorphism associated with large-scale mountain building.

Rock cleavage The tendency of rocks to split along parallel, closely spaced surfaces. These surfaces are often highly inclined to the bedding planes in the rock.

Schistosity A type of foliation that is characteristic of coarser-grained metamorphic rocks. Such rocks have a parallel arrangement of platy minerals such as the micas.

Slaty cleavage A type of foliation that is characteristic of slates, in which there is a parallel arrangement of fine-grained metamorphic minerals.

Subduction zone metamorphism High-pressure, low-temperature metamorphism that occurs where sediments are carried to great depths by a subducting plate.

Texture The size, shape, and distribution of the particles that collectively constitute a rock.

Thermal metamorphism See Contact metamorphism.

Geologic Time

From Chapter 9 of *Earth: An Introduction to Physical Geology*, Eleventh Edition. Edward J. Tarbuck, Frederick K. Lutgens, Dennis Tasa.
Copyright © 2014 by Pearson Education, Inc. All rights reserved.

Geologic Time

The Colorado River winding through Canyonlands National Park, Utah. The strata exposed in the canyon walls contain clues to millions of years of Earth history. (Photo by Gerhard Zwerger-Schon)

Each statement represents the primary learning objective for the corresponding major heading within the chapter. After you complete the chapter you should be able to:

1 Distinguish between numerical and relative dating and apply relative dating principles to determine a time sequence of geologic events.

2 Define *fossil* and discuss the conditions that favor the preservation of organisms as fossils. List and describe various types of fossils.

3 Explain how rocks of similar age that are in different places can be matched up.

4 Discuss three types of radioactive decay and explain how radioactive isotopes are used to determine numerical dates.

5 Distinguish among the four basic time units that make up the geologic time scale and explain why the time scale is considered to be a dynamic tool.

6 Explain how reliable numerical dates are determined for layers of sedimentary rock.

n the late eighteenth century, James Hutton recognized the immensity of Earth history and the importance of time as a component in all geologic processes. In the nineteenth century, Sir Charles Lyell and others effectively demonstrated that Earth had experienced many episodes of mountain building and erosion, which must have required great spans of geologic time. Although these pioneering scientists understood that Earth was very old, they had no way of determining its age in years. Was it tens of millions, hundreds of millions, or even billions of years old? Long before geologists could establish a geologic calendar that included numerical dates in years, they gradually assembled a time scale using relative dating principles. What are these principles? What part do fossils play? With the discovery of radioactivity and radiometric dating techniques, geologists now can assign quite accurate dates to many of the events in Earth history. What is radioactivity? Why is it a good "clock" for dating the geologic past?

Fossils are important tools in the study of Earth history. These Jurassic age ammonite fossils are from Germany. (Photo by James L. Amos/Photo Researchers, Inc.)

1 Creating a Time Scale—Relative Dating Principles

FIGURE 1 shows a hiker resting atop the Kaibab Formation at Cape Royal on the North Rim of the Grand Canyon. A great span of Earth history is concealed in the strata beneath the hiker.

The Importance of a Time Scale

Like the pages in a long and complicated history book, rocks record the geologic events and changing life-forms of the past. The book, however, is not complete. Many pages, especially in the early chapters, are missing. Others are tattered, torn, or smudged. Yet enough of the book remains to allow much of the story to be deciphered.

Interpreting Earth history is a prime goal of the science of geology. Like a modern-day sleuth, a geologist must interpret the clues found preserved in the rocks. By studying rocks, especially sedimentary rocks, and the features they contain, geologists can unravel the complexities of the past.

Geologic events by themselves, however, have little meaning until they are put into a time perspective. Studying history, whether it is the Civil War or the age of dinosaurs, requires a calendar. Among geology's major contributions to human knowledge are the *geologic time scale* and the discovery that Earth history is exceedingly long.

Numerical and Relative Dates

The geologists who developed the geologic time scale revolutionized the way people think about time and perceive our planet. They learned that Earth is much older than anyone had previously imagined and that its surface and interior have been changed over and over again by the same geologic processes that operate today.

Numerical Dates During the late 1800s and early 1900s, attempts were made to determine Earth's age. Although some of the methods appeared promising at the time, none of those early efforts proved to be reliable. What those scientists were seeking was a **numerical date**. Such dates specify the actual number of years that have passed since an event occurred. Today, our understanding of radioactivity allows us to accurately determine numerical dates for rocks that represent important events in Earth's distant past. We will study radioactivity later in this chapter. Prior to the discovery of radioactiv-

FIGURE 1 Contemplating geologic time
This hiker is resting atop the Kaibab Formation, the uppermost layer in the Grand Canyon. (Photo by Michael Collier)

ity, geologists had no reliable method of numerical dating and had to rely solely on relative dating.

Relative Dates When we place rocks in their proper *sequence of formation*—which formed first, second, third, and so on—we are establishing **relative dates**. Such dates cannot tell us how long ago something took place, only that it followed one event and preceded another. The relative dating techniques that were developed are valuable and still widely used. Numerical dating methods did not replace these techniques; they simply supplemented them. To establish a relative time scale, a few basic principles or rules had to be discovered and applied. Although they may seem obvious to us today, they were major breakthroughs in thinking at

E.J. Tarbuck

FIGURE 2 Superposition
Applying the principle of superposition to these layers in the upper portion of the Grand Canyon, the Supai Group is oldest and the Kaibab Limestone is youngest.

Geologist's Sketch

Youngest

Kaibab Limestone: shallow marine limestone that rims much of the canyon

Toroweap Formation: shallow marine, thin-to-medium bedded sandy limestone

Coconino Sandstone: cliff-forming cross-bedded sandstone

Hermit Shale: red, slope-forming thinly-bedded shales and siltstones

Supai Group: alternating layers of sandstone, siltstone and shale

Oldest

the time, and their discovery was an important scientific achievement.

Principle of Superposition

Nicolas Steno, a Danish anatomist, geologist, and priest (1638–1686), is credited with being the first to recognize a sequence of historical events in an outcrop of sedimentary rock layers. Working in the mountains of western Italy, Steno applied a very simple rule that has come to be the most basic principle of relative dating—the **principle of superposition** (*super* = above; *positum* = to place). The law simply states that in an undeformed sequence of sedimentary rocks, each bed is older than the one above and younger than the one below. Although it may seem obvious that a rock layer could not be deposited with nothing beneath it for support, it was not until 1669 that Steno clearly stated this principle.

This rule also applies to other surface-deposited materials, such as lava flows and beds of ash from volcanic eruptions. Applying the law of superposition to the beds exposed in the upper portion of the Grand Canyon, we can easily place the layers in their proper order. Among those that are pictured in FIGURE 2, the sedimentary rocks in the Supai Group are the oldest, followed in order by the Hermit Shale, Coconino Sandstone, Toroweap Formation, and Kaibab Limestone.

EYE on Earth

This image shows West Cedar Mountain in southern Utah. The gray rocks are shale that originated as muddy river delta deposits. The sediments composing the orange sandstone were deposited by a river. (Photo by Michael Collier)

Question 1 Place the events related to the geologic history of this area in proper sequence. Explain your logic. Include the following: uplift, sandstone, erosion, and shale.

Question 2 What term is applied to the type of dates you established for this site?

Shale

Sandstone

FIGURE 3 Original horizontality
Most layers of sediment are deposited in a nearly horizontal position. When we see strata that are folded or tilted, we can assume that they were moved into that position by crustal disturbances *after* their deposition. (Photo by Marco Simoni/Robert Harding World Imagery)

Principle of Original Horizontality

Steno is also credited with recognizing the importance of another basic principle, called the **principle of original horizontality**, which says that layers of sediment are generally deposited in a horizontal position. Thus, if we observe rock layers that are flat, it means they have not been disturbed and still have their *original* horizontality. The layers in the Grand Canyon illustrate this in Figures 1 and 2. But if they are folded or inclined at a steep angle, they must have been moved into that position by crustal disturbances sometime *after* their deposition (FIGURE 3).

Principle of Lateral Continuity

The **principle of lateral continuity** refers to the fact that sedimentary beds originate as continuous layers that extend in all directions until they eventually grade into a different type of sediment or until they thin out at the edge of the basin of deposition (FIGURE 4). For example, when a river creates a canyon, we can assume that identical or

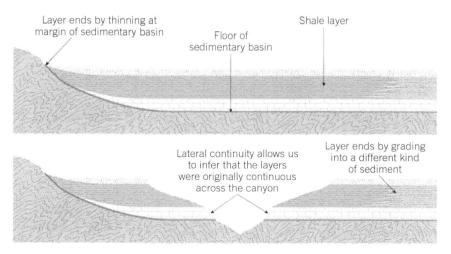

Layer ends by thinning at margin of sedimentary basin

Floor of sedimentary basin

Shale layer

Lateral continuity allows us to infer that the layers were originally continuous across the canyon

Layer ends by grading into a different kind of sediment

FIGURE 4 Lateral continuity
Sediments are deposited over a large area in a continuous sheet. Sedimentary strata extend continuously in all directions until they thin out at the edge of a depositional basin or grade into a different type of sediment.

FIGURE 5 Lateral continuity in the Grand Canyon

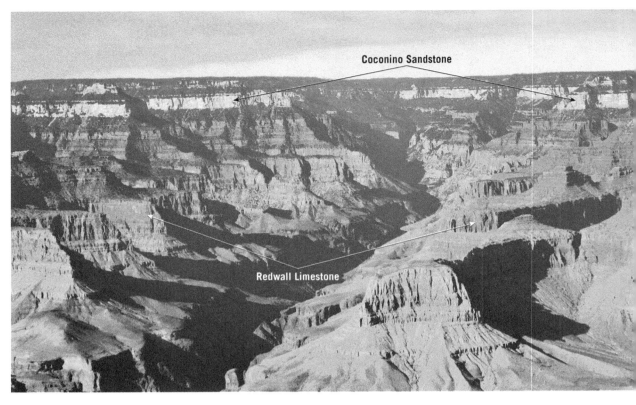

FIGURE 5 Lateral continuity in the Grand Canyon Although rock exposures are separated by many miles, we know they were once continuous. (Photo by bcampbell65/Shutterstock)

similar strata on opposite sides once spanned the canyon. Although rock outcrops may be separated by a considerable distance, the principle of lateral continuity tells us those outcrops once formed a continuous layer (FIGURE 5). This principle allows geologists to relate rocks in isolated outcrops to one another. Combining the principles of lateral continuity and superposition lets us extend relative age relationships over broad areas. This process, called *correlation*, is examined later in the chapter.

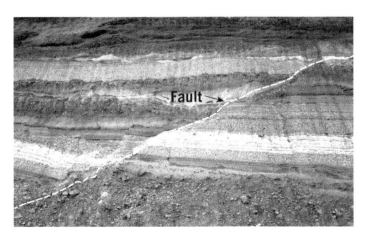

FIGURE 6 Cross-cutting fault The rocks are older than the fault that displaced them. (Morley Read/Alamy)

Principle of Cross-Cutting Relationships

FIGURE 6 shows a mass of rock that is offset by a fault, a fracture in rock along which displacement occurs. It is clear that the rocks must be older than the fault that broke them. The **principle of cross-cutting relationships** states that geologic features that cut across rocks must form *after* the rocks they cut through. Igneous intrusions provide another example. The dike shown in FIGURE 7 is a tabular mass of igneous rock that cuts through the surrounding rocks. The magmatic heat from igneous intrusions often creates a narrow "baked" zone of contact metamorphism on the adjacent rock, also indicating that the intrusion occurred after the surrounding rocks were in place.

Inclusions

Sometimes inclusions can aid in the relative dating process. **Inclusions** (*includere* = to enclose) are fragments of one rock unit that have been enclosed within another. The basic principle is logical and

FIGURE 7 Cross-cutting dike
An igneous intrusion is younger than the rocks that are intruded. (Photo by Ken M. Johns/Photo Researchers, Inc.)

representing certain spans of geologic time. However, no place on Earth has a complete set of conformable strata.

Throughout Earth history, the deposition of sediment has been interrupted over and over again. All such breaks in the rock record are termed *unconformities*. An **unconformity** represents a long period during which deposition ceased, erosion removed previously formed rocks, and then deposition resumed. In each case, uplift and erosion are followed by subsidence and renewed sedimentation. Unconformities are important features because they represent significant geologic events in Earth history. Moreover, their recognition helps us identify what intervals of time are not represented by strata and thus are missing from the geologic record.

There are three basic types of unconformities.

Angular Unconformity

Perhaps the most easily recognized unconformity is an **angular unconformity**. It consists of tilted or folded sedimentary rocks that are overlain by younger, more flat-lying strata. An angular unconformity indicates that during the pause in deposition, a period

straightforward. The rock mass adjacent to the one containing the inclusions must have been there first in order to provide the rock fragments. Therefore, the rock mass that contains inclusions is the younger of the two. For example, when magma intrudes into surrounding rock, blocks of the surrounding rock may become dislodged and incorporated into the magma. If these pieces do not melt, they remain as inclusions, known as *xenoliths*. In another example, when sediment is deposited atop a weathered mass of bedrock, pieces of the weathered rock become incorporated into the younger sedimentary layer (FIGURE 8).

Unconformities

When we observe layers of rock that have been deposited essentially without interruption, we call them **conformable**. Particular sites exhibit conformable beds

These inclusions of igneous rock contained in the adjacent sedimentary layer indicate the sediments were deposited atop the weathered igneous mass and thus are younger.

Sedimentary layers

Igneous intrusion

Xenoliths are inclusions in an igneous intrusion that form when pieces of surrounding rock are incorporated into magma.

SMARTFIGURE 8
Inclusions
The rock containing inclusions is younger than the inclusions.

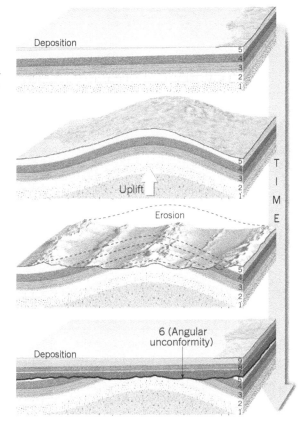

Formation of an angular unconformity
An angular unconformity represents an extended period during which deformation and erosion occurred.

Deposition

Uplift

Erosion

TIME

6 (Angular unconformity)

Deposition

FIGURE 10 Siccar Point, Scotland
James Hutton studied this famous unconformity in the late 1700s. (Photo by Marli Miller)

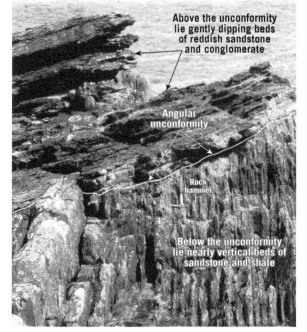

Above the unconformity lie gently dipping beds of reddish sandstone and conglomerate

Angular unconformity

Rock hammer

Below the unconformity lie nearly vertical beds of sandstone and shale

Disconformity
Gap in the rock record represents a period of nondeposition and erosion

Younger, horizontal sedimentary rocks

Older, horizontal sedimentary rocks

FIGURE 11 Disconformity
The layers on both sides of this gap in the rock record are essentially parallel.

of deformation (folding or tilting) and erosion occurred (FIGURE 9).

When James Hutton studied an angular unconformity in Scotland more than 200 years ago, it was clear to him that it represented a major episode of geologic activity (FIGURE 10). He and his colleagues also appreciated the immense time span implied by such relationships. When a companion later wrote of their visit to this site, he stated that "the mind seemed to grow giddy by looking so far into the abyss of time."

Disconformity A **disconformity** is a gap in the rock record that represents a period during which erosion rather than deposition is occurring. Imagine that a series of sedimentary layers is deposited in a shallow marine setting. Following this period of deposition, sea level falls or the land rises, exposing some the sedimentary layers. During this span, when the sedimentary beds are above sea level, no new sediment accumulates, and some of the existing layers are eroded away. Later, sea level rises or the land subsides, submerging the landscape. Now the surface is again below sea level, and a new series of sedimentary beds is deposited. The boundary separating the two sets of beds is a disconformity—a span for which there is no rock record (FIGURE 11). Because the layers above and below a disconformity are parallel, these features are sometimes difficult to identify unless you notice evidence of erosion such as a buried stream channel.

Nonconformity The third basic type of unconformity is a **nonconformity**, in which younger sedimentary strata overlie older metamorphic or intrusive igneous rocks (FIGURE 12). Just as angular unconformities and some disconformities imply crustal movements, so too do nonconformities. Intrusive igneous masses and metamorphic rocks originate far below the surface. Thus, for a nonconformity to develop, there must be a period of uplift and erosion of overlying rocks. Once exposed at the surface, the igneous or metamorphic rocks are subjected to weathering and erosion prior to subsidence and the renewal of sedimentation.

Unconformities in the Grand Canyon

The rocks exposed in the Grand Canyon of the Colorado River represent a tremendous span of geologic history. It is a wonderful place to take a trip through time. The canyon's colorful strata record a long history of sedimentation in a variety of environments—advancing seas, rivers and deltas, tidal flats and sand dunes. But the record is not continuous. Unconformities represent vast amounts of time that have not been recorded in the canyon's layers. FIGURE 13 is a geologic cross section of the Grand Canyon. All three types of unconformities can be seen in the canyon walls.

FIGURE 12 Nonconformity
Younger sedimentary rocks rest atop older metamorphic or igneous rocks.

Nonconformity
Period of uplift and erosion that exposed the deep rocks at the surface

Younger, sedimentary layers deposited atop erosion surface

Older, igneous and/or metamorphic rocks that formed deep within the crust

FIGURE 13 Cross section of the Grand Canyon
All three types of unconformities are present. (Center photo by Marli Miller; other photos by E. J. Tarbuck)

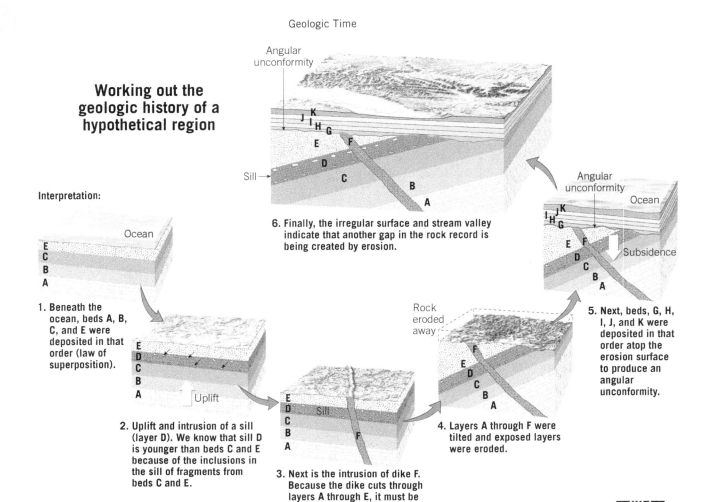

Working out the geologic history of a hypothetical region

Geologic Time

Angular unconformity

J K
I H G
E F
Sill → D
C
B
A

Interpretation:

Ocean

E
C
B
A

1. Beneath the ocean, beds A, B, C, and E were deposited in that order (law of superposition).

E
D
C
B
A
Uplift

2. Uplift and intrusion of a sill (layer D). We know that sill D is younger than beds C and E because of the inclusions in the sill of fragments from beds C and E.

E
D
C Sill
B
A
F

3. Next is the intrusion of dike F. Because the dike cuts through layers A through E, it must be younger (principle of cross-cutting relationships).

6. Finally, the irregular surface and stream valley indicate that another gap in the rock record is being created by erosion.

Rock eroded away

F
E
D
C
B
A

4. Layers A through F were tilted and exposed layers were eroded.

Angular unconformity

Ocean

J K
I H G
E F
D
C Subsidence
B
A

5. Next, beds, G, H, I, J, and K were deposited in that order atop the erosion surface to produce an angular unconformity.

SMARTFIGURE 14 Applying principles

Applying Relative Dating Principles

If you apply the principles of relative dating to the hypothetical geologic cross section in FIGURE 14, you can place in proper sequence the rocks and the events they represent. The statements within the figure summarize the logic used to interpret the cross section.

In this example, we establish a relative time scale for the rocks and events in the area of the cross section. Remember that this method gives us no idea how many years of Earth history are represented, for we have no numerical dates. Nor do we know how this area compares to any other.

Dating the Lunar Surface

Just as we use relative dating principles to determine the sequence of geologic events on Earth, so too can we apply such principles to the surface of the Moon.

Numerical Dates

Radiometric dating of Moon rocks brought back from Apollo missions showed that the age of the highlands is greater than 4 billion years, whereas the maria have ages ranging from 3.2 to 3.9 billion years.

Crater Density

Highlands

Maria

Older regions have been exposed to meteorite impact longer and therefore have more craters. Using this technique, we can infer that the highly cratered highlands are older than the dark areas called maria. The number of craters per unit area (called crater density) is obviously much greater in the highlands.

Superposition

This image shows the forward margin of a lava flow "frozen" in place. By applying the law of superposition, we know that this flow is younger than the adjacent layer that disappears beneath it. (Photos by NASA Headquarters/Lick Observatory Publications Office)

Cross-Cutting

Older

Younger

The most obvious features on the lunar surface are craters. Most were produced by the impact of rapidly moving objects called meteorites. When we observe one impact crater that overlaps another, we know the continuous unbroken crater came after the one it cuts across.

2 Fossils: Evidence of Past Life

Fossils, the remains or traces of prehistoric life, are important inclusions in sediment and sedimentary rocks. They are basic and important tools for interpreting the geologic past. The scientific study of fossils is called **paleontology**. It is an interdisciplinary science that blends geology and biology in an attempt to understand all aspects of the succession of life over the vast expanse of geologic time. Knowing the nature of the life-forms that existed at a particular time helps researchers understand past environmental conditions. Further, fossils are important time indicators and play a key role in correlating rocks of similar ages that are from different places.

Types of Fossils

Fossils are of many types. The remains of relatively recent organisms may not have been altered at all. Such objects as teeth, bones, and shells are common examples (FIGURE 15). Far less common are entire animals, flesh included, that have been preserved because of rather unusual circumstances. Remains of prehistoric elephants called mammoths that were frozen in the Arctic tundra of Siberia and Alaska are examples, as are the mummified remains of sloths preserved in a dry cave in Nevada.

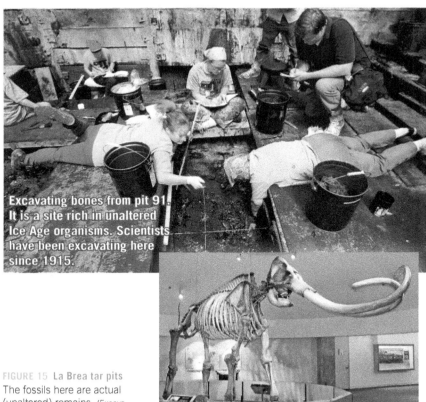

Excavating bones from pit 91. It is a site rich in unaltered Ice Age organisms. Scientists have been excavating here since 1915.

FIGURE 15 La Brea tar pits The fossils here are actual (unaltered) remains. (Excavation photo by Reed Saxon/AP Wide World Photo; skeleton photo by Martin Shields/Alamy)

Skeleton of a mammoth, a prehistoric relative of modern elephant, from the La Brea tar pits.

Permineralization When mineral-rich groundwater permeates porous tissue such as bone or wood, minerals precipitate out of solution and fill pores and empty spaces, a process called *permineralization*. The formation of *petrified wood* involves permineralization with silica, often from a volcanic source such as a surrounding layer of volcanic ash. The wood is gradually transformed into chert, sometimes with colorful bands from impurities such as iron or carbon (FIGURE 16A). The word *petrified* literally means "turned into stone." Sometimes the microscopic details of the petrified structure are faithfully retained.

Molds and Casts Another common class of fossils is *molds* and *casts*. When a shell or other structure is buried in sediment and then dissolved by underground water, a *mold* is created. The mold faithfully reflects only the shape and surface marking of the organism; it does not reveal any information concerning its internal structure. If these hollow spaces are subsequently filled with mineral matter, *casts* are created (FIGURE 16B).

Carbonization and Impressions A type of fossilization called *carbonization* is particularly effective at preserving leaves and delicate animal forms. It occurs when fine sediment encases the remains of an organism. As time passes, pressure squeezes out the liquid and gaseous components and leaves behind a thin residue of carbon (FIGURE 16C). Black shale deposited as organic-rich mud in oxygen-poor environments often contains abundant carbonized remains. If the film of carbon is lost from a fossil preserved in fine-grained sediment, a replica of the surface, called an *impression*, may still show considerable detail (FIGURE 16D).

Amber Delicate organisms, such as insects, are difficult to preserve, and consequently they are relatively rare in the fossil record. Not only must they be protected from decay, but they must not be subjected to any pressure that would crush them. One way in which some insects have been preserved is in *amber*, the hardened resin of ancient trees. The fly in FIGURE 16E was preserved after being trapped in a drop of sticky resin. Resin sealed off the insect from the atmosphere and protected the remains from damage by water and air. As the resin hardened, a protective pressure-resistant case was formed.

Trace Fossils In addition to the fossils already mentioned, there are numerous other types, many of them only traces of prehistoric life. Examples of such indirect evidence include:

1. Tracks—animal footprints made in soft sediment that later turned into sedimentary rock.
2. Burrows—tubes in sediment, wood, or rock made by an animal. These holes may later become filled with mineral matter and preserved. Some of the oldest-known fossils are believed to be worm burrows.
3. Coprolites—fossil dung and stomach contents that can provide useful information pertaining to the size and food habits of organisms (FIGURE 16F).
4. Gastroliths—highly polished stomach stones that were used in the grinding of food by some extinct reptiles.

Conditions Favoring Preservation

Only a tiny fraction of the organisms that have lived during the geologic past have been preserved as fossils. Normally, the remains of an animal or plant are destroyed. Under what circumstances are they preserved? Two special conditions appear to be necessary: rapid burial and the possession of hard parts.

When an organism perishes, its soft parts usually are quickly eaten by scavengers or decomposed by bacteria. Occasionally, however, the remains are buried by sediment. When this occurs, the remains are protected from the environment, where destructive processes operate. Rapid burial, therefore, is an important condition favoring preservation.

In addition, animals and plants have a much better chance of being preserved as part of the fossil record if they have hard parts. Although traces and imprints of soft-bodied animals such as jellyfish, worms, and insects exist, they are not common. Flesh usually decays so rapidly that preservation is exceedingly unlikely. Hard parts such as shells, bones, and teeth predominate in the record of past life.

Because preservation is contingent on special conditions, the record of life in the geologic past is biased. The fossil record of those organisms with hard parts that lived in areas of sedimentation is quite abundant. However, we get only an occasional glimpse of the vast array of other life-forms that did not meet the special conditions favoring preservation.

2 CONCEPT CHECKS

1. Describe several ways that an animal or a plant can be preserved as a fossil.
2. List three examples of trace fossils.
3. What conditions favor the preservation of an organism as a fossil?

Geologic Time

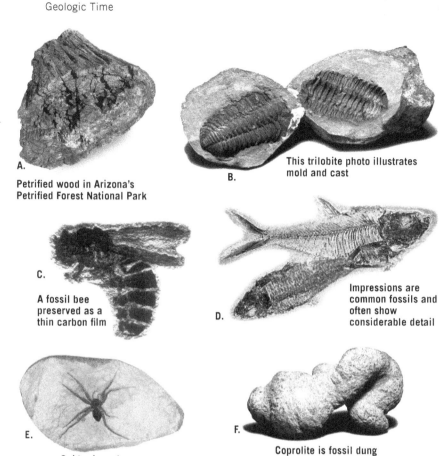

A. Petrified wood in Arizona's Petrified Forest National Park

B. This trilobite photo illustrates mold and cast

C. A fossil bee preserved as a thin carbon film

D. Impressions are common fossils and often show considerable detail

E. Spider in amber

F. Coprolite is fossil dung

FIGURE 16 Types of fossils

(Photos by **A**, Bernhard Edmaier/Photo Researchers, Inc.; **B**, E. J. Tarbuck; **C**, Florissant Fossil Beds National Monument; **D**, E. J. Tarbuck; **E**, Colin Keates/Dorling Kindersley Media Library; **F**, E. J. Tarbuck)

EYE on Earth

This close-up shows pieces of diorite (darkest rock) in granite. The thin white line is a vein of quartz. Think of a vein as a tiny dike.

Question 1 What term is applied to the pieces of diorite?

Question 2 Place the quartz vein, diorite, and granite in order from oldest to youngest.

Marli Miller

3 Correlation of Rock Layers

To develop a geologic time scale that is applicable to the entire Earth, rocks of similar age in different regions must be matched up. Such a task is referred to as **correlation**. By correlating the rocks from one place to another, a more comprehensive view of the geologic history of a region is possible. **FIGURE 17**, for example, shows the correlation of strata at three sites on the Colorado Plateau in southern Utah and northern Arizona. No single locale exhibits the entire sequence, but correlation reveals a more complete picture of the sedimentary rock record.

FIGURE 17 Correlation Matching strata at three locations on the Colorado Plateau. (Photos by E. J. Tarbuck)

Correlation Within Limited Areas

Within a limited area, correlating rocks of one locality with those of another may be done simply by walking along the outcropping edges. However, this may not be possible when the rocks are mostly concealed by soil and vegetation. Correlation over short distances is often achieved by noting the position of a bed in a sequence of strata. Or a layer may be identified in another location if it is composed of distinctive or uncommon minerals.

Many geologic studies involve relatively small areas. Although they are important in their own right, their full value is realized only when they are correlated with other regions. Although the methods just described are sufficient to trace a rock formation over relatively short distances, they are not adequate for matching up rocks that are separated by great distances. When correlation between widely separated areas or between continents is the objective, geologists must rely on fossils.

Fossils and Correlation

The existence of fossils had been known for centuries, yet it was not until the late 1700s and early 1800s that their significance as geologic tools was made evident. During this period, an English engineer and canal builder, William Smith, discovered that each rock formation in the canals he worked on contained fossils unlike those in the beds either above or below. Further, he noted that sedimentary strata in widely separated areas could be identified—and correlated—by their distinctive fossil content.

Principle of Faunal Succession
Based on Smith's classic observations and the findings of many geologists who followed, one of the most important and basic principles in historical geology was formulated: *Fossil organisms succeed one another in a definite and determinable order, and therefore any time period can be recognized by its fossil content.* This has come to be known as the **principle of fossil succession**. In other words, when fossils are arranged according to their age, they do not present a random or haphazard picture. To the contrary, fossils document the evolution of life through time.

For example, an Age of Trilobites is recognized quite early in the fossil record. Then, in succession, paleontologists recognize an Age of Fishes, an Age of Coal Swamps, an Age of Reptiles, and an Age of Mammals. These "ages" pertain to groups that were especially plentiful and characteristic during particular time periods. Within each of the "ages" are many subdivisions, based, for example, on certain species of trilobites and certain types of fish, reptiles, and so on. This same succession of dominant organisms, never out of order, is found on every continent.

FIGURE 18 **Index fossils** Since microfossils are often very abundant, widespread, and quick to appear and become extinct, they constitute ideal index fossils. This scanning electron micrograph shows marine microfossils from the Miocene epoch. (Photo by Biophoto Associates/Photo Researchers, Inc.)

Index Fossils and Fossil Assemblages
When fossils were found to be time indicators, they became the most useful means of correlating rocks of similar age in different regions. Geologists pay particular attention to certain fossils called **index fossils** (FIGURE 18). These fossils are widespread geographically and are limited to a short span of geologic time, so their presence provides an important method of matching rocks of the same age. Rock formations, however, do not always contain a specific index fossil. In such situations, a group of fossils, called a **fossil assemblage**, is used to establish the age of the bed. FIGURE 19 illustrates how an assemblage of fossils may be used to date rocks more precisely than could be accomplished by the use of any one of the fossils.

Environmental Indicators
In addition to being important, and often essential, tools for correlation, fossils are important environmental indicators. Although much can be deduced about past environments by studying the nature and characteristics of sedimentary rocks, a close examination of the fossils present can usually provide a great deal more information. For example, when the remains of certain clam shells are found in limestone, a geologist quite reasonably assumes that the region was once covered by a shallow sea. Also, by using what we know of living organisms, we can conclude that fossil animals with thick shells, capable of withstanding pounding and surging waves, inhabited shorelines.

On the other hand, animals with thin, delicate shells probably indicate deep, calm offshore waters. Hence, by looking closely at the types of fossils, the approximate

Fossil assemblage
Overlapping ranges of fossils help date rocks more exactly than using a single fossil.

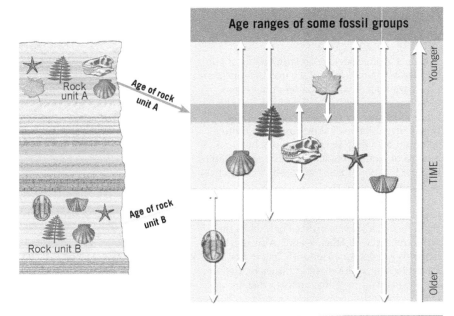

position of an ancient shoreline may be identified. Further, fossils can be used to indicate the former temperature of the water. Certain kinds of present-day corals must live in warm and shallow tropical seas like those around Florida and The Bahamas. When similar types of coral are found in ancient limestones, they indicate the marine environment that must have existed when they were alive. These examples illustrate how fossils can help unravel the complex story of Earth history.

3 CONCEPT CHECKS

1. What is the goal of correlation?
2. State the principle of fossil succession in your own words.
3. Contrast index fossil and fossil assemblage.
4. Other than being important time indicators, how else are fossils useful to geologists?

EYE on Earth

This scene in Montana's Glacier National Park shows layers of Precambrian sedimentary rocks. The darker layer contained in the sedimentary layers is igneous. The narrow, light-colored areas adjacent to the igneous rock were created when the molten material that formed the igneous rock baked the adjacent rock.

Marli Miller

Question 1 Is the igneous layer more likely a lava flow that was laid down at the surface prior to the deposition of the layers above it or a sill that was intruded after all the sedimentary layers were deposited? Explain.

Question 2 With which feature, a lava flow or a sill, would you most likely find rock with a vesicular texture? Explain.

How is paleontology different from archaeology?

People frequently confuse these two areas of study because a common perception of both paleontologists and archaeologists is of scientists carefully extracting important clues about the past from layers of rock or sediment. While it is true that scientists in both disciplines "dig" a lot, the focus of each is different.

Archaeology

Archaeologists help us learn about how our human ancestors met the challenges of life in the past.

Archaeologists focus on the material remains of past human life. These remains include both the objects used by people long ago, called *artifacts*, and the buildings and other structures associated with where people lived, called *sites*.

Paleontology

Paleontologists study fossils and are concerned with all life forms in the geologic past. These scientists are excavating the fossil remains of *Albertasaurus*, a carnivore similar to *Tyrannosaurus rex*.

Richard T. Nowitz/Photo Researchers, Inc.

Richard T. Nowitz/Science Source/Photo Researchers, Inc.

335

4 Dating with Radioactivity

In addition to establishing relative dates by using the principles described in the preceding sections, it is also possible to obtain reliable numerical dates for events in the geologic past. For example, we know that Earth is about 4.6 billion years old and that the dinosaurs became extinct about 65 million years ago. Dates that are expressed in millions and billions of years truly stretch our imagination because our personal calendars involve time measured in hours, weeks, and years. Nevertheless, the vast expanse of geologic time is a reality, and radiometric dating allows us to measure it. In this section you will learn about radioactivity and its application in radiometric dating.

Reviewing Basic Atomic Structure

Each atom has a *nucleus* that contains protons and neutrons and the nucleus is orbited by electrons. *Electrons* have a negative electrical charge, and *protons* have a positive charge. A *neutron* is actually a proton and an electron combined, so it has no charge (it is neutral).

The *atomic number* (each element's identifying number) is the number of protons in the nucleus. Every element has a different number of protons and thus a different atomic number (hydrogen = 1, carbon = 6, oxygen = 8, uranium = 92, etc.). Atoms of the same element always have the same number of protons, so the atomic number stays constant.

Practically all of an atom's mass (99.9 percent) is in the nucleus, indicating that electrons have virtually no mass at all. So, by adding the protons and neutrons in an atom's nucleus, we derive the atom's *mass number.* The number of neutrons can vary, and these variants, or *isotopes*, have different mass numbers.

To summarize with an example, uranium's nucleus always has 92 protons, so its atomic number is always 92. But its neutron population varies, so uranium has three isotopes: uranium-234 (protons + neutrons = 234), uranium-235, and uranium-238. All three isotopes are mixed in nature. They look the same and behave the same in chemical reactions.

Radioactivity

The forces that bind protons and neutrons together in the nucleus are usually strong. However, in some isotopes, the nuclei are unstable because the forces that bind protons and neutrons together are not strong enough. As a result, the nuclei spontaneously break apart, or decay, in a process called **radioactivity**.

Common Examples of Radioactive Decay What happens when unstable nuclei break apart? Three common types of radioactive decay are illustrated in FIGURE 20 and can be summarized as follows:

- *Alpha particles* (α particles) may be emitted from the nucleus. An alpha particle is composed of 2 protons and 2 neutrons. Thus, the emission of an alpha particle means that the mass number of the isotope is reduced by 4, and the atomic number is lowered by 2.
- When a *beta particle* (β particle), or an electron, is given off from a nucleus, the mass number remains unchanged because electrons have practically no mass. However, because the electron has come from a neutron (remember, a neutron is a combination of a proton and an electron), the nucleus contains one more proton than before. Therefore, the atomic number increases by 1.

FIGURE 20 **Common types of radioactive decay** Notice that in each example, the number of protons (atomic number) in the nucleus changes, thus producing a different element.

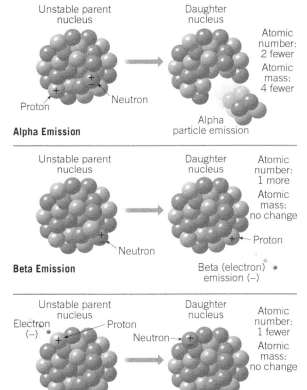

Unstable parent nucleus — Daughter nucleus

Atomic number: 2 fewer
Atomic mass: 4 fewer

Proton — Neutron

Alpha Emission — Alpha particle emission

Unstable parent nucleus — Daughter nucleus

Atomic number: 1 more
Atomic mass: no change

Neutron — Proton

Beta Emission — Beta (electron) emission (−)

Unstable parent nucleus — Daughter nucleus

Electron (−) — Proton — Neutron

Atomic number: 1 fewer
Atomic mass: no change

Electron Capture

- Sometimes an electron is captured by the nucleus. The electron combines with a proton and forms a neutron. As in the last example, the mass number remains unchanged. However, because the nucleus now contains one less proton, the atomic number decreases by 1.

An unstable radioactive isotope is referred to as the *parent*, and the isotopes resulting from the decay of the parent are termed the *daughter products*. FIGURE 21 provides an example of radioactive decay. Here it can be seen that when the radioactive parent, uranium-238 (atomic number 92, mass number 238) decays, it follows a number of steps, emitting 8 alpha particles and 6 beta particles before finally becoming the stable daughter product lead-206 (atomic number 82, mass number 206). One of the unstable daughter products produced during this decay series is radon.

Radiometric Dating   Certainly among the most important results of the discovery of radioactivity is that it provided a reliable means of calculating the ages of rocks and minerals that contain particular radioactive isotopes. The procedure is called **radiometric dating**. Why is radiometric dating reliable? Because the rates of decay for many isotopes have been precisely measured and do not vary under the physical conditions that exist in Earth's outer layers. Therefore, each radioactive isotope used for dating has been decaying at a fixed rate since the formation of the minerals in which it occurs, and the products of decay have been accumulating at a corresponding rate. For example, when uranium is incorporated into a mineral that crystallizes from magma, there is no lead (the stable daughter product) from previous decay. The radiometric "clock" starts at this point. As the uranium in this newly formed mineral disintegrates, atoms of the daughter product are trapped, and measurable amounts of lead eventually accumulate.

Half-Life

The time required for half of the nuclei in a sample to decay is called the **half-life** of the isotope. Half-life is a common way of expressing the rate of radioactive disintegration. FIGURE 22 illustrates what occurs when a radioactive parent decays directly into its stable daughter product. When the quantities of parent and daughter are equal (ratio 1:1), we know that one half-life has transpired. When one-quarter of the original parent atoms remain and three-quarters have decayed to the daughter product, the parent/daughter ratio is 1:3, and we know that two half-lives have passed. After three half-lives, the ratio of parent atoms to daughter atoms is 1:7 (one parent atom for every seven daughter atoms).

If the half-life of a radioactive isotope is known and the parent/daughter ratio can be determined, the age of the sample can be calculated. For example,

FIGURE 21 Decay of U-238 Uranium-238 is an example of a radioactive decay series. Before the stable end product (Pb-206) is reached, many different isotopes are produced as intermediate steps.

assume that the half-life of a hypothetical unstable isotope is 1 million years, and the parent/daughter ratio in a sample is 1:15. This ratio indicates that four half-lives have passed and that the sample must be 4 million years old.

Using Various Isotopes

Notice that the *percentage* of radioactive atoms that decay during one half-life is always the same: 50 percent. However, the *actual number* of atoms that decay with the passing of each half-life continually decreases. Thus, as the percentage of radioactive parent atoms declines, the proportion of stable daughter atoms rises, with the

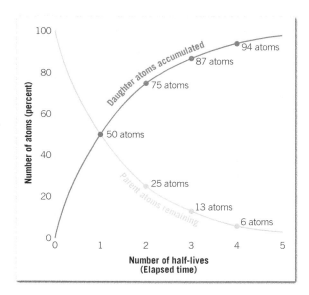

SMARTFIGURE 22
Radioactive decay curve
Change is exponential. Half of the radioactive parent remains after one half-life. After a second half-life, one-quarter of the parent remains, and so forth.

TABLE 1	Isotopes Frequently Used in Radiometric Dating	
Radioactive Parent	Stable Daughter Product	Currently Accepted Half-Life Values
Uranium-238	Lead-206	4.5 billion years
Uranium-235	Lead-207	704 million years
Thorium-232	Lead-208	14.1 billion years
Rubidium-87	Strontium-87	47.0 billion years
Potassium-40	Argon-40	1.3 billion years

increase in daughter atoms just matching the drop in parent atoms. This fact is the key to radiometric dating.

Of the many radioactive isotopes that exist in nature, five have proved particularly useful in providing radiometric ages for ancient rocks (TABLE 1). Rubidium-87, thorium-232, and the two isotopes of uranium are used only for dating rocks that are millions of years old, but potassium-40 is more versatile.

Potassium-Argon Although the half-life of potassium-40 is 1.3 billion years, analytical techniques make possible the detection of tiny amounts of its stable daughter product, argon-40, in some rocks that are younger than 100,000 years. Another important reason for its frequent use is that potassium is an abundant constituent of many common minerals, particularly micas and feldspars.

Although potassium (K) has three natural isotopes, ^{39}K, ^{40}K, and ^{41}K, only ^{40}K is radioactive. When ^{40}K decays, it does so in two ways. About 11 percent changes to argon-40 (^{40}Ar) by means of electron capture (see Figure 20C). The remaining 89 percent of ^{40}K decays to calcium-40 (^{40}Ca) by beta emission (see Figure 20B). The decay of ^{40}K to ^{40}Ca, however, is not useful for radiometric dating because the ^{40}Ca produced by radioactive disintegration cannot be distinguished from calcium that may have been present when the rock formed.

The potassium-argon clock begins when potassium-bearing minerals crystallize from a magma or form within a metamorphic rock. At this point the new minerals will contain ^{40}K but will be free of ^{40}Ar because this element is an inert gas that does not chemically combine with other elements. As time passes, the ^{40}K steadily decays by electron capture. The ^{40}Ar produced by this process remains trapped within the mineral's crystal lattice. Because no ^{40}Ar was present when the mineral formed, all of the daughter atoms trapped in the mineral must have come from the decay of ^{40}K. To determine a sample's age, the $^{40}K/^{40}Ar$ ratio is measured precisely and the known half-life for ^{40}K applied.

A Complex Process Bear in mind that although the basic principle of radiometric dating is simple, the actual procedure is quite complex. The analysis that determines the quantities of parent and daughter must be painstakingly precise. In addition, some radioactive materials do not decay directly into the stable daughter product, as was the case with our hypothetical example, a fact that may further complicate the analysis. In the case of uranium-238, there are 13 intermediate unstable daughter products formed before the 14th and last daughter product, the stable isotope lead-206, is produced (see Figure 21).

Sources of Error It is important to realize that an accurate radiometric date can be obtained only for a mineral that remained a closed system during the entire period since its formation. Obtaining a correct date is not possible unless there was neither addition nor loss of parent or daughter isotopes. This is not always the case. In fact, an important limitation of the potassium-argon method arises from the fact that argon is a gas, and it may leak from minerals, throwing off measurements. Indeed, losses can be significant if the rock is subjected to relatively high temperatures.

Of course, a reduction in the amount of daughter product, ^{40}Ar, would lead to an underestimation of the rock's actual age. Sometimes temperatures are high enough for a sufficiently long period that all argon escapes. When this happens, the potassium-argon clock is reset, and dating the sample gives only the time of thermal resetting, not the true age of the rock. For other radiometric clocks, a loss of daughter atoms can occur if the rock has been subjected to weathering or leaching. To avoid such a problem, one simple safeguard is to use only fresh, unweathered material and not samples that exhibit signs that they have been chemically altered.

Earth's Oldest Rocks Radiometric dating methods have produced literally thousands of dates for events in Earth history. Rocks exceeding 3.5 billion years in age are found on all of the continents. Earth's oldest rocks (so far) may be as old as 4.28 billion years (b.y.). Discovered in northern Quebec, Canada, on the shores of Hudson Bay, these rocks may be remnants of Earth's earliest crust. Rocks from western Greenland have been dated at 3.7 to 3.8 b.y., and rocks nearly as old are found in the Minnesota River valley and northern Michigan (3.5 to 3.7 b.y.), in southern Africa (3.4 to 3.5 b.y.), and in western Australia (3.4 to 3.6 b.y.). Tiny crystals of the mineral zircon having radiometric ages as old as 4.3 b.y. have been found in younger sedimentary rocks in western Australia. The source rocks for these tiny durable grains either no longer exist or have not yet been found.

Radiometric dating has vindicated the ideas of Hutton, Darwin, and others, who more than 150 years ago inferred that geologic time must be immense. Indeed, modern dating methods have proved that there has been enough time for the processes we observe to have accomplished tremendous tasks.

Dating with Carbon-14

To date relatively recent events, carbon-14 is used. Carbon-14 is the radioactive isotope of carbon. The process is often called **radiocarbon dating**. Because the half-life of carbon-14 is only 5730 years, it can be used for dating events from the historic past as well as those from very recent geologic history. In some cases carbon-14 can be used to date events as far back as 70,000 years.

Carbon-14 is continuously produced in the upper atmosphere as a consequence of cosmic-ray bombardment. Cosmic rays (high-energy nuclear particles) shatter the nuclei of gas atoms, releasing neutrons. Some of the neutrons are absorbed by nitrogen atoms (atomic number 7, mass number 14), causing each nucleus to emit a proton. As a result, the atomic number decreases by 1 (to 6), and a different element, carbon-14, is created (FIGURE 23A). This isotope of carbon quickly becomes incorporated into carbon dioxide, which circulates in the atmosphere and is absorbed by living matter. As a result, all organisms—including you—contain a small amount of carbon-14.

As long as an organism is alive, the decaying radiocarbon is continually replaced, and the proportions of carbon-14 and carbon-12 remain constant. Carbon-12 is the stable and most common isotope of carbon. However, when any plant or animal dies, the amount of carbon-14 gradually decreases as it decays to nitrogen-14 by beta emission (FIGURE 23B). By comparing the proportions of carbon-14 and carbon-12 in a sample, radiocarbon dates can be determined. It is important to emphasize that carbon-14 is only useful in dating organic materials, such as wood, charcoal, bones, flesh, and cloth.

Although carbon-14 is only useful in dating the last small fraction of geologic time, it has become a very valuable tool for anthropologists, archaeologists, and historians, as well as for geologists who study very recent Earth history (FIGURE 24). In fact, the development of radiocarbon dating was considered so important that the chemist who discovered this application, Willard F. Libby, received a Nobel Prize in 1960.

A. Production of carbon-14

Nitrogen-14 atomic number 7 atomic mass 14

Neutron capture

Carbon-14 atomic number 6 atomic mass 14

Proton emission

B. Decay of carbon-14

Neutron

Carbon-14

Proton

Nitrogen-14

(−)

Beta (electron) emission

FIGURE 23 Carbon-14 Production and decay of radiocarbon. These sketches represent the nuclei of the respective atoms.

FIGURE 24 Cave art Chauvet Cave in southern France, discovered in 1994, contains some of the earliest-known cave paintings. Radiocarbon dating indicates that most of the images were drawn between 30,000 and 32,000 years ago. (Photo by Javier Trueba/MSF/Photo Researchers, Inc.)

4 CONCEPT CHECKS

1. List three types of radioactive decay. For each type, describe how the atomic number and atomic mass change.
2. Sketch a simple diagram to explain the idea of half-life.
3. Why is radiometric dating a reliable method for determining numerical dates?
4. For what time span does radiocarbon dating apply?

5 The Geologic Time Scale

Geologists have divided the whole of geologic history into units of varying length. Together, they compose the **geologic time scale** of Earth history (FIGURE 25). The major units of the time scale were delineated during the nineteenth century, principally by scientists in Western Europe and Great Britain. Because radiometric dating was unavailable at that time, the entire time scale was created using methods of relative dating. It was only in the twentieth century that radiometric methods permitted numerical dates to be added.

FIGURE 25 Geologic time scale
Numbers on the time scale represent time in millions of years before present. Numerical dates were added long after the time scale was established using relative dating techniques.

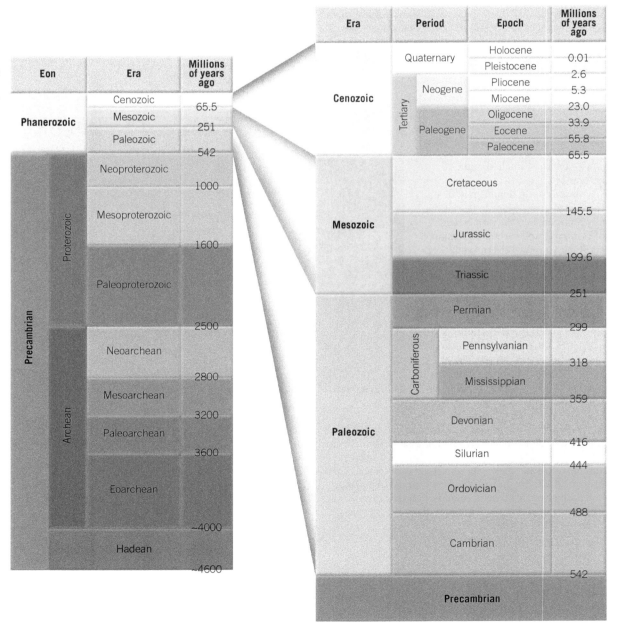

Structure of the Time Scale

The geologic time scale subdivides the 4.6-billion-year history of Earth into many different units and provides a meaningful time frame within which the events of the geologic past are arranged. As shown in Figure 25, **eons** represent the greatest expanses of time. The eon that began about 542 million years ago is the **Phanerozoic**, a term derived from Greek words meaning "visible life." It is an appropriate description because the rocks and deposits of the Phanerozoic eon contain abundant fossils that document major evolutionary trends.

Another glance at the time scale reveals that eons are divided into **eras**. The Phanerozoic eon consists of the **Paleozoic era** (*paleo* = ancient, *zoe* = life), the **Mesozoic era** (*meso* = middle, *zoe* = life), and the **Cenozoic era** (*ceno* = recent, *zoe* = life). As the names imply, these eras are bounded by profound worldwide changes in life-forms.

Each era of the Phaneroic eon is further divided into time units known as **periods**. The Paleozoic has seven, and the Mesozoic and Cenozoic each have three. Each of these periods is characterized by a somewhat less profound change in life-forms as compared with the eras.

Each of the periods is divided into still smaller units called **epochs**. As you can see in Figure 25, seven epochs have been named for the periods of the Cenozoic. The epochs of other periods usually are simply termed *early*, *middle*, and *late*.

Precambrian Time

Notice that the detail of the geologic time scale does not begin until about 542 million years ago, the date for the beginning of the Cambrian period. The nearly 4 billion years prior to the Cambrian are divided into two eons, the **Archean** (*archaios* = ancient) and the **Proterozoic** (*proteros* = before, *zoe* = life). It is also common for this vast expanse of time to simply be referred to as the **Precambrian**. Although it represents about 88 percent of Earth history, the Precambrian is not divided into nearly as many smaller time units as the Phanerozoic eon.

Why is the huge expanse of Precambrian time not divided into numerous eras, periods, and epochs? The reason is that Precambrian history is not known in great enough detail. The quantity of information that geologists have deciphered about Earth's past is somewhat analogous to the detail of human history. The further back we go, the less that is known. Certainly more data and information exist about the past 10 years than for the first decade of the twentieth century; the events of the nineteenth century have been

documented much better than the events of the first century A.D.; and so on. So it is with Earth history. The more recent past has the freshest, least disturbed, and most observable record. The further back in time a geologist goes, the more fragmented the record and clues become. There are other reasons to explain our lack of a detailed time scale for this vast segment of Earth history:

1. The first abundant fossil evidence does not appear in the geologic record until the beginning of the Cambrian period. Prior to the Cambrian, simple life-forms such as algae, bacteria, fungi, and worms predominated. All of these organisms lack hard parts, an important condition favoring preservation. For this reason, there is only a meager Precambrian fossil record. Many exposures of Precambrian rocks have been studied in some detail, but correlation is often difficult when fossils are lacking.
2. Because Precambrian rocks are very old, most have been subjected to a great many changes. Much of the Precambrian rock record is composed of highly distorted metamorphic rocks. This makes the interpretation of past environments difficult because many of the clues present in the original sedimentary rocks have been destroyed.

Radiometric dating has provided a partial solution to the troublesome task of dating and correlating Precambrian rocks. But untangling the complex Precambrian record still remains a daunting task.

Terminology and the Geologic Time Scale

There are some terms that are associated with the geologic time scale but are not "officially" recognized as being a part of it. The best known, and most common, example is *Precambrian*—the informal name for the eons that came before the current Phanerozoic eon. Although the term *Precambrian* has no formal status on the geologic time scale, it has been traditionally used as though it does.

Hadean is another informal term that is found on some versions of the geologic time scale and is used by many geologists. It refers to the earliest interval (eon) of Earth history—before the oldest-known rocks. When the term was coined in 1972, the age of Earth's oldest rocks was about 3.8 billion years. Today that number stands at slightly greater than 4 billion, and, of course, is subject to revision. The name *Hadean* derives from *Hades*, Greek for *underworld*—a reference to the "hellish" conditions that prevailed on Earth early in its history.

Effective communication in the geosciences requires that the geologic time scale consist of standardized divisions and dates. So, who determines which names and dates on the geologic time scale are "official"? The organization that is largely responsible for maintaining and updating this important document is the International Committee on Stratigraphy (ICS), a committee of the International Union of Geological Sciences. Advances in the geosciences require that the scale be periodically updated to include changes in unit names and boundary age estimates.

For example, the geologic time scale shown in Figure 25 was updated as recently as July 2009. After considerable dialogue among geologists who focus on very recent Earth history, the ICS changed the date for the start of the Quaternary period and the pleistocene epoch from 1.8 million to 2.6 million years ago. Who knows? Perhaps by the time you read this, other changes will have been made.

If you were to examine a geologic time scale from just a few years ago, it is quite possible that you would see the Cenozoic era divided into the Tertiary and Quaternary periods. However, on more recent versions, the space formerly designated as Tertiary is divided into the Paleogene and Neogene periods. As our understanding of this time span has changed, so too has its designation on the geologic time scale. Today, the Tertiary period is considered a "historic" name and is given no official status on the ICS version of the time scale. Many time scales still contain references to the Tertiary period, though, including Figure 25. One reason for this is that a great deal of past (and some current) geologic literature uses this name.

For those who study historical geology, it is important to realize that the geologic time scale is a dynamic tool that continues to be refined as our knowledge and understanding of Earth history evolves.

5 CONCEPT CHECKS

1. List the four basic units that make up the geologic time scale.
2. Why is -zoic part of so many names on the geologic time scale?
3. What term applies to all of geologic time prior to the Phanerozoic eon? Why is this span not divided into as many smaller time units as the Phanerozoic eon?
4. To what does Hadean apply? Is it an "official" part of the geologic time scale?

EYE on Earth

This image if from the bottom of the Grand Canyon, a zone called the Inner Gorge. The dark rock is the Vishnu Schist. The light-colored rock, called the Zoroaster Granite, is a series of dikes. Both rocks date from Precambrian time. Suppose you are on a raft trip through the Grand Canyon. Your companions are bright and curious but are not trained in geology as you are. Sitting around the campfire the night before you reached the site pictured here, you and your fellow rafters discussed the geologic time scale and the magnitude of geologic time.

Question 1 When you arrive at this site, someone asks why Precambrian history seems so sketchy and why this time span is not divided into nearly as many subdivisions as Phanerozoic time. Use this setting as you answer these questions.

Question 2 Which is older, the Vishnu Schist or the Zoroaster Granite? Explain.

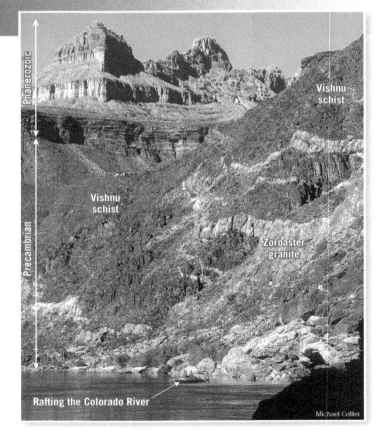

Rafting the Colorado River

Michael Collier

Did Humans and Dinosaurs Ever Coexist?

GEOGRAPHICS

Many old and not-so-old movies and TV shows show humans and dinosaurs living side-by-side. This is also true of many cartoons and comic strips. Although we know these stories are fiction, many people still have the impression that these two life forms coexisted.

OFFICE

Hanna-Barbera/Everett Collection

This well-known fossil of a human ancestor (*Australopithecus afarensis*) known as Lucy was discovered in Ethiopia and is 3.2 million years old. The oldest bones thus far assigned to the human genus *Homo*, are from the early Pleistocene epoch and are about 2.4 million years old.
(Andrew Holt/Alamy)

Tyrannosaurus rex dates from the late Cretaceous period. Dinosaurs became extinct more than 65 million years before humans evolved.
(Sabena Jane Black Bird/Alamy)

251 MYA	199.6 MYA	145.5 MYA	65.5 MYA	23 MYA	2.6 MYA
	MESOZOIC			CENOZOIC	
TRIASSIC	JURASSIC	CRETACEOUS		TERTIARY	QUATERNARY
				PALEOGENE	NEOGENE

Dinosaurs first appear in the Triassic period.

Dinosaurs did not become gigantic until the Jurassic period.

Dinosaurs became extinct at the close of the Cretaceous period 65.5 million years ago.

Humans (*Homo sapiens*) evolved in East Africa slightly more than 150,000 years ago.

6 Determining Numerical Dates for Sedimentary Strata

Although reasonably accurate numerical dates have been worked out for the periods of the geologic time scale (see Figure 25), the task is not without difficulty. The primary difficulty in assigning numerical dates to units of time is the fact that not all rocks can be dated by using radiometric methods. For a radiometric date to be useful, all the minerals in the rock must have formed at about the same time. For this reason, radioactive isotopes can be used to determine when minerals in an igneous rock crystallized and when pressure and heat created new minerals in a metamorphic rock.

However, samples of sedimentary rock can only rarely be dated directly by radiometric means. Although a detrital sedimentary rock may include particles that contain radioactive isotopes, the rock's age cannot be accurately determined because the grains composing the rock are not the same age as the rock in which they occur. Rather, the sediments have been weathered from rocks of diverse ages.

Radiometric dates obtained from metamorphic rocks may also be difficult to interpret because the age of a particular mineral in a metamorphic rock does not necessarily represent the time when the rock initially formed. Instead, the date might indicate any one of a number of subsequent metamorphic phases.

If samples of sedimentary rocks rarely yield reliable radiometric ages, how can numerical dates be assigned to sedimentary layers? Usually a geologist must relate the strata to datable igneous masses, as in FIGURE 26. In this example, radiometric dating has determined the ages of the volcanic ash bed in the Morrison Formation and the dike cutting the Mancos Shale and Mesaverde Formation. The sedimentary beds below the ash are obviously older than

the ash, and all the layers above the ash are younger. The dike is younger than the Mancos Shale and the Mesaverde Formation but older than the Wasatch Formation because the dike does not intrude these Paleogene age rocks.

From this kind of evidence, geologists estimate that the last part of the Morrison Formation was deposited about 160 million years ago, as indicated by the ash bed. Further, they conclude that the Paleogene period began after the intrusion of the dike, 66 million years ago. This is one example of literally thousands that illustrate how datable materials are used to bracket the various episodes in Earth history within specific time periods. It shows the necessity of combining laboratory dating methods with field observations of rocks.

6 CONCEPT CHECKS

1. Briefly explain why it is often difficult to assign a reliable numerical date to a sample of sedimentary rock.
2. How might a numerical date for a layer of sedimentary rock be determined?

FIGURE 26 Dating sedimentary strata Numerical dates for sedimentary layers are usually determined by examining their relationship to igneous rocks.

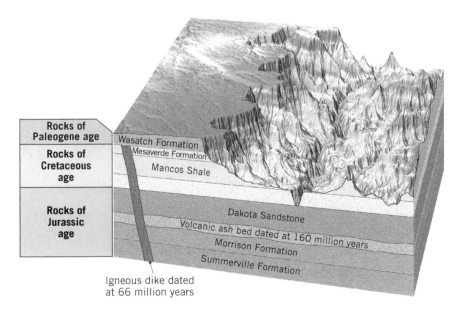

Rocks of Paleogene age

Rocks of Cretaceous age

Rocks of Jurassic age

Wasatch Formation
Mesaverde Formation
Mancos Shale
Dakota Sandstone
Volcanic ash bed dated at 160 million years
Morrison Formation
Summerville Formation

Igneous dike dated at 66 million years

EYE on Earth

Close-up view of the detrital sedimentary rock conglomerate. This rock contains radioactive isotopes that will yield numerical dates.

Question 1 Although radioactive isotopes are present, a reliable numerical date for this conglomerate cannot be *accurately* determined. Explain.

Question 2 How might a numerical age range be established for the conglomerate layer?

E.J. Tarbuck

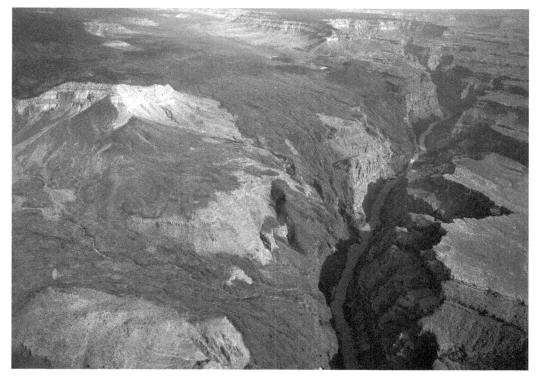

This aerial view in the Grand Canyon shows basaltic lava draped over layers of sedimentary rock. The relationship between igneous and sedimentary rocks is often a key factor in determining numerical dates for sedimentary rocks. (Photo by Michael Collier)

CONCEPTS IN REVIEW: GEOLOGIC TIME

1 Creating A Time Scale—Relative Dating Principles

Distinguish between numerical and relative dating and apply relative dating principles to determine a time sequence of geologic events.

KEY WORDS numerical date, relative date, principle of superposition, principle of original horizontality, principle of lateral continuity, principle of cross-cutting relationships, inclusion, conformable, unconformity, angular unconformity, disconformity, nonconformity

- One of geology's main contributions to human knowledge is a scientific interpretation of what has happened in the distant past.
- We can figure out the sequence of geologic events by determining how old rocks and structures are relative to one another as well as their actual age, expressed as a number of years.
- Five principles guide relative dating. First is the idea that in a stack of sedimentary or volcanic layers that accumulate on Earth's surface, the oldest will be at the bottom, and the most recently deposited will lie on the top. Second, these layers are originally deposited in a more-or-less horizontal sheet, and therefore if you find them in a non-horizontal orientation, it suggests that they have been tilted since their deposition. Third, when these sheets of sediment were deposited, they were laterally continuous, but they may later be dissected by erosion so that pieces of the original layer become increasingly isolated over time.

Basalt xenolith (oldest)

Granite dike (youngest)

Granite (middle)

Mike Beauregard

- The fourth principle, of cross-cutting relationships, suggests that a geologic structure that cuts across or through another rock or structure must be younger. Before something can be cut, it must first exist. The cutter is always younger. Fifth is the principle of relative dating by inclusions, which says that a rock must first exist before a piece of it could be broken off and included inside another rock.
- No place on Earth has a complete record of every moment of geologic time. Unconformities are gaps in the geologic record generated either by time going by without the deposition of strata or by the erosion of older deposits. The recognition of unconformities was a fundamental insight into the true depths of geologic time.

COMPARE State the age of your instructor in both relative and numerical terms.

2 Fossils: Evidence of Past Life

Define *fossil* and discuss the conditions that favor the preservation of organisms as fossils. List and describe various types of fossils.

KEY WORDS fossil, paleontology

- Fossils are the remains or traces of ancient life. Paleontology is the branch of geology that studies fossils.

- Fossils can form through many different processes. For an organism to be preserved as a fossil, it must be buried rapidly. Also, an organism's hard skeletal materials are most likely to be preserved, as soft tissue decays rapidly in most circumstances.

R.I.P. In which of the following locations would a plant leaf be most likely to be preserved as a fossil: in a swamp, in a desert dune field, or in a river bed? Explain.

3 Correlation of Rock Layers

Explain how rocks of similar age that are in different places can be matched up.

KEY WORDS correlation, principle of fossil succession, index fossil, fossil assemblage

- Most rock units don't exist in isolation. The act of matching up different exposures of rock that represent the same age of formation is called correlation. By correlating rock units from around the world, geologists have attained a fuller perspective on Earth history.
- Fossils are useful tools for correlating strata. Index fossils are particularly useful fossils because they provide a rapid index to the age of the strata in which they are found. No organism that became an index fossil lasted very long. The sequence of different index fossils provides a sixth principle

of relative dating, the principle of fossil succession, which states that fossil organisms succeed one another in a definite order. If you can identify the fossil content of a particular rock, then you can deduce its age.

- The overlapping time spans of fossils in an assemblage may also be used to establish an age for a particular rock unit that contains multiple fossil organisms.
- Fossils may also be used to establish ancient environmental conditions that existed at the time of sedimentary deposition.

COMPARE Which would make a better index fossil for the modern era: a penguin or a pigeon? Why?

E.J. Tarbuck

4 Dating with Radioactivity

Discuss three types of radioactive decay and explain how radioactive isotopes are used to determine numerical dates.

KEY WORDS radioactivity, radiometric dating, half-life, radiocarbon dating

- Atoms with unstable nuclei break apart over time, releasing smaller particles in a process called radioactivity. Unstable atoms are called parent isotopes, and the isotopes that are produced through radioactive decay are called daughter products.
- Because the rate at which each parent isotope decays can be measured with some precision, it can be used as the basis for numerical dating of rocks. The amount of time it takes for half of the remaining parent isotope to decay is the isotope's half-life. This amount of time is distinct for each individual isotope.
- Only certain minerals take parent isotopes into their crystal structure but exclude daughter isotopes. Only rocks containing these few critical minerals are suitable candidates for radiometric dating.
- Radiocarbon dating utilizes the decay of carbon-14 in organic matter as a basis for dating relatively recent material that was once alive, such as wood or charcoal. Because it has a very short half-life, carbon-14 is useful only for material less than 70,000 years old.

CALCULATE IT Measurement of zircon crystals from a granite yield parent/daughter ratios of 25 percent parent (uranium-235) and 75 percent daughter (lead-206). The half-life of uranium-235 is 704 million years. How old is the granite?

Parent isotope		Daughter isotope	
Initial	After one half-life	After two half-lives	After three half-lives

5 The Geologic Time Scale

Distinguish among the four basic time units that make up the geologic time scale and explain why the time scale is considered to be a dynamic tool.

KEY WORDS geologic time scale, eon, Phanerozoic, era, Paleozoic, Mesozoic, Cenozoic, period, epoch, Archean, Proterozoic, Precambrian

- The geologic history of Earth is subdivided into units of time on the geologic time scale. Eons are subdivided into eras, which each contain multiple periods, and periods are subdivided into epochs.
- Precambrian time includes the Archean and Proterozoic eons. It is followed by the Phanerozoic eon, which is well documented by abundant fossil evidence, resulting in many subdivisions.
- The geologic time scale is a work in progress, continually being refined to greater precision based on new information.

CLASSIFY IT Is the Mesozoic an example of an eon, an era, a period, or an epoch? What about the Jurassic?

Dennis Tasa

Eurypterids were a diverse group related to spiders that became extinct in the Permian period. Fossils were critical tools for the construction of the geologic time scale.

6 Determining Numerical Dates for Sedimentary Strata

Explain how reliable numerical dates are determined for layers of sedimentary rock.

- Sedimentary strata are not capable of being directly dated using radiometric techniques because they are from products produced through the weathering of other rocks. A grain of sand in a sandstone comes from some older source rock. If you were to date it using isotopes, you would get the age of the source rock, not the sedimentary deposit.
- The principles of relative dating combine with the techniques of numerical dating to provide precise age constraints on sedimentary strata. Maximum and minimum ages based on superposition and cross-cutting relationships of other, datable rock units (usually igneous) help to "bracket" the ages of sedimentary formations and the fossils they contain.

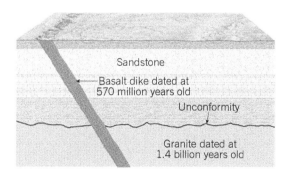

Sandstone

Basalt dike dated at 570 million years old

Unconformity

Granite dated at 1.4 billion years old

BRACKET IT Determine the age of the sandstone unit in the figure as precisely as possible.

GIVE IT SOME THOUGHT

1. The accompanying image shows the metamorphic rock gneiss, a basaltic dike, and a fault. Place these three features in their proper sequence and explain your logic.

Marli Miller

2. A mass of granite is in contact with a layer of sandstone. Using a principle described in this chapter, explain how you might determine whether the sandstone was deposited on top of the granite or whether the magma that formed the granite was intruded after the sandstone was deposited.

3. The accompanying photo shows two layers of sedimentary rock. The lower layer is shale from the late **Mesozoic** era. Note the old river channel that was carved into the shale after it was deposited. Above is a younger layer of boulder-rich breccia. Are these layers conformable? Explain why or why not. What term from relative dating applies to the line separating the two layers?

Callan Bentley

4. Refer to Figure 10, which shows the historic angular unconformity at Scotland's Siccar Point that James Hutton studied in the late 1700s. Refer to this photo for the following exercises.
   a. Describe in general what occurred to produce this feature.
   b. Suggest ways in which at least three of Earth's four spheres could have been involved.
   c. The Earth system is powered by energy from two sources. How are both sources represented in the Siccar Point unconformity?

5. These polished stones are called *gastroliths*. Explain how such objects can be considered fossils. What category of fossil is it? Name another example of a fossil in this category.

Francois Gohier/Photo Researchers, Inc.

0   1   2
Centimeters

6. If a radioactive isotope of thorium (atomic number 90, mass number 232) emits 6 alpha particles and 4 beta particles during the course of radioactive decay, what are the atomic number and mass number of the stable daughter product?

7. A hypothetical radioactive isotope has a half-life of 10,000 years. If the ratio of radioactive parent to stable daughter product is 1:3, how old is the rock containing the radioactive material?

8. Solve the problems below that relate to the magnitude of Earth history. To make calculations easier, round Earth's age to 5 billion years.
   a. What percentage of geologic time is represented by recorded history? (Assume 5000 years for the length of recorded history.)
   b. Humanlike ancestors (hominids) have been around for roughly 5 million years. What percentage of geologic time is represented by these ancestors?
   c. The first abundant fossil evidence does not appear until the beginning of the Cambrian period, about 540 million years ago. What percentage of geologic time is represented by abundant fossil evidence?

9. A portion of a popular college text in historical geology includes 10 chapters (281 pages) in a unit titled "The Story of Earth." Two chapters (49 pages) are devoted to Precambrian time. By contrast, the last two chapters (67 pages) focus on the most recent 23 million years,

with 25 of those pages devoted to the Holocene epoch, which began 10,000 years ago.

a. Compare the percentage of pages devoted to the Precambrian to the actual percentage of geologic time that this span represents.

b. How does the number of pages about the Holocene compare to its actual percentage of geologic time?

c. Suggest some reasons why the text seems to have such an unequal treatment of Earth history.

10. The accompanying diagram is a cross section of a hypothetical area. Place the lettered features in the proper sequence, from oldest to youngest. Where in the sequence can you identify an unconformity?

MasteringGeology™

Glossary

Angular unconformity An unconformity in which the older strata dip at an angle different from that of the younger beds.

Archean eon The first eon of Precambrian time. The eon preceding the Proterozoic. It extends between 4.5 and 2.5 billion years ago.

Cenozoic era A time span on the geologic time scale beginning about 65.5 million years ago, following the Mesozoic era.

Conformable layers Rock layers that were deposited without interruption.

Correlation The process of establishing the equivalence of rocks of similar age in different areas.

Disconformity A type of unconformity in which the beds above and below are parallel.

Eon The largest time unit on the geologic time scale, next in order of magnitude above era.

Epoch A unit of the geologic time scale that is a subdivision of a period.

Era A major division on the geologic time scale; eras are divided into shorter units called periods.

Fossil The remains or traces of organisms preserved from the geologic past.

Fossil assemblage The overlapping ranges of a group of fossils (assemblage) collected from a layer. By examining such an assemblage, the age of the sedimentary layer can be established.

Geologic time scale The division of Earth history into blocks of time—eons, eras, periods, and epochs. The time scale was created using relative dating principles.

Half-life The time required for one-half of the atoms of a radioactive substance to decay.

Inclusion A piece of one rock unit that is contained within another. Inclusions are used in relative dating. The rock mass adjacent to the one containing the inclusion must have been there first in order to provide the fragment.

Index fossil A fossil that is associated with a particular span of geologic time.

Mesozoic era A time span on the geologic time scale between the Paleozoic and Cenozoic eras—from about 248 to 65.5 million years ago.

Nonconformity An unconformity in which older metamorphic or intrusive igneous rocks are overlain by younger sedimentary strata.

Numerical date The number of years that have passed since an event occurred.

Paleontology The systematic study of fossils and the history of life on Earth.

Paleozoic era A time span on the geologic time scale between the Precambrian and Mesozoic eras—from about 542 million to 251 million years ago.

Period A basic unit of the geologic time scale that is a subdivision of an era. Periods may be divided into smaller units called epochs.

Phanerozoic eon The part of geologic time that is represented by rocks containing abundant fossil evidence. The eon extending from the end of the Proterozoic eon (540 million years ago) to the present.

Precambrian All geologic time prior to the Phanerozoic eon. A term encompassing both the Archean and Proterozoic eons.

Principle of fossil succession A principle by which fossil organisms succeed one another in a definite and determinable order, and any time period can be recognized by its fossil content.

Principle of original horizontality A principle by which layers of sediment are generally deposited in a horizontal or nearly horizontal position.

Principle of Superposition A principle which states that in any undeformed sequence of sedimentary rocks, each bed is older than the one above and younger than the one below.

Proterozoic eon The eon following the Archean and preceding the Phanerozoic. It extends between 2500 and 542 million years ago.

Radioactivity See Radioactive decay.

Radiocarbon (carbon-14) dating Dating of events from the very recent geologic past (the past few tens of thousands of years) based on the fact that the radioactive isotope of carbon is produced continuously in the atmosphere.

Radiometric dating The procedure of calculating the absolute ages of rocks and minerals that contain certain radioactive isotopes.

Relative dating A process of determining the chronological order of events by placing rocks and structures in their proper sequence or order.

Unconformity A surface that represents a break in the rock record, caused by erosion and nondeposition.

Crustal Deformation

From Chapter 10 of *Earth: An Introduction to Physical Geology*, Eleventh Edition. Edward J. Tarbuck, Frederick K. Lutgens, Dennis Tasa.

Crustal Deformation

Sheep Mountain Anticline, Wyoming. (Michael Collier)

Each statement represents the primary learning objective for the corresponding major heading within the chapter. After you complete the chapter you should be able to:

1 Describe the three types of differential stress and contrast stress with strain.

2 Compare and contrast brittle and ductile deformation.

3 List and describe five types of folds.

4 Sketch and briefly describe the relative motion of rock bodies located on opposite sides of normal, reverse, and thrust faults as well as both types of strike-slip faults.

5 Define *strike* and *dip* and explain what these measurements tell geologists about the orientations of rock structures located mainly below Earth's surface.

E arth is a dynamic planet. Shifting lithospheric plates gradually change the face of our planet by moving continents across the globe. The results of this tectonic activity are perhaps most strikingly apparent in Earth's major mountain belts. Rocks containing fossils of marine organisms are found thousands of meters above sea level, and massive rock units are bent, contorted, overturned, and sometimes riddled with fractures.

In the Canadian Rockies, for example, rock strata have been thrust hundreds of kilometers over the top of other layers. On a smaller scale, crustal movements of a few meters occur along faults during major earthquakes. Even in the stable interiors of the continents, rocks reveal a history of deformation that shows that these areas were once sites of former mountain belts.

This chapter explores the forces that deform rock and the rock structures that result. It is devoted to the major structural features of Earth's crust and the tectonic forces that produce them.

Panamint Butte, Death Valley, California
These sedimentary beds have been intensely folded and faulted.
(Michael Collier)

1 What Causes Rock to Deform?

Every body of rock, no matter how strong, has a point at which it will deform by bending or breaking. **Deformation** (*de* = out, *forma* = form) is a general term that refers to the changes in the shape or position of a rock body in response to differential stress. Most crustal deformation occurs along plate boundaries. Plate motions and the interactions along plate margins generate the tectonic forces that cause rock to deform.

The basic geologic features that form as a result of the forces generated by the interactions of tectonic plates are called **rock structures**, or **geologic structures** (FIGURE 1). Rock structures include *folds* (wave-like undulations), *faults* (fractures along which one rock body slides past another), *joints* (cracks), and small-scale structures associated with metamorphic rocks such as *foliation* and *rock cleavage*.

Stress: The Force That Deforms Rocks

From everyday experience, you know that if a door is stuck, you must expend energy, called *force*, to open it. Geologists use the term **stress** to describe the forces that deform rocks. Whenever the stresses acting on a rock body exceed its strength, the rock will deform—usually by one or more of the following processes: folding, flowing, fracturing, or faulting.

The magnitude of stress is not simply a function of the amount of force applied but also relates to the area on which the force acts. For example, if you are walking barefoot on a hard surface, the force (weight) of your body is distributed across your entire foot, so the stress acting on any one point of your foot is low. However, if you step on a small pointed rock (ouch!), the stress concentration at that point on your foot will be high. Thus, you can think of stress as a measure of how much force is applied over a particular area.

When stress is applied uniformly in all directions, it is called **confining pressure**. By contrast, when stress is applied unequally in different directions, it is termed **differential stress**. We will consider three types of differential stress:

SMARTFIGURE 1
Deformed sedimentary strata
These deformed strata are exposed in a road cut near Palmdale, California. In addition to the obvious folding, light-colored beds are offset along a fault located on the right side of the photograph. (Photo by E. J. Tarbuck)

Deformed sedimentary strata exposed along road cut

Fault

Anticline

Fold

Syncline

Palmdale, California

Geologist's Sketch

FIGURE 2 Three types
of stresses:
Compressional, tensional,
and shear

A. Undeformed rock

**B. Compressional stress
(shortening)**

**C. Tensional stress
(stretching)**

**D. Shear stress
(sliding and tearing)**

1. **Compressional stress.** Differential stress that squeezes a rock mass as if placed in a vise is known as **compressional stress** (*com* = together, *premere* = to press) (FIGURE 2B). Compressional stresses are most often associated with convergent plate boundaries. When plates collide, Earth's crust is generally shortened horizontally and thickened vertically. Over millions of years, this deformation produces mountainous terrains.

2. **Tensional stress.** Differential stress that pulls apart or elongates rock bodies is known as **tensional stress** (*tendere* = to stretch) (FIGURE 2C). Along divergent plate boundaries where plates are moving apart, tensional stresses stretch and lengthen rock bodies. For example, in the Basin and Range Province in the western United States, tensional forces have fractured and stretched the crust by as much as twice its original width.

3. **Shear stress.** Differential stress can also cause rock to **shear**, which involves the movement of one part of a rock body past another (FIGURE 2D). Shear is similar to the slippage that occurs between individual playing cards when the top of the deck is moved relative to the bottom (FIGURE 3). Small-scale deformation of rocks by shear stress occur along closely spaced parallel surfaces of weakness,

By sliding the top of the deck relative to the bottom, we can illustrate the type of shearing that commonly occurs along closely spaced planes of weakness in rocks.

Shear stress causes the circle in this deck of cards to become an ellipse, which can be used to measure the amount and type of strain.

FIGURE 3 Shearing and the resulting deformation (strain)
An ordinary deck of playing cards with a circle embossed on its side illustrates shearing and the resulting strain.

FIGURE 4 Deformed trilobite
Compare the fossil of this common Paleozoic life-form with the fossil of another trilobite to see the extent of change.
(Photo by Marli Miller)

such as foliation surfaces and microscopic fractures where slippage changes the shape of rocks. By contrast, at transform fault boundaries, such as the San Andreas Fault, shear stress causes large segments of Earth's crust to slip horizontally past one another.

Strain: A Change in Shape Caused by Stress

When flat-lying sedimentary layers are uplifted and tilted, their orientations change, but their shapes are often retained. Differential stresses can also change the shape of a rock body, referred to as **strain**. Like the circle shown in Figure 3, *strained bodies lose their original configuration during deformation.* Strain is illustrated by the deformed trilobite fossil show in FIGURE 4. When we compare the deformed specimen to a trilobite fossil of the same species that has not been deformed, the type of strain that occurred to the surrounding rock body can be determined. *Stress* is the force that acts to deform rock bodies, while *strain* is the resulting deformation (distortion), or change in the shape of the rock body.

1 CONCEPT CHECKS

1. What is rock deformation? How might a rock body change during deformation?
2. List the three types of differential stress and briefly describe the changes they impart to rock bodies.
3. What type of plate boundary is most commonly associated with compressional stress?
4. How is strain different from stress?

2 | How Do Rocks Deform?

When rocks are subjected to stresses that exceed their strength, they deform, usually by bending or breaking. It is easy to visualize how rocks break because we normally think of rocks as being brittle. But how can large masses of rock be *bent* into intricate folds without fracturing in the process? To answer this question, geologists performed laboratory experiments where rocks were subjected to differential stress under conditions experienced at various depths within Earth's crust. Geologists determined that although different rocks deform under somewhat different conditions and rates, all rocks experience three types of deformation: *elastic*, *brittle*, and *ductile*.

Elastic, Brittle, and Ductile Deformation

When stress is applied *gradually*, rocks initially respond by deforming elastically. Changes that result from **elastic deformation** are recoverable; that is, like a rubber band, the rock will snap back to nearly its original size and shape when the stress is removed. During elastic deformation, the chemical bonds of the minerals within a rock are stretched but do not break. When the stress is removed, the bonds snap back to their original length. The energy for most earthquakes comes from stored elastic energy that is released as rock snaps back to its original shape.

Once the elastic limit (strength) of a rock is surpassed, it either bends or breaks. Rocks that break into smaller pieces exhibit **brittle deformation** (*bryttian* = to shatter). From our everyday experience, we know that glass objects, wooden pencils, china plates, and even our bones exhibit brittle failure once their strength is surpassed. Brittle deformation occurs when stress breaks the chemical bonds that hold a material together.

Ductile deformation is a type of solid-state flow that produces a change in the shape of an object without fracturing (FIGURE 5). Ordinary objects that display ductile behavior include modeling clay, beeswax, taffy, and some metals. For example, a coin placed on a railroad track will be flattened (without breaking) by the forces applied by a passing train (FIGURE 6).

Ductile deformation may occur by slippage along planes of weakness such as bedding surfaces and foliation in rock bodies. Individual mineral grains may also change shape through the process of solid-state flow.

These rocks were deformed at great depth and were subsequently exposed at the surface. Vishnu Schist, Grand Canyon National Park, Arizona.

FIGURE 5 Rocks exhibiting ductile deformation (Photo by Michael Collier)

FIGURE 6 A Coin deformed by a passing train (Photo by Anthony Pleva/Alamy)

Factors That Affect Rock Strength

The major factors that influence the strength of a rock and how it will deform include temperature, confining pressure, rock type, and time.

The Role of Temperature

The effect of temperature on the strength of a material can be easily demonstrated with a piece of glass tubing commonly found in a chemistry lab. If the tubing is dropped on a hard surface, it will shatter. However, if the tubing is heated over a Bunsen burner, it can be easily bent into a variety of shapes. Rocks respond to heat similarly. Where temperatures are high (deep in Earth's crust), rocks tend to soften and become more malleable, so they deform by folding or flowing (ductile deformation). Likewise, where temperatures are low (at or near the surface), rocks tend to behave like brittle solids and fracture.

The Role of Confining Pressure

Pressure, like temperature, increases with depth as the thickness of the overlying rock increases. Buried rocks are subjected to confining pressure, which is much like water pressure, where the forces are applied equally in all directions. Confining pressure "squeezes" the materials in Earth's crust, which makes it stronger and thus harder to break. Therefore, rocks that are deeply buried are "held together" by the immense pressure and tend to bend rather than fracture.

The Influence of Rock Type

In addition to the physical environment, the mineral composition and texture of rock greatly influence how it will deform. For example, crystalline rocks composed of minerals that have strong internal chemical bonds tend to fail by brittle fracture. By contrast, sedimentary rocks that are weakly cemented or metamorphic rocks that contain zones of weakness, such as foliation, are more susceptible to ductile deformation.

Weak rocks that are most likely to behave in a ductile manner (bend or flow) when subjected to differential stress include rock salt, shale, limestone, and schist. In fact, rock salt is so weak that large masses of it often rise through overlying beds of sedimentary rocks, much as hot magma rises toward the surface. Perhaps the weakest naturally occurring solid to exhibit ductile flow is glacial ice.

Igneous and some metamorphic rocks (quartzite, for example) tend to be strong and brittle. In a near-surface environment, strong, brittle rocks will fail by breaking when subjected to stresses that exceed their strength. At increasing depths, however, the strength of all rock types decreases significantly.

Some outcrops consist of a sequence of interbedded weak and strong rock layers that have been moderately deformed by folding—for example, shale and well-cemented sandstone beds. In these settings, the strong sandstone layers are often highly fractured, while the weak shale beds form broad undulating folds. The formation of diverse structures (one brittle and one ductile) within the same rock mass can be illustrated by placing a Milky Way® or similar chocolate-over-caramel candy bar into a refrigerator. When the cool candy bar is slowly bent, it will exhibit brittle deformation in the chocolate and ductile deformation in the caramel.

Time as a Factor

One key factor that researchers are unable to duplicate in the laboratory is how rocks respond to small stresses applied gradually over long spans of *geologic time*. However, insights into the effects of time on deformation are provided in everyday settings. For example, marble benches have been known to sag under their own weight over a time span of 100 years or so, and wooden bookshelves may bend within a few months after being loaded with books.

In general, when tectonic forces are applied slowly over long time spans, rocks tend to display ductile behavior and deform by bending or flowing. However, the same rocks may shatter if force is applied suddenly. An analogous situation occurs when you take a taffy bar and slowly move the two ends together. The taffy will deform by folding. However, if you hit the taffy swiftly against the edge of a table, it will break into two or more pieces, exhibiting brittle failure.

Ductile Versus Brittle Deformation and the Resulting Rock Structures

You have probably seen a drinking glass drop on a hard surface and shatter into pieces. What you witnessed is analogous to brittle deformation that occurs in Earth's

A. Joints **B. Fault**

FIGURE 7 Joints versus faults
Joints are fractures along which no appreciable displacement has occurred, whereas faults are fractures along which one rock body slides past another. (Photos by E. J. Tarbuck)

How Rocks Respond to Differential Stress

Type of stress	COMPRESSION (Compression causes shortening)	TENSION (Tension causes stretching)	SHEAR (Shear distorts rock)
At shallow depths rocks exhibit brittle fracture	At shallow depths shortening occurs by brittle deformation along faults where one rock mass is thrust over another.	At shallow depths tensional stresses cause rocks to fracture and pull apart.	At shallow depths shear stress causes offsets in crustal blocks along faults.
At deeper crustal depths rocks deform by ductile flow	At deeper crustal levels where temperatures are high, compressional forces squeeze and fold rock masses.	At deeper crustal levels where temperatures are high, tensional forces stretch and elongate crustal materials by ductile flow.	At deeper crustal levels where temperatures are high, shear stress distorts rock masses by ductile flow, usually along shear zones.

crust. In nature, brittle deformation occurs when stresses exceed the strength of a rock, causing it to break or fracture.

In the upper crust, to depths of about 10 kilometers (6 miles), most rocks tend to exhibit brittle behavior by fracturing or faulting. When tectonic forces cause up-warping of the crust, rocks near the surface are stretched and pulled apart, forming fractures called **joints** (FIGURE 7A). **Faults**, on the other hand, are fractures in Earth's crust where the rocks on one side of the fault are displaced relative to the rocks on the other side (FIGURE 7B).

Folds, common features of deformed sedimentary rocks, provide evidence that rocks can bend without breaking. Rocks that display evidence of ductile deformation usually were generated at depth in high-temperature and high-pressure environments. The resulting rocks often exhibit contorted folds that give the impression that the strength of the rock was akin to that of soft putty (see Figure 5). Weak rocks, however, bend or flow without breaking in less extreme environments.

FIGURE 8 illustrates deformation of Earth's crust as a result of the three types of stress: compressional,

tensional, and shear stress. Compressional stresses associated with convergent plate boundaries tend to *shorten* and *thicken* Earth's crust by folding, flowing, and faulting, whereas tensional stresses along divergent plate boundaries tend to *lengthen* rock bodies by displacement along faults in the upper crust and by ductile flow at depth. Shearing, often associated with transform plate boundaries, tends to produce fault zones in the upper crust and ductile flow at depth. Brittle deformation—fracturing and faulting—dominates in the upper crust, where temperatures and relatively cool. By contrast, at greater depths, rocks exhibit ductile behavior and deform by folding or flowing.

2 CONCEPT CHECKS

1. Describe elastic deformation.
2. How is brittle deformation different from ductile deformation?
3. List and describe the four factors that affect rock strength.
4. Compare rock deformation at shallow depths with the type of deformation that occurs deep within Earth's crust.

FIGURE 8 Deformation caused by three types of stress
Brittle deformation (fracturing and faulting) dominates in the upper crust, where the temperatures are comparatively cool. By contrast, at depths greater than about 10 kilometers (6 miles), where temperatures are high, rock deforms by ductile flow and folding.

3 Folds: Rock Structures Formed by Ductile Deformation

Along convergent plate boundaries, flat-lying sedimentary strata, tabular intrusions, and volcanic rocks are often bent into a series of wavelike undulations called **folds**. Folds in sedimentary strata are much like those that would form if you were to hold the ends of a sheet of paper on a flat surface and then push them together. In nature, folds come in a wide variety of sizes and configurations. Some folds are broad flexures in which strata hundreds of meters thick have been slightly warped. Others are very tight microscopic structures found in metamorphic rocks. Size differences notwithstanding, most folds result from *compressional stresses that result in a shortening and thickening of the crust.*

To aid our understanding of folds and folding, it is important to become familiar with the terminology used to name the parts of a fold. Folds are geologic structures consisting of stacks of originally horizontal surfaces, such as sedimentary strata, that have been bent as a result of permanent deformation. Each layer is bent around an imaginary axis called a *hinge line*, or simply a *hinge*. In some folds, the hinge lines are horizontal as shown in FIGURE 9. However, in some folds the hinge lines are inclined at an angle known as the *plunge* (see Figure 12).

Folds are also described by their *axial plane*, which is a surface that connects all the hinge lines of the folded strata. In simple folds, the axial plane is vertical and divides the fold into two roughly symmetrical *limbs*. However, the axial plane often leans to one side so that one limb is steeper and shorter than the other. In extreme cases, the axial plane can be tilted so that it has a horizontal orientation as shown in FIGURE 10.

Anticlines and Synclines

The two most common types of folds are anticlines and synclines (FIGURE 11). **Anticlines** usually arise by upfolding, or arching, of sedimentary layers and are sometimes spectacularly displayed along highways that have been cut through deformed strata. Typically found in association with anticlines are downfolds, or troughs, called **synclines**. Notice in Figure 11 that the limb of an anticline is also a limb of the adjacent syncline.

Depending on their orientation, these basic folds are described as *symmetrical* when the limbs are mirror

---

By strict definition, an anticline is a structure in which the oldest strata are found in the center. A syncline is a structure in which the youngest strata are found in the center.

FIGURE 9 **Features associated with symmetrical folds** The axial plane divides a fold as symmetrically as possible, while the hinge line traces the points of maximum curvature of any layer.

Axial plane — Hinge line

Axial plane —

Limb — Limb

Before erosion

Axial plane —

Limb — Limb

After erosion

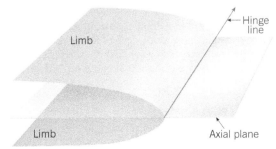

Hinge line

Limb

Limb

Axial plane

FIGURE 10 **Recumbent folds** Recumbent folds are said to "lie on their side" and have nearly horizontal axial planes. (Photo by Marli Miller)

SMARTFIGURE 11 Common types of folds
The upfolded, or arched, structures are *anticlines*. The downfolds, or troughs, are *synclines*. Notice that the limb of an anticline is also the limb of the adjacent syncline.

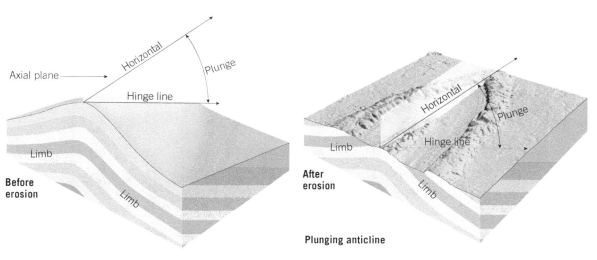

Plunging anticline

FIGURE 12 A plunging anticline
The ends of a fold plunge when the axis (hinge line) of the fold penetrates the ground.

Sheep Mountain Anticline, Wyoming

SMARTFIGURE 13 Sheep Mountain, Wyoming
Eroded plunging anticlines, like Sheep Mountain, have an outcrop pattern that "points" in the direction of plunge. (Photo by Michael Collier)

images of each other and *asymmetrical* when they are not. An asymmetrical fold is said to be *overturned* if one or both limbs are tilted beyond the vertical (Figure 11). An overturned fold can also "lie on its side" so the axial plane is horizontal. These *recumbent* folds are common in highly deformed mountainous regions such as the Alps (see Figure 10).

Folds do not continue forever; rather, their ends die out much like the wrinkles in cloth. The ends of folds are said to *plunge* because the axis of a fold penetrates the ground (FIGURE 12). Sheep Mountain, Wyoming, is an example of a plunging anticline. FIGURE 13 shows the pattern produced when erosion removes the upper layers of plunging folds and exposes their interiors. Note that the outcrop pattern of an anticline points in the direction it is plunging. The opposite is true for a syncline. A good example of topography that results when erosional forces attack folded sedimentary strata is found in the Valley and Ridge Province of the Appalachians.

It is important to realize that ridges are not necessarily associated with anticlines, nor are valleys related to synclines. Rather, ridges and valleys result because of differential weathering and erosion. For example, in the Valley and Ridge Province, resistant sandstone beds remain as imposing ridges separated by valleys cut into more easily eroded shale or limestone beds.

Domes and Basins

Broad upwarps in basement rock may deform the overlying cover of sedimentary strata and generate large folds. When this upwarping produces a circular or slightly elongated structure, the feature is called a **dome** (FIGURE 14A). The Black Hills of western South Dakota is a large structural dome generated by upwarping. Here erosion has stripped away the highest portions of the overlying sedimentary beds, exposing

SMARTFIGURE 14 Domes versus basins
Gentle upwarping and downwarping of crustal rocks produce **A**. domes and **B**. basins. Erosion of these structures results in an outcrop pattern that is roughly circular or slightly elongate.

A. Upwarping produces a *dome*.

B. Downwarping produces a *basin*.

FIGURE 15 The Black Hills of South Dakota, a large structural dome
The central core of the Black Hills is composed of resistant Precambrian age igneous and metamorphic rocks. The surrounding rocks are mainly younger limestones and sandstones.

FIGURE 16 The bedrock geology of the Michigan Basin
The youngest rocks are centrally located, whereas the oldest beds flank this structure.

crust to subside. A few structural basins may have resulted from giant meteorite impacts.

Because large basins contain sedimentary beds sloping at low angles, they are usually identified by the age of the rocks composing them. The youngest rocks are found near the center, and the oldest rocks are at the flanks. This is just the opposite order of a dome, such as the Black Hills, where the oldest rocks form the core.

older igneous and metamorphic rocks in the center (FIGURE 15).

Structural domes can also be formed by the intrusion of magma (laccoliths). In addition, the upward migration of buried salt deposits can produce salt domes like those surrounding the Gulf of Mexico. Salt domes are economically important rock structures because when salt migrates upward, the surrounding oil-bearing sedimentary strata deforms to form oil reservoirs.

Downwarped structures having a similar shape are termed **basins** (FIGURE 14B). Several large basins exist in the United States (FIGURE 16). The basins of Michigan and Illinois have gently sloping beds similar to saucers. These basins are thought to result from large accumulations of sediment, whose weight caused the

Monoclines

Although we have separated our discussion of folds and faults, folds can be uniquely coupled with faults. Examples of this close association are broad, regional features called *monoclines*. Particularly prominent features of the Colorado Plateau, **monoclines** (*mono* = one, *kleinen* = incline) are large, steplike folds in otherwise horizontal sedimentary strata (FIGURE 17). These folds appear to have resulted from the reactivation of ancient, steep-dipping faults located in basement rocks beneath the plateau. As large blocks of basement rock were displaced upward, the comparatively ductile sedimentary strata above responded by draping over the fault like clothes hanging over a bench. Displacement along these reactivated faults often exceeds 1 kilometer (Figure 17).

East Kaibab Monocline, Arizona

Monocline

Monocline

Sedimentary strata removed by erosion

Fault in basement rock

Michael Collier

FIGURE 17 **The East Kaibab Monocline, Arizona**
This monocline consists of bent sedimentary beds that were deformed by faulting in the bedrock below. The thrust fault shown is called a *blind thrust* because it does not reach the surface.

Examples of monoclines found on the Colorado Plateau include the East Kaibab Monocline, the Raplee Anticline, the Waterpocket Fold, and the San Rafael Swell. The inclined strata shown in Figure 17 once extended over the sedimentary layers now exposed at the surface—evidence that a tremendous volume of rock has been eroded from this area.

3 CONCEPT CHECKS

1. Distinguish between anticlines and synclines, between domes and basins, and between anticlines and domes.
2. Draw a cross-sectional view of a symmetrical anticline. Include a line to represent the axial plane and label both limbs.
3. The Black Hills of South Dakota is a good example of what type of geologic structure?
4. Where do the youngest rocks in an eroded basin outcrop: near the center or near the flanks?
5. Describe the formation of a monocline.

EYE on Earth

This image features a large geologic structure that outcrops in Death Valley National Park, California.

Question 1 What name would you give to this geologic structure?

Question 2 Based on this image, would you describe this fold as symmetrical or asymmetrical?

Question 3 Do these rock units mainly display ductile deformation or brittle deformation?

Michael Collier

4 Faults and Joints: Rock Structures Formed by Brittle Deformation

Faults form where brittle deformation leads to fracturing and displacement of Earth's crust. Occasionally, small faults can be recognized in road cuts where sedimentary beds have been offset a few meters, as shown in FIGURE 18. Faults of this scale usually occur as single discrete breaks. By contrast, large faults, like the San Andreas Fault in California, have displacements of hundreds of kilometers and consist of many interconnecting fault surfaces. These structures, described as *fault zones*, can be several kilometers wide and are often easier to identify from aerial photographs than at ground level.

Sudden movements along faults are the cause of most earthquakes. However, the vast majority of faults are remnants of past deformation and are inactive. On some fault surfaces, the rocks become highly polished and striated, or grooved, as the crustal blocks slide past one another. These polished and striated surfaces, called *slickensides* (*sliken* = smooth), provide geologists with evidence for the direction of the most recent displacement along the fault (FIGURE 19).

Dip-Slip Faults

Faults in which movement is primarily parallel to the *inclination* (also called *dip*) of the fault surface are called **dip-slip faults**. Geologists identify the rock surface immediately above the fault as the **hanging wall block** and the rock surface below as the **footwall block** (FIGURE 20). These names were first used by prospectors and miners who excavated metallic ore deposits such as gold that had precipitated from hydrothermal solutions along inactive fault zones. The miners would walk on the rocks below the mineralized fault zone (*the footwall block*) and

hang their lanterns on the rocks above (*the hanging wall block*).

Vertical displacements along dip-slip faults tend to produce long, low cliffs called **fault scarps** (*scarpe* = a slope). Fault scarps, such as the one shown in FIGURE 21, are produced by rapid vertical slips that generate earthquakes.

Normal Faults   Dip-slip faults are classified as **normal faults** when the hanging wall block moves down relative to the footwall block (FIGURE 22A). Normal faults are found in a variety of sizes. Some are small, having displacements of only a meter or so, like the one shown in the road cut in Figure 18. Others, however, extend for tens of kilometers and may sinuously trace the boundary of a mountain front. Most large normal faults have relatively steep dips that tend to flatten out with depth. Normal faults tend to be associated with tensional stresses that pull rock units apart, thereby lengthening the crust. This "pulling apart" can be accomplished either by uplifting that causes the surface to stretch and break or by horizontal forces that have opposing orientations.

In the western United States, large normal faults are associated with structures called **fault-block mountains**. Excellent examples of fault-block mountains are found in the Basin and Range Province, a region that encompasses Nevada and portions of the surrounding states (FIGURE 23). Here the crust has been elongated and broken to create more than 200 relatively small mountain ranges. Averaging about 80 kilometers (50 miles) in length, the ranges rise 900 to 1500 meters (3000 to 5000 feet) above the adjacent down-faulted basins.

The topography of the Basin and Range Province evolved in association with a system of normal faults trending roughly north–south. Movements along these faults produced alternating uplifted fault blocks called **horsts** and down-dropped blocks called **grabens** (*graben* = ditch). Horsts form the ranges and are the source of sediments that have accumulated in the basins created by the grabens. As Figure 23 illustrates, structures called **half-grabens**, which are tilted fault blocks, also contribute to the alternating topographic highs and lows in the Basin and Range Province.

FIGURE 19 Slickensides As two rock bodies slide past one another, their fault surfaces often become polished and grooved into *slickensides*. (Photo by Michael Collier)

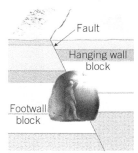

FIGURE 20 Hanging wall block and footwall block The rock immediately above a fault surface is the *hanging wall block*, and the one below is called the *footwall block*. These names came from miners who excavated ore deposits that formed along fault zones. The miners hung their lanterns on the rocks above the fault trace (hanging wall block) and walked on the rocks below the fault trace (footwall block).

FIGURE 18 Faults are fractures where slip has occurred (Photo by E. J. Tarbuck)

FIGURE 21 Fault scarp
This fault scarp was created in 1959 when a fault near Hebgen Lake, Montana, ruptured. The earthquake, which measured 7.5 on the Richter scale, triggered a massive landslide in the canyon of the Madison River that claimed 28 lives. Note the person for scale. (Photo by Russell Losco)

A. Normal fault

B. Reverse fault

C. Thrust fault

SMARTFIGURE 22 Types of dip-slip faults
The upper diagrams illustrate the relative displacement that occurs between the blocks on either side of a fault. The lower diagrams show how erosion may alter the upfaulted blocks.

Also notice in Figure 23 that the slopes of the large normal faults associated with the Basin and Range Province decrease with depth and eventually join to form a nearly horizontal fault called a **detachment fault**. These faults represent a major boundary between the rocks below, which exhibit ductile deformation, and the rocks above, which exhibit mainly brittle deformation.

Reverse and Thrust Faults

Dip-slip faults in which the hanging wall block moves up relative to the footwall block are called **reverse faults** (see Figure 22B). **Thrust faults** are a type of reverse faults having dips less than 45 degrees, so the overlying block moves nearly horizontally over the underlying block (see Figure 22C). Reverse faults result from compressional stresses that produce horizontal shortening of the crust.

Most high-angle reverse faults are small and accommodate local displacements in regions dominated by other types of faulting. Thrust faults, on the other hand, exist at all scales, with some large thrust faults having displacements ranging from tens to hundreds of kilometers.

Thrust faulting is most pronounced along convergent plate boundaries. Compressional forces associated with colliding plates generally create folds as well as thrust faults that thicken and shorten the crust to produce mountainous topography (FIGURE 24). Examples of mountainous belts produced by this type of compressional tectonics include the Alps, Northern Rockies, Himalayas, and Appalachians.

Montana's Glacier National Park is a classic site of thrust faulting (FIGURE 25). Mountain peaks that provide the park's majestic scenery have been carved mainly from a thick sheet of Precambrian limestones that were displaced, as essentially one unit, over much younger Cretaceous shale deposits. This block of sedimentary rock was 6 kilometers (4 miles) thick and slid a distance of about 100 kilometers (60 miles) along the Lewis Thrust Fault. At the eastern edge of Glacier National Park is a peak called Chief Mountain. This well-known landmark is an isolated remnant of a thrust sheet that was severed by the erosional forces of glacial ice and running water. An isolated block, like

FIGURE 23 Normal faulting in the Basin and Range province
Here, tensional stresses have elongated and fractured the crust into numerous blocks. Movement along these faults has tilted the blocks, producing parallel mountain ranges called *fault-block mountains*. The down-faulted blocks (*grabens*) form basins, whereas the upfaulted blocks (*horsts*) erode to form rugged mountainous topography. In addition, numerous tilted blocks (*half-grabens*) form both basins and mountains. (Photo by Michael Collier)

Chief Mountain, is called a **klippe** (*klippe* = cliff) (Figure 25).

Strike-Slip Faults

A fault in which the dominant displacement is horizontal and parallel to the *trend* (direction) of the fault surface is called a **strike-slip fault** (FIGURE 26). The earliest scientific records of strike-slip faulting were

FIGURE 24
Compressional stresses produce folds and thrust faults
At convergent plate boundaries, compressional stresses thicken and shorten the crust, resulting in mountainous topography.

COMPRESSIONAL STRESS

Large-scale movement along the Lewis Thrust Fault displaced Precambrian rock over Cretaceous strata in what is now Glacier National Park, Montana. (D, photo by Phillippe Clement/ AGE/Fotostock)

A. Geologic setting prior to thrust faulting

Stress

Incipient thrust fault

Stress

Cretaceous rocks

Precambrian rocks

B. Movement along the Lewis Thrust Fault displaced mainly Precambrian rocks over Cretaceous strata in what is now Glacier National Park, Montana.

Stress

Thrust fault

Stress

Precambrian rocks

Cretaceous rocks

C. Erosion sculpted the thrust sheet into a majestic landscape and created an isolated remnant of the thrust sheet called Chief Mountain.

Glacier National Park

Lewis Thrust Fault

Chief Mountain

Precambrian rocks

Cretaceous rocks

D. Chief Mountain in Glacier National Park, Montana, is a klippe.

made following surface ruptures that produced large earthquakes. One of the most noteworthy of these was the great San Francisco earthquake of 1906. During this strong earthquake, structures such as fences and roads that were built across the San Andreas Fault were displaced as much as 4.7 meters (15 feet). Because movement along the San Andreas Fault causes the crustal block on the opposite side of the fault to move to the right as you face the fault, it is called a *right-lateral* strike-slip fault.

The Great Glen Fault in Scotland, which exhibits the opposite sense of displacement, is a well-known example of a *left-lateral* strike-slip fault. The total displacement along the Great Glen Fault is estimated to exceed 100 kilometers (60 miles). Also associated with this fault trace are numerous lakes, including Loch Ness, home of the legendary monster.

Although sudden displacement along any fault can produce an earthquake, some of the most destructive earthquakes occur along strike-slip faults. One of the most noteworthy of these was the earthquake that struck near Port-au-Prince, Haiti, in 2010. During this strong earthquake, an estimated 230,000 people lost their lives and 300,000 homes were destroyed (FIGURE 27).

Some strike-slip faults slice through Earth's crust and accommodate motion between two tectonic plates. These major strike-slip faults are called **transform faults** (*trans* = across, *forma* = form). Numerous transform faults cut the oceanic lithosphere and link spreading oceanic ridges. Others accommodate displacement between continental blocks that slip horizontally past each other. Some of the best-known transform faults include California's San Andreas Fault, New Zealand's Alpine Fault, the Middle East's Dead Sea Fault, and Turkey's North Anatolian Fault (FIGURE 28).

Notice that the ridge of light-colored rock in the top-right portion of the photo was offset to the right relative to the portion of the same ridge that appears at the bottom left of the image. (Photo by Marli Miller)

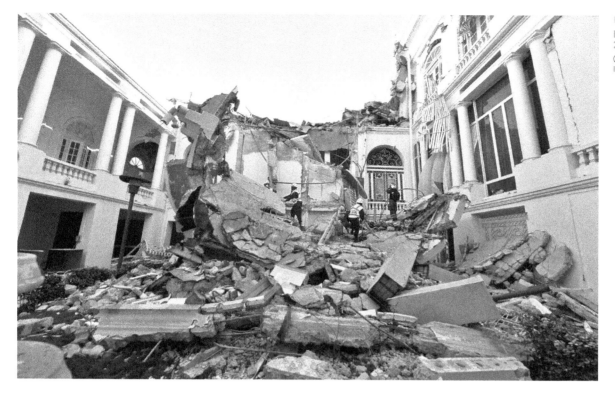

Large transform faults, like these, accommodate relative displacements of up to several hundred kilometers.

Rather than being a single fracture along which movement takes place, most continental transform faults consist of a zone of roughly parallel fractures. The zone may be up to several kilometers wide. The most recent movement, however, is often along a strand only a few meters wide, which may offset features such as stream channels. Crushed and broken rocks produced during faulting are more easily eroded, so linear valleys or sag ponds often mark the locations of large strike-slip faults.

Oblique-Slip Faults

Faults that exhibit both dip-slip and strike-slip movement, called **oblique-slip faults**, are caused by a combination of shearing and tensional or compressional stress (FIGURE 29). Nearly all faults have minor components of both dip-slip and strike-slip movement, so defining a fault as oblique requires that both types of slip be significant enough to be observed and measured.

FIGURE 28 The Alpine Fault, New Zealand
The Alpine Fault is a large strike-slip fault, called a *transform fault*, that accommodates movement between two tectonic plates. Displacement along this fault accommodates the relative movement of the Australian plate, which is moving toward the northeast, and the westward-moving Pacific plate.

FIGURE 29 Oblique-slip faults
Oblique-slip faults exhibit a combination of dip-slip and strike-slip movement.

FIGURE 30 Devil's Tower
National Monument,
Wyoming
This imposing structure
exhibits columnar joints.
Columnar joints form as
igneous rocks cool and
develop shrinkage fractures
that produce five- to seven-
sided elongated, pillarlike
structures. (Photo by Michael
Collier)

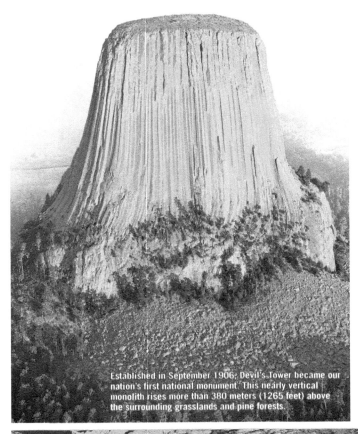

Established in September 1906, Devil's Tower became our nation's first national monument. This nearly vertical monolith rises more than 380 meters (1265 feet) above the surrounding grasslands and pine forests.

Michael Collier

FIGURE 31 Nearly parallel
joints in the Navajo
Sandstone, Arches
National Park, Utah
Weathering and erosion
along the joints have produced a topography known
in the park as "fins."

Joints

Among the most common rock structures are fractures called joints. Unlike faults, **joints** are fractures along which no appreciable displacement has occurred. Although some joints have a random orientation, most occur in roughly parallel groups.

Columnar joints form when igneous rocks cool and develop shrinkage fractures that produce elongated, pillarlike columns (FIGURE 30). In addition, sheeting produces a pattern of gently curved joints that develop more or less parallel to the surface of large exposed igneous bodies such as batholiths. Here the jointing results from the gradual expansion that occurs when erosion removes the overlying load.

Most joints are produced when rocks in the outermost crust are deformed, causing the rock to fail by brittle fracture. Extensive joint patterns often develop in response to relatively subtle and often barely perceptible regional upwarping and downwarping of the crust. In many cases, the cause of jointing at a particular locale is not particularly obvious.

Many rocks are broken by two or even three sets of intersecting joints that slice the rock into numerous regularly shaped blocks. These joint sets often exert a strong influence on other geologic processes. For example, chemical weathering tends to be concentrated along joints, and joint patterns influence how groundwater moves through the crust (FIGURE 31).

Joints may also be significant from an economic standpoint. Some of the world's largest and most important mineral deposits are located along joint systems. Hydrothermal solutions (mineralized fluids) can migrate into fractured host rocks and precipitate economically significant amounts of copper, silver, gold, zinc, lead, and uranium.

Highly jointed rocks present a risk to construction projects, including bridges, highways, and dams. On June 5, 1976, 14 lives were lost and nearly $1 billion in property damage occurred when the Teton Dam in Idaho failed. This earthen dam, constructed of very erodible clays and silts, was situated on highly fractured volcanic rocks. Although attempts were made to fill the voids in the jointed rock, water gradually penetrated the subsurface fractures and undermined the dam's foundation. Eventually the moving water cut a tunnel into the easily erodible clays and silts. Within minutes the dam failed, sending a 20-meter- (65-foot-) high wall of water down the Teton and Snake Rivers.

4 CONCEPT CHECKS

1. Contrast the movements that occur along normal and reverse faults. What type of stress is indicated by each fault?
2. What type of faults are associated with fault-block mountains?
3. How are reverse faults different from thrust faults? In what way are they the same?
4. Describe the relative movement along a strike-slip fault.
5. How are joints different from faults?

 EYE on Earth

This group of linear collapsed valleys is located in the Needles District of Canyonlands National Park, Utah. About 10 million years ago, as the Colorado Plateau was being uplifted, the Colorado River and its tributaries started to downcut through the rock layers in this area, carrying the sediment to the Pacific. About 55 thousand years ago, the Colorado River encountered and began to cut through a thick layer of Pennsylvanian age salt that underlies the surface rocks of the Needles. Once the salt layer was breached, the weight of the overlying rock caused salt to flow toward the Colorado River like thick toothpaste squeezed from a tube. The result was the stretching of Earth's crust and formation of the collapsed valleys shown in this photograph.

Question 1 What name do geologists give to these down-faulted linear valleys?

Question 2 What type of deformation do the salt deposits experience as they flow toward the Colorado River (ductile or brittle)?

Question 3 Name the type of faults that border these collapsed structures.

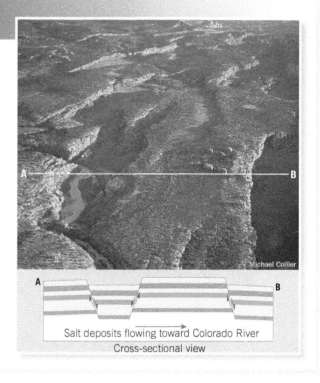

Michael Collier

Salt deposits flowing toward Colorado River

Cross-sectional view

The San Andreas Fault System

The San Andreas Fault system is a 1,300 kilometer (780 miles) long transform fault that slices through two thirds of the length of California. Geologists have determined that this fault zone measures tens of kilometers wide in some locations, and extends to a depth of at least 18 kilometers.

Photo: Sacramento Bee/John Trotter/Newscom

Map: USGS

Because of its great length and complexity, the San Andreas Fault is more appropriately referred to as a "fault system" which consists of the San Andreas Fault and several other major branches, including the Hayward and Calaveras faults located in the San Francisco Bay area.

CALIFORNIA

Hayward Fault

San Francisco

Calaveras Fault

Garlock Fault

Los Angeles

San Jacinto Fault

Imperial Fault

Eastern California Shear Zone

San Andreas Fault

Although the 1989 Loma Prieta earthquake was centered in a remote section of the Santa Cruz Mountains, major damage occurred in the Marina District of San Francisco. Hundreds of small earthquakes are generated every year on the San Andreas Fault system, while moderate earthquakes (magnitude greater than 6) occur about every 20 years or so. Large destructive earthquakes (magnitude greater than 8) occur about every 150 years, on average.

Directional stress that is deforming the crust in the Los Angeles area produced several low-angle thrust faults that uplifted large crustal blocks including those of the San Gabriel Mountains. Because some thrust faults do not penetrate Earth's surface, they are called blind thrusts. Movement on such a blind thrust produced the 1994 earthquake in the Northridge area of Los Angeles.

Hayward Fault

Greenville Fault

San Francisco

Oakland

San Andreas Fault

San Jose

Calaveras Fault

Range Front Fault

San Gregorio Fault

Sargent Fault

Photo: Chad Ehlers

Simi Fault

Northridge Hills Fault

San Gabriel Fault zone

SAN ANDREAS FAULT

Thousand Oaks

San Fernando Valley

Sierra Madre Fault zone

Santa Monica Fault

Santa Monica

Los Angeles

Newport Inglewood Fault zone

Whittier Fault

Torrance

Palos Verdes Fault

Irvine

Los Angeles

Mojave Desert

San Andreas Fault Zone

San Gabriel Mountains

Sierra Madre Thrust Fault

Stress

Stress

BRITTLE CRUST

DUCTILE

Tomales Bay is a narrow inlet located north of San Francisco that nearly separates Point Reyes Peninsula from mainland North America. This linear depression, now filled with seawater, formed as a result of displacement along the San Andreas Fault system. Tomales Bay is more than one mile wide, suggesting that the San Andreas system, which consists of numerous roughly parallel fault traces, is equally as wide.

Photo: NASA

Tomales Bay

Drakes Bay

Point Reyes

San Andreas Fault

N

Photo: Michael Collier

Along the San Andreas Fault, the Pacific plate grinds horizontally past the North American plate at a rate of about 5 centimeters per year. At its southern end, the San Andreas connects with a spreading center located in the Gulf of California. In the north, the fault enters the Pacific Ocean at Point Arena, where it continues its northwestwardly trend, eventually joining the Mendocino fracture zone.

Basin and Range Province

Extension

Great Valley

San Andreas Fault

Photo: Michael Collier

Calaveras Fault

Rather than generating earthquakes, some segments of the San Andreas Fault experience creep, a somewhat continuous movement along the fault without measurable earthquake activity. This once straight sidewalk and concrete wall were built decades ago in Hollister, California, and show effects of creep along the Calaveras Fault.

The Carrizo Plain is an expansive grassland that is bisected by the San Andreas Fault. For nearly 50 miles, a linear trough, offset stream channels, narrow ridges, and sag ponds mark the trace of this iconic fault. From ground level, however, surface expressions of faults are much more difficult to detect.

Photo: Michael Collier

Pinnacles National Monument lies near the San Andreas Fault about 80 miles south of the San Francisco Bay area. It is composed of highly eroded volcanic rocks that spewed from Earth's interior about 23 million years ago. A strikingly similar group of rocks called the Neenach Volcanic Formation is located to the southeast, near Tejon Pass. It is thought that the Pinnacles were sliced from the Neenach Volcanic Formation and transported by the Pacific plate 195 miles toward the northeast. By matching these and other rock units across the fault, geologists have determined that the total displacement along the San Andreas Fault system from earthquakes and creep exceeds 340 miles.

Photo: Kevin Schafer/AGE Fotostock

5 Mapping Geologic Structures

By studying the orientations of faults, folds, and tilted sedimentary formations, geologists can often reconstruct the original geologic setting and determine the nature of the forces that generated these structures. In this way, the complex events of Earth's geologic history are unraveled.

Frequently, structures are so large that only a small portion is visible from any particular vantage point. In many situations, most of the bedrock is concealed by vegetation or buried by recent sedimentation. Consequently, reconstruction must be done using data gathered from a limited number of *outcrops*, sites where bedrock is exposed at the surface. Despite these challenges, a number of mapping techniques enable geologists to infer the shape and orientation of rock structures below the surface. In recent years, this work has been aided by advances in aerial photography, satellite imagery, and the development of the Global Positioning System (GPS). In addition, seismic reflection profiling and drill holes provide data on the composition and orientation of rock structures that lie at depth.

Strike and Dip

Sedimentary rock units, because they are usually deposited in horizontal layers, are most useful when studying rock deformation. If the sedimentary rock layers are horizontal, geologists infer that the area is undisturbed structurally. Inclined, bent, or broken strata indicate that a period of deformation occurred following deposition.

Geologists use measurements called *strike* (trend) and *dip* (inclination) to help determine the orientation of planar rock features, such as sedimentary bedding and fault surfaces (FIGURE 32). By knowing the strike and dip of rocks at the surface, geologists can predict the nature and structure of rock units hidden beneath the surface.

Strike is the compass bearing (direction) of the line produced by the intersection of an inclined rock layer (or fault) with a horizontal plane (Figure 32). The strike, or compass bearing, is generally expressed as an angle relative to north. For example, N10°E means the line of strike is 10 degrees to the east of north.

Dip is the maximum angle of inclination of the surface of a rock unit or fault, measured from a horizontal plane. Dip includes both an angle of inclination and a direction toward which the rock is inclined. In Figure 32 the dip angles of the rock layer are 20 degrees on one limb of the anticline and 60 degrees on the other. The direction of dip will always be at a 90-degree angle to the strike.

In the field, geologists measure the strike (trend) and dip (inclination) of sedimentary strata at as many outcrops as practical. These data are then plotted on a topographic map or an aerial photograph, using T-shaped symbols. From the orientation of the strata, an inferred orientation and shape of the buried structure can be established, as shown in FIGURE 33. Using this information, geologists can reconstruct the pre-erosional structures and begin to interpret the region's geologic history.

FIGURE 32 Strike and dip of rock layers

FIGURE 33 Mapping geologic structures
By establishing the strike and dip of outcropping sedimentary beds and placing them on a map, geologists can infer the orientation of the rock structures below the surface.

A. Map view

B. Block diagram

5 CONCEPT CHECKS

1. What two measurements are used to establish the orientation of deformed strata? Distinguish between them.
2. Briefly describe the method geologists use to infer the orientation of rock units that lie mainly below Earth's surface.

CONCEPTS IN REVIEW: CRUSTAL DEFORMATION

1   What Causes Rock to Deform?

Describe the three types of differential stress and contrast stress with strain.

KEY WORDS   deformation, rock structure (geologic structure), stress, confining pressure, differential stress, compressional stress, tensional stress, shear, strain

- Rock structures are generated when preexisting rocks are deformed by bending or breaking due to differential stress. Crustal deformation produces geologic structures that include folds, faults, joints, foliation, and rock cleavage.
- Stress, or force applied over some area, drives rock deformation. Stress may be the same magnitude in every direction, in which case we call it confining pressure. Alternatively, the amount of stress coming from

one direction might be greater in magnitude than the amount of stress coming from another direction. In this case, we have a difference between the stress amounts in different directions, and we call it differential stress. There are three main types of differential stress: compressional, tensional, and shear stress.

- If rocks are strong, small stresses don't affect them. However, if stresses are strong, rocks may deform, or strain. Strain results from stresses that are greater than the strength of the rock.

CLASSIFY IT   Classify the following everyday situations as confining pressure, compressional stress, tensional stress, or shear stress: (a) a watermelon being run over by a steamroller, (b) a person diving into the deep end of the swimming pool, (c) playing a game of tug-of-war, (d) kneading bread dough, (e) slipping on a banana peel. Which examples include strain? Which don't?

2   How Do Rocks Deform?

Compare and contrast brittle and ductile deformation.

KEY WORDS   elastic deformation, brittle deformation, ductile deformation, joint, fault

- There are several types of deformation. Elastic deformation is a temporary stretching of the chemical bonds in a rock, but not past their breaking point. When the stress is released, the bonds snap back to their original lengths. When stress is greater than the strength of the bonds, the rock deforms in either a brittle or ductile fashion. Brittle deformation is the breaking of rocks into smaller pieces, whereas ductile deformation is flow in the manner of modeling clay or warm wax.
- Which type of deformation (ductile or brittle) occurs depends on four variables. One is temperature: If the rock is warm, it is more likely to flow than break. Second, if the rock is under high confining pressure, it is more likely to flow than break. Thus, conditions in the shallow crust are more likely to result in brittle deformation, while ductile deformation is more likely in the deeper crust.
- Rock type is a third variable influencing the type of deformation (ductile or brittle) that occurs. Some rocks are stronger; other rocks are weaker.

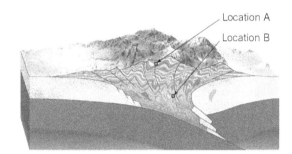

Location A
Location B

Strong rocks are more likely to deform in a brittle fashion, whereas many sedimentary layers will readily deform in a ductile fashion because they are weaker. The fourth variable is the amount of time over which the stress is applied. Silly Putty provides a good analogy: Sudden applications of stress are more likely to break it, while slow applications of the same stress encourage ductile flow.

INTERPRET IT   Examine this illustration of tectonic compression. Compare the deformation you would expect at locations A and B. Suggest possible exceptions to the general predictions you make.

3   Folds: Rock Structures Formed by Ductile Deformation

List and describe five types of folds.

KEY WORDS   fold, anticline, syncline, dome, basin, monocline

- Folds are wavelike undulations in layered rocks that develop through ductile deformation in rocks undergoing compressional stress.
- Folds may be described in terms of their geometric configuration: If the limbs of a fold dip away from the hinge, the fold has an overall arch-like structure and is called an anticline. If the limbs of a fold dip toward the hinge, the fold has an overall trough-like structure and is called a syncline. Anticlines and synclines may be symmetrical, asymmetrical, overturned, or recumbent.
- The shape of a fold does not necessarily correlate to the shape of the landscape above it. Rather, surface topography usually reflects

patterns of differential weathering. A fold is said to plunge when its axis penetrates the ground at an angle. This results in a V-shaped outcrop pattern of the folded layers.

- Domes and basins are large folds that produce "bull's-eye"–shaped outcrop patterns. They don't have a linear axis but rather a single point of maximum uplift or subsidence. The overall shape of a dome or basin is like a saucer or a bowl, either right-side-up (basin) or inverted (dome).
- Monoclines are large folds in which strata are locally tilted on top of a subsurface fault. Imagine a carpet draped over a short staircase to envision how the strata can go from horizontal to tilted and back to horizontal again.

DISTINGUISH THEM   What do domes and anticlines have in common? What sets them apart from one another? Similarly, compare synclines and basins. Use a bath towel to quickly generate models of each of these four fold types, as well as monoclines.

4 Faults and joints: Structures Formed by Brittle Deformation

Sketch and briefly describe the relative motion of rock bodies located on opposite sides of normal, reverse, and thrust faults as well as both types of strike-slip faults.

KEY WORDS fault, dip-slip fault, hanging wall block, footwall block, fault scarp, normal fault, fault-block mountain, horst, graben, half-graben, detachment fault, reverse fault, thrust fault, klippe, strike-slip fault, transform fault, oblique-slip fault, joint

- Faults and joints are fractures in rock that form through brittle deformation. Faults show offset of the rocks on either side of the fracture; joints do not show offset.
- The offset on a fault may be determined by comparing the blocks of rock on either side of the fault surface. If the movement is in the direction of the fault's dip (or inclination), then the rock above the fault plane is the hanging wall block, and the rock below the fault is the footwall block. If the hanging wall moves *down* relative to the footwall, the fault is a normal fault. If the hanging wall moves *up* relative to the footwall, the fault is a reverse fault. Large normal faults with low dip angles are detachment faults. Large reverse faults with low dip angles are thrust faults.
- Faults that intersect Earth's surface may produce a "step" in the land known as a fault scarp. Areas of tectonic extension, such as the Basin and Range Province, produce fault-block mountains—horsts separated by neighboring grabens or half-grabens.
- Areas of tectonic compression, such as mountain belts, are dominated by reverse faults that shorten the crust horizontally while thickening it vertically. Erosion of thrust sheets may isolate scraps of thrust-faulted rock to form a klippe, such as Chief Mountain, Montana.
- Strike-slip faults see most of their movement in the direction of the horizontal trend of the fault trace. There is minimal up- or down-oriented

East Africa

Canadian Rockies

movement; instead, the motion is either right-lateral or left-lateral. Transform faults are strike-slip faults that serve as tectonic boundaries between lithospheric plates.
- Oblique-slip faults display a blend of dip-slip motion and strike-slip motion.
- Joints form in the shallow crust when rocks are stressed under brittle conditions. They are important for groundwater movement, mineralization of economic resources, and human hazards.

COMPARE & CONTRAST Examine the diagrams depicting the structure of East Africa and the Canadian Rockies. Characterize the type of faulting found at each location and infer the differential stresses and the type of plate boundary that were responsible.

5 Mapping Geologic Structures

Define *strike* and *dip* and explain what these measurements tell geologists about the orientations of rock structures located mainly below Earth's surface.

KEY WORDS strike, dip

- Geologists gather structural data from numerous individual outcrops in order to infer larger-scale patterns of Earth's rock structures. This act of mapping allows the reconstruction of geologic histories and the interpretation of the shape and orientation of rock structures at depth—an important thing to be able to do for resource extraction and hazard assessment.
- Strike and dip are measurements of the orientation of planar rock features such as sedimentary bedding. Strike is the compass direction of the line at the intersection between a perfectly horizontal plane and the geologic surface of interest. Dip is the angle of inclination between the horizontal plane and a line that is perpendicular to the strike. Using a special compass, field geologists measure the strike and dip of rock outcrops and plot them on a map using T-shaped symbols. By matching up rock units with these measured orientations, the shape of subterranean structures such as faults or folds may be inferred.

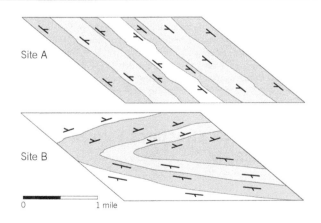

Site A

Site B

0   1 mile

MAP IT Examine the two different maps showing outcrop patterns of the four sedimentary units. By checking the strike and dip symbols, interpret the geologic structures that exist in these two areas.

GIVE IT SOME THOUGHT

1. Describe an environment within Earth in which you might expect rocks to experience ductile deformation. Suggest a scenario in which brittle rather than ductile deformation might occur.

2. Is granite or mica schist more likely to fold or flow rather than fracture when subjected to differential stress? Explain.

3. Refer to the accompanying diagrams to answer the following:
   a. What type of dip-slip fault is shown in Diagram 1? Were the dominant forces during faulting tensional, compressional, or shear?
   b. What type of dip-slip fault is shown in Diagram 2? Were the dominant forces during faulting tensional, compressional, or shear?
   c. Match the correct pair of arrows in Diagram 3 to the faults in Diagrams 1 and 2.

Diagram 1   Diagram 2   Diagram 3

4. Refer to the accompanying photo to answer the following:

USGS

   a. The white line shows the approximate location of a fault that displaced these furrows created by a plow. What type of fault caused the offset shown?
   b. Is this a right-lateral or left-lateral fault? Explain.

5. With which of the three types of plate boundaries does normal faulting predominate? Thrust faulting? Strike-slip faulting?

6. Write a brief statement describing each of the accompanying photos, using terms from the following list: strike-slip, dip-slip, normal, reverse, right-lateral, left-lateral.

A.

B.

7. The accompanying photo, taken near the bottom of the Grand Canyon, shows a quartz vein that has been deformed.

Michael Collier

   a. What type of deformation is exhibited—ductile or brittle?
   b. Did this deformation most likely occur near Earth's surface or at great depth?

8. Refer to the accompanying photo to answer the following questions.

E. J. Tarbuck

   a. Name the type of fold shown.
   b. Would you describe this fold as symmetrical or asymmetrical?
   c. What name is given to the part of the fold labeled A?
   d. Is point B located along the fold line, hinge line, or dip line of this particular fold?

9. The accompanying simplified geologic map shows the strike and dip of outcropping sedimentary beds. From these measurements, describe the rock structure that is most likely beneath Earth's surface, using terms from the following list: anticline, syncline, dome, basin, symmetrical, asymmetrical.

Map view

MasteringGeology™

Glossary

Anticline A fold in sedimentary strata that resembles an arch.

Basin A circular downfolded structure.

Compressional stress Differential stress that shortens a rock body.

Confining pressure Stress that is applied uniformly in all directions.

Deformation General term for the processes of folding, faulting, shearing, compression, or extension of rocks as the result of various natural forces.

Detachment fault A nearly horizontal fault that may extend for hundreds of kilometers below the surface. Such a fault represents a boundary between rocks that exhibit ductile deformation and rocks that exhibit brittle deformation.

Differential stress Forces that are unequal in different directions.

Dip-slip fault A fault in which the movement is parallel to the dip of the fault.

Dip The angle at which a rock layer or fault is inclined from the horizontal. The direction of dip is at a right angle to the strike.

Dome A roughly circular upfolded structure.

Ductile deformation A type of solid-state flow that produces a change in the size and shape of a rock body without fracturing. Occurs at depths where temperatures and confining pressures are high.

Elastic deformation Rock deformation in which the rock will return to nearly its original size and shape when the stress is removed.

Fault-block mountain A mountain that is formed by the displacement of rock along a fault.

Fault A break in a rock mass along which movement has occurred.

Fault scarp A cliff created by movement along a fault. It represents the exposed surface of the fault prior to modification by weathering and erosion.

Fold A bent layer or series of layers that were originally horizontal and subsequently deformed.

Footwall block The rock surface below a fault.

Geologic structure See Rock structure.

Graben A valley formed by the downward displacement of a fault-bounded block.

Half graben A tilted fault block in which the higher side is associated with mountainous topography and the lower side is a basin that fills with sediment.

Hanging wall block The rock surface immediately above a fault.

Horst An elongate, uplifted block of crust bounded by faults.

Joint A fracture in rock along which there has been no movement.

Klippe A remnant or an outlier of a thrust sheet that was isolated by erosion.

Monocline A one-limbed flexure in strata. The strata are usually flat-lying or very gently dipping on both sides of the monocline.

Normal fault A fault in which the rock above the fault plane has moved down relative to the rock below.

Oblique slip fault A fault that exhibits both dip-slip and strike-slip movement.

Reverse fault A fault in which the material above the fault plane moves up in relation to the material below.

Rock structure All features created by the processes of deformation from minor fractures in bedrock to a major mountain chain.

Shear Stress that causes two adjacent parts of a body to slide past one another.

Strain An irreversible change in the shape and size of a rock body caused by stress.

Stress The force per unit area acting on any surface within a solid.

Strike-slip fault A fault along which movement occurs horizontally.

Strike The compass direction of the line of intersection created by a dipping bed or fault and a horizontal surface. A strike is always perpendicular to the direction of dip.

Syncline A linear downfold in sedimentary strata; the opposite of anticline.

Tensional stress The type of stress that tends to pull a body apart.

Thrust fault A low-angle reverse fault.

Transform fault A major strike-slip fault that cuts through the lithosphere and accommodates motion between two plates.

Earthquakes and Earthquake Hazards

From Chapter 11 of *Earth: An Introduction to Physical Geology*, Eleventh Edition. Edward J. Tarbuck, Frederick K. Lutgens, Dennis Tasa.

Earthquakes and Earthquake Hazards

Tsunami striking the coast of Japan on March 11, 2011. (Photo by Sadatsugu Tomizawa/AFP/Getty Images)

Each statement represents the primary learning objective for the corresponding major heading within the chapter. After you complete the chapter you should be able to:

1 Sketch and describe the mechanism that generates most earthquakes.

2 List the basic types of faults and describe the tectonic setting where each type of faulting tends to dominate.

3 Compare and contrast the types of seismic waves and describe the principle of the seismograph, which is used to detect them.

4 Distinguish between intensity scales and magnitude scales.

5 Summarize the major destructive forces that can be triggered by earthquake vibrations.

6 Locate Earth's major earthquake belts on a world map and label the regions associated with the largest earthquakes.

7 Compare and contrast the goals of short-range earthquake predictions and long-range forecasts.

O
n January 12, 2010, an estimated 316,000 people lost their lives when a 7.0-magnitude earthquake struck the small Caribbean nation of Haiti, the poorest country in the Western Hemisphere. In addition to the staggering death toll, there were more than 300,000 injuries, and more than 280,000 houses were destroyed or damaged.

The quake originated only 25 kilometers (15 miles) from the country's densely populated capital city of Port-au-Prince. It occurred along a San Andreas–like fault at a depth of just 10 kilometers (6 miles). Because of the quake's shallow depth, ground shaking was exceptional for an event of this magnitude. Other factors that contributed to the Port-au-Prince disaster included the city's geologic setting and the nature of its buildings. The city is built on sediment, which is quite susceptible to ground shaking during an earthquake. More importantly, inadequate or nonexistent building codes meant that buildings collapsed far more readily than they should have. At least 52 aftershocks, measuring magnitude 4.5 or greater, jolted the area and added to the trauma survivors experienced for days after the original quake.

Destruction in Port-au-Prince, Haiti following a devastating earthquake in January 2010. (Photo by Orlando Barria/EFE/Newscom)

1 What Is an Earthquake?

An **earthquake** is ground shaking caused by the sudden and rapid movement of one block of rock slipping past another along fractures in Earth's crust called **faults**. Most large earthquakes occur along preexisting faults where past earthquakes have caused the crustal rocks to rupture or break into two or more units. The location where slippage begins is called the **hypocenter**, or **focus**. Earthquake waves radiate from this spot outward into the surrounding rock. The point on Earth's surface directly above the hypocenter is called the **epicenter** (FIGURE 1).

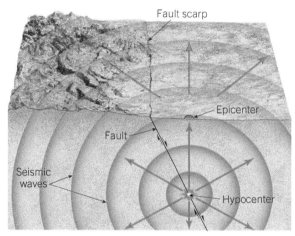

FIGURE 1 Earthquake hypocenter and epicenter
The *hypocenter* is the zone at depth where the initial displacement occurs. The *epicenter* is the surface location directly above the hypocenter.

Large earthquakes release huge amounts of stored-up energy as **seismic waves**—a form of energy that causes the material that transmits them to shake. Seismic waves are analogous to waves produced when a stone is dropped into a calm pond. Just as the impact of the stone creates a pattern of circular waves, an earthquake generates waves that radiate outward in all directions from the hypocenter. Although seismic energy dissipates rapidly as it moves away from the quake's hypocenter, sensitive instruments can detect earthquakes even when they occur on the opposite side of Earth.

Thousands of earthquakes occur around the world every day. Fortunately, most are small and cannot be detected by people. Of these, only about 15 strong earthquakes (magnitude 7 or greater) are recorded each year, many of them occurring in remote regions. Occasionally, a large earthquake is triggered near a major population center. Such events are among the most destructive natural forces on Earth. The shaking of the ground, coupled with the liquefaction of soils, wreaks havoc on buildings, roadways, and other structures. In addition, when a quake occurs in a populated area, power and gas lines are

often ruptured, causing numerous fires. In the famous 1906 San Francisco earthquake, much of the damage was caused by fires that became uncontrollable when broken water mains left firefighters with only trickles of water (FIGURE 2).

Discovering the Causes of Earthquakes

The energy released by volcanic eruptions, massive landslides, and meteorite impacts can generate earthquakelike waves, but these events are usually weak. What mechanism produces a destructive earthquake? As you have learned, Earth is not a static planet. We know that large sections of Earth's crust have been thrust upward because fossils of marine organisms have been discovered thousands of meters above sea level. Other regions, such as California's Death Valley, exhibit evidence of extensive subsidence. In addition to these vertical displacements, offsets in fences, roads, and other structures indicate that horizontal movements between blocks of Earth's crust are also common (FIGURE 3).

The actual mechanism of earthquake generation eluded geologists until H. F. Reid of Johns Hopkins University conducted a landmark study following the 1906 San Francisco earthquake. This earthquake was accompanied by horizontal surface displacements of several meters along the northern portion of the San Andreas Fault. Field studies determined that during this single earthquake, the Pacific plate lurched as much as 9.7 meters (32 feet) northward past the adjacent North American plate. To better visualize this, imagine standing on one side of the fault and watching a person on the other side suddenly slide horizontally 32 feet to your right.

What Reid concluded from his investigations is illustrated in FIGURE 4. Over tens to hundreds of years, differential stress slowly bends the crustal rocks on both sides of a fault. This is much like a person bending a limber wooden stick, as shown in Figure 4. Frictional resistance keeps the fault from rupturing and slipping. (Friction acts against slippage and is enhanced

San Francisco in flames following the 1906 quake, when broken water mains left firefighters without water.

Fire triggered when a gas line ruptured during the 1994 Northridge earthquake in southern California.

FIGURE 2 Earthquakes can trigger fires
(Reproduced from the collection of the Library of Congress) (Inset photo by Hal Garb/AFP/Getty Images)

by irregularities that occur along the fault surface.) At some point, the stress along the fault overcomes the frictional resistance, and slip initiates. Slippage allows the deformed (bent) rock to "snap back" to its original, stress-free, shape; a series of earthquake waves radiate as it slides (Figure 4C,D). Reid termed the "springing back" **elastic rebound** because the rock behaves elastically, much like a stretched rubber band does when it is released.

Aftershocks and Foreshocks

Strong earthquakes are followed by numerous earthquakes of lesser magnitude, called **aftershocks**, which are the result of crust along the fault surface adjusting to the displacement caused by the main shock. Aftershocks gradually diminish in frequency and intensity over a period of several months following an earthquake. In a little more than one month following the 2010 Haiti earthquake, the U.S. Geological Survey detected nearly 60 aftershocks with magnitudes of 4.5 or greater. The two largest aftershocks had magnitudes of 6.0 and 5.9, both large enough to inflict damage. Hundreds of minor tremors were also felt.

Although aftershocks are weaker than the main earthquake, they often trigger the destruction of already weakened structures. For example, in northwestern Armenia in 1988, where many people lived in large apartment buildings constructed of brick and concrete slabs, a

FIGURE 3 Displacement of structures along a fault
(Color photo by John S. Shelton/University of Washington Libraries; inset photo by G.K. Gilbert/USGS)

Slippage along a fault produced this offset in an orange grove east of Calexico, California.

This fence was offset 2.5 meters (8.5 feet) during the 1906 San Francisco earthquake.

Deformation of rocks

Deformation of a limber stick

SMARTFIGURE 4 Elastic rebound

Tens to hundreds of years

Seconds to a few minutes

Time

A. Original position of rocks on opposite sides of a fault.

B. The movement of tectonic plates causes the rocks to bend and store elastic energy.

C. Once the strength of the rocks is exceeded, slippage along the fault produces an earthquake.

D. The rocks return to their original shape, but in a new location.

moderate earthquake of magnitude 6.9 weakened many structures, and a strong aftershock of magnitude 5.8 completed the demolition.

In contrast to aftershocks, small earthquakes called **foreshocks** often, but not always, precede major earthquakes by days or, in some cases, by several years. Monitoring of foreshocks to predict forthcoming earthquakes has been attempted with only limited success.

1 CONCEPT CHECKS

1. What is an earthquake? Under what circumstances do most large earthquakes occur?
2. How are faults, hypocenters, and epicenters related?
3. Who was first to explain the mechanism by which most earthquakes are generated?
4. Explain what is meant by *elastic rebound*.

2 ▮ Faults and Earthquakes

Earthquakes take place along both new and preexisting faults, in places where differential stresses cause Earth's crust to break. Some faults are large and capable of generating major earthquakes. One example is the San Andreas Fault, which is the transform fault boundary that separates two great sections of Earth's lithosphere: the North American plate and the Pacific plate. Most large faults are not perfectly straight or continuous; instead, they consist of numerous branches and smaller fractures that display kinks and offsets.

The slippage that occurs along faults can be explained by the plate tectonics theory, which states that large slabs of Earth's lithosphere are continually grinding past one another. These mobile plates interact with neighboring plates, straining and deforming the rocks at their edges. Faults associated with plate boundaries are the source of most large earthquakes.

Types of Faults

There are three basic types of faults: *normal faults, reverse faults* (including thrust faults), and *strike-slip faults* (FIGURE 5). Normal faults occur where tensional stress causes Earth's crust to be stretched and elongated. Therefore, most earthquakes along normal faults are associated with divergent plate boundaries, mainly seafloor spreading centers and continental rifts. Normal faulting, although common, is not generally associated with earthquakes (Figure 5A).

Reverse faults, including low-angle thrust faults, are mostly associated with convergent plate boundaries. These faults are generated by compressional forces along subduction zones and where continental collisions result in mountain building. The plate boundary between a subducting slab of oceanic lithosphere and the overlying plate is called a **megathrust fault** (Figure 5B). Because these large thrust faults lie beneath the ocean floor and experience vertical motion that can displace the overlying water, they are capable of generating destructive tsunamis. Megathrust faults have produced the majority of Earth's most powerful earthquakes, including the 2011 Japan quake (magnitude [M] 9.0), the 2004 Indian Ocean quake in Sumatra (M 9.1), the 1964 Alaska quake (M 9.2), and the largest earthquake yet recorded, the 1960 Chile quake (M 9.5).

Strike-slip faults, by contrast, are the result of shear stresses and exhibit mainly horizontal slip that result in large segments of Earth's crust to grind past each other (Figure 5C). Large strike-slip faults, like the San Andreas Fault, are called *transform faults* when they form plate boundaries.

The San Andreas is undoubtedly the most studied fault system in the world. From this and other research, geologists have learned that displacement along large faults occurs in discrete segments that often behave differently from one another. Some sections of the San Andreas Fault exhibit slow, gradual displacement known as **fault creep**, which occurs without the accumulation of significant strain. These sections of the fault produce little seismic shaking. Other segments slip at relatively closely spaced intervals, producing numerous small to

FIGURE 5 Major fault types

Normal faults occur where the crust is stretched and elongated.

Tensional stresses

Normal faults

A. Normal faults are associated with divergent plate boundaries, mainly seafloor spreading centers and continental rifting.

Reverse and thrust faults occur where crustal rocks are shortened and thickened.

Compressional stresses

Megathrust fault

Overriding plate

Reverse and thrust faults

Subducting plate

B. Reverse and thrust faults are associated with subduction zones and continental collisions.

Strike-slip faults occur where large segments of Earth's crust slip horizontally past each other.

Strike-slip fault

Shear stresses

C. Large strike-slip faults may form transform plate boundaries.

moderate earthquakes. Still other segments remain stuck tight and store elastic energy for a few hundred years before they break loose. The result of this breaking loose is often a major earthquake.

Earthquakes that occur along locked segments of the San Andreas Fault tend to be repetitive: As soon as one is over, strain immediately begins accumulating due to the continuous motion of the plates. Decades or centuries later, the fault fails again.

Fault Rupture and Propagation

Most faults are locked, except for brief, abrupt movements when sudden slippage produces an earthquake. Faults are locked because the confining pressure exerted by the overlying crust is enormous, causing these fractures in the crust to be "squeezed shut."

Faults do not slip at all once. The initial slip begins at the hypocenter and propagates (travels) along the fault surface, at 2 to 4 kilometers per second—faster than a rifle shot (FIGURE 6). The propagation of the rupture zone along a 300-kilometer-long fault, for example, takes about 1.5 minutes, as compared to about 30 seconds for a 100-kilometer-long fault. Slippage on one section of the fault adds stress to the adjacent segment that may also slip. As this zone of slippage advances, it can slow down, speed up, or even jump to a nearby fault segment. Earthquake waves are generated at every point along the fault as that portion of the fault begins to slip.

Although a rupture can propagate in both horizontal directions from the hypocenter, it often travels mainly in one direction. For example, during the 1906 San Francisco earthquake, the rupture began near the southern end of the 477-kilometer (296-mile) rupture zone of the San Andreas Fault and traveled mainly northward. In contrast, the Fort Tejon earthquake began at the northern end of the rupture zone, and the zone of slippage propagated southward.

Moderate earthquakes result from slippage along relatively small faults or small segments of large faults. The amount of displacement on the fault surface, called **fault slip**, is typically no more than a few meters. By contrast, during the largest earthquakes, fault slips of 50 meters (160 feet) have been observed. The maximum displacement during the 2011 earthquake in Japan is estimated to have exceeded 40 meters (130 feet), one of the largest yet measured. In addition, the fault surface that ruptures during a large quake can exceed 1000 kilometers (620 miles) in length. Therefore, the ground shaking produced by large earthquakes is not only stronger but also lasts

FIGURE 6 Fault propagation

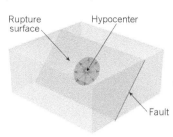

During an earthquake the initial slippage begins at the hypocenter.

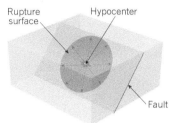

The rupture surface propagates (travels) along the fault surface, at a rate of 2 to 3 kilometers per second.

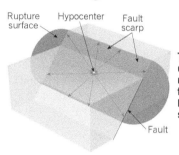

The rupture surface continues to grow until it reaches a section of the fault where the rocks have not been sufficiently strained to rupture.

longer than the vibrations produced by slippage along small fault segments.

Why do earthquake ruptures stop rather than continue along the entire fault? Evidence suggests that slippage usually stops when the rupture reaches a section of the fault where the rocks have not been sufficiently strained to overcome frictional resistance, such as in a section of the fault that has recently experienced an earthquake. The rupture may also stop if it encounters a large kink, or an offset along the fault surface.

---

2 CONCEPT CHECKS

1. What type of fault tends to produce the most destructive earthquakes?
2. During an earthquake the entire length of a fault slips in a single event that lasts less than 1 second. True or false?
3. Defend or rebut this statement: Faults that do not experience fault creep may be considered safe.

3 Seismology: The Study of Earthquake Waves

The study of earthquake waves, **seismology**, dates back to attempts made in China almost 2000 years ago to determine the direction from which these waves originated. The earliest known instrument, invented by Zhang Heng, was a large hollow jar that contained a weight suspended from the top (FIGURE 7). The suspended weight (similar to a clock pendulum) was connected to the jaws of several large dragon figurines that encircled the container. The jaws of each dragon held a metal ball. When earthquake waves reached the instrument, the relative motion between the suspended mass and the jar would dislodge some of the metal balls into the waiting mouths of frogs directly below.

FIGURE 7 Ancient Chinese seismograph During an Earth tremor, the dragons located in the direction of the main vibrations would drop a ball into the mouth of a frog below. (Photo by James E. Patterson Collection)

Zhang Heng likely understood that the first strong ground motion from an earthquake is directional, and when it is strong enough, all poorly supported items will topple over in the same direction. He used this fact, in addition to the position of the dislodged balls, to detect the direction of an earthquake's source.

Instruments That Record Earthquakes

In principle, modern **seismographs**, or **seismometers**, are similar to the instruments used by early Chinese researchers. A seismograph has a weight freely suspended from a support that is securely attached to bedrock (FIGURE 8). When vibrations from an earthquake reach the instrument, the **inertia** of the weight keeps it relatively stationary, while Earth and the support move. Inertia can be simply described by this statement: Objects at rest tend to stay at rest, and objects in motion tend to remain in motion unless either is acted upon by an outside force.

You probably have experienced inertia when you have tried to stop your automobile quickly and your body has continued to move forward.

Earthquakes cause both vertical and horizontal ground motion; therefore, more than one type of seismograph is needed to accurately describe the intensity of shaking. The instrument shown in Figure 8 detects horizontal ground motion, while vertical ground motion is detected if the weight is suspended from a spring, as shown in FIGURE 9.

To detect very weak earthquakes or a great earthquake that has occurred in another part of the world, most seismographs are designed to amplify ground motion. In earthquake-prone areas, the instruments used can withstand the violent shaking that can occur near the epicenter.

Seismic Waves

The records obtained from seismographs, called **seismograms**, provide useful information about the nature of seismic waves. Seismograms reveal that two main types of seismic waves are generated by the slippage of a rock mass. One of these wave types, called **surface waves**, travels in the rock layers just below Earth's surface (FIGURE 10). The other wave types travel through Earth's interior and are called body waves.

Body Waves Body waves are further divided into two types—called **primary**, or **P, waves** and **secondary**, or **S, waves**—and are identified by their mode of travel through intervening materials. P waves are "push/pull" waves; they momentarily push (compress) and pull (stretch) rocks in the direction the wave is traveling (FIGURE 11A). This wave motion is similar to that generated

FIGURE 8 Principle of the seismograph The inertia of the suspended weight tends to keep it motionless while the recording drum, which is anchored to bedrock, vibrates in response to seismic waves. The stationary weight provides a reference point from which to measure the amount of displacement occurring as a seismic wave passes through the ground. (Photo courtesy of Zephyr/Photo Researchers, Inc.)

Bedrock

Wire

Pivot

Seismograph recording earthquake tremors

Suspended weight

Support

Horizontal ground motion

Rotating drum

Bedrock

A.

B.

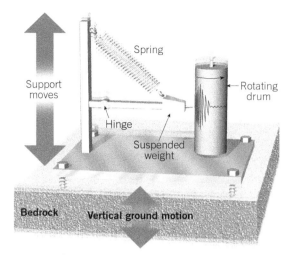

FIGURE 9 Seismograph designed to record vertical ground motion

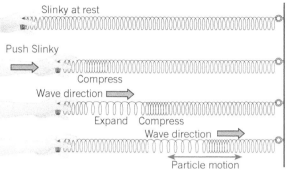

A. As illustrated by a toy Slinky, P waves alternately compress and expand the material through which they pass.

Slinky at rest

Push Slinky

Compress

Wave direction

Expand   Compress

Wave direction

Particle motion

B. S waves cause material to oscillate at right angles to the direction of wave motion.

Rope at rest

Shake rope

Wave direction   Particle motion

Wave direction   Particle motion

FIGURE 11 The characteristic motion of P waves and S waves During a strong earthquake, ground shaking consists of a combination of various kinds of seismic waves.

by human vocal cords as they move air back and forth to create sound. Solids, liquids, and gases resist stresses that change their volume when compressed and, therefore, elastically spring back once the stress is removed. Therefore, P waves can travel through all these materials.

By contrast, S waves "shake" the particles at right angles to their direction of travel. This can be illustrated by fastening one end of a rope and shaking the other end, as shown in FIGURE 11B. Unlike P waves, which temporarily change the *volume* of intervening material by alternately squeezing and stretching it, S waves change the *shape* of the material that transmits them. Because fluids (gases and liquids) do not resist stresses that cause changes in shape—meaning fluids do not return to their original shape once the stress is removed—liquids and gases will not transmit S waves.

Epicenter

P waves
S waves

Surface waves

P waves
S waves

S waves   P waves

Core

Mantle

Seismograph #1

P waves | S waves | Surface waves
1 minute

Seismograph #2

P waves | S waves | Surface waves
1 minute

Seismograph #3

P waves | S waves and surface waves have not yet arrived
1 minute

SMARTFIGURE 10 Body waves (P and S waves) versus surface waves
P and S waves travel through Earth's interior, while surface waves travel in the layer directly below the surface. P waves are the first to arrive at a seismic station, followed by S waves, and then surface waves.

FIGURE 12 Two types of surface waves

One type of surface wave travels along Earth's surface similar to rolling ocean waves. The red arrows show the movement of rock as the wave passes.

Wave motion

Wave direction

A second type of surface wave moves the ground from side to side and can be particularly damaging to building foundations.

Side-by-side motion

Wave direction

Surface Waves There are two types of surface waves. One type causes Earth's surface and anything resting upon it to move, much like ocean swells toss a ship (FIGURE 12A). The second type of surface wave causes Earth's materials to move side to side. This latter motion is particularly damaging to the foundations of structures (FIGURE 12B).

Body Waves Versus Surface Waves By examining the seismic record shown in FIGURE 13, you can

see that the major difference among seismic waves is their speed of travel. P waves are the first to arrive at a recording station, then S waves, and finally surface waves. Generally, in any solid Earth material, P waves travel about 1.7 times faster than S waves, and S waves are roughly 10 percent faster than surface waves.

In addition to velocity differences, notice in Figure 13 that the height, or *amplitude*, of these wave types also varies. S waves have slightly greater amplitudes than P waves, and surface waves exhibit even greater amplitudes. Surface waves also retain their maximum amplitude longer than P and S waves. As a result, surface waves tend to cause greater ground shaking and, hence, greater property damage, than either P or S waves.

FIGURE 13 Typical seismogram

Note the time interval (about 5 minutes) between the arrival of the first P wave and the arrival of the first S wave.

Surface waves

First P wave

First S wave

1 minute

(Earlier)   T I M E   (Later)

---

3 CONCEPT CHECKS

1. Describe the principle of a seismograph.
2. List the major differences between P, S, and surface waves.
3. Which type of seismic waves tend to cause the greatest destruction to buildings?

Finding the Epicenter of an Earthquake

The difference in the velocities of P and S waves provides a method for locating the epicenter of an earthquake. Since P waves travel faster than S waves, the further the epicenter is from the recording instrument, the greater the difference in the arrival times of the first P wave compared to the first S wave.

THREE SEISMOGRAMS

Seismogram A – New York, NY

1 minute

FIRST P WAVE   FIRST S WAVE

Seismogram B – Nome, Alaska

FIRST P WAVE   FIRST S WAVE

Seismogram C – Mexico City, Mexico

FIRST P WAVE   FIRST S WAVE

Thony Belizaire/AFP/Getty Images

STEP 1

Using the seismogram on the left for a seismic recording station in New York, determine the time difference between the arrival of the first P wave and the arrival of the first S wave. In this example, the P-S time interval is 5 minutes.

STEP 2

Find the place on the travel-time graph where the vertical separation between the P and S curves is equal to the P-S interval determined in Step 1.

STEP 3

From this position, draw a vertical line that extends to the bottom of the graph and read the distance to the epicenter. The distance from our seismograph in New York to the earthquake epicenter is 2300 miles.

STEP 4

To find an earthquake epicenter, seismograms from three different stations are needed in order to "triangulate the location." Therefore, you need to determine the distance that two other seismic stations (Nome, Alaska, and Mexico City, Mexico) are from the epicenter, using the procedure described above. Using a compass, draw a circle around each seismograph with a radius equal to its distance from the epicenter. The point where all three circles intersect is the approximate location of the earthquake epicenter.

Building destroyed by 2010 earthquake, Port-au-Prince, Haiti

TRAVEL-TIME GRAPH

Distance from epicenter in kilometers

1000   2000   3000   4000   5000   6000

Time in minutes since earthquake

S-WAVE CURVE

P-WAVE CURVE

1000   2000   3000

Distance from epicenter in miles

Nome

2750 miles

New York

2300 miles

1800 miles   Mexico City

0   1000   2000   3000 MILES
0   1000   2000   3000   4000   5000 KILOMETERS

4 Determining the Size of Earthquakes

Seismologists use a variety of methods to determine two fundamentally different measures that describe the size of an earthquake—*intensity* and *magnitude*. The first of these to be used was **intensity**—a measure of the amount of ground shaking at a particular location, based on observed property damage. Later, with the development of seismographs, it became possible to measure ground motion using instruments. This quantitative measurement, called **magnitude**, relies on data gleaned from seismic records to estimate the amount of energy released at an earthquake's source.

Intensity and magnitude provide useful, though different, information about earthquake strength. Consequently, both measures are used to describe earthquake severity.

Intensity Scales

Until the mid-1800s, historical records provided the only accounts of the severity of earthquake shaking and destruction. Perhaps the first attempt to scientifically describe the aftermath of an earthquake came following the great Italian earthquake of 1857. By systematically mapping effects of the earthquake, a measure of the intensity of ground shaking was established. The map generated by this study used lines to connect places of equal damage and hence equal ground shaking. Using this technique, zones of intensity were identified, with the zone of highest intensity located near the center of maximum ground shaking and often (but not always) the earthquake epicenter.

In 1902, Giuseppe Mercalli developed a more reliable intensity scale, which in a modified form is still used today. The **Modified Mercalli Intensity scale**, shown in TABLE 1, was developed using California buildings as its standard. For example, on the 12-point Mercalli intensity scale, if some well-built wood structures and most masonry buildings were destroyed by an earthquake, the affected area would be assigned a Roman numeral X (ten). FIGURE 14 shows the zone of destruction for the 1989 Loma Prieta earthquake, where the intensity of ground shaking was based on the Modified Mercalli Intensity scale.

More recently, the U.S. Geological Survey has developed a webpage called "Did You Feel It," where Internet users enter their zip code and answer questions such as "Did objects fall off shelves?" Within a few hours, a Community Internet Intensity Map, like the one in FIGURE 15 for the 2011 central Virginia earthquake, is generated. Shaking was reported from Maine to Florida, an area occupied by one-third of the U.S. population. Several national landmarks, including the Washington Monument and the Washington National Cathedral located about 130 kilometers (80 miles) away, were damaged. Because the crustal rocks east of the Rocky Mountains are cool and strong, earthquakes are felt over a much larger area than those of similar magnitudes in the west (Figure 15).

TABLE 1	Modified Mercalli Intensity Scale
I	Not felt except by a very few under especially favorable circumstances.
II	Felt only by a few persons at rest, especially on upper floors of buildings.
III	Felt quite noticeably indoors, especially on upper floors of buildings, but many people do not recognize that an earthquake is occurring.
IV	During the day felt indoors by many, outdoors by few. Sensation like a heavy truck striking a building.
V	Felt by nearly everyone, many awakened. Disturbances of trees, poles, and other tall objects sometimes noticed.
VI	Felt by all; many frightened and run outdoors. Some heavy furniture moved; few instances of fallen plaster or damaged chimneys. Damage slight.
VII	Everybody runs outdoors. Damage negligible in buildings of good design and construction; slight to moderate in well-built ordinary structures; considerable in poorly built or badly designed structures.
VIII	Damage slight in specially designed structures; considerable in ordinary substantial buildings with partial collapse; great in poorly built structures. (Fall of chimneys, factory stacks, columns, monuments, walls.)
IX	Damage considerable in specially designed structures. Buildings shifted off foundations. Ground cracked conspicuously.
X	Some well-built wooden structures destroyed. Most masonry and frame structures destroyed. Ground badly cracked.
XI	Few, if any, (masonry) structures remain standing. Bridges destroyed. Broad fissures in ground.
XII	Damage total. Waves seen on ground surfaces. Objects thrown upward into air.

Seismic intensity map, Loma Prieta, 1989
Intensity levels are based on the Modified Mercalli Intensity
Scale, which uses Roman numerals to represent the intensity
categories. The zone of maximum intensity during this event
roughly corresponded to the epicenter, but this is not always the
case.

Magnitude Scales

To more accurately compare earthquakes around the
globe, scientists searched for a way to describe the
energy released by earthquakes that did not rely on
factors, such as building practices, that vary considerably from one part of the world to another. As a consequence, several magnitude scales were developed.

Richter Magnitude In 1935 Charles Richter of
the California Institute of Technology developed
the first magnitude scale to use seismic records. As
shown in FIGURE 16 (top), the **Richter scale** is calculated by measuring the amplitude of the largest seismic wave (usually an S, or surface, wave) recorded on
a seismogram. Because seismic waves weaken as the
distance between the hypocenter and the seismograph
increases, Richter developed a method that accounts for
the decrease in wave amplitude with increasing distance.
Theoretically, as long as equivalent instruments are used,
monitoring stations at different locations will obtain the
same Richter magnitude for each recorded earthquake.
In practice, however, different recording stations

often obtain slightly different magnitudes for the same
earthquake—a consequence of the variations in rock
types through which the waves travel.

Earthquakes vary enormously in strength, and great
earthquakes produce wave amplitudes that are thousands
of times larger than those generated by weak tremors. To
accommodate this wide variation, Richter used a *logarithmic scale* to express magnitude, in which a *tenfold*
increase in wave amplitude corresponds to an increase of
1 on the magnitude scale. Thus, the intensity of ground
shaking for a 5-magnitude earthquake is 10 times greater
than that produced by an earthquake having a Richter
magnitude of 4 (FIGURE 17).

In addition, each unit of increase in Richter magnitude equates to roughly a *32-fold increase in the energy
released*. Thus, an earthquake with a magnitude of 6.5
releases 32 times more energy than one with a magnitude
of 5.5 and roughly 1000 times (32×32) more energy than
a 4.5-magnitude quake. A major earthquake with a magnitude of 8.5 releases millions of times more energy than the
smallest earthquakes felt by humans (FIGURE 18).

Although the Richter scale has no theoretical upper
limit, the largest magnitude ever recorded was 8.9. Great
shocks such as these release an amount of energy that is
roughly equivalent to the detonation of 1 billion tons of explosives. Conversely, earthquakes with a Richter magnitude
of less than 2.0 are generally not felt by humans. Richter

**The green dots on the national map show locations of
people who reported feeling earthquakes of similar
magnitude, one that occurred in California versus one
that occurred in Virginia. The difference is
attributable to the rigidity of the bedrock.**

Key for USGS Community Internet Intensity Map

INTENSITY	I	II–III	IV	V	VI	VII	VIII	IX	X
SHAKING	Not felt	Weak	Light	Moderate	Strong	Very strong	Severe	Violent	Extreme
DAMAGE	none	none	none	Very light	Light	Moderate	Moderate/Heavy	Heavy	Very Heavy

SMARTFIGURE 15 USGS Community Internet Intensity Map
Maps like this one are prepared using data collected over the Internet from people responding to questions such as "Did objects fall off
shelves?"

FIGURE 16 Determining the Richter magnitude of an earthquake

1. Meaure the height (amplitude) of the largest wave on the seismogram (23 mm) and plot it on the amplitude scale (right).

2. Determine the distance to the earthquake using the time interval separating the arrival of the first P wave and the arrival of the first S wave (24 seconds) and plot it on the distance scale (left).

3. Draw a line connecting the two plots and read the Richter magnitude (M$_L$ 5) from the magnitude scale (center).

Magnitude vs. Ground Motion and Energy

Magnitude Change	Ground Motion Change (amplitude)	Energy Change (approximate)
4.0	10,000 times	1,000,000 times
3.0	1000 times	32,000 times
2.0	100 times	1000 times
1.0	10.0 times	32 times
0.5	3.2 times	5.5 times
0.1	1.3 times	1.4 times

FIGURE 17 Magnitude versus ground motion and energy released
An earthquake that is one magnitude stronger than another (M 6 versus M 5) produces seismic waves that have a maximum amplitude 10 times greater, and they release about 32 times more energy than the waves of the weaker quake.

Moment Magnitude For measuring medium and large earthquakes, seismologists have come to favor a newer scale called **moment magnitude** (M$_W$), which measures the total energy released during an earthquake. Moment magnitude is calculated by determining the average amount of slip on the fault, the area of the fault surface that slipped, and the strength of the faulted rock.

Moment magnitude can also be calculated by modeling data obtained from seismograms. The results are converted to a magnitude number, as in other magnitude scales. In addition, as in the Richter scale, each unit increase in moment magnitude equates to roughly a 32-fold increase in the energy released.

Because moment magnitude estimates the total energy released, it is better for measuring very large earthquakes. In light of this, seismologists have recalculated the magnitudes of older, strong earthquakes using the moment magnitude scale. For example, the 1964 Alaskan earthquake, which was originally given a Richter magnitude of 8.3, has since been recalculated using the moment magnitude scale, resulting in an upgrade to 9.2. Conversely, the 1906 San Francisco earthquake that was given a Richter magnitude of 8.3, was downgraded to a M$_W$ 7.9. The strongest earthquake on record is the 1960 Chilean subduction zone earthquake, with a moment magnitude of 9.5.

magnitude was designed to classify earthquakes in southern California, near the California Institute of Technology (local), where Richter worked, and is designated by the symbol (M$_L$)—where M is for *magnitude* and L is for *local*.

The convenience of describing the size of an earthquake by a single number that can be calculated quickly from seismograms makes the Richter scale a powerful tool. Seismologists have since modified Richter's work and developed other Richter-like magnitude scales.

Despite its usefulness, the Richter scale is not adequate for describing very large earthquakes. For example, the 1906 San Francisco earthquake and the 1964 Alaskan earthquake have roughly the same Richter magnitudes. However, based on the relative size of the affected areas and the associated tectonic changes, the Alaskan earthquake released considerably more energy than the San Francisco quake. Thus, the Richter scale is considered *saturated* for major earthquakes because it cannot distinguish among them. Despite this shortcoming, Richter-like scales are still used because they can be calculated quickly.

4 CONCEPT CHECKS

1. What does the Modified Mercalli Intensity scale tell us about an earthquake?
2. What information is used to establish the lower numbers on the Mercalli scale?
3. How much more energy does a magnitude 7.0 earthquake release than a 6.0 earthquake?
4. Why is the moment magnitude scale favored over the Richter scale?

Frequency and Energy Released by Earthquakes of Different Magnitudes

Magnitude (Mw)	Average Per Year	Description	Examples	Energy Release (equivalent kilograms of explosive)
9	<1	**Largest recorded earthquakes–** destruction over vast area massive loss of life possible	Chile, 1960 (M 9.5); Alaska, 1964 (M 9.0); Japan, 2011 (M 9.0)	56,000,000,000,000
8	1	**Great earthquakes–** severe economic impact large loss of life	Sumatra, 2006 (M 8.6); Mexico City, 1980 (M 8.1)	1,800,000,000,000
7	15	**Major earthquakes–** damage ($ billions) loss of life	New Madrid, Missouri 1812 (M 7.7); Turkey, 1999 (M 7.6); Charleston, South Carolina, 1886 (M 7.3)	56,000,000,000
6	134	**Strong earthquakes–** can be destructive in populated areas	Kobe, Japan, 1995 (M 6.9); Loma Prieta, California, 1989 (M 6.9); Northridge, California, 1994 (M 6.7)	1,800,000,000
5	1319	**Moderate earthquakes–** property damage to poorly constructive buildings	Mineral, Virginia, 2011 (M 5.8); Northern New York, 1994 (M 5.8); East of Oklahoma City, Oklahoma, 2011 (M5.6)	56,000,000
4	13,000	**Light earthquakes–** noticable shaking of items indoors, some property damage	Western Minnesota, 1975 (M 4.6); Arkansas, 2011 (M 4.7)	1,800,000
3	130,000	**Minor earthquakes–** felt by humans, very light property damage, if any	New Jersey, 2009 (M3.0) Maine, 2006 (M3.8)	56,000
2	1,300,000	**Very minor earthquakes–** felt by humans, no property damage		1,800
	Unknown	Generally not felt by humans, but may be recorded		56

Data from USGS

FIGURE 18 Annual occurrence of earthquakes with various magnitudes (Data from U.S. Geological Survey)

EYE on Earth

The Calaveras Fault, a branch of the San Andreas Fault system, cuts directly through the town of Hollister, California. Rather than being "locked," this section of the fault is slowly slipping, producing noticeable offsets and damage to curbs, sidewalks, roads, and buildings. The concrete wall and sidewalk shown here were straight when they were originally constructed.

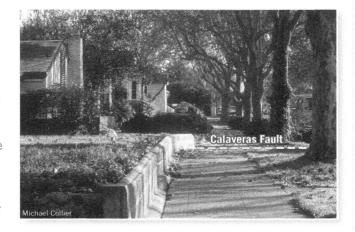

Question 1 What term is used to describe the phenomenon observed in Hollister along the Calaveras Fault?

Question 2 Are faults that exhibit this type of slippage considered likely to generate a major earthquake? Explain.

Question 3 Based on this image, does this strike-slip fault exhibit right-lateral or left-lateral motion?

Historic Earthquakes East of the Rockies

Large earthquakes are relatively uncommon in the middle of continents, far from the places where plates collide or grind past one another, or where one plate slides beneath another. Nevertheless, several damaging earthquakes have occurred in the central and eastern United States since colonial times.

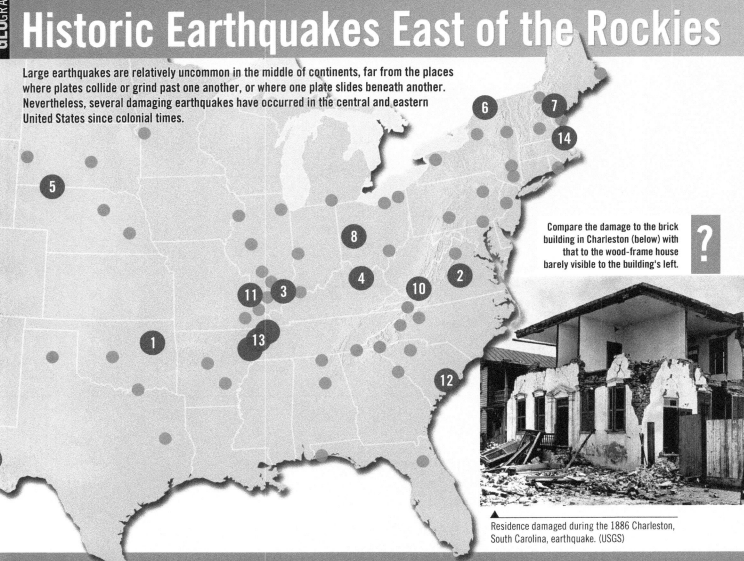

Compare the damage to the brick building in Charleston (below) with that to the wood-frame house barely visible to the building's left.

Residence damaged during the 1886 Charleston, South Carolina, earthquake. (USGS)

LOCATION	DATE	INTENSITY	MAGNITUDE*	COMMENTS
1 East of Oklahoma City	2011	VII	5.6	Fourteen homes destroyed
2 Mineral, Virginia	2011	VII	5.8	Felt by many due to its proximity to large population centers
3 Southeastern Illinois	2008	VII	5.4	Occurred along the Wabash Valley Seismic Zone
4 Northeast Kentucky	1980	VII	5.2	Largest earthquake ever recorded in Kentucky
5 Merriman, Nebraska	1964	VII	5.1	Largest earthquake ever recorded in Nebraska
6 Northern New York	1944	VIII	5.8	Left several structures unsafe for occupancy
7 Ossipee Lake, New Hampshire	1947	VII	5.5	Two earthquakes occurred four days apart
8 Western Ohio	1937	VIII	5.4	Extensive damage to chimneys and plaster walls
9 Valentine, Texas	1931	VIII	5.8	Brick buildings were severely damaged
10 Giles County, Virginia	1897	VIII	5.9	Changed the flow of natural springs
11 Charleston, Missouri	1895	VIII	6.6	Structural damage and liquefaction reported
12 Charleston, South Carolina	1886	X	7.3	Caused 60 deaths, destroyed many buildings
13 New Madrid, Missouri	1811-1812	X	7.7	Three strong earthquakes occurred in remote areas
14 Cape Ann, Massachusetts	1755	VIII	?	Chimneys leveled and brick buildings damaged in Boston

Source: U.S. Geological Survey
*Intensity and magnitudes have been estimated for many of these events.

New Madrid Seismic Zone

Three large earthquakes that were centered near the Mississippi River Valley in southeastern Missouri occurred on December 16, 1811, January 23, 1812, and February 7, 1812. Having estimated magnitudes of 7.7, 7.5, and 7.7, these earthquakes and numerous smaller aftershocks destroyed the town of New Madrid, Missouri. These quakes also triggered massive landslides, inflicted damage in the surrounding states of Illinois, Indiana, Kentucky, Arkansas, and Tennessee and were felt over the entire Midwest because of the rigid bedrock that underlies that region. Chimneys collapsed as far away as Cincinnati, Ohio. Destruction of property from the New Madrid earthquakes was minimal, primarily because the Midwest was sparsely populated in the early 1800s. Memphis, Tennessee, located near the epicenter, had not yet been established, and St. Louis, Missouri, was a small frontier town. Today, these metropolitan areas each have populations that exceed one million residents.

Eric Foltz/Getty Images

Reelfoot Lake, Tennessee, located about 14 miles south of New Madrid, formed in an area of subsidence that was produced during the February 7, 1812, event. Subsidence that exceeded 6 meters (20 feet) in some places occurred on the down-dropped side of the Reelfoot Fault.

The largest historical earthquake in the eastern United States occurred in Charleston, South Carolina, in 1886. This one-minute event resulted in 60 deaths, numerous injuries, and great economic loss within 200 kilometers (120 miles) of Charleston. Minutes after the quake, strong vibrations shook the upper floors of buildings in Chicago, Illinois, and St. Louis, Missouri, causing people to rush outdoors. In Charleston, more than one hundred buildings were destroyed, and 90 percent of the remaining structures were damaged.

5 Earthquake Destruction

The most violent earthquake ever recorded in North America—the Alaskan earthquake—occurred at 5:36 P.M. on March 27, 1964. Felt over most of the state, the earthquake had a moment magnitude (M_W) of 9.2 and lasted 3 to 4 minutes. This event left 128 people dead and thousands homeless, and it badly disrupted the economy of the state. Within 24 hours of the initial shock, 28 aftershocks were recorded, 10 of them exceeding a magnitude of 6. The location of the epicenter and the towns hardest hit by the quake are shown in FIGURE 19.

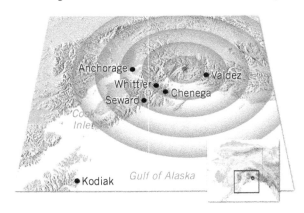

FIGURE 19 Region most affected by the Alaskan earthquake, 1964

Many factors determine the degree of destruction that will accompany an earthquake. The most obvious is *the magnitude of the earthquake and its proximity to a populated area.* During an earthquake, the region within 20 to 50 kilometers (12 to 30 miles) of the epicenter tends to experience roughly the same degree of ground shaking, and beyond this limit, vibrations usually diminish rapidly. Earthquakes that occur in the stable continental interior, such as the New Madrid earthquake of 1811–1812, are generally felt more over a much larger area than those in earthquake-prone areas such as California.

Destruction from Seismic Vibrations

The 1964 Alaskan earthquake provided geologists with insights into the role of ground shaking as a destructive force. As the energy released by an earthquake travels along Earth's surface, it causes the ground to vibrate in a complex manner by involving up-and-down as well side-to-side motion. The amount of damage to human-made structures attributable to the vibrations depends on several factors, including (1) *the intensity* and (2) *the duration of the vibrations,* (3) *the nature of the material upon which structures rest,* and (4) *the nature of building materials and construction practices of the region.*

All of the multi-story structures in Anchorage were damaged by the vibrations. The more flexible wood-frame residential buildings fared best. A striking example of how construction variations affect earthquake damage is shown in FIGURE 20. You can see that the steel-frame building on the left withstood the vibrations, whereas the poorly designed JCPenney building was badly damaged. Engineers have learned that buildings built of blocks and bricks that are not reinforced with steel rods are the most serious safety threats in earthquakes. Unfortunately, most of the structures in the developing world are constructed of unreinforced concrete slabs and bricks made of dried mud—a primary reason the death toll in poor countries such as Haiti is usually higher than for earthquakes of similar size in the United States.

The 1964 Alaskan earthquake damaged most large structures in Anchorage, even though they were built according to the earthquake provisions of the Uniform Building Code. Perhaps some of that destruction can be attributed to the unusually long duration of the earthquake. Most quakes involve tremors that last less than a minute. For example, the 1994 Northridge earthquake was felt for about 40 seconds, and the strong vibrations of the 1989 Loma Prieta earthquake lasted less than 15 seconds. But the Alaska quake reverberated for 3 to 4 minutes.

FIGURE 20 Comparing damage to structures The extensively damaged five-story JCPenney building, Anchorage, Alaska. Very little structural damage was incurred by the adjacent building. (Courtesy of NOAA/Seattle)

FIGURE 21 Ground failure caused the street to collapse (Photo by USGS)

FIGURE 22 Liquefaction These "mud volcanoes" were produced by the Loma Prieta earthquake of 1989. They formed when geysers of sand and water shot from the ground, an indication that liquefaction occurred. (Photo by Richard Hilton)

Amplification of Seismic Waves

Although the region near the epicenter experiences about the same intensity of ground shaking, destruction may vary considerably within this area. These differences are usually attributable to the nature of the ground on which the structures are built. Soft sediments, for example, generally amplify the vibrations more than solid bedrock. Thus, the buildings in Anchorage that were situated on unconsolidated sediments experienced heavy structural damage (FIGURE 21). In contrast, most of the town of Whittier, although much nearer the epicenter, rested on a firm foundation of solid bedrock and suffered much less damage from seismic vibrations.

Liquefaction

The intense shaking of an earthquake can cause loosely packed water-logged materials, such as sandy stream deposits or fill, to be transformed into a substance that acts like fluids (FIGURE 22). The phenomenon of transforming a somewhat stable soil into mobile material capable of rising toward Earth's surface is known as **liquefaction**. When liquefaction occurs, the ground may not be capable of supporting buildings, and underground storage tanks and sewer lines may literally float toward the surface (FIGURE 23). During the 1989 Loma Prieta earthquake, in San Francisco's Marina District, foundations failed, and geysers of sand and water shot from the ground, evidence that liquefaction had occurred (Figure 22). Liquefaction also contributed to the damage inflicted on San Francisco's water system during the 1906 earthquake. During the 2011 Japan earthquake, liquefaction caused entire buildings to sink several feet.

Seiches

The effects of great earthquakes may be felt thousands of kilometers from their source. Ground motion may generate *seiches*, the rhythmic sloshing of water in lakes, reservoirs, and enclosed basins such as the Gulf of Mexico. The 1964 Alaskan earthquake, for example, generated 2-meter waves off the coast of Texas, and dam-

A. Before earthquake:
Loose, saturated, sandy material

B. During earthquake:
Water and upper sandy layer mobilize

C. After earthquake:
Sandy material becomes more tightly packed

aged small craft, while much smaller waves were noticed in swimming pools in both Texas and Louisiana.

Seiches can be particularly dangerous when they occur in reservoirs retained by earthen dams. These waves have been known to slosh over reservoir walls and weaken the structures, thereby endangering property as well as the lives of those downstream.

FIGURE 23 Effects of liquefaction (Photo by James L. Beck)

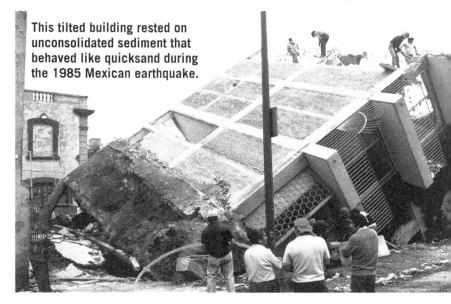

This tilted building rested on unconsolidated sediment that behaved like quicksand during the 1985 Mexican earthquake.

399

Landslides and Ground Subsidence

The greatest earthquake-related damage to structures is often caused by landslides and ground subsidence triggered by earthquake vibrations. This was the case during the 1964 Alaskan earthquake in Valdez and Seward, where the violent shaking caused coastal sediments to slump, carrying both waterfronts away. In Valdez, 31 people died when a dock slid into the sea. Because of the threat of recurrence, the entire town of Valdez was relocated to more stable ground about 7 kilometers away.

Much of the damage in Anchorage was attributed to landslides. Homes were destroyed in Turnagain Heights when a layer of clay lost its strength and over 200 acres of land slid toward the ocean (FIGURE 24). A portion of this spectacular landslide was left in its natural condition, as a reminder of this destructive event. The site was appropriately named "Earthquake Park." Downtown Anchorage was also disrupted as sections of the main business district dropped by as much as 3 meters (see Figure 21).

SMARTFIGURE 24
Turnagain Heights slide caused by the 1964 Alaskan Earthquake
(Photo courtesy of the U.S. Geological Survey)

Vibrations from the Alaskan earthquake caused cracks to appear near the edge of the Turnagain Heights bluff.

Blocks of land began to slide toward the sea on a weak layer called the Botlegger Cove clay and in less than 5 minutes, as much as 200 meters of the Turnagain Heights bluff area had been destroyed.

Photo of a small area of destruction caused by the Turnagain Heights slide.

Fire

More than 100 years ago, San Francisco was the economic center of the western United States, largely because of gold and silver mining. Then, at dawn on April 18, 1906, a violent earthquake struck, triggering an enormous firestorm (see Figure 2). Much of the city was reduced to ashes and ruins. It is estimated that 3000 people died and more than half of the city's 400,000 residents were left homeless.

The historic San Francisco earthquake reminds us of the formidable threat of fire, which started when gas and electrical lines were severed. The initial ground shaking broke the city's water lines into hundreds of disconnected pieces, which made controlling the fires virtually impossible. The fires, which raged out of control for 3 days, were finally contained when buildings were dynamited along a wide boulevard to provide a fire break, similar to the strategy used in fighting forest fires.

While few deaths were attributed to the San Francisco fires, other earthquake-initiated fires have been more destructive and have claimed many more lives. For example, the 1923 earthquake in Japan triggered an estimated 250 fires, devastating the city of Yokohama and destroying more than half the homes in Tokyo. More than 100,000 deaths were attributed to the fires, which were driven by unusually high winds.

What Is a Tsunami?

Major undersea earthquakes occasionally set in motion a series of large ocean waves that are known by the Japanese name **tsunami** (which means "harbor wave"). Most tsunamis are generated by displacement along a megathrust fault that suddenly lifts a large slab of seafloor (FIGURE 25). Once generated, a tsunami resembles a series of ripples formed when a pebble is dropped into a pond. In contrast to ripples, tsunamis advance across the ocean at amazing speeds, about 800 kilometers (500 miles) per hour—equivalent to the speed of a commercial airliner. Despite this striking characteristic, a tsunami in the open ocean can pass undetected because its height (amplitude) is usually less than 1 meter, and the distance separating wave crests ranges from 100 to 700 kilometers. However, upon entering shallow coastal waters, these destructive waves "feel bottom" and slow, causing the water to pile up (Figure 25). A few exceptional tsunamis have exceeded 30 meters (100 feet) in height. As the crest of a tsunami approaches the shore, it appears as a rapid rise in sea level with a turbulent and chaotic surface; it does not resemble a breaking wave (FIGURE 26).

The first warning of an approaching tsunami is often the rapid withdrawal of water from beaches, the result of the trough of the first large wave preceding the crest. Some inhabitants of the Pacific basin have learned to heed this warning and quickly move to higher ground.

FIGURE 25 Tsunami generated by displacement of the ocean floor
The speed of a wave correlates with ocean depth. Waves moving in deep water advance at speeds in excess of 800 kilometers (500 miles) per hour. Speed gradually slows to 50 kilometers (30 miles) per hour at depths of 20 meters (65 feet). As waves slow in shallow water, they grow in height until they rush onto shore with tremendous force. The size and spacing of these swells are not to scale.

FIGURE 26 Tsunami generated off the coast of Sumatra, 2004
(AFP/Getty Images, Inc.—Agence France Presse)

Japan Tsunami Because of Japan's location along the circum-Pacific belt and the subduction zone that parallels its coastline, it is especially vulnerable to tsunami destruction. The most powerful earthquake to strike Japan in the age of modern seismology was the 2011 Tōhoku earthquake (M_W 9.0). This historic event resulted in at least 15,861 deaths, more than 3000 people missing, and 6107 injured. Nearly 400,000 buildings, 56 bridges, and 26 railways were destroyed or damaged by the earthquake and devastating tsunami.

The majority of human casualties and damage was inflicted by a Pacific-wide tsunami that reached a maximum height of about 40 meters (130 feet) and traveled inland 10 kilometers (6 miles) in the Sendai region

FIGURE 27 2011 Japan tsunami
Devastation in Natori City.
(Photo by Mike Clark/AFP/Getty Images)

Approximately 5 to 30 minutes after the retreat of water, a surge capable of extending several kilometers inland occurs. In a successive fashion, each surge is followed by a rapid oceanward retreat of the sea. Therefore, people experiencing a tsunami should not return to the shore once the first surge of water retreats.

Tsunami Damage from the 2004 Indonesian Earthquake A massive undersea earthquake of M_W 9.1 occurred near the island of Sumatra on December 26, 2004, sending waves of water racing across the Indian Ocean and Bay of Bengal (Figure 26). It was one of the deadliest natural disasters of any kind in modern times, claiming more than 230,000 lives. As water surged several kilometers inland, cars and trucks were flung around like toys in a bathtub, and fishing boats were rammed into homes. In some locations, the backwash of water dragged bodies and huge amounts of debris out to sea.

The destruction was indiscriminate, destroying luxury resorts as well as poor fishing hamlets along the Indian Ocean. Damages were reported as far away as the coast of Somalia in Africa, 4100 kilometers (2500 miles) west of the earthquake epicenter.

(FIGURE 27). In addition, meltdowns occurred at three nuclear reactors in Japan's Fukushima Daiichi Nuclear Complex. Across the Pacific in California, Oregon, Peru, and Chile, a few people were killed and several houses, boats, and docks were destroyed. The tsunami was generated when a slab of seafloor located 60 kilometers off the east coast of Japan was suddenly "thrust up" an estimated 5 to 8 meters.

Tsunami Warning System   In 1946, a large tsunami struck the Hawaiian islands without warning. A wave more than 15 meters (50 feet) high left several coastal villages in shambles. This destruction motivated the U.S. Coast and Geodetic Survey to establish a tsunami warning system for coastal areas of the Pacific that today includes 26 countries. Seismic observatories throughout the region report large earthquakes to the Tsunami Warning Center in Honolulu. Scientists at the center use deep-sea buoys equipped with pressure sensors to detect energy released by an earthquake. In addition, tidal gauges measure the rise and fall in sea level that accompany tsunamis, and warnings are issued within an hour. Although tsunamis travel very rapidly, there is sufficient time to warn all except those in the areas nearest the epicenter. For example, a tsunami generated near the Aleutian Islands would take 5 hours to reach Hawaii, and one generated near the coast of Chile would travel 15 hours before reaching the shores of Hawaii (FIGURE 28).

FIGURE 28 Tsunami travel times
Travel times to Honolulu, Hawaii, from selected locations throughout the Pacific. (Data from NOAA)

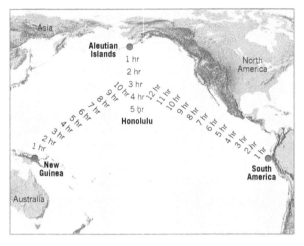

5 CONCEPT CHECKS

1. List four factors that affect the amount of destruction that seismic vibrations cause to human-made structures.
2. In addition to the destruction created directly by seismic vibrations, list three other types of destruction associated with earthquakes.
3. What is a *tsunami*? How are tsunamis generated?
4. List at least three reasons an earthquake with a magnitude of 7.0 might inflict more death and destruction than a quake with a magnitude of 8.0.

EYE on Earth

Water-saturated sandy soil provides students an opportunity to experience the phenomenon of liquefaction. Liquefaction may occur when ground shaking causes a layer of saturated material to lose strength and act like a fluid.

Question 1 Describe what you think would happen to a structure built on sandy soil that suddenly experienced liquefaction during an earthquake.

Question 2 How might a nearly empty underground storage tank be affected by liquefaction of the surrounding soil?

6 Earthquake Belts and Plate Boundaries

About 95 percent of the energy released by earthquakes originates in the few relatively narrow zones, shown in FIGURE 29. The zone of greatest seismic activity, called the *circum-Pacific belt*, encompasses the coastal regions of Chile, Central America, Indonesia, Japan, and Alaska, including the Aleutian Islands (Figure 29). Most earthquakes in the circum-Pacific belt occur along convergent plate boundaries where one plate slides at a low angle beneath another. The contacts between the subducting and overlying plates are *megathrust faults*, along which Earth's largest earthquakes are generated (FIGURE 30).

FIGURE 29 Earthquake belts Distribution of nearly 15,000 earthquakes with magnitudes equal to or greater than 5 for a 10-year period. (Data from U.S. Geological Survey)

There are more than 40,000 kilometers (25,000 miles) of subduction boundaries in the circum-Pacific belt where displacement is dominated by thrust faulting. Ruptures occasionally occur along segments that are nearly 1000 kilometers (600 miles) in length, generating catastrophic *megathrust earthquakes* with magnitudes of (M_W) 8 or greater.

Another major concentration of strong seismic activity, referred to as the *Alpine-Himalayan belt*, runs through the mountainous regions that flank the Mediterranean Sea and extends past the Himalayan Mountains (see Figure 29). Tectonic activity in this region is mainly attributed to collisions of the African plate with Eurasia and of the Indian plate with Southeast Asia. These plate interactions created many thrust and strike-slip faults that remain active. In addition, numerous faults located a considerable distance from these plate boundaries have been reactivated as India continues its northward advance into Asia. For example, slippage on a complex fault system in 2008 in the Sichuan Province of China killed at least 70,000 people and left 1.5 million others homeless. The "culprit" was the Indian subcontinent continually shoving the Tibetan Plateau eastward against the rocks of the Sichuan basin.

Figure 29 shows another continuous earthquake belt that extends for thousands of kilometers through the world's oceans. This zone coincides with the oceanic ridge system, which is an area of frequent but weak seismic activity. As tensional forces pull the plates apart during seafloor spreading, displacement along normal faults generates most of the earthquakes in this zone. The remaining seismic activity is associated with slippage along transform faults located between ridge segments.

Transform faults and smaller strike-slip faults also run through continental crust, where they may generate large earthquakes that tend to occur on a cyclical basis. Examples include California's San Andreas Fault, New Zealand's Alpine Fault, and Turkey's North Anatolian Fault, which produced a deadly earthquake in 1999.

FIGURE 30 Distribution of earthquakes of magnitude 7.5 or greater since 1900

Geologist's Sketch

6 CONCEPT CHECKS

1. Where does the greatest amount of seismic activity occur?
2. What type of plate boundary is associated with Earth's largest earthquakes?
3. Name another major concentration of strong earthquake activity.

7 Can Earthquakes Be Predicted?

The vibrations that shook the San Francisco area in 1989 caused 63 deaths, heavily damaged the Marina District, and caused the collapse of a double-decked section of I-880 in Oakland, California (FIGURE 31). This level of destruction was the result of an earthquake of moderate intensity (M_W 6.9). Seismologists warn that other earthquakes of comparable or greater strength can be expected along the San Andreas system, which cuts a nearly 1300-kilometer (800-mile) path through the western third of the state. An obvious question is: Can these earthquakes be predicted?

Short-Range Predictions

The goal of short-range earthquake prediction is to provide a warning of the location and magnitude of a large earthquake within a narrow time frame (TABLE 2). Substantial efforts to achieve this objective have been attempted in Japan, the United States, China, and Russia—countries where earthquake risks are high. This research has concentrated on monitoring possible *precursors*—events or changes that precede a forth-coming earthquake and thus may provide warning. In California, for example, seismologists monitor changes in ground elevation and variations in strain levels near active faults. Other researchers measure changes in groundwater levels, while still others try to predict earthquakes based on an increase in the frequency of fore-shocks that precede some, but not all, earthquakes.

Japanese and Chinese scientists have been known to monitor anomalous animal behavior. A few days before the May 12, 2008, earthquake in China's Sichuan Province,

the streets of a village near the fault were filled with toads migrating from the mountains. Was this a warning? Perhaps. Walter Mooney, a USGS seismologist, put it best: "Everyone hopes that animals can tell us something we don't know. . . . but animal behavior is way too unreliable." Although precursors may exist, we have yet to determine effective ways to interpret and utilize the information.

One claim of a successful short-range prediction, based on an increase in foreshocks, was made by the Chinese government after the February 4, 1975, earth-quake in Liaoning Province. According to reports, very few people were killed—even though more than 1 million lived near the epicenter—because the earthquake was pre-dicted, and the residents were evacuated. Some Western seismologists have questioned this claim and suggest instead that an intense swarm of foreshocks, which began 24 hours before the main earthquake, may have caused many people to evacuate of their own accord.

One year after the Liaoning earthquake, an esti-mated 240,000 people perished in the Tangshan, China,

FIGURE 31 Collapse of the double-decked section of I-880 This section of a double-decked highway, known as the Cypress Viaduct, collapsed during the 1989 Loma Prieta earthquake. (Photo by Paul Sakuma/AP Photo)

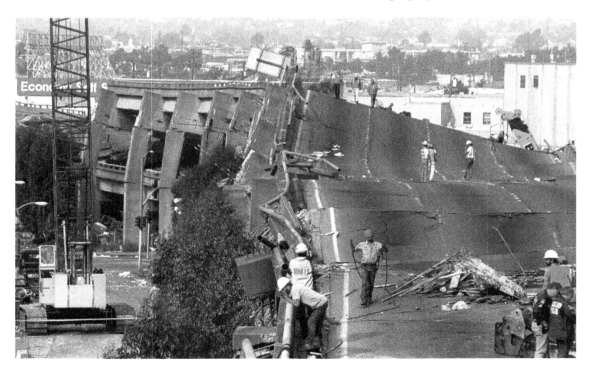

TABLE 2	Some Notable Earthquakes			
Year	Location	Deaths (est.)	Magnitude*	Comments
856	Iran	200,000		
893	Iran	150,000		
1138	Syria	230,000		
1268	Asia Minor	60,000		
1290	China	100,000		
1556	Shensi, China	830,000		Possibly the greatest natural disaster
1667	Caucasia	80,000		
1727	Iran	77,000		
1755	Lisbon, Portugal	70,000		Tsunami damage extensive
1783	Italy	50,000		
1908	Messina, Italy	120,000		
1920	China	200,000	7.5	Landslide buried a village
1923	Tokyo, Japan	143,000	7.9	Fire caused extensive destruction
1948	Turkmenistan	110,000	7.3	Almost all brick buildings near epicenter collapsed
1960	Southern Chile	5,700	9.5	The largest-magnitude earthquake ever recorded
1964	Alaska	131	9.2	Greatest-magnitude North American earthquake
1970	Peru	70,000	7.9	Great rockslide
1976	Tangshan, China	242,000	7.5	Estimates for the death toll are as high as 655,000
1985	Mexico City	9,500	8.1	Major damage occurred 400 km from epicenter
1988	Armenia	25,000	6.9	Poor construction practices
1990	Iran	50,000	7.4	Landslides and poor construction practices led to great damage
1993	Latur, India	10,000	6.4	Located in stable continental interior
1995	Kobe, Japan	5,472	6.9	Damages estimated to exceed $100 billion
1999	Izmit, Turkey	17,127	7.4	Nearly 44,000 injured and more than 250,000 displaced
2001	Gujarat, India	20,000	7.9	Millions homeless
2003	Bam, Iran	31,000	6.6	Ancient city with poor construction
2004	Indian Ocean (Sumatra)	230,000	9.1	Devastating tsunami damage
2005	Pakistan/Kashmir	86,000	7.6	Many landslides; 4 million homeless
2008	Sichuan, China	87,000	7.9	Millions homeless, some towns will not be rebuilt
2010	Port-au-Prince, Haiti	316,000	7.0	More than 300,000 injured and 1.3 million homeless
2011	Japan	20,000	9.0	Majority of the casualties due to a tsunami

* Widely differing magnitudes have been estimated for some of these earthquakes. When available, moment magnitudes are used.

Source: U.S. Geological Survey.

earthquake, which was *not* predicted. There were no foreshocks. Predictions can also lead to false alarms. In a province near Hong Kong, people reportedly evacuated their dwellings for over a month, but no earthquake followed.

In order for a short-range prediction scheme to warrant general acceptance, it must be both accurate and reliable. Thus, *it must have a small range of uncertainty in regard to location and timing, and it must produce few failures or false alarms.* Can you imagine the debate that would precede an order to evacuate a large city in the United States, such as Los Angeles or San Francisco? The cost of evacuating millions of people, arranging for living accommodations, and providing for their lost work time and wages would be staggering.

Currently, no reliable method exists for making short-range earthquake predictions. In fact, leading seismologists in the past 100 years have generally concluded that short-range earthquake prediction is not feasible.

Long-Range Forecasts

In contrast to short-range predictions, which aim to predict earthquakes within a time frame of hours or days, long-range forecasts are estimates of how likely it is for an earthquake of a certain magnitude to occur on a time scale of 30 to 100 years or more. These forecasts give statistical estimates of the expected intensity of ground motion for a given area over a specified time frame. Although long-range forecasts are not as informative as we might like, these data are useful for providing important guides for building codes so that buildings, dams,

FIGURE 32 Trans-Alaskan oil pipeline
This pipeline was designed and built to withstand several meters of horizontal displacement where it crosses the Denali Fault. During a magnitude 7.9 earthquake in 2002, the pipeline moved as predicted, and no oil spill occurred. This illustrates the importance of estimating potential ground motion and designing structures to mitigate the risks. (Photo courtesy of USGS/U.S. Department of the Interior)

and roadways are constructed to withstand expected levels of ground shaking.

For example, in the 1970s, before the 1300-kilometer-long (800-mile-long) Trans-Alaskan oil pipeline was built, geologists did a hazards study of the Denali fault system—a major tectonic structure across Alaska. It was determined that during a magnitude 8 earthquake, the Denali Fault would experience a 6-meter (20-foot) horizontal displacement. As a result of this investigation, the pipeline was designed to be able to slide horizontally without breaking (FIGURE 32). In 2002, the Denali Fault ruptured, producing a 7.9-magnitude earthquake. Although the total displacement along the fault was about 5 meters (18 feet), there was no oil spill.

Most long-range forecasting strategies are based on evidence that many large faults break in a cyclical manner, producing similar quakes at roughly similar intervals. In other words, as soon as a section of a fault ruptures, the continuing motions of Earth's plates begin to build strain in the rocks again until they fail once more. Seismologists have therefore studied historical records of earthquakes to see if there are any discernible patterns so that they can establish the probability of recurrence.

Seismic Gaps Seismologists began to plot the distribution of rupture zones associated with great earthquakes around the globe. The maps revealed that individual rupture zones tend to occur adjacent to one another, without appreciable overlap, thereby tracing out a plate boundary. Because plates are moving at known velocities, the rate at which strain builds can also be estimated.

When these researchers studied historical records, they discovered that some seismic zones had not produced a large earthquake in more than a century or, in some locations, for several centuries. These quiet zones, called **seismic gaps**, are believed to be zones that are storing strain that will be released during a future earthquake. FIGURE 33 shows a patch (seismic gap) of the megathrust fault that lies offshore of Padang, a low-lying city of 800,000 people off the coast of Sumatra that has not ruptured since 1797. Scientists are particularly concerned about this particular seismic gap because, in 2004, a rupture of an adjacent segment of this megathrust fault that lies to the north generated a tsunami that claimed 230,000 lives.

Paleoseismology Another method of long-term forecasting involves *paleoseismology* (*palaois* = ancient, *seismos* = shake, *ology* = study of), the study of the timing, location, and size of prehistoric earthquakes. Paleoseismology studies are often conducted by digging a trench across a suspected fault zone and then looking for evidence of ancient faulting, such as offset sedimentary strata or mud volcanoes (FIGURE 34). A large vertical offset of the layers of sediments indicates a large earthquake. Sometimes buried plant debris can be carbon dated, allowing for the timing of recurrence to be established.

SMARTFIGURE 33 Seismic gaps: Tools for forecasting earthquakes
Seismic gaps are "quiet zones" thought to be inactive zones that are storing elastic strain that will eventually produce major earthquakes. This seismic gap occurs along a patch of the megathrust fault where oceanic lithosphere is being subducted beneath Sumatra, near Padang, a low-lying coastal city with a population of 800,000 people.

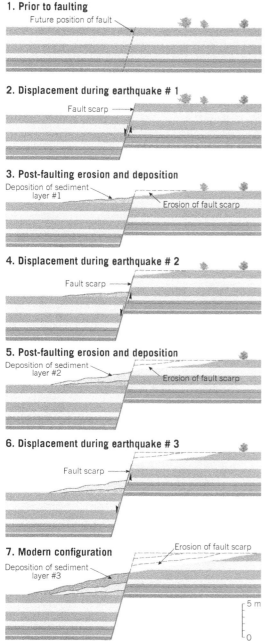

1. Prior to faulting
Future position of fault

2. Displacement during earthquake # 1
Fault scarp

3. Post-faulting erosion and deposition
Deposition of sediment layer #1
Erosion of fault scarp

4. Displacement during earthquake # 2
Fault scarp

5. Post-faulting erosion and deposition
Deposition of sediment layer #2
Erosion of fault scarp

6. Displacement during earthquake # 3
Fault scarp

7. Modern configuration
Erosion of fault scarp
Deposition of sediment layer #3
5 m
0

A.

B. The events depicted in the accompanying art where deciphered by digging a trench (shown here) across the fault zone and studying the displaced sedimentary beds.

FIGURE 34 Paleoseismology: The study of prehistoric earthquakes
These studies are often conducted by digging a trench across a fault zone and then looking for evidence of ancient displacements, such as offset sedimentary strata. This simplified diagram shows that vertical displacement occurred on this fault three different times, with each event producing an earthquake. Based on the size of the vertical displacement, these paleoearthquakes had estimated magnitudes of 6.8 and 7.4. (Photo courtesy of U.S. Geological Survey)

along the fault zone. Trenches excavated across the creek bed have exposed sediments that have been displaced by several large earthquakes over a span of 1500 years. From these data, it was determined that strong earthquakes occur an average of once every 135 years. The last major event, called the Fort Tejon earthquake, occurred on this segment of the San Andreas Fault in 1857, roughly 150 years ago. Because earthquakes occur on a cyclical basis, a major event in southern California could be imminent.

Using other paleoseismology techniques, researchers determined that several powerful earthquakes (magnitude 8 or larger) have repeatedly struck the coastal Pacific Northwest over the past several thousand years. The most recent event, which occurred about 300 years ago, generated a destructive tsunami. As a result of these findings, public officials have taken steps to strengthen some of the region's existing buildings, dams, bridges, and water systems. Even the private sector responded. The U.S. Bancorp building in Portland, Oregon, was strengthened at a cost of $8 million.

One investigation that used this method focused on a segment of the San Andreas Fault that lies north and east of Los Angeles. At this site, the drainage of Pallet Creek has been repeatedly disturbed by successive ruptures

7 CONCEPT CHECKS

1. Are accurate, short-range earthquake predictions currently possible using modern seismic instruments? Explain.
2. What is the value of long-range earthquake forecasts?

Seismic Risks
on the San Andreas Fault System

California's San Andreas Fault runs diagonally from southeast to northwest for nearly 1300 kilometers (800 miles) through much of the western part of the state. For years researchers have been trying to predict the location of the next "Big One"—an earthquake with a magnitude of 8 or greater—along this fault system.

CALIFORNIA

The 1906 San Francisco earthquake caused displacement on the 477-kilometer-long northernmost section of the fault. This event, which had an estimated magnitude of 7.8, likely relieved much of the strain that had been building during the previous 200 years or so.

1906 epicenter
San Francisco ●

Located just south of the 1906 rupture is a section of the San Andreas Fault that exhibits fault creep. When plates gradually slide past each other, less strain accumulates than when the fault is locked, diminishing the possibilities of an eventual large quake.

1857
epicenter

The 1906 San Francisco earthquake was the most devastating in California's history. The quake and resulting fires caused an estimated 3000 deaths and extensively damaged buildings throughout the city. The business district was devastated largely because it was built on land made by filling in a cove. (USGS)

This 300-kilometer-long section of the San Andreas Fault System produced the Fort Tejon earthquake of 1857 that had an estimated magnitude of 7.9. Because a portion of the fault has likely accumulated considerable strain since the Fort Tejon quake, the U.S. Geological Survey gives it a 60 percent probability of producing a major earthquake in the next 30 years.

● **Los Angeles**

The next major quake on the San Andreas may well be on its southernmost 200 kilometers—an area that has not produced a large event in about 300 years.

Adam Teitelbaum/AFP/Getty Images

On October 17, 1989, millions of television viewers around the world were settling in to watch the third game of the World Series. Instead, they saw their TVs go to black as tremors hit San Francisco's Candlestick Park, where power and communication lines were severed in what came to be known as the Loma Prieta earthquake. Although the quake was centered in a remote section of the Santa Cruz Mountains—100 miles to the south—major damage occurred in the Marina District of San Francisco.

62%

The U. S. Geological Survey concluded that between 2003 and 2032 there is a 62 percent probability of at least one magnitude 6.7 or greater earthquake striking somewhere in the San Francisco Bay area. They also predict that this quake would be roughly comparable to the 1989 Loma Prieta event (MW 6.9) and capable of causing significant damage.

This is the probability for one or more magnitude 6.7 or greater earthquakes between 2003 to 2032. This result incorporates 14% odds of quakes occurring on faults not shown on this map.

% Probability of magnitude 6.7 or greater quake before 2032 on the indicated faults

Increasing probability along fault segments

In mid-January 1994, less than five years after the Loma Prieta event, the Northridge earthquake struck an area slightly north of Los Angeles. Although not the fabled "Big One," this moderate 6.7-magnitude earthquake claimed the lives of 57 people. Nearly 300 schools were severely damaged, and one dozen major roadways buckled. Among these were two of California's major arteries—sections of the Santa Monica Freeway and the Golden State Freeway (I-5) where an overpass collapsed completely and blocked the highway.

Rogers Creek fault

Napa

Concord-Green Valley fault

27%

San Andreas fault

4%

Walnut Creek

Hayward fault

Greenville fault

Mt. Diablo thrust fault

San Francisco

Oakland

3%

21%

San Francisco Bay

3%

Palo Alto

San Jose

Calaveras fault

10%

San Gregorio fault

11%

5 NORTH 14
Autos

EXTENT OF RUPTURE IN THE LOMA PRIETA QUAKE

PACIFIC OCEAN

Monterey Bay

Monterey

Tom McHugh/Photo Researchers, Inc.

409

CONCEPTS IN REVIEW: EARTHQUAKES AND EARTHQUAKE HAZARDS

1 What Is an Earthquake?

Sketch and describe the mechanism that generates most earthquakes.

KEY WORDS earthquake, fault, hypocenter (focus), epicenter, seismic wave, elastic rebound, aftershock, foreshock

- Earthquakes are caused by the sudden movement of blocks of rock on opposite sides of faults. The spot where the rock begins to slip is the hypocenter (or focus). Seismic waves radiate from this spot outward into the surrounding rock. The point on Earth's surface directly above the hypocenter is the epicenter.
- Elastic rebound explains why most earthquakes happen: Rock is stressed by movement of Earth's crust. However, frictional resistance keeps the fault locked in place, and the rock bends elastically. Stress builds up until it is greater than the resistance, and the blocks of rock suddenly slip, releasing the pent-up energy, in the form of seismic waves. As elastic rebound occurs, the blocks of rock on either side of the fault return to their original shapes, but they are now in new positions.
- Foreshocks are smaller earthquakes that precede larger earthquakes. Aftershocks are smaller earthquakes that happen after large earthquakes, as the crust readjusts to the new, post-earthquake state of stress.

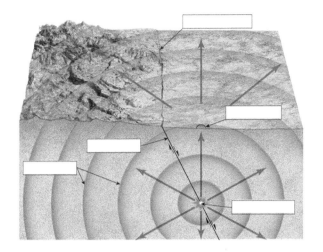

LABEL IT Label the blanks on the diagram, showing the relationship between earthquakes and faults.

2 Faults and Earthquakes

List the basic types of faults and describe the tectonic setting where each type of faulting tends to dominate.

KEY WORDS megathrust fault, fault creep, fault slip

- Faults associated with plate boundaries are the source of most earthquakes, because that is where movement of crustal blocks generates the most differential stress. Normal faults generally don't generate large earthquakes.
- Subduction zones are marked by megathrust faults, large reverse faults that are responsible for the largest earthquakes in recorded history. Megathrust faults are also capable of generating tsunamis.
- Strike-slip faults are also important earthquake makers. The San Andreas Fault in California is an example of a large strike-slip fault. Portions of it generate destructive earthquakes. Other parts move slowly and gradually by fault creep; these sections do not produce significant earthquakes because they do not accumulate sufficient strain.
- The total amount of displacement of the rock on one side of a fault relative to the other side is called *fault slip*. Fault slip occurs on one section of the fault at a time, not the entire fault surface all at once.

DRAW IT Sketch the sorts of faults that would be most likely at (1) convergent, (2) divergent, and (3) transform plate boundaries. Include arrows on your sketches to show the direction of offset.

3 Seismology: The Study of Earthquake Waves

Compare and contrast the types of seismic waves and describe the principle of the seismograph, which is used to detect them.

KEY WORDS seismology, seismograph (seismometer), inertia, seismogram, surface waves, body waves, P waves (primary waves), S waves (secondary waves)

- Seismology is the study of seismic waves. An instrument called a seismograph measures these waves, using the principle of inertia. While the body of the machine moves with the waves, a weight in the center keeps a pen (or an electronic sensor) stationary and records the relative difference between the two. The resulting record of the waves is called a seismogram.
- Seismograms reveal that there are three main categories of earthquake waves: P waves and S waves (which are both body waves, capable of moving through Earth's interior) and surface waves (which travel along the upper surface of the lithosphere). P waves are the fastest, S waves are intermediate in speed, and surface waves are the slowest. However, surface waves have the greatest amplitude, while S waves are intermediate, and P waves have the least amplitude. Large-amplitude waves produce the most shaking, so surface waves are responsible for most damage during earthquakes.
- P waves and S waves exhibit different kinds of motion. P waves show compressional motion: They change the volume of the rock as they pass through it. In contrast, S waves impart a shaking motion to rock as they pass through it. This changes the shape of the rock but doesn't alter its volume. As a result, P waves can travel through liquids, but S waves cannot. Liquids can be compressed but not sheared.

ACT IT OUT How could you physically demonstrate the difference between P waves and S waves to a friend who hasn't taken a geology course? (Caution: Don't hurt your friend!)

4 Determining the Size of Earthquakes

Distinguish between intensity scales and magnitude scales.

KEY WORDS intensity, magnitude, Modified Mercalli Intensity scale, Richter scale, moment magnitude

- Intensity and magnitude are different measures of earthquake strength. Intensity measures the amount of ground shaking a place experiences due to an earthquake, and magnitude is an estimate of the actual amount of energy released during the earthquake.
- The Modified Mercalli Intensity scale is a tool for measuring an earthquake's intensity at different locations. The scale is based on verifiable physical evidence to quantify intensity on a 12-point scale. However, it's hard to measure intensity if there are no buildings or people present at a particular location.
- The Richter scale was the first attempt at measuring an earthquake's magnitude. The scale takes into account both the maximum amplitude of the seismic waves measured at a given seismograph and the distance of that seismograph from the hypocenter. The Richter scale is logarithmic, meaning that each numerical unit up on the scale represents seismic wave amplitudes that are 10 times greater than those of the next number down. Seismic waves with larger amplitudes possess more energy, so each numerical Richter unit represents about 32 times as much energy release as the next number below it.

- The Richter scale isn't good at distinguishing among really large earthquakes, so another scale was devised that can handle data from major quakes. The moment magnitude scale measures the total energy released from an earthquake. It considers the strength of the faulted rock, the amount of slip, and the area of the fault that slipped. Moment magnitude is the modern standard for measuring the size of earthquakes.

CALCULATE IT On the Richter scale diagram, first determine the (M_L) for an earthquake at 400 kilometers distance, with a maximum amplitude of 0.5 millimeters. Second, for this same earthquake (same M_L), determine the amplitude of the biggest waves for a seismograph only 40 kilometers from the hypocenter.

5 Earthquake Destruction

List and describe the major destructive forces that can be triggered by earthquake vibrations.

KEY WORDS liquefaction, tsunami

- Several factors influence how much destruction results from an earthquake. The earthquake's magnitude and distance are important, but we must also consider (1) the intensity of the shaking, (2) how long shaking persists, (3) what sort of ground underlies buildings, and (4) building construction standards. Buildings made of unreinforced masonry are more likely than other types of buildings to collapse in a quake.
- Buildings may be constructed on solid bedrock or on deposits of loose sediment. In general, bedrock-grounded buildings fare better in an earthquake, as loose sediments amplify seismic shaking.
- A particular hazard occurs with water-logged sediments or soil: When shaken at certain frequencies, the material will flow like a liquid. Liquefaction can cause sand "volcanoes." Buildings may sink into the ground, or underground tanks or sewer lines may float up to the surface.

- A seiche is a "sloshing" motion of water in an enclosed basin such as a lake. It can be dangerous not only for boats riding the seiche waves but also when the waves overtop earthen dams.
- Earthquakes may also trigger landslides or ground subsidence, and they may break gas lines, which can initiate devastating fires.
- Tsunamis are large ocean waves that form when water is displaced, usually by a megathrust fault rupturing on the seafloor. Crossing the ocean at the same speed as a commercial airplane, a tsunami is hardly noticeable in deep water. However, when it gets into shallower coastal waters, the tsunami slows down and piles up, sometimes producing waves more than 30 meters in height. A tsunami does not look like a curling breaker wave. It looks like a rapid rise in sea level and may be choked with sediment and other debris. Tsunami warning systems have been established in several ocean basins, including the Pacific.

LOCAL EFFECTS Of the secondary earthquake hazards discussed in this section, which is (are) of the greatest concern in the region where you live? Why?

6 Earthquake Belts and Plate Boundaries

Locate Earth's major earthquake belts on a world map and label the regions associated with the largest earthquakes.

- Most earthquake energy is released in the circum-Pacific belt, the ring of megathrust faults rimming the Pacific Ocean. Another earthquake belt is the Alpine–Himalayan belt, which runs along the collisional zone between Eurasia and the Indian–Australian and African plates.
- Earth's divergent oceanic ridge system produces another belt of earthquake activity where seafloor spreading generates many frequent quakes of small magnitude. Strike-slip faults in the continental crust, including the San Andreas Fault, can produce large earthquakes.

BELT IT OUT From memory, outline Earth's major earthquake belts on this map. Describe the tectonic stresses responsible for producing each belt.

7 Can Earthquakes Be Predicted?

Compare and contrast the goals of short-range earthquake predictions to long-range forecasts.

KEY WORD seismic gap

- Successful earthquake prediction has been an elusive goal of seismology for many years. Shorter-range predictions (for hours or days) are based on precursor events such as changes in ground elevation or variations in strain levels near a fault. Unfortunately, they haven't been found to be consistently reliable.
- Long-range forecasts (for time scales of 30 to 100 years) are statistical estimates of how likely it is for an earthquake of a given magnitude to occur. Long-range forecasts are useful because they can be used to guide building codes and infrastructure development.
- Scientists have identified seismic gaps, portions of faults that have been storing strain for a long time without releasing it. Knowing the location of seismic gaps can help in the preparation of long-range forecasts. Another tool used in making long-range forecasts is paleoseismology, the study of ancient earthquakes. Because earthquakes occur on a cyclical basis, determining how frequently they have occurred in the past can suggest when they are most likely to occur again.

MIND THE GAP If you were considering moving to a city located in a seismic gap, how would you figure out if it was safe or foolhardy? Which factors would be most influential in your decision?

GIVE IT SOME THOUGHT

1. Draw a sketch that illustrates the concept of elastic rebound. Develop an analogy other than a rubber band to illustrate this concept.

2. The accompanying map shows the locations of many of the largest earthquakes in the world since 1900. Using a map of Earth's plate boundaries, determine which type of plate boundary is most often associated with these destructive events.

3. Use the accompanying seismogram to answer the following questions:
   a. Which of the three types of seismic waves reached the seismograph first?
   b. What is the time interval between the arrival of the first P wave and the arrival of the first S wave?
   c. Use your answer from Question b and the travel-time graph earlier in the chapter to determine the distance from the seismic station to the earthquake.
   d. Which of the three types of seismic waves had the highest amplitude when they reached the seismic station?

4. You go for a jog on a beach and choose to run near the water where the sand is well packed and solid under your feet. With each step, you notice that your footprint quickly fills with water but not water coming in from the ocean. What is this water's source? For what earthquake-related hazard is this phenomenon a good analogy?

5. Make a sketch that illustrates why a tsunami often causes a rapid withdrawal of water from beaches before the first surge.

6. Why is it possible to issue a tsunami warning but not a warning for an impending earthquake? Describe a scenario in which a tsunami warning would be of little value.

7. Using the accompanying map of the San Andreas Fault, answer the following questions:
   a. Which of the four segments (1–4) of the San Andreas Fault do you think is experiencing fault creep?
   b. Paleoseismology studies have found that the section of the San Andreas Fault that failed during the Fort Tejon quake (segment 3) produces a major earthquake every 135 years, on average. Based on this information, how would you rate the chances of a major earthquake occurring along this section in the next 30 years? Explain.
   c. Do you think San Francisco or Los Angeles has the greater risk of experiencing a major earthquake in the near future? Defend your selection.

8. The accompanying image shows a double-decked section of Interstate 880 (Nimitz Freeway) that collapsed during the 1989 Loma Prieta earthquake and caused 42 deaths. About 1.4 kilometers of this freeway section, commonly called the Cypress Viaduct, collapsed, while a similar section survived the vibration. Both sections were subsequently demolished and rebuilt as a single-level structure, at a cost of $1.2 billion. Examine the map and seismograms from an aftershock that shows the intensity of shaking observed at three nearby locations to answer the following questions:

   a. What type of ground material experienced the least amount of shaking during the aftershock?

   b. What type of ground materials experienced the greatest amount of ground shaking during the same event?

   c. Which of the two sections of the Cypress Viaduct shown on the map do you think collapsed? Explain.

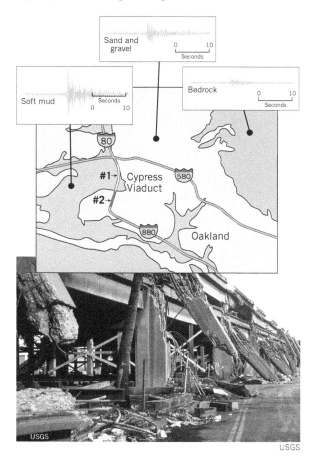

USGS

9. Strike-slip faults, like the San Andreas Fault, are not perfectly straight but bend gradually back and forth. In some locations, the bends are oriented such that blocks on opposite sides of the fault pull away from each other, as shown in the accompanying sketch. As a result, the ground between the bends sags, forming a depression or basin. These depressions often fill with water.

   a. What name is given to the depression in the accompanying photo?

   b. Describe what would happen if these two blocks began moving in opposite directions.

Michael Collier

MasteringGeology™

Glossary

Aftershock A smaller earthquake that follows the main earthquake.

Elastic rebound The sudden release of stored strain in rocks that results in movement along a fault.

Epicenter The location on Earth's surface that lies directly above the focus of an earthquake.

Fault A break in a rock mass along which movement has occurred.

Fault creep Gradual displacement along a fault. Such activity occurs relatively smoothly and with little noticeable seismic activity.

Focus (earthquake) The zone within Earth where rock displacement produces an earthquake.

Foreshocks Small earthquakes that often precede a major earthquake.

Hypocenter See *Focus (earthquake)*.

Inertia A property by which objects at rest tend to remain at rest, and objects in motion tend to stay in motion unless either is acted upon by an outside force.

Intensity (earthquake) A measure of the degree of earthquake shaking at a given locale, based on the amount of damage.

Liquefaction The transformation of a stable soil into a fluid that is often unable to support buildings or other structures.

Magnitude (earthquake) An estimate of the total amount of energy released during an earth-quake, based on seismic records.

Megathrust fault The plate boundary separating a subducting slab of oceanic lithosphere and the overlying plate.

Modified Mercalli Intensity scale A 12-point scale developed to evaluate earthquake intensity, based on the amount of damage to various structures.

Moment magnitude A more precise measure of earthquake magnitude than the Richter scale that is derived from the amount of displacement that occurs along a fault zone.

Primary (P) wave A type of seismic wave that involves alternating compression and expansion of the material through which it passes.

Richter scale A scale of earthquake magnitude based on the amplitude of the largest seismic wave.

Secondary (S) wave A seismic wave that involves oscillation perpendicular to the direction of propagation.

Seismic gap A segment of an active fault zone that has not experienced a major earthquake over a span when most other segments have. Such segments are probable sites for future major earthquakes.

Seismic sea wave A rapidly moving ocean wave, generated by earthquake activity, that is capable of inflicting heavy damage in coastal regions.

Seismogram A record made by a seismograph.

Seismograph An instrument that records earthquake waves.

Surface waves Seismic waves that travel along the outer layer of Earth.

Tsunami The Japanese word for a seismic sea wave.

Earth's Interior

From Chapter 12 of *Earth: An Introduction to Physical Geology*, Eleventh Edition. Edward J. Tarbuck, Frederick K. Lutgens, Dennis Tasa.

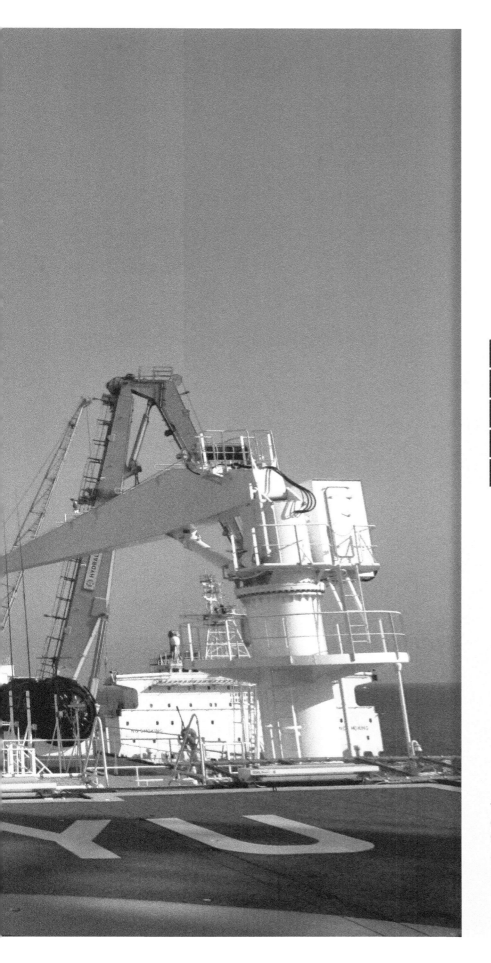

Earth's Interior*

1 **Earth's Internal Structure**

2 **Probing Earth's Interior**

3 **Earth's Layers**

4 **Earth's Temperature**

5 **Earth's Three-Dimensional Structure**

The Japanese high-tech drilling ship *Chikyu* is capable of drilling 7000 meters (nearly 4.5 miles) into the ocean floor. (Photo by Katsumi Kasahara/AP Photo)

*This chapter was originally prepared by Professor Michael Wysession, Washington University.

Each statement represents the primary learning objective for the corresponding major heading within the chapter. After you complete the chapter you should be able to:

1   Explain how Earth acquired its layered structure.
2   Describe how seismic waves are used to probe Earth's interior.
3   List and describe each of the layers of Earth's interior.
4   Describe the processes of heat transfer that operate within Earth's interior and where each of these processes dominates.
5   Discuss what the studies of Earth's gravity, seismic tomography, and Earth's magnetic field have revealed about our planet.

Vibroseis trucks are used to probe Earth's upper crust
This vibroseis truck produces artificial seismic waves using a baseplate, visible between the wheels, that vibrates Earth's surface. The waves that are generated probe the underlying rock structure in a manner similar to ultrasound. (Photo by David Parker/Photo Researchers, Inc.)

I f you could look inside a planet, you would quickly notice its distinct layers. The heaviest materials (metals) appear in the center, lighter solids (rocks) occupy the middle, and less dense liquids and gases are found at the top. For planet Earth, we know these layers as the iron core, the rocky mantle and crust, the liquid ocean, and the gaseous atmosphere. More than 95 percent of the variations in composition and temperature within Earth are due to this seemingly simple layered structure. However, Earth's interior is much more complex, sustaining what might otherwise be a lifeless cinder floating in space.

In addition to Earth's layers, small horizontal variations in composition and temperature at various depths verify that the interior of our planet is a dynamic place. The rocks of Earth's mantle and crust are constantly moving because of plate tectonics. In addition, material is continuously recycling between the surface and the deep interior. It is also from Earth's deep interior that the water and air of our oceans and atmosphere are replenished, allowing life to exist at the surface.

1 Earth's Internal Structure

Earth's interior consists of three major layers defined by their chemical composition—the crust, mantle, and core. In addition, Earth's three compositionally distinct layers can be further subdivided into zones, based on physical properties that include whether the layer is solid or liquid and how weak or strong it is. Knowledge of both types of layers is essential to our understanding of basic geologic processes, such as volcanism, earthquakes, and mountain building (FIGURE 1).

Gravity and Layered Planets

If a bottle filled with clay, iron filings, water, and air were shaken, it would appear to have a single, muddy composition. If that bottle were then allowed to sit undisturbed, the different materials would separate and settle into layers. The iron filings, which are the densest, would be the first to sink to the bottom. Above the iron would be a layer of clay, then water, and, finally, air.

This is similar to what happens inside planets. At their birth, planets accumulate huge quantities of nebular debris that melts and quickly segregates into layers. The iron sinks to form the core, rocky substances form the mantle and crust, and gases rise to create an atmosphere. All large bodies in the solar system have iron cores and rocky mantles, including the predominantly gaseous bodies Jupiter, Saturn, and the Sun. The force of gravity is responsible for the layering in both the bottle of muddy water and the planets.

Mineral Phase Changes

Another effect of gravity is that density changes occur not only between layers but also within layers; this happens because materials may compress when they are squeezed. Rocks in the upper mantle have a density of about 3.3 grams per cubic centimeter (g/cm^3). However, the density of these same rocks when taken to the base of the mantle increases to 5.6 g/cm^3, nearly twice the original density. This increase in density occurs partly because atoms shrink and occupy less space when subjected

FIGURE 1 Earth's layered structure
The properties of Earth's layers include the physical state of the material (solid, liquid, or gas) as well as how strong the material is—for example, the distinction between the strong lithosphere and weak asthenosphere. Studies have shown that Earth's layers are mainly determined by density, with the heaviest materials (iron) at the center and the lightest ones (gases and liquids) on the outside.

Crust (strong, rocky layer 5–70 km thick)

Mantle

Lower mantle (hot, but strong because of high pressure)

Upper mantle (rocky, includes weak and strong layers)

Temperature and pressure increase with depth

Outer core (liquid iron)

—2900 km

Hydrosphere (liquid)

Atmosphere (gas)

Oceanic crust

Lithosphere (strong, rocky layers) ~100 km

Lithospheric mantle (strong layer)

Continental crust

Moho

Core

Asthenosphere (hot, weak, rocky layer)

—5150 km

Upper mantle

Inner core (solid iron)

—6371 km

600 km

to immense pressure. In addition, atoms compress at various rates, and it is easier to compress negative ions than positive ions.

Negative ions have more electrons than protons and tend to be "fluffier" than positive ions. For example, when rocks are squeezed, the negative ions (such as O^{-2}) compress more easily than the positive ions (such as Si^{+4} and Mg^{+2}), so the ratios of ionic sizes change. As these ratios change, the structure may eventually become unstable, and the atoms rearrange into a more stable and denser structure. This is called a **mineral phase change**. For example, at depths between 300 and 400 kilometers, the intense pressure of the overlying rocks causes the mineral *olivine* to become unstable. As

a result, the atoms in olivine rearrange into a denser and more stable crystalline structure. The increase in density of mantle rocks is due both to the compression of existing minerals and to the formation of new "high-pressure" minerals.

1 CONCEPT CHECKS

1. List the three compositionally distinct layers of Earth's interior.
2. Describe the process that produced layering during Earth's formation.
3. What causes a mineral phase change?

Volcanic eruptions, such as the one in this image in Iceland, provide important data about the composition of Earth's upper mantle. (Photo by Vilhelm Gunnersson/ EPA/Newscom)

2 Probing Earth's Interior

Discovering the structure and properties of Earth's deep interior has not been easy. Light does not travel through rock, so we must find other ways to "see" into our planet. The ideal way to learn about Earth's interior would be to dig or drill a hole and examine what is extracted. Unfortunately, this is only possible at shallow depths. The deepest a drill has ever penetrated is only 12.3 kilometers (7.5 miles), about 1/500 of the way to Earth's center—an extraordinary accomplishment due to the rapid increases in temperature and pressure with depth.

"Seeing" Seismic Waves

Fortunately for seismologists, many earthquakes are large enough that their seismic waves travel all the way through Earth and can be detected on the other side (FIGURE 2). This property of seismic waves is similar to how medical X-rays image our bones and organs. There are about 100 to 200 earthquakes each year that are large enough (about $M_W > 6$) to be recorded by seismographs around the globe. These large quakes provide the means to "see" into our planet and have been the source of much of the data that allow us to more fully understand Earth's interior.

When traveling through Earth, seismic waves spread out from an earthquake source (hypocenter) as circular features called *wave fronts*.

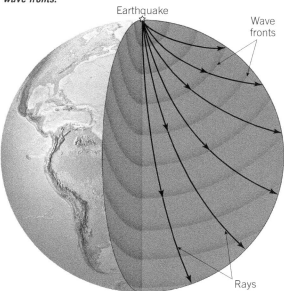

The paths taken by these waves can also be considered *seismic rays*, lines drawn perpendicular to the wave front as shown here.

SMARTFIGURE 2 Seismic waves provide a way to "see" into our planet Illustration of seismic waves traveling through Earth's interior, assuming uniform materials along the path.

Seismic Velocities

Recall that the various seismic waves travel at different speeds. In addition, the speed at which P waves and S waves travel through Earth's layers depends largely on the properties of the materials that transmit them. In general, seismic waves travel fastest when rock is *stiff* (*rigid*) or *less compressible*. These properties of stiffness and compressibility are used to interpret the composition and temperature of the rock. For instance, when rock is heated, it becomes less stiff (imagine warming a frozen chocolate bar), and waves travel through it more slowly. When P waves enter the outer core, which is liquid, they slow dramatically while S waves are not transmitted (Figure 7).

Likewise, waves travel at different speeds through Earth materials that have different compositions. For example, seismic waves travel faster through oceanic crust, which is composed of basalt, than through the continental crust, which has an overall composition akin to granite. Thus, the speed at which seismic waves travel through a layer can help determine both the type of material and its temperature.

Interactions Between Seismic Waves and Earth's Layers

Interpreting the waves recorded on seismograms is challenging because seismic waves usually do not travel along straight paths. Instead, seismic waves interact with Earth's layers and are *reflected* and *refracted* as they pass through our planet (FIGURE 3). You are

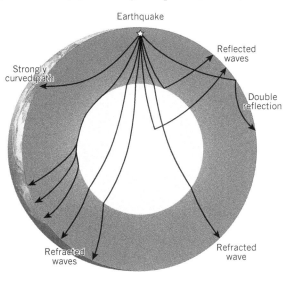

FIGURE 3 Possible paths that seismic rays follow through Earth

FIGURE 4 Reflection and refraction

When seismic waves (rays) encounter a boundary between materials with different properties, such as air and water, the energy splits into reflected and refracted (bent) waves.

When the velocity of seismic waves increases as they pass from one layer into another, the waves refract (bend) toward the boundary separating the layers.

When the velocity of seismic waves decreases as they pass from one layer into another, the waves refract (bend) away from the boundary separating them.

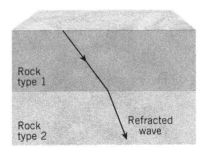

FIGURE 5 Paths of seismic waves though the mantle
The rays follow curved (refracting) paths rather than straight paths because the seismic velocity of rocks increases with depth as a result of a steady increase in pressure.

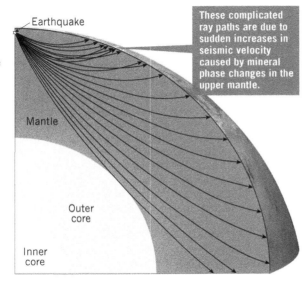

These complicated ray paths are due to sudden increases in seismic velocity caused by mineral phase changes in the upper mantle.

familiar with reflected sound waves that we call echoes. When a seismic wave hits a boundary between different Earth materials, such as the boundary between the crust and the mantle, some of the waves are **reflected** back toward the surface (FIGURE 4). The remaining energy passes though the boundary and is **refracted** (bent). This is similar to how light is refracted (bent) as it passes from air to water.

One of the most noticeable behaviors of seismic waves is that they follow strongly curved (refracted) paths because their velocities generally increase with depth (FIGURE 5). Within a particular layer, the speed of seismic waves increases with depth because pressure increases and squeezes the rock into a more compact, rigid material.

Within Earth's mantle, where there are both distinct boundaries and gradual seismic velocity changes caused by changes in mineral properties, the pattern of seismic waves is complex. FIGURE 6 shows what S waves look like when they travel from a deep earthquake through the mantle. Note how the single wave from the shock is soon broken into many different waves that appear on seismograms as separate signals.

---

2 CONCEPT CHECKS

1. What characteristic of seismic waves makes them useful for probing Earth's interior?
2. Briefly describe the difference between reflection and refraction.
3. Why do seismic waves travel along curved paths through the mantle?

Time = 300 s

Inner core | Outer core | Mantle

Time = 900 s

Inner core | Outer core | Mantle

Time = 1800 s

Inner core | Outer core

Mantle

FIGURE 6 Three snapshots showing the locations of S waves within the mantle
In addition to refracting, S waves reflect from boundaries such as the core–mantle boundary.

Recreating the Deep Earth

Seismology alone cannot determine the nature of the materials deep in Earth's interior. Additional information must be obtained by other techniques. Mineral physics experiments can measure physical properties of rocks and minerals such as stiffness, compressibility, and density while simulating the extreme conditions of the mantle and core.

C.Arache, D. Jackson and S.T. Weir/Lawrence Livermore National Laboratory

Most mineral physics experiments are conducted using presses with hard carbonized steel tips that simulate the enormous pressures at depth by squeezing mineral samples. The highest pressures are obtained using diamond-anvil presses like the one shown here. These take advantage of two important properties of diamonds—hardness and transparency. The tips of two diamonds are cut off, and a small sample of mineral or rock is placed between them. By squeezing two diamonds together, pressures as high as our planet's interior have been simulated. High temperatures are achieved by firing a laser beam through the diamond and into the mineral sample.

Douglas L. Peck Photography

PRESSURE   PRESSURE

DIAMOND

METALLIC GASKET

TINY MINERAL SAMPLE

DIAMOND

PRESSURE   PRESSURE

One experiment determines the temperature at which minerals begin to melt under various pressures. Another examines the temperatures and pressures at which one mineral phase will become unstable and convert into a new "high-pressure" phase. These experiments are useful because they help identify where phase changes take place within Earth.

These experiments have also helped identify where changes in temperature, pressure, and density occur in Earth's interior, as shown in the graphs below.

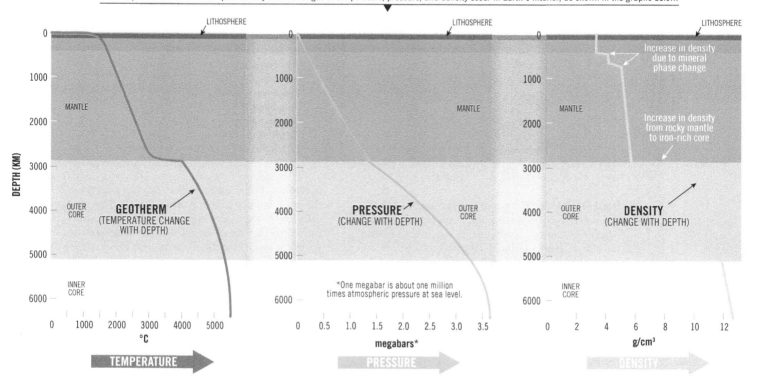

3 Earth's Layers

Combining the data obtained from seismological studies and mineral physics experiments has given us a layer-by-layer understanding of Earth's composition. The variations in seismic velocities with depth are shown in FIGURE 7. By examining the behavior of a variety of rocks at the pressures corresponding to these depths, geologists have made important discoveries about the compositions of Earth's crust, mantle, and core.

SMARTFIGURE 7 Average velocities of P and S waves at each depth S waves are an indication of how rigid (stiff) the material is; faster velocities indicate greater rigidity. The inner core is less rigid than the mantle, and the liquid outer core has no rigidity.

Earth's Crust

Earth's **crust** consists of two distinct types—continental crust and oceanic crust. Continental crust and oceanic crust have very different compositions, histories, and ages. In fact, oceanic crust is compositionally more similar to the mantle than to the continental crust.

Oceanic Crust The ocean crust averages about 7 kilometers (4.5 miles) thick and forms at mid-ocean ridges, which separate two diverging tectonic plates. Ocean crust has a density of about 3.0 g/cm^3, which compares to measured values for the rocks basalt and gabbro.

Continental Crust While oceanic crust is fairly uniform, no two continental regions have the same structure or composition. Continental crust averages about 40 kilometers

(25 miles) thick but can be more than 70 kilometers (45 miles) thick in mountainous regions such as the Himalayas and the Andes. The thinnest crust in North America is beneath the Basin and Range region in the western United States, where the crust is as thin as 20 kilometers (12 miles). The thickest North American crust, beneath the Rockies, is more than 50 kilometers (30 miles) thick.

Seismic velocities within continents are quite variable, suggesting that the composition of continental crust must also vary greatly. Continents have an average density of about 2.7 g/cm^3, which is much lower than the densities of both oceanic crust and mantle rock. This low density explains why continents are buoyant—acting like giant rafts, floating atop tectonic plates—and why they cannot be readily subducted into the mantle.

Discovering Boundaries: The Moho The boundary between the crust and mantle, called the **Moho**, was one of the first features of Earth's interior discovered using seismic waves. In 1909, Croatian seismologist Andrija Mohorovičić discovered this boundary that now bears his name. At the base of the continents, P waves travel about 6 kilometers per second (km/s) but abruptly increase to 8 km/s at a slightly greater depth.

Mohorovičić cleverly used this large jump in seismic velocity to make his discovery. He noticed that two different sets of seismic waves were recorded at seismographs located within a few hundred kilometers of an earthquake. One set of waves moved through the ground at about 6 km/s, while the other set of waves traveled about 8 km/s—allowing Mohorovičić to correctly determine that the different waves were traveling through two different layers.

During a shallow earthquake, *direct waves* travel along a nearly straight path through the crust, as shown in FIGURE 8. Other seismic waves follow a path through the crust and along the top of the mantle. These are called *refracted waves* because they are bent, or refracted, as they enter the mantle. Seismographs near the epicenter record the direct waves first. However, seismographs further from the epicenter record the refracted waves first. The point at which both waves arrive at the same time, called the *cross-over*, can be used to determine the depth of the Moho. Thus, using data from these two sets of waves and seismographs at various distances from an earthquake's epicenter, the thickness of the crust for any location can be calculated.

The difference between travel times for direct and refracted waves is comparable to driving to a destination on local roads versus on interstate highways. For short distances, you will typically arrive sooner if you drive the most direct route using local roads. For long distances, the trip may take less time if you take a less direct route that involves mostly interstate highways. The cross-over point, where both routes take an equal amount of time, is directly related to how far you must drive before reaching the interstate highway. Applied to determining the depth of the Moho, the cross-over is related to how far seismic waves travel through the crust (slow layer) before they reach the mantle (fast layer): The greater the cross-over distance, the deeper the Moho. The Moho lies about 25 to 70 kilometers (15 to 45 miles) beneath the continents and about 5 to 10 kilometers (3 to 6 miles) below the ocean floor.

Earth's Mantle

More than 82 percent of Earth's volume is contained within the **mantle**, a nearly 2900-kilometer-thick shell extending from the base of the crust (Moho) to the liquid outer core (see Figure 1). Because S waves readily travel through the mantle, we know that it is a solid rocky layer composed of silicate minerals that are rich in iron and magnesium. However, despite its solid nature, rock in the mantle is quite hot and capable of flow, albeit at very slow velocities.

The Upper Mantle Earth's **upper mantle** extends from the Moho to a depth of about 660 kilometers and can be divided into three shells:

1. The uppermost mantle is called the **lithospheric mantle**, and it ranges in thickness from only a few kilometers under the mid-oceanic ridges to perhaps as much as 200 kilometers under the stable continental interiors. This layer and the crust make up Earth's rigid outer shell, called the *lithosphere*.
2. Beneath the lithospheric mantle is a weak layer called the **asthenosphere**. The lithospheric mantle and asthenosphere are compositionally similar; however, lithospheric mantle is strong, and the asthenosphere is weak, as a result of Earth's temperature structure—a topic we will consider later.
3. The lower portion of the upper mantle, at depths between 410 and 660 kilometers, is called the **transition zone**.

Rocks brought to the surface by volcanism and other geologic processes have provided geologists with valuable information about the composition of the upper mantle, which is composed mainly of the rock peridotite (FIGURE 9). Peridotite is an ultramafic rock that consists of the minerals *olivine* and *pyroxene*, minerals that are rich in iron and magnesium. As a result, the mantle is

Over a short distance the direct waves arrive first.

A.

For greater distances, the refracted waves arrive first.

B.

At the cross-over point, both waves arrive at the same time. The distance to the cross-over point increases as the depth of the Moho increases, and therefore can be used to determine the thickness of the crust at different locations.

C.

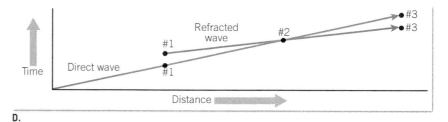

D.

FIGURE 8 Determining the depth of the Moho

denser than either the continental crust or the oceanic crust that lie above it.

At the depth (and pressures) of the transition zone, the mineral olivine, which is stable in the uppermost mantle, is subjected to greater pressure and collapses into denser structures. In the top half of the transition zone, olivine converts to a more compact structure similar to the mineral spinel and pyroxene converts to a garnet-like structure.

Water cycles slowly through Earth and is brought into the mantle by subducting oceanic lithosphere and

FIGURE 9 Peridotite: A rock from Earth's mantle This sample of peridotite (green rock that is olivine rich) was carried up from the mantle and provides clues to the composition of Earth's interior. The mantle fragment (xenolith) was contained within a volcanic bomb from Vulken-Eifel, Germany. €1coin for scale. (Photo by Woudloper)

carried back to the surface by rising plumes of mantle rock. Mineral physics experiments have revealed that the transition zone is capable of holding a great deal of water—up to 2 percent of its weight. This is considerably more than for the rocks of the uppermost mantle, which can hold only about 0.1 percent of their weight as water. Because the transition zone represents 10 percent of Earth's volume, it could potentially hold up to five times the volume of Earth's oceans. How much water is actually contained within the transition zone has not been determined.

The Lower Mantle The **lower mantle** lies between the transition zone (660 kilometers) and the liquid core (2900 kilometers). Beneath the 660-kilometer discontinuity, both olivine and pyroxene take the

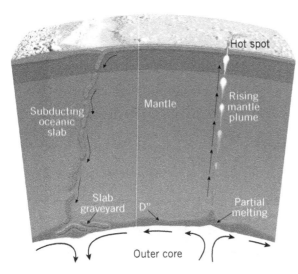

FIGURE 10 The variable and unusual D″ layer lies at the base of the mantle The D″ layer contains large, horizontal variations in both temperature and composition. Many geologists feel that the D″ layer is the graveyard of subducted oceanic lithosphere and the birthplace of some mantle plumes.

structure of the mineral *perovskite* (Fe, Mg) SiO_3 and related minerals. Because the lower mantle is undoubtedly Earth's largest layer, occupying 56 percent of the volume of the planet, perovskite-structured silicate minerals are the single most abundant material within Earth.

The D″ Layer In the lowest few hundred kilometers of the mantle is a highly variable and unusual region called D″ (pronounced "dee double-prime"). The **D″ layer**, the boundary layer between the rocky mantle and the liquid iron outer core, is thought to have large variations in composition as well as temperature (FIGURE 10). Cool areas in the D″ layer are thought to be the graveyard of subducted oceanic lithosphere, whereas the hot areas are the birthplace of deep mantle plumes.

The very base of D″, the part of the mantle in direct contact with the hot liquid iron core, is like Earth's surface in that there are "upside-down mountains" of rock that protrude into the core. Furthermore, in some regions of the core–mantle boundary, the base of D″ may be hot enough to be partially molten. Evidence for partial melting comes from zones at the very base of the mantle where S-wave velocities decrease by 30 percent, an indication that the material there is quite weak.

Discovering Boundaries: The Core–Mantle Boundary Evidence that Earth has a distinct central core was uncovered in 1906 by British geologist Richard Dixon Oldham. At locations beyond approximately 100 degrees from the epicenter of a large earthquake, Oldham observed that P and S waves were absent or very weak. In other words, Oldham found evidence for a central core that produced a **shadow zone** for seismic waves (FIGURE 11). In 1914, Beno Gutenberg calculated 2900 kilometers to the core boundary depth, which remains the accepted value.

As Oldham predicted, Earth's core exhibits markedly different properties from the mantle above, which causes considerable refraction of P waves—similarly to how light is refracted as it passes from air to water. In addition, because the outer core is liquid iron, it blocks the transmission of S waves. (Recall that S waves do not travel through liquids.)

The locations of the P- and S-wave shadow zones and how their paths are affected by the core are shown in Figure 11. Whereas some P and S waves still arrive in the shadow zone, they differ greatly from those expected in a planet without a core.

A. The P-wave shadow zone exists because P waves interact with the low-velocity liquid iron of the outer core, which causes their rays to be refracted downward. This creates a shadow zone where no direct P waves are recorded (although reflected P waves travel there).

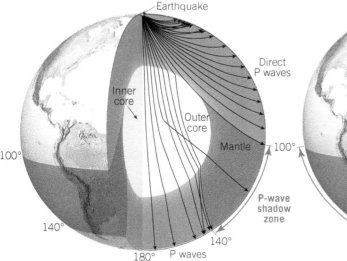

B. The core is an obstacle to S waves, because they cannot pass through liquids. Therefore, a large shadow zone exists for direct S waves.

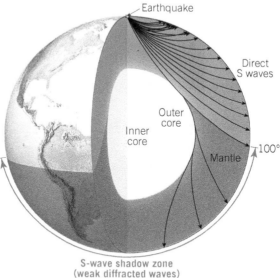

A. The P waves that travel through the core are called PKP waves. The "K" represents the path through the core and comes from the German word for core, which is *kern*. The increase in seismic velocity at the top of the inner core can refract waves sharply, so some arrive within the shadow zone, shown here as a single ray. **B.** Some S waves are bent around the core and are recorded on the other side of the planet within the S-wave shadow zone.

Earth's Core

The Outer Core   The boundary between Earth's mantle and outer core, called the *core–mantle boundary*, is significant because of its varied material properties. P wave velocities drop dramatically as they cross the core–mantle boundary, and S waves do not penetrate the outer core. Because S waves do not pass through liquids, their absence in the **outer core** indicates its liquid state. The change in density at the core–mantle boundary from 5.6 to 9.9 g/cm³ is even larger than the air–rock difference observed at Earth's surface.

Based on our knowledge of the composition of meteorites, geologists expect Earth to contain a significantly higher percentage of iron than is observed in rocks found in the crust and mantle. This fact, coupled with the great density of the core, indicates that the outer core consists mostly of iron, with lesser amounts of nickel, which has a density similar to that of iron.

Density and seismic studies suggest that in addition to iron and nickel, about 15 percent of the outer core consists of lighter elements. Based on mineral physics experiments, these are likely to include sulfur, oxygen, silicon, and hydrogen. For instance, an iron–sulfur mixture melts at a much lower temperature than pure iron. As Earth was forming, high-velocity impacts of nebular debris and the decay of radioactive elements caused the temperature of our planet to increase.

When heated sufficiently, iron in the presence of sulfur would begin to melt before pure iron. Melting produced liquid blobs of an iron–sulfur alloy that sank to form the core. In a similar manner, other light elements were dragged down into the core.

The **core** accounts for about one-sixth of Earth's volume but one-third of its mass because it is composed mostly of iron, which is the most dense of the common elements. In fact, iron is Earth's most abundant element when measured by mass.

The Inner Core   At the center of the core is the **inner core**, a solid dense sphere (around 13 g/cm³) of iron with trace amounts of other elements. Because the inner core is a sphere whereas Earth's other layers are shells, drawings make the inner core appear much larger than it really is (see Figure 1). The inner core is actually relatively small, only 1/142 of the volume of Earth (less than 1 percent). The inner core did not exist early in Earth's history, when our planet was hotter. However, as Earth cooled, iron began to crystallize at the center to form the solid inner core. Even today, the inner core continues to grow larger—at the expense of the outer core—as the planet cools.

Separated from the mantle by the liquid outer core, the solid inner core is free to rotate independently from Earth's outer layers. Recent studies suggest that the inner core rotates faster than the crust and mantle, lapping them every few hundred years

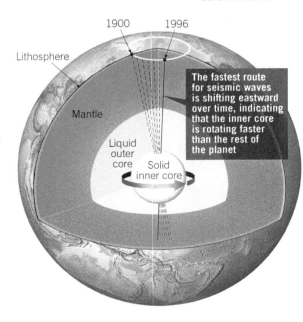

FIGURE 12 The solid inner core moves independently of Earth's other layers Slight variations in the travel times of seismic waves through the core, measured over many decades, suggest that the inner core actually rotates faster than the mantle. The reason for this is not yet understood.

1900   1996

Lithosphere

Mantle

Liquid outer core

Solid inner core

The fastest route for seismic waves is shifting eastward over time, indicating that the inner core is rotating faster than the rest of the planet

(FIGURE 12). The inner core's small size and great distance from the surface make it the most difficult-to-examine region of Earth.

Discovering Boundaries: The Inner Core–Outer Core Boundary The boundary between the solid inner core and liquid outer core was discovered in 1936 by Danish seismologist Inge Lehman. By examining seismograph records, Lehman discovered that some P waves were strongly refracted (bent) by a sudden increase in seismic velocities at a boundary within Earth's core. The waves she observed were bent enough to arrive within the P-wave shadow zone, as shown in Figure 11A. Because of the work of Lehman and other scientists, it is now understood that the inner core is an integral part of the activities of Earth's interior.

3 CONCEPT CHECKS

1. How do continental crust and oceanic crust differ?
2. What is the Moho? How were seismic waves used to discover the Moho and determine its depth?
3. Why is the asthenosphere weaker than the lithosphere?
4. List and briefly describe the composition and physical properties of the layers of the mantle.
5. How are Earth's inner and outer cores different? How are they similar?

Kimberly diamond mine, South Africa, also called the Big Hole, is considered a "window" into Earth. Because diamonds can form only in high-temperature, high-pressure environments, these diamond-bearing structures are thought to originate in the mantle at least 150 kilometers (90 miles) below Earth's surface, and perhaps much deeper. (Photo by Ann and Steve Toon/Alamy)

4 Earth's Temperature

Deciphering Earth's temperature structure and how temperature changes with depth is important for determining the movements of rock within our planet. As you are probably aware, heat flows from hotter regions toward colder regions. Earth is about 5500° C at its center and 0° C at its surface. As a result, heat flows toward Earth's surface.

The rate at which Earth is cooling can be estimated by determining the rate at which heat escapes Earth's surface—a mere 87 milliwatts per square meter. At this rate, it would require all the energy emitted from about 690 square meters, roughly the size of a baseball diamond, to power one 60-watt light bulb. However, because Earth's surface is so large, heat leaves at a rate about three times greater than the world rate of energy consumption.

FIGURE 13 illustrates that heat does not escape Earth's surface at the same rate in all locations. Heat flow is highest near mid-ocean ridges, where hot magma is consistently rising toward the surface. The rate of heat flow is also high in continental regions where the rocks are enriched in radioactive isotopes. Heat flow is lowest in the deep abyssal plains, which are areas of old, cold oceanic seafloor.

How Did Earth Get So Hot?

Like all other planets in our solar system, Earth has experienced two thermal stages (FIGURE 14). The first stage occurred during Earth's formation and lasted about 50 million years—a relatively short time span in geologic terms—and involved a rapid increase in internal temperature. The second stage has been the very slow process of cooling over the remaining 4.5 billion years of Earth history.

Several factors contributed to the early increase in temperature. Earth formed through a very violent process involving the collisions of countless planetesimals ("baby planets") during the birth of our solar system. With each collision, the kinetic energy of motion was converted into thermal energy. As the early Earth grew in size, its temperature rapidly increased. Our young planet also contained many short-lived radioactive isotopes, such as aluminum-26 and calcium-41. As these isotopes decayed to stable forms, they released a great deal of energy, called *radiogenic heat.*

Another significant event that heated our planet was the collision of a Mars-sized object with Earth that led to the formation of the Moon. At that time, the entire core, and most, if not all, of the mantle was molten. From that point, about 4.5 billion years ago, to the present, Earth has gradually cooled.

If Earth's only heat came from its early formation and the decay of short-lived radioactive isotopes, our planet would have cooled to a frozen cinder long ago. However, the mantle and crust also contain long-lived radioactive isotopes that keep our planet cooking as if on a slow burner. The half-lives of the four main

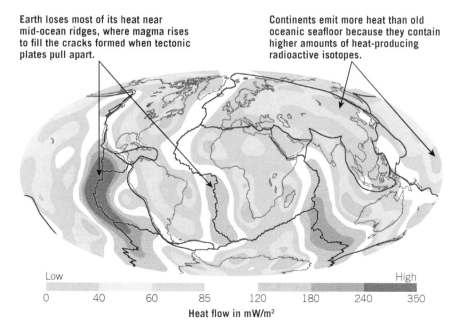

Earth loses most of its heat near mid-ocean ridges, where magma rises to fill the cracks formed when tectonic plates pull apart.

Continents emit more heat than old oceanic seafloor because they contain higher amounts of heat-producing radioactive isotopes.

FIGURE 13 Rate of heat flow at Earth's surface A map of the rate of heat flow out of Earth as it gradually cools over time, measured in milliwatts per square meter.

Low   High

| 0 | 40 | 60 | 85 | 120 | 180 | 240 | 350 |

Heat flow in mW/m²

SMARTFIGURE 14
Earth's thermal history
through time

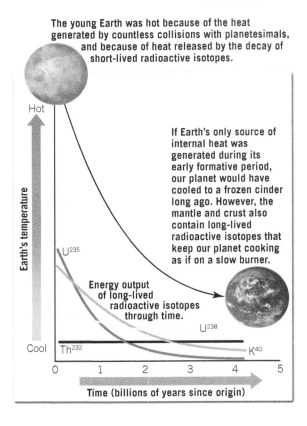

The young Earth was hot because of the heat generated by countless collisions with planetesimals, and because of heat released by the decay of short-lived radioactive isotopes.

If Earth's only source of internal heat was generated during its early formative period, our planet would have cooled to a frozen cinder long ago. However, the mantle and crust also contain long-lived radioactive isotopes that keep our planet cooking as if on a slow burner.

Energy output of long-lived radioactive isotopes through time.

Hot

Earth's temperature

U^{235}

Cool   Th^{232} U^{238} K^{40}

0   1   2   3   4   5

Time (billions of years since origin)

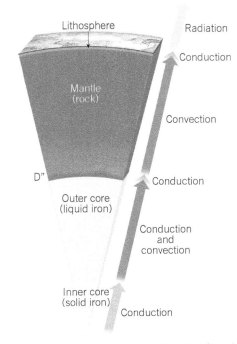

FIGURE 15 Dominant types of heat transfer at various depths Heat travels from Earth's interior to the surface through the processes of convection and conduction. However, Earth ultimately loses its heat to space through radiation.

isotopes—uranium-235, uranium-238, thorium-232, and potassium-40—are billions of years long.

Radioactivity plays two vital roles in geology. It is the means for determining the ages of rocks. More importantly, it is the source of radiogenic heat that drives mantle convection and, ultimately, the movement of Earth's tectonic plates.

Heat Flow

Heat travels from Earth's interior to space via three different mechanisms: *convection*, *conduction*, and *radiation*. The layers where these mechanisms contribute significantly to the outward flow of thermal energy are shown in FIGURE 15. Only two of these processes, convection and conduction, operate within Earth's interior. The third, radiation, transports heat away from Earth's surface and eventually back to space.

Convection   The transfer of heat in a fluid-like manner where hot materials displace cooler materials (or vice versa) is called **convection**. It is the primary means of heat transfer within Earth. You are familiar with convection if you have ever watched boiling water in a pot. The water appears to be rolling—rising in the middle

and sinking down the sides of the pot (FIGURE 16). This pattern, called a *convection cycle*, occurs within Earth's mantle and outer core, and possibly within the inner core as well.

Convection occurs because of several factors: thermal expansion, gravity-induced buoyancy, and fluidity. When water at the bottom of a pot is heated, it expands and rises, replacing the cooler, denser water at the top. Gravity is the driving force for convection. Hot water is less dense (more buoyant) than cold water, so it rises, and the cold water sinks to take its place. If you tried to boil water in outer space, where there is no strong gravity, you would find that the pot of water would not convect.

Materials must also be weak enough to flow. Scientists usually measure a material's fluidity in terms of its *resistance* to flow, called its **viscosity**. Water flows easily and has a low viscosity. The liquid iron of Earth's outer core likely has a viscosity similar to that of water, and it convects easily as well. Materials that are viscous do not flow as easily as water but can still flow. For example, ketchup flows, although it is thousands of times more viscous than water. Rock in the lower mantle is 10 trillion trillion (10^{25}) times more viscous than water, but yet it flows.

Temperature differences between the top and bottom of a convection cycle determine how vigorous the

Conduction   The flow of heat *through a material* is called **conduction**. Heat conducts in two ways: (1) through the collisions of atoms and (2) through the flow of electrons. In rocks, atoms are locked in place but are constantly oscillating. If one side of a rock is heated, the atoms on that side will oscillate more energetically. This increases the intensity of the collisions with neighboring atoms, and in a domino effect, the energy slowly propagates through the rock. Conduction occurs much more quickly in metals than in rocky substances. Although the atoms in metals are also locked in place, some of their electrons are free to move through the material, and these electrons can carry heat quickly from one side of a metallic object to another.

Materials conduct at vastly different rates. For example, heat conducts about 40,000 times more easily through a diamond than through air. Most rocks are poor conductors of heat, so conduction is not an efficient way to move heat through most of Earth. However, it is an important mechanism in places such as the lithosphere, the D″ layer, and the core.

Heat Flow in Earth's Interior   The dominant types of heat transfer in Earth's interior are illustrated in Figure 15. Conduction is thought to be the most important process in the solid inner core. When heat conducts from the inner core to the outer core, convection begins to play a more significant role in carrying heat to the top of the core.

Convective flow in the outer core is thought to be driven by three main mechanisms:

1. As heat conducts out of the core into the overlying mantle, the material in the outermost core cools, becomes denser, and sinks. This is a form of top-down, thermally driven convection.
2. Crystallization of solid iron near the bottom of the outer core sinks to form the inner core and leaves behind fluids that are less dense because they are depleted of iron. As this buoyant fluid rises, away from the inner core boundary, it drives a type of chemical convection.

FIGURE 16 Convection: Heat transfer that involves the movement of a substance
The flame warms the water in the bottom of the beaker. The heated water expands, becomes less dense (more buoyant), and rises. Simultaneously, the cooler, denser water near the top sinks.

convection will be. Earth's surface is extremely cold compared to the interior, so newly formed oceanic lithosphere cools rapidly (FIGURE 17). This causes oceanic lithosphere to contract, become denser and heavier, and, in time, sink back into the mantle at subduction zones. As these cold sinking slabs descend, they absorb heat. Some of this crustal material eventually becomes warm and buoyant enough to return to the surface. Cool oceanic lithosphere can therefore be thought of as the top of the mantle convection cycle, whereas rising mantle rock below spreading centers and the warm buoyant rocks called **mantle plumes** are the upward-flowing arms of this convection cycle (Figure 17).

Convection sometimes occurs when differences in density arise through chemical rather than thermal means. *Chemical convection* is an important mechanism operating in the outer core. As iron crystallizes and sinks to form the solid inner core, it leaves behind a molten material that contains a higher percentage of lighter elements. Because this liquid is more buoyant than the surrounding iron-rich material, it rises and contributes to convective flow in the outer core.

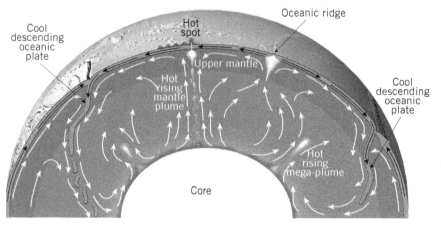

FIGURE 17 Whole-mantle convection
According to this model, the entire mantle is in motion, driven by the sinking of cold oceanic lithosphere back into the deep mantle. This is like stirring a pot of stew with downward strokes of a spoon. The upward flow of rock likely occurs through a combination of mantle plumes and a broad return flow of rock to replace the oceanic lithosphere that leaves the surface at subduction zones. Not all scientists agree with this model.

3. There are thought to be radioactive isotopes, such as potassium-40, within the core that could provide additional heat to drive thermal convection.

The transfer of energy from the core to the mantle occurs by conduction because the iron-rich material of the core is too dense to intrude (convect) into the less dense mantle rocks. For thermal energy to leave the core, it must conduct across the core–mantle boundary and up through the D" layer. Once it reaches the lower mantle, thermal energy is carried toward the surface through slow, sluggish mantle convection.

Most of the thermal energy that reaches the upper mantle makes its final journey to the surface by slowly conducting across the stiff, rigid lithosphere. The remaining energy is carried to the surface along divergent plate boundaries and other sites of volcanic activity where rising molten rock erupts.

Earth's Temperature Profile

The profile of Earth's average temperature at each depth is called the **geothermal gradient**, or **geotherm** (FIGURE 18A). Within the crust, temperatures increase rapidly—as much as 30° C per kilometer of depth. The deepest diamond mines in South Africa are more than 3 kilometers below Earth's surface, where temperatures

SMARTFIGURE 18
The geotherm and melting point curve are valuable tools for investigating Earth materials at depth If you compare these two graphs, you can see that rocks are weakest and flow more easily at depths where the temperatures of rocks are close to melting (the asthenosphere and D" layer). High viscosities, like those of the crust and lithosphere, show rock that is stiffer and flows less easily.

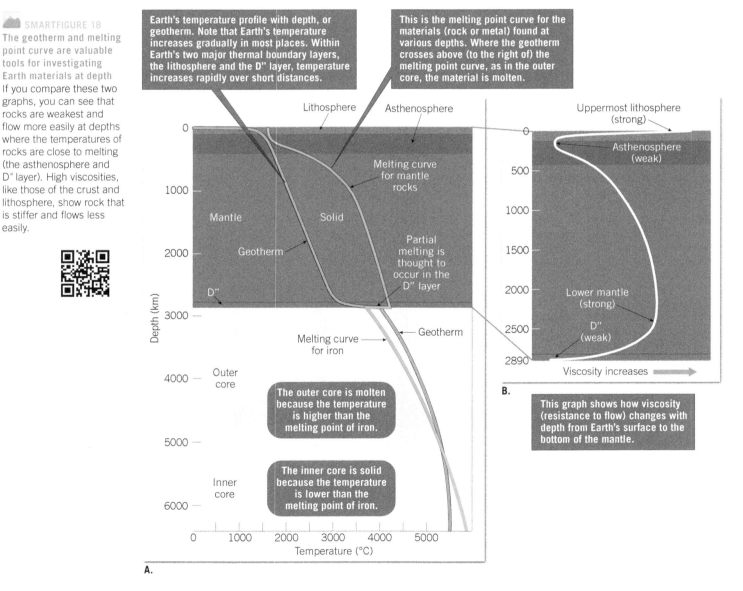

Earth's temperature profile with depth, or geotherm. Note that Earth's temperature increases gradually in most places. Within Earth's two major thermal boundary layers, the lithosphere and the D" layer, temperature increases rapidly over short distances.

This is the melting point curve for the materials (rock or metal) found at various depths. Where the geotherm crosses above (to the right of) the melting point curve, as in the outer core, the material is molten.

The outer core is molten because the temperature is higher than the melting point of iron.

The inner core is solid because the temperature is lower than the melting point of iron.

This graph shows how viscosity (resistance to flow) changes with depth from Earth's surface to the bottom of the mantle.

exceed 50° C (120° F). However, temperature increases do not continue at this rapid rate; if they did, our planet would be molten ball surrounded by a 100-kilometer-thick outer shell.

At the base of the lithosphere, about 100 kilometers down, the temperature is roughly 1400° C. You would need to descend to nearly the bottom of the mantle before the temperature doubled to 2800° C. For most of the mantle, the temperature increases very slowly—about 0.3° C per kilometer. The exception to this pattern is within the thin D″ layer, which acts as a thermal boundary, where temperatures increase by more than 1000° C from top to bottom.

Determining temperatures deep within Earth is difficult, and uncertainties remain. The temperature at Earth's center has been estimated to be between 5000° and 8000° C. For our discussion, we use 5500° C as the temperature at Earth's center.

Figure 18A shows the geotherm (average temperature at each depth) as well as the curve for the melting point of material at each depth. Note that the melting point curves generally increase gradually with depth as a result of the continual increase in pressure exerted by the overlying material. Squeezing a material makes it more difficult to melt because in their liquid form, materials usually take up more volume than in their solid form. As a result, higher pressures result in higher melting temperatures.

Considered together, the geotherm and the melting point curve are valuable tools for investigating the behavior of Earth's materials. In layers where the geotherm (temperature at depth) is greater than the melting temperature, the material is molten. As shown in Figure 18A, this situation occurs in the outer core.

The relationship between the geotherm and the melting temperature not only determines whether a material is molten but also indicates its stiffness, or viscosity. Notice how viscosity, shown in FIGURE 18B, is directly related to the proximity of the geotherm curves to the melting point curves in Figure 18A. When rock approaches its melting point, it begins to soften and weaken. Low-viscosity regions, such as the asthenosphere and D″, are weak. High-viscosity regions, such as the lithosphere, are rigid.

Most of the lower mantle is very stiff, so rock moves sluggishly there (Figure 18B). Researchers have determined that convective flow is several times slower in the lower mantle than in the upper mantle. However, at the very base of the mantle, temperature increases rapidly with depth. As a result, rock in the D″ layer is relatively weak, flows more easily, and may experience some melting.

In the core, temperature increases much more slowly than pressure. From the core–mantle boundary to Earth's center, the temperature increases by only about 40 percent, or from about 4000° to 5500° C. Pressure, however, nearly triples, increasing from 1.36 to 3.64 megabars (1 megabar is 1 million times greater than standard atmospheric pressure). Although the temperature is cooler in the outer core than it is in the inner core, the outer core remains a liquid because it is under less pressure. Conversely, iron in the inner core remains solid at these high temperatures because its melting temperature increases dramatically at these extreme pressures.

4 CONCEPT CHECKS

1. In general, how does temperature change between Earth's surface and its core?
2. What were the two main sources of Earth's original internal heat?
3. How is heat transferred inside Earth?
4. What happens to rock as the geotherm approaches the rock's melting temperature?

5 | Earth's Three-Dimensional Structure

As you have seen, Earth is not perfectly layered. At the surface, a variety of compositional and structural differences exist: oceans, continents, mountains, valleys, trenches, and mid-ocean ridges. Geophysical observations show that horizontal variations are not limited to the surface; they also occur within Earth and are directly related to the process of mantle convection and plate tectonics. Three-dimensional structures within Earth have been identified by studying variations in Earth's gravitational and magnetic fields and imaging called *seismic tomography*.

Earth's Gravity

Earth's rotation is the most significant cause for the differences in the force of gravity observed at the surface. Because Earth rotates around its axis the acceleration due to gravity[*] is less at the equator (9.78 m/s²) than at the poles (9.83 m/s²). Two reasons account for this phenomenon. Earth's rotation causes a centrifugal force that is in proportion to the distance from the axis of rotation. In a manner similar to the force that throws you sideways in a vehicle going too quickly around a curve or corner, centrifugal force acts to throw objects outward at the equator, where the force is greatest.

Earth's shape is also affected by its rotation—with the equator slightly further from Earth's center (6378 kilometers) than the poles (6357 kilometers) (FIGURE 19). Earth, therefore, is not a perfect sphere but instead bulges at the equator—a shape called an *oblate ellipsoid*. This difference causes the force of gravity to be slightly weaker at the equator than at the poles because gravitational attraction is less when objects are further apart. In fact, your body weight is 0.5 percent less at the equator than at the poles.

Gravity measurements show that there are other variations that cannot be explained by Earth's rotation. For instance, when a large body of unusually dense rock is underground, the increase in mass will cause a larger-than-average gravitational force at the surface directly above. Because metals and metal ores tend to be much denser than silicate rocks, local *gravity anomalies* (differences from the expected) have long been used to help prospect for ore deposits.

A map of regional gravity anomalies for the United States is shown in FIGURE 20. A narrow *positive gravity anomaly* (stronger than expected) that runs down the middle of the country is the mid-continent rift (red), where thick, dense volcanic rocks filled a rupture in the crust more than 1 billion years ago. The *negative gravity anomaly* (blue) in the Basin and Range region is a result of warm, low-density crust being stretched and thinned as it was intruded by hot buoyant magma bodies.

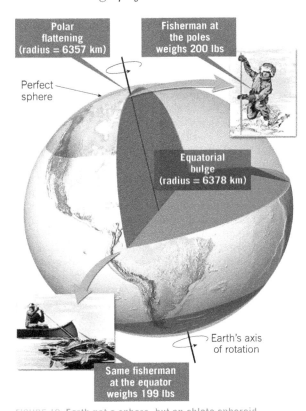

FIGURE 19 Earth not a sphere, but an oblate spheroid
Because Earth rotates, it bulges at the equator and flattens at the poles. The combination of Earth's elliptical shape and its daily rotation actually causes the force of gravity to be slightly weaker at the equator than at the poles. This difference is large enough to be measured on a bathroom scale. Imagine two fishermen of equal mass both standing at sea level. If the one at the North Pole weighs 200 pounds, the one at the equator would weigh only 199 pounds.

Some large-scale differences in density deep beneath the surface have been detected using satellites. These gravity anomalies result from the large upwellings and downwellings of mantle convection. Areas of upwelling are associated with hot mantle plumes, whereas downwelling occurs where cold oceanic slabs descend into the mantle.

---

[*]The force of gravity causes objects, such as apples, to accelerate as they fall to the ground, hence the expression "acceleration due to gravity."

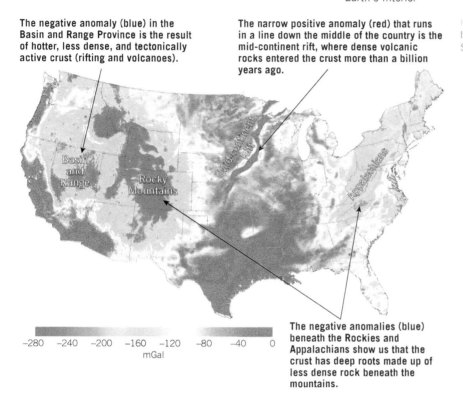

The negative anomaly (blue) in the Basin and Range Province is the result of hotter, less dense, and tectonically active crust (rifting and volcanoes).

The narrow positive anomaly (red) that runs in a line down the middle of the country is the mid-continent rift, where dense volcanic rocks entered the crust more than a billion years ago.

FIGURE 20 Gravity anomalies beneath the continental United States

The negative anomalies (blue) beneath the Rockies and Appalachians show us that the crust has deep roots made up of less dense rock beneath the mountains.

-280 -240 -200 -160 -120 -80 -40 0
mGal

Seismic Tomography

The three-dimensional changes in composition and density that are detected with gravity measurements can also be viewed using seismology. The technique, called **seismic tomography**, involves collecting signals from many different earthquakes recorded at many seismograph stations, in order to "see" all parts of Earth's interior. Seismic tomography is similar to medical tomography, in which doctors use technology such as CT scans to make three-dimensional images of humans' internal organs.

Seismic tomography identifies regions where P or S waves travel faster or slower than average for a particular depth. These *seismic velocity anomalies* are then interpreted as variations in material properties such as temperature, composition, mineral phase, or water content. For instance, increasing the temperature of rock about 100° C can decrease S-wave velocities about 1 percent, so images from seismic tomography are often interpreted in terms of temperature variations.

A seismic tomography cross section for the mantle centered beneath North America is shown in FIGURE 21. Regions where waves travel slower than average (negative anomalies) are red, and regions where waves travel faster than average (positive anomalies) are blue. Significant patterns can be observed in this diagram. For example, the lithosphere beneath the interiors of North America and Africa exhibits faster seismic velocities than oceanic lithosphere because continental lithosphere is older and has been cooling for billions of years. Seismic imaging also shows that continental lithosphere (deep blue areas) can be quite thick, extending more than 300 kilometers into the mantle. Conversely, oceanic ridges such as the Mid-Atlantic Ridge, exhibit slow seismic velocities because they are extremely hot (Figure 21).

In the mantle beneath North America, you can see a sloping zone of fast seismic velocities (blue/green) representing a sheet of descending oceanic lithosphere known as the Farallon plate. The segment of this former slab of seafloor seen in Figure 21 is currently sinking and warming as it moves toward the core–mantle boundary. Given enough time, this slab may become hot and buoyant enough to begin to rise back to the surface.

The large region of slow seismic velocities beneath Africa (the large reddish orange region at the lower right of Figure 21) is called the *African superplume*—a region of upward flow in the mantle. These slow velocities are likely due to both unusually high temperatures and rock that is highly enriched in iron. The rising rock cannot easily break through the thick African crust, so it seems

Earth's Interior

FIGURE 21 A seismic tomographic slice showing the structure of the mantle Colors show variations in the speed of S waves from their average value. Cool, strong rock produces fast S waves and is shown in blue, while warm, weak rock produces slow S waves and is shown in red.

The western United States is tectonically active, making that portion of the continent warmer and weaker (shown by the color red), which slows S waves.

The large blue structure extending far beneath North America is likely to be a sheet of cold, dense, ancient Pacific seafloor that is sinking toward the base of the mantle.

Older portions of continents, America and Africa, are cold and strong—the blue color indicates fast S wave speeds.

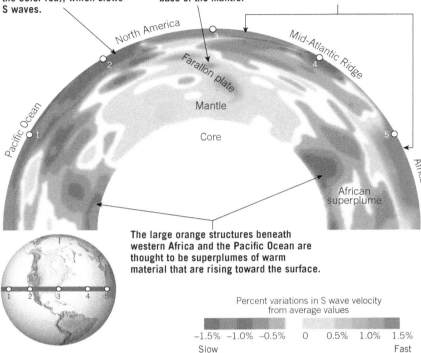

The large orange structures beneath western Africa and the Pacific Ocean are thought to be superplumes of warm material that are rising toward the surface.

Percent variations in S wave velocity from average values

−1.5% −1.0% −0.5% 0 0.5% 1.0% 1.5%
Slow   Fast

to be deflected to both sides of the continent, perhaps supplying magma to both the Mid-Atlantic and Indian Ocean spreading centers.

Earth's Magnetic Field

Convection of liquid iron in the outer core is vigorous, which makes the outer core *appear* uniform when viewed with seismic waves. In *reality*, however, patterns of flow in the outer core create variations in Earth's magnetic field that are measurable at the surface and tell a different story.

The Geodynamo Earth's magnetic field has a complex structure that reflects the processes that generate it. As iron-rich fluid in the outer core rises, its path becomes twisted because of Earth's rotation. As a result, the fluid moves in spiraling columns that align with Earth's axis of rotation (**FIGURE 22**). Because the iron-rich fluid is electrically charged and flowing, it generates a magnetic field—a phenomenon called a **geodynamo**. This process is similar to how an electromagnet generates a magnetic field. When a wire is wrapped around an iron nail and an electric current passes through it, the nail becomes a magnet

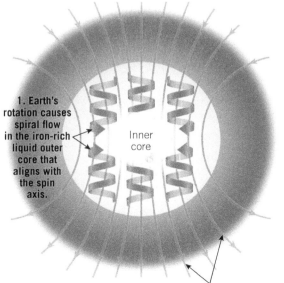

1. Earth's rotation causes spiral flow in the iron-rich liquid outer core that aligns with the spin axis.

Inner core

2. The electrically-charged spiral flow in the outer core generates Earth's magnetic field. This is similar to how an electromagnet works.

FIGURE 22 How Earth's magnetic field is generated in the liquid, iron-rich outer core

436

This simple electromagnet consists of a nail wrapped in a coil of wire that has an electrical current traveling through it.

It was once thought that Earth's core acted like a large bar magnet. Now scientists think that Earth's magnetic field is similar to that produced by an electromagnet. The cylinders of spiraling liquid iron shown in Figure 22 behave like the electric current passing through the coil wire of an electromagnet.

FIGURE 23 Similarities between Earth's magnetic field and an electromagnet

A. Electromagnet (Dipolar field)

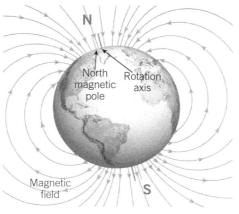

B. Earth's magnetic field (Dipolar field)

that generates a magnetic field that resembles the one that surrounds a bar magnet (FIGURE 23A,B). This type of magnetic field is called a *dipolar field* because it has two poles (north and south magnetic poles). The magnetic field that emanates from Earth's outer core has the same dipolar form (Figure 23).

However, the convection in the outer core is considerably more complex. More than 90 percent of Earth's magnetic field is dipolar, but the remainder is a result of more complicated patterns of convection. In addition, some of the features of Earth's magnetic field change over time. For centuries, sailors have used compasses to navigate, primarily keeping track of the direction in which compass needles point. From these observations, it was determined that the positions of the magnetic poles gradually change. Understanding this phenomenon requires an examination of how the magnetic field is measured.

Measuring Earth's Magnetic Field and Its Changes Anywhere on Earth's surface, the direction of the magnetic field is measured with two angles, called *declination* and *inclination*. The declination measures the direction to the magnetic north pole with respect to the direction to the geographic North Pole (Earth's axis of rotation). The inclination measures the downward tilt of the magnetic lines of force at any location—what a compass would show if tilted on its side. At the magnetic north pole, the field points directly downward, while at the equator, it is horizontal (FIGURE 24). In the central United States it tilts downward at an intermediate angle.

Recent studies have shown that the locations of the magnetic poles change significantly over time. Earth's magnetic north pole was previously located in Canada but moved northward into the Arctic Ocean during the past decade. Currently, it is moving northwestward between 50 and 65 kilometers (34 and 37 miles) per year (FIGURE 25). While the magnetic north pole has been moving toward the geographic North Pole, the magnetic south pole has been moving *away* from the geographic South Pole, passing from Antarctica to the Pacific Ocean.

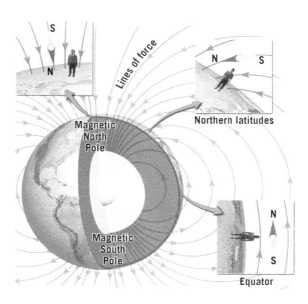

FIGURE 24 Inclination or dip of the magnetic field at different locations Although a compass measures only the horizontal direction of the magnetic field (the *declination*), at most locations, the field also dips in or out of the surface at various angles (*inclination*).

FIGURE 25 Locations of
the north magnetic pole
over time
The patterns of convec-
tion within the outer core
change fast enough that
we can see the strength
and position of the
magnetic field change significantly over our lifetimes.

emitted by the Sun. If the strength of the magnetic
field decreases significantly during a reversal, the increased amounts of ionized particles reaching Earth's
surface could cause health hazards for humans and
other life-forms.

Global Dynamic Connections The layers of planet
Earth are not isolated from one another; rather, they are
connected by their thermally driven motions. These connected motions do not necessarily interact in a predictable, steady manner; instead, they tend to occur episodically or in pulses. One example is the possible connection
between magnetic reversals, hot-spot volcanism, and the
breakup of the supercontinent Pangaea.

Pangaea began to break up about 200 million years
ago, and the accompanying increase in plate motion
resulted in the subduction of large amounts of seafloor.
About 80 million years later, the magnetic reversal

Magnetic Reversals Although the pattern of convection in the core changes over time, causing the magnetic
poles to move, the locations of the magnetic poles averaged over thousands of years align with Earth's axis of
rotation (geographic poles). One major exception occurs
during periods of magnetic field reversals. At apparently
random times, Earth's magnetic field reverses polarity so
that the *north* needle on a compass would point *south*.
During a reversal, the strength of the magnetic field decreases to about 10 percent of normal, and the locations
of the poles begin to wander, going so far as to cross the
equator (FIGURE 26). When the strength of the magnetic
field returns to normal levels, the field is regenerated
with reverse polarity. The entire process takes only a few
thousand years.

The rate at which the magnetic field reverses provides evidence that convection patterns in the outer core
change over relatively short time spans. This complex
process is now being modeled using high-speed computers (Figure 26). In addition, Figure 26 illustrates how the
magnetic field lines twist in a complex manner before
returning to a more uniform, simpler dipolar pattern.

The existence of magnetic reversals has been
extremely important to geoscientists in providing the
foundation for the theory of plate tectonics. However,
magnetic reversals have potentially harmful consequences for Earth's land dwellers. An atmospheric
magnetic layer, known as the *magnetosphere*, surrounds our planet and protects Earth's surface from
bombardment by ionized particles, called *solar wind*,

**A. Normal orientation of
magnetic field**

**B. Magnetic field weakens and
poles begin to wander**

**C. Poles wander across the
equator**

**D. Reversal complete with
north pole pointing south**

FIGURE 26 Computer simulations showing how Earth's
magnetic field might reverse direction
The white circle represents the core–mantle boundary, and
the dashed white line represents the projected position of
the equator. The arrows point to the north (N) and south
(S) magnetic poles. During a reversal, the strength of the
magnetic field weakens, and the poles begin to wander
greatly, going so far as to cross the equator. When the
strength of the field returns to normal levels, the field is
regenerated with reverse polarity.

process shut down, preventing Earth's magnetic field from reversing for 35 million years. During this period, several enormous outpourings of lava have been linked to the arrival of new hot-spot mantle plumes at the surface.

In one hypothesis, these three events are closely connected. In the 80 million years following the breakup of Pangaea, a large amount of subducted lithosphere is thought to have plunged to the base of the mantle. This would have displaced hot rock at the base of the mantle, causing much of it to rise toward the surface and erupt as flood basalts. India's Deccan Traps are an example of such a process. At the same time, the sudden infusion of comparatively cold oceanic lithosphere next to the hot core at the core–mantle boundary would have chilled the uppermost core. This increased the temperature gradient—hotter at the bottom, cooler at the top—in the outer core. The result was more vigorous convection that

prevented the magnetic field from weakening and reversing. This hypothesis, if deemed accurate, is an important reminder that Earth is a complex, churning, pulsing planet that is active in a variety of geologic functions.

5 CONCEPT CHECKS

1. Is the force of gravity the same over Earth's entire surface? Explain why or why not.
2. Give examples of tectonic features of Earth's three-dimensional structure that are revealed by seismic tomography.
3. What is thought to produce Earth's magnetic field?
4. Describe how Earth's magnetic field changes though time.

CONCEPTS IN REVIEW: EARTH'S INTERIOR

1 Earth's Internal Structure

Explain how Earth acquired its layered structure.

KEY WORD mineral phase change

- The layered internal structure of Earth developed due to gravitational sorting of Earth materials early in the history of the planet. The densest material sunk to the center, and the least dense material rose to the exterior.

- Within layers such as the mantle, atoms in a mineral may rearrange into a more compact crystal structure. Given sufficient pressure, such a mineral phase change can pack the same amount of matter into a smaller volume. This results in an increased density. For example, olivine undergoes a phase change to become a more compact mineral at a depth of about 400 kilometers.

ORDER IT Arrange the following Earth layers to be in order from most dense to least dense: crust, atmosphere, core, mantle, oceans.

2 Probing Earth's Interior

Describe how seismic waves are used to probe Earth's interior.

KEY WORDS reflection, refraction

- Seismic waves allow geoscientists to "look" into Earth's interior, which would otherwise be invisible to scientific investigation. Like X-rays passing through a person's body, seismic waves from large earthquakes reveal details about Earth's layered structure.
- Seismic waves travel most rapidly through stiff, elastic materials, so when P or S waves cross a mineral phase change at depth, seismographs can detect their increased velocity. In general, seismic waves follow curved paths through Earth's interior because the deeper part of the wave travels slightly faster than the shallower part of the wave. When seismic waves pass through partially molten material, the seismic waves slow down because magma is less rigid and less elastic than solid rock. S waves cannot be transmitted through liquids, but P waves can.
- When seismic waves encounter a different layer, they may either reflect or refract. Reflection is like "bouncing": It's a change in the direction of the wave away from the new layer. With refraction, the wave continues into the new layer, but it bends, changing its path to a different trajectory.

PICK THE PLANET

Examine the seismic refraction profiles for two hypothetical planets, A and B. Which of the layered structures (1 or 2) best matches each profile? Which planet has a liquid layer?

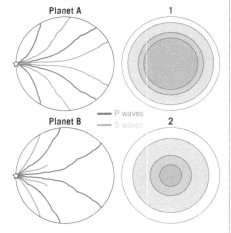

Planet A   1

Planet B   2

— P waves
— S waves

- The base of the crust is the Mohorovičić discontinuity, or Moho. It was discovered because seismic waves travel faster below the Moho (in the mantle) than they do above it (in the crust). Beneath the continents, the Moho lies 25 to 70 kilometers below the surface. In oceanic lithosphere, the Moho occurs at a depth of about 7 kilometers.
- Earth's mantle may be divided by density into upper (3.3 g/cm^3) and lower (5.6 g/cm^3) portions. The upper mantle includes the lithospheric mantle (which makes up the bulk of rigid tectonic plates) and the weak asthenosphere beneath it. There is a transition zone at the bottom of the upper mantle, between 410 and 660 kilometers in depth. The lower mantle lies below the transition zone. At its base, just above the core, is the unusual layer called D″. Seismic velocities slow dramatically in the D″ layer, indicating that it may be partially molten. This may be where subducted mantle slabs go before being recycled as mantle plumes.
- When an earthquake occurs, Earth's core casts a seismic "shadow" on the side of the planet opposite the quake. The size of this shadow zone reveals the size of the core: about one-sixth the volume of Earth. The composition of the core is likely a mix of iron, nickel, and lighter elements. Iron and nickel are common heavy elements in meteorites, the leftover "building blocks" of Earth. The outer core is dense (around 9.9 g/cm^3). It is known to be liquid, as S waves cannot pass through it. The inner core is solid, very dense (around 13 g/cm^3), and spins slightly faster than the rest of the planet.

WALK IT OUT Use the depth data from this figure to lay out a model section of Earth's layers. Use a metric measuring tape and a scale of 1 centimeter in the model to represent each kilometer of depth in the actual Earth. Mark major layer boundaries, and then walk from the surface to the core, noting the changes you "encounter" along the way.

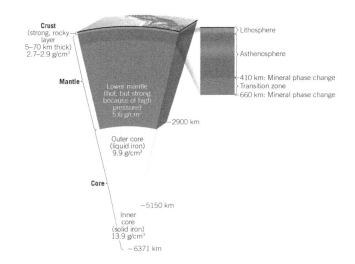

Crust (strong, rocky layer 5–70 km thick) 2.7–2.9 g/cm^3

Lithosphere

Asthenosphere

410 km: Mineral phase change
Transition zone
660 km: Mineral phase change

Mantle

Lower mantle (hot, but strong because of high pressure) 5.6 g/cm^3

—2900 km

Outer core (liquid iron) 9.9 g/cm^3

Core

—5150 km

Inner core (solid iron) 13.9 g/cm^3

—6371 km

3 Earth's Layers

List and describe each of the layers of Earth's interior.

KEY WORDS crust, Moho, mantle, upper mantle, lithospheric mantle, asthenosphere, transition zone, lower mantle, D″ layer, shadow zone, outer core, core, inner core

- Earth has two distinct kinds of crust: oceanic and continental. Oceanic crust is thinner, denser, and more iron and magnesium rich than continental crust. Oceanic crust also tends to be younger than continental crust, since it readily subducts but continents do not.

4   Earth's Temperature

Describe the processes of heat transfer that operate within Earth's interior and where each of these processes dominates.

KEY WORDS convection, viscosity, mantle plume, conduction, geothermal gradient (geotherm)

- Heat flows from Earth's interior outward, toward the surface. Heat flow through the crust is higher in places where the crust is thin and where magma is close to the surface. There are two main sources of heat in Earth's interior. First is residual kinetic energy left over from the amalgamation of the planet during the formation of the solar system. The second source of heat is radioactivity. Early in Earth's history, short-lived isotopes (now extinct) generated additional heat by radioactive decay. Radioactivity of long-lived isotopes (such as uranium-235 and potassium-40) continues to add heat at a lower rate today.
- Heat flows through Earth's interior via several mechanisms. Most important are convection and conduction. Conduction is the movement of heat (but not matter) through a body, and convection is the movement where hot materials displace cold materials due to the difference in their densities. Convection is the most important mechanism of heat transfer in Earth's interior, as large masses of warm material rise in a viscous fashion. Convection occurs in the liquid outer core, and then the core conducts heat to the mantle, and the mantle convects, carrying heat to the base of the lithosphere. When heat reaches Earth's surface, some of it radiates into space.
- The geothermal gradient is the profile of Earth's temperature versus depth. Temperature increases rapidly relative to depth in both the lithosphere and the D″ layer. Other than those two layers, there is a relatively gentle geotherm of 0.3° C per kilometer. The position of the melting point curve relative to the geotherm is a key relationship responsible for the behavior of Earth's interior layers. In layers where the geotherm is greater than the melting point curve, the material will be partially or totally molten.

YOU'RE GETTING WARMER   How can the outer core be molten if the solid inner core is even hotter? Explain this "paradox."

5   Earth's Three-Dimensional Structure

Discuss what the studies of Earth's gravity, seismic topography, and Earth's magnetic field have revealed about our planet.

KEY WORDS seismic tomography, geodynamo

- Earth exhibits not only vertical variations (layering) but horizontal variations as well (differences within a given layer). The composition and thickness of the mantle and core vary from place to place, just like the crust.
- Gravity anomalies occur where rock is more dense (often because it is cold) and less dense (often because it is warm).
- Seismic tomography is a technique for imaging Earth's interior on the basis of whether seismic waves speed up or slow down when they pass through it. These changes are usually interpreted in terms of temperature differences. Slower waves indicate relatively warm rock, which is likely rising due to convection.
- Convection of the liquid outer core generates a magnetic field that is larger than the entire planet. The magnetic field that results from this self-sustaining geodynamo changes in both the (1) position and (2) orientation of its poles over time.
- There may be a connection between deep Earth processes and the surface. For instance, as Pangaea broke up, displaced oceanic lithosphere would have subducted. If it sunk to the base of the mantle, it could sap heat from the core. Since the magnetic field is driven by temperature differences in the outer core, this could explain the anomalously stable magnetic polarity of the mid-Cretaceous. The subducted lithosphere, warmed by the heat transfer, might then have mobilized in plumes that ultimately erupted as flood basalts at the surface.

EDIBLE ANALOGY   If you were baking a cake to mimic some of the characteristics of Earth's interior, how would you deal with the issue of horizontal variation? Sketch your cake and describe the rationale behind your choice of ingredients.

GIVE IT SOME THOUGHT

1. Explain how S waves "tell us" the mantle is solid.

2. The accompanying diagram shows one incoming ray and three possible outgoing ray paths, labeled 1, 2, and 3. Match each of the outgoing ray paths with one of these descriptions:
   a. Reflected ray.
   b. Refracted ray going from a region of low velocity to high velocity.
   c. Refracted ray going from a region of high velocity to low velocity.

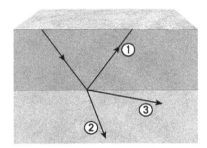

3. What are the two major reasons for the increase in density with depth in Earth's mantle?

4. Explain how the core is only one-sixth of Earth's volume, yet it is one-third of Earth's mass.

5. The accompanying diagram shows the internal structures of Earth, Mars, and Earth's Moon. Based on what you know about the composition of the layers shown and how density increase with depth, list these three bodies in order from the most dense to the least dense.

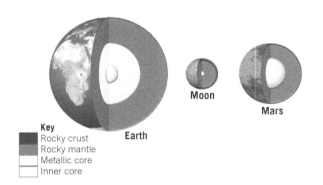

6. Describe how Earth's inner core grows in size.

7. Explain why convection is an inefficient means of heat transfer in materials with high viscosity.

8. Imagine that you are exploring another planet and using seismic data to determine the planet's internal structure. Based on the ray paths for the S waves shown in the accompanying diagram, answer the following questions:
   a. How many distinct layers does this planet appear to have (not including its outer surface)?
   b. Which of these layers is the thickest? Which is the thinnest?
   c. Does this planet have a liquid layer? If so, which one?

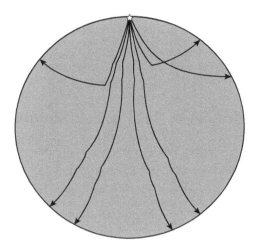

9. Earth once rotated much faster than it currently does. How would Earth's shape have been different in the past than it is today?

10. Why might a magnetic reversal be dangerous to humans?

11. The temperatures reach 50° C (120° F) in the deepest diamond mines in South Africa—which are about 3 kilometers below Earth's surface. Assuming an average surface temperature of 10° C, calculate the geothermal gradient for this region.

Peter Horree/Alamy Images

12. Earthquakes below the Yellowstone caldera originate at very shallow depths, about 4 kilometers on average. Below this depth, the rocks are at least 400° C, too hot and weak to store elastic energy. Based on this data, answer the following questions:

  a. What is the minimum geothermal gradient in the first 4 kilometers beneath the Yellowstone caldera, assuming an average surface temperature of 0° C (32° F)?

  b. At about what depth is the groundwater below the Yellowstone caldera hot enough to "boil" and therefore capable of generating a geyser?

Flirt/SuperStock

MasteringGeology™

www.masteringgeology.com

Looking for additional review and test prep materials? Visit the Study Area in MasteringGeology to enhance your understanding of this chapter's content by accessing a variety of resources, including **Self-Study Quizzes,** **Geoscience Animations, GEODe Tutorials, RSS feeds, flashcards, web links, self-study quizzes,** and an optional **Pearson eText.**

Glossary

Asthenosphere A subdivision of the mantle situated below the lithosphere. This zone of weak material exists below a depth of about 100 kilometers (60 miles) and in some regions extends as deep as 700 kilometers (430 miles). The rock within this zone is easily deformed.

Conduction The transfer of heat through matter by molecular activity.

Convection The transfer of heat by the mass movement or circulation of a substance.

Core The innermost layer of Earth. It is thought to be largely an iron–nickel alloy, with minor amounts of oxygen, silicon, and sulfur.

Crust The very thin, outermost layer of Earth.

D"layer A region in roughly the lowermost 200 kilometers (125 miles) of the mantle where P waves experience a sharp decrease in velocity.

Geothermal gradient The gradual increase in temperature with depth in the crust. The average is 30° C per kilometer in the upper crust.

Inner core The solid innermost layer of Earth, about 1216 kilometers (754 miles) in radius.

Lithosphere The rigid outer layer of Earth, including the crust and upper mantle.

Lower mantle See *Mesosphere*.

Mantle One of Earth's compositional layers. The solid rocky shell that extends from the base of the crust to a depth of 2900 kilometers (1800 miles).

Mantle plume A mass of hotter-than-typical mantle material that ascends toward the surface, where it may lead to igneous activity. These plumes of solid yet mobile material may originate as deep as the core–mantle boundary.

Mineral phase change A change that occurs when a mineral is subjected to intense pressure; in this change, the structure of a mineral may become unstable, causing its atoms to rearrange into a denser, more stable structure.

Mohorovičić discontinuity (Moho) The boundary separating the crust and the mantle, discernible by an increase in seismic velocity.

Outer core A layer beneath the mantle about 2270 kilometers (1410 miles) thick, which has the properties of a liquid.

Seismology The study of earthquakes and seismic waves.

Shadow zone The zone between 105 and 140 degrees from an earthquake epicenter. Direct waves do not penetrate the shadow zone because of refraction by Earth's core.

Viscosity A measure of a fluid's resistance to flow.

Divergent Boundaries: Origin and Evolution of the Ocean Floor

From Chapter 13 of *Earth: An Introduction to Physical Geology*, Eleventh Edition. Edward J. Tarbuck, Frederick K. Lutgens, Dennis Tasa.
Copyright © 2014 by Pearson Education, Inc. All rights reserved.

Divergent Boundaries: Origin and Evolution of the Ocean Floor

The Maldives are a chain of atolls located in the Indian Ocean.
(Photo by Sakis Papadopoulos/Robert Harding)

Each statement represents the primary learning objective for the corresponding major heading within the chapter. After you complete the chapter you should be able to:

1. Define *bathymetry* and explain the various bathymetric techniques used to map the ocean floor.
2. Compare and contrast a passive continental margin with an active continental margin and list the major features of each.
3. List and describe the major features of the deep-ocean basin.
4. Sketch and label a cross-sectional view of the Mid-Atlantic Ridge. Explain how a cross section of the East Pacific Rise would look different.
5. Write a statement that describes how spreading rates affect ridge topography.
6. List the four layers of oceanic crust and explain how oceanic crust forms and how it is different from continental crust.
7. Outline the steps by which continental rifting results in the formation of new ocean basins. Describe the supercontinent cycle.
8. Compare and contrast spontaneous subduction and forced subduction.

The ocean is Earth's most prominent feature, covering more than 70 percent of its surface. Yet, prior to the 1950s, information about the ocean floor was extremely limited. With the development of modern instruments, our understanding of the diverse topography of the ocean floor improved dramatically. Particularly significant was the discovery of the global oceanic ridge system, a broad elevated landform that stands 2 to 3 kilometers higher than the adjacent deep-ocean basins and is the longest topographic feature on Earth.

Today we know that oceanic ridges mark divergent plate margins where new oceanic lithosphere is born. Oceanographic studies also discovered deep-ocean trenches, where oceanic lithosphere descends into the mantle. Because the processes of plate tectonics continuously create oceanic crust at mid-ocean ridges and consume it at subduction zones, oceanic crust is perpetually renewed and recycled.

In this chapter we will examine the topography of the ocean floor and look at the processes that generate its varied features.

The University of Hawaii's research vessel, *Kilo Moana*, arriving at Kodiak, Alaska. (U.S. Coast Guard, Marshalena Delaney/AP Photo)

1 An Emerging Picture of the Ocean Floor

If all water could be drained from the ocean basins, a great variety of features would be observed, including volcanic peaks, deep trenches, extensive plains, linear ridges, and large plateaus. In fact, the topography would be nearly as diverse as that on the continents.

Mapping the Seafloor

The complex nature of ocean-floor topography did not unfold until the historic 3½-year voyage of the HMS *Challenger* (FIGURE 1). From December 1872 to May 1876, the *Challenger* expedition made the first comprehensive study of the global ocean ever attempted. During the 127,500-kilometer (79,200-mile) voyage, the ship and its crew of scientists traveled to every ocean except the Arctic. Throughout the voyage, they sampled a multitude of ocean properties, including water depth, which was accomplished by laboriously lowering long weighted lines overboard. The HMS *Challenger* measured the depth of the deepest spot on the seafloor in 1875. Today, this spot is called the Challenger Deep.

FIGURE 1 HMS *Challenger* The first systematic bathymetric survey of the ocean was made aboard the HMS *Challenger* during its historic 3½-year voyage. (Photo courtesy of the Library of Congress)

Modern Bathymetric Techniques The measurement of ocean depths and the charting of the shape or topography of the ocean floor is known as **bathymetry** (*bathos* = depth, *metry* = measurement). Today, sound energy is often used to measure water depths. The basic approach employs **sonar**, an acronym for *sound navigation and ranging*. The first devices that used sound to measure water depth, called **echo sounders**, were developed early in the twentieth century. Echo sounders work by transmitting a sound wave (called a *ping*) into the water in order to produce an echo when it bounces off any object, such as a large marine organism or the ocean floor (FIGURE 2). A sensitive receiver intercepts the reflected echo, and a clock precisely measures the travel time to fractions of a second. Using the speed of sound waves in water—about 1500 meters (4900 feet) per second—and measuring the time required for the energy pulse to reach the ocean floor and return, the depth can be calculated: Depth = ½ (1500 m/sec × Echo travel time). Bathymetry determined from continuous monitoring of these echoes is plotted to obtain a profile of the ocean floor. By laboriously combining numerous profiles, a detailed chart of the seafloor has been produced (FIGURE 3).

Following World War II, the U.S. Navy developed *sidescan sonar* to look for explosive devices that had been deployed in shipping lanes (FIGURE 4A). These torpedo-shaped instruments were towed behind ships, where they send out a fan of sound extending on either side of the ship's path. By combining swaths of sidescan

FIGURE 2 Echo sounder An echo sounder determines the water depth by measuring the time interval required for an acoustic wave to travel from a ship to the seafloor and back.

Outgoing signal

Reflected signal

Seafloor

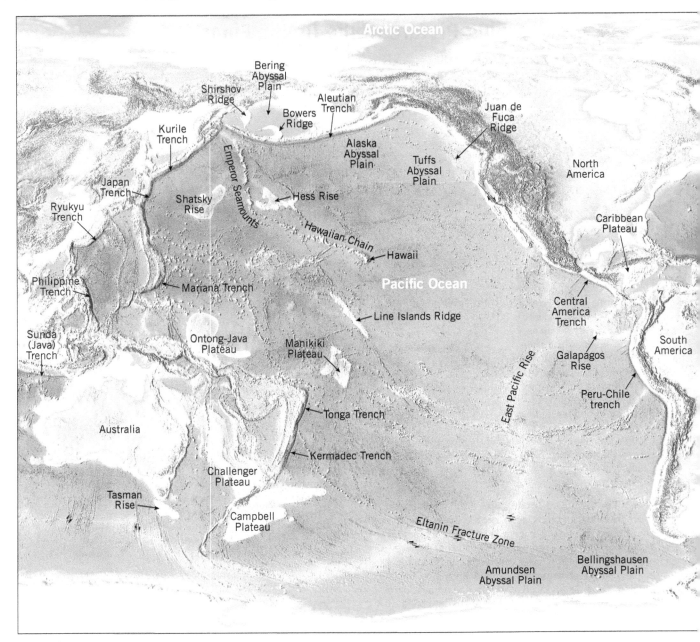

FIGURE 3 Major features of the seafloor

sonar data, oceanographers produced the first photograph-like images of the seafloor. Although sidescan sonar provides valuable views of the seafloor, it does not provide bathymetric (water depth) data.

This drawback was resolved with the development of *high-resolution multibeam* instruments (Figure 4A). These systems use hull-mounted sound sources that send out a fan of sound and then record reflections from the seafloor through a set of narrowly focused receivers aimed at different angles. Rather than obtain the depth

of a single point every few seconds, this technique allows a survey ship to map a swath of ocean floor tens of kilometers wide. In addition, these systems collect bathymetric data of such high resolution that they can distinguish depths that differ by less than 1 meter (3 feet). When multibeam sonar is used to map sections of seafloor, the ship travels in a regularly spaced back-and-forth pattern known as "mowing the lawn."

Despite their greater efficiency and enhanced detail, research vessels equipped with multibeam sonar travel

Greenland

Arctic
Mid-Ocean Ridge

Iceland

North Atlantic
Igneous Province

Eurasia

Gibbs
Fracture
Zone

Porcupine
Abyssal
Plain

Sohn Abyssal
Plain

**Atlantic
Ocean**

Puerto-Rico
Trench

Red Sea
Rift

Chagos-Laccadive
Ridge

Gambia
Abyssal
Plain

Sunda
(Java)
Trench

Mid-Atlantic Ridge

Africa

Demerara
Abyssal Plain

Mid-Indian Ridge

**Indian
Ocean**

South
America

Mid-Indian
Abyssal
Plain

Ninety
East
Ridge

Angola
Abyssal
Plain

Walvis
Ridge

Seychelles
Bank

Rio Grande
Rise

Broken
Ridge

Southwest Indian Ridge

Southeast Indian Ridge

North Scotia Ridge

Kerguelen
Plateau

South Sandwich
Trench

South Scotia
Ridge

Weddell
Abyssal Plain

Antarctica

FIGURE 3 Major features of
the seafloor (*continued*)

at a mere 10 to 20 kilometers (6 to 12 miles) per hour. It would take at least 100 vessels outfitted with this equipment hundreds of years to map the entire seafloor. This explains why only about 5 percent of the seafloor has been mapped in detail (FIGURE 4B).

Mapping the Ocean Floor from Space Another technological breakthrough that led to an enhanced understanding of the seafloor involves measuring the shape of the ocean surface from space. After compensating for

waves, tides, currents, and atmospheric effects, it was discovered that the water's surface is not perfectly "flat." Because massive structures such as seamounts and ridges exert stronger-than-average gravitational attraction, they produce elevated areas on the ocean surface. Conversely, canyons and trenches create slight depressions.

Satellites equipped with *radar altimeters* are able to measure subtle differences in sea level by bouncing microwaves off the sea surface (FIGURE 5). These devices can measure variations as small as a few centimeters. Such

FIGURE 4 Sidescan and multibeam sonar

A. Sidescan sonar and multibeam sonar operating from the same research vessel.

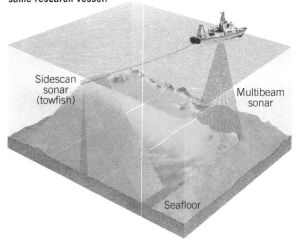

B. Color enhanced perspective map of the seafloor and coastal landforms in the Los Angeles area of California.

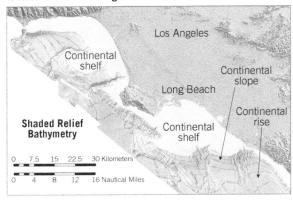

SMARTFIGURE
5 Satellite altimeter
A satellite altimeter measures the variation in sea surface elevation, which is caused by gravitational attraction and mimics the shape of the seafloor. The sea surface anomaly is the difference between the measured ocean surface and the theoretical ocean surface.

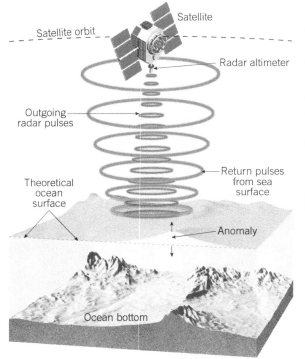

data have added greatly to our knowledge of ocean-floor topography. Combined with traditional sonar depth measurements, the data are used to produce detailed ocean-floor maps, such as the one in Figure 3.

Provinces of the Ocean Floor

Oceanographers studying the topography of the ocean floor identify three major areas: *continental margins, deep-ocean basins,* and *oceanic (mid-ocean) ridges.* The map in FIGURE 6 outlines these provinces for the North Atlantic Ocean, and the profile at the bottom shows the varied topography. Profiles of this type usually have their vertical dimension exaggerated many times (40 times, in this case) to make topographic features more conspicuous. Vertical exaggeration, however, makes slopes appear *much* steeper than they actually are.

1 CONCEPT CHECKS

1. Define *bathymetry*.
2. Assuming that the average speed of sound waves in water is 1500 meters (4900 feet) per second, determine the water depth if the signal sent out by an echo sounder requires 6 seconds to strike bottom and return to the recorder.
3. Describe how satellites orbiting Earth can determine features on the seafloor without being able to directly observe them beneath several kilometers of seawater.
4. What are the three major topographic provinces of the ocean floor?

Divergent Boundaries: Origin and Evolution of the Ocean Floor

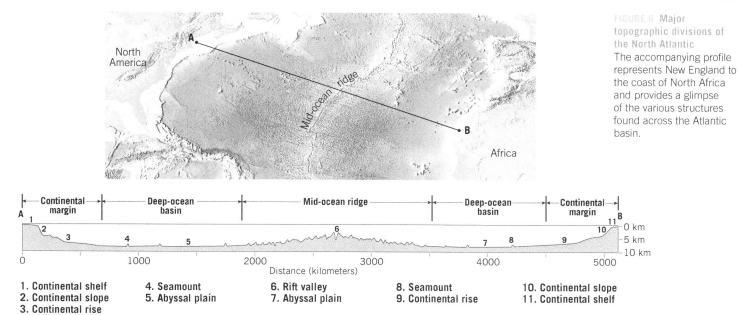

FIGURE 6 Major topographic divisions of the North Atlantic The accompanying profile represents New England to the coast of North Africa and provides a glimpse of the various structures found across the Atlantic basin.

1. Continental shelf
2. Continental slope
3. Continental rise
4. Seamount
5. Abyssal plain
6. Rift valley
7. Abyssal plain
8. Seamount
9. Continental rise
10. Continental slope
11. Continental shelf

Delgada Canyon, a large submarine canyon off the coast of northern California. Like Monterey Submarine Canyon, it begins near shore and carries large quantities of sediment unto the seafloor forming a deep-sea fan. (Courtesy of NOAA)

2 Continental Margins

As the name implies, the **continental margins** are the outer margins of the continents, where continental crust transitions to oceanic crust. Two types of continental margin have been identified—*passive* and *active*. Nearly the entire Atlantic Ocean and a large portion of the Indian Ocean are surrounded by passive continental margins (see Figure 3). By contrast, most of the Pacific Ocean is bordered by active continental margins that are represented by subduction zones in FIGURE 7. Notice that many of those active subduction zones lie far beyond the margins of the continents.

FIGURE 7 Distribution of Earth's subduction zones
Notice that most of Earth's active subduction zones surround the Pacific basin.

Most passive margins are relatively wide and are sites where large quantities of sediments are deposited. The features comprising passive continental margins include the continental shelf, the continental slope, and the continental rise (FIGURE 8).

Continental Shelf The **continental shelf** is a gently sloping, submerged surface extending from the shoreline toward the deep-ocean basin. It consists mainly of continental crust capped with sedimentary rocks and sediments eroded from adjacent landmasses.

The continental shelf varies greatly in width. Although it is almost nonexistent along some continents, the shelf extends seaward more than 1500 kilometers (930 miles) along others. The average inclination of the continental shelf is only about one-tenth of 1 degree, a slope so slight that it would appear to an observer to be a horizontal surface.

The continental shelf tends to be relatively featureless; however, some areas are mantled by extensive glacial deposits and thus are quite rugged. In addition, some continental shelves are dissected by large valleys running from the coastline into deeper waters. Many of these *shelf valleys* are the seaward extensions of river valleys on the adjacent landmass. They were eroded during the last Ice Age (Quaternary period), when enormous quantities of water were stored in vast ice sheets on the continents, causing sea level to drop at least 100 meters (330 feet). Because

Passive Continental Margins

Passive continental margins are geologically inactive regions located some distance from plate boundaries. As a result, they are not associated with strong earthquakes or volcanic activity. Passive continental margins develop when continental blocks rift apart and are separated by continued seafloor spreading. As a result, the continental blocks are firmly attached to the adjacent oceanic crust.

FIGURE 8 Passive continental margins
The slopes shown for the continental shelf and continental slope are greatly exaggerated. The continental shelf has an average slope of one-tenth of 1 degree, while the continental slope has an average slope of about 5 degrees.

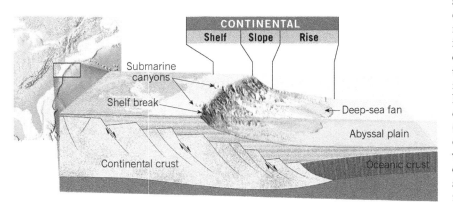

of this sea-level drop, rivers extended their courses, and land-dwelling plants and animals migrated to the newly exposed portions of the continents. Dredging off the coast of North America has retrieved the ancient remains of numerous land dwellers, including mammoths, mastodons, and horses—providing further evidence that portions of the continental shelves were once above sea level.

Although continental shelves represent only 7.5 percent of the total ocean area, they have economic and political significance because they contain important reservoirs of oil and natural gas and support important fishing grounds.

Continental Slope   Marking the seaward edge of the continental shelf is the **continental slope**, a relatively steep structure that marks the boundary between continental crust and oceanic crust. Although the inclination of the continental slope varies greatly from place to place, it averages about 5 degrees and in places exceeds 25 degrees.

Continental Rise   The continental slope merges into a more gradual incline known as the **continental rise**, which may extend seaward for hundreds of kilometers.

The continental rise consists of a thick accumulation of sediment that has moved down the continental slope and onto deep-ocean floor. Most of the sediments are delivered to the seafloor by **turbidity currents**, mixtures of sediment and water that periodically flow down **submarine canyons**. When these muddy slurries emerge from the mouth of a canyon onto the relatively flat ocean floor, they deposit sediment that forms a **deep-sea fan** (Figure 8). As fans from adjacent submarine canyons grow, they merge to produce a continuous wedge of sediment at the base of the continental slope forming the continental rise.

Active Continental Margins

Active continental margins are located along convergent plate boundaries, where oceanic lithosphere is being subducted beneath the leading edge of a continent (FIGURE 9). Deep-ocean trenches are the major topographic expression at convergent plate boundaries. These deep, narrow furrows surround most of the Pacific Rim. One exception is the Puerto Rico Trench, which forms the boundary between the Caribbean Sea and the Atlantic Ocean (FIGURE 10).

Active continental margins are located along convergent plate boundaries where oceanic lithosphere is being subducted beneath the leading edge of a continent.

SMARTFIGURE 9 Active continental margins

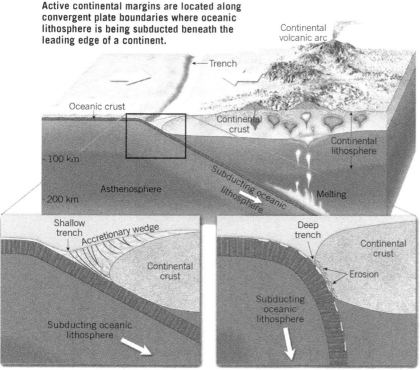

A. Accretionary wedges develop along subduction zones where sediments from the ocean floor are scraped from the descending oceanic plate and pressed against the edge of the overriding plate.

B. Subduction erosion occurs where sediment and rock scraped off the bottom of the overriding plate is carried into the mantle by the subducting plate.

FIGURE 10 **The Puerto Rico Trench**
This trench separates the Caribbean Sea from the Atlantic Ocean. (Photo by USGS)

Along some subduction zones, sediments from the ocean floor and pieces of oceanic crust are scraped from the descending oceanic plate and plastered against the edge of the overriding plate (Figure 9A). This chaotic accumulation of deformed sediment and scraps of oceanic crust is called an **accretionary wedge** (*ad* = toward, *crescere* = to grow). Prolonged plate subduction can produce massive accumulations of sediment along active continental margins.

The opposite process, known as **subduction erosion**, characterizes many other subduction zones (Figure 9B). Rather than sediment accumulating along the front of the overriding plate, sediment and rock are scraped off the bottom of the overriding plate and transported into the mantle by the subducting plate. Subduction erosion is particularly effective where cold, dense oceanic lithosphere subducts at a steep angle as

exemplified by the Mariana Trench. Sharp bending of the subducting plate causes faulting in the ocean crust and a rough surface, as shown in Figure 9C.

2 CONCEPT CHECKS

1. List the three major features of a passive continental margin. Which of these features is considered a flooded extension of the continent? Which one has the steepest slope?
2. Describe the differences between active and passive continental margins and give a geographic example of each type of margin.
3. How are active continental margins related to plate tectonics?
4. Briefly explain how an accretionary wedge forms.
5. What is meant by *subduction erosion*?

Argus, a remotely operated vehicle that is towed behind a surface vessel, was designed to explore the floor of the Gulf of Mexico. In addition to five cameras, *Argus* is equipped with a subsurface profiler that revealed the geologic structures below the seafloor, as well as multi-beam sonar used to map the surface of the seafloor. (Courtesy of NOAA).

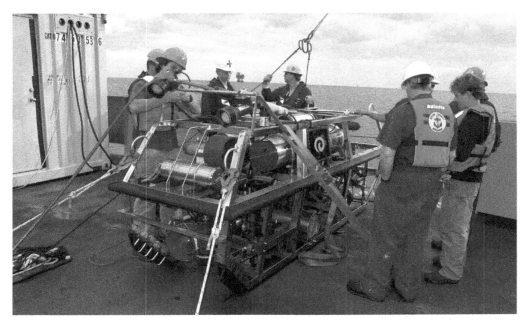

3 Features of Deep-Ocean Basins

Between the continental margin and the oceanic ridge lies the **deep-ocean basin** (see Figure 6). The size of this region—almost 30 percent of Earth's surface—is roughly comparable to the percentage of land above sea level. This region contains *deep-ocean trenches*, which are extremely deep linear depressions in the ocean floor; remarkably flat areas known as *abyssal plains*; tall volcanic peaks called *seamounts* and *guyots*; and large, elevated flood basalt provinces called *oceanic plateaus*.

Deep-Ocean Trenches

Deep-ocean trenches are long, narrow creases in the seafloor that represent the deepest parts of the ocean floor. Most trenches are located along the margins of the Pacific Ocean, where many exceed 10 kilometers (6 miles) in depth (see Figure 3). The Challenger Deep, located in the Mariana Trench, has been measured at 10,994 meters (36,069 feet) below sea level, making it the deepest known part of the world ocean (FIGURE 11). Only two trenches are located in the Atlantic—the Puerto Rico Trench adjacent to the Lesser Antilles arc and the South Sandwich Trench.

Although deep-ocean trenches represent a very small portion of the area of the ocean floor, they are nevertheless significant geologic features. Trenches are sites of plate convergence where slabs of oceanic lithosphere subduct and plunge back into the mantle. In addition to earthquakes being created as one plate "scrapes" against another, volcanic activity is also triggered by plate subduction. As a result, some trenches run parallel to an arc-shaped row of active volcanoes called a **volcanic island arc**. Furthermore, **continental volcanic arcs**, such as those making up portions of the Andes and Cascades, are located parallel to subduction zones that lie adjacent to continental margins. The volcanic activity associated with the trenches that surround the Pacific Ocean explains why this region is called the *Ring of Fire*.

Abyssal Plains

Abyssal plains (*a* = without, *byssus* = bottom) are flat features of the deep-ocean floor; in fact, they are likely the most level places on Earth (see Figure 3). The abyssal plain found off the coast of Argentina, for example, has less than 3 meters (10 feet) of relief over a distance exceeding 1300 kilometers (800 miles). The monotonous topography of abyssal plains is occasionally interrupted by the protruding summit of a partially buried volcanic peak (seamount).

Using **seismic reflection profilers**, researchers have determined that the relatively featureless topography of abyssal plains is due to thick accumulations of sediment that have buried an otherwise rugged ocean floor (FIGURE 12). The nature of the sediment indicates that these plains consist primarily of three materials: (1) fine sediments transported far out to sea by turbidity

FIGURE 11 The Challenger Deep Located near the southern end of the Mariana Trench, the Challenger Deep is the deepest place in the global ocean, about 10,994 meters (36,069 feet) deep. Film director James Cameron (*Titanic* and *Avatar*) made news in March 2012 as the first person to dive to the bottom of the Challenger Deep in more than 50 years.

FIGURE 12 Seismic profile of the ocean floor
This seismic cross section and matching sketch across a portion of the Madeira abyssal plain in the eastern Atlantic Ocean show the irregular oceanic crust buried by sediments. (Image courtesy of Charles Hollister, Woods Hole Oceanographic Institution)

Seismic reflection profile

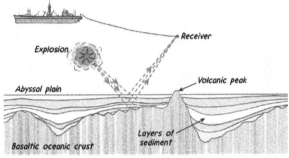

Geologist's Sketch

currents, (2) mineral matter that has precipitated out of seawater, and (3) shells and skeletons of microscopic marine organisms.

Abyssal plains are found in all oceans. However, the Atlantic Ocean has the most extensive abyssal plains because it has few trenches to act as traps for sediment carried down the continental slope.

Volcanic Structures on the Ocean Floor

Dotting the sea floor are numerous volcanic structures of various sizes. Many occur as isolated features that resemble volcanic cones on land. Others occur in nearly linear chains that stretch for thousands of kilometers, while still others are massive structures that cover areas the size of Texas.

Seamounts and Volcanic Islands Submarine volcanoes, called **seamounts**, may rise hundreds of meters above the surrounding topography. It is estimated that more than a million seamounts exist. Some grow large enough to become oceanic islands, but most do not have a sufficiently long eruptive history to build a structure above sea level. Although seamounts are found on the floors of all the oceans, they are most common in the Pacific.

Some, like the Hawaiian Island–Emperor Seamount chain, which stretches from the Hawaiian Islands to the Aleutian trench, form over volcanic hot spots. Others are born near oceanic ridges.

If a volcano grows large enough before it is carried from its magma source by plate motion, the structure may emerge as a **volcanic island**. Examples of volcanic islands include Easter Island, Tahiti, Bora Bora, the Galapagos Islands, and the Canary Islands.

EYE on Earth

This perspective view of the Pacific margin is looking southwest toward the Palos Verdes Peninsula, with Los Angeles in the background.

Question 1 Match the features labeled 1 to 4 with the following terms: continental shelf, continental slope, continental rise, and submarine canyon.

Question 2 Based on the features shown, describe the type of continental margin in the image.

Guyots   During their existence, inactive volcanic islands are gradually but inevitably lowered to near sea level by the forces of weathering and erosion. As a moving plate slowly carries volcanic islands away from the elevated oceanic ridge or hot spot over which they formed, they gradually sink and disappear below the water surface. Submerged, flat-topped seamounts that formed in this manner are called **guyots**.*

Oceanic Plateaus   The ocean floor also contains several massive **oceanic plateaus**, which resemble the flood basalt provinces found on the continents. Oceanic plateaus, which can be more than 30 kilometers (20 miles) thick, are generated from vast outpourings of fluid basaltic lavas.

*The term *guyot* is named after Arnold Guyot, Princeton University's first geology professor. It is pronounced "GEE-oh" with a hard *g*, as in "give."

Some oceanic plateaus appear to have formed quickly in geologic terms. Examples include the Ontong Java Plateau, which formed in less than 3 million years, and the Kerguelen Plateau, which formed in 4.5 million years (see Figure 3). Like flood basalt provinces on land, oceanic plateaus are thought to form when the bulbous head of a rising mantle plume melts, producing a vast outpouring of basaltic lava.

3 CONCEPT CHECKS

1. Explain how deep-ocean trenches are related to plate boundaries.
2. Why are abyssal plains more extensive on the floor of the Atlantic than on the floor of the Pacific?
3. How does a flat-topped seamount, called a *guyot*, form?
4. What features on the ocean floor most resemble flood basalt provinces on the continents?

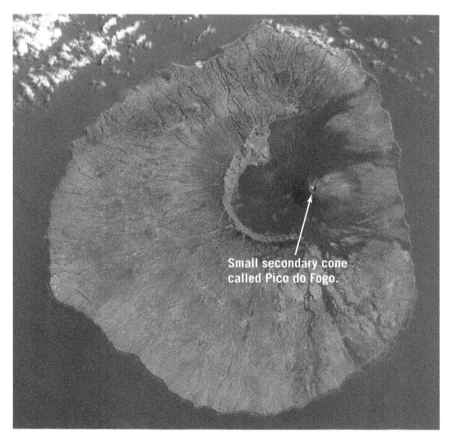

Small secondary cone called Pico do Fogo.

Fogo, the most active volcano of the Cape Verdi Islands, is located about 640 kilometers off the westernmost edge of Africa. This shield volcano is similar to the island of Hawaii, because it is the product of hot spot volcanism. However, Fogo is a single cone that grew from the deep ocean floor whereas the island of Hawaii consists of five overlapping volcanoes. (Courtesy of NASA)

4   Anatomy of the Oceanic Ridge

Along well-developed divergent plate boundaries, the seafloor is elevated, forming a broad linear swell called the **oceanic ridge**, or **mid-ocean ridge** or **rise**. Our knowledge of the oceanic ridge system comes from soundings of the ocean floor, core samples from deep-sea drilling, visual inspection using deep-diving submersibles (**FIGURE 13**), and firsthand inspection of slices of ocean floor that have been thrust onto dry land during continental collisions.

FIGURE 13 The deep-diving submersible *Alvin*
This submersible is 7.6 meters long, weighs 16 tons, has a cruising speed of 1 knot, and can reach depths of 4000 meters. A pilot and two scientific observers are along during a normal 6- to 10-hour dive.
(Photo by Rod Catanach KRT/ Newscom)

The oceanic ridge system winds through all major oceans in a manner similar to the seam on a baseball, and it is the longest topographic feature on Earth, exceeding 70,000 kilometers (43,000 miles) in length (**FIGURE 14**). The crest of the ridge typically stands 2 to 3 kilometers above the adjacent deep-ocean basins and marks the plate boundary, where new oceanic crust is created.

Notice in Figure 14 that large sections of the oceanic ridge system have been named based on their locations within the various ocean basins. A ridge may run through the middle of an ocean basin, where it is appropriately called a *mid-ocean ridge*. The Mid-Atlantic Ridge and the Mid-Indian Ridge are examples. By contrast, the East Pacific Rise is *not* a "mid-ocean" feature. Rather, as its name implies, it is located in the eastern Pacific, far from the center of the ocean.

The term *ridge* is somewhat misleading because these features are not narrow and steep, as the term implies, but have widths from 1000 to 4000 kilometers (600 to 2500 miles) and the appearance of broad, elongated swells that exhibit varying degrees of ruggedness. Furthermore, the ridge system is broken into segments that range from a few tens to hundreds of kilometers in length.

FIGURE 14 Distribution of the oceanic ridge system The map shows ridge segments that exhibit slow, intermediate, and fast spreading rates.

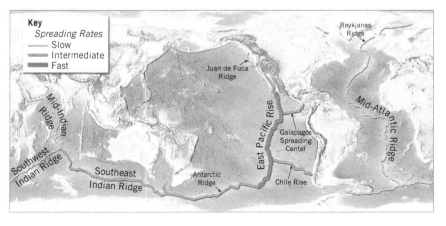

Each segment is offset from the adjacent segment by a transform fault.

Oceanic ridges are as high as some mountains on the continents, but the similarities end there. Whereas most mountain ranges on land form when the compressional forces associated with continental collisions fold and metamorphose thick sequences of sedimentary rocks, oceanic ridges form where upwelling from the mantle generates new oceanic crust. Oceanic ridges consist of layers and piles of newly formed basaltic rocks that are buoyantly uplifted by the hot mantle rocks from which they formed.

Along the axis of some segments of the oceanic ridge system are deep, down-faulted structures called **rift valleys** because of their striking similarity to the continental rift valleys found in East Africa (FIGURE 15). Some rift valleys, including those along the rugged Mid-Atlantic Ridge, are typically 30 to 50 kilometers (20 to 30 miles) wide and have walls that tower 500 to 2500 meters (1600 to 8200 feet) above the valley floor. This makes them comparable to the deepest and widest part of Arizona's Grand Canyon.

FIGURE 15 **Rift valleys** The axis of some segments of the oceanic ridge system contains deep down-faulted structures called *rift valleys* that may exceed 30 to 50 kilometers in width and 500 to 2500 meters in depth.

4 CONCEPT CHECKS

1. Briefly describe the oceanic ridge system.
2. Although oceanic ridges can be as tall as some mountains found on the continents, list some ways in which the features are different.
3. Where do rift valleys form along the oceanic ridge system?

EYE on Earth

Offshore drilling rigs are used to tap oil and natural gas reserves on the continental shelf and beyond. Notable offshore fields are found in the Gulf of Mexico, the North Sea, and the Persian Gulf, as well as off the coasts of West Africa, Brazil, and Newfoundland. Drilling rigs can be fixed to the seafloor or may float. The latter group includes semi-submersibles, anchored platforms that are partially filled with seawater and drill ships that typically use dynamic positioning to remain over the drilling location.

Peter Bowater/Photo Researchers, Inc.

Question 1 What was the name of the drilling rig that caused a major oil spill in the Gulf of Mexico and sank in 2010?

Question 2 One of the world's deepest platforms, the Perdito, located in the Gulf of Mexico, is floating in 2,438 meters (7997 feet) of water. Explain at least one logistic issue or difficulty posed by drilling in water this deep.

Explaining Coral Atolls: Darwin's Hypothesis

Douglas Peebles Photography/Alamy

Coral atolls are ring-shaped structures that often extend from slightly above sea level to depths of several thousand meters. What causes atolls to form, and how do they attain such great thicknesses?

Reef-building corals only grow in warm, clear sunlit water. The depth of most active reef growth is limited to warm tropical water no more than about 45 meters (150 feet) deep. The strict environmental conditions required for coral growth create an interesting paradox: How can corals—which require warm, shallow, sunlit water no deeper than a few dozen meters—create massive structures such as coral atolls that extend to great depths?

Most corals secrete a hard external skeleton made of calcium carbonate. Colonies of these corals build large calcium carbonate structures, called reefs, where new colonies grow atop the strong skeletons of previous colonies. Sponges and algae may attach to the reef, further enlarging the structure.

TENTACLE → POLYP

MOUTH

CALCIUM CARBONATE
SUPPORT STRUCTURE

STOMACH

Corals: Tiny colonial animals
Corals are marine animals that typically live in compact colonies of many identical organisms called polyps.

NOAA

NOAA

Reinhard Dirsherl/AGE Fotostock

462

Fringing reef · David Hiser/Getty Images

Barrier reef · Freng Flint Images/Getty Images

Atoll · imagebroker/Alamy Images

What Darwin observed Naturalist Charles Darwin was one of the first to formulate a hypothesis on the origin of these ringed-shaped atolls. Aboard the British ship HMS *Beagle* during its famous global circumnavigation, Darwin noticed a progression of stages in coral reef development from (1) a fringing reef along the margins of a volcano to (2) a barrier reef with a volcano in the middle to (3) an atoll, consisting of a continuous or broken ring of coral reef surrounding a central lagoon.

Fringing coral reef

Barrier reef

Atoll

Darwin's hypothesis Darwin's hypothesis asserts that, in addition to being lowered by erosional forces, many volcanic islands gradually sink. Darwin also suggested that corals respond to the gradual change in water depth caused by the subsiding volcano by building the reef complex upward. During Darwin's time, however, there was no plausible mechanism to account for how, or why so many volcanic islands sink.

Plate tectonics and coral atolls The plate tectonics theory provides the most current scientific explanation regarding how volcanic islands become extinct and sink to great depths over long periods of time. Some volcanic islands form over relatively stationary mantle plumes, causing the lithosphere to be buoyantly uplifted. Over spans of millions of years, these volcanic islands gradually sink as moving plates carry them away from the region of hot-spot volcanism because the oceanic lithosphere cools, becomes denser, and sinks.

Fringing coral reef

Barrier reef

Lagoon

Atoll

Oceanic lithosphere

Plate motion

Rising mantle plume

5 | Oceanic Ridges and Seafloor Spreading

The greatest volume of magma (more than 60 percent of Earth's total yearly output) is produced along the oceanic ridge system in association with seafloor spreading. As plates diverge, fractures created in the oceanic crust fill with molten rock that gradually wells up from the hot mantle below. This molten material slowly cools and crystallizes, producing new slivers of seafloor. This process repeats itself in episodic bursts, generating new lithosphere that moves away from the ridge crest in a conveyor belt fashion.

Seafloor Spreading

Harry Hess of Princeton University formulated the concept of seafloor spreading in the early 1960s. Later, geologists were able to verify Hess's view that seafloor spreading occurs along the crests of oceanic ridges, where hot mantle rock rises to replace the material that has shifted horizontally (Figure 15). As rock rises, it experiences a decrease in confining pressure that may lead to *decompression melting.*

Partial melting of ultramafic mantle rock produces basaltic magma that has a surprisingly consistent chemical composition. The newly formed melt separates from the mantle rock and rises toward the surface. Along some ridge segments, the melt collects in small elongated reservoirs located just beneath the ridge crest. Eventually, about 10 to 20 percent of the melt migrates upward along fissures and erupts as lava flows on the ocean floor, while the remainder crystallizes at depth to form the lower crust. This activity continuously adds new basaltic rock to diverging plate margins, temporarily welding them together; they are then broken as spreading continues. Along some ridges, outpourings of pillow lavas build submerged shield volcanoes (seamounts) as well as elongated lava ridges. At other locations, more voluminous lava flows pave the surface to create a relatively subdued topography.

Why Are Oceanic Ridges Elevated?

The primary reason for the elevated position of the ridge system is that newly created oceanic lithosphere is hot and therefore less dense than cooler rocks of the deep-ocean basin. As the newly formed basaltic crust travels away from the ridge crest, it is cooled from above as seawater circulates through the pore spaces and fractures in the rock. In addition, it cools because it gets farther and farther from the zone of hot mantle upwelling. As a result, the lithosphere gradually cools, contracts, and becomes denser. This thermal contraction accounts for the greater ocean depths that occur away from the ridge. After about 80 million years of cooling and contraction, rock that was once part of an elevated ocean-ridge system becomes part of the deep-ocean basin.

As lithosphere is displaced away from the ridge crest, cooling also causes a gradual increase in lithospheric thickness. This happens because the boundary between the lithosphere and asthenosphere is a thermal (temperature) boundary. Recall that the lithosphere is Earth's cool, stiff outer layer, whereas the asthenosphere is a comparatively hot and weak layer. As material in the uppermost asthenosphere ages (cools), it becomes stiff and rigid. Thus, the upper portion of the asthenosphere is gradually converted to lithosphere simply by cooling. Oceanic lithosphere continues to thicken until it is about 80 to100 kilometers (50 to 60 miles) thick. Thereafter, its thickness remains relatively unchanged until it is subducted.

Spreading Rates and Ridge Topography

When researchers studied various segments of the oceanic ridge system, it became clear that there were topographic differences. These differences appear to be the result of differences in spreading rates—which largely determine the amount of melt generated at a rift zone. At fast spreading centers, more magma wells up from the mantle than at slow spreading centers. This difference in output causes differences in the structure and topography of various ridge segments.

Oceanic ridges that exhibit slow spreading rates from 1 to 5 centimeters per year have prominent rift valleys and rugged topography (FIGURE 16A). The Mid-Atlantic and Mid-Indian Ridges are examples. The vertical displacement of large slabs of oceanic crust along normal faults is responsible for the steep walls of the rift valleys. Furthermore, volcanism produces numerous cones in the rift valley, which enhance the rugged topography of the ridge crest.

By contrast, along the Galapagos Ridge, an intermediate spreading rate of 5 to 9 centimeters per year is the norm. As a result, the rift valleys that develop are relatively shallow—often less than 200 meters (660 feet) deep. In addition, their topography is more subdued compared to ridges that have slower spreading rates.

At fast spreading centers (greater than 9 centimeters per year), such as along much of the East Pacific Rise,

A. At slow spreading rates a prominent central rift valley develops along the ridge crest, and the topography of the ridge is typically rugged.

B. Along fast spreading centers, medial rift valleys do not develop and the topography is comparatively smooth.

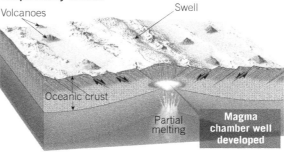

FIGURE 16 Topography of slow and fast spreading centers

rift valleys are generally absent (FIGURE 16B). Instead, the ridge axis is elevated. These elevated structures, called *swells*, are built from lava flows up to 10 meters (30 feet) thick that have incrementally paved the ridge crest with volcanic rocks (Figure 16B). In addition, because the depth of the ocean depends largely on the age of the sea-floor, ridge segments that exhibit faster spreading rates tend to have more gradual profiles than ridges that have slower spreading rates (FIGURE 17). Because of these differences in topography, the gently sloping, less rugged portions of fast-spreading ridges are called *rises*.

---

5 CONCEPT CHECKS

1. What is the source of magma for seafloor spreading?
2. What is the primary reason for the elevated position of the oceanic ridge system?
3. Why does the lithosphere thicken as it moves away from the ridge as a result of seafloor spreading?
4. Compare and contrast a slow spreading center such as the Mid-Atlantic Ridge with one that exhibits a faster spreading rate, such as the East Pacific Rise.

Ridges that have fast spreading rates are characterized by smooth topography, gently sloping flanks, and a central swell.

SMARTFIGURE 17 Ridge segments that exhibit fast, intermediate, and slow spreading rates

Ridges that have intermediate spreading rates are characterized by small rift valleys (less than 500 meters deep) and moderately sloping flanks.

Ridges that have slow spreading rates are characterized by rugged topography, well-developed rift valleys (500-2500 meters deep) and steeply sloping flanks.

6   The Nature of Oceanic Crust

An interesting aspect of oceanic crust is that its thickness and structure are remarkably consistent throughout the entire ocean basin. Seismic soundings indicate that its thickness averages only about 7 kilometers (5 miles). Furthermore, it is composed almost entirely of mafic rocks that are underlain by a layer of the ultramafic rock peridotite, which forms the lithospheric mantle.

Although most oceanic crust forms out of view, far below sea level, geologists have been able to examine the structure of the ocean floor firsthand. In locations such as Newfoundland, Cyprus, Oman, and California, slivers of oceanic crust and underlying mantle have been thrust high above sea level. From these exposures and core samples collected by deep-sea drilling ships, researchers have concluded that the ocean crust consists of four distinct layers (FIGURE 18):

- **Layer 1.** The upper layer is a sequence of deep-sea sediments or sedimentary rocks. Sediments are very thin near the axes of oceanic ridges but may be several kilometers thick next to continents.
- **Layer 2.** Below the layer of sediments is a rock unit composed mainly of basaltic lavas that contain abundant pillowlike structures called *pillow basalts.*
- **Layer 3.** The middle, rocky layer is made up of numerous interconnected dikes that have a nearly vertical orientation, called the *sheeted dike complex.* These dikes are former pathways where magma rose to feed pillow basalts on the ocean floor.
- **Layer 4.** The lowest unit is mainly gabbro, the coarse-grained equivalent of basalt, which crystallized deeper in the crust without erupting.

When fragments of oceanic crust and the underling mantle are discovered on land they are called an **ophiolite complex**. From studies of various ophiolite complexes around the globe and related data, geologists have pieced together a scenario for the formation of the ocean floor.

How Does Oceanic Crust Form?

The molten rock that forms new oceanic crust originates from partial melting of the ultramafic mantle rock. This process generates basaltic melt that is less dense than the surrounding solid rock. The newly formed melt rises through the upper mantle along thousands of tiny conduits that feed into a few dozen larger, elongated channels, perhaps 100 meters (300 feet) or more wide. These structures, in turn, feed lens-shaped magma chambers located directly beneath the ridge crest. With the addition of melt from below, the pressure inside the magma chambers steadily increases. As a result, the rocks above these reservoirs periodically fracture, allowing the melt to ascend along numerous vertical fractures that develop in the ocean crust. Some of the melt cools and solidifies to form dikes. New dikes intrude older dikes, which are still warm and weak, to form a **sheeted dike complex**. This portion of the oceanic crust is usually 1 to 2 kilometers thick.

Roughly 10 to 20 percent of the melt eventually erupts on the ocean floor. Because the surface of these submarine lava flows is chilled quickly by seawater, these flows generally travel no more than a few kilometers before completely solidifying. The forward motion occurs as lava accumulates behind the congealed margin and then breaks through. This process occurs repeatedly, as molten basalt is extruded—like toothpaste from a tightly squeezed tube (FIGURE 19). The result is protuberances resembling large bed pillows stacked one atop the other, hence the name **pillow basalts** (FIGURE 20).

In some settings, pillow lavas may build volcano-size mounds that resemble shield volcanoes, whereas in other situations they form elongated ridges tens of kilometers long. These structures are eventually separated from their supply of magma as they are carried away from the ridge crest by seafloor spreading.

The lowest unit of the ocean crust develops from crystallization within the central magma chamber itself. The first minerals to crystallize are olivine, pyroxene, and occasionally chromite (chromium oxide), which settle through the magma to form a layered zone near the floor

FIGURE 18 Ophiolite complex: Structure of the oceanic crust
This view of the layered structure of oceanic crust is based on data obtained from ophiolite complexes, seismic profiling, and core samples obtained from deep-sea drilling expeditions.

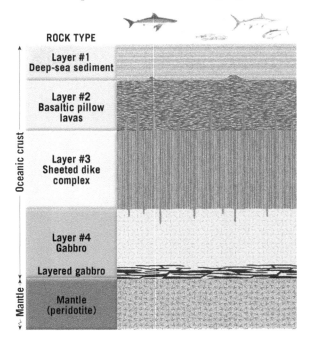

ROCK TYPE

Oceanic crust
- Layer #1 Deep-sea sediment
- Layer #2 Basaltic pillow lavas
- Layer #3 Sheeted dike complex
- Layer #4 Gabbro
- Layered gabbro

Mantle
- Mantle (peridotite)

FIGURE 19 **Erupting pillow lava**
The orange glow of magma erupting on the ocean floor. These toothpaste-like extrusions are called *pillow lava.* (Image courtesy of NOAA)

of the reservoir. The remaining melt tends to cool along the walls of magma chambers to form massive amounts of coarse-grained gabbro. This portion accounts for up to 5 of the 7 kilometers (3 to 4.3 miles) of ocean crust thickness.

Although molten rock rises continuously from the mantle toward the surface, seafloor spreading occurs in pulse-like bursts. As the melt begins to accumulate in the lens-shaped reservoirs, it is blocked from continuing upward by the stiff overlying rocks. As the amount of melt entering the magma reservoirs increases, pressure rises. Periodically, the pressure exceeds the strength of the overlying rocks, which fracture and initiate a short episode of seafloor spreading.

Interactions Between Seawater and Oceanic Crust

In addition to serving as a mechanism for the dissipation of Earth's internal heat, the interaction between seawater and the newly formed basaltic crust alters both the seawater and the crust. The permeable and highly fractured lava of the upper oceanic crust allows seawater to penetrate to depths of 2 to 3 kilometers (1 to 2 miles). As seawater circulates through the hot crust, it is heated and chemically reacts with the basaltic rock in a process called *hydrothermal* (hot water) *metamorphism*. This alteration causes the dark silicates (olivine and pyroxene) in basalt to form new metamorphic minerals such as chlorite and serpentine. Simultaneously, the hot seawater dissolves ions of silica, iron, copper, and occasionally silver and gold from the hot basalts. When the water temperature reaches a few hundred degrees Celsius, these mineral-rich fluids buoyantly rise along fractures and eventually spew out on the ocean floor.

FIGURE 20 **Cross-sectional view of pillow lava**
This pillow lava is exposed along a sea cliff at Cape Wanbrow, New Zealand. Notice that each "pillow" shows an outer dark glassy layer created by rapid cooling enclosing a dark gray basalt interior. (Photo by GR Roberts/Photo Researchers, Inc.)

Studies conducted by submersibles along several segments of the oceanic ridge have photographed these metallic-rich solutions gushing from the seafloor to form particle-filled clouds called **black smokers**. As the hot liquid (up to 400° C [750°F]) mixes with the cold, mineral-laden seawater, the dissolved minerals precipitate to form massive metallic sulfide deposits, some of which are economically important. Occasionally these deposits grow upward to form underwater chimney-like structures equivalent in height to skyscrapers.

6 CONCEPT CHECKS

1. Briefly describe the four layers of the ocean crust.
2. How does a *sheeted dike complex* form?
3. How does hydrothermal metamorphism alter the basaltic rocks that make up the seafloor? How is seawater changed during this process?
4. What is a black smoker?

Deep-Sea Hydrothermal Vents

Deep-sea hydrothermal vents are openings in the oceanic crust from which geothermally heated water rises. They are found main along the oceanic ridge system where tectonic plates rift apart, resulting in the production of new seafloor by upwelling magma.

When these hot, mineral-rich fluids reach the seafloor their temperatures can exceed 350 °C, but because of the extremely high pressures exerted by the water column above, they do not boil. When this hydrothermal fluid comes into contact with the much colder chemical-rich seawater, mineral matter rapidly precipitates to form shimmering smoke-like clouds called "*black smokers.*" The particles that compose the black smokers eventually settle out of the seawater. These deposits may contain economically significant amounts of iron, copper, zinc, lead, and occasionally silver and gold.

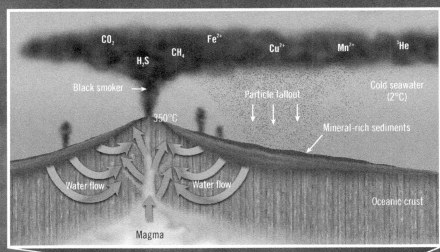

CO_2 Fe^{2+} Cu^{2+} Mn^{2+} ^3He
H_2S CH_4

Black smoker

Cold seawater (2°C)

Particle fallout

350°C

Mineral-rich sediments

Water flow   Water flow

Oceanic crust

Magma

At oceanic ridges, cold seawater circulates hundreds of meters down into the highly fractured basaltic crust, where it is heated by magmatic sources. Along the way, the hot water strips metals and other elements such as sulfur from surrounding rock. This heated fluid eventually becomes hot and buoyant enough to rise along conduits and fractures towards the surface.

Some minerals immediately solidify and contribute to the formation of spectacular chimney-like structures, which can be as tall as 15-story buildings, and are appropriately given names like *Godzilla* and *Inferno*.

NOAA

468

Tubeworms

Fisheries and Oceans Canada/Uvic-Verena Tunnicliffe/Newscom

B. Murton/Southampton Oceanography/Photo Researchers Inc.

Hydrothermal vents are also remarkable for the marine biology they support. In these environments, completely devoid of sunlight, microorganisms utilize mineral-rich hydrothermal fluid to perform chemosynthesis—the conversion of carbon atoms into organic compounds without sunlight for energy. The microbial communities, in turn, support larger, more complex animals such as fish, crabs, worms, mussels, clams, and perhaps the most unique, the tubeworm. With their white chitinous tubes and bright red plumes, these conspicuous creatures rely entirely on bacteria growing in their trophosome, an internal organ designed for harvesting bacteria. These symbiotic bacteria rely on the tubeworm to provide them with a suitable habitat and, in return, they use chemosynthesis to provide carbon-based building blocks (nutrients) to the tubeworms.

Where are hydrothermal vents found?

Most hydrothermal vents are found around the oceanic ridge system including some small spreading centers such as the Juan de Fuca Ridge and Galapagos Rift, as well as in the back arc basins that lie behind subduction zones.

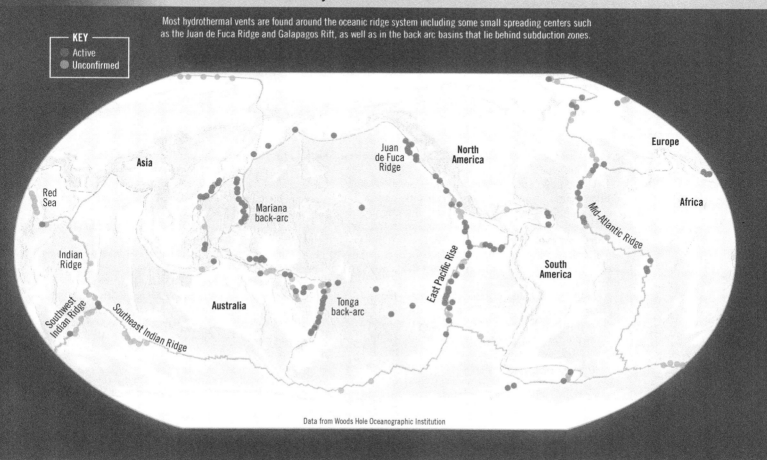

KEY
- Active
- Unconfirmed

Red Sea
Asia
Indian Ridge
Mariana back-arc
Juan de Fuca Ridge
North America
Europe
Africa
Mid-Atlantic Ridge
Southwest Indian Ridge
Southeast Indian Ridge
Australia
Tonga back-arc
East Pacific Rise
South America

Data from Woods Hole Oceanographic Institution

7 | Continental Rifting: The Birth of a New Ocean Basin

The reason Pangaea began splitting apart nearly 200 million years ago is a subject debated among geoscientists. Nevertheless, the breakup of Pangaea illustrates that ocean basins, such as the Atlantic, originate when continents break apart.

Evolution of an Ocean Basin

The opening of a new ocean basin begins with the formation of a **continental rift**, an elongated depression along which the entire lithosphere is stretched and thinned. Where the lithosphere is thick, cool, and strong, rifts tend to be narrow—often less than a few hundred kilometers wide. Modern examples of narrow continental rifts include the East African Rift, the Rio Grande Rift (southwestern United States), the Baikal Rift (south-central Siberia), and the Rhine Valley (northwestern Europe). By contrast, where the crust is thin, hot, and weak, rifts can be more than 1000 kilometers (600 miles) wide, as exemplified by the Basin and Range region in the western United States.

In settings where rifting continues, the rift system evolves into a young, narrow ocean basin, such as the present-day Red Sea. Continued seafloor spreading eventually results in the formation of a mature ocean basin bordered by rifted continental margins. The Atlantic Ocean is such a feature.

What follows is an overview of ocean basin evolution, using modern examples to represent the various stages of rifting.

East African Rift The East African Rift is a continental rift that extends through eastern Africa for approximately 3000 kilometers (2000 miles). It consists of several interconnected rift valleys that split into eastern and western sections around Lake Victoria (FIGURE 21). Whether this rift will eventually develop into a spreading center, with the Somali subplate separating from the rest of the continent of Africa, is uncertain.

The most recent period of rifting began about 20 million years ago, as upwelling in the mantle intruded the base of the lithosphere (FIGURE 22A). Buoyant uplifting of the heated lithosphere led to doming and stretching of the crust. Consequently, the upper crust was broken along high-angle normal faults, producing down-faulted blocks, or *grabens*, while the lower crust deformed by ductile stretching (FIGURE 22B).

In the early stages of rifting, magma generated by decompression melting of the rising mantle rocks intruded the crust. Occasionally, some of the magma migrated upward along fractures and erupted at the surface. This activity produced extensive basaltic flows within the rift as well as volcanic cones—some forming more than 100 kilometers (60 miles) from the rift axis. Examples include Mount Kenya and Mount Kilimanjaro,

FIGURE 21 East African Rift Valley

the highest point in Africa, rising almost 6000 meters (20,000 feet) above the Serengeti Plain.

Red Sea Gradually, a rift valley will lengthen and deepen, eventually extending to the margin of the continent (FIGURE 22C). At this point, the continental rift becomes a narrow linear sea with an outlet to the ocean, similar to the Red Sea.

The Red Sea formed when the Arabian Peninsula rifted from Africa beginning about 30 million years ago. Steep fault scarps that rise as much as 3 kilometers above sea level flank the margins of this water body. Thus, the escarpments surrounding the Red Sea are similar to the steep cliffs that border the East African Rift. Although the Red Sea reaches oceanic depths (up to 5 kilometers) in only a few locations, symmetrical magnetic stripes indicate that typical seafloor spreading has been occurring for at least the past 5 million years.

Atlantic Ocean If spreading continues, the Red Sea will grow wider and develop an elevated oceanic ridge

A. Tensional forces and buoyant uplifting of the heated lithosphere cause the upper crust to be broken along normal faults, while the lower crust deforms by ductile stretching.

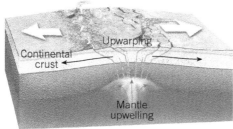

Illustration of the separation of South America and Africa to form the South Atlantic.

FIGURE 22 Formation of an ocean basin

B. As the crust is pulled apart, large slabs of rock sink, generating a rift valley.

C. Further spreading generates a narrow sea.

D. Eventually, an expansive ocean basin and ridge system are created.

similar to the Mid-Atlantic Ridge (FIGURE 22D). The Atlantic Ocean shows what the Red Sea could eventually become over tens of millions of years. As the Atlantic formed, new oceanic crust was added to the diverging plates, and the rifted continental margins gradually receded from the region of upwelling. As a result, they cooled, contracted, and sank.

Over time, continental margins subsided below sea level, and material that had eroded from the adjacent highlands blanketed this once-rugged topography. The result was a *passive continental margin* on both sides of the Atlantic consisting of rifted continental crust that has been covered by a thick wedge of relatively undisturbed sediment and sedimentary rock.

Interrupted Rifting Not all continental rift valleys develop into full-fledged spreading centers. In the central United States, a failed rift extends from Lake Superior

into Kansas (FIGURE 23). This once-active rift valley is
filled with clastic sedimentary and basaltic rocks that
were extruded onto the crust more than a billion years
ago. Why one rift valley develops into a full-fledged active spreading center while others fail to develop is not
fully understood.

Mechanisms for Continental Rifting

At least two supercontinents existed in the geologic past.
Pangaea, the most recent of them, was assembled into a
supercontinent between 450 and 230 million years ago,
only to break up shortly after it formed. Geologists have
concluded that the formation of supercontinents followed
by continental splitting is an integral part of plate tectonics. This process, which involves the formation and dispersal of supercontinents, is called the **supercontinent
cycle**.

The supercontinent cycle must involve major changes
in the direction and nature of the forces that drive plate
motion. In other words, over long periods of geologic
time, the forces that drive plate motions tend to organize
crustal fragments into a single supercontinent, only to
change directions and disperse them again. Mechanisms
that are thought to contribute to continental rifting include plumes of hot mobile rock rising from deep in the
mantle, upwelling from shallow levels in the asthenosphere, and forces that arise from plate motions.

Mantle Plumes and Hot-Spot Volcanism A *mantle
plume* consists of hotter-than-normal mantle rock that
has a large mushroom-shaped head hundreds of kilometers in diameter attached to a long, narrow, trailing tail. As the plume head nears the base of the rigid
lithosphere, it spreads laterally. Decompression melting
within the plume generates huge volumes of basaltic

magma that rises and triggers *hot-spot volcanism* at the
surface.

Research suggests that mantle plumes tend to
concentrate beneath a supercontinent because once assembled, a large landmass forms an insulating "blanket"
that traps heat in the mantle. The resulting temperature
increase leads to the formation of mantle plumes that
serve to dissipate heat.

Evidence that mantle plumes play a role in the
breakup of at least some landmasses can be observed in
modern passive continental margins. In several regions
on both sides of the Atlantic, continental rifting was preceded by crustal uplift and massive outpourings of basaltic lava. Examples include the Etendeka flood basalts of
southwest Africa and the Paraná basalt province of South
America (FIGURE 24A).

About 130 million years ago, when South America
and Africa were a single landmass, vast outpourings of lava
produced a large continental basalt plateau (FIGURE 24B).

**A. Relationship of the Paraná and Etendeka basalt plateaus to
the Tristan da Cunha hotspot.**

**B. Location of these flood-basalt plateaus 130 million years
ago, just before the South Atlantic began to open.**

FIGURE 24 The role that mantle plumes might play in
continental rifting

Next, the South Atlantic began to open, splitting the basalt province into two parts—the Etendeka and Paraná basalt plateaus. As the ocean basin grew, the tail of the plume produced a string of seamounts on each side of the newly formed ridge (Figure 24A). The modern area of hot-spot activity is centered around the volcanic island of Tristan da Cunha, on the Mid-Atlantic Ridge.

When hot, buoyant mantle plumes reach the base of the lithosphere, they cause the overlying crust to dome and weaken. Doming—of perhaps as much as 1000 meters (3300 feet)—tends to produce *three rifts*, or *arms*, that join in the area above the rising plume, called a **triple junction**. Frequently, continental breakup and the formation of an ocean basin occur along two of the rift arms, whereas the third arm may be less developed and constitute a failed rift that becomes filled with sediments. FIGURE 25 illustrates the location of a few mantle plumes that have generated large flood basalt plateaus and were presumably involved in the breakup of Pangaea.

One mantle plume is currently located beneath Iceland, near the crest of the Mid-Atlantic Ridge (FIGURE 26). Vast outpourings of basaltic lava began about 55 million years ago; evidence of these outpourings occurs in eastern Greenland, as well as across the Atlantic, in the Hebridean Islands of northern Scotland. The oldest magnetic stripes between Greenland and Europe are the same age, supporting the connection between the emergence of the Icelandic plume and seafloor spreading in the North Atlantic.

The Afar plume, which is associated with the split of the Arabian Peninsula from Africa, is located beneath a region of northeastern Ethiopia called the Afar Lowlands, an area of extensive volcanism (see Figure 21). This plume generated a typical rift system consisting of three arms that meet at a triple junction. Two of these rifts, the Red Sea and the Gulf of Aden, are active spreading centers. The third arm is the East African Rift, which may represent the initial stage in the breakup of a continent, as described earlier, or it may be destined to become a failed rift.

It is important to note that hot-spot volcanism does not necessarily lead to rifting. For example, vast outpourings of basaltic lava that constitute the Columbia River basalts in the Pacific Northwest, as well as Russia's Siberian Traps, are not associated with the fragmentation of a continent. Furthermore, along some rifted continental margins, stretching and thinning of the lithosphere was not accompanied by large-scale volcanism and melting. Consequently, other forces that contribute to continental fragmentation must exist.

Role of Tensional Stress
Continental rifting requires tensional stresses that are sufficiently strong to tear the lithosphere. In the Basin and Range region, where the lithosphere is thin, hot, and weak, small

Approximate surface location of mantle plumes prior to the breakup of Pangaea. The location of the plume that produced the Central Atlantic Province is unknown and may have involved a superplume that was deflected by the unusually thick lithosphere beneath western Africa. The Central Atlantic Province includes lava flows, sills, and dikes in northeastern South America, northwestern Africa, southwestern Europe, and eastern North America.

Timing of the breakup of Pangaea along various rift zones and the plume volcanism that was associated with each period of continental fragmentation. In most cases, volcanism appears to precede breakup by a few million years, or more.

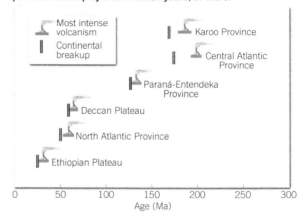

stresses are sufficient to cause spreading. During the past 20 million years, a broad zone of upwelling within the asthenosphere is thought to have caused considerable stretching and thinning of the crust in this region. In such settings, rifting is accompanied by large-scale melting and volcanism.

FIGURE 26 **Eruption of fluid basaltic lava, Iceland, 2010**
Iceland is located over a mantle plume that began to build this large volcanic island more than 20 million years ago. (Photo by Pakos Photography/Alamy)

Tensional stresses that result from plate motions are also thought to be particularly significant in continental rifting. In settings where a continent is attached to a subducting slab of oceanic lithosphere, it is pulled along by the descending slab. However, continental lithosphere is thick and tends to resist being towed, which creates tensional stresses that may be sufficient to tear the landmass. The zones of rifting in the fragmentation of a supercontinent may be influenced by a preexisting weakness, such as sutures—the sites where continents collided to form the supercontinent.

7 CONCEPT CHECKS

1. Name a modern example of a continental rift.
2. Briefly describe each of the four stages in the evolution of an ocean basin.
3. What role do hot spots and mantle plumes play in the breakup of a supercontinent?

EYE on Earth

Gas hydrates are natural gas reservoirs in icelike crystalline solids found in sediments on the deep-ocean floor and in Arctic permafrost areas deeper than 200 meters (660 feet). Gas hydrates contain methane molecules—the main ingredient of most natural gas—which is trapped within a lattice-like cage of water molecules. These deposits, called "ice that burns" are stable only at relatively high pressures and/or low temperatures.

Yonhap News/Newscom

Question 1 At surface temperatures and pressures, in what state of matter is methane? With this in mind, what problems exist for the extraction of gas hydrate deposits?

Question 2 Explain why gas hydrates are not found in sediments at shallow depths such as those found on continental shelves.

474

8 Destruction of Oceanic Lithosphere

Although new lithosphere is continually being produced at divergent plate boundaries, Earth's surface area is not growing larger. In order to balance the amount of newly created lithosphere, there must be a process whereby oceanic plates are destroyed.

Why Oceanic Lithosphere Subducts

The process of plate subduction is complex, and the ultimate fate of oceanic lithosphere is still being debated. Does subducted oceanic crust pile up at the boundary between the upper and lower mantle, where it is assimilated into the mantle? Or do most plates descend to the core–mantle boundary, where they are heated and eventually rise back toward Earth's surface as mantle plumes?

What is known with some certainty is that oceanic lithosphere will resist subduction unless its overall density is greater than that of the underlying asthenosphere. It takes at least 15 million years for a young slab of oceanic lithosphere to cool sufficiently to become denser than the supporting asthenosphere.

Spontaneous Subduction Subduction zones can be subdivided into two basic types, based on the nature of the subducting plate. The first type, referred to as a *Mariana-type subduction zone*, is characterized by old, dense lithosphere sinking into the mantle by its own weight. The lithosphere entering the Mariana Trench is about 185 million years old, some of the oldest and densest lithosphere in today's oceans. Along this trench, the subducting slab descends into the mantle at a steep angle that approaches 90 degrees (FIGURE 27A). Steep subduction angles produces deep trenches, which account in part for the depth of the Challenger Deep, located at the southern limb of the Mariana Trench. The Mariana and most of the other subduction zones in the western Pacific involve cold, dense lithosphere and therefore exhibit **spontaneous subduction**.

It is important to note that the *lithospheric mantle*, which makes up about 80 percent of the descending oceanic slab, drives subduction. Even when the *oceanic crust* is quite old, its density is still less than that of the underlying asthenosphere. Subduction, therefore, depends on lithospheric mantle that is colder and therefore denser than the underlying asthenosphere.

When an oceanic slab descends to about 400 kilometers (250 miles), mineral phase changes (the transition from low-density mineral to high-density mineral) enhance subduction. At this depth, the transition from olivine to its high-density form that has the spinel-structure increases the density of the slab, which helps pull the plate into the subduction zone.

Forced Subduction The second type of subduction zone, called the *Peru–Chile–type subduction*, is characterized by younger, hotter, and less-dense lithosphere

that dips at shallower angles (FIGURE 27B). Along Peru–Chile–type boundaries, the lithosphere is too buoyant to subduct spontaneously; rather, it is *forced* beneath the overlying plate by compressional forces.

In areas where **forced subduction** occurs, a strong coupling develops between the overlying plate and the subducting plate that can result in particularly strong and frequent earthquakes. Stated another way, plate motion generates horizontal compressional forces that cause the upper plate and underlying plate to grind against each other. The result can be folding and thickening of the upper plate and sometimes the formation of mountainous terrains like we see today in the Andes. Shallow subduction and strong coupling have also been observed in the past decade along the Sunda subduction zone, off the coast of Sumatra, another region that has experienced several major earthquakes.

It has also been determined that unusually thick units of oceanic crust, those that approach 30 kilometers (20 miles) in thickness, are likely to resist subduction. The Ontong Java Plateau, for example, is a thick oceanic plateau, about the size of Alaska, located in the western Pacific. About 20 million years ago, this plateau reached the trench that forms the boundary between the subducting Pacific plate and the overriding Australian–Indian plate. Apparently too buoyant to subduct, the Ontong Java Plateau clogged the trench.

FIGURE 27 The angle of plate subduction depends on its density
A. In parts of the Pacific, some oceanic lithosphere exceeds 180 million years in age and descends into the mantle at angles approaching 90 degrees. **B.** Young oceanic lithosphere is warm and buoyant, and it tends to subduct at a low angle.

Old, cold, dense lithosphere subducts at a steep angle

Young, warm, buoyant lithosphere subducts at a low angle

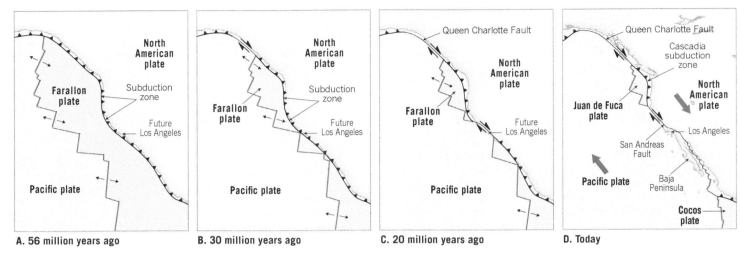

A. 56 million years ago   B. 30 million years ago   C. 20 million years ago   D. Today

SMARTFIGURE 28 **The demise of the Farallon plate**
Because the Farallon plate was subducting faster than it was being generated, it continually got smaller and smaller. The remaining fragments of the once-mighty Farallon plate are the Juan de Fuca, Cocos, and Nazca plates.

Subducting Plates: The Demise of Ocean Basins

In the 1970s, geologists began using magnetic stripes and fracture zones on the ocean floor to reconstruct the past 200 million years of plate movement. This research showed that parts of, or even entire, ocean basins have been destroyed along subduction zones. For example, during the breakup of Pangaea shown in the GEOgraphic, notice that the African plate moved northward, eventually colliding with Eurasia. During this event, the floor of the intervening Tethys Ocean was almost entirely consumed into the mantle, leaving behind a few small remnants—the Eastern Mediterranean Sea and the Black Sea.

Reconstructions of the breakup of Pangaea also helped investigators understand the demise of the Farallon plate—a large oceanic plate that once occupied much of the eastern Pacific basin. At the time of the breakup of Pangaea, the Farallon plate was situated on the eastern side of a spreading center, as shown in FIGURE 28A. The spreading center, which generated both the Farallon and Pacific plates, is the East Pacific Rise.

Beginning about 180 million years ago, the Americas were propelled westward, as Pangaea broke up and the Atlantic Ocean started to open. As a result, the Farallon plate began subducting beneath the Americas faster than it was being generated, causing it to decrease in size (FIGURE 28B). The three remaining fragments of the once-extensive Farallon plate include the modern Juan de Fuca, Cocos, and Nazca plates.

The westward migration of North America also caused a section of the East Pacific Rise to enter the subduction zone that once lay off the coast of California (Figure 28B). As this spreading center subducted, it was destroyed and replaced by a transform fault system that currently accommodates the differential motion between the North American and Pacific plates. Because of this change in plate geometry, the Pacific plate has captured a sliver of North America (the Baja Peninsula and a portion of southern California) and carries it northwestward toward Alaska at a rate of about 6 centimeters (2.5 inches) per year.

As more of the ridge subducted, the transform fault system, which we now call the San Andreas Fault, increased in length (FIGURE 28C). Today, the southern end of the San Andreas Fault connects to a young spreading center that is generating the Gulf of California (FIGURE 29). A similar event generated the Queen Charlotte transform fault, located off the west coast of Canada and southeastern Alaska.

8 CONCEPT CHECKS

1. Explain why oceanic lithosphere subducts even though the oceanic crust is less dense than the underlying asthenosphere.
2. Compare spontaneous subduction and forced subduction. Provide examples of places where each operates.
3. What role do mineral phase changes play in plate subduction?
4. Explain what happened when the spreading center that generated the Farallon plate collided with the North American plate.

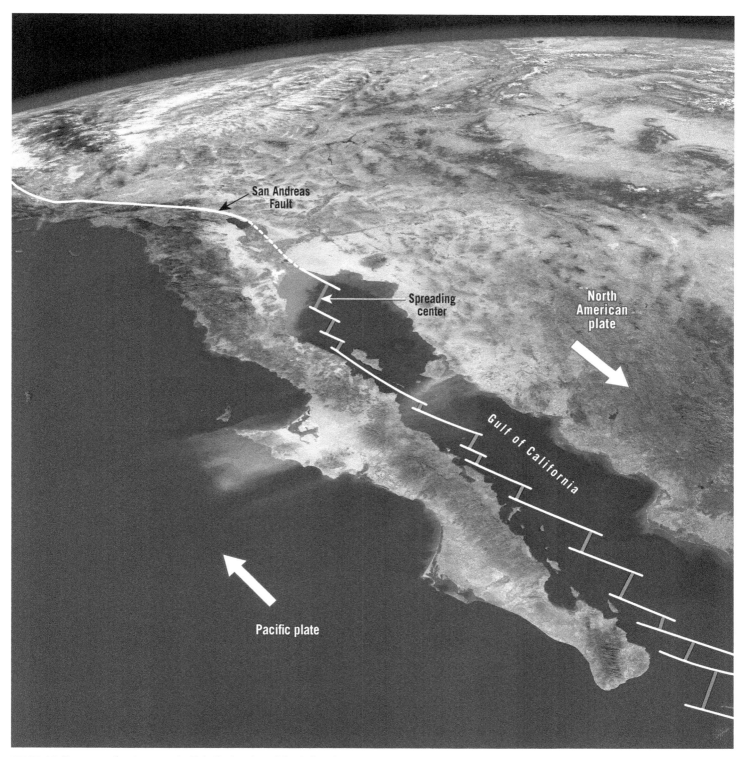

FIGURE 29 The separation between the Baja Peninsula and North America (SeaWiFS Project/ORBIGMAGE/NASA/Goddard Space Flight Center)

CONCEPTS IN REVIEW: DIVERGENT BOUNDARIES: ORIGIN AND EVOLUTION OF THE OCEAN FLOOR

1   An Emerging Picture of the Ocean Floor

Define *bathymetry* and explain the various bathymetric techniques used to map the ocean floor.

KEY WORDS   bathymetry, sonar, echo sounder

- Seafloor mapping is done with sonar—shipboard instruments that emit pulses of sound that "echo" off the bottom. Satellites are also used to map the ocean floor. Their instruments measure slight variations in sea level that result from differences in the gravitational pull of features on the seafloor. Accurate maps of seafloor topography can be made using these data.
- Mapping efforts have revealed three major areas of the ocean floor: continental margins, deep-ocean basins, and oceanic ridges.

CALCULATE IT   How many seconds would it take an echo sounder's ping to make the trip from a ship to the Challenger Deep (10,994 meters) and back? Recall that Depth = ½ (1500 m/sec × Echo travel time).

2   Continental Margins

Compare and contrast a passive continental margin with an active continental margin and list the major features of each.

KEY WORDS   continental margin, passive continental margin, continental shelf, continental slope, continental rise, turbidity current, submarine canyon, deep-sea fan, active continental margin, accretionary wedge, subduction erosion

- Continental margins are transitional zones between continental and oceanic crust. Active continental margins occur where a plate boundary and the edge of a continent coincide, usually on the leading edge of a plate. Passive continental margins are on the trailing edge of continents, far from plate boundaries.
- Heading offshore from the shoreline of a passive margin, a submarine traveler would first encounter the gently sloping continental shelf and then the steeper continental slope, which marks the end of the continental crust and the beginning of the oceanic crust. Below it is another gently sloping section, the continental rise: It is made of sediment transported by turbidity currents through submarine canyons and piled up in deep-sea fans atop the oceanic crust. Finally, in the deepest water, lies the abyssal plain.
- At an active continental margin, material may be added to the leading edge of a continent in the form of an accretionary wedge (common at shallow-angle subduction zones), or material may be scraped off the edge of a continent by subduction erosion (common at steeply dipping subduction zones).

CONSTANT CHANGES   How might Earth's land surface along a passive continental margin change over time as compared with the land along an active continental margin? Explain.

3   Features of Deep-Ocean Basins

List and describe the major features of the deep-ocean basin.

KEY WORDS   deep-ocean basin, deep-ocean trench, volcanic island arc, continental volcanic arc, abyssal plain, seismic reflection profiler, seamount, volcanic island, guyot, oceanic plateau

- The deep-ocean basin makes up about half of the ocean floor's area. Much of it is abyssal plain (deep, featureless sediment-draped crust). Subduction zones and deep-ocean trenches also occur in deep-ocean basins. Paralleling trenches are volcanic island arcs (if the subduction goes underneath oceanic lithosphere) or continental volcanic arcs (if the overriding plate has continental lithosphere on its leading edge).
- A variety of volcanic structures poke up from the abyssal plain. Seamounts are submarine volcanoes; if they pierce the surface of the ocean, we call them volcanic islands. Guyots are old volcanic islands that have had their tops eroded off before they subside below the sea. Oceanic plateaus are submarine flood basalt provinces—unusually thick sections of oceanic crust formed by massive underwater eruptions of lava.

IDENTIFY IT   On the cross-sectional view of a deep-ocean basin, label the following features: a seamount, a guyot, a volcanic island, an oceanic plateau, and an abyssal plain.

Oceanic crust

4 Anatomy of the Oceanic Ridge

Sketch and label a cross-sectional view of the Mid-Atlantic Ridge. Explain how a cross section of the East Pacific Rise would look different.

KEY WORDS oceanic ridge (mid-ocean ridge or rise), rift valley

- The oceanic ridge system is the longest topographic feature on Earth, wrapping around the world through all major ocean basins. It is a few kilometers tall, a few thousand kilometers wide, and a few tens of thousands of kilometers long. The summit is the place where new oceanic crust is generated, often marked by a rift valley.

WHERE IS IT? Do all oceanic ridges qualify as mid-ocean ridges? Explain.

5 Oceanic Ridges and Seafloor Spreading

Write a statement that describes how spreading rates affect ridge topography.

- Oceanic ridges form due to seafloor spreading: As plates of oceanic lithosphere move apart, the warm mantle beneath undergoes decompression, and it partially melts. The resulting magma is basaltic in composition. Some of it erupts along the ridge axis, but much of it crystallizes at depth. The freshly cooled basalt or gabbro makes up new oceanic crust.
- Oceanic ridges are elevated features because they are warm, and therefore less dense than older, colder oceanic lithosphere. Heat loss causes the oceanic crust to subside and be buried. After 80 million years, crust that was once an oceanic ridge can become an abyssal plain.
- The rate at which seafloor spreading occurs will determine the shape of the oceanic ridge. Ridges with slow spreading rates (1 to 5 centimeters per year) have prominent rift valleys and rugged topography. Those with fast spreading rates (greater than 9 centimeters per year) lack rift valleys and show a smoother, more subdued topography.

DATABLE DATA What can be said about the age of oceanic crust that is located on the flank of an oceanic ridge at some distance from the ridge crest? (*Hint:* Think about maximum and minimum ages.)

6 The Nature of Oceanic Crust

List the four layers of oceanic crust and explain how oceanic crust forms and how it is different from continental crust.

KEY WORDS ophiolite complex, sheeted dike complex, pillow basalt, black smoker

- Ophiolite complexes contain slices of oceanic crust that have been thrust above sea level. They have four distinct layers (from the top down): (1) deep-sea sediment, (2) pillow basalt, (3) a sheeted dike complex, and (4) gabbro.
- As two divergent plates move apart, fractures open perpendicular to the stretching direction, and lava moves up through these cracks, toward the seafloor. Once the lava has cooled and sealed these fractures shut, they become preserved as dikes of the sheeted dike complex. Magma that cools at depth crystallizes to become gabbro. Any lava that makes it to the seafloor is erupted as pillow basalt. (Pillow basalts are gradually buried by deep-sea sedimentation.)
- Along mid-ocean ridges, seawater flows through fissures in the oceanic crust and gets warmed by nearby pockets of magma. The warmer the seawater gets, the more chemically active it becomes. As it flows through the crust, the water causes hydrothermal metamorphism and dissolves metal ions. These hot, dark solutions may spew out of the crust at black smokers. The resulting sulfide mineral deposits can be economically important as sources of metals.

INTERPRET IT The photo shows a sea arch near Point Bonita, California—a headland just north of San Francisco. Look closely at the rock that makes up the arch. Identify the portion of the ophiolite complex that it represents and interpret how (and where) these structures originally formed. How might they have gotten from their place of origin to San Francisco?

Adam Talmadge

7 Continental Rifting: The Birth of a New Ocean Basin

Outline the steps by which continental rifting results in the formation of new ocean basins. Describe the supercontinent cycle.

KEY WORDS continental rift, supercontinent cycle, triple junction

- When continents rift apart, new ocean basins may form. In the modern world, the East African Rift shows an example of the initial stages of continental breakup, with rift valleys that are sites of basaltic volcanism and the deposition of detrital sediment. The Red Sea is a modern example of more advanced rifting in which seafloor spreading is occurring and the rift is submerged below sea level. Over time, the rift may widen through seafloor spreading, and an ocean basin will form, flanked by passive continental margins. A modern example of this stage is the Atlantic Ocean.

- Continental rifting may be initiated by mantle plumes, or perhaps continents are more likely to break when sites of preexisting mechanical weakness are subjected to tensional stresses. The assembly and breakup of supercontinents has been called the supercontinent cycle. At least two supercontinents have formed in Earth's past.

COMPARE & CONTRAST Consider the Baja Peninsula of Mexico (Figure 29). Which step of continental rifting does the Gulf of California most closely match? What differences distinguish it from the example described in the chapter?

8 Destruction of Oceanic Lithosphere

Compare and contrast spontaneous subduction and forced subduction.

KEY WORDS spontaneous subduction, forced subduction

- Every unit of oceanic lithosphere produced by seafloor spreading is matched by an equivalent amount that gets destroyed. Subduction takes oceanic lithosphere into the mantle, where its ultimate fate is still uncertain.

- If oceanic lithosphere is sufficiently old (and therefore cold), it may begin to sink because of its increased density. The resulting spontaneous subduction zone will plunge at close to 90 degrees and be marked by a deep trench. The Mariana Trench is an example.

- Forced subduction shoves relatively buoyant oceanic lithosphere underneath another plate. This results in shallow subduction angles and big earthquakes along megathrust faults. The Peru–Chile Trench is an example.

- Regardless of its initial cause, subduction serves to close ocean basins. This may eventually bring the once widely separated landmasses into contact with one another.

FORCING THE QUESTION Which type of subduction is occurring in this figure? Explain. Describe the age of the oceanic lithosphere at both the deep-ocean trench and the oceanic ridge as fully as you can.

GIVE IT SOME THOUGHT

1. Refer to the accompanying map showing the eastern seaboard of the United States to complete the following:
   a. Which letter is associated with each of the following: continental shelf, continental rise, and shelf-break?
   b. How does the size of the continental shelf that surrounds the state of Florida compare with the size of the Florida peninsula?
   c. Why are there no deep-ocean trenches on this map?

2. Search Wikipedia for "Mataiva," a small atoll in Tuamotus, French Polynesia. Using the map on the Wikipedia site, determine the approximate number of atolls in this small region of the western Pacific. What conclusion can you draw about the abundance of atolls in the western Pacific?

3. Referring to Figure 17, compare and contrast the topography of the crest of an oceanic ridge that exhibits a slow spreading rate with one that exhibits a fast spreading rate. Give examples of each.

4. Briefly explain why the ocean floor generally gets deeper the farther one travels from the ridge crest.

5. The accompanying photo is a false-color sonar image that shows the ridge crest (linear pink area) of a section of a spreading center.
   a. Is the structure along the ridge crest characteristic of a fast or slow spreading center? Explain.
   b. What name is given to the submerged conical-shaped structure in the lower-left portion of this image?

Dr. Ken C. Macdonald

6. Name a location where a new ocean basin may develop in the future. Explain why you chose that site.

7. Propose one or two ideas to explain why some continental rifts evolve into active plate boundaries while others do not.

8. Refer to Figure 3. At which of the following locations would you expect to have the highest angle of subduction: the Puerto Rico subduction zone or the Cascadia subduction zone? Explain.

9. Refer to Figure 28. Predict the fate of the Juan de Fuca plate. What type of boundary might the Cascadia subduction zone become in the future? Explain.

10. Explain this statement: The oceans are 4 billion years old, but the oldest ocean basin is only about 200 million years old.

11. This image shows lava at a temperature of about 1200° C erupting on the seafloor west of the Tonga trench. What name is given to lava flows like these that erupt underwater?

NOAA

MasteringGeology™
www.masteringgeology.com

Looking for additional review and test prep materials? Visit the Study Area in MasteringGeology to enhance your understanding of this chapter's content by accessing a variety of resources, including **Self-Study Quizzes**, **Geoscience Animations, GEODe Tutorials, RSS feeds, flashcards, web links, self-study quizzes,** and an optional **Pearson eText.**

Glossary

Abyssal plain A very level area of the deep-ocean floor, usually lying at the foot of the continental rise.

Accretionary wedge A large wedge-shaped mass of sediment that accumulates in subduction zones. Here sediment is scraped from the subducting oceanic plate and accreted to the overriding crustal block.

Active continental margin A margin that is usually narrow and consists of highly deformed sediments. Such margins occur where oceanic lithosphere is being subducted beneath the margin of a continent.

Bathymetry The measurement of ocean depths and the charting of the topography of the ocean floor.

Black smoker A hydrothermal vent on the ocean floor that emits a black cloud of hot, metal-rich water.

Continental margin The portion of the seafloor that is adjacent to the continents. It may include the continental shelf, continental slope, and continental rise.

Continental rift A linear zone along which continental lithosphere stretches and pulls apart. Its creation may mark the beginning of a new ocean basin.

Continental rise The gently sloping surface at the base of the continental slope.

Continental shelf The gently sloping submerged portion of the continental margin, extending from the shoreline to the continental slope.

Continental slope The steep gradient that leads to the deep-ocean floor and marks the seaward edge of the continental shelf.

Continental volcanic arc Mountains formed in part by igneous activity associated with the subduction of oceanic lithosphere beneath a continent. Examples include the Andes and the Cascades.

Deep-ocean basin The portion of seafloor that lies between the continental margin and the oceanic ridge system. This region comprises almost 30 percent of Earth's surface.

Deep-ocean trench A narrow, elongated depression of the seafloor.

Deep-sea fan A cone-shaped deposit at the base of the continental slope. The sediment is transported to the fan by turbidity currents that follow submarine canyons.

Echo sounder An instrument used to determine the depth of water by measuring the time interval between emission of a sound signal and the return of its echo from the bottom.

Forced subduction A process that occurs at Peru–Chile–type subduction zones in which lithosphere is too buoyant to subduct spontaneously but is forced beneath the overriding plate.

Guyot A submerged, flat-topped seamount.

Mid-ocean ridge A continuous mountainous ridge on the floor of all the major ocean basins and varying in width from 500 to 5000 kilometers (300 to 3000 miles). The rifts at the crests of these ridges represent divergent plate boundaries.

Oceanic plateau An extensive region on the ocean floor that is composed of thick accumulations of pillow basalts and other mafic rocks that, in some cases, exceed 30 kilometers (20 miles) in thickness.

Oceanic ridge See Mid-ocean ridge.

Ophiolite complex The sequence of rocks that make up the oceanic crust. The three-layer sequence includes an upper layer of pillow basalts, a middle zone of sheeted dikes, and a lower layer of gabbro.

Passive continental margin A margin that consists of a continental shelf, continental slope, and continental rise. They are not associated with plate boundaries and therefore experience little volcanism and few earthquakes.

Pillow basalts Basaltic lava that solidifies in an underwater environment and develops a structure that resembles a pile of pillows.

Rift valley A long, narrow trough bounded by normal faults. It represents a region where divergence is taking place.

Seamount An isolated volcanic peak that rises at least 1000 meters (3300 feet) above the deep-ocean floor.

Seismic reflection profile A method of viewing the rock structure beneath a blanket of sediment by using strong, low-frequency sound waves that penetrate the sediments and reflect off the contacts between rock layers and fault zones.

Sheeted dike complex A large group of nearly parallel dikes.

Sonar An instrument that uses acoustic signals (sound energy) to measure water depths. Sonar is an acronym for sound navigation and ranging.

Spontaneous subduction A process that occurs at Mariana-type subduction zones in which old, dense lithosphere sinks into the mantle at a steep angle by its own weight creating a deep trench.

Subduction erosion A process in subduction zones in which sediment and rock are scraped off the bottom of the overriding plate and transported into the mantle.

Submarine canyon A seaward extension of a valley that was cut on the continental shelf during a time when sea level was lower, or a canyon carved into the outer continental shelf, slope, and rise by turbidity currents.

Supercontinent cycle The idea that the rifting and dispersal of one supercontinent is followed by a long period during which the fragments gradually reassemble into a new supercontinent.

Triple junction A point where three lithospheric plates meet.

Turbidity current A downslope movement of dense, sediment-laden water created when sand and mud on the continental shelf and slope are dislodged and thrown into suspension.

Volcanic island arc A chain of volcanic islands generally located a few hundred kilometers from a trench where there is active subduction of one oceanic plate beneath another.

Convergent Boundaries: Origin of Mountains

From Chapter 14 of *Earth: An Introduction to Physical Geology*, Eleventh Edition. Edward J. Tarbuck, Frederick K. Lutgens, Dennis Tasa.
Copyright © 2014 by Pearson Education, Inc. All rights reserved.

Convergent Boundaries: Origin of Mountains

Hiker ascending the Alpinisteig climbing route in the Italian Dolomites.
(Photo by allesfoto/imagebroker/AGE fotostock)

Each statement represents the primary learning objective for the corresponding major heading within the chapter. After you complete the chapter you should be able to:

1   Locate and name Earth's major mountain belts on a world map.
2   List and describe the four major features associated with subduction zones.
3   Sketch a cross section of an Andean-type mountain belt and describe how its major features are generated.
4   Summarize the stages in the development of an Alpine-type mountain belt such as the Appalachians.
5   Compare and contrast the formation of fault-block mountains with compressional mountains.
6   Explain the principle of isostasy and how it contributes to the elevated topography of young mountain belts like the Himalayas.

Mountains are spectacular features that rise abruptly above the surrounding terrain. Some mountains occur as isolated masses; the volcanic cone Kilimanjaro stands almost 6000 meters (20,000 feet) above sea level, overlooking the expansive grasslands of East Africa. Other peaks are parts of extensive mountain belts, such as the American Cordillera, which runs almost continuously from the southern tip of South America through Alaska. Chains such as the Himalayas consist of geologically young, towering peaks that are still rising, whereas others, including the Appalachian Mountains in the eastern United States, are much older and have eroded far below their once-lofty heights.

Most major mountain belts show evidence of enormous compressional forces that have folded, faulted, and generally deformed large sections of Earth's crust. Although tectonic processes contribute to the majestic appearance of mountains, much of their beauty must be credited to weathering and the work of running water and glacial ice, which continually sculpt these uplifted masses. In this chapter, we will examine the nature of mountains and the processes that form them.

This peak is in Pakistan's Karakoram Range, part of the Himalayan system. (Photo by Art Wolfe/Getty)

1 Mountain Building

Mountain building has occurred in the recent geologic past at several locations around the world. Young mountain belts include the American Cordillera (cordillera means "spine" or "backbone"), which runs along the western margin of the Americas from Cape Horn at the tip of South America to Alaska and includes the Andes; the Alpine–Himalaya chain, that extends along the margin of the Mediterranean, through Iran to northern India and into Indochina; and the mountainous terrains of the western Pacific, which include volcanic island arcs that comprise Japan, the Philippines, and Sumatra. Most of these young mountain belts have come into existence within the past 100 million years (FIGURE 1). Some, including the Himalayas, began their growth as recently as 50 million years ago.

In addition to these young mountain belts, there are several chains of Paleozoic-age mountains on Earth. Although these older mountain belts are deeply eroded and topographically less prominent, they exhibit the same structural features found in younger mountains. The Appalachians in the eastern United States and the Urals in Russia are classic examples of this group of older, well-worn mountain belts.

The term for the processes that collectively produce a mountain belt is **orogenesis** (*oros* = mountain, *genesis* = to come into being). Most major mountain belts display striking visual evidence of great compressional forces that have shortened the crust horizontally while thickening it vertically. These **compressional mountains** contain large quantities of preexisting sedimentary and crystalline rocks that have been faulted and contorted into a series of folds (FIGURE 2). Although folding and thrust faulting are often the most conspicuous signs of orogenesis, varying degrees of metamorphism and igneous activity are always present.

How do mountain belts form? Since the time of the ancient Greeks, this question has intrigued philosophers and scientists. One early proposal suggested that mountains are simply wrinkles in Earth's crust, produced as the planet cooled from its original semi-molten state. According to this idea, Earth contracted and shrank as it lost heat, which caused the crust to deform in a manner similar to how an orange peel wrinkles as the fruit dries out. However, neither this nor any other early hypothesis withstood scientific scrutiny.

FIGURE 1 Earth's major mountain belts
Notice the east–west trend of major mountain belts in Eurasia in contrast to the north–south trend of the North and South American Cordillera.

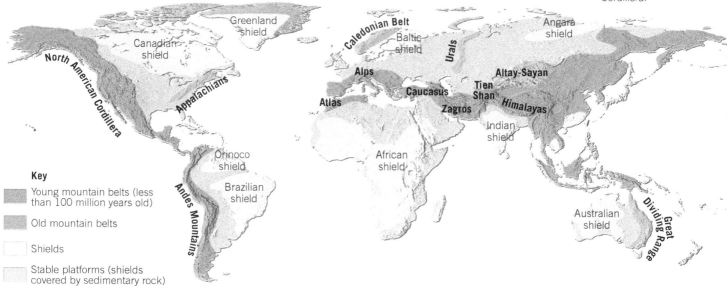

Key

Young mountain belts (less than 100 million years old)

Old mountain belts

Shields

Stable platforms (shields covered by sedimentary rock)

SMARTFIGURE 2
Mount Kidd, Alberta,
Canada

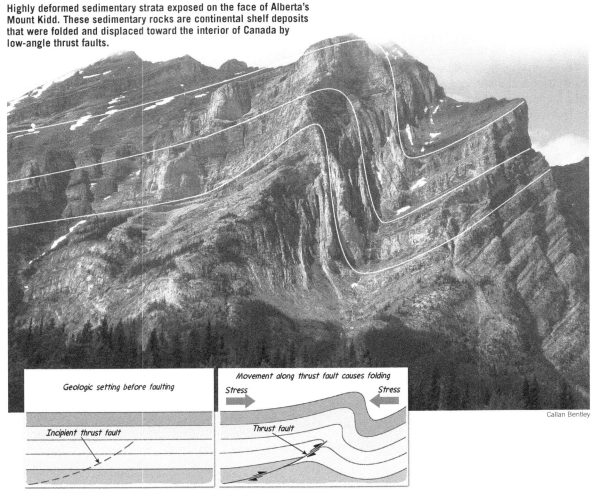

Highly deformed sedimentary strata exposed on the face of Alberta's Mount Kidd. These sedimentary rocks are continental shelf deposits that were folded and displaced toward the interior of Canada by low-angle thrust faults.

Callan Bentley

Geologist's Sketch

The theory of plate tectonics provides a model for orogenesis with excellent explanatory power and accounts for the origin of virtually all the present mountain belts and most of the ancient ones. According to this model, the tectonic processes that generate Earth's major mountainous terrains occurs along convergent plate boundaries, where oceanic lithosphere subducts into the mantle. We will first look at the nature of convergent plate boundaries and then examine how the process of subduction has driven mountain building around the globe.

1 CONCEPT CHECKS

1. Define *orogenesis*.
2. In the plate tectonics model, which type of plate boundary is most directly associated with Earth's major mountain belts?

2 Convergence and Subducting Plates

In their ongoing quest to unravel the events that produce mountains, researchers examine ancient mountain belts as well as sites where orogenesis is currently active. Of particular interest are convergent plate boundaries, where lithospheric plates subduct. The subduction of oceanic lithosphere generates Earth's strongest earthquakes and most explosive volcanic eruptions, and it plays a pivotal role in generating most of Earth's mountain belts.

Major Features of Subduction Zones

Subduction zones can be roughly divided into four regions: (1) a *volcanic arc*, which is built on the overlying plate; (2) a *deep-ocean trench*, which forms where subducting slabs of oceanic lithosphere bend and descend into the asthenosphere; (3) a *forearc region*, which is located between a trench and a volcanic arc; and (4) a *back-arc region*, which is located on the side of the volcanic arc opposite the trench.

Volcanic Arcs Perhaps the most obvious structure generated by subduction is a *volcanic arc* (FIGURE 3). Where two oceanic slabs converge, one is subducted beneath the other, initiating partial melting of the mantle wedge located above the subducting plate. This eventually leads to the growth of a **volcanic island arc**, or simply an **island arc**, on the ocean floor. Examples of active island arcs include the Mariana, Tonga, and Aleutian arcs in the Pacific (FIGURE 4).

When oceanic lithosphere is subducted beneath a continental block, a **continental volcanic arc** results. Continental volcanic arcs build on the topography of older continental rocks, resulting in volcanic peaks that may reach 6000 meters (nearly 20,000 feet) above sea level.

Deep-Ocean Trenches Deep-ocean trenches are created where oceanic lithosphere bends as it descends into the mantle. Trench depth is strongly related to the age, and therefore the temperature, of the subducting oceanic slab as well as the availability of sediments. In the western Pacific, where oceanic lithosphere is cold, dense oceanic slabs descend into the mantle at steep angles, producing trenches with average depths of 7 to 8 kilometers below sea level. A well-known example is the Mariana trench, where the deepest area is an amazing 10,994 meters (36,069 feet) below sea level. By contrast, the Cascadia subduction zone off the coasts of Washington and Oregon lacks a well-defined trench, partly because the warm, buoyant Juan de Fuca plate subducts at a very low angle. In addition, a massive amount of sediment from the Columbia River basin fills most of what would otherwise be a shallow trench—2 to 3 kilometers deep.

Forearc and Back-Arc Regions Located between developing volcanic arcs and deep-ocean trenches are

Continuous subduction of oceanic lithosphere results in the development of thick units of continental-like crust upon the overlying plate.

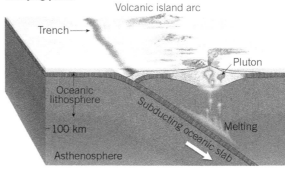

FIGURE 3 Development of a volcanic island arc A volcanic island arc forms where one slab of oceanic lithosphere is subducted beneath another slab of the same material.

forearc regions, where pyroclastic material from the volcanic arc, as well as sediments eroded from the adjacent landmass, accumulate. Ocean-floor sediments are also carried to forearc regions by subducting plates.

Another site where sediments and volcanic debris accumulate is the *back-arc* region, which is located on the backside of the volcanic arc when viewed from the trench.

Geologist's Sketch

FIGURE 4 Three of many volcanic islands that comprise the Aleutian Arc This narrow band of volcanism results from the subduction of the Pacific plate. In the distance is the Great Sitkin volcano (1772 meters [5812 feet]), which the Aleuts call the "Great Emptier of Bowels" because of its frequent activity. (Photo by Bruce D. Marsh)

FIGURE 5 Formation of a
back-arc basin

Subduction and "roll back" of an oceanic slab creates flow
in the mantle, called slab suction, that "pulls" the upper
(non-subducting) plate toward the retreating trench.

Slab suction causes the overlying plate to become
elongated and thinned, often resulting in the formation of
a basin and spreading center behind the volcanic arc.

Some back-arc basins, like the one shown, develop into
well-developed spreading centers that generate a deep
ocean basin behind the volcanic arc.

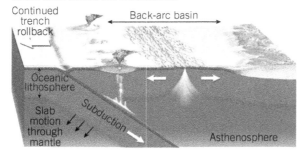

In these regions, tensional forces are usually prevalent,
causing Earth's crust to be stretched and thinned.

Extension and Back-Arc Spreading

Because subduction zones form where two plates converge,
it is logical to assume that large compressional forces deform the plate margins. However, convergent margins are
not necessarily regions dominated by compressional forces.
Along some convergent plate margins, tensional stresses
act on the overlying plates and cause extension—stretching
and thinning—of the crust. But how do extensional processes operate where two plates are moving together?

The age of the subducting oceanic slab is thought to
play a significant role in determining the dominant forces
acting on the overriding plate. When a relatively cold,
dense slab subducts, it does *not* follow a fixed path into
the asthenosphere. Rather, it sinks vertically as it descends
along an angled path. This causes the trench to retreat, or
"roll back," as shown in FIGURE 5. As the subducting plate
sinks, it creates a flow in the asthenosphere called *slab
suction* that "pulls" the upper plate toward the retreating
trench. (Visualize what would have happened if you were in
a lifeboat unable to move away from the *Titanic* as it sank!)

Slab suction, in turn, produces tensional stress that
causes the overriding plate to become elongated and
thinned, most often creating a basin in the region behind the volcanic arc (Figure 5B). Thinning of the crust
results in upwelling of hot mantle rock and accompanying decompression melting. Continued extension may
initiate seafloor spreading, which increases the size of
the newly formed basin. Basins of this type, located
"behind" a volcanic arc, are referred to as **back-arc basins** (Figure 5C). Seafloor spreading is currently enlarging the back-arc basins found landward of the Mariana
and Tonga islands.

---

2 CONCEPT CHECKS

1. List the four major features of a subduction zone.
2. Briefly describe how back-arc basins form.

3 | Subduction and Mountain Building

The subduction of oceanic lithosphere is the driving force in mountain building (orogenesis). Where oceanic lithosphere subducts beneath an oceanic plate, a *volcanic island arc* and related tectonic features develop. Subduction beneath a continental block, on the other hand, results in the formation of a *continental volcanic arc* and mountainous topography along the margin of a continent. In addition, volcanic island arcs and other crustal fragments "drift" across the ocean basin until they reach a subduction zone, where they collide and become welded to another crustal fragment or a larger continental block. If subduction continues long enough, it can ultimately result in the collision of two or more continents.

Island Arc–Type Mountain Building

Island arcs result from the steady subduction of oceanic lithosphere, which may last for 200 million years or more. Periodic volcanic activity, the emplacement of igneous plutons at depth, and the accumulation of sediment that is scraped from the subducting plate gradually increase the volume of crustal material capping the upper plate. Some large volcanic island arcs, such as Japan, owe their size to having been built on fragments of continental crust that have rifted from a large landmass or the joining of multiple island arcs over time.

The continued growth of a volcanic island arc can result in the formation of mountainous topography consisting of nearly parallel belts of igneous and metamorphic rocks. This activity, however, is viewed as just one phase in the development of Earth's major mountain belts. As you will see later, some volcanic arcs are carried by subducting plates to the margin of large continental blocks, where they become involved in large-scale mountain-building episodes.

Andean-Type Mountain Building

Andean-type mountain building is characterized by subduction beneath a continent rather than oceanic lithosphere. Subduction along these active continental margins is associated with long-lasting magmatic activity that builds continental volcanic arcs. The result is crustal thickening, with the crust reaching thicknesses of more than 70 kilometers (45 miles).

The first stage in the development of Andean-type mountain belts, named after the Andes Mountains of South America, occurs along *passive continental margins*. The East Coast of the United States provides a modern example of a passive continental margin where sedimentation has produced a thick platform of shallow-water sandstones, limestones, and shales (FIGURE 6A). At some point, the forces that drive plate motions change, and a subduction zone develops along the margin of the continent. In order for a new subduction zone to form, oceanic lithosphere must be old and dense enough to create a downward force capable of shearing the lithosphere. Alternatively, strong compressional forces tear off the oceanic lithosphere along a continental margin, thereby initiating subduction.

Building Volcanic Arcs Recall that as oceanic lithosphere descends into the mantle, increasing temperatures

FIGURE 6 Andean-type mountain building

A. Passive continental margin with an extensive platform of sediments and sedimentary rocks.

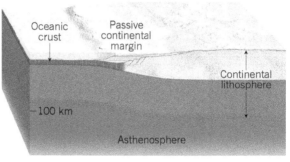

B. Plate convergence generates a subduction zone, and partial melting produces a continental volcanic arc. Compressional forces and igneous activity further deform and thicken the crust, elevating the mountain belt.

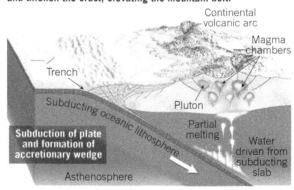

C. Subduction ends and is followed by a period of uplift.

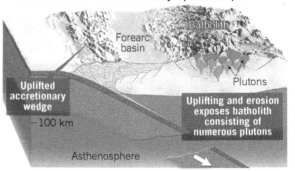

and pressures drive volatiles (mostly water and carbon dioxide) from the crustal rocks. These mobile fluids migrate upward into the wedge-shaped region of mantle between the subducting slab and upper plate. At a depth of about 100 kilometers (60 miles), these water-rich fluids sufficiently reduce the melting point of hot mantle rock to trigger some melting (FIGURE 6B). Partial melting of the ultramafic rock peridotite generates *primary magmas*, with mafic (basaltic) compositions. Because these newly formed basaltic magmas are less dense than the rocks from which they originated, they will buoyantly rise. Upon reaching the base of the low-density materials of the continental crust, they typically collect, or pond.

Continued ascent through the thick continental crust is generally achieved through magmatic differentiation, in which heavy ferromagnesian minerals crystallize and settle out of the magma, leaving the remaining melt enriched in silica and other "light" components. Hence, through magmatic differentiation, a comparatively dense basaltic magma can generate low-density, buoyant *secondary magma* composed of intermediate and/or felsic composition.

Emplacement of Batholiths

Because of its low density and great thickness, continental crust significantly impedes the ascent of molten rock. Consequently, a high percentage of the magma that intrudes the crust never reaches the surface; instead, it crystallizes at depth to form massive igneous plutons called *batholiths*. The result of this activity is thickening of the crust.

Eventually, uplifting and erosion exhume the batholiths that consist of numerous interconnected plutons (FIGURE 6C). The American Cordillera contains several large batholiths, including the Sierra Nevada of California, the Coast Range Batholith of western Canada, and several large igneous bodies in the Andes (FIGURE 7). Most batholiths consist of intrusive igneous rocks that range in composition from granite to diorite.

Development of an Accretionary Wedge

During the development of volcanic arcs, unconsolidated sediments that are carried on the subducting plate, as well as fragments of oceanic crust, may be scraped off and plastered against the edge of the overriding plate. The resulting chaotic accumulation of deformed and thrust-faulted sediments and scraps of ocean crust is called an **accretionary wedge** (see Figure 6B). The processes that deform these sediments are comparable to a wedge of soil being scraped and pushed in front of an advancing bulldozer.

Some of the sediments that comprise an accretionary wedge are muds that accumulated on the ocean floor and were subsequently carried to the subduction zone by plate motion. Additional materials are derived from an adjacent continent or volcanic arc and consist of volcanic debris and products of weathering and erosion.

In regions where sediment is plentiful, prolonged subduction may thicken a developing accretionary wedge sufficiently that it protrudes above sea level. This has occurred along the southern end of the Puerto Rico Trench, where the Orinoco River basin of Venezuela is a major source of sediments. The resulting wedge emerges to form the island of Barbados. By contrast, some subduction zones have small accretionary wedges or none at all. The Mariana Trench, for example, has a poorly developed accretionary wedge, partially because of its distance from a significant source of sediment.

Forearc Basins

As an accretionary wedge grows upward, it tends to act as a barrier to the movement of sediment from the volcanic arc to the trench. As a result, sediments begin to collect between the accretionary wedge and the volcanic arc. This region, which is composed of relatively undeformed layers of sediment and sedimentary rocks, is called a **forearc basin** (see Figure 6B,C). Subsidence and continued sedimentation in forearc basins can generate a sequence of nearly horizontal sedimentary strata that can attain thicknesses of several kilometers.

Sierra Nevada, Coast Ranges, and Great Valley

California's Sierra Nevada, Coast Ranges, and Great Valley are excellent examples of the tectonic structures that are typically generated along an Andean-type subduction zone (FIGURE 8). These structures were produced by the subduction of a portion of the Pacific basin (Farallon plate) under the western margin of California. The Sierra Nevada Batholith is a remnant of the continental volcanic arc that was produced by many surges of magma during a time span that exceeded 100 million years. The Coast Ranges

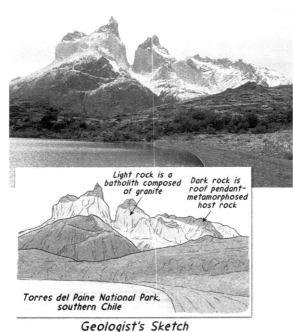

FIGURE 7 Torres del Paine National Park, Chile This mountainous area, east of the high southern Andes, consists mainly of large granite plutons (light color) between layers of sedimentary and metamorphic rocks (dark color). Magma intruded and metamorphosed the adjacent sedimentary host rock to form these rock bodies that were uplifted and exhumed by erosional forces. (Photo by Michael Collier)

Light rock is a batholith composed of granite

Dark rock is roof pendant-metamorphosed host rock

Torres del Paine National Park, southern Chile

Geologist's Sketch

FIGURE 8 Mountains
and landform regions of the
western United States

(After Thelin and Pike, U.S. Geological Survey)

Beginning about 30 million years ago, subduction gradually ceased along much of the margin of North America, as the spreading center that produced the Farallon plate entered the California Trench. The uplifting and erosion that followed removed most of the evidence of past volcanic activity and exposed a core of crystalline igneous and associated metamorphic rocks that make up the Sierra Nevada (see Figure 6C). The Coast Ranges were uplifted only recently, as evidenced by the young, unconsolidated sediments that currently blanket portions of these highlands.

California's Great Valley is a remnant of the forearc basin that formed between the Sierra Nevada and the accretionary prism and trench that lay offshore. Throughout much of its history, portions of the Great Valley lay below sea level. This sediment-laden basin contains thick marine deposits and debris eroded from the adjacent continental volcanic arc.

3 CONCEPT CHECKS

1. How are magmas that exhibit an intermediate-to-felsic composition thought to be generated from mantle-derived basaltic magmas?
2. What is a batholith? In what modern tectonic setting are batholiths being generated?
3. In what ways are the Sierra Nevada and the Andes similar?
4. What is an accretionary wedge? Briefly describe its formation.
5. Describe and give an example of a passive continental margin.
6. The formation of mountainous topography at a volcanic island arc is considered just one phase in the development of a major mountain belt. Explain.

were built from the vast accumulation of sediments (accretionary wedge) that collected along the continental margin, or perhaps an island arc that lay offshore.

EYE on Earth

These interbedded layers of chert and shale have been strongly folded during the growth of an accretionary wedge. A recent period of uplift has exposed these deformed strata near Marin Headlands, north of San Francisco, California.

Question 1 What is the nature of the stress that most likely generated these highly folded strata: compressional or tensional?

Question 2 Along what type of plate boundaries do accretionary wedges form?

Question 3 What type of plate boundary is found today in the San Francisco Bay area?

0   1
Meter

Michael Collier

4 Collisional Mountain Belts

Most major mountain belts are generated when one or more buoyant crustal fragments collide with a continental margin as a result of subduction. Whereas oceanic lithosphere, which is relatively dense, readily subducts, continental lithosphere contains significant amounts of low-density crustal rocks and is therefore too buoyant to undergo subduction. Consequently, the arrival of a crustal fragment at a trench results in a collision and usually ends further subduction.

Cordilleran-Type Mountain Building

A Cordilleran-type orogeny, named after the North American Cordillera, is associated with a Pacific-like ocean—Pacific-like in that unlike the Atlantic, the Pacific may never close. The rapid rate of seafloor spreading in the Pacific basin is balanced by a high rate of subduction. In this setting, it is highly likely that island arcs or small crustal fragments will be carried along until they collide with an active continental margin. The process of collision and accretion (joining together) of comparatively small crustal fragments to a continental margin has generated many of the mountainous regions that rim the Pacific. Geologists refer to these accreted crustal blocks as *terranes*. The term **terrane** is used to describe a crustal fragment consisting of a distinct and recognizable series of rock formations that has been transported by plate tectonic processes. By contrast, the term *terrain* is used when describing the shape of the surface topography, or "lay of the land."

The Nature of Terranes

What is the nature of crustal fragments, and where did they originate? Research suggests that prior to their accretion to a continental block, some of these fragments may have been **microcontinents** similar to the modern-day island of Madagascar, located east of Africa in the Indian Ocean. Many others were island arcs similar to Japan, the Philippines, and the Aleutian Islands. Still others may have been submerged oceanic plateaus created by massive outpourings of basaltic lavas associated with mantle plumes. More than 100 of these relatively small crustal fragments, most of which are in the Pacific, are known to exist.

Accretion and Orogenesis

As oceanic plates move, they carry embedded oceanic plateaus, volcanic island arcs, and microcontinents to an Andean-type subduction zone. When an oceanic plate contains small seamounts, these structures are generally subducted along with the

A. A microcontinent and a volcanic island arc are being carried toward a subduction zone.

B. The volcanic island arc is sliced off the subducting plate and thrust onto the continent.

SMARTFIGURE 9
Collision and accretion of small crustal fragments to a continental margin

C. A new subduction zone forms seaward of the old subduction zone.

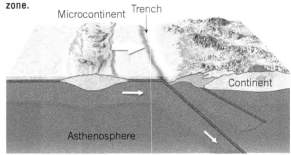

D. The accretion of the microcontinent to the continental margin shoves the remnant island arc further inland and grows the continental margin seaward.

descending oceanic slab. However, large, thick units of oceanic crust, such as the Ontong Java Plateau, which is the size of Alaska, or an island arc composed of abundant "light" igneous rocks, render the oceanic lithosphere too buoyant to subduct. In these situations, a collision between the crustal fragment and the continental margin occurs.

The sequence of events that happen when small crustal fragments reach a Cordilleran-type margin is shown in FIGURE 9. Rather than subduct, the upper crustal layers of these thickened zones are peeled from the descending plate and thrust in relatively thin sheets on the adjacent continental block. Convergence does not generally end with the accretion of a crustal fragment. Rather, new subduction zones typically form, and they can carry other island arcs or microcontinents toward a collision with the continental margin. Each collision displaces earlier accreted terranes further inland, adding to the zone of deformation as well as to the thickness and lateral extent of the continental margin.

The North American Cordillera   The correlation between mountain building and the accretion of crustal fragments arose primarily from studies conducted in the North American Cordillera (FIGURE 10). Researchers determined that some of the rocks in the orogenic belts of Alaska and British Columbia contained fossil and paleomagnetic evidence which indicated that these strata previously lay much closer to the equator.

It is now known that many of the terranes that make up the North American Cordillera were scattered throughout the eastern Pacific, like the island arcs and oceanic plateaus currently distributed in the western Pacific. During the breakup of Pangaea, the eastern portion of the Pacific basin (Farallon plate) began to subduct under the western margin of North America. This activity resulted in the piecemeal addition of crustal fragments to the entire Pacific margin of the continent—from Mexico's Baja Peninsula to northern Alaska (Figure 10). Geologists expect that many modern microcontinents will likewise be accreted to active continental margins surrounding the Pacific, producing new orogenic belts.

Alpine-Type Mountain Building: Continental Collisions

Alpine-type orogenies, named after the Alps that have been studied intensely for more than 200 years, occur where two continental masses collide. This type of orogeny may also involve the accretion of continental fragments or island arcs that occupied the ocean basin that once separated the two continental blocks. Mountain belts that were formed by the closure of major ocean basins include the Himalayas, Appalachians, Urals, and Alps. Continental collisions result in the development

FIGURE 10 Terranes that have been added to western North America during the past 200 million years Paleomagnetic studies and fossil evidence indicate that some of these terranes originated thousands of kilometers to the south of their present locations. (After D. R. Hutchinson and others)

of mountains characterized by shortened and thickened crust, achieved through folding and large-scale thrust faulting.

The zone where two continents collide and are "welded" together is called the **suture**. This portion of the mountain belt often preserves slivers of oceanic lithosphere (ophiolites) that were trapped between the colliding plates. As a result of their unique structure, these pieces of oceanic lithosphere help identify the collision boundary.

Noteworthy features of most collisional mountain ranges are **fold-and-thrust belts**. These mountainous zones result from the deformation of thick sequences of shallow marine sedimentary rocks like those currently found along passive continental margins of the Atlantic. During continental collisions, sedimentary rocks are pushed inland, away from the core of the developing mountain belt and over the stable continental interior. In essence, crustal shortening is achieved by displacement along thrust faults where once relatively flat-lying strata are "sliced" into thick layers that are eventually stacked one upon another. During this displacement, material caught between the thrust faults is often folded, thereby forming the other major structure of a fold-and-thrust belt. Excellent examples of fold-and-thrust belts are found in the Appalachian Valley and Ridge Province, the Canadian Rockies, the Lesser (southern) Himalayas, and the northern Alps.

Next, we will take a closer look at two examples of collisional mountains—the Himalayas and the Appalachians. The Himalayas are Earth's youngest collisional mountains and are still rising. By contrast, the Appalachians are a much older mountain belt, in which active mountain building ceased about 250 million years ago.

The Himalayas

The mountain-building episode that created the Himalayas began roughly 50 million years ago, when India began to collide with Asia. Prior to the breakup of Pangaea, India was located between Africa and Antarctica in the Southern Hemisphere. As Pangaea fragmented, India moved rapidly, geologically speaking, a few thousand kilometers in a northward direction.

The subduction zone that facilitated India's northward migration was near the southern margin of Asia (FIGURE 11A). Continued subduction along Asia's margin created an Andean-type plate margin that contained a well-developed continental volcanic arc and an accretionary wedge. India's northern margin, on the other hand, was a passive continental margin consisting of a thick platform of shallow-water sediments and sedimentary rocks.

Geologists have determined that one, or perhaps more, small crustal fragments were positioned on the subducting plate somewhere between India and Asia. During the closing of the intervening ocean basin, a small crustal fragment, which now forms southern Tibet, reached the trench. This event was followed by the docking of India itself. The tectonic forces involved in the collision of India with Asia were immense and caused the more deformable materials located on the seaward edges of these landmasses to become highly folded and

FIGURE 11 Continental collision, the formation of the Himalayas
These diagrams illustrate the collision of India with the Eurasian plate that produced the spectacular Himalayas.

Prior to the collision of India and Asia, India's northern margin consisted of a thick platform of continental shelf sediments, whereas Asia's was an active continental margin with a well developed accretionary wedge and volcanic arc.

The ensuing continental collision folded and faulted the crustal rocks that lay along the margins of these continents to form the Himalayas. This event was followed by the gradual uplift of the Tibetan Plateau as the subcontinent of India was shoved under Asia.

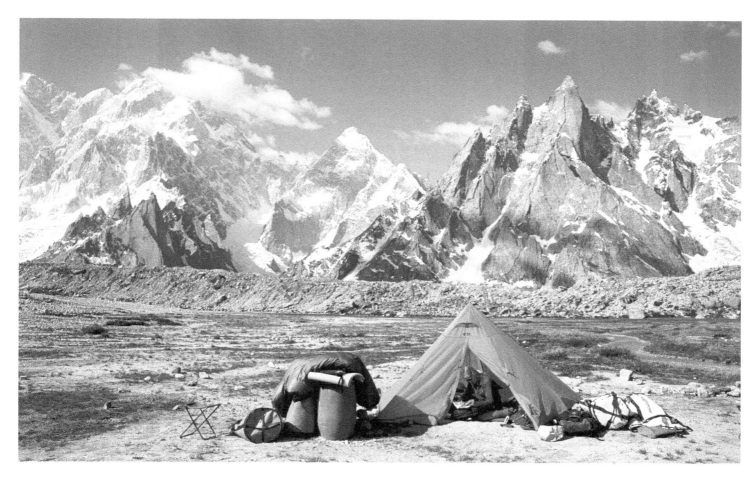

faulted (see FIGURE 11B). The shortening and thickening of the crust elevated great quantities of crustal material, thereby generating the spectacular Himalaya Mountains (FIGURE 12). As a result, tropical marine limestones that formed along the continental shelf now lie at the summit of Mount Everest.

In addition to uplift, crustal shortening caused rocks at the "bottom of the pile" to become deeply buried—an environment where these rocks experienced elevated temperatures and pressures (see Figure 11B). Partial melting within the deepest and most-deformed region of the developing mountain belt produced magmas that intruded the overlying rocks. These environments generate the metamorphic and igneous cores of collisional mountains.

The formation of the Himalayas was followed by a period of uplift that raised the Tibetan Plateau. Seismic evidence suggests that a portion of the Indian subcontinent was thrust beneath Tibet—a distance of perhaps 400 kilometers (250 miles). If this occurred, the added crustal thickness would account for the lofty landscape of southern Tibet, which has an average elevation higher than Mount Whitney, the highest point in the contiguous United States.

The collision with Asia slowed but did not stop the northward migration of India, which has since penetrated at least 2000 kilometers (1200 miles) into the mainland of Asia. Crustal shortening accommodated some of this motion. Much of the remaining penetration into Asia caused lateral displacement of large blocks of the Asian crust by a mechanism described as *continental escape.* As shown in FIGURE 13, when India continued its northward trek, parts of Asia were "squeezed" eastward, out of the collision zone. These displaced crustal blocks include much of Southeast Asia (the region between India and China) and sections of China.

Why was the interior of Asia deformed to such a large extent, while India has remained essentially intact? The answer lies in the nature of these diverse crustal blocks. Much of India is a continental shield composed mainly of Precambrian rocks (see Figure 1). This thick, cold slab of crustal material has been intact for more than 2 billion years and is mechanically strong as a result. By contrast, Southeast Asia was assembled more recently, from the collision of several smaller crustal fragments. Consequently, it is still relatively "warm and weak" from recent periods of mountain building (Figure 13B).

The Appalachians

The Appalachian Mountains provide great scenic beauty near the eastern margin of North America, from Alabama to Newfoundland. In addition, mountain belts of similar origin that formed during the same period and were once contiguous are found in the British Isles,

FIGURE 12 Bold peaks of the Karakoram Range, part of the "Greater Himalayas" The second highest peak in the world, K2, is located in the Karakoram Range. (Photo by Jimmy Chin/National GeographicSociety/Getty Images)

Map view showing the southeastward displacement of China and
the mainland of Southeast Asia as India plowed into Asia.

**Re-creation of the
deformation of Asia,
using a rigid block to
represent India that is
pushed into a mass of
modeling clay
representing Asia.**

Scandinavia, northwestern Africa, and Greenland. The orogeny that generated this extensive mountain system lasted a few hundred million years and was one of the stages in assembling the supercontinent of Pangaea. Detailed studies of the Appalachians indicate that the formation of this mountain belt was complex and resulted from three distinct episodes of mountain building.

Our simplified overview begins roughly 750 million years ago, with the breakup of a supercontinent called Rodinia that predates Pangaea. Similar to the breakup of Pangaea, this episode of continental rifting and seafloor spreading generated a new ocean between the rifted continental blocks. Located within this developing ocean basin was an active volcanic arc that lay off the coast of what would later become North America and a microcontinent situated closer to Africa (FIGURE 14A).

About 600 million years ago, for reasons geologists do not completely understand, plate motion changed dramatically, and the ancient ocean basin began to close. This led to three main orogenic events that culminated with the collision of North America and Africa.

Taconic Orogeny Around 450 million years ago, the marginal sea between the volcanic island arc and ancestral North America began to close. The collision that ensued, called the *Taconic Orogeny*, caused the volcanic arc along with ocean sediments that were located on the upper plate to be thrust over the larger continental block. The remnants of this volcanic arc and oceanic sediments are recognized today as the metamorphic rocks found across much of the western Appalachians, especially in New York (FIGURE 14B). In addition to the pervasive regional metamorphism, numerous magma bodies intruded the crustal rocks along the entire continental margin.

Acadian Orogeny A second episode of mountain building, called the *Acadian Orogeny*, occurred about 350 million years ago. The continued closing of this ancient ocean basin resulted in the collision of a microcontinent with North America (FIGURE 14C). This orogeny involved thrust faulting, metamorphism, and the intrusion of several large granite bodies. In addition, this event added substantially to the width of North American, particularly in the region occupied by the southern Appalachians.

Alleghanian Orogeny The final orogeny, called the *Alleghanian Orogeny*, occurred between 250 and 300 million years ago, when Africa collided with North America. The result was the displacement of the material that was accreted earlier by as much as 250 kilometers (155 miles) toward the interior of North America. This

North America — Taconic volcanic arc — Avalonia (microcontinent) — Africa

A.

Closing of an Ocean Basin
About 600 million years ago, the precursor to the North Atlantic began to close. Located within this ocean basin was an active volcanic arc that lay off the coast of North America and a microcontinent situated closer to Africa.

SMARTFIGURE 14
Formation of the Appalachian Mountains
The Appalachians formed during the closing of a precursor to the Atlantic Ocean. This event involved three separate stages of mountain building that spanned more than 300 million years. (Based on Zve Ben Avraham, Jack Oliver, Larry Brown, and Frederick Cook)

North America — Taconic Orogeny — Avalonia — Africa

B.

Taconic Orogeny Around 450 million years ago, the marginal sea between the volcanic island arc and North America closed. The collision that ensued, called the Taconic Orogeny, thrust the island arc over the eastern margin of North America.

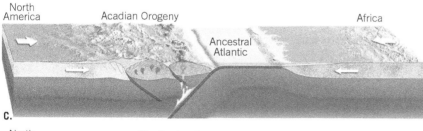

North America — Acadian Orogeny — Ancestral Atlantic — Africa

C.

Acadian Orogeny A second episode of mountain building, called the Acadian Orogeny, occurred about 350 million years ago and involved the collision of a microcontinent with North America.

North America — Alleghanian Orogeny — Africa

D.

Alleghanian Orogeny The final event, the Alleghanian Orogeny, occurred between 250 and 300 million years ago, when Africa collided with North America. The result was the formation of the Appalachian Mountains, perhaps once as majestic as the Himalayas. The Appalachians lay in the interior of the newly assembled supercontinent of Pangaea.

Appalachian Plateau — Valley and Ridge — Blue Ridge — Piedmont — Coastal Plain — Developing North Atlantic — Africa

Remnant of Africa

E.

Rifting of Pangaea Then, about 180 million years ago, Pangaea began to break into smaller fragments, a process that ultimately created the modern Atlantic Ocean. Because this new zone of rifting occurred east of the suture that formed when Africa and North America collided, remnants of African crust remain "welded" to the North American plate.

event also displaced and further deformed the shelf sediments and sedimentary rocks that had once flanked the eastern margin of North America (FIGURE 14D). Today these folded and thrust-faulted sandstones, limestones, and shales make up the largely unmetamorphosed rocks of the Valley and Ridge province (FIGURE 15). Outcrops of

the folded and thrust-faulted structures that characterize collisional mountains are found as far inland as central Pennsylvania and West Virginia.

With the collision of Africa and North America, the Appalachians, perhaps as majestic as the Himalayas, lay in the interior of Pangaea. Then, about 180 million years

FIGURE 15 **The Valley and Ridge province**
This region of the Appalachian Mountains consists of folded and faulted sedimentary strata that were displaced landward along thrust faults as a result of the collision of Africa with North America. (NASA/GSFC/ JPL, MISR Science Team)

Valley and Ridge   Blue Ridge   Piedmont   Coastal Plain

ago, this newly formed supercontinent began to break into smaller fragments, a process that ultimately created the modern Atlantic Ocean. Because this new zone of rifting occurred east of the suture that formed when Africa and North America collided, remnants of Africa remain "welded" to the North American plate (FIGURE 14E). The crust underlying Florida is an example.

Other mountain ranges that exhibit evidence of continental collisions include the Alps and the Urals. The Alps formed as Africa and at least two smaller crustal fragments collided with Europe during the closing of the Tethys Sea. Similarly, the Urals were uplifted during the assembly of Pangaea, when northern Europe and northern Asia collided, forming a major portion of Eurasia.

4 CONCEPT CHECKS

1. Differentiate between *terrane* and *terrain*.
2. During the formation of the Himalayas, the continental crust of Asia was deformed more than India proper. Why was this the case?
3. Where might magma be generated in a newly formed collisional mountain belt?
4. How can the Appalachian Mountains be considered a collision-type mountain range when the nearest continent is 5000 kilometers (3000 miles) away?
5. How does the plate tectonics theory help explain the existence of fossil marine life in rocks atop compressional mountains?

5 | Fault-Block Mountains

Most mountain belts form in compressional environments, as evidenced by the predominance of large thrust faults and folded strata. However, other tectonic processes, such as continental rifting, can also produce topographic mountains. Recall that continental rifting occurs when tensional forces stretch and thin the lithosphere, resulting in upwelling of hot mantle rock. Upwelling heats the thinned lithosphere, which becomes less dense (more buoyant) and rises. This accounts, in part, for the elevated topography associated with continental rifts. Simultaneously, stretching elongates the rigid upper crust, which breaks into large crustal blocks that are bounded by high-angle normal faults. Continued rifting causes the blocks to tilt, with one edge rising as the other drops. Mountains that form in these tectonic settings are termed **fault-block mountains**.

The Teton Range in western Wyoming is an excellent example of fault-block mountains. This lofty structure was faulted and uplifted along its eastern flank as the block tilted downward to the west. Looking west from Jackson Hole, Wyoming, the eastern front of this mountain rises more than 2 kilometers above the valley, making it one of the most imposing mountain fronts in the United States (FIGURE 16).

The Basin and Range Province

Located between the Sierra Nevada and Rocky Mountains is one of Earth's largest regions of fault-block mountains—the Basin and Range province. This region extends in a roughly north–south direction for nearly 3000 kilometers (2000 miles) and encompasses all of Nevada and portions of the surrounding states, as well as parts of southern Canada and western Mexico. In this region, Earth's brittle upper crust has been broken into hundreds of fault blocks. Tilting of these faulted structures, called *half-grabens*, produced nearly

parallel mountain ranges, averaging about 80 kilometers (50 miles) in length, which rise above adjacent sediment-filled basins.

Several hypotheses have been proposed to explain the events that generated the Basin and Range region. The most widely accepted view proposes that a change in the nature of the plate boundary along the western margin of California caused the formation of the Basin and Range region (FIGURE 17). About 30 million years ago, the dominant forces acting on the western margin of North America were compressional, caused by the buoyant subduction of a segment of the Farallon plate (Figure 17A). Starting about 25 million years ago, subduction gradually ceased along the California coast as the spreading center that separated the Farallon plate from the Pacific began to subduct beneath North America. This event spawned the San Andreas Fault, with its strike-slip motion, that currently separates the Pacific plate from the North American plate (Figure 17B). According to this hypothesis, the northwestward motion of the Pacific plate produced tensional forces that stretched and fractured the crust

FIGURE 16 Wyoming's Teton Range, an example of fault-block mountains (Photo by Rob Marmion/ Shutterstock)

A.
Grand Teton Range
Jackson Hole Valley
B.

501

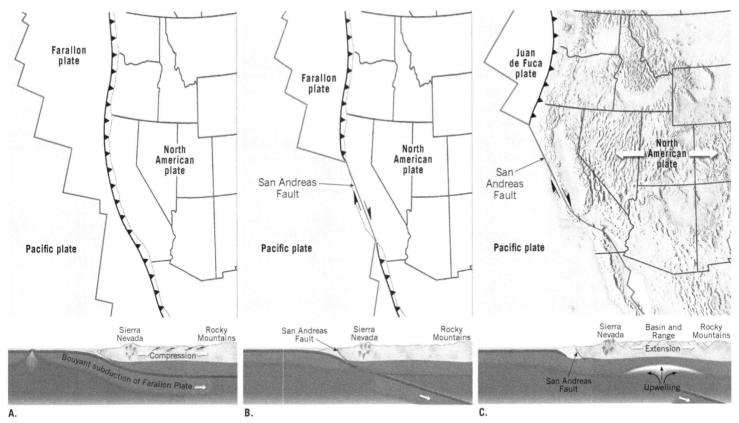

FIGURE 17 Model for the formation of the Basin and Range province The Basin and Range region consists of more than 100 fault-block mountains that were generated during the past 20 million years. Upwelling of hot mantle rock and perhaps gravitational collapse (crustal sliding) may have contributed to considerable stretching and thinning of the crust.

of the North American plate to produce the fault-block mountains of the Basin and Range region (Figure 17C). In addition, stretching and thinning of the lithosphere led to upwelling that accounts for the higher–than-average elevation of the Basin and Range region.

Another model contends that about 20 million years ago, the cold, dense lithospheric mantle located beneath the Basin and Range region decoupled (separated) from the overlying crustal layer and slowly sank into the mantle. This process, called *delamination*, resulted in upwelling and lateral spreading of hot mantle rock that produced tensional forces that stretched and thinned the overlying crust. According to this view, these elevated

crustal blocks began to gravitationally slide from their lofty perches to generate the fault-block topography of the Basin and Range province.

5 CONCEPT CHECKS

1. Name one process that accounts for the elevated topography of at least some fault-block mountains.
2. In what way does the formation of fault-block mountains differ from the processes that generate most other major mountain belts?
3. Briefly describe the basic structure of the Basin and Range province and identify its geographic extent.

6 · What Causes Earth's Varied Topography?

The causes of Earth's varied topography are complex and cumulative. Geologists know that colliding plates provide the tectonic forces that thicken and elevate crustal rocks during mountain building. Simultaneously, weathering and erosion sculpt Earth's surface into a vast array of landforms, while up-and-down motions in the mantle can change the elevation of a region.

The Principle of Isostasy

During the 1840s, researchers discovered that Earth's low-density crust "floats" on top of the high-density, deformable rocks of the mantle. The concept of a floating crust in gravitational balance is called **isostasy**. The principle of isostasy helps us understand many large-scale variations on Earth' surface—from towering mountains to deep-ocean basins.

One way to explore the concept of isostasy is to envision a series of wooden blocks of different heights floating in water, as shown in FIGURE 18. Note that the thicker wooden blocks float higher than the thinner blocks. Similarly, compressional mountains stand high above the surrounding terrain because crustal thickening creates buoyant crustal "roots" that extend deep into the supporting material below. Thus, lofty mountains such as the Himalayas are much like the thicker wooden blocks shown in Figure 18.

How Is Isostasy Related to Changes in Elevation?
Visualize what would happen if another small block of wood were placed atop one of the blocks in Figure 18. The combined block would sink until it reached a new isostatic (gravitational) balance. At this point, the top of the combined block would be higher than before, and the bottom would be lower. This process of establishing a new level of gravitational balance by loading or unloading is called **isostatic adjustment**.

Applying the concept of isostatic adjustment, we should expect that when weight is added to the crust, it will respond by subsiding and will rebound when weight is removed. (Visualize what happens when a ship's cargo is loaded or unloaded.) Evidence for crustal subsidence followed by crustal rebound is provided by Ice Age glaciers. When continental ice sheets occupied portions of North America during the Pleistocene epoch, the added weight of 3-kilometer-thick masses of ice caused downwarping of Earth's crust by hundreds of meters. In the 8000 years since this last ice sheet melted, gradual uplift of as much as 330 meters (1000 feet) has occurred in Canada's Hudson Bay region, where the thickest ice had accumulated.

One of the consequences of isostatic adjustment is that, as erosion lowers the summits of mountains, the crust rises in response to the reduced load (FIGURE 19). The processes of uplift and erosion continue until the mountain block reaches "normal" crustal thickness. When this occurs, these once-elevated structures will be near sea level, and the once-deeply buried interior of the mountain will be exposed at the surface. In addition, as mountains are worn down, the eroded sediment is deposited on adjacent landscapes, causing these areas to subside (Figure 19).

How High Is Too High?
Where compressional forces are great, such as those driving India into Asia, lofty mountains such as the Himalayas result. Is there a limit on how high a mountain can rise? As mountaintops are elevated, gravity-driven processes such as erosion and mass wasting are accelerated, carving the deformed strata into rugged landscapes. Equally important, however, is the fact that gravity also acts on the rocks within these massive structures. The higher the mountain, the greater the downward force on rocks near the base. Eventually, the rocks deep within the developing mountain, which are relatively warm and weak, begin to flow laterally, as shown in FIGURE 20. This is analogous to what happens when a ladle of very thick pancake batter is poured onto a hot griddle. Similarly, mountains are altered by a process called **gravitational collapse**, which involves ductile spreading at depth and normal faulting and subsidence in the upper, brittle portion of Earth's crust.

Considering these factors, a seemingly logical question follows: "What keeps the Himalayas standing?" Simply, the horizontal compressional forces that are driving India into Asia are greater than the vertical force of gravity. However, when India's northward trek ends, the downward pull of gravity, as well as weathering and erosion, will become the dominant forces acting on this mountainous region.

FIGURE 18 The principle of isostasy
Illustration of how wooden blocks of different thicknesses float in water. In a similar manner, thick sections of crustal material float higher than thinner crustal slabs.

SMARTFIGURE 19
The effects of isostatic adjustment and erosion on mountainous topography This sequence illustrates how the combined effects of erosion and isostatic adjustment result in a thinning of the crust in mountainous regions.

Mountain range

When compressional mountains are young they are composed of thick, low density crustal rocks that float on the denser asthenosphere below.

Michael Collier

As erosion lowers the mountains, the crust rises in response to the reduced load in order to maintain isostatic balance.

Mark Karrass/CORBIS RF

Erosion and uplift continue until the mountains reach "normal" crustal thickness.

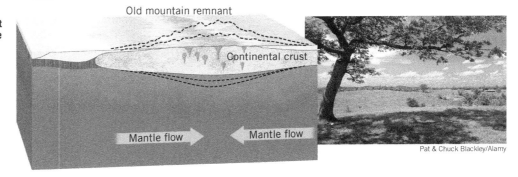

Pat & Chuck Blackley/Alamy

Mantle Convection: A Cause of Vertical Crustal Movement

Based on studies of Earth's gravitational field, it became apparent that up-and-down convective flow in the mantle also affects the elevation of Earth's major landforms. The buoyancy of hot rising material accounts for broad upwarping in the overlying lithosphere, whereas downward flow causes downwarping.

Uplifting Whole Continents Southern Africa is one region where large-scale vertical motion is evident. The topography of the region consists of an expansive plateau that has an average elevation of nearly 1500 meters (5000 feet)—much higher than what would be predicted for a stable continental platform.

Evidence from seismic tomography indicates that a large mass of hot mantle rock is centered below the southern tip of Africa. This structure, called a *superplume*, extends upward about 2900 kilometers (1800 miles) from the core–mantle boundary and has a lateral expanse of a few thousand kilometers. Researchers have determined that the upward flow associated with this huge mantle plume is sufficient to elevate southern Africa.

Crustal Subsidence Extensive areas of downwarping also occur at Earth's surface. In the United States, large,

A. Horizontal compressional forces dominate

Compression causes shortening and thickening of the crust

Uplift

Compressional stress

Subsidence

TIME

Subsidence

Gravitational collapse results in stretching and thinning of the crust

Ductile spreading

Uplift

B. Gravitational forces dominate

FIGURE 20 **Gravitational collapse**
Without compressional forces to support them, mountains gradually collapse under their own weight. Gravitational collapse involves normal faulting in the upper, brittle portion of the crust and ductile spreading in the warm, weak rocks at depth.

nearly circular basins are found in Michigan and Illinois. Similar structures are known on other continents as well.

The cause of the downwarping that created these basins may be linked to the subduction of slabs of oceanic lithosphere. One proposal suggests that when subduction ceases, the descending slab detaches from the trailing lithosphere and continues its descent into the mantle. As this detached lithospheric slab sinks, it creates a downward flow in its wake that tugs at the base of the overriding continent. In some settings, the crust is apparently pulled down sufficiently to produce a large basin that eventually fills with sediments. As the oceanic slab sinks deeper into the mantle, the pull of the trailing wake weakens, and the continent "floats" back into isostatic balance.

6 CONCEPT CHECKS

1. Define *isostasy*.
2. Give one example of evidence that supports the concept of crustal uplift.
3. What happens to a floating object when weight is added? Subtracted?
4. Briefly describe how the principle of isostatic adjustment applies to changes in the elevations of mountains.
5. Explain the process whereby mountainous regions experience gravitational collapse.

The Laramide Rockies

The portion of the Rocky Mountains that extends from southwestern Montana to New Mexico was produced during a period of deformation known as the Laramide Orogeny. This event, which created some of the most picturesque scenery in the United States, peaked about 60 million years ago.

Where are the Laramide Rockies?
Sometimes called the Central and Southern Rockies, this mountain belt lies to the east of the Colorado Plateau and includes the Bighorns of Wyoming, the Front Range of Colorado, the Uintas of Utah, and the Sangre de Cristo of southern Colorado and New Mexico.

Colorado Rockies near Steamboat Springs
photo by Michael Collier

NASA

Uintas
Front Range
Sawatch Range
Denver
San Juans
Sangre de Cristo

Bighorns
Black Hills
LARAMIDE ROCKIES
Wyoming Basin
Uintas
Front Range
Sawatch Range
San Juans
Sangre de Cristo
Colorado Plateau
Great Plains

What is the geologic history of the Laramide Rockies?
These mountain ranges formed when Precambrian age basement rocks were uplifted nearly vertically along reverse and thrust faults, upwarping the overlying layers of younger sedimentary rocks. Uplifting accelerated the processes of weathering and erosion, which removed much of the younger sedimentary cover from the highest portions of the uplifted blocks. Intrusion of igneous plutons and volcanism occurred simultaneously with this period of mountain building.

LARAMIDE UPLIFT

Basin

Basin

Crystalline core

Uplift

KEY

Paleogene sedimentary rocks
Mesozoic sedimentary rocks
Paleozoic sedimentary rocks
Precambrian sedimentary rocks
Precambrian crystalline rocks

What is responsible for the steep, rugged form of these mountains?

The resulting mountainous topography consists mainly of individual, elongated blocks of igneous and metamorphic rocks flanked by upturned sedimentary strata and separated by sediment filled basins. The cores of these large uplifted blocks include some of the highest and most scenic topography in the west, including Long's Peak, Maroon Bells, and Mount Sneffels, all located in Colorado. Much of the scenic beauty of these structures can be credited to the work of glaciers.

Long's Peak
photo by Daniel H. Bailey/Alamy

Maroon Bells
photo by Raymond Forbes/SuperStock

How did this mountain belt form?

Because the Laramide Rockies lie more than 1500 kilometers from the plate boundary that produced the Cordilleran Orogeny, it has been difficult to identify the mechanism which produced them. The most widely accepted model proposes that a thickened slab of the Farallon Plate began to subduct under the west coast of California about 85 million years ago. Because of its thickness, this buoyant slab resisted subduction as it was shoved beneath the continent. As the thick slab continued eastward under the Colorado Plateau it triggered uplift of at least 2 kilometers and built several monoclines. Upon reaching the Rockies compressional forces squeezed the crust, which responded by developing high angle faults along which igneous and metamorphic basement rock was uplifted. These crystalline blocks form the cores of many of the high peaks that comprise this mountain belt.

Sierra Nevada · Colorado Plateau · Laramide Rockies · Great Plains

Bouyant subduction of Farallon plate

Compressional stress

Partial melting

Over-thicken slab of oceanic crust

Asthenosphere

CONCEPTS IN REVIEW: CONVERGENT BOUNDARIES

1 Mountain Building

Locate and name Earth's major mountain belts on a world map.

KEY WORDS orogenesis, compressional mountain

- Orogenesis is the making of mountains. Most orogenesis occurs along convergent plate boundaries, where compressional forces cause folding and faulting of the rock, thickening the crust vertically and shortening it horizontally. Some mountain belts are very old, while others are actively forming today.

LOCATION, LOCATION, LOCATION Look at the South American plate on the map. Make a statement that relates the position of the Andes Mountains on the plate to the direction of the plate's motion.

2 Convergence and Subducting Plates

List and describe the four major features associated with subduction zones.

KEY WORDS volcanic island arc (island arc), continental volcanic arc, back-arc basin

- Sites of subduction are marked by volcanic arcs, deep-ocean trenches, and forearc basins located between them. A subduction zone may also contain a back-arc basin, a site of tectonic extension that forms due to trench rollback and the sinking of old, cold, dense oceanic lithosphere.

POSSIBLE PLANETS If you were a planetary geologist assessing a newly discovered ocean-covered moon and found that the moon had both deep-ocean trenches and volcanic island arcs, would you expect that it would also have an oceanic ridge system? Explain.

3 Subduction and Mountain Building

Sketch a cross section of an Andean-type mountain belt and describe how its major features are generated.

KEY WORDS accretionary wedge, forearc basin

- Subduction leads to orogenesis. If a subducted plate is overridden by oceanic lithosphere, island arc–type mountain building results, with a thick accumulation of erupted volcanic rocks mixed with sediment scraped off the subducted plate. Andean-type mountain building occurs where subduction takes place beneath continental lithosphere.
- Release of water from a subducted slab triggers melting in the wedge of mantle above the slab. These primary magmas have mafic compositions. They rise to the base of the continental crust and pond. Fractional crystallization then separates ferromagnesian minerals from a melt that grows increasingly felsic in composition.

- The evolved magma rises further and may either cool and crystallize below the surface to form a batholith of granite or diorite, or it may erupt at the surface to form a continental volcanic arc.
- Sediment scraped off the subducting plate builds up in an accretionary wedge. The thickness of the wedge varies in accordance with the amount of sediment available. Between the accretionary wedge and the volcanic arc is a relatively calm site of sedimentary deposition, the forearc basin.
- The geography of central California preserves an accretionary wedge (Coast Ranges), a forearc basin (Great Valley), and the roots of a continental volcanic arc (Sierra Nevada).

CHANGES Over geologic time, what processes would have to take place in the Andes to make the landscape of western South America resemble the landscape of modern California?

4 Collisional Mountain Belts

Summarize the stages in the development of an Alpine-type mountain belt such as the Appalachians.

KEY WORDS terrane, microcontinent, suture, fold-and-thrust belt

- Terranes are relatively small crustal fragments (microcontinents, volcanic island arcs, or oceanic plateaus). Terranes may be accreted to

continents when subduction brings them to a trench, but they cannot subduct due to their relatively low density. The terranes are "peeled off" the subducted slab and thrust onto the leading edge of the continent.
- The presence of ophiolites (accreted pieces of oceanic crust) may mark the suture zone between two landmasses. Fold-and-thrust belts of folded and faulted sedimentary strata flank the sides of a collisional mountain belt.

• The Himalayas and Appalachians have similar origins in the collision of continents formerly separated by (now-subducted) ocean basins. The Appalachians are older and were caused by the collision of ancestral North America with ancestral Africa more than 250 million years ago. In contrast, the Himalayas are younger, having been formed by the collision of India and Eurasia starting around 50 million years ago. They are still rising today.

PREDICT IT Identify modern examples of (1) a microcontinent, (2) a volcanic island arc, and (3) an oceanic plateau on a world map. Suggest a location where these future terranes might someday be accreted, if plate motions continue in the same direction.

5 Fault-Block Mountains

Compare and contrast the formation of fault-block mountains with compressional mountains.

KEY WORD fault-block mountain

• Mountains can also form in extensional tectonic settings. When the crust is thinned and stretched, normal faulting breaks the landscape into chunks, some of which slide down relative to their neighbors. Fault-block mountains are common in the Basin and Range province in the western United States. The Teton Range is an example: It is a north–south–trending mountain range with a normal fault separating it from the half-graben of Jackson Hole lying immediately to the east.

CALCULATE IT Mount Moran (3842 meters elevation) in the Teton Range rises 1.8 kilometers above Jackson Hole, Wyoming, and is capped by a layer of Flathead Sandstone. On the other side of the Teton Fault, the same Flathead Sandstone lies 7 kilometers below Jackson Hole. The Teton Fault dips to the east at 45 to 75 degrees. For the sake of simplicity, use a value of 60 degrees to estimate displacement. Calculate the total offset on the Teton Fault.

Wyoming's Teton Range, an example of fault-block mountains (Photo by Rob Marmion/ Shutterstock)

6 What Causes Earth's Varied Topography?

Explain the principle of isostasy and how it contributes to the elevated topography of young mountain belts like the Himalayas.

KEY WORDS isostasy, isostatic adjustment, gravitational collapse

- Isostasy is the principle that the elevation of the crust can change in accordance with gravitational balance. If additional weight is placed on the crust (a flood basalt, a thick layer of sediments, or an ice sheet), the crust will sink into the mantle until it comes to equilibrium with the extra load. If the new mass is removed, the crust will rebound upward.
- When mountains form and rock mass is pushed up to the height of a young compressional mountain belt such as the Himalayas, the rocks at the base of the mountains become warmer and weaker. As the overlying rock mass pushes down on them through gravity, these deeper rocks flow out of the way. This causes the mountain belt to collapse outward into a wider, lower-elevation region.
- Convection in the mantle can influence the vertical position of the crust. Areas of crust above sites of mantle upwelling may bulge upward, while the crust above sites of mantle downwelling may sink into broad basin-like structures.

CAUSES AND EFFECTS   Based on the principle of isostasy, predict what would happen to the elevation of the highest peaks in a mountain range if rivers and glaciers eroded deep valleys through the mountains and removed large amounts of rock.

Plate tectonics is the dominant theory to explain the origin of Earth's major features, including mountains, continents, and ocean basins. Grand Teton Range, Wyoming. (Photo by Michael Collier).

GIVE IT SOME THOUGHT

1. Refer to the accompanying map, which shows the location of the Galapagos Rise and the Rio Grande Rise to answer the following questions:
   a. Compare the continental margin of the west coast of South America with the continental margin along the east coast.
   b. Based on your answer to the question above, is the Galapagos Rise or the Rio Grande Rise more likely to end up accreted to a continent? Explain your choice.
   c. In the distant future, how might a geologist determine that this accreted landmass is distinct from the continental crust to which it accreted?

2. Suppose that a sliver of oceanic crust were discovered in the interior of a continent. Would this refute the theory of plate tectonics? Explain.

3. The Ural Mountains exhibit a north–south orientation through Eurasia. How does the theory of plate tectonics explain the existence of this mountain belt in the interior of an expansive landmass?

4. Briefly describe the major differences between the evolution of the Appalachian Mountains and the North American Cordillera.

5. Which of the accompanying sketches best illustrates an Andean-type orogeny, a Cordilleran-type orogeny, and an Alpine-type orogeny?

6. What processes (besides formation and melting of large ice sheets) could cause isostatic adjustments?

MasteringGeology™   www.masteringgeology.com

Looking for additional review and test prep materials? Visit the Study Area in MasteringGeology to enhance your understanding of this chapter's content by accessing a variety of resources, including **Self-Study Quizzes,**

Geoscience Animations, GEODe Tutorials, RSS feeds, flashcards, web links, self-study quizzes, and an optional **Pearson eText.**

Glossary

Accretionary wedge A large wedge-shaped mass of sediment that accumulates in subduction zones. Here sediment is scraped from the subducting oceanic plate and accreted to the overriding crustal block.

Backarc basin A basin that forms on the side of a volcanic arc away from the trench.

Compressional mountains Mountains in which great horizontal forces have shortened and thickened the crust. Most major mountain belts are of this type.

Continental volcanic arc Mountains formed in part by igneous activity associated with the subduction of oceanic lithosphere beneath a continent. Examples include the Andes and the Cascades.

Fault-block mountain A mountain that is formed by the displacement of rock along a fault.

Fold-and-thrust belts Regions within compressional mountain systems where large areas have been shortened and thickened by the processes of folding and thrust faulting, as exemplified by the Valley and Ridge province of the Appalachians.

Forearc basin The region located between a volcanic arc and an accretionary wedge where shallow-water marine sediments typically accumulate.

Gravitational collapse The gradual subsidence of mountains caused by lateral spreading of weak material located deep within these structures.

Island arc See *Volcanic island arc.*

Isostasy The concept that Earth's crust is "floating" in gravitational balance upon the material of the mantle.

Isostatic adjustment Compensation of the lithosphere when weight is added or removed. When weight is added, the lithosphere responds by subsiding, and when weight is removed, there is uplift.

Microcontinents Relatively small fragments of continental crust that may lie above sea level, such as the island of Madagascar, or that may be submerged, as exemplified by the Campbell Plateau located near New Zealand.

Orogenesis The processes that collectively result in the formation of mountains.

Suture A zone along which two crustal fragments are jointed together. For example, following a continental collision, the two continental blocks are sutured together.

Terrane A crustal block bounded by faults, whose geologic history is distinct from the histories of adjoining crustal blocks.

Volcanic island arc A chain of volcanic islands generally located a few hundred kilometers from a trench where there is active subduction of one oceanic plate beneath another.

Mass Wasting: The Work of Gravity

From Chapter 15 of *Earth: An Introduction to Physical Geology*, Eleventh Edition. Edward J. Tarbuck, Frederick K. Lutgens, Dennis Tasa.
Copyright © 2014 by Pearson Education, Inc. All rights reserved.

Mass Wasting: The Work of Gravity

This rock avalanche along England's White Cliffs of Dover occurred in March 2012. (Photo by Rex Features via AP Images)

Each statement represents the primary learning objective for the corresponding major heading within the chapter. After you complete the chapter you should be able to:

1 Discuss situations in which mass-wasting processes can cause natural disasters and discuss the role that mass wasting plays in the development of landforms.

2 Summarize the factors that control and trigger mass-wasting processes.

3 List and explain the criteria that are commonly used to classify mass-wasting processes.

4 Distinguish among slump, rockslide, debris flow, and earthflow.

5 Review the general characteristics of slow mass-wasting processes and describe the unique issues associated with a permafrost environment.

E arth's surface is never perfectly flat but instead consists of slopes of many different varieties. Some are steep and precipitous; others are moderate or gentle. Some are long and gradual; others are short and abrupt. Slopes can be mantled with soil and covered by vegetation or consist of barren rock and rubble. Taken together, slopes are the most common elements in our physical landscape. Although most slopes may appear to be stable and unchanging, the force of gravity causes material to move downslope. At one extreme, the movement may be gradual and practically imperceptible. At the other extreme, it may consist of a roaring debris flow or a thundering rock avalanche. Landslides are a worldwide natural hazard. When these hazardous processes lead to loss of life and property, they become natural disasters.

A small rock fall in progress. (Photo by Herb Dunn/DunnRight Photography)

1 The Importance of Mass Wasting

Some mass-wasting processes are dangerous events that represent significant geologic hazards. Perhaps less well known is the fact that mass-wasting processes play an important role in the development and evolution of many of Earth's varied landforms.

Landslides as Geologic Hazards

The chapter-opening photo is a spectacular example of a phenomenon that many people would call a landslide. For most of us, the word *landslide* implies a sudden event in which large quantities of rock and soil plunge down steep slopes. When people and communities are in the way, a natural disaster may result. Landslides constitute major geologic hazards that each year in the United States cause billions of dollars in damages and the loss of 25 to 50 lives. As you will see, many landslides occur in connection with other major natural disasters, including earthquakes, volcanic eruptions, wildfires, and severe storms.

If you were to view several images of events called landslides, you would likely notice that the term seems to refer to several different things—from mudflows to rock avalanches. This variety reflects the fact that although many people, including geologists, frequently use the word *landslide*, the term has no specific definition in geology. Rather, it is a popular, nontechnical word used to describe any or all relatively rapid forms of mass wasting.

Landslides are spectacular examples of a basic geologic process called mass wasting. **Mass wasting** refers to the downslope movement of rock, regolith, and soil under the direct influence of gravity. It is distinct from the erosional processes because mass wasting does not require a transporting medium such as water, wind, or glacial ice.

The Role of Mass Wasting in Landform Development

In the evolution of most landforms, mass wasting is the step that follows weathering. By itself, weathering does not produce significant landforms. Rather, landforms develop as products of weathering are removed from the places where they originate. Once weathering weakens and breaks rock apart, mass wasting transfers the debris downslope, where a stream or glacier, acting as a conveyor belt, usually carries it away. Although there may be many intermediate stops along the way, the sediment is eventually transported to its ultimate destination: the sea.

The combined effects of mass wasting and running water produce stream valleys, which are the most common and conspicuous of Earth's landforms. If streams alone were responsible for creating the valleys in which they flow, the valleys would be very narrow features resembling the canyon in FIGURE 1. However, the fact that most river valleys are much wider than they are deep is a strong indication of the significance of mass-wasting processes in supplying material to streams. This is illustrated by the Grand Canyon (FIGURE 2). The walls of the canyon extend far from the Colorado River, due to the transfer of weathered debris downslope to the river and its tributaries by mass-wasting processes. In this manner, streams and mass wasting combine to modify and sculpt the surface. Of course, glaciers, groundwater, waves, and wind are also important agents in shaping landforms and developing landscapes.

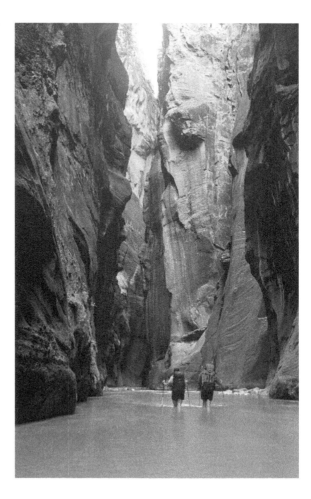

FIGURE 1 Zion Narrows The Virgin River in southern Utah is responsible for cutting this narrow canyon through the Navajo Sandstone. (Photo by James Kay/SC Photos/Alamy Images)

SMARTFIGURE 2 **Excavating the Grand Canyon**
The walls of the canyon extend far from the channel of the Colorado River. This results primarily from the transfer of weathered debris downslope to the river and its tributaries by mass-wasting processes. (Photo by Bryan Brazil/Shutterstock)

Geologist's Sketch

Slopes Change Through Time

It is clear that if mass wasting is to occur, there must be slopes that rock, soil, and regolith can move down. It is Earth's mountain building and volcanic processes that produce these slopes through sporadic changes in the elevations of landmasses and the ocean floor. If dynamic internal processes did not continually produce regions having higher elevations, the system that moves debris to lower elevations would gradually slow and eventually cease.

Most rapid and spectacular mass-wasting events occur in areas of rugged, geologically young mountains. Newly formed mountains are rapidly eroded by rivers and glaciers into regions characterized by steep and unstable slopes. It is in such settings that massive destructive landslides, such as those described at the beginning of the chapter, occur. As mountain building subsides, mass wasting and erosional processes lower the land. Through time, steep and rugged mountain slopes give way to gentler, more subdued terrain. Thus, as a landscape ages, massive and rapid mass-wasting processes give way to smaller, less dramatic downslope movements that are often imperceptibly slow.

1 CONCEPT CHECKS

1. Discuss the meaning of the term *landslide*.
2. What is the controlling force of mass wasting?
3. In what environment are rapid mass-wasting processes most likely to occur?
4. Sketch or describe how mass wasting contributes to the development of a valley.

EYE on Earth

Landslide debris atop Buckskin Glacier in Denali National Park in the rugged Alaska Range. The glacier feeds a river that flows into Cook Inlet, just west of the city of Anchorage. Cook Inlet is an arm of the North Pacific.

Question 1 Is the material deposited by landslide well sorted? Why or why not?

Question 2 Would you expect particles in landslide debris to be rounded or angular? Explain.

Question 3 These mountains are clearly being sculpted by glaciers. However, other processes also have important roles. Identify these processes and briefly describe the role that each plays in the evolution of this mountainous landscape.

Michael Collier

Landslides as Natural Disasters

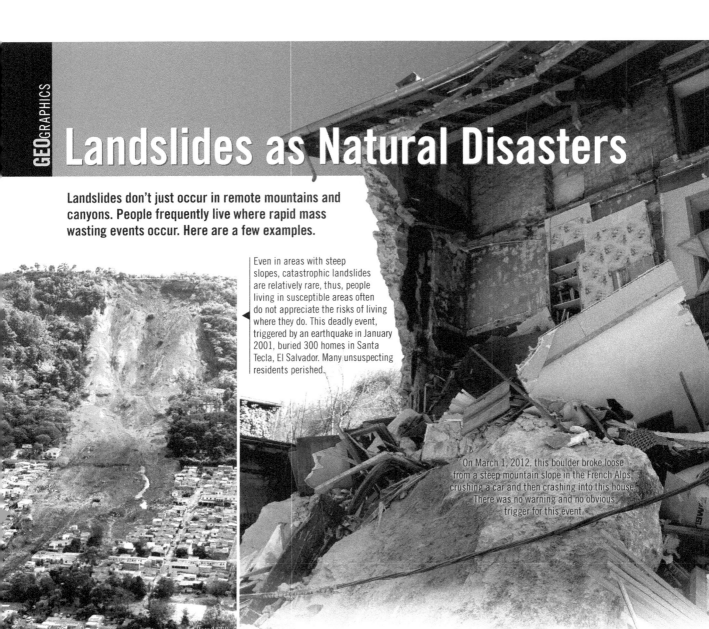

Landslides don't just occur in remote mountains and canyons. People frequently live where rapid mass wasting events occur. Here are a few examples.

Even in areas with steep slopes, catastrophic landslides are relatively rare, thus, people living in susceptible areas often do not appreciate the risks of living where they do. This deadly event, triggered by an earthquake in January 2001, buried 300 homes in Santa Tecla, El Salvador. Many unsuspecting residents perished.

On March 1, 2012, this boulder broke loose from a steep mountain slope in the French Alps, crushing a car and then crashing into this house. There was no warning and no obvious trigger for this event.

Thevenot-Laurent/PHOTOPQR/LE PROGRES/Newscom

Ed Harp/USGS

Weathered rock, precipitous slopes, and the shock of an earthquake combined to produce many rockfalls and rock avalanches in and around Christchurch, New Zealand on February 22, 2011.

Neil Sands/AFP/Getty Images

Marty Melville/AFP/Getty Images

In January 2011, following a period of torrential rains, this thick slurry of mud, appropriately called a mudflow, buried these cars in Nova Friburgo, Brazil. Heavy rains are an important trigger of mass wasting processes.

www.gridpneus.com.br

Ed Harp/USGS

2 Controls and Triggers of Mass Wasting

Gravity is the controlling force of mass wasting, but several factors play an important role in overcoming inertia and creating downslope movements. Long before a landslide occurs, various processes work to weaken slope material, gradually making it more and more susceptible to the pull of gravity. During this span, the slope remains stable but gets closer and closer to being unstable. Eventually, the strength of the slope is weakened to the point that something causes it to cross the threshold from stability to instability. Such an event that initiates downslope movement is called a *trigger*. Remember that a trigger is not the sole cause of a mass-wasting event but just the last of many causes. Among the common factors that trigger mass-wasting processes are saturation of material with water, oversteepening of slopes, removal of anchoring vegetation, and ground vibrations from earthquakes.

The Role of Water

Mass wasting is sometimes triggered when heavy rains or periods of snow-melt saturate surface materials. The water does not transport the material. Rather, it allows gravity to more easily set the material in motion. This was the case in January 2005, when a massive debris flow (popularly called a mudslide) swept through La Conchita, California, a small coastal community northwest of Los Angeles (FIGURE 3).

When the pores in sediment become filled with water, the cohesion among particles is destroyed, allowing them to move past one another with relative ease. For example, when sand is slightly moist, it sticks together quite well. However, if enough water is added to fill the openings between the grains, the sand will ooze out in all directions (FIGURE 4). Thus, saturation reduces the internal resistance of materials, which are then easily set in motion by the force of gravity. When clay is wetted, it becomes very slick—another example of the "lubricating" effect of water. Water also adds considerable weight to a mass of material. The added weight in itself may be enough to cause the material to slide or flow downslope.

Scar created by 1995 landslide

Road wiped out by debris flow

2005 debris flow

Houses buried in mud and debris. The thick debris moved some houses instead of flowing around them.

January 10, 2005—the debris flow occurred after the heaviest rainfall of an exceptionally wet rainy season

Rainfall (centimeters)

11/1/04 11/10/04 11/20/04 11/30/04 12/10/04 12/20/04 12/30/04 1/9/05 1/19/05

FIGURE 3 Heavy rains trigger debris flow On January 10, 2005, a massive debris flow swept through La Conchita, California, a small coastal town situated on a narrow coastal strip between the shoreline and a steep bluff. The event occurred after a span of near-record amounts of rainfall. (Photos by Kevork Djansezian/AP Images)

FIGURE 4 Saturation reduces friction
When water saturates soil, friction among particles is reduced, allowing soil to move downslope.

Dry sand

Damp sand

Wet sand

Dry sand grains are bound mainly by friction with one another

Small amounts of water increase the cohesion among sand grains

Saturation reduces friction and causes the sand to flow

FIGURE 4 Saturation reduces friction
When water saturates soil, friction among particles is reduced, allowing soil to move downslope.

Oversteepened Slopes

Oversteepening of slopes is another trigger of many mass movements. There are many situations in nature where oversteepening takes place. For example, as a stream cuts into a valley wall, it removes material from the base of the wall. This causes the slope to become too steep and material to fall or slide into the stream. Furthermore, through their activities, people often create oversteepened and unstable slopes that become prime sites for mass wasting (FIGURE 5).

FIGURE 5 Unstable slopes
Natural processes such as stream and wave erosion can oversteepen slopes. Changing the slope to accommodate a new house or road can also lead to instability and a destructive mass-wasting event.

Heavy rainfall

Oversteepened hillslope   **Fill**

Loose, granular particles (sand-size or coarser) assume a stable slope called the **angle of repose** (*reposen* = to be at rest). This is the steepest angle at which material remains stable (FIGURE 6). Depending on the size and shape of the particles, the angle varies from 25 to 40 degrees. The larger, more angular particles maintain the steepest slopes. If the angle is increased, the rock debris will adjust by moving downslope.

Oversteepening is not just important because it triggers movements of unconsolidated granular materials. Oversteepening also produces unstable slopes and mass movements in cohesive soils, regolith, and bedrock. The response will not be immediate, as with loose, granular material, but sooner or later, one or more mass-wasting processes will eliminate the oversteepening and restore stability to the slope.

Removal of Vegetation

Plants protect against erosion and contribute to the stability of slopes because their root systems bind soil and regolith together. In addition, plants shield the soil surface from the erosional effects of raindrop impact. Where plants are lacking, mass wasting is enhanced, especially if slopes are steep and water is plentiful. When anchoring vegetation is removed by forest fires or by people (for timber, farming, or development), surface materials frequently move downslope.

An unusual example illustrating the anchoring effect of plants occurred several decades ago, on steep slopes near Menton, France. Farmers replaced olive trees, which have deep roots, with a more profitable but shallow-rooted crop: carnations. When the less stable slope failed, the landslide took 11 lives.

In July 1994 a severe wildfire swept Storm King Mountain west of Glenwood Springs, Colorado, denuding the slopes of vegetation. Two months later, heavy rains resulted in numerous debris flows—rapid mass-wasting events involving water-saturated rock and soil. One debris flow blocked Interstate 70 and threatened to dam the Colorado River. A 5-kilometer (3-mile) length of the highway was inundated with tons of rock, mud, and burned trees. The closure of Interstate 70 imposed costly delays on this major highway.

Wildfires are inevitable in the western United States, and fast-moving, highly destructive debris flows triggered by intense rainfall are some of the most dangerous post-fire hazards (FIGURE 7). Such events are particularly dangerous because they tend to occur with little warning. Their mass and speed make them particularly destructive. Post-fire debris flows are most common in the 2 years after a fire. Some of the largest debris-flow events have been triggered by the very first intense rain event following a wildfire. It takes much less rain to trigger debris flows in burned areas than in unburned areas. In southern California, as little as 7 millimeters (0.3 inch) of rain in 30 minutes has triggered debris flows.

How large can these flows be? According to the U.S. Geological Survey, documented debris flows from burned areas in southern California and other western states have ranged in volume from as small as 600 cubic meters to as much as 300,000 cubic meters. This larger volume

FIGURE 6 Angle of repose
The angle of repose is the steepest angle at which an accumulation of granular particles remains stable. Larger, more angular particles maintain the steepest slopes.

The angle of repose for this granular material is about 30°.

G. Leavens/Photo Reseachers, Inc.

As sand accumulates along a dune crest, the slope gets steeper. Eventually, some sand slides down the oversteepened slope.

Michael Collier

FIGURE 7 Aftermath of a wildfire
This image shows the aftermath of a wildfire that occurred northwest of Flagstaff, Arizona, in 2010. The loss of anchoring vegetation sets the stage for accelerated mass wasting.
(Photo by Michael Collier)

is enough material to cover a football field with mud and rocks to a depth of about 65 meters (almost 215 feet)!

In addition to eliminating plants that anchor the soil, fire can promote mass wasting in other ways. Following a wildfire, the upper part of the soil may become dry and loose. As a result, even in dry weather, the soil tends to move down steep slopes. Moreover, fire can also "bake" the ground, creating a water-repellant layer at a shallow depth. This nearly impermeable barrier prevents or slows the infiltration of water, resulting in increased surface runoff during rains. The consequence can be dangerous torrents of viscous mud and rock debris.

Earthquakes as Triggers

Conditions that favor mass wasting may exist in an area for a long time without movement occurring. An additional factor is sometimes necessary to trigger the movement. Among the most important and dramatic triggers are earthquakes. An earthquake and its aftershocks can dislodge enormous volumes of rock and unconsolidated material (FIGURE 8).

Examples from California and China A memorable United States example occurred in January 1994, when a quake struck the Los Angeles region of southern California. Named for its epicenter in the town of Northridge, the 6.7-magnitude event produced

estimated losses of $20 billion. Some of the losses resulted from more than 11,000 landslides in an area of about 10,000 square kilometers (3900 square miles) that were set in motion by the quake. Most were shallow rock falls and slides, but some were much larger and filled canyon bottoms with jumbles of soil, rock, and plant debris. The debris in canyon bottoms created a secondary threat because it can mobilize during rainstorms, producing debris flows. Such flows are common and often disastrous in southern California.

On May 12, 2008, a magnitude 7.9 earthquake struck near the city of Chengdu in China's Sichuan Province. Compounding the tragic effects caused directly by the severe ground shaking were hundreds of landslides triggered by the quake and its many aftershocks. Rock avalanches and debris slides thundered down steep mountain slopes, burying buildings and blocking roads and rail lines. The landslides also dammed rivers, creating more than two dozen lakes. Earthquake-created lakes present a dual danger. Apart from the upstream floods that occur as the lake builds behind the natural dam, the piles of rubble that form the dam may be unstable. Another quake, or simply the pressure of water behind it, could burst the dam, sending a wall of water downstream. Such floods may also occur when water begins to cascade over the top of the dam. The largest of the lakes created by the May 12 earthquake, Tangjiashan Lake, threatened roughly 1.3

FIGURE 8 Earthquakes as triggers
A major earthquake in China's mountainous Sichuan Province in May 2008 triggered hundreds of landslides. The landslide shown here took 51 lives.
(Photo by Lynn Highland/U.S. Geological Survey)

million people. In this instance, a disaster was avoided when Chinese engineers successfully breached the landslide dam and safely drained the lake.

Liquefaction   Intense ground shaking during earthquakes can cause water-saturated surface materials to lose their strength and behave as fluidlike masses that flow (FIGURE 9). This process, called *liquefaction*, was a major cause of property damage in Anchorage, Alaska, during the massive 1964 Good Friday earthquake—the largest quake to strike North America in the twentieth century.

Landslides Without Triggers?

Do rapid mass-wasting events always require some sort of trigger, such as heavy rains or an earthquake? The answer is no; such events sometimes occur without being triggered. For example, on the afternoon of May 9, 1999, a landslide killed 10 hikers and injured many others at Sacred Falls State Park near Hauula, on the north shore of Oahu, Hawaii. The tragic event occurred when a mass of rock from a canyon wall plunged 150 meters (500 feet) down a nearly vertical slope to the valley floor. Because of safety concerns, the park was closed so that landslide specialists from the U.S. Geological Survey could investigate the site. Their study concluded that the landslide occurred *without triggering* from any discernible external conditions.

Many rapid mass-wasting events occur without a discernible trigger. Slope materials gradually weaken over

FIGURE 9 The effects of liquefaction Ground shaking during an earthquake can cause water-saturated ground to lose strength, causing roads and buildings to shift and tilt. These vehicles sank due to liquefaction triggered by an earthquake in Christchurch, New Zealand, in February 2011. (Photo by Mason Woodall/AFP/Getty Images/Newscom)

time under the influence of long-term weathering, infiltration of water, and other physical processes. Eventually, if the strength falls below what is necessary to maintain slope stability, a landslide will occur. The timing of such events is random, and thus accurate prediction is impossible.

2 CONCEPT CHECKS

1. How does water affect mass-wasting processes?
2. Describe the significance of the angle of repose.
3. How might a wildfire influence mass wasting?
4. Describe the relationship between earthquakes and landslides.

EYE on Earth

During summer, wildfires are common occurrences in many parts of the western United States. Millions of acres are burned each year. This wildfire occurred near Santa Clarita, California, in July 2004. We have learned that Earth is a system in which various parts of its four major spheres interact in uncountable ways. Let's relate this idea to the situation pictured here.

Question 1 What atmospheric conditions might have preceded and thus set the stage for this wildfire?

Question 2 What might have ignited the blaze? Suggest a natural possibility and a human possibility.

Question 3 Describe at least two ways that wildfires, like the one shown here, might influence future mass-wasting events in the area.

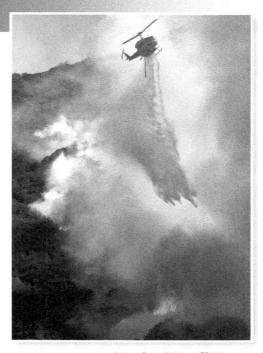

Joshua Gates Weisberg/EPA Newscom

3 Classification of Mass-Wasting Processes

Geologists use the term *mass wasting* to describe a broad array of different processes. Generally, the different types are classified based on the type of material involved, the kind of motion displayed, and the velocity of the movement.

Type of Material

The classification of mass-wasting processes on the basis of the material involved in the movement depends on whether the descending mass began as unconsolidated material or as bedrock. If soil and regolith dominate, terms such as *debris*, *mud*, or *earth* are used in the description. In contrast, when a mass of bedrock breaks loose and moves downslope, the term *rock* may be part of the description.

Type of Motion

In addition to characterizing the type of material involved in a mass-wasting event, the way in which the material moves may also be important. Generally, the kind of motion is described as either a fall, a slide, or a flow.

Fall When the movement in a mass-wasting event involves the free fall of detached individual pieces of any size, it is termed a **fall**. Fall is a common form of movement on slopes that are so steep that loose

material cannot remain on the surface. The rock may fall directly to the base of the slope or move in a series of leaps and bounds over other rocks along the way. Rock falls are the primary way in which **talus slopes** are built and maintained (FIGURE 10). Many falls result when freeze and thaw cycles and/or the action of plant roots loosen rock to the point that gravity takes over. Although signs along bedrock cuts on highways warn of falling rock, few of us have actually witnessed such an event. However, as FIGURE 11 illustrates, they do indeed occur.

When large masses of rock plunge from great heights, they hit the ground with enormous force and often trigger additional mass-wasting events. One deadly example occurred in Peru. In May 1970, an earthquake caused a huge mass of rock and ice to break free from the precipitous north face of Nevados Huascaran, the loftiest peak in the Peruvian Andes. The material plunged nearly

FIGURE 10 Talus slopes
These large talus slopes (sometimes called *talus cones*) are in Canada's Banff National Park. (Photo by Marli Miller) The image of the hiker shows that talus slopes are steep features. (Photo by Whit Richardson/Alamy Images)

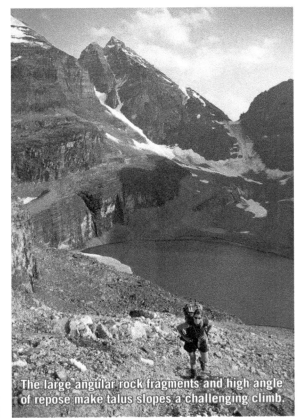

In the mountains, mechanical weathering produces angular rock fragments that fall to the base of a cliff. Over time, a talus slope forms.

The large angular rock fragments and high angle of repose make talus slopes a challenging climb.

2 Controls and Triggers of Mass Wasting

Gravity is the controlling force of mass wasting, but several factors play an important role in overcoming inertia and creating downslope movements. Long before a landslide occurs, various processes work to weaken slope material, gradually making it more and more susceptible to the pull of gravity. During this span, the slope remains stable but gets closer and closer to being unstable. Eventually, the strength of the slope is weakened to the point that something causes it to cross the threshold from stability to instability. Such an event that initiates downslope movement is called a *trigger*. Remember that a trigger is not the sole cause of a mass-wasting event but just the last of many causes. Among the common factors that trigger mass-wasting processes are saturation of material with water, oversteepening of slopes, removal of anchoring vegetation, and ground vibrations from earthquakes.

The Role of Water

Mass wasting is sometimes triggered when heavy rains or periods of snow-melt saturate surface materials. The water does not transport the material. Rather, it allows gravity to more easily set the material in motion. This was the case in January 2005, when a massive debris flow (popularly called a mudslide) swept through La Conchita, California, a small coastal community northwest of Los Angeles (FIGURE 3).

When the pores in sediment become filled with water, the cohesion among particles is destroyed, allowing them to move past one another with relative ease. For example, when sand is slightly moist, it sticks together quite well. However, if enough water is added to fill the openings between the grains, the sand will ooze out in all directions (FIGURE 4). Thus, saturation reduces the internal resistance of materials, which are then easily set in motion by the force of gravity. When clay is wetted, it becomes very slick—another example of the "lubricating" effect of water. Water also adds considerable weight to a mass of material. The added weight in itself may be enough to cause the material to slide or flow downslope.

Scar created by 1995 landslide

Road wiped out by debris flow

2005 debris flow

Houses buried in mud and debris. The thick debris moved some houses instead of flowing around them.

10
9
8
7
6
5
4
3
2
1
0

Rainfall (centimeters)

January 10, 2005—the debris flow occurred after the heaviest rainfall of an exceptionally wet rainy season

11/1/04 11/10/04 11/20/04 11/30/04 12/10/04 12/20/04 12/30/04 1/9/05 1/19/05

FIGURE 3 Heavy rains trigger debris flow On January 10, 2005, a massive debris flow swept through La Conchita, California, a small coastal town situated on a narrow coastal strip between the shoreline and a steep bluff. The event occurred after a span of near-record amounts of rainfall. (Photos by Kevork Djansezian/AP Images)

FIGURE 4 Saturation reduces friction
When water saturates soil, friction among particles is reduced, allowing soil to move downslope.

Dry sand

Dry sand grains are bound mainly by friction with one another

Damp sand

Small amounts of water increase the cohesion among sand grains

Wet sand

Saturation reduces friction and causes the sand to flow

Oversteepened Slopes

Oversteepening of slopes is another trigger of many mass movements. There are many situations in nature where oversteepening takes place. For example, as a stream cuts into a valley wall, it removes material from the base of the wall. This causes the slope to become too steep and material to fall or slide into the stream. Furthermore, through their activities, people often create oversteepened and unstable slopes that become prime sites for mass wasting (FIGURE 5).

FIGURE 5 Unstable slopes
Natural processes such as stream and wave erosion can oversteepen slopes. Changing the slope to accommodate a new house or road can also lead to instability and a destructive mass-wasting event.

Heavy rainfall

Oversteepened hillslope   Fill

Loose, granular particles (sand-size or coarser) assume a stable slope called the **angle of repose** (*reposen* = to be at rest). This is the steepest angle at which material remains stable (FIGURE 6). Depending on the size and shape of the particles, the angle varies from 25 to 40 degrees. The larger, more angular particles maintain the steepest slopes. If the angle is increased, the rock debris will adjust by moving downslope.

Oversteepening is not just important because it triggers movements of unconsolidated granular materials. Oversteepening also produces unstable slopes and mass movements in cohesive soils, regolith, and bedrock. The response will not be immediate, as with loose, granular material, but sooner or later, one or more mass-wasting processes will eliminate the oversteepening and restore stability to the slope.

Removal of Vegetation

Plants protect against erosion and contribute to the stability of slopes because their root systems bind soil and regolith together. In addition, plants shield the soil surface from the erosional effects of raindrop impact. Where plants are lacking, mass wasting is enhanced, especially if slopes are steep and water is plentiful. When anchoring vegetation is removed by forest fires or by people (for timber, farming, or development), surface materials frequently move downslope.

An unusual example illustrating the anchoring effect of plants occurred several decades ago, on steep slopes near Menton, France. Farmers replaced olive trees, which have deep roots, with a more profitable but shallow-rooted crop: carnations. When the less stable slope failed, the landslide took 11 lives.

In July 1994 a severe wildfire swept Storm King Mountain west of Glenwood Springs, Colorado, denuding

FIGURE 11 Watch Out for Falling Rock! This rock fall blocked Highway 140 near the Arch Rock entrance to California's Yosemite National Park in January 1997. (Photo by Roger J. Wyan/ AP/Wide World Photos; sign photo by Harris Shiffman/Shutterstock)

a kilometer and pulverized on impact. The rock avalanche that followed rushed down the mountainside, made fluid by trapped air and ice. Along the way, it ripped loose millions of tons of additional debris that ultimately and tragically buried more than 20,000 people in the towns of Yungay and Ranrahirca.

A different effect triggered by a rock fall occurred in Yosemite National Park on July 10, 1996. When two large rock masses broke loose from steep cliffs and fell about 500 meters (1640 feet) to the floor of Yosemite Valley, the impacts were great enough to be recorded at seismic stations 200 kilometers (125 miles) from the site. As the dislodged rock masses struck the ground, they generated atmospheric pressure waves that were comparable in velocity to a tornado or hurricane. The force of the air blasts uprooted and snapped more than 1000 trees, including some that were 40 meters (130 feet) tall.

Slide   Many mass-wasting processes are described as **slides**. The term refers to mass movements in which there is a distinct zone of weakness separating the slide material from the more stable underlying material. Two basic types of slides are recognized. *Rotational slides* are those in which the surface of rupture is a concave-upward curve that resembles the shape of a spoon and the descending material exhibits a downward and outward rotation. By contrast, a *translational slide* is one in which a mass of material moves along a relatively flat surface such as a joint, fault, or bedding plane. Such slides exhibit little rotation or backward tilting.

Flow   The third type of movement common to mass-wasting processes is termed **flow**. Flow occurs when material moves downslope as a viscous fluid. Most flows are saturated with water and typically move as lobes or tongues.

Rate of Movement

Some of the events that have been described so far in this chapter involved very rapid rates of movement. For example, it is estimated that the debris that rushed down the slopes of Peru's Nevados Huascaran moved at speeds in excess of 200 kilometers (125 miles) per hour. This most rapid type of mass movement is termed a **rock avalanche** (*avaler* = to descend). Researchers now understand that rock avalanches, such as the one that produced the scene in FIGURE 12, must literally "float on air" as they move downslope. That is, high velocities result when air becomes trapped and compressed beneath the falling mass of debris, allowing it to move as a buoyant, flexible sheet across the surface.

Most mass movements, however, do not move with the speed of a rock avalanche. In fact, a great deal of mass wasting is imperceptibly slow. One process that we will examine later, termed *creep*, results in particle movements that are usually measured in millimeters or centimeters per year. Thus, as you can see, rates of movement can be spectacularly sudden or

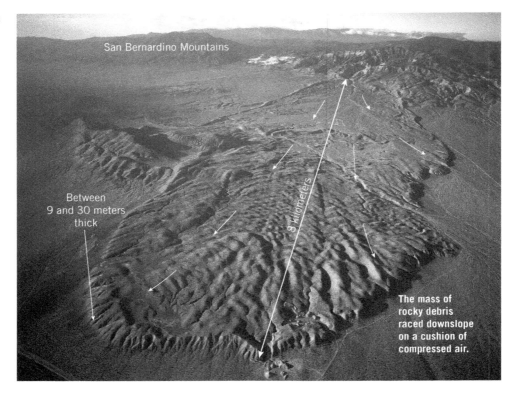

FIGURE 12 Blackhawk rock avalanche
This prehistoric event is considered one of the largest known landslides in North America. (Photo by Michael Collier)

San Bernardino Mountains

Between 9 and 30 meters thick

8 kilometers

The mass of rocky debris raced downslope on a cushion of compressed air.

exceptionally gradual. Although various types of mass wasting are often classified as either rapid or slow, such a distinction is highly subjective because a wide range of rates exists between the two extremes. Even the velocity of a single process at a particular site can vary considerably.

3 CONCEPT CHECKS

1. What terms are used to describe the way material moves during mass wasting?
2. Why can rock avalanches move at such great speeds?

EYE on Earth

The rugged terrain in this image is in California's Sierra Nevada. Notice the accumulation of angular rock fragments at the base of the sheer rock wall.

Question 1 What term is applied to a pile of rock debris such as this?

Question 2 Describe the process(es) that produced this feature.

Question 3 Did the feature form rapidly or gradually?

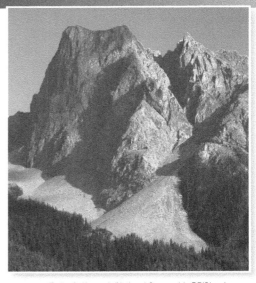

Taylor S. Kennedy/National Geographic RF/Glow Images

4 Rapid Forms of Mass Wasting

The common rapid mass-wasting processes discussed in this section include slump, rockslide, debris flow, and earthflow. They are most common where slopes are steep. The speed of movement varies from barely perceptible to very rapid.

Slump

Slump refers to the downward sliding of a mass of rock or unconsolidated material moving as a unit along a curved surface (FIGURE 13). Usually the slumped material does not travel spectacularly fast nor very far. This is a common form of mass wasting, especially in thick accumulations of cohesive materials such as clay. The ruptured surface is characteristically spoon shaped and concave upward or outward. As the movement occurs, a crescent-shaped scarp is created at the head, and the block's upper surface is sometimes tilted backward. Although slump may involve a single mass, it often consists of multiple blocks. Sometimes water collects between the base of the scarp and the top of the tilted block. As this water percolates downward along the surface of rupture, it may promote further instability and additional movement.

Slump commonly occurs because a slope has been oversteepened. The material on the upper portion of a slope is held in place by the material at the bottom of the slope. As this anchoring material at the base is removed, the material above is made unstable and reacts to the pull of gravity. One relatively common example is a valley wall that becomes oversteepened by a meandering river. The photo in FIGURE 14 provides an example in which a coastal cliff has been undercut by wave action at its base. Slumping may also occur when a slope is overloaded, causing internal stress on the material below. This type of slump often occurs where weak, clay-rich material underlies layers of stronger, more resistant rock such as sandstone. The seepage of water through the upper layers reduces the strength of the clay below, resulting in slope failure.

Rockslide

Rockslides occur when blocks of bedrock break loose and slide down a slope (FIGURE 15). If the material involved is largely unconsolidated, the term **debris slide** is used instead. Such events are among the fastest and most destructive mass movements. Usually rockslides take place in a geologic setting where the

Slump occurs when material slips downslope en masse along a curved surface of rupture. It is an example of a rotational slide. Earthflows frequently form at the base of the slump.

rock strata are inclined, or where joints and fractures exist parallel to the slope. When such a rock unit is undercut at the base of the slope, it loses support, and the rock eventually gives way. Sometimes the rockslide is triggered when rain or melting snow lubricates the underlying surface to the point that friction is no longer sufficient to hold the rock unit in place. As a result, rockslides tend to be most common during the spring, when heavy rains and melting snow are most prevalent.

Waves undercut the base of the steep slope, making it unstable. (Photo by John S. Shelton/University of Washington Libraries)

Geologist's Sketch

FIGURE 15 Rockslide
These rapid movements are classified as translational slides in which the material moves along a relatively flat surface with little or no rotation or backward tilting.

Surface of rupture

Rockslide

As mentioned earlier, earthquakes can trigger rockslides and other mass movements. There are many well-known examples. The 1811 earthquake at New Madrid, Missouri, caused slides in an area of more than 13,000 square kilometers (5000 square miles) along the Mississippi River valley. On August 17, 1959, a severe earthquake west of Yellowstone National Park triggered a massive slide in the canyon of the Madison River in southwestern Montana. In a matter of moments, an estimated 27 million cubic meters of rock, soil, and trees slid into the canyon. The debris dammed the river and buried a campground and highway. More than 20 unsuspecting campers perished.

Heavy rains and melting snow, rather than an earthquake, triggered another major rockslide in the Yellowstone region. Not far from the site of the Madison Canyon slide, the legendary Gros Ventre rockslide occurred 34 years earlier. The Gros Ventre River flows west from the northernmost part of the Wind River Range in northwestern Wyoming, through Grand Teton National Park, and eventually empties into the Snake River. On June 23, 1925, a massive rockslide took place in its valley, just east of the small town of Kelly. In the span of just a few minutes, a great mass of sandstone, shale, and soil crashed down the south side of the valley, carrying with it a dense pine forest. The volume of debris, estimated at 38 million cubic meters (50 million cubic yards), created a 70-meter-high (230 feet) dam on the Gros Ventre River. Because the river was completely blocked, a lake was formed. It filled so quickly that a house that had been 18 meters (60 feet) above the river was floated off its foundation 18 hours after the slide. In 1927, the lake overflowed the dam, partially draining the lake and resulting in a devastating flood downstream.

Why did the Gros Ventre rockslide take place? FIGURE 16 shows a diagrammatic cross-sectional view of the geology of the valley. You will notice that (1) the sedimentary strata in this area dip (tilt) 15 to 21 degrees; (2) underlying the bed of sandstone is a relatively thin layer of clay; and (3) at the bottom of the valley, the river had cut through much of the sandstone layer. During the spring of 1925, water from heavy rains and melting snow seeped through the sandstone, saturating the clay below. Because much of the sandstone layer had been cut through by the Gros Ventre River, the layer had virtually no support at the bottom of the slope. Eventually the sandstone could no longer hold its position on the wetted clay, and gravity pulled the mass down the side of the valley. The circumstances at this location were such that the event was inevitable.

 SMARTFIGURE 16
Gros Ventre rockslide
This massive slide occurred on June 23, 1925, just east of the small town of Kelly, Wyoming. (Photo by Michael Collier)

The side of the mountain gave way when the tilted sandstone bed, that had been cut through by the river, could no longer maintain its position atop the saturated bed of clay.

Gros Ventre landslide debris

Former land surface

Scar

Lake

Clay bed

Rupture surface

Sandstone

Limestone

0   0.5   1
Kilometer

Even though the Gros Ventre rockslide occurred in 1925, the scar left on the side of Sheep Mountain is still a prominent feature.

Debris Flow

Debris flow is a relatively rapid type of mass wasting that involves a flow of soil and regolith containing a large amount of water (FIGURE 17). The La Conchita debris flow in Figure 3 is one example.

Debris flows are sometimes called **mudflows** when the material is primarily fine-grained. Although they can occur in many different climate settings, they tend to occur more frequently in semiarid mountainous regions. Debris flows, called *lahars*, are also common on the steep slopes of some volcanoes. Because of their fluid properties, debris flows frequently follow canyons and stream channels. In populated areas, debris flows can pose a significant hazard to life and property.

Debris Flows in Semiarid Regions

When a cloudburst or rapidly melting mountain snows create a sudden flood in a semiarid region, large quantities of soil and regolith are washed into nearby stream channels because there is usually little vegetation to anchor the surface material. The end product is a flowing tongue of well-mixed mud, soil, rock, and water. Its consistency may range from that of wet concrete to a soupy mixture not much thicker than muddy water. The rate of flow, therefore, depends not only on the slope but also on the water content. When dense, debris flows are capable of carrying or pushing large boulders, trees, and even houses with relative ease.

Debris flows pose a serious hazard to development in relatively dry mountainous areas such as southern California. The construction of homes on canyon hillsides and the removal of native vegetation by brush fires and other means have increased the frequency of these destructive events. Moreover, when a debris flow reaches the end of a steep, narrow canyon, it spreads out, covering the area beyond the mouth of the canyon with a mixture of wet debris. This material contributes to the buildup of fan-like deposits, called *alluvial fans*, at canyon mouths. The fans are relatively easy to build on, often have nice views, and are close to the mountains; in fact, like the nearby canyons, many have become preferred sites for development. Because debris flows occur only sporadically, the public is often unaware of the potential hazard of such sites.

Lahars

Debris flows composed mostly of volcanic materials on the flanks of volcanoes are called *lahars*. The word originated in Indonesia, a volcanic region that has experienced many of these often-destructive events. Historically, lahars have been some of the deadliest volcano hazards. They can occur either during an eruption or when a volcano is quiet. They take place when highly unstable layers of ash and debris become saturated

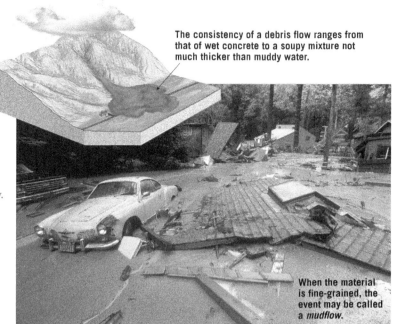

The consistency of a debris flow ranges from that of wet concrete to a soupy mixture not much thicker than muddy water.

When the material is fine-grained, the event may be called a *mudflow.*

FIGURE 17 Debris flow
Debris flow is a moving tongue of well-mixed mud, soil rock, and water. (Photo by Michael Collier)

with water and flow down steep volcanic slopes, generally following existing stream channels (FIGURE 18). Heavy rainfalls often trigger these flows. Others are initiated when large volumes of ice and snow are melted by heat

FIGURE 18 Lahar at Redoubt Volcano
An eruption in April 2009 of this volcano on Alaska's Kenai Peninsula, sent lahars down the valley of the Drift River. The dark color of the lahar contrasts sharply with the surrounding snow-covered landscape. (NASA)

Lahar following valley of Drift River

Mt. Redoubt erupting ash column

Ash-covered snow

Ash-plume spreading downwind

Cook Inlet

N

Geologist's Sketch

FIGURE 19 Lahar at Mount St. Helens
The force of this viscous debris flow that followed the Toutle River tore the end section from a house and lodged it in the trees. (Photo by D. R. Crandell, U.S. Geological Survey, Denver)

FIGURE 20 Earthflow
This small tongue-shaped earthflow occurred on a newly formed slope along a recently constructed highway in central Illinois. It formed in clay-rich material following a period of heavy rain. Notice the small slump at the head of the earthflow. (Photo by E. J. Tarbuck)

flowing to the surface from within the volcano or by the hot gases and near-molten debris emitted during a violent eruption.

When Mount St. Helens erupted in May 1980, several lahars were created. The flows and accompanying floods raced down the valleys of the north and south forks of the Toutle River at speeds that were often in excess of 30 kilometers (20 miles) per hour. Fortunately, the affected area was not densely settled. Nevertheless, more than 200 homes were destroyed or severely damaged (**FIGURE 19**). Most bridges met a similar fate. According to the U.S. Geological Survey:

Even after traveling many tens of miles from the volcano and mixing with cold waters, the mudflows maintained temperatures in the range of about 84°

to 91 °C; they undoubtedly had higher temperatures closer to the eruption source. . . . Locally the mudflows surged up the valley walls as much as 360 feet and over hills as high as 250 feet. From the evidence left by the "bathtub-ring" mudlines, the larger mudflows at their peak averaged from 33 to 66 feet deep.

Eventually the lahars in the Toutle River drainage area carried more than 50 million cubic meters of material to the lower Cowlitz and Columbia Rivers. The deposits temporarily reduced the water-carrying capacity of the Cowlitz River by 85 percent, and the depth of the Columbia River navigational channel was decreased from 12 meters to less than 4 meters.

In November 1985, lahars were produced during the eruption of Nevado del Ruiz, a 5300-meter (17,400-foot) volcano in the Andes Mountains of Colombia. The eruption melted much of the snow and ice that capped the uppermost 600 meters (2000 feet) of the peak, producing torrents of hot, viscous mud, ash, and debris. The lahars moved outward from the volcano, following the valleys of three rain-swollen rivers that radiate from the peak. The flow that moved down the valley of the Lagunilla River was the most destructive. It devastated the town of Armero, 48 kilometers (30 miles) from the mountain. Most of the more than 25,000 deaths caused by the event occurred in this once-thriving agricultural community.

Death and property damage due to the lahars also occurred in 13 other villages within the 180-square-kilometer (70-square-mile) disaster area. Although a great deal of pyroclastic material was explosively ejected from Nevado del Ruiz, it was the lahars triggered by this eruption that made this such a devastating natural disaster. In fact, it was the worst volcanic disaster to occur since the 1902 eruption of Mount Pelée on the Caribbean island of Martinique that killed 28,000 people.

Earthflow

We have seen that debris flows are frequently confined to channels in semiarid regions. In contrast, **earthflows** most often form on hillsides in humid areas during times of heavy precipitation or snowmelt. When water saturates the soil and regolith on a hillside, the material may break away, leaving a scar on the slope and forming a tongue- or teardrop-shaped mass that flows downslope (**FIGURE 20**).

Geologist's Sketch

Robert I. Tilling, *Eruptions of Mount St. Helens: Past, Present, and Future.* Washington, DC: U.S. Government Printing Office, 1987.

The materials most commonly involved are rich in clay and silt and contain only small proportions of sand and coarser particles. Earthflows range in size from bodies a few meters long, a few meters wide, and less than a meter deep to masses more than 1 kilometer long, several hundred meters wide, and more than 10 meters deep. Because earthflows are quite viscous, they generally move at slower rates than the more fluid debris flows described in the preceding section. They are characterized by a gradual movement that may go on for periods ranging from days to years. Depending on the steepness of the slope and the material's consistency, measured velocities range from less than a millimeter a day up to several meters a day. Over the time span that earthflows are active, movement is typically faster during wet periods than during drier times. In addition to occurring as isolated hillside phenomena, earthflows commonly take place in association with large slumps. In this situation, they may be seen as tongue-like flows at the base of the slump block.

4 CONCEPT CHECKS

1. Without looking at Figures 13 and 14, sketch and label a simple cross section (side view) of a slump.
2. Both slumps and rockslides move by sliding. How do these processes differ?
3. What factors led to the massive rockslide at Gros Ventre, Wyoming?
4. How is a lahar different from a debris flow that might occur in southern California?
5. Contrast earthflows and debris flows.

EYE on Earth

Heavy rains in late July 2010 triggered the mass wasting that occurred in this mountain valley near Durango, Colorado. Heavy equipment is clearing away material that blocked railroad tracks and significantly narrowed the adjacent stream channel.

Question 1 What is the likely type of mass wasting that occurred here? Explain your choice.

Question 2 Most of us are familiar with the phrase "One thing leads to another." It certainly applies to the Earth system. Suppose the material from the mass-wasting event had completely filled the stream. What other natural hazard might have developed?

Soaring Tree Adventures

SMARTFIGURE 21
Creep
The repeated expansion
and contraction of the
surface material causes a
net downslope migration
of soil and rock particles.
(Marli Miller)

5 Slow Movements

Movements such as rockslides, rock avalanches, and lahars are certainly the most spectacular and catastrophic forms of mass wasting. These dangerous events deserve intensive study to enable more effective prediction, timely warnings, and better controls to save lives. However, because of their large size and spectacular nature, they give us a false impression of their importance as mass-wasting processes. Indeed, sudden movements are responsible for moving less material than the slower and far more subtle action of creep. Whereas rapid types of mass wasting are characteristic of mountains and steep hillsides, creep takes place on both steep and gentle slopes and is thus much more widespread.

Creep

Creep is a type of mass wasting that involves the gradual downhill movement of soil and regolith. One factor that contributes to creep is the alternating expansion and contraction of surface material caused by freezing and thawing or wetting and drying. As shown in FIGURE 21, freezing or wetting lifts particles at right angles to the slope, and thawing or drying allows the particles to fall back to a slightly lower level. Each cycle therefore moves the material a tiny distance downslope. Creep is aided by anything that disturbs the soil, such as raindrop impact and disturbance by plant roots and burrowing animals. Creep is also promoted when the ground becomes saturated with water. Following a heavy rain or snowmelt, a water-logged soil may lose its internal cohesion, allowing gravity to pull the material downslope. Because creep is imperceptibly slow, the process cannot be observed in action. What can be observed, however, are the effects of creep. Creep causes fences and utility poles to tilt and retaining walls to be displaced (FIGURE 22).

Expansion
caused by
freezing

Contraction
during thaws

Surface when
frozen

Surface when
thawed

Creep

Regolith

Bedrock

FIGURE 22 Effects of creep
Although creep is an imperceptibly slow movement, its effects are often visible. (Photos by D. Bradley/NOAA, Marli Miller, and Tim McGuire Images, Inc./Alamy)

Bent rock
layers

Curved
tree trunk

Tilted
fence

Zone of creep

Broken
retaining
wall

Tension
cracks

Solifluction

When soil is saturated with water, the soggy mass may flow downslope at a rate of a few millimeters or a few centimeters per day or per year. Such a process is called **solifluction** (literally, "soil flow"). It is a type of mass wasting that is common wherever water cannot escape from the saturated surface layer by infiltrating to deeper levels. A dense clay hardpan in soil or an impermeable bedrock layer can promote solifluction.

Solifluction is also common in regions underlain by *permafrost*. Permafrost refers to the permanently frozen ground that occurs in association with Earth's harsh tundra and subarctic climates. (There is more about permafrost in the next section.) Solifluction occurs in a zone above the permafrost called the *active layer*, which thaws to a depth of about a meter during the brief high-latitude summer and then refreezes in winter. During the summer season, water is unable to percolate into the impervious permafrost layer below. As a result, the active layer becomes saturated and slowly flows. The process can occur on slopes as gentle as 2 to 3 degrees. Where there is a well-developed mat of vegetation, a solifluction sheet may move in a series of well-defined lobes or as a series of partially overriding folds (FIGURE 23).

The Sensitive Permafrost Landscape

Many of the mass-wasting disasters described in this chapter had sudden and disastrous impacts on people. When the activities of people cause ice contained in permanently frozen ground to melt, the impact is more gradual and less deadly. Nevertheless, because permafrost regions are sensitive and fragile landscapes, the scars resulting from poorly planned actions can remain for generations.

Permanently frozen ground, known as **permafrost**, occurs where summers are too short and cool to melt more than a shallow surface layer (FIGURE 24). Deeper ground remains frozen year-round. Strictly speaking, permafrost is defined only on the basis of temperature; that is, it is ground with temperatures that have remained below 0° C (32° F) continuously for 2 years or more. The degree to which ice is present in the ground strongly affects the behavior of the surface material. Knowing how much ice is present and where it is located is very important when it comes to constructing roads, buildings, and other projects in areas underlain by permafrost.

Permafrost is extensive in the lands surrounding the Arctic Ocean. It covers more than 80 percent of Alaska, about 50 percent of Canada, and a substantial portion of northern Siberia (FIGURE 25). Near the southern margins of the region, the permafrost consists of relatively thin, isolated masses. Farther north, the area and thickness gradually increase to the point where the permafrost is essentially continuous, and its thickness may approach or even exceed 500 meters (1600 feet). In the discontinuous

FIGURE 23 Solifluction lobes near the Arctic Circle in Alaska Solifluction occurs in permafrost regions when the active layer thaws in summer. (Photo by James E. Patterson Collection)

Active layer (thawed in summer)

Frozen layer (permafrost)

Geologist's Sketch

zone, land-use planning is frequently more difficult than in the continuous zone farther north because the occurrences of permafrost are patchy and difficult to predict.

When people disturb the surface, such as by removing the insulating vegetation mat or by constructing roads and buildings, the delicate thermal balance is disturbed, and the permafrost can thaw. Thawing produces unstable ground that may slide, slump, subside, and undergo severe frost heaving. When a heated structure is built directly on permafrost that contains a high proportion of ice, thawing creates soggy material into which a building can sink (FIGURE 26). One solution is to place buildings and other structures on piles, like stilts. Such piles allow subfreezing air to circulate between the floor of the building and the soil and thereby keep the ground frozen.

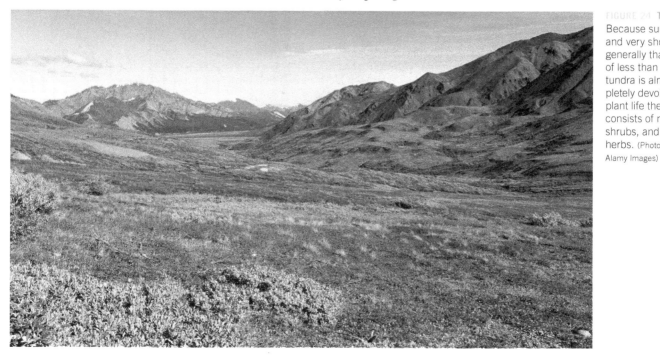

FIGURE 24 Tundra Because summers are cool and very short, frozen soils generally thaw to depths of less than 1 meter The tundra is almost completely devoid of trees, and plant life there frequently consists of mosses, low shrubs, and flowering herbs. (Photo by imagebroker/Alamy Images)

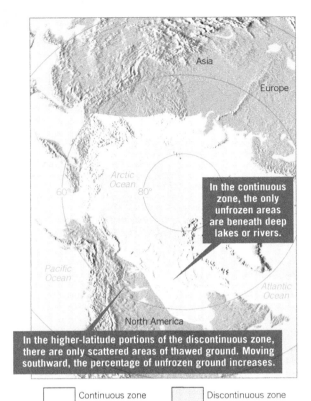

24

In the continuous zone, the only unfrozen areas are beneath deep lakes or rivers.

In the higher-latitude portions of the discontinuous zone, there are only scattered areas of thawed ground. Moving southward, the percentage of unfrozen ground increases.

Continuous zone   Discontinuous zone

FIGURE 25 Distribution of permafrost in the northern hemisphere
More than 80 percent of Alaska and about 50 percent of Canada are underlain by permafrost.

Heat

Permafrost

SMARTFIGURE 26 When permafrost thaws
This building, located south of Fairbanks, Alaska, subsided because of thawing permafrost. Notice that the right side, which was heated, settled much more than the unheated porch on the left. (Photo by Steve McCutcheon, U.S. Geological Survey)

When oil was discovered on Alaska's North Slope, many people were concerned about the building of a pipeline linking the oil fields at Prudhoe Bay to the ice-free port of Valdez 1300 kilometers (800 miles) to the south. There was serious concern that such a massive project might damage the sensitive permafrost environment. Many also worried about possible oil spills.

Because oil must be heated to about 60° C (140° F) to flow properly, special engineering procedures had to be developed to isolate this heat from the permafrost. Methods included insulating the pipe, elevating portions of the pipeline above ground level, and even placing cooling devices in the ground to keep it frozen (FIGURE 27). The Alaskan pipeline is clearly one of the most complex and costly projects ever built in the Arctic tundra. Detailed studies and careful engineering helped minimize adverse effects resulting from the disturbance of frozen ground.

Pipeline

FIGURE 27 Trans-Alaska pipeline
In places, the pipeline is suspended above ground to prevent melting of delicate permafrost. (Photos by Michael Collier)

5 CONCEPT CHECKS

1. Describe the basic mechanisms that contribute to creep. How might you recognize that creep is occurring?
2. During what season does solifluction in the Arctic occur? Explain why it occurs only during that season.
3. What is permafrost? How might disturbing permafrost lead to unstable ground that may slide, flow, or subside?

Landslide Risks:
United States and Worldwide

According to the U. S. Geological Survey, each year in the United States, landslides cost nearly $4 billion (2010 dollars) in damage repair and cause between 25 and 50 deaths. All states experience rapid mass-wasting processes, but not all areas have the same landslide potential. What's the risk where you live?

U.S. LANDSLIDE POTENTIAL

KEY
VERY HIGH POTENTIAL
HIGH POTENTIAL
MODERATE POTENTIAL
LOW POTENTIAL

❶ In parts of the **Seattle area,** volcanic mudflows called lahars are a potential threat.

❷ In the mountainous parts of the **Pacific Northwest**, heavy rains and melting snow often trigger rapid forms of mass wasting.

❸ **Coastal California's** steep slopes have a high landslide potential often triggered by winter storms or ground shaking associated with earthquakes.

❹ Strong wave activity undercuts and oversteepens coastal cliffs.

❺ In the **center of the country**, the plains states are relatively flat, so landslide potential is mostly low-to-moderate.

❻ High potential occurs along steep bluffs that flank river valleys.

❼ **Florida** and the adjacent Atlantic and Gulf coastal plains have some of the lowest potential because steep slopes are largely absent.

❽ In the **East**, landslides are most common in the Appalachian Mountains

Reuters/Japan Coast

GLOBAL LANDSLIDE RISKS

NASA scientists compiled this risk map based on topographic data, land cover classifications and soil types.

Purple and dark red indicate areas at highest risk.

Black dots identify locations of major landslides over a four-year span (2003-2006)

LANDSLIDE RISK
SLIGHT ← → MODERATE ← → SEVERE

Xinhua/Photoshot/Newscom

CONCEPTS IN REVIEW: MASS WASTING: THE WORK OF GRAVITY

1 The Importance of Mass Wasting

Discuss situations in which mass-wasting processes can cause natural disasters and discuss the role that mass wasting plays in the development of landforms.

KEY WORD mass wasting

- After weathering breaks rock apart, gravity moves the debris downslope, in a process called mass wasting. Sometimes this occurs rapidly as a landslide, and at other times the movement is slower. Landslides are a significant geologic hazard, taking many lives and destroying property every year.
- Mass wasting serves an important role in landscape development. It widens stream-cut valleys and helps tear down the mountains thrust up by plate tectonics.

ANOTHER EARTH Imagine a planet with stronger rocks and less gravity. Imagine a second planet with weaker rocks and much greater gravity. Assume that plate tectonics and mass wasting are forces that work on these two planets. How might the landscapes of these planets compare to those on Earth? Speculate about which would be a safer planet to build an outpost.

Gregory S. Springer

2 Controls and Triggers of Mass Wasting

Summarize the factors that control and trigger mass-wasting processes.

KEY WORD angle of repose

- An event that initiates a mass-wasting process is referred to as a trigger. The addition of water, oversteepening of the slope, removal of vegetation, and shaking due to an earthquake are four important examples. Not all landslides are triggered by one of these four processes, but many are.
- Water added to a slope can expand the pore space between grains, causing them to lose their cohesion. Water also lubricates the contacts between the grains and adds a significant amount of mass to a wetted slope.

- Granular materials can pile up to a certain angle of slope, but granular piles steeper than that critical angle will spontaneously collapse outward to form a gentler slope. For most geologic materials, this angle of repose varies between 25 and 40 degrees from horizontal. Oversteepened slopes are likely to fail with a landslide.
- The roots of plants (especially plants with deep roots) act as a three-dimensional "net" that holds soil and regolith particles in place. When the plants die, the soil loses an important support structure. Plants may be removed naturally (through wildfires, for instance) or by humans seeking to harvest timber, plant crops, or build structures.
- Earthquakes are significant triggers that deliver an energetic jolt to slopes poised on the brink of failure.

PLAN IT If you were buying a home on a hill, how would you assess the landslide risk? What steps might you take to mitigate that risk?

3 Classification of Mass-Wasting Processes

List and explain the criteria that are commonly used to classify mass-wasting processes.

KEY WORDS fall, talus slope, slide, flow, rock avalanche

- There are a variety of Earth materials (rock, soil, regolith) and a variety of rates of mass wasting movement. The type of material and the nature of the motion are combined into classifying terms for the different types of mass wasting.
- Rock falls occur when pieces of bedrock detach and fall freely through the air, slamming into the ground below with tremendous force. Repeated rock falls generate a talus slope, the characteristic "apron" of angular rock debris that accumulates below mountain cliffs. Slides occur

when discrete blocks of rock or unconsolidated material slip downslope on a planar or curved surface. Unlike in a fall, the material in a slide does not drop through the air. Flows occur when individual grains or particles move randomly in a slurry, a viscous mixture of water-saturated materials.
- Rock avalanches move incredibly rapidly over surprising distances (tens of kilometers in a few minutes) because they ride along a layer of compressed air, in the same way that a hovercraft slides over the land with minimal friction. Other forms of mass wasting are much slower, moving perhaps only millimeters per year.

EXPLAIN IT Relate the formation of talus slopes to both weathering and mass-wasting processes.

4 Rapid Forms of Mass Wasting

Distinguish among slump, rockslide, debris flow, and earthflow.

KEY WORDS slump, rockslide, debris slide, debris flow, mudflow, earthflow

- A slump is a distinctive and common form of mass wasting in which coherent blocks of material move downhill on a spoon-shaped slip surface. Slumps are often marked by curved scarps that open up at their tops. They are frequently triggered by oversteepening, such as that caused by stream erosion of a valley wall.
- Rockslides are rapid forms of mass wasting in which a coherent block of rock slides downhill along a planar surface. Often this is a preexisting structure such as a joint or a bedding plane. Situations where these surfaces dip into a valley at an angle are especially risky.

- Debris flows occur when unconsolidated soil or regolith becomes saturated with water and moves downhill in a slurry, picking up other objects (trees, houses, livestock) along the way. Varieties of debris flow include mudflows, which are dominated by small particle sizes, and lahars, which involve volcanic material. Debris flows can move quickly—up to 30 kilometers (nearly 20 miles) per hour.
- Earthflow is characterized by a similar loss of coherence between grains in unconsolidated material, but it is much slower than a debris flow. Typically, sites of earthflow show an uphill scarp and a lobe of viscous soil on the downhill side.

RISK ASSESSMENT Examine the three situations shown here. Each depicts a cross-section through a valley cut into sedimentary strata. Which one of these situations would have the highest risk for a rockslide?

5 Slow Movements

Review the general characteristics of slow mass-wasting processes and describe the unique issues associated with a permafrost environment.

KEY WORDS creep, solifluction, permafrost

- Creep is a widespread and important form of mass wasting that is very slow. It occurs when freezing (or wetting) causes soil particles to be pushed out away from the slope, only to drop down to a lower position following thawing (or drying). In contrast, solifluction is the gradual flow of a saturated surface layer that is underlain by an impermeable zone. In arctic regions, the impermeable zone is permafrost.
- Permafrost, permanently frozen ground, covers large portions of North America and Siberia. Constructing buildings and other infrastructure in such regions requires special planning. Leaking heat can melt permafrost, causing a loss of volume and triggering flow in the formerly frozen soil. The resulting subsidence can be devastating.

CRITICAL MASS Examine the photograph of a house near Fairbanks, Alaska, a region of permafrost. What sort of damage can you detect? What processes might be causing this damage? Explain your reasoning.

Michael Collier

GIVE IT SOME THOUGHT

1. Describe a type of mass wasting that might occur in your home area. Remember to consider characteristics such as climate, surface materials, and steepness of slopes. Does your example have a trigger?

2. Rivers, groundwater, glaciers, wind, and waves can all move and deposit sediment. Geologists refer to these phenomena as *agents of erosion*. Mass wasting also involves the movement and deposition of sediment, yet it is *not* classified as an agent of erosion. How is mass wasting different?

3. Internal processes include such phenomena as earthquakes, mountain building, and volcanic activity. External processes, such as weathering, mass wasting, and erosion, modify Earth's surface. In the accompanying photo, external processes are clearly active. Describe the role mass wasting is playing. Identify one feature that is the result of mass wasting.

Michael Collier

4. Describe at least one situation in which an internal process might cause or contribute to a mass-wasting event.

5. Do you think it is likely that landslides frequently occur on the Moon? Explain why or why not.

6. This image shows the aftermath of a rock avalanche that occurred in the mountains of Kyrgyzstan, a country in central Asia. This deposit resembles a talus slope. How is the formation of this feature different from that of a talus slope?

Marli Miller

7. The GEOgraphic feature includes a world map showing global landslide risks. What criteria were used to construct the map? What additional data could be considered that would make this risk map even more useful?

8. In August 1959, a strong earthquake struck an area along Montana's Madison River, just west of Yellowstone National Park. Based on what you see in the accompanying photo, prepare a brief summary that explains how the area changed as a result of the earthquake. In addition, suggest one or more *new* natural hazard(s) that exists now but did not exist before the quake occurred.

Marli Miller

9. Mass wasting is influenced by many processes associated with all four spheres of the Earth system. Select two items from the list below. For each, outline a series of events that relate the item to various spheres and to a mass-wasting process. Here is an example which assumes that "frost wedging" is an item on the list: *Frost wedging involves rock (geosphere) being broken when water (hydrosphere) freezes. Freeze–thaw cycles (atmosphere) promote frost wedging. When frost wedging loosens a rock on a cliff, the fragment tumbles to the base of the cliff. This event, rock fall, is an example of mass wasting.* Now you give it a try. Use your imagination.

   - Deforestation
   - Spring thaw/melting snow
   - Highway road cut
   - Crashing waves
   - Cavern formation

10. When the rail line in the accompanying photo was built in rural Alaska in the 1930s, the terrain was relatively level. Not long after the railroad was completed, a great deal of subsidence and shifting of the ground occurred, turning the tracks into the "roller coaster" shown here. As a result the rail line had to be abandoned. Suggest a reason why the ground became unstable and shifted.

L.A. Yehle/O.J. Ferrians, Jr./USGS

MasteringGeology™

Glossary

Angle of repose The steepest angle at which loose material remains stationary without sliding downslope.

Creep The slow downhill movement of soil and regolith.

Debris flow A flow of soil and regolith that contains a large amount of water. Most common in semiarid mountainous regions and on the slopes of some volcanoes.

Debris slide See Rockslide.

Earthflow The downslope movement of water-saturated, clay-rich sediment. Most characteristic of humid regions.

Fall A type of movement that is common to mass-wasting processes that refers to the free falling of detached individual pieces of any size.

Flow A type of movement common to mass-wasting processes in which water-saturated material moves downslope as a viscous fluid.

Mass wasting The downslope movement of rock, regolith, and soil under the direct influence of gravity.

Mudflow See Debris flow.

Permafrost Any permanently frozen subsoil. Usually found in the subarctic and arctic regions.

Rock avalanche Very rapid downslope movement of rock and debris. These rapid movements may be aided by a layer of air trapped beneath the debris, and they have been known to reach speeds of over 200 kilometers (125 miles) per hour.

Rockslide The rapid slide of a mass of rock downslope, along planes of weakness.

Slide A movement common to mass-wasting processes in which the material moving downslope remains fairly coherent and moves along a well-defined surface.

Slump The downward slipping of a mass of rock or unconsolidated material moving as a unit along a curved surface.

Solifluction The slow, downslope flow of water-saturated materials common to permafrost areas.

Talus An accumulation of rock debris at the base of a cliff.

Running Water

From Chapter 16 of *Earth: An Introduction to Physical Geology*, Eleventh Edition. Edward J. Tarbuck, Frederick K. Lutgens, Dennis Tasa.

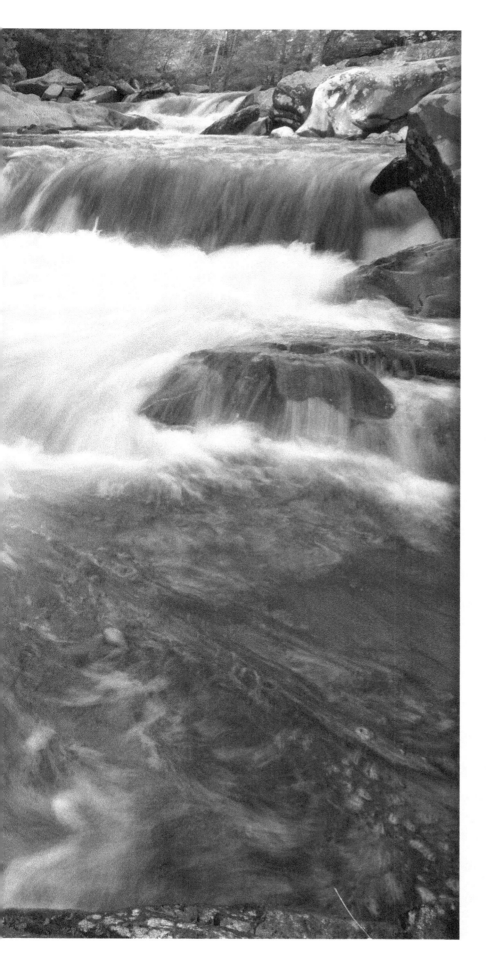

Running Water

Turbulent flow in the Little River in northeastern Alabama
(Photo by Michael Collier)

Each statement represents the primary learning objective for the corresponding major heading within the chapter. After you complete the chapter you should be able to:

1 List the hydrosphere's major reservoirs and describe the different paths that water takes through the hydrologic cycle.

2 Describe the nature of drainage basins and river systems.

3 Discuss streamflow and the factors that cause it to change.

4 Outline the ways in which streams erode, transport, and deposit sediment.

5 Contrast bedrock and alluvial stream channels. Distinguish between two types of alluvial channels.

6 Contrast narrow V-shaped valleys, broad valleys with floodplains, and valleys that display incised meanders or stream terraces.

7 List the major depositional landforms associated with streams and describe the formation of these features.

8 Sketch and explain basic drainage patterns.

9 Summarize the various categories of floods and the common measures of flood control.

R ivers have always played an important role in human affairs. All the early great civilizations rose on the banks of large rivers: Mesopotamia sat on the banks of the Tigris and Euphrates; Egypt lay in the fertile valley of the Nile; the Yellow River, called "the Mother River," was the cradle of early Chinese civilization; and the Indus River on the subcontinent of India was the birthplace of Indus Valley Civilization. Because rivers change naturally over time, as a result of climatic and tectonic influences, the "engineers" of ancient history tried to minimize the effects of floods and channel changes.

Modern river engineers are challenged by similar problems. Although their carefully designed structures are often successful in managing flood control, navigation, and channel stabilization, they are costly to build and maintain. Ultimately, through these efforts we have learned that rivers cannot always be controlled by humans.

Consider the bittersweet relationship we have with rivers. They are vital economic tools—used as highways to move goods and sources of water for irrigation and energy—as well as prime locations for recreation. When considered as part of the Earth system, rivers and streams represent a fundamental link in the constant cycling of our planet's water. Running water is the dominant agent of landscape alteration, eroding more terrain and transporting more sediment than any other process. Because human populations gravitate toward rivers, flooding represents enormous potential for destruction.

This chapter provides an overview of the hydrologic cycle, the nature of river systems, the types of river channels and the factors that produce them, the influences of running water on our planet's landscapes, and the nature of floods and their impact on people.

Halls Creek Narrows is a classic slot canyon in Utah's Capitol Reef National Park. (Photo by Michael Collier)

1 Earth as a System: The Hydrologic Cycle

We live on a planet that is unique in the solar system—it is in just the right location and is just the right size. If Earth were appreciably closer to the Sun, water would exist only as a vapor. Conversely, water would be forever frozen if our planet were much farther away. Moreover, Earth is large enough to have a hot mantle that supports convective flow, which carries water to the surface through volcanism. Water that rose from Earth's interior through mantle convection generated our planet's oceans and atmosphere. Thus, by coincidence of favorable size and location, Earth is the only planet in the solar system that has a global ocean and a hydrologic cycle.

Water is found almost everywhere on Earth—in the oceans, glaciers, rivers, lakes, air, soil, and living tissue. All these "reservoirs" constitute Earth's hydrosphere, which contains about 1.39 billion cubic kilometers (333 million cubic miles) of water. The vast majority of it, an estimated 96.5 percent, is stored in the global ocean. Ice sheets and glaciers account for another 1.74 percent, leaving less than 2 percent divided among lakes, streams, subsurface water, and the atmosphere (FIGURE 1).

> All the rivers run into the sea; yet the sea is not full;
> unto the place from whence the rivers come, thither
> they return again.
>
> Ecclesiastes 1:7

As the perceptive writer of Ecclesiastes implied, water is constantly moving among Earth's different spheres—the *hydrosphere*, the *atmosphere*, the *geosphere*, and the *biosphere*. This unending circulation of water, called the **hydrologic cycle**, describes what happens as water evaporates from the ocean, plants, and soil; moves through the atmosphere; and eventually falls as precipitation (FIGURE 2). Precipitation that falls onto the ocean has completed its cycle and is ready to begin another.

When precipitation falls on land, it either soaks into the ground, a process called **infiltration**, flows over the surface as **runoff**, or immediately evaporates. Much of the water that infiltrates or runs off eventually finds its way back to the atmosphere via evaporation from soil, lakes, and streams. In addition, some of the water that soaks into the ground is absorbed by plants, which later release it into the atmosphere. This process is called **transpiration** (*trans* = across, *spiro* = to breathe). Because both evaporation and transpiration involve the transfer of water from the surface directly to the atmosphere, they are often considered together as the combined process of **evapotranspiration**.

More water falls on land as precipitation than is lost by evapotranspiration. The excess is carried back to the ocean mainly by streams; less than 1 percent returns as groundwater. However, much of the water that flows in rivers is not transmitted directly into river channels after falling as precipitation. Instead, a large percentage first soaks into the soil and then gradually flows as

FIGURE 1 Distribution of Earth's water

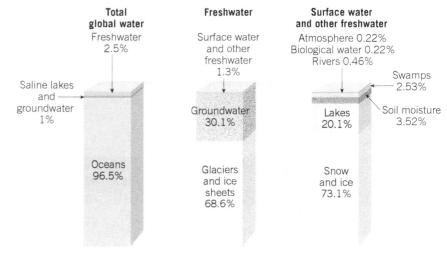

FIGURE 2 The hydrologic cycle

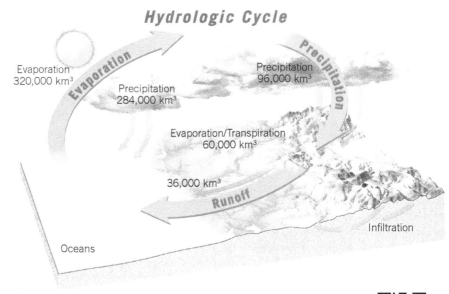

SMARTFIGURE 2 The hydrologic cycle
The primary movement of water through the cycle is shown by the large arrows. A number refers to the annual amount of water taking a particular path.

groundwater to river channels. In this manner, groundwater provides a form of storage that sustains the flow of streams between storms and during periods of drought.

When precipitation falls in very cold areas—at high elevations or high latitudes—the water may not immediately soak in, run off, or evaporate. Instead, it becomes part of a snowfield or a glacier. In this way, glaciers store large quantities of water. If present-day glaciers were to melt and release their stored water, sea level would rise by several tens of meters worldwide and submerge many heavily populated coastal areas. Over the past 2 million years, huge ice sheets have formed and melted on several occasions, each time changing the balance of the hydrologic cycle.

Figure 2 also shows that Earth's hydrologic cycle is balanced. This basically means that although water is constantly moving from one reservoir to another, the overall amount of water in the oceans and on land remains about the same. Each year, solar energy evaporates about 320,000 cubic kilometers of water from the oceans, but only 284,000 cubic kilometers return to the oceans as precipitation. A balance is achieved by the 36,000 cubic kilometers that are carried to the ocean as runoff. Although runoff makes up a small percentage of the total, running water is, nevertheless, *the single most important erosional agent sculpting Earth's land surface.*

1 CONCEPT CHECKS

1. Describe or sketch the movement of water through the hydrologic cycle. Once precipitation has fallen on land, what paths might the water take?
2. What is meant by the term *evapotranspiration?*
3. Over the oceans, evaporation exceeds precipitation, yet sea level does not drop. Explain why.

EYE on Earth

This photo shows the famous Thousand Springs along the Snake River in southern Idaho. The springs are natural outlets for groundwater.

Question 1 Is there water in this image that can't be seen? If so, where might it be?

Question 2 Prepare a story that speculates on the answers to the following questions. Suggest several possibilities for both questions:

    a. What journeys did the water in this image take to get to this place?

    b. What paths might the water follow when it makes its way back to the ocean?

David R. Frazier/Alamy Images

2 Running Water

Recall that most of the precipitation that falls on land either enters the soil (infiltration) or remains at the surface, moving downslope as runoff. The amount of water that runs off rather than soaking into the ground depends on several factors: (1) the intensity and duration of rainfall, (2) the amount of water already in the soil, (3) the nature of the surface material, (4) the slope of the land, and (5) the extent and type of vegetation. When the surface material is highly impermeable or when it becomes saturated, runoff is the dominant process. Runoff is also high in urban areas because large areas are covered by impermeable buildings, roads, and parking lots.

Runoff initially flows in broad, thin sheets across slopes in a process called *sheet flow*. This thin, unconfined flow eventually develops threads of current that form tiny channels called *rills*. Rills meet to form *gullies*, which join to form brooks, creeks, or streams. Then, when they reach an undefined size, they are called rivers. Although the terms *river* and *stream* are often used interchangeably, geologists define **stream** as water that flows in a channel, regardless of size. **River**, on the other hand, is a general term for streams that carry substantial amounts of water and have numerous tributaries.

In humid regions, the water to support streamflow comes from two sources: overland flow that sporadically enters the stream and groundwater that enters the channel. In areas where the bedrock is composed of soluble rocks such as limestone, large openings may exist that facilitate the transport of groundwater to streams. In arid regions, however, the *water table* may be below the level of the stream channel, in which case the stream loses water to the groundwater system by outflow through the streambed.

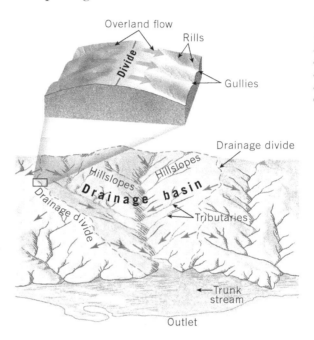

FIGURE 3 Drainage basin and divide
A drainage basin is the area drained by a stream and its tributaries. Boundaries between basins are called divides.

Drainage Basins

Every stream drains an area of land called a **drainage basin** (FIGURE 3). Each drainage basin is bounded by an imaginary line called a **divide**, something that is clearly visible as a sharp ridge in some mountainous areas but can be more difficult to determine when the topography is subdued. The outlet, where the stream exits the drainage basin, is at a lower elevation than the rest of the basin.

Drainage divides range in scale from a small ridge separating two gullies on a hillside to a *continental divide* that splits an entire continent into enormous drainage basins. The Mississippi River has the largest drainage basin in North America, collecting and carrying 40 percent of the flow in the United States (FIGURE 4).

By looking at the drainage basin in Figure 3, it should be obvious that slopes cover most of the area. Water erosion on the hillsides is aided by the impact of falling rain and surface flow, moving downslope as sheets or in rills toward a stream channel. Hillslope erosion is

the main source of fine particles (clays and fine sand) carried in stream channels.

River Systems

Rivers drain much of the land area, with the exception of extremely arid regions or polar areas that are permanently frozen. To a large extent, the variety of rivers that exist is a reflection of the different environments in which they are found. For example, although the Paraná-La Plata river system in South America drains an area roughly the same size as the Nile in Egypt, it carries nearly 10 times more water to the ocean. Because its drainage basin is entirely in a rainy tropical climate, the Paraná-La Plata system has a huge discharge. By contrast, the Nile, which also originates in a humid region, flows through an expansive arid landscape, where significant amounts of water evaporate or are withdrawn to

SMARTFIGURE 4
Mississippi River drainage
basin

The drainage basin of the
Mississippi River, North
America's largest, covers
about 3 million square kilometers (almost 1.2 million
square miles) and consists
of many smaller drainage
basins. The drainage basin
of the Yellowstone River is
one of many that contrib-
ute water to the Missouri
River, which, in turn, is one
of many that make up the
drainage basin of the
Mississippi River.

sustain agriculture. Thus, climatic differences and human intervention can significantly influence the character of a river. Later, we will examine other factors that contribute to stream variability.

River systems not only involve a network of stream channels but the entire drainage basin. Based on the dominant processes operating within them, river systems can be divided into three zones: *sediment production*—where erosion dominates, *sediment transport*, and *sediment deposition* (FIGURE 5). It is important to recognize that sediment is being eroded, transported, and deposited along the entire length of a stream, regardless of which process is dominant within each zone.

Sediment Production   The zone of *sediment production*, where most of the sediment is derived, is located in the headwaters region of the river system. Much of the sediment carried by streams begins as bedrock that is subsequently broken down by weathering and

then moved downslope by mass wasting and by way of sheet flow and rills. Bank erosion can also contribute significant amounts of sediment. In addition, scouring of the channel bed deepens the channel and adds to the stream's sediment load.

Sediment Transport   Sediment acquired by a stream is transported through the channel network along sections referred to as *trunk streams*. When trunk streams are in balance, the amount of sediment eroded from their banks equals the amount deposited elsewhere in the channel. Although trunk streams rework their channels over time, they are not a source of sediment, nor do they accumulate or store it.

Sediment Deposition   When a river reaches the ocean or another large body of water, it slows and the energy to transport sediment is greatly reduced. Most of the sediments either accumulate at the mouth of the river to form a delta, are reconfigured by wave action to form a variety of coastal features, or are moved far offshore by ocean currents. Because coarse sediments tend to be deposited upstream, it is primarily the fine sediments (clay, silt, and fine sand) that eventually reach the ocean. Taken together, erosion, transportation, and deposition are the processes by which rivers move Earth's surface materials and sculpt landscapes.

FIGURE 5 Zones of a river
Each of the three zones
is based on the dominant
process that is operating
in that part of the river
system.

2 CONCEPT CHECKS

1. List several factors that cause infiltration and runoff to vary from place to place and time to time.
2. Draw a simple sketch of a drainage basin and a divide and label each.
3. What are the three main parts (zones) of a river system?

3 Streamflow

The water in river channels moves under the influence of gravity. In very slowly flowing streams, water moves in nearly straight-line paths parallel to the stream channel, called **laminar flow**. However, streams typically exhibit **turbulent flow**, in which the water moves in an erratic fashion characterized by a series of horizontal and vertical swirling motions (FIGURE 6). Strong turbulent behavior occurs in whirlpools and eddies, as well as in roiling whitewater rapids. Even streams that appear smooth on the surface often exhibit turbulent flow near the bottom and sides of the channel, where flow resistance is greatest. Turbulence contributes to a stream's ability to erode its channel because it acts to lift sediment from the streambed.

Running the rapids in the Grand Canyon— an extreme example of turbulent flow.

This water is not standing still. It is moving slowly toward the bottom of the image. The flow in the foreground is primarily laminar.

FIGURE 6 Laminar and turbulent flow
Most often streamflow is turbulent. (Photos by Michael Collier)

An important factor influencing stream turbulence is the water's flow velocity. As the velocity of a stream increases, the flow becomes more turbulent. Flow velocities can vary significantly from place to place along a stream channel, as well as over time, in response to variations in the amount and intensity of precipitation. If you have ever waded into a stream, you may have noticed that the strength of the current increased as you moved into deeper parts of the channel. This is related to the fact that frictional resistance is greatest near the banks and bed of a stream channel.

Flow velocities are determined at gaging stations by averaging measurements taken at various locations across the stream's channel. Some sluggish streams have flow velocities of less than 1 kilometer (0.62 mile) per hour, whereas stretches of some fast-flowing rivers may exceed 30 kilometers (19 miles) per hour.

Factors Affecting Flow Velocity

The ability of a stream to erode and transport material is directly related to its flow velocity. Even slight variations in flow rate can lead to significant changes in the sediment load transported by a stream. Several factors influence flow velocities and, therefore, control a stream's potential to do "work." These factors include (1) channel slope or gradient, (2) channel cross-sectional shape, (3) channel size and roughness, and (4) discharge, or the amount of water flowing in the channel.

Gradient   The slope of a stream channel, expressed as the vertical drop of a stream over a specified distance, is called **gradient**. Portions of the lower Mississippi River have very low gradients, about 10 centimeters or less per kilometer. By contrast, some mountain streams have

Cross-sectional area = 10 square units
Wetted perimeter = 12 units
Ratio = $\frac{10}{12}$ = 0.83

Wide, shallow channel

Cross-sectional area = 10 square units
Wetted perimeter = 9 units
Ratio = $\frac{10}{9}$ = 1.11

Narrow, deep channel

channels that drop at a rate of more than 40 meters per kilometer—a gradient 400 times steeper than the lower Mississippi. Gradient also varies along the length of a particular channel. When the gradient is steeper, more gravitational energy is available to drive channel flow.

Channel Shape   As water in a stream channel moves downslope, it encounters a significant amount of frictional resistance. The *cross-sectional shape* (a slice taken across the channel) determines, to a large extent, the amount of flow in contact with the banks and bed of the channel. This measure is referred to as the **wetted perimeter**. The most efficient channel is one with the least wetted perimeter for its cross-sectional area. FIGURE 7 compares two channels that differ only in shape: One is wide and shallow, the other is narrow and deep. Although the cross-sectional area of both is identical, the narrow and deep one has less water in contact with the channel (a smaller wetted perimeter) and therefore less frictional drag. As a result, if all other factors are equal, the water will flow more efficiently and at a higher velocity in a deep and narrow channel compared to a wide and shallow channel.

Channel Size and Roughness   Water depth also affects the frictional resistance that the channel exerts on flow. Maximum flow velocity occurs when a stream is *bankfull*, before water starts to inundate the floodplain. At this stage, the channel's ratio of the cross-sectional area to wetted perimeter is highest and streamflow is

most efficient. Similarly, an increase in water depth increases the ratio of cross-sectional area to wetted perimeter and, therefore, increases channel efficiency. All other factors being equal, flow velocities are higher in large channels than in small channels.

Most streams have channels that can be described as *rough*. Elements such as boulders, irregularities in the channel bed, and woody debris create turbulence that significantly impedes flow.

Discharge   Streams vary in size from small headwater creeks less than a meter wide to large rivers with widths of several kilometers. The size of a stream channel is largely determined by the amount of water supplied from the drainage basin. The measure most often used to compare the size of streams is **discharge**—the volume of water flowing past a certain point in a given unit of time. Discharge, usually measured in cubic meters per second or cubic feet per second, is determined by multiplying a stream's cross-sectional area by its velocity.

The discharge of a river system changes over time because of variations in the amount of precipitation received by the drainage basin. Studies show that when discharge increases, the width, depth, and flow velocity of the channel all increase predictably. As we saw earlier, when the size of the channel increases, proportionally less water is in contact with the bed and banks of the channel. Thus, friction, which acts to retard the flow, is reduced, resulting in an increase in the rate of flow.

Monitoring Streamflow   The U.S. Geological Survey maintains a network of about 7500 stream gaging stations that collect basic data about the country's surface water resources (FIGURE 8). Data collected include flow velocity, discharge, and river stage. *Stage* is the height of the water surface relative to a fixed reference point. This measurement is frequently reported by the media, especially when a river approaches or surpasses *flood stage*. Streamflow measurements are essential components of river models used to make flood forecasts and warnings. There are other applications as well. The data are used in making decisions dealing with water supply allocations, operating wastewater treatment plants, planning the design of highway bridges, and recreation activities.

Changes Downstream

One useful way of studying a stream is to examine its **longitudinal profile**. Such a profile is simply a cross-sectional view of a stream from its source area (called the **head**, or **headwaters**) to its **mouth**, the point downstream where it empties into another water body—a river, a lake, or an ocean. FIGURE 9 shows that the most obvious feature of a typical longitudinal

The U.S. Geological Survey operates and maintains nearly 7500 stream gaging stations.

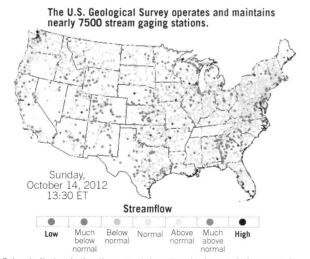

Sunday,
October 14, 2012
13:30 ET

Streamflow

Low	Much below normal	Below normal	Normal	Above normal	Much above normal	High

Colors indicate whether the current river stage is above or below normal.

A stilling well, used to determine the stage of a river, is connected to the stream with pipes. When the water level in the stream changes, the water level in the well changes. A float is connected to a recorder. Data can be sent via satellite to various agencies.

FIGURE 8 Stream gaging stations
The United States has a dense network of stream gaging stations. To determine discharge, it is necessary to survey the channel to determine its shape and calculate its area. A stilling well measures the stage and a current meter determines flow velocity.

profile is its concave shape—a result of the decrease in slope that occurs from the headwaters to the mouth. In addition, local irregularities exist in the profiles of most streams; the flatter sections may be associated with lakes or reservoirs, and the steeper sections are sites of rapids or waterfalls.

The change in slope observed on most stream profiles is usually accompanied by an increase in discharge and channel size and a reduction in sediment particle size (FIGURE 10). For example, data from successive gaging stations along most rivers show that, in humid regions, discharge increases toward the mouth. This should come as no surprise because, as we move downstream, more and more tributaries contribute water to

the main channel. In the case of the Amazon, for example, about 1000 tributaries join the main river along its 6500-kilometer (4000-mile) course across South America.

In order to accommodate the growing volume of water, channel size typically increases downstream as well. Recall that flow velocities are higher in large channels than in small channels. Furthermore, observations show a general decline in sediment size downstream, making the channel smoother and more efficient.

Although the channel slope decreases toward a stream's mouth, the flow velocity generally increases. This fact contradicts our intuitive assumptions of swift, narrow headwater streams and wide, placid rivers flowing

FIGURE 9 Longitudinal profile
California's Kings River originates high in the Sierra Nevada and flows into the San Joaquin Valley.

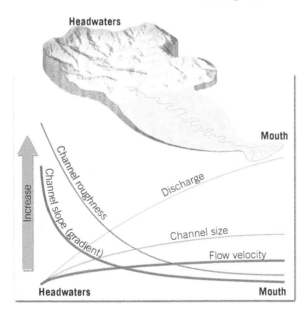

SMARTFIGURE 10
Channel changes from head to mouth
Although the gradient decreases toward the mouth, increases in discharge and channel size and decreases in roughness more than offset the decrease in slope. Consequently, flow velocity usually increases toward the mouth.

across more subtle topography. Increases in channel size and discharge and decreases in channel roughness that occur downstream compensate for the decrease in slope—thereby making the stream more efficient (see Figure 10). Thus, the average flow velocity is typically lower in headwater streams than in wide, placid-appearing rivers.

---

3 CONCEPT CHECKS

1. Contrast laminar and turbulent flow.
2. Summarize the factors that influence flow velocity.
3. What is a longitudinal profile?
4. What typically happens to channel width, channel depth, flow velocity, and discharge between the headwaters and mouth of a stream? Briefly explain why these changes occur.

An autumn scene along the Oconaluftee River in North Carolina's Great Smoky Mountains. If channel roughness was less and the cross-sectional shape was more efficient, flow velocity would increase. (Photo by Michael Collier)

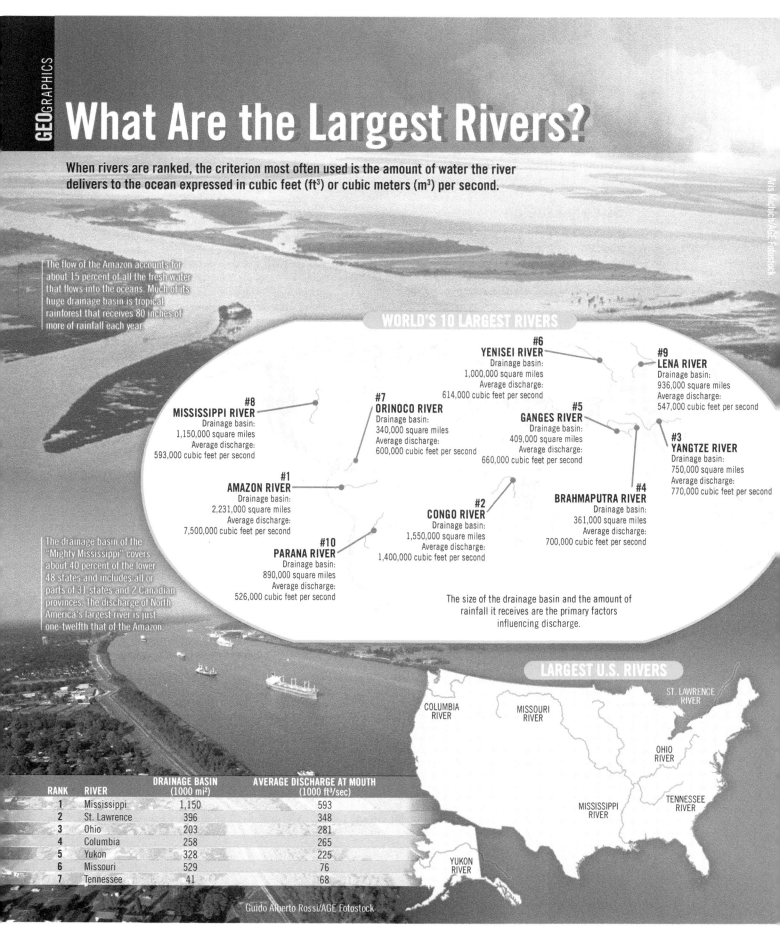

GEOGRAPHICS

What Are the Largest Rivers?

When rivers are ranked, the criterion most often used is the amount of water the river delivers to the ocean expressed in cubic feet (ft³) or cubic meters (m³) per second.

The flow of the Amazon accounts for about 15 percent of all the fresh water that flows into the oceans. Much of its huge drainage basin is tropical rainforest that receives 80 inches of more of rainfall each year.

WORLD'S 10 LARGEST RIVERS

#6 YENISEI RIVER
Drainage basin:
1,000,000 square miles
Average discharge:
614,000 cubic feet per second

#9 LENA RIVER
Drainage basin:
936,000 square miles
Average discharge:
547,000 cubic feet per second

#8 MISSISSIPPI RIVER
Drainage basin:
1,150,000 square miles
Average discharge:
593,000 cubic feet per second

#7 ORINOCO RIVER
Drainage basin:
340,000 square miles
Average discharge:
600,000 cubic feet per second

#5 GANGES RIVER
Drainage basin:
409,000 square miles
Average discharge:
660,000 cubic feet per second

#3 YANGTZE RIVER
Drainage basin:
750,000 square miles
Average discharge:
770,000 cubic feet per second

#1 AMAZON RIVER
Drainage basin:
2,231,000 square miles
Average discharge:
7,500,000 cubic feet per second

#2 CONGO RIVER
Drainage basin:
1,550,000 square miles
Average discharge:
1,400,000 cubic feet per second

#4 BRAHMAPUTRA RIVER
Drainage basin:
361,000 square miles
Average discharge:
700,000 cubic feet per second

#10 PARANA RIVER
Drainage basin:
890,000 square miles
Average discharge:
526,000 cubic feet per second

The drainage basin of the "Mighty Mississippi" covers about 40 percent of the lower 48 states and includes all or parts of 31 states and 2 Canadian provinces. The discharge of North America's largest river is just one-twelfth that of the Amazon.

The size of the drainage basin and the amount of rainfall it receives are the primary factors influencing discharge.

LARGEST U.S. RIVERS

COLUMBIA RIVER
MISSOURI RIVER
ST. LAWRENCE RIVER
OHIO RIVER
MISSISSIPPI RIVER
TENNESSEE RIVER
YUKON RIVER

RANK	RIVER	DRAINAGE BASIN (1000 mi²)	AVERAGE DISCHARGE AT MOUTH (1000 ft³/sec)
1	Mississippi	1,150	593
2	St. Lawrence	396	348
3	Ohio	203	281
4	Columbia	258	265
5	Yukon	328	225
6	Missouri	529	76
7	Tennessee	41	68

Guido Alberto Rossi/AGE Fotostock

Aris Mihich/AGE Fotostock

4 The Work of Running Water

Streams are Earth's most important erosional agents. Not only do they have the ability to downcut and widen their channels, but streams also have the capacity to transport enormous quantities of sediment delivered to them by overland flow, mass wasting, and groundwater. Eventually, much of this material is deposited to create a variety of landforms.

Stream Erosion

A stream's ability to accumulate and transport soil and weathered rock is aided by the work of raindrops, which knock sediment particles loose. When the ground is saturated, rainwater cannot infiltrate, so it flows downslope, transporting some of the material it dislodges. On barren slopes the flow of muddy water (sheet flow) often produces small channels (rills), which in time can evolve into larger gullies.

Once flow is confined in a channel, the erosional power of a stream is related to its slope and discharge. The rate of erosion, however, is also dependent on the relative resistance of the bank and bed material. In general, channels composed of unconsolidated materials are more easily eroded than channels cut into bedrock.

When a channel is sandy, the particles are easily dislodged from the bed and banks, and they are lifted into the moving water. Moreover, banks consisting of sandy material are often undercut, dumping even more loose debris into the water to be carried downstream. Banks that consist of coarse gravels or cohesive clay and silt particles tend to be relatively resistant to erosion. Thus, channels with cohesive silty banks are generally narrower than comparable ones with sandy banks.

Streams cut channels into bedrock through three main processes: *quarrying*, *abrasion*, and *corrosion*.

Quarrying   **Quarrying** involves the removal of blocks from the bed of the channel. This process is aided by fracturing and weathering that loosen the blocks sufficiently so they are moveable during times of high flow rates. Quarrying is mainly the result of the impact forces exerted by flowing water.

Abrasion   The process by which the bed and banks of a bedrock channel are ceaselessly bombarded by particles carried into the flow is termed **abrasion**. The individual sediment grains are also abraded by their many impacts with the channel and with one another. Thus, by scraping, rubbing, and bumping, abrasion erodes a bedrock channel and simultaneously smooths and rounds the abrading particles. That is why smooth, rounded cobbles and pebbles are found in streams.

Abrasion also results in a reduction in the size of the sediments transported by streams.

Features common to some bedrock channels are circular depressions known as **potholes**, created by the abrasive action of particles swirling in fast-moving eddies (FIGURE 11). The rotational motion of sand and pebbles acts like a drill to bore the holes. As the particles wear down to nothing, they are replaced by new ones that continue to drill the streambed. Eventually, smooth depressions several meters across and deep may result.

Corrosion   Bedrock channels formed in soluble rock such as limestone are susceptible to **corrosion**—a process in which rock is gradually dissolved by the flowing water. Corrosion is a type of chemical weathering between the solutions in the water and the mineral matter that makes up the bedrock.

Transport of Sediment by Streams

All streams, regardless of size, transport some weathered rock material (FIGURE 12). Streams also sort the solid sediment they transport because finer, lighter material is carried more readily than larger, heavier particles. Streams transport their load of sediment in three ways: (1) in solution (**dissolved load**), (2) in suspension (**suspended load**), and (3) by sliding, skipping, or rolling along the bottom (**bed load**).

It is estimated that each year the world's rivers transport about 10 cubic kilometers (2.4 cubic miles) of weathered material to lakes and oceans either as detrital sediment or as dissolved ions. If distributed evenly over Earth's land surface, this quantity of sediment represents a lowering of about 7 millimeters over a 100-year span.

Dissolved Load   Most of the dissolved load is brought to a stream by groundwater and is dispersed throughout the flow. When water percolates through the ground, it acquires soluble soil compounds. Then, it seeps through cracks and pores in bedrock, dissolving additional mineral matter. Eventually much of this mineral-rich water finds its way into streams.

The velocity of streamflow has essentially no effect on a stream's ability to carry its dissolved load; material

A.

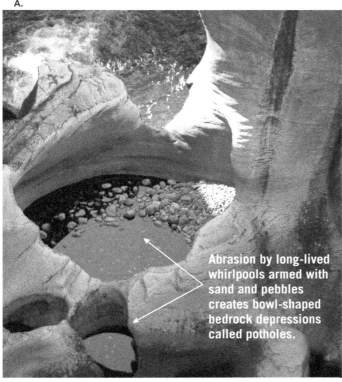

Abrasion by long-lived whirlpools armed with sand and pebbles creates bowl-shaped bedrock depressions called potholes.

FIGURE 11 **Potholes**
The rotational motion of swirling pebbles acts like a drill to create potholes.
(Close-up photo by Elmari Joubert/Alamy Images; canyon photo by Michael Collier)

B.

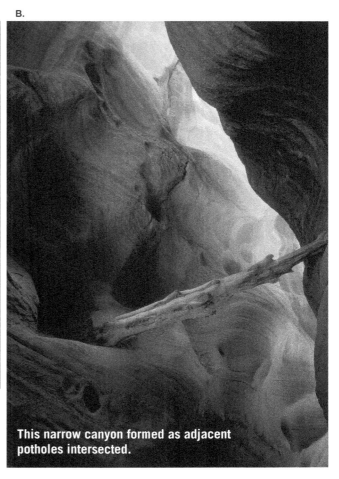

This narrow canyon formed as adjacent potholes intersected.

in the solution goes wherever the stream goes. Precipitation of the dissolved mineral matter occurs when the chemistry of the water changes, when organisms create hard parts, or when the water enters an inland "sea,"

FIGURE 12 **Transport of sediment**
Streams transport their load of sediment in three ways. The dissolved and suspended loads are carried in the general flow. The bed load includes coarse sand, gravel, and boulders that move by rolling, sliding, and saltation.

located in an arid climate where the rate of evaporation is high.

Suspended Load Most streams carry the largest part of their load in *suspension*. Indeed, the muddy appearance created by suspended sediment is the most obvious portion of a stream's load (FIGURE 13). Usually only very fine sand, silt, and clay particles are carried this way, but during flood stage, larger particles can also be transported in suspension. During flood stage, the total quantity of material carried in suspension also increases dramatically, verifiable by people whose homes have become sites for the deposition of this material. For example, during its flood stage, the Yellow River (Hwang Ho) of China is reported to carry an amount of sediment equal in weight to the water that carries it. Rivers such as this are appropriately described as "too thick to drink but too thin to cultivate."

The type and amount of material carried in suspension are controlled by two factors: the flow velocity and

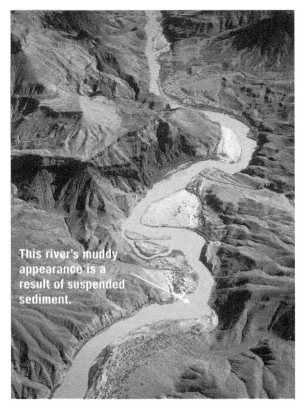

FIGURE 13 Suspended load
FIGURE 13 Suspended load
An aerial view of the Colorado River in the Grand Canyon. Heavy rains washed sediment into the river. (Photo by Michael Collier)

This river's muddy appearance is a result of suspended sediment.

the settling velocity of each sediment grain. **Settling velocity** is defined as the speed at which a particle falls through a still fluid. The larger the particle, the more rapidly it settles toward the streambed (FIGURE 14). In addition to size, the shape and specific gravity of particles also influence settling velocity. Flat grains sink through water more slowly than spherical grains, and dense particles fall toward the bottom more rapidly than less dense particles. The slower the settling velocity and higher the flow velocity, the longer a sediment particle

FIGURE 14 Settling velocity
The speed at which a particle falls through still water is its settling velocity. Deposition of suspended particles occurs when their settling velocities are greater than the stream's flow velocity.

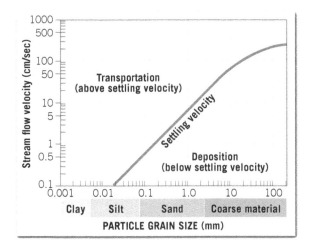

will stay in suspension, and the farther it will be carried downstream.

Bed Load Coarse material, including coarse sands, gravels, and even boulders typically move along the bed of a channel as bed load (FIGURE 15). The particles that make up the bed load move by rolling, sliding, and saltation. Sediment moving by **saltation** (*saltare* = to leap) appears to jump or skip along the streambed (see Figure 12). This occurs as particles are propelled upward by collisions or lifted by the current and then carried downstream a short distance until gravity pulls them back to the bed of the stream. Particles that are too large or heavy to move by saltation either roll or slide along the bottom, depending on their shapes.

Compared with suspended load, the movement of bed load through a stream network tends to be less rapid and more localized. A study conducted on a glacially fed river in Norway determined that suspended sediments

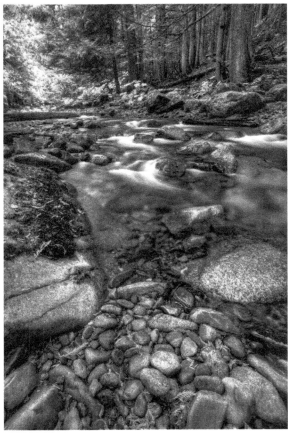

FIGURE 15 Bed load
Although the bed load of many rivers consists of sand, the bed load of this stream is made of boulders and is easily seen during periods of low water. During floods, the seemingly immovable rocks in this channel are rolled along the bed of the stream. (Photo by Gregory Johnston/Shutterstock)

took only a day to exit the drainage basin, while the bed load required several decades to travel the same distance. Depending on the discharge and slope of the channel, coarse gravels may only be moved during times of high flow, while boulders move only during exceptional floods. Once set in motion, large particles are usually carried short distances. Along some stretches of a stream, bed load cannot be carried at all until it is broken into smaller particles.

Capacity and Competence   A stream's ability to carry solid particles is described using two criteria—*capacity* and *competence*. **Capacity** is the maximum load of solid particles a stream can transport per unit time. The greater the discharge, the greater the stream's capacity for hauling sediment. Consequently, large rivers with high flow velocities have large capacities.

Competence is a measure of a stream's ability to transport particles based on size rather than quantity. Flow velocity is key: Swift streams have greater competencies than slow streams, regardless of channel size. A stream's competence increases proportionately to the square of its velocity. Thus, if the velocity of a stream doubles, the impact force of the water increases four times; if the velocity triples, the force increases nine times, and so forth. Hence, large boulders, such as those in Figure 15, that are often visible in low water and seem immovable can, in fact, be transported during exceptional floods because of the stream's increased competence.

By now it should be clear why the greatest erosion and transportation of sediment occur during periods of high water associated with floods. The increase in discharge results in greater capacity; the increased velocity produces greater competency. Rising velocity makes the water more turbulent, and larger particles are set in motion. In the course of a few days, or perhaps a few hours, a stream at flood stage can erode and transport more sediment than it does during several months of normal flow.

Deposition of Sediment by Streams

Deposition occurs whenever a stream slows, causing a reduction in competence. Put another way, particles are deposited when flow velocity is less than the settling velocity; as a stream's flow velocity decreases, sediment begins to settle, largest particles first. In this manner, stream transport provides a mechanism by which solid particles of various sizes are separated. This process, called **sorting**, explains why particles of similar size are deposited together.

The general term for sediment deposited by streams is **alluvium**. Many different depositional features are composed of alluvium. Some occur within stream channels, some occur on the valley floor adjacent to a channel, and some are found at the mouth of a stream. We will consider the nature of these features later in the chapter.

4 CONCEPT CHECKS

1. Describe two processes by which streams cut channels in bedrock.
2. In what three ways does a stream transport its load? Which part of the load moves slowest?
3. Explain the difference between capacity and competency.
4. What is settling velocity? What factors influence settling velocity? What part of a stream's load is not affected by settling velocity?

EYE on Earth

The meandering White River in Arkansas is a tributary of the Mississippi River.

Question 1 In this aerial view, the color of the White River is brown. What part of the stream's load gives it this color?

Question 2 If a channel were created across the narrow neck of land shown by the arrow, how would the river's gradient change?

Question 3 How would the flow velocity be affected by the formation of such a channel?

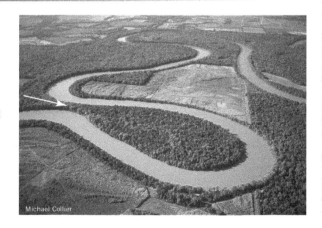

Michael Collier

5 Stream Channels

A basic characteristic that distinguishes streamflow from overland flow is that it is confined in a channel. A stream channel can be thought of as an open conduit consisting of the streambed and banks that act to confine flow except, of course, during floods.

Although somewhat oversimplified, we can divide stream channels into two basic types. *Bedrock channels* are channels in which the streams are actively cutting into solid rock. In contrast, when the bed and banks are composed mainly of unconsolidated sediment or alluvium, the channel is called an *alluvial channel.*

Bedrock Channels

As the name suggests, **bedrock channels** are cut into the underlying strata and typically form in the headwaters of river systems where streams have steep slopes. The energetic flow tends to transport coarse particles that actively abrade the bedrock channel. Potholes are often visible evidence of the erosional forces at work.

Steep bedrock channels often develop a sequence of *steps* and *pools*, relatively flat segments (pools) where alluvium tends to accumulate, and steep segments (steps) where bedrock is exposed. The steep areas contain rapids or, occasionally, waterfalls.

The channel pattern exhibited by streams cutting into bedrock is controlled by the underlying geologic structure. Even when flowing over rather uniform bedrock, streams tend to exhibit winding or irregular patterns rather than flowing in straight channels. Anyone who has gone white-water rafting has observed the steep, winding nature of a stream flowing in a bedrock channel.

Alluvial Channels

Alluvial channels form in sediment that was previously deposited in the valley. When the valley floor reaches sufficient width, material deposited by the stream can form a *floodplain* that borders the channel. Because the banks and beds of alluvial channels are composed of unconsolidated sediment (alluvium), they can undergo major changes in

SMARTFIGURE 16
Formation of cut banks and point bars
By eroding its outer bank and depositing material on the inside of the bend, a stream is able to shift its channel.

Maximum velocity

Maximum velocity

Erosion of a cut bank along the Newaukum River in southwestern Washington State.

Deposition of point bar

Erosion of cut bank

Maximum velocity

Maximum velocity

White River near Vernal, Utah

The cut bank forms on the outside of a meander where flow velocity and turbulence are greatest.

Point bar

As water slows on the inside of a meander, coarser material is deposited as a point bar.

Michael Collier

shape as material is continually being eroded, transported, and redeposited. The major factors affecting the shapes of these channels are the average size of the sediment being transported, the channel's gradient, and discharge.

Alluvial channel patterns reflect a stream's ability to transport its load at a uniform rate while expending the least amount of energy. Thus, the size and type of sediment being carried help determine the nature of the stream channel. Two common types of alluvial channels are *meandering channels* and *braided channels*.

Meandering Channels Streams that transport much of their load in suspension generally move in sweeping bends called **meanders**. These streams flow in relatively deep, smooth channels and primarily transport mud (silt and clay), sand, and occasionally fine gravel. The lower Mississippi River exhibits this type of channel.

Meandering channels evolve over time as individual bends migrate across the floodplain. Most of the erosion is focused at the outside of the meander, where velocity and turbulence are greatest. In time, the outside bank is undermined, especially during periods of high water. Because the outside of a meander is a zone of active erosion, it is often referred to as a **cut bank** (FIGURE 16). Debris acquired by the stream at the cut bank moves downstream, where the coarser material is generally deposited as **point bars** on the insides of bends. In this manner, meanders migrate laterally by eroding the outside of the bends and depositing sediment on the inside, without appreciably changing their shape.

In addition to migrating laterally, the bends in a channel also migrate down the valley. This occurs because erosion is more effective on the downstream (downslope) side of the meander. Sometimes the downstream migration of a meander is slowed when it reaches a more resistant bank material. This allows the next meander upstream to gradually erode the material between the two meanders, as shown in FIGURE 17. Eventually, the river may erode through the narrow neck of land, forming a new, shorter channel segment called a **cutoff**. Because of its shape, the abandoned bend is called an **oxbow lake** (Figure 17).

Braided Channels Some streams consist of a complex network of converging and diverging channels that thread their way among numerous islands or gravel bars (FIGURE 18). Because these channels have an interwoven appearance, they are called **braided channels**. Braided channels form where a large portion of a stream's load consists of coarse material (sand and gravel) and the stream has a highly variable discharge.

FIGURE 17 Formation of an oxbow lake
Oxbow lakes occupy abandoned meanders. Aerial view of an oxbow lake created by the meandering Green River near Bronx, Wyoming. (Photo by Michael Collier)

Geologist's Sketch

Because the bank material is readily erodible, braided channels are wide and shallow.

One setting in which braided streams form is at the end of glaciers, where there is a large seasonal variation in discharge. During the summer, large amounts of ice-eroded sediment are dumped into the meltwater streams flowing away from the glacier. However, when flow is sluggish, the stream deposits the coarsest material as elongated structures called *bars*. This process causes the flow to split into several paths around the bars. During the next period of high flow, the laterally shifting channels erode and redeposit much of this coarse sediment, thereby transforming the entire streambed. In some braided streams, the bars have built semipermanent islands anchored by vegetation.

5 CONCEPT CHECKS

1. Are bedrock channels more likely to be found near the head or the mouth of a stream?
2. Describe or sketch the evolution of a meander, including how an oxbow lake forms.
3. Describe a situation that might cause a stream channel to become braided.

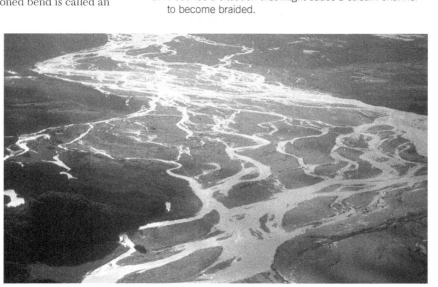

FIGURE 18 Braided stream
The Knik River is a classic braided stream with multiple channels separated by migrating gravel bars. The Knik is choked with sediment from four melting glaciers in the Chugach Mountains north of Anchorage, Alaska. (Photo by Michael Collier)

6 Shaping Stream Valleys

A **stream valley** consists of a channel and the surrounding terrain that directs water to the stream. It includes the *valley floor*, which is the lower, flatter area that is partially or totally occupied by the stream channel, and the sloping *valley walls* that rise above the valley floor on both sides. Alluvial channels often flow in valleys that have wide valley floors consisting of sand and gravel deposited in the channel and clay and silt deposited by floods. Bedrock channels, on the other hand, tend to be located in narrow V-shaped valleys. In some arid regions, where weathering is slow and rock is particularly resistant, narrow valleys having nearly vertical walls are also found. Such features are called *slot canyons*. Stream valleys exist on a continuum from narrow, steep-sided valleys to valleys that are so flat and wide that the valley walls are not discernible.

Streams, with the aid of weathering and mass wasting, shape the landscape through which they flow. As a result, streams continuously modify the valleys they occupy.

Base Level and Graded Streams

In 1875 John Wesley Powell, the pioneering geologist who first explored the Grand Canyon and later headed the U.S. Geological Survey, introduced the concept of a downward limit to stream erosion, which he called **base level**. A fundamental concept in the study of stream activity, base level is defined as the lowest elevation to which a stream can erode its channel. Essentially this is the level at which the mouth of a stream enters the ocean, a lake, or a trunk stream. Powell determined that two types of base level exist: "We may consider the level of the sea to be a grand base level, below which the dry lands cannot be eroded; but we may also have,

for local and temporary purposes, other base levels of erosion." [*]

Sea level, which Powell called "grand base level," is now referred to as **ultimate base level**. **Local** (or **temporary**) **base levels** include lakes, resistant layers of rock, and rivers that act as base levels for their tributaries. All limit a stream's ability to downcut its channel.

Changes in base level cause corresponding adjustments in the "work" that streams perform. When a dam is built along a stream course, the reservoir that forms behind it raises the base level of the stream (FIGURE 19). Upstream from the reservoir, the stream gradient is reduced, lowering its velocity and, hence, its sediment-transporting ability. As a result, the stream deposits material, thereby building up its channel. This process continues until the stream again has a gradient sufficient to carry its load. The profile of the new channel will be similar to the old, but somewhat higher.

If, on the other hand, base level is lowered by a drop in sea level, the stream will have excess energy and downcut its channel to establish a balance with its new base level. Erosion first occurs near the mouth and then progresses upstream, creating a new stream profile.

Observing streams that adjust their profiles to changes in base level led to the concept of a graded stream. A **graded stream** has the necessary slope and other channel characteristics to maintain the minimum velocity required to transport the material supplied to it. On average, a graded system is neither eroding nor depositing material but simply transporting it. When a stream reaches equilibrium, it becomes a self-regulating system in which a change in one characteristic causes a change in the others to counteract the effect.

Consider what would happen if displacement along a fault were to raise a layer of resistant rock along the

FIGURE 19 Building a dam The base level upstream from the reservoir is raised, which reduces the stream's flow velocity and leads to deposition and a reduced gradient.

Ultimate base level

Sea

Profile of stream adjusted to base level

New stream profile formed by deposition of sediment

New base level

Reservoir

Dam

Sea

Original profile

---

[*]*Exploration of the Colorado River of the West* (Washington, DC: Smithsonian Institution, 1875), p. 203.

course of a graded stream. As shown in FIGURE 20, the resistant rock forms a waterfall and serves as a temporary base level for the stream. Because of the increased gradient, the stream concentrates its erosive energy on the resistant rock along an area called a *knickpoint*. Eventually, the river erases the knickpoint from its path and reestablishes a smooth profile.

Valley Deepening

When a stream's gradient is steep and the channel is well above base level, downcutting is the dominant activity. Abrasion caused by bed load sliding and rolling along the bottom, and the hydraulic power of fast-moving water, slowly lowers the streambed. The result is usually a V-shaped valley with steep sides. A classic example of a V-shaped valley is the section of the Yellowstone River shown in FIGURE 21.

The most prominent features of V-shaped valleys are *rapids* and *waterfalls*. Both occur where the stream's gradient increases significantly, a situation usually caused by variations in the erodibility of the bedrock into which a stream channel is cutting. Resistant beds create rapids by acting as a temporary base level upstream while allowing downcutting to continue downstream.

FIGURE 20 Changes in base level
A resistant layer of rock can act as a temporary base level. The stream concentrates its erosive energy on the resistant rock at the knickpoint. Eventually the river eliminates the knickpoint and reestablishes a smooth profile.

FIGURE 21 Yellowstone River
The V-shaped valley, rapids, and waterfalls indicate that the river is vigorously downcutting. (Photo by Charles A. Blakeslee/AGE Fotostock)

563

FIGURE 22 **The Retreat of Niagara Falls**
The force of the plunging Niagara River is causing the falls to retreat.
(Photo by Michael Collier)

As the river plunges over the falls, it erodes the weaker rocks beneath the more resistant Lockport Dolostone. As a section of dolostone is undercut, it loses support and breaks off.

Geologist's Sketch

Headward erosion of Niagara Falls

Lockport dolostone

Weak shale layers

Lake Erie

Niagara River

Niagara Falls

Niagara gorge

Niagara Escarpment

Former position of Niagara Falls

Lake Ontario

The Niagara River flows from Lake Erie to Lake Ontario. The falls have retreated upstream (toward Lake Erie) more than 11 kilometers (7 miles) during the last 12,000 years.

Recall that, in time, erosion usually eliminates the resistant rock.

Waterfalls occur where streams make vertical drops. One type of waterfall is exemplified by Niagara Falls (FIGURE 22). These famous falls are supported by a resistant bed of dolostone that is underlain by less resistant shale. As the water plunges over the lip of the falls, it erodes the less resistant shale, undermining a section of overlying rock, which eventually breaks off. In this manner, the waterfall retains its vertical cliff while slowly, but continually, retreating upstream. Over the past 12,000 years, Niagara Falls has retreated more than 11 kilometers (7 miles) upstream.

Valley Widening

As a stream approaches a graded condition, downcutting becomes less dominant. At this point the stream's channel takes on a meandering pattern, and more of its energy is directed from side to side. As a result, the valley widens as the river cuts away at one bank and then the other. The continuous lateral erosion caused by shifting meanders gradually produces a broad, flat valley floor covered with alluvium (FIGURE 23). This feature, called a **floodplain**, is appropriately named because when a river overflows its banks during flood stage, it inundates the floodplain. Over time the floodplain will widen to a point where the stream is actively eroding the valley walls in

only a few places. In the case of the lower Mississippi River, for example, the distance from one valley wall to another sometimes exceeds 160 kilometers (100 miles).

When a river erodes laterally and creates a floodplain as described, it is called an *erosional floodplain*. Floodplains can be depositional as well. *Depositional floodplains* are produced by major fluctuations in conditions, such as changes in base level or climate. The floodplain in California's Yosemite Valley is one such feature; it was produced when a glacier gouged the valley floor about 300 meters (1000 feet) deeper than its former level. After the glacial ice melted, running water refilled the valley with alluvium. The Merced River currently winds across a relatively flat floodplain that forms much of the floor of Yosemite Valley.

Incised Meanders and Stream Terraces

We usually find streams with highly meandering courses on floodplains in wide valleys. However, some rivers have meandering channels that flow in steep, narrow bedrock valleys. Such meanders are called **incised meanders** (*incisum* = to cut into) (FIGURE 24).

How do these features form? Originally the meanders probably developed on the floodplain of a stream that was in balance with its base level. Then, a change in base level caused the stream to begin downcutting.

Running Water

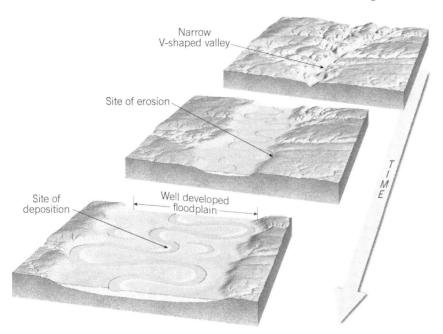

Narrow
V-shaped valley

Site of erosion

Site of
deposition

Well developed
floodplain

T
I
M
E

Continuous side-to-side
erosion by shifting meanders
gradually produces a broad,
flat valley floor. Alluvium deposited during floods covers
the valley floor.

Incised meanders
Aerial view of incised
meanders of the Colorado
River on the Colorado
Plateau. (Photo by Michael
Collier)

Before uplift of the Colorado
Plateau, the river was meandering
on a floodplain.

During uplift of the plateau, the
meanders downcut because of the
steepening gradient.

FIGURE 25 Stream terraces Terraces result when a stream adjusts to a relative drop in base level. (Photo by Greg Hancock)

Stream meandering on its floodplain
Floodplain

Because of a relative drop in base level, the river erodes downward through previously deposited alluvium. Eventually a new floodplain forms. Terraces represent elevated remnants of the former floodplain.
Terrace
Terrace

These stream terraces developed along the Wind River in Wyoming

Terraces
Terraces

When there is another relative drop in base level, a second set of terraces forms.

One of two events likely occurred: Either the base level dropped or the land on which the river was flowing was uplifted. For example, regional uplifting of the Colorado Plateau in the southwestern United States generated incised meanders on several rivers. As the plateau gradually rose, meandering rivers began downcutting because of their steepening gradient (Figure 24).

After a river has adjusted in this manner, it may once again produce a floodplain at a level below the old one. The remnants of a former floodplain are sometimes present as relatively flat surfaces called **terraces** (FIGURE 25).

6 CONCEPT CHECKS

1. Define *base level* and distinguish between ultimate base level and local, or temporary, base level.
2. What is a graded stream?
3. Explain why V-shaped valleys often contain rapids and/or waterfalls.
4. Describe or sketch how an erosional floodplain develops.
5. Describe two situations that would trigger the formation of incised meanders.

EYE on Earth

The Middle Fork of the Salmon River flows for about 175 kilometers (110 miles) through a wilderness area in central Idaho.

Question 1 Is the river flowing in an alluvial channel or a bedrock channel? Explain.

Question 2 What process is dominant here: valley deepening or valley widening?

Question 3 Is the area shown in this image more likely near the mouth or the head of the river?

Michael Collier

7 | Depositional Landforms

Recall that streams continually pick up sediment in one part of their channel and deposit it downstream. These small-scale channel deposits are called **bars**. Such features, however, are only temporary, as the material will be picked up again and eventually carried to the ocean. In addition to sand and gravel bars, streams also create other depositional features that have somewhat longer life spans. These include *deltas, natural levees,* and *alluvial fans.*

Deltas

Deltas form where sediment-charged streams enter the relatively still waters of a lake, an inland sea, or the ocean (**FIGURE 26**). As the stream's forward motion is slowed, sediments are deposited by the dying current, producing three types of beds. *Foreset beds* are composed of coarse particles that drop almost immediately upon entering the water to form layers that slope downcurrent from the delta front. The foreset beds are usually covered by thin, horizontal *topset beds* deposited during flood stage. The finer silts and clays settle away from the mouth in nearly horizontal layers called *bottomset beds.*

Topset beds are deposited atop the foreset beds during floods.

Distributaries

Foreset beds consist of coarse particles that drop soon after entering the water body. As the delta grows, these beds cover the bottomset beds.

Bottomset beds consist of fine silt and clay particles that settled beyond the mouth of the river.

As the stream extends its channel, the gradient is reduced. During flood stage some of the flow is diverted to a shorter, higher-gradient route forming a new distributary.

FIGURE 26 Formation of a simple delta Structure and growth of a simple delta that forms in relatively quiet waters.

As a delta grows outward from the shoreline, the stream's gradient continually decreases. This circumstance eventually causes the channel to become choked with sediment. As a consequence, the river seeks shorter, higher-gradient routes to base level. Figure 26 shows the main channel dividing into several smaller ones, called **distributaries** that carry water away from the main channel in varying paths to base level. After numerous shifts in the main flow from one distributary to the next, a delta may grow into the triangular shape of the Greek letter delta (Δ), although several other shapes exist. Differences in the configurations of shorelines and variations in the nature and strength of wave activity are responsible for the shape and structure of each delta. Many of the world's great rivers have created massive deltas, each with its own peculiarities and typically more complex than the one illustrated in Figure 26.

Not all rivers have deltas. A river that transports a large sediment load may lack a delta because ocean waves and powerful currents quickly redistribute the material soon after it is deposited. The Columbia River in the Pacific Northwest is an example. In other cases, rivers do not carry sufficient quantities of sediment to build a delta. The St. Lawrence River, for example, has little opportunity to pick up much sediment between its head in Lake Ontario and its mouth in the Gulf of St. Lawrence.

The Mississippi River Delta

The Mississippi River delta resulted from the accumulation of huge quantities of sediment derived from the vast region drained by the river and its tributaries. New Orleans currently rests where there was once ocean.

History and Structure   FIGURE 27 shows the portion of the Mississippi delta that has accumulated over the past 6000 years. As the figure illustrates, the delta is actually a series of seven coalescing subdeltas. Each subdelta formed when the main flow was diverted from one channel to a shorter, more direct path to the Gulf of Mexico. The individual subdeltas intertwine and partially cover each other to produce a complex structure. It is also apparent from Figure 27 that after each channel was abandoned, coastal erosion modified the newly formed subdelta. The present subdelta (number 7 in Figure 27), called a *bird-foot* delta because of the configuration of its distributaries, has been built by the Mississippi over the past 500 years.

At present, this active bird-foot delta has extended seaward almost as far as natural forces will allow. In fact, for many years the river has been "struggling" to cut through a narrow neck of land and shift its course to the Atchafalaya River (see inset in Figure 27). If this were to happen, the Mississippi would abandon the lowermost 500 kilometers (300 miles) of its channel in favor of the Atchafalaya's much shorter 225-kilometer (140-mile) route to the Gulf.

In a concerted effort to keep the Mississippi on its present course, a damlike structure was erected at the site where the channel was trying to break through. A flood in 1973 weakened the control structure, and the river again threatened to shift. This event caused the U.S. Army Corps of Engineers to construct a massive auxiliary dam that was completed in the mid-1980s. For the time being, at least, the inevitable has been avoided, and the Mississippi River continues to flow past Baton Rouge and New Orleans on its way to the Gulf of Mexico.

Vanishing Wetlands The delta of the Mississippi River in Louisiana is a biologically significant region that includes about 12,000 square kilometers (3 million acres) of coastal wetlands—40 percent of all coastal wetlands in the contiguous United States (FIGURE 28). These flat areas that are only slightly above sea level are sheltered

FIGURE 28 Coastal wetlands These low-lying, sediment-starved swamps, marshes, and bayous are disappearing at an alarming rate. (Photo by Michael Collier)

from the wave action of hurricanes and winter storms by low-lying offshore barrier islands. Both the wetlands and offshore islands were formed and maintained by sediments carried to the Gulf of Mexico by the Mississippi River.

The coastal wetlands of Louisiana are disappearing at an alarming rate—accounting for 80 percent of the wetland loss in the lower 48 states. According to the U.S. Geological Survey, Louisiana has lost more than 5000 square kilometers (1900 square miles) of coastal land since the early 1930s. If wetland loss continues at this rate, another 3000 square kilometers (1170 square miles) will vanish by the year 2050. Why is this occurring?

Before Europeans settled the delta, the Mississippi River regularly overflowed its banks in seasonal floods. Huge quantities of sediment were deposited atop the delta, which kept the land elevated above sea level. However, with settlement came flood-control efforts and the desire to maintain and improve navigation on the river. Artificial levees (earthen mounds built parallel to the river) were constructed to contain the rising river during flood stage. Over time the levees were extended all the way to the mouth of the Mississippi to keep the channel open to navigation.

The effects have been straightforward: The levees prevent sediment from being dispersed onto the wetlands. As a result, sediment is not added in sufficient quantities to offset compaction, subsidence, and wave erosion. Thus, the size of the delta and the extent of the wetlands are shrinking. The problem has been exacerbated by a decline in the sediment load of the Mississippi, which has decreased approximately 50 percent over the past 100 years. A substantial portion of the reduction results from sediment being trapped upstream by dams on the river's many tributaries.

Natural Levees

Meandering rivers that occupy valleys with broad floodplains tend to build **natural levees** (*lever* = to raise) that parallel their channels on both banks (FIGURE 29). Natural levees are built by years of successive floods. When a stream overflows onto the floodplain, the water flows over the surface as a broad sheet. Because the flow velocity drops significantly, the coarser portion of the suspended load is immediately deposited adjacent to the channel. As the water spreads across the floodplain, a thin layer of fine sediment is laid down over the valley floor. This uneven distribution of material produces the gentle, almost imperceptible, slope of the natural levee (Figure 29).

The natural levees of the lower Mississippi River rise 6 meters (20 feet) above the adjacent valley floor. The area behind a levee is characteristically poorly drained for the obvious reason that water cannot flow over the levee and into the river. Marshes called **back swamps** often result. When a tributary stream enters a river valley that has a substantial natural levee, it often flows for many kilometers through the back swamp before finding an opening where it enters the main river. Such streams are called **yazoo tributaries**, after the Yazoo River, which parallels the lower Mississippi River for more than 300 kilometers (185 miles).

FIGURE 29 Formation of a natural levee
These gently sloping structures that parallel a river channel are created by repeated floods. Because the ground next to the channel is higher than the adjacent floodplain, back swamps and yazoo tributaries may develop.

FIGURE 30 Alluvial fan in Death Valley

Fans are deposited at the mouth of a valley that emerges from a mountainous or upland area onto a relatively flat lowland. Usually coarse material is dropped near the apex of the fan, while finer materials are carried toward the base of the deposit. California's Death Valley has many large fans. As adjacent fans grow larger, they may coalesce to form a steep apron of sediment called a *bajada*. (Photo by Michael Collier)

Geologist's Sketch

Dry channels

Dry stream channel

Alluvial fan

Road

Death Valley

its gradient drops and it deposits a large portion of its sediment load. Although alluvial fans are more prevalent in arid climates, they are occasionally found in humid regions.

Mountain streams, because of their steep gradients, carry much of their sediment load as coarse sand and gravel. Because alluvial fans are composed of these same coarse materials, water that flows across them readily soaks in. When a stream emerges from its valley onto an alluvial fan, its flow divides itself into several distributary channels. The fan shape is produced because the main flow swings back and forth between the distributaries from a fixed point where the stream exits the mountain.

Between rainy periods in deserts, little or no water flows across an alluvial fan, evident by the many dry channels that cross its surface. Thus, fans in dry regions grow intermittently, receiving considerable water and sediment only during wet periods. Steep canyons in dry regions are prime locations for debris flows. Therefore, as would be expected, many alluvial fans have debris-flow deposits interbedded with the coarse alluvium.

7 CONCEPT CHECKS

1. Sketch a cross section of a simple delta and distinguish among the three types of beds that compose it.
2. Explain why the Mississippi delta consists of seven coalescing subdeltas.
3. What is causing the area of the Mississippi delta and its wetlands to shrink?
4. Briefly describe the formation of a natural levee. How is this feature related to back swamps and yazoo tributaries?
5. Describe the formation of an alluvial fan.

Alluvial Fans

As FIGURE 30 illustrates, **alluvial fans** are fan-shaped deposits that accumulate along steep mountain fronts. When a mountain stream emerges onto a relatively flat lowland,

EYE on Earth

This satellite image shows the delta of the Yukon River. The river originates in northern British Columbia. It flows through the Yukon Territory and across the tundra of Alaska before entering the Bering Sea, a distance of nearly 3200 kilometers (about 2000 miles).

Question 1 Explain why the river breaks into numerous channels as it crosses the delta.

Question 2 What term is applied to the channels that radiate across the delta?

Question 3 Notice the cloud of sediment in the water surrounding the delta. Are these sediments more likely sand and gravel or silt and clay? Explain.

Question 4 After the cloud of material settles to the seafloor and the delta expands farther into the Bering Sea, which beds of the delta will these sediments become?

NASA

8 Drainage Patterns

Drainage systems are interconnected networks of streams that form a variety of patterns. These different patterns occur primarily in response to the type of material on which the streams developed and/or the structural pattern of fractures, faults, and folds. FIGURE 31 illustrates four drainage patterns.

Dendritic pattern
develops on relatively
uniform surface materials

Rectangular pattern
develops on highly jointed bedrock

Radial pattern
develops on isolated
volcanic cones or domes

Volcano

Trellis pattern
develops in areas of alternating
weak and resistant bedrock

Ridges of
resistant
rock

Valleys cut in
less-resistant
rock

FIGURE 31 Drainage patterns
Networks of streams form a variety of patterns.

The most common, the **dendritic drainage pattern**, is characterized by irregular branching of tributary streams that resemble the branching pattern of a deciduous tree. In fact, the word *dendritic* means "treelike." This drainage pattern develops whenever underlying bedrock is relatively uniform, such as flat-lying sedimentary strata or massive igneous rocks. Because the underlying material is essentially uniform in its resistance to erosion, it does not control the pattern of streamflow. Rather, the pattern is primarily determined by the slope of land.

When streams diverge from a central area, like spokes from the hub of a wheel, it is called a **radial drainage pattern**. This pattern typically develops on isolated volcanic cones and domal uplifts.

A **rectangular drainage pattern**, exhibits many right-angle bends. This pattern typically develops where the bedrock is crisscrossed by a series of joints. Because fractured rock tends to weather and erode more easily than unbroken rock, the geometric pattern of joints guides the direction of streams as they carve their valleys.

A **trellis drainage pattern**, is a rectangular pattern in which tributary streams are nearly parallel to one another and have the appearance of a garden trellis. This pattern forms in areas underlain by alternating bands of resistant and less resistant rock and is particularly well displayed in the folded Appalachian Mountains, where both weak and strong strata outcrop in nearly parallel belts.

Formation of a Water Gap

To fully understand the drainage pattern displayed by a stream, we must consider the stream's entire history. For example, river valleys occasionally cut through a ridge or mountainous topography that lies across their path. The steep-walled notch followed by the river through a tectonic structure is called a **water gap** (FIGURE 32).

Why do streams cut across such structures and not flow around them? One possibility is that a stream existed before the ridge or mountain was uplifted. In this situation, the stream, called an **antecedent stream**, downcut its bed at a pace equal to the rate of uplift. That is, the stream would maintain its course as folding or faulting gradually raised the structure across its path.

FIGURE 32 **Development of a superposed stream** This is one way in which a water gap can form. (Photo by Michael Collier)

The river establishes its course on relatively uniform strata that cover a structural feature below.

As the stream erodes downward, it encounters and cuts through the resistant rock units creating water gaps. By this process the river is superimposed on the ridges.

The Bighorn River is a superposed stream that created a water gap through Wyoming's Sheep Mountain.

A second possibility is that a **superposed stream** eroded its channel into an existing structure (see Figure 32). This can occur when folded beds or resistant rocks are buried beneath layers of relatively flat-lying sediments or sedimentary strata. Streams originating on the overlying strata establish their courses without regard to the structures below. Then, as the valley deepens, the river continues to cut its valley into the structure below. The folded Appalachians feature several superposed rivers, including the Potomac and the Susquehanna, which cut their channels through folded strata on their way to the Atlantic.

Headward Erosion and Stream Piracy

Streams lengthen their courses by **headward erosion**—that is, by extending the heads of their valleys upslope. In their headwater sections, streams tend to downcut their channels. This leads to increased rates of erosion on the steeper slopes, which lie in the opposite direction of streamflow. Thus, through headward erosion, a valley is extended into previously undissected terrain. In FIGURE 33, the tributaries to Utah's San Rafael River illustrate this process.

Headward erosion can result in one stream entering the drainage basin of an adjacent stream. This process, called **stream piracy**, is the capture of drainage that previously flowed to another stream. Numerous situations can lead to stream piracy. In FIGURE 34 a drainage divide separates stream A from stream B. Headward erosion by stream A gradually narrows the divide and eventually breaches it. When the head of stream A intersects the channel of stream B, it captures the flow of stream B, diverting it through the newly formed water gap and down the valley to the mouth of stream A.

8 CONCEPT CHECKS

1. Prepare a simple sketch of the four drainage patterns discussed in this section.
2. How does geology influence each of these drainage patterns?
3. Contrast antecedent and superposed streams.
4. Relate headward erosion to stream piracy.

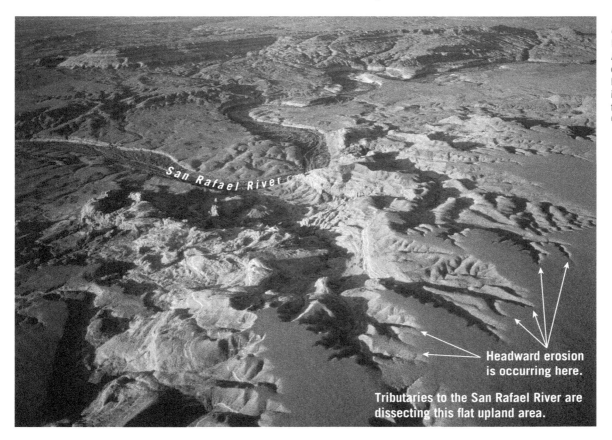

Headward erosion
is occurring here.

Tributaries to the San Rafael River are
dissecting this flat upland area.

San Rafael River

Headward erosion
A stream lengthens its
course by extending the
head of its valley upslope
into previously undissected
terrain. (Photo by Michael
Collier)

Divide separating the drainage basins
of stream A and stream B

Stream A

Stream B

**Before
capture**

Headward erosion
by stream A gradually
cuts through the divide and
intercepts the flow of stream B

Water gap created by
headward erosion by
stream A

Captured
stream

Point of
capture

**After
capture**

Dry former
channel of stream B

FIGURE 34 **Stream piracy**
Headward erosion by one
stream intercepts and captures the flow of another
stream.

Flash floods

Flash floods are local floods of great volume and short duration. The rapidly rising surge of water usually occurs with little advance warning and can destroy roads, bridges, homes, and other substantial structur

The power of a flash flood is illustrated by the Big Thompson River flood of July 31, 1976, in Colorado. During a four-hour span more than 30 centimeters (12 inches) of rain fell on portions of the river's small drainage basin. This amounted to nearly three-quarters of the average yearly total. The flash flood in the narrow canyon lasted only a few hours, but cost 139 people their lives.

Urban development increases runoff. As a result, peak discharge and flood frequency increase. A recent study indicated that the area of impervious surfaces in the 48 contiguous United States is roughly equal to the area of the state of Ohio (44,000 mi²).

Most people do not appreciate the power of moving water. Many automobiles will float and be swept away in a strong current that is only 2 feet deep. More than half of all U.S. flash-flood fatalities are auto related!

Average Annual Storm-Related Deaths in the United States

In most years floods are responsible for the greatest number of storm-related deaths. The average number of hurricane deaths was dramatically affected by Hurricane Katrina in 2005 (more than 1000). For all other years on this graph, hurricane fatalities numbered fewer than 20.

30 year average (1981–2010) 10 year average (2001–2010)

Effect of Urban Development on Flooding

Streamflow in Mercer Creek, an urban stream in western Washington, increases more quickly, reaches a higher peak discharge, and has a larger volume during a one-day storm on February 1, 2000, than streamflow in Newaukum Creek, a nearby rural stream. Streamflow during the following week, however, was greater in Newaukum Creek.

JANUARY 2000   FEBRUARY 2000

9 Floods and Flood Control

A **flood** occurs when the flow of a stream becomes so great that it exceeds the capacity of its channel and overflows its banks. Among the most deadly and most destructive of all geologic hazards, floods are, nevertheless, simply part of the *natural* behavior of streams.

Types of Floods

Floods can result from several naturally occurring and human-induced factors. Most floods are caused by atmospheric processes that can vary greatly in both time and space. An hour or less of intense thunderstorm rainfall can trigger flash floods in small valleys. By contrast, major floods in large river valleys often result from an extraordinary series of precipitation events over a broad region for many days or weeks. Common flood types include *regional floods, flash floods, ice-jam floods*, and *dam-failure floods.*

Regional Floods
Most regional floods are seasonal. Rapid melting of snow in spring and/or heavy spring rains often overwhelm rivers. For example, the extensive 1997 flood along the Red River of the North was preceded by an especially snowy winter and an early spring blizzard. Early April brought rapidly rising temperatures, melting the snow in a matter of days, causing a record-breaking 500-year flood. Roughly 4.5 million acres were underwater, and the losses in the Grand Forks, North Dakota, region exceeded $3.5 billion.*

Regional floods can also result from numerous heavy rain events. The Great Flood of 1993 in the Upper Mississippi River basin is likely the country's worst non-hurricane flooding disaster, with damages that approached $29 billion (2011 dollars). Unprecedented rainfall produced the wettest spring and early summer in more than a century, with large parts of Minnesota, Wisconsin, Iowa, Illinois, and Missouri receiving more than twice the average April–July precipitation (FIGURE 35).

Flash Floods
Flash floods often occur with little warning and are potentially deadly because they produce rapid rises in water levels and can have devastating flow velocities. Rainfall intensity and duration, surface conditions, and topography are among the factors that influence flash flooding. Mountainous areas are especially susceptible because steep slopes can funnel runoff into narrow valleys with disastrous consequences.

A recent episode of flash flooding occurred in late August 2011, when heavy rains from the remnants of Hurricane Irene swamped parts of the Northeast. The hilly and mountainous terrain of upstate New York and Vermont were hit especially hard (FIGURE 36). Flash floods

FIGURE 35 The Great Flood of 1993 These satellite images show the St. Louis area where the Mississippi, Illinois, and Missouri Rivers join. The upper image shows the rivers during a drought that occurred in the summer of 1988. The lower image shows the peak of the 1993 flood. In all, nearly 14 million acres were inundated, displacing at least 50,000 people. (Courtesy of GeoEye Inc.)

washed out dozens of roads and bridges, isolating numerous small towns and rural areas.

Urban areas are also susceptible to flash floods because a high percentage of the surface area is composed of impervious roofs, streets, and parking lots, where infiltration is minimal and runoff is rapid.

Ice-Jam Floods
Frozen rivers are especially susceptible to ice-jam floods. As the level of a stream rises, it breaks up ice and creates ice floes that can accumulate on channel obstructions. Jams of this nature create temporary ice dams across the channel. Water trapped upstream can rise rapidly and overflow the channel banks. When an ice dam fails, water behind the dam is often released with sufficient force to inflict considerable damage downstream.

---

*Ice jams also contribute to floods on the Red River of the North. See the section "Ice-Jam Floods" on this page.

FIGURE 36 Flash floods in Vermont
In late August 2011 the remnants of Hurricane Irene brought torrential rains that caused record-breaking flash floods in Vermont and parts of up-state New York. (AP Photo/ Toby Talbot)

The scale of destruction was unprecedented including nearly 2000 damaged road segments and 300 damaged or destroyed bridges. In addition, more than 800 homes and businesses and several rail and telecommunications lines were damaged or destroyed.

Graph showing river stages for Otter Creek near Rutland, Vermont. The stream rose about 14 feet in less than a day and then subsided quickly.

Dam-Failure Floods

Human interference with stream systems can cause floods. A prime example is the failure of a dam or an artificial levee designed to contain small or moderate floods. When larger floods occur, the dam or levee may fail, resulting in the water behind it being released as a flash flood. The bursting of a dam in 1889 on the Little Conemaugh River caused the devastating Johnstown, Pennsylvania, flood that took over 2200 lives.

Flood Recurrence Intervals

Land-use planning in river basins requires an understanding of the frequency and magnitude of floods. For any particular river, a relationship exists between the size of a flood and the frequency with which it occurs. The larger the flood, the less often it is expected to occur. You have may heard of a *100-year flood*. This describes the *recurrence interval*, which is an estimate of how often a flood of a given size can be expected to occur. A 25-year event would be much smaller but would be four times more likely to occur than a 100-year flood.

The phrase "100-year flood" does not mean that 100 years must pass between each flood of equal or greater magnitude. Floods happen irregularly! Rather, it means that there is a 1 percent (1 in 100) probability in a given year for a flood of that size. It is possible that a 100-year flood could occur 2 or 3 years in a row. It is also possible that such a flood might not occur over a span exceeding 100 years.

In order to make a reasonable calculation, stream gage data must be collected for at least 10 to 30 years. The longer the record, the better the prediction will likely be. Other factors influence the accuracy of flood recurrence estimates as well. Climate cycles that involve extensive drought or rainy periods are an example. Land-use changes, such as when extensive rural areas become urbanized, typically trigger reevaluation of flood recurrence intervals.

These floods are often associated with northward-flowing rivers in the Northern Hemisphere. The Red River of the North mentioned earlier is an example. The Siberian region of Russia has several northward-flowing rivers, such as the Ob, Lena, and Yenisei, that frequently experience these floods (FIGURE 37). The reason is that when spring arrives, ice melts in the warmer southern portions of a river and its drainage basin while farther north the river remains frozen. As a consequence, water flowing from the south "backs up" behind the frozen northern portion of the river.

FIGURE 37 Northward-flowing Siberian Rivers
Ice-jam floods are relatively common in late spring and early summer in Siberia because its large rivers flow north into the Arctic Ocean.

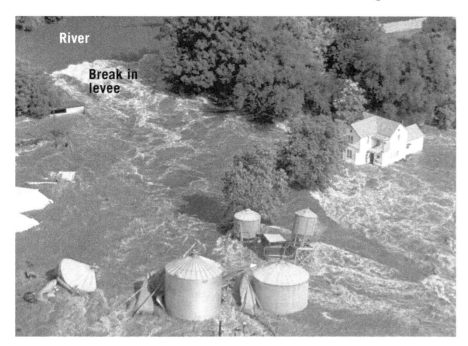

River

Break in levee

FIGURE 38 Broken levee Water rushes through a break in an artificial levee in Monroe County, Illinois. During the record-breaking 1993 Midwest floods, many artificial levees could not withstand the force of the floodwaters. Sections of many weakened structures were overtopped or simply collapsed. (Photo by James Finley/AP Wide World Pictures)

Flood Control

Several strategies have been devised to eliminate or lessen the catastrophic impact of floods on our lives and environment. Engineering efforts include the construction of artificial levees, river channelization, and the building of flood-control dams.

Artificial Levees *Artificial levees* are earthen mounds built on river banks to increase the volume of water the channel can hold. Levees, used since ancient times, are the most commonly used stream-containment structures. In some locations, concrete floodwalls are constructed that function as artificial levees.

Many artificial levees were not built to withstand periods of extreme flooding. For example, numerous levees failed during the summer of 1993, when the upper Mississippi and many of its tributaries experienced record flooding (FIGURE 38). During that event, floodwalls at St. Louis, Missouri, created a bottleneck for the river that led to increased flooding upstream of the city.

Channelization *Channelization* involves altering a stream channel in order to make the flow more efficient. This may simply involve clearing a channel of obstructions or dredging a channel to make it wider and deeper. Another alteration involves straightening, and thus shortening a channel by creating *artificial cutoffs*. Shortening a stream increases the channel's flow velocity.

Between 1929 and 1942, the Army Corps of Engineers removed 16 meander bends on the lower Mississippi for the purpose of increasing the slope of the channel and, thereby reducing the threat of flooding. This river, a vital transportation corridor, was shortened about 240 kilometers (150 miles). These efforts have been somewhat successful in reducing the maximum height of the river during flood stage. However, channel shortening led to increased gradients and accelerated erosion of bank material, both of which necessitated further intervention. Following the creation of artificial cutoffs, massive bank protection was installed along several stretches of the lower Mississippi.

A similar case in which artificial cutoffs accelerated bank erosion occurred on the Blackwater River in Missouri, whose meandering course was shortened in 1910. Among the many effects of this project was a significant increase in the channel's width due to increased velocity. One particular bridge over the river collapsed in 1930 because of bank erosion. During the following 17 years, the bridge was replaced three times, each time requiring a longer span.

Flood-Control Dams *Flood-control dams* are built to store floodwater and then release it slowly, in a controlled manner. Since the 1920s, thousands of dams have been built on nearly every major river in the United States. Many dams have significant non-flood-related functions, such as providing water for irrigated agriculture and for hydroelectric power generation. Many reservoirs are also major regional recreational facilities.

Although dams are effective in reducing flooding and provide other benefits, their construction and maintenance also have significant costs and consequences. For example, reservoirs created by dams may cover valuable farmland, forests, historic sites, and scenic valleys. Large dams can also cause significant damage to river ecosystems that have developed over thousands of years.

Furthermore, building dams is not a permanent solution to flooding. Sedimentation behind a dam gradually diminishes the volume of its reservoir, reducing the long-term effectiveness of this flood-control measure.

A Nonstructural Approach All the flood-control measures described so far employ structural solutions to "control" rivers. These solutions are typically expensive and often give those who reside on the floodplain a false sense of security.

Many scientists and engineers advocate a nonstructural approach to flood control. They suggest that sound floodplain management is an alternative to artificial levees, dams, and channelization. By identifying high-risk flood areas, appropriate zoning regulations can be implemented to minimize development and promote safer, more appropriate land use.

9 CONCEPT CHECKS

1. List and distinguish among four types of floods.
2. Does a 100-year flood necessarily occur every 100 years? Explain.
3. Describe three basic flood-control strategies. What are some drawbacks of each?
4. What is meant by a *nonstructural* approach to flood control?

EYE on Earth

Building a dam is one method of regulating the flow of a river to control flooding. Dams and their reservoirs may also provide recreational opportunities and water for irrigation and hydroelectric power generation. This image, from near Page, Arizona, shows Glen Canyon Dam on the Colorado River upstream from the Grand Canyon and a portion of Lake Powell, the reservoir it created.

Question 1 How did the behavior of the stream likely change upstream from Lake Powell?

Question 2 How might the behavior of the Colorado River downstream from the dam have been affected?

Question 3 Given enough time, how might the reservoir change?

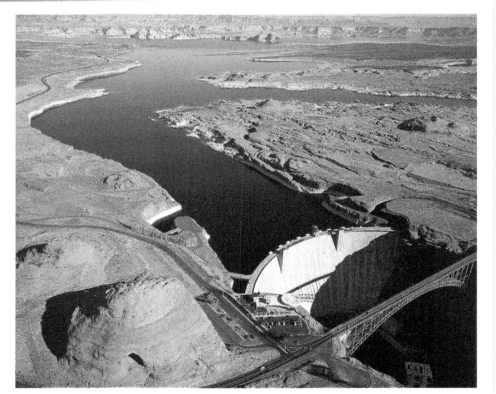

Michael Collier

CONCEPTS IN REVIEW: RUNNING WATER

1 Earth as a System: The Hydrologic Cycle

List the hydrosphere's major reservoirs and describe the different paths that water takes through the hydrologic cycle.

KEY WORDS hydrologic cycle, infiltration, runoff, transpiration, evapotranspiration

- Water moves through the hydrosphere's many reservoirs by evaporating, condensing into clouds, and falling as precipitation.

Once it reaches the ground surface, rain can either soak into the soil, evaporate, be returned to the atmosphere by plant transpiration, or run off over the surface. Running water may be a small portion of the total water on Earth, but it is the most important agent in sculpting Earth's varied landscapes.

SCENARIO SPECULATION Suggest some ways that the hydrologic cycle might be affected if the average temperature of Earth's lower atmosphere were several degrees warmer.

2 Running Water

Describe the nature of drainage basins and river systems.

KEY WORDS stream, river, drainage basin, divide

- Streams flow in channels. Big streams are often called rivers. Streams gain water from overland runoff, from groundwater, and from other streams (tributaries). Each stream drains an area of land known as its drainage basin. An individual drainage basin is separated from its neighbors by a drainage divide.
- River systems tend to erode at their upstream end, transport sediment through the middle section of the river, and deposit sediment at the downstream end of the river.

WATERSHED MOMENT The map shows two rivers and their tributary streams. Draw in the approximate boundaries of the divides that separate the streams' drainage basins.

3 Streamflow

Discuss streamflow and the factors that cause it to change.

KEY WORDS laminar flow, turbulent flow, gradient, wetted perimeter, discharge, longitudinal profile, head (headwaters), mouth

- The flow of water in a stream may be laminar or turbulent. A stream's flow velocity is influenced by four factors: channel gradient, channel size and cross-sectional shape, channel roughness, and the amount of water flowing in the channel. Streamflow is measured at gaging stations.

- A longitudinal profile along the length of a stream will typically show a steeper gradient at the headwaters and a gentler gradient toward the mouth. Though the gradient may be less at the downstream end of the profile, a greater discharge in a smoother channel makes the streamflow more efficient, and so velocities will typically be higher than at the headwaters.

DRAW IT Sketch a typical longitudinal stream profile and label the key features along its length. Where does most erosion happen? Where do most sediment transport and sediment deposition occur?

4 The Work of Running Water

Outline the ways in which streams erode, transport, and deposit sediment.

KEY WORDS quarrying, abrasion, pothole, corrosion, dissolved load, suspended load, bed load, settling velocity, saltation, capacity, competence, sorting, alluvium

- Streams are powerful agents of erosion that carve solid rock through quarrying, abrasion, and the focused "drilling" that results in potholes. Turbulent water also lifts loose particles from the streambed. In areas of soluble bedrock such as limestone, stream water can also corrode the landscape by dissolving the rock.

- Sediment is transported in a stream either in solution, suspended in the water, or rolling or saltating along the bottom of the stream. Fast-moving rivers have an ability to carry a greater total amount of sediment (capacity) and larger individual particles (competence). Flooding increases both capacity and competence, which is why rivers do most of their work during short-lived times of peak flow.
- Sediment deposited by streams is called alluvium. Typically, streams are efficient agents of sorting, meaning that they deposit similarly sized grains in the same area.

A PINCH OF SALT Consider the dissolved load of streams, and compare it to the ocean. Why is the ocean salty, but streams are considered "fresh" water?

5 Stream Channels

Contrast bedrock and alluvial stream channels. Distinguish between two types of alluvial channels.

KEY WORDS bedrock channel, alluvial channel, meander, cut bank, point bar, cutoff, oxbow lake, braided channel

- Bedrock channels are cut into solid rock. They typically show steps (highlighted by waterfalls or rapids) and pools (segments that are relatively flat).
- Alluvial channels are dominated by streamflow moving through sediment previously deposited by the river. A floodplain usually covers much of a valley floor, with the river itself moving through a channel that may meander or exhibit a braided pattern.
- Meanders are enhanced through erosion at the cut bank (outside edge of the meander) and deposition of sediment on the point bar (inside edge of the meander). The shape of the meander may grow more and more exaggerated until it loops back on itself. Once a cutoff is formed, the old meander loop will be abandoned by the main current and become an oxbow lake.
- Braided channels occur in streams that experience a high degree of variability in discharge. During times of low flow, the river moves in an interwoven network of channels between bars of coarse-grained alluvium.

MEANDERING HISTORY The town of Carter Lake is the *only* portion of the state of Iowa that lies on the west side of the Missouri River. It is bounded on the north by its namesake, Carter Lake, on the south by the Missouri River, and on the east and west by Nebraska. Examine the map shown here and hypothesize how this unusual situation could have developed.

6 Shaping Stream Valleys

Contrast narrow V-shaped valleys, broad valleys with floodplains, and valleys that display incised meanders or stream terraces.

KEY WORDS stream valley, base level, ultimate base level, local (temporary) base level, graded stream, floodplain, incised meander, terrace

- A stream valley includes the channel itself, the adjacent floodplain, and relatively steep valley walls. Stream valley width and shape vary a lot from bedrock channels (which tend to be V-shaped, with a narrow floodplain) to alluvial channels, which may have broad floodplains of alluvium and relatively subdued valley walls.
- Streams erode downward until they approach base level, which is usually the level at which the stream enters another stream, a lake, or the ocean. A river flowing toward the sea (ultimate base level) may encounter several local base levels along its route. These could be lakes or resistant rock units that retard the downcutting of the stream. A graded stream has reached equilibrium with its base level, and primarily works to transport sediment.
- Stream valleys are widened through the meandering action of the stream, which erodes the valley walls and widens the floodplain. If the base level drops, the stream downcuts. If it is underlain by bedrock, the stream may then develop incised meanders. Streams underlain by deep alluvium are likely to develop terraces.

Michael Collier

EXPLAIN THE PARADOX Meanders are associated with a river that is eroding from side to side, whereas narrow canyons are associated with rivers that are vigorously downcutting. The river in this image is confined to a narrow canyon but is also meandering. Explain.

7 Depositional Landforms

List the major depositional landforms associated with streams and describe the formation of these features

KEY WORDS bar, delta, distributary, natural levee, back swamp, yazoo tributary, alluvial fan

- A delta may form where a river deposits sediment in another water body at its mouth. The partitioning of streamflow into multiple distributaries spreads sediment in different directions. In the United States, the Mississippi River is an example of a major river with a dynamic delta system.

- Natural levees result from sediment deposited along the margins of a river channel by many years of successive floods. Because they slope gently away from the channel, the surrounding land is poorly drained, resulting in back swamps.
- Alluvial fans are fan-shaped deposits of alluvium that form where steep mountain fronts drop down into adjacent valleys.

COMPARE & CONTRAST At first glance, deltas and alluvial fans may look quite similar. How are they alike, and what sets them apart?

8   Drainage Patterns

Sketch and explain basic drainage patterns.

KEY WORDS dendritic drainage pattern, radial drainage pattern, rectangular drainage pattern, trellis drainage pattern, water gap, antecedent stream, superposed stream, headward erosion, stream piracy

- Drainage patterns are large-scale patterns that result when the structure of the landscape interacts with a river's downcutting. In areas where the underlying material offers relatively equal resistance to erosion, a branch-like dendritic drainage pattern will result. A radial drainage pattern is associated with streams that flow away (radiate from) a central high area. Rectangular drainage patterns result from stream erosion of fractured bedrock. In the Appalachian Mountains and other eroded mountain belts, the differential erosion of resistant and weak rocks may produce a trellis drainage pattern, where the tributaries flow parallel to local mountain ridges. Water gaps occur where streams flow across resistant, ridge-forming rock units.

- A stream erodes most efficiently in a headward direction, lengthening the stream's profile. If headward erosion by one stream results in the capture of another stream's headwaters, stream piracy is said to have occurred.

EXPLAIN IT   Examine the satellite photograph of central Pennsylvania. Identify the features seen where the Susquehanna River crosses the five mountain ridges and explain how these features came to be.

Susquehanna River

5 km

N

NASA

9   Floods and Flood Control

Summarize the various categories of floods and the common measures of flood control.

KEY WORD flood

- When a stream receives more discharge than its channel can hold, a flood occurs. The statistical probability that a flood of a given size will occur in a year is described with a recurrence interval. Four major factors that can cause a flood are large amounts of precipitation (or melting) across a region, sudden pulses of precipitation in areas of high runoff, temporary dams made of floating ice (which then break up, releasing impounded water), and the failure of human-built dams, causing the sudden escape of water from a reservoir.

- Three main structural strategies exist for coping with floods: construction of artificial levees to constrain streamflow to the channel, alterations to make a stream channel's flow more efficient, and building of dams on a river's tributaries so that a sudden influx of water will be temporarily stored and released slowly to the river system. A nonstructural approach is sound floodplain management. Here, a solid scientific understanding of flood dynamics informs policy and regulation of areas that are subject to flooding.

LESSER OF TWO FLOODS   Artificial levees are constructed to protect property from floods. Sometimes artificial levees in rural areas are intentionally opened up to protect a city from experiencing flooding. How does this work?

GIVE IT SOME THOUGHT

1. What factors influence how much of this rain will soak into the ground compared to how much will run off?

elwynn/Shutterstock

2. A river system consists of three zones, based on the dominant process operating in each zone. On the accompanying diagram, match each process with one of the three zones:
   a. Sediment production (erosion)
   b. Sediment deposition
   c. Sediment transportation

3. If you collect a jar of water from a stream, what part of its load will settle to the bottom of the jar? What portion will remain in the water indefinitely? What part of the stream's load would probably not be represented in your sample?

4. Streamflow is affected by several variables, including discharge, gradient, and channel roughness, size, and shape. Develop a scenario in which a mass wasting event influences a stream's flow. Explain what led up to, or triggered, the event and describe how the mass wasting process influenced the stream's flow.

5. Which description best describes each of the accompanying photos?
   a. Bedrock channel
   b. Alluvial channel (meandering)
   c. Alluvial channel (non-meandering)
   d. Alluvial channel (braided)

6. Use the photos referred to in the previous question to answer the following:
   a. Which of these streams is actually downcutting its channel?
   b. Which is/are transporting coarse sediments?
   c. Which is/are mainly transporting silt- and clay-size particles?
   d. Which of these streams do you think is most likely being fed by a melting glacier?

7. Describe and explain what happens to a stream's ability to erode during periods of drought and during periods of heavy rainfall. Suggest other factors besides a change in precipitation that could change a stream's ability to erode.

8. This satellite image shows portions of the Ohio and Wabash Rivers in May 2011. What is the base level for the Wabash River? What is base level for the Ohio River (referring to Figure 4 will help)? Are either of the base levels you just noted considered *ultimate base level*? Explain.

9. Several times during the past 2.5 million years, huge ice sheets (continental-size glaciers) formed and spread across large parts of Northern Hemisphere landmasses and then gradually melted away.
   a. How do you think the formation of ice sheets affected sea level?
   b. How would rivers flowing into the ocean have been affected as the ice sheets expanded?
   c. What kind of adjustments would these rivers make as the glacial ice melted?

10. Look at Figure 27. Based on the locations of the seven subdeltas of the Mississippi River, briefly describe the history of flow at the mouth of the Mississippi River. Why would people be concerned with the possibility of the Mississippi River shifting from its current path and following the path of the Atchafalaya River?

11. Describe three ways that a stream can lengthen its course. How might a stream get shorter?

12. One day you and a friend are discussing the aftermath of a major (100-year) flood that occurred on a nearby river in your area just a few months earlier. At the close of your conversation your friend remarks, "At least we won't have to worry about another one of those in our lifetime." How would you respond?

13. This satellite image from September 2, 2011, shows the lower portions of two rivers that flow into Long Island Sound a few days after heavy rains fell in the region. The muddy-looking Connecticut River clearly has a significant suspended load. To the east, the Thames River appears to be carrying very little sediment. Suggest a reason that might explain the contrasting sediment loads of the Connecticut and Thames Rivers.

MasteringGeology™

Looking for additional review and test prep materials? Visit the Study Area in MasteringGeology to enhance your understanding of this chapter's content by accessing a variety of resources, including **Self-Study Quizzes,** **Geoscience Animations, GEODe Tutorials, RSS feeds, flashcards, web links, self-study quizzes,** and an optional **Pearson eText.**

Glossary

Abrasion The grinding and scraping of a rock surface by the friction and impact of rock particles carried by water, wind, and ice.

Alluvial channel A stream channel in which the bed and banks are composed largely of unconsolidated sediment (alluvium) that was previously deposited in the valley.

Alluvial fan A fan-shaped deposit of sediment formed when a stream's slope is abruptly reduced.

Alluvium Unconsolidated sediment deposited by a stream.

Antecedent stream A stream that continued to downcut and maintain its original course as an area along its course was uplifted by faulting or folding.

Backswamp A poorly drained area on a floodplain resulting when natural levees are present.

Bar Common term for sand and gravel deposits in a stream channel.

Base level The level below which a stream cannot erode.

Bed load Sediment moved along the bottom of a stream by moving water, or particles moved along the ground surface by wind.

Bedrock channel A channel in which a stream is cutting into solid rock. Such channels typically form in the headwaters or river systems where gradients are high.

Braided stream A stream that consists of numerous intertwining channels.

Capacity The total amount of sediment that a stream is able to transport.

Competence A measure of the largest particle a stream can transport; a factor dependent on velocity.

Corrosion The process by which soluble rock is gradually dissolved by flowing water.

Cut bank The area of active erosion on the outside of a meander.

Cutoff A short *cha*nnel segment created when a river erodes through the narrow neck of land between meanders.

Delta An accumulation of sediment formed where a stream enters a lake or an ocean.

Dendritic pattern A stream system that resembles the pattern of a branching tree.

Discharge The quantity of water in a stream that passes a given point in a period of time.

Dissolved load The portion of a stream's load that is carried in solution.

Distributary A section of a stream that leaves the main flow.

Divide An imaginary line that separates the drainage of two streams, often found along a ridge.

Drainage basin The land area that contributes water to a stream.

Evapotranspiration The combined effect of evaporation and transpiration.

Flood The overflow of a stream channel that occurs when discharge exceeds the channel's capacity. The most common and destructive geologic hazard.

Floodplain The flat, low-lying portion of a stream valley subject to periodic inundation.

Graded stream A stream that has the correct channel characteristics to maintain exactly the velocity required to transport the material supplied to it.

Gradient The slope of a stream, generally expressed as the vertical drop over a fixed distance.

Head (stream) The beginning or source area for a stream. Also called the headwaters.

Headward erosion The extension upslope of the head of a valley due to erosion.

Hydrologic cycle The unending circulation of Earth's water supply. The cycle is powered by energy from the Sun and is characterized by continuous exchanges of water among the oceans, the atmosphere, and the continents.

Incised meander A meandering channel that flows in a steep, narrow valley. It forms either when an area is uplifted or when the base level drops.

Infiltration The movement of surface water into rock or soil through cracks and pore spaces.

Laminar flow The movement of water particles in straight-line paths that are parallel to the channel. The water particles move downstream without mixing.

Local base level See Temporary (local) base level.

Longitudinal profile A cross section of a stream channel along its descending course from the head to the mouth.

Meander A looplike bend in the course of a stream.

Mouth The point downstream where a river empties into another stream or water body.

Natural levee An elevated landform composed of alluvium that parallels some stre*ams and acts* to confine their waters, except during floodstage.

Oxbow lake A curved lake that is created when a stream cuts off a meander.

Point bar A crescent-shaped accumulation of sand and gravel deposited on the inside of a meander.

Pothole A depression formed in a stream channel by the abrasive action of the water's sediment load.

Quarrying Removing loosened blocks from the bed of a channel during times of high flow rates.

Radial pattern A system of streams running in all directions, away from a central elevated structure, such as a volcano.

Rectangular pattern A drainage pattern characterized by numerous right angle bends that develops on jointed or fractured bedrock.

River A general term for a stream that carries a substantial amount of water and has numerous tributaries.

Runoff Water that flows over land rather than infiltrating into the ground.

Saltation Transportation of sediment through a series of leaps or bounces.

Settling velocity The speed at which a particle falls through a still fluid. The size, shape, and specific gravity of particles influence settling velocity.

Sorting The degree of similarity in particle size in sediment or sedimentary rock.

Stream A general term to denote the flow of water with*in any natural* channel. Thus, a small creek and a large river are both streams.

Stream piracy Diversion of the drainage of one stream that results from the headward erosion of another stream.

Stream valley The channel, valley floor, and sloping valley walls of a stream.

Superposed stream A stream that cuts through a ridge lying across its path. The stream established its course on uniform layers at a higher level without regard to underlying structures and subsequently downcut.

Suspended load Fine sediment carried within the body of flowing water or air.

Temporary (local) base level The level of a lake, resistant rock layer, or any other base level that stands above sea level.

Terrace A flat, benchlike structure produced by a stream, which was left elevated as the stream cut downward.

Transpiration The release of water vapor to the atmosphere by plants.

Trellis drainage pattern A system of streams in which nearly parallel tributaries occupy valleys cut in folded strata.

Turbulent flow Erratic movement of water often characterized by swirling, whirlpool-like eddies. Most streamflow is of this type.

Ultimate base level Sea level; the lowest level to which stream erosion could lower the land.

Water gap A pass through a ridge or mountain in which a stream flows.

Wetted perimeter The total distance in a linear cross-section of a stream that is in contact with water.

Yazoo tributary A tributary that flows parallel to the main stream because a natural levee is present.

Groundwater

From Chapter 17 of *Earth: An Introduction to Physical Geology*, Eleventh Edition. Edward J. Tarbuck, Frederick K. Lutgens, Dennis Tasa.

Groundwater

Geysers are a type of hot spring in which columns of water and steam erupt with great force. This is Castle Geyser in Yellowstone National Park. (Photo by Michael Just/AGE Fotostock)

Each statement represents the primary learning objective for the corresponding major heading within the chapter. After you complete the chapter you should be able to:

1 Describe the importance of groundwater as a source of freshwater and groundwater's roles as a geologic agent.

2 Prepare a sketch with labels that summarizes the distribution of water beneath Earth's surface.

3 Discuss the factors that cause variations in the water table and describe the interactions between groundwater and streams.

4 Summarize the factors that influence the storage and movement of groundwater.

5 Sketch a simple groundwater flow system and explain it. Discuss how groundwater movement is measured and the different scales of movement.

6 Discuss water wells and their relationship to the water table.

7 Sketch and label a simple artesian system.

8 Distinguish among springs, hot springs, and geysers.

9 List and discuss important environmental problems associated with groundwater.

10 Explain the formation of caverns and the development of karst topography.

lthough it is hidden from view, vast quantities of water exist in the cracks, crevices, and pore spaces of rock and soil. Groundwater occurs almost everywhere beneath Earth's surface and is a major source of water worldwide. Groundwater is a valuable natural resource that provides about half of our drinking water and is essential to the vitality of agriculture and industry. In addition to human uses, groundwater plays a crucial role in sustaining streamflow between precipitation events—especially during protracted dry periods. Many ecosystems depend on groundwater discharge into streams, lakes, and wetlands. In some regions, large-scale development has caused groundwater levels to decline, resulting in water shortages, streamflow depletion, land subsidence, contamination by saltwater, and increased pumping costs. Groundwater pollution is also a serious issue in some places.

The tropical plants of a desert oasis are fed by groundwater. (Photo by Trans-World Photos/SuperStock)

1 The Importance of Groundwater

Groundwater is one of our most important and widely available resources, yet people's perceptions of the subsurface environment from which it comes are often unclear and incorrect. The reason is that the groundwater environment is largely hidden from view except in caves and mines, and the impressions people gain from these subsurface openings are misleading. Observations on the land surface give an impression that Earth is "solid." This view remains when we enter a cave and see water flowing in a channel that appears to have been cut into solid rock.

Because of such observations, many people believe that groundwater occurs only in underground "rivers." In reality, most of the subsurface environment is not "solid" at all. It includes countless tiny *pore spaces* between grains of soil and sediment, plus narrow joints and fractures in bedrock. Together, these spaces add up to an immense volume. It is in these small openings that groundwater collects and moves.

Groundwater and the Hydrosphere

Considering the entire hydrosphere, or all of Earth's water, only about six-tenths of 1 percent occurs underground. Nevertheless, this small percentage, stored in the rocks and sediments beneath Earth's surface, is a vast quantity. When the oceans are excluded and only sources of freshwater are considered, the significance of groundwater becomes more apparent.

FIGURE 1 contains estimates of the distribution of freshwater in the hydrosphere. Clearly the largest volume occurs as glacial ice. Second in rank is groundwater, with slightly more than 14 percent of the total. However, when ice is excluded and just liquid water is considered, more than 94 percent of all freshwater is groundwater. Without question, *groundwater represents the largest reservoir of freshwater that is readily available to humans.* Its value in terms of economics and human well-being is incalculable.

One of the advantages of groundwater is that it exists almost everywhere across the country and, thus, is often available in places that lack reliable surface sources such as lakes and rivers. Water in a groundwater system is stored in subsurface pore spaces and fractures. As water is withdrawn from a well, the connected pore spaces and fractures act as a "pipeline" that allows water to gradually move from one part of the hydrologic system to where it is being withdrawn.

Geologic Importance of Groundwater

Geologically, groundwater is important as an erosional agent. The dissolving action of groundwater slowly removes soluble rock such as limestone, allowing surface depressions known as *sinkholes* to form as well as creating subterranean caverns (FIGURE 2). Groundwater is also an equalizer of streamflow. Much of the water that flows in rivers is not direct runoff from rain and snowmelt. Rather, a large percentage of precipitation soaks in and then moves slowly

Share of Total Volume of Freshwater

Lakes 0.549%
Soil moisture 0.294%
Water vapor in atmosphere 0.294%
Rivers 0.004%
Groundwater 14.6%
Ice sheets and glaciers 84.945%

Share of all Liquid Freshwater

Lakes 3.64%
Soil moisture 1.95%
Water vapor in atmosphere 0.049%
Rivers 0.03%
Groundwater 94.05%

FIGURE 1 Earth's freshwater Groundwater is the major reservoir of liquid freshwater.

underground to stream channels. Groundwater is thus a form of storage that sustains streams during periods when rain does not fall. Therefore, when we see water flowing in a river during a dry period, it is rain that fell at some earlier time and was stored underground.

1 CONCEPT CHECKS

1. What percentage of Earth's total freshwater supply is groundwater?
2. What share of Earth's liquid freshwater is groundwater?
3. List two geologic roles that groundwater plays.

FIGURE 2 Carlsbad Caverns, New Mexico The dissolving action of acidic groundwater created these caverns. Later, groundwater deposited the limestone decorations. (Photo by Dennis Tasa)

Our Water Supply

Water is basic to life. It has been called the "bloodstream" of both the biosphere and society. The needs of the world's rapidly growing population are putting Earth's water supply under unprecedented pressure.

FRESH WATER IN THE UNITED STATES

SOURCES OF FRESH WATER IN THE UNITED STATES

23% GROUNDWATER 79 BILLION GALLONS PER DAY

77% SURFACE WATER 270 BILLION GALLONS PER DAY

GROUNDWATER
Use by category

68.4% IRRIGATION

19.3% PUBLIC SUPPLY

THERMOELECTRIC **0.05%**
MINING **0.92%**
AQUACULTURE **1.3%**
LIVESTOCK **1.3%**
INDUSTRIAL **4.3%**
DOMESTIC **4.2%**

Irrigation is number one

There are nearly 60 million acres (nearly 243,000 square kilometers or about 93,700 square miles) of irrigated land in the United States. That is an area nearly the size of the state of Wyoming. About 42 percent of the water used for irrigation is groundwater.

DRILLING DOWN

Countries are increasingly meeting demand by withdrawing groundwater from nonrenewable sources. Groundwater withdrawal worldwide tripled between 1950 and 2010 according to the United Nations. India has had the largest growth and accounts for about one-quarter of the total.

THE WATER WE USE EACH DAY

According to the American Water Works Association, daily indoor per capita use in an average single family home is nearly 70 gallons.

GROUNDWATER EXTRACTION (KM³ PER YEAR)

300
250
200
150
100
50
0

1950 1960 1970 1980 1990 2000 2010

PER CAPITA USE (GALLONS)
5 10 15 20

SHOWERS & BATHS
CLOTHES WASHERS
DISHWASHERS
TOILETS
LEAKS
OTHER USES

10 15 20 25 30
PERCENT OF DAILY USE

RMBrown/Alamy

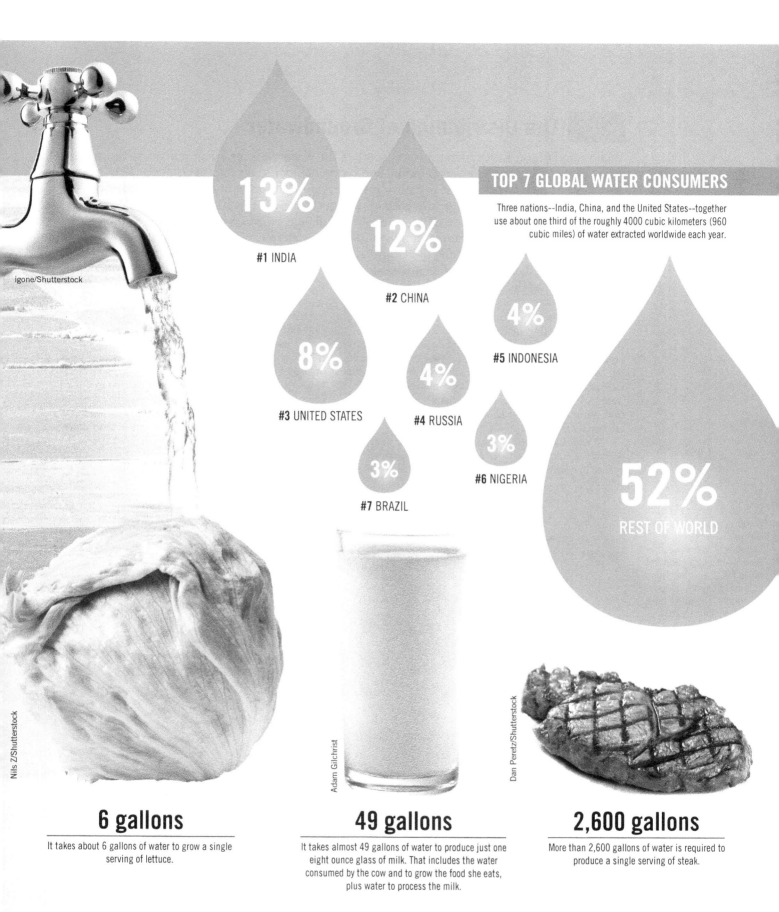

13%

#1 INDIA

12%

#2 CHINA

Three nations--India, China, and the United States--together use about one third of the roughly 4000 cubic kilometers (960 cubic miles) of water extracted worldwide each year.

8%

#3 UNITED STATES

4%

#4 RUSSIA

4%

#5 INDONESIA

3%

#6 NIGERIA

3%

#7 BRAZIL

52%

REST OF WORLD

igone/Shutterstock

Nils Z/Shutterstock

Adam Gilchrist

Dan Peretz/Shutterstock

6 gallons

It takes about 6 gallons of water to grow a single serving of lettuce.

49 gallons

It takes almost 49 gallons of water to produce just one eight ounce glass of milk. That includes the water consumed by the cow and to grow the food she eats, plus water to process the milk.

2,600 gallons

More than 2,600 gallons of water is required to produce a single serving of steak.

2 The Distribution of Groundwater

When rain falls on Earth's land surface, some of the water runs off, some returns to the atmosphere by evaporation and transpiration, and the remainder soaks into the ground. This last path is the primary source of practically all subsurface water. The amount of water that takes each of these paths, however, varies greatly both in time and space. Influential factors include steepness of slope, nature of surface material, intensity of rainfall, and type and amount of vegetation. Heavy rains falling on steep slopes underlain by impervious materials will obviously result in a high percentage of the water running off. Conversely, if rain falls steadily and gently on more gradual slopes composed of materials that are easily penetrated by the water, a much larger percentage of water soaks into the ground.

Some of the water that soaks in does not travel far because it is held by molecular attraction as a surface film on soil particles. This near-surface zone is called the **zone of soil moisture**. It is crisscrossed by roots, voids left by decayed roots, and animal and worm burrows that enhance the infiltration of rainwater into the soil. Soil water is used by plants in life functions and transpiration. Some water also evaporates directly back into the atmosphere.

Water that is not held as soil moisture percolates downward until it reaches a zone where all the open spaces in sediment and rock are completely filled with water (FIGURE 3). This is the **zone of saturation** (also called the **phreatic zone**). Water in the zone of saturation is called **groundwater**. The upper limit of this zone is known as the **water table**. Extending upward from the water table is the **capillary fringe** (*capillus* = hair). Here groundwater is held by surface tension in tiny passages between grains of soil or sediment. The area above the water table that includes the capillary fringe and the zone of soil moisture is called the **unsaturated zone** (also known as the **vadose zone**). The pore spaces in this zone contain both air and water. Although a considerable amount of water can be present in the unsaturated zone, this water cannot be pumped by wells because it clings too tightly to rock and soil particles. By contrast, below the water table, the water pressure is great enough to allow water to enter wells, thus permitting groundwater to be withdrawn for use. We will examine wells more closely later in the chapter.

 SMARTFIGURE 3
Water beneath Earth's surface
The shape of the water table is usually a subdued replica of the surface topography. During periods of drought, the water table falls, reducing streamflow and drying up some wells.

2 CONCEPT CHECKS

1. When rain falls on land, what factors influence the amount of water that soaks in?
2. Define *groundwater* and relate it to the water table.

Soil moisture

Unsaturated zone

Water table

Capillary fringe

Zone of saturation

Groundwater

Stream

Well

Normal water table

Water table during drought

3 The Water Table

The water table, the upper limit of the zone of saturation, is a very significant feature of the groundwater system. The water table level is important in predicting the productivity of wells, explaining the changes in the flow of springs and streams, and accounting for fluctuations in the levels of lakes.

Variations in the Water Table

The depth of the water table is highly variable and can range from zero, when it is at the surface, to hundreds of meters in some places. An important characteristic of the water table is that its configuration varies seasonally and from year to year because the addition of water to the groundwater system is closely related to the quantity, distribution, and timing of precipitation. Except where the water table is at the surface, we cannot observe it directly. However, the elevation of the water table is mapped and studied in detail by examining water levels in wells (FIGURE 4). The U.S. Geological Survey and state agencies maintain and monitor an extensive network of observation wells to provide statistics about groundwater levels. Such data are the basis for maps that reveal that the water table is rarely level, as we might expect a table to be (FIGURE 5). Instead, its shape is usually a subdued replica of the surface topography, reaching its highest elevations beneath hills and then descending toward valleys (see Figure 3). Where a wetland (swamp) is encountered, the water table is right at the surface. Lakes and streams generally occupy areas low enough that the water table is above the land surface.

Several factors contribute to the irregular surface of the water table. One important influence is the fact that groundwater moves very slowly and at varying rates under different conditions. Because of this, water tends to "pile up" beneath high areas between stream valleys. If rainfall were to cease completely, these water table "hills" would slowly subside and gradually approach the level of the valleys. However, new supplies of rainwater are

Radio antenna

Photovoltaic panel

Recorder box

Counterweight Float

Water table

Water level data can be accessed remotely.

A groundwater network is an array of wells where water levels are routinely measured. The U. S. Geological Survey in conjunction with state agencies maintains an extensive network of about 20,000 observation wells. This map shows the network of wells in Missouri.

Kansas City

St. Louis

The steady drop in water level from late May to November is the result of water discharging from the aquifer to feed springs and streams but not being replaced by recharge.

April 13–14
1.6 in. of rain

January 12–15
2.54 in. of rain

November 29–30
4.39 in. of rain

Depth to water level, feet below land surface

Dry weather

Jul 01 2006 · Sep 01 2006 · Nov 01 2006 · Jan 01 2007 · Mar 01 2007

Groundwater recharge and discharge at the Akers observation well in Shannon County, Missouri. The height of the water table in this well and many others in this region shows a steady decline between spring and fall. This occurs because recharge is low during these months. However, water continues to move through the aquifer to supply springs and streams in the area maintaining their flow even in dry years.

FIGURE 4 Monitoring the water table
Water level measurements from observation wells are a basic and important source of data. The well location highlighted in red on the map is the well whose data are shown below. (Photo by Missouri Dept. of Natural Resources)

usually added frequently enough to prevent this. Nevertheless, in times of extended drought, the water table may drop enough to dry up shallow wells (see Figure 3). Other causes for the uneven water table are variations in rainfall and permeability from place to place.

Interaction Between Groundwater and Streams

The interaction between the groundwater system and streams is a basic link in the hydrologic cycle. It can take

Groundwater

FIGURE 5 Mapping the water table
The water table coincides with the water level in observation wells.

●121.2   ●145.2   ●151.3

119.4●   ●141.6

            ●124.8   133.3 ●

      ●115.7   ●121.9

106.5●

                    114.4 ●

Step 1 The locations of observation wells and the elevations of the water table above sea level are plotted on the map.

●121.2   ●145.2 ─150─ ●151.3

119.4●   ●141.6

─140─

            ●124.8 ─130─   133.3 ●

─120─

      ●115.7   ●121.9

106.5● ─110─

                    114.4 ●

Step 2 Data points are used to guide the drawing of water-table contour lines. Groundwater flow lines can be added to show water movement in the upper portion of the zone of saturation. Groundwater moves perpendicular to the contours and down the slope of the water table.

place in one of three ways. Streams may gain water from the inflow of groundwater through the streambed. Such streams are called **gaining streams** (FIGURE 6A). For this to occur, the elevation of the water table must be higher than the level of the surface of the stream. Streams may lose water to the groundwater system by outflow through the streambed. The term **losing stream** is applied to

this situation (FIGURE 6B,C). When this happens, the elevation of the water table must be lower than the surface of the stream. The third possibility is a combination of the first two: A stream gains in some sections and loses in others.

Losing streams can be connected to the groundwater system by a continuous saturated zone or they can be disconnected from the groundwater system by an unsaturated zone. Compare parts B and C in Figure 6. When the stream is disconnected, the water table may have a discernible bulge beneath the stream if the rate of water movement through the streambed and unsaturated zone is greater than the rate of groundwater movement away from the bulge.

In some settings, a stream might always be a gaining stream or might always be a losing stream. However, in many situations, flow direction can vary a great deal along a stream; some sections receive groundwater and other sections lose water to the groundwater system. Moreover, the direction of flow can change over a short time span as the result of storms adding water near the stream bank or when temporary flood peaks move down the channel.

Groundwater contributes to streams in most geologic and climatic settings. Even where streams are primarily losing water to the groundwater system, certain sections may receive groundwater inflow during some seasons. In one study of 54 streams in all parts of the United States, the analysis indicated that 52 percent of the streamflow was contributed by groundwater. The groundwater contribution ranged from a low of 14 percent to a maximum of 90 percent. Groundwater is also a major source of water for lakes and wetlands.

FIGURE 6 Interactions between the groundwater system and streams

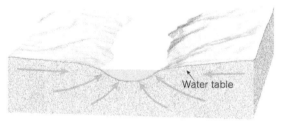

A. Gaining stream Gaining streams receive water from the groundwater system.

B. Losing stream (connected) Losing streams provide water to the groundwater system.

C. Losing stream (disconnected) When losing streams are separated from the groundwater system by the unsaturated zone, a bulge may form in the water table.

3 CONCEPT CHECKS

1. A kitchen table is flat. Is this usually the case for a water table? Why?
2. Contrast a gaining stream and a losing stream.

labels in Figure 6 images: Water table, Unsaturated zone

4 Factors Influencing the Storage and Movement of Groundwater

The nature of subsurface materials strongly influences the rate of groundwater movement and the amount of groundwater that can be stored. Two factors are especially important—porosity and permeability.

Porosity

Water soaks into the ground because bedrock, sediment, and soil contain countless voids or openings. These openings are similar to those of a sponge and are often called *pore spaces.* The quantity of ground-water that can be stored depends on the **porosity** of the material, which is the percentage of the total volume of rock or sediment that consists of pore spaces (FIGURE 7). Voids most often are spaces between sedimentary particles, but also common are joints, faults, cavities formed by the dissolving of soluble rock such as limestone, and vesicles (voids left by gases escaping from lava).

Variations in porosity can be great. Sediment is commonly quite porous, and open spaces may occupy 10 to 50 percent of the sediment's total volume. Pore space depends on the size and shape of the grains, how they are packed together, the degree of sorting, and in sedimentary rocks, the amount of cementing material. For example, clay may have a porosity as high as 50 percent, whereas some gravels may have only 20 percent voids.

Where sediments are poorly sorted, the porosity is reduced because the finer particles tend to fill the openings among the larger grains. Most igneous and metamorphic rocks, as well as some sedimentary rocks, are composed of tightly interlocking crystals so the voids between the grains may be negligible. In these rocks, fractures must provide the porosity.

Permeability, Aquitards, and Aquifers

Porosity alone cannot measure a material's capacity to yield groundwater. Rock or sediment may be very porous yet still not allow water to move through it. The pores must be *connected* to allow water flow, and they must be *large enough* to allow flow. Thus, the **permeability** (*permeare* = to penetrate) of a material—its ability to *transmit* a fluid—is also very important.

The beaker on the left is filled with 1000 ml of sediment. The beaker on the right is filled with 1000 ml of water.

The sediment-filled beaker now contains 500 ml of water. Pore spaces (porosity) must represent 50 percent of the volume of the sediment.

FIGURE 7 Porosity demonstration Porosity is the percentage of the total volume of rock or sediment that consists of pore spaces.

Groundwater moves by twisting and turning through small interconnected openings. The smaller the pore spaces, the more slowly the water moves. This idea is clearly illustrated by examining the information about the water-yielding potential of different materials in TABLE 1. Here groundwater is divided into two categories: (1) the portion that will drain under the influence of gravity (called *specific yield*) and (2) the part that is retained as a film on particle and rock surfaces and in tiny openings (called *specific retention*). Specific yield indicates how much water is actually available for use, whereas specific retention indicates how much water remains bound in the material. For example, the ability of a clay deposit to store water may be great, due to high porosity, but its pore spaces are so small that water is unable to move through it. Thus, the clay's porosity is high but because its permeability is poor, it has a very low specific yield.

TABLE 1 Selected Values of Porosity, Specific Yield, and Specific Retention*			
Material	Porosity	Specific Yield	Specific Retention
Clay	50	2	48
Sand	25	22	3
Gravel	20	19	1
Limestone	20	18	2
Sandstone (semiconsolidated)	11	6	5
Granite	0.1	0.09	0.01
Basalt (fresh)	11	8	3

*Values in percent by volume.

Source: U.S. Geological Survey, Water Supply Paper 2220, 1987.

Impermeable layers that hinder or prevent water movement are termed **aquitards** (*aqua* = water, *tard* = slow). Clay is a good example. On the other hand, larger particles, such as sand or gravel, have larger pore spaces. Therefore, the water moves with relative ease. Permeable rock strata or sediment that transmit groundwater freely are called **aquifers** (*aqua* = water, *fer* = carry). Sands and gravels are common examples.

In summary, porosity is not always a reliable guide to the amount of groundwater that can be produced, and permeability is significant in determining the rate of groundwater movement and the quantity of water that might be pumped from a well.

4 CONCEPT CHECKS

1. Distinguish between porosity and permeability.
2. What is the difference between an aquifer and an aquitard?

EYE on Earth

Marshes are characterized by saturated, poorly drained soils. This wetland is located southwest of Fort McMurray, Alberta, Canada. (Photo by Michael Collier)

Question 1 Describe the position of the water table in this image.

Question 2 Suggest two situations that might cause the marsh to disappear. Include one natural cause and one cause related to human activities.

5 How Groundwater Moves

The movement of water in the atmosphere and on the land surface is relatively easy to visualize, but the movement of groundwater is not. Near the beginning of the chapter, we mentioned the common misconception that groundwater occurs in underground rivers that resemble surface streams. Although subsurface streams do exist, they are *not* common (**FIGURE 8**). Rather, as you learned in the preceding sections, groundwater exists in the pore spaces and fractures in rock and sediment. Thus, contrary to any impressions of rapid flow that an underground river might evoke, the movement of most groundwater is exceedingly slow, from pore to pore.

One method of measuring the rate of groundwater movement involves introducing dye into a well. The time is measured until the coloring agent appears in another well at a known distance from the first. A typical rate for many aquifers is about 15 meters per year (about 4 centimeters per day).

A Simple Groundwater Flow System

FIGURE 9 depicts a simple example of a *groundwater flow system*—a three-dimensional body of Earth material saturated with moving groundwater. It shows groundwater moving along flow paths from areas of **recharge**, where groundwater is being replenished, to a **discharge area** along a stream where groundwater is flowing back to the surface. Discharge also occurs at springs, lakes, or wetlands, and in coastal areas, as groundwater seeps into bays or the ocean. Transpiration by plants whose roots extend to near the water table represents another form of groundwater discharge. Wells, where groundwater is being pumped to the surface, represent artificial discharge areas.

The energy that makes groundwater move is provided by the force of gravity. In response to gravity, water moves from areas where the water table is high to zones where the water table is lower. Although some water takes the most direct path down the slope of the water table, much of the water follows long, curving paths.

Figure 9 shows water percolating into a stream from all possible directions. Some paths clearly turn upward, apparently against the force of gravity, and enter through the bottom of the channel. This is easily explained: The deeper you go into the zone of saturation, the greater is the water pressure. Thus, the looping curves followed by water in the saturated zone may be thought of as a compromise between the downward pull of gravity and the tendency of water to move toward areas of reduced pressure. As a result, water at any given height is under greater pressure beneath a hill than beneath a stream channel, and the water tends to migrate toward points of lower pressure.

Measuring Groundwater Movement

The foundations of our modern understanding of groundwater movement began in the mid-nineteenth century with the work of the French engineer Henry Darcy.

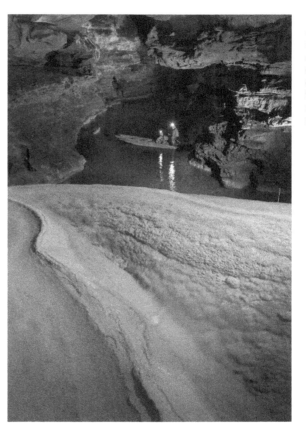

FIGURE 8 Underground rivers—a common misconception Although subsurface channels of flowing water occasionally occur, such as this one in France, they are rare. (Photo by SUDRES Jean-Daniel/AGE Fotostock)

The looping flow lines may be thought of as a compromise between the downward pull of gravity and the tendency of groundwater to move toward areas of reduced pressure.

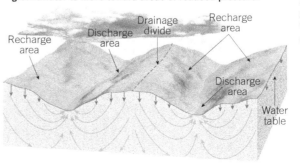

FIGURE 9 Groundwater movement Arrows show paths of groundwater movement through uniformly permeable material.

FIGURE 10 Hydraulic gradient

The hydraulic gradient is determined by measuring the difference in elevation between two points on the water table ($h_1 - h_2$) divided by the distance between them, d. Wells are used to determine the height of the water table.

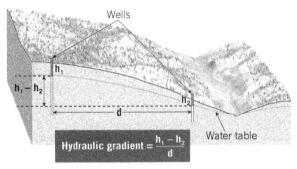

During this time, Darcy made measurements and conducted experiments in an attempt to determine whether the water needs of the city of Dijon in east-central France could be met by tapping local supplies of groundwater. Among the experiments Darcy carried out was one which showed that the velocity of ground-water flow is proportional to the slope of the water table—the steeper the slope, the faster the water moves (because the steeper the slope, the greater the pressure difference between two points). The water table slope is known as the **hydraulic gradient** and can be expressed as follows:

$$\text{Hydraulic gradient} = \frac{h_1 - h_2}{d}$$

where h_1 is the elevation of one point on the water table, h_2 is the elevation of a second point, and d is the horizontal distance between the two points (FIGURE 10).

Darcy also experimented with different materials, such as coarse sand and fine sand, by measuring the rate of flow through sediment-filled tubes that were tilted at varying angles. He found that flow velocity varied with the permeability of the sediment: Ground-water flows more rapidly through sediments having greater permeability than through materials having lower permeability. This factor is known as **hydraulic conductivity** and is a coefficient that takes into account the permeability of the aquifer and the viscosity of the fluid.

To determine discharge (Q)—that is, the actual volume of water that flows through an aquifer in a specified time—the following equation is used:

$$Q = \frac{KA(h_1 - h_2)}{d}$$

where $\dfrac{h_1 - h_2}{d}$ is the hydraulic gradient, K is the coefficient that represents hydraulic conductivity, and A is the cross-sectional area of the aquifer. This expression has come to be called **Darcy's law**, in honor of the pioneering French scientist-engineer. Using this equation, if you know an aquifer's hydraulic gradient, conductivity, and cross-sectional area, you can calculate its discharge.

Different Scales of Movement

The geographic extent of groundwater flow systems varies from a few square kilometers or less to tens of thousands of square kilometers. The length of flow paths ranges from a few meters to tens and sometimes hundreds of kilometers. FIGURE 11 is a cross section of a hypothetical region in which a deep groundwater flow system is overlain by and connected to several, more shallow local flow systems. The subsurface geology exhibits a complicated arrangement of high

SMARTFIGURE 11
Hypothetical groundwater flow system
The diagram includes sub-systems at three different scales. Variations in surface topography and subsurface geology can produce a complex situation. The horizontal scale of the figure could range from tens to hundreds of kilometers.

Explanation

High hydraulic-conductivity aquifer

Low hydraulic-conductivity aquitard unit

-------- Water table

⟵ Groundwater movement in near-surface local systems

⟵ Groundwater movement in a subregional system

⟵ Groundwater movement in a deep regional system

hydraulic-conductivity aquifer units and low hydraulic-conductivity aquitard units.

Starting near the top of Figure 11, the blue arrows represent water movement in several local groundwater systems that occur in the upper water table aquifer. They are separated by groundwater divides at the center of the hills and discharge into the nearest surface water body. Beneath these most shallow systems, red arrows show water movement in a somewhat deeper system in which groundwater does not discharge into the nearest surface water body, but into a more distant one. Finally, the black arrows show groundwater movement in a deep regional system that lies beneath the more shallow ones and is connected to them. The horizontal scale of the figure could range from tens to hundreds of kilometers.

5 CONCEPT CHECKS

1. What factors cause water to follow the paths shown in Figure 9?
2. Relate groundwater movement to hydraulic gradient and hydraulic conductivity.
3. Contrast groundwater movement in a near-surface local system with that in a deep regional system.

EYE on Earth

The drainage basin of the Republican River occupies portions of Colorado, Nebraska, and Kansas. A significant part of the basin is considered semiarid. In 1943, the three states made a legal agreement regarding sharing the river's water. In 1998, Kansas went to court to force farmers in southern Nebraska to substantially reduce the amount of groundwater used for irrigation. Nebraska officials claimed that the farmers were not taking water from the Republican River and thus were not violating the 1943 agreement. The court ruled in favor of Kansas. (Photo by Michael Collier)

Question 1 Explain why the court ruled that groundwater in southern Nebraska should be considered part of the Republican River system.

Question 2 How might heavy irrigation in a drainage basin influence the flow of a river?

Michael Collier

6 Wells

The most common method for removing groundwater is to use a **well**, a hole bored into the zone of saturation (FIGURE 12). Wells serve as small reservoirs into which groundwater migrates and from which it can be pumped to the surface. The use of wells dates back many centuries and continues to be an important method of obtaining water today. Groundwater is the principal source of drinking water for about 50 percent of the U.S. population and provides about 96 percent of the water used for rural domestic supplies.

FIGURE 12 Wells
Wells are the most common means by which people obtain groundwater.
(Top photo by Shutterstock; bottom photo by ASP/YPP/AGE Fotostock)

The water table level may fluctuate considerably during the course of a year, dropping during dry periods and rising following periods of rain. Therefore, to ensure a continuous supply of water, a well must penetrate below the water table. Whenever water is withdrawn from a well, the water table around the well is lowered. This effect, termed **drawdown**, decreases with increasing distance from the well. The result is a depression in the water table, roughly conical in shape, known as a **cone of depression** (FIGURE 13). Because the cone of depression increases the hydraulic gradient near the well, groundwater will flow more rapidly toward the opening. For most smaller domestic wells, the cone of depression is negligible. However, when wells are heavily pumped for irrigation or for industrial purposes, the withdrawal of water can be great enough to create a very wide and steep cone of depression. This may substantially lower the water table in an area and cause nearby shallow wells to become dry. Figure 13 illustrates this situation.

Digging a successful well is a familiar challenge for people in areas where groundwater is the primary source of supply. One well may be successful at a depth of 10 meters (33 feet), whereas a neighbor may have to go twice as deep to find an adequate supply. Still others may be forced to go deeper or try a different site altogether. When subsurface materials are heterogeneous, the amount of water a well is capable of providing may vary a great deal over short distances. For example, when two nearby wells are drilled to the same level and only one is successful, it may be because there is a perched water table beneath one of them. As FIGURE 14 illustrates, a **perched water table** forms where an aquitard is situated above the main water table. Massive igneous and metamorphic rocks provide

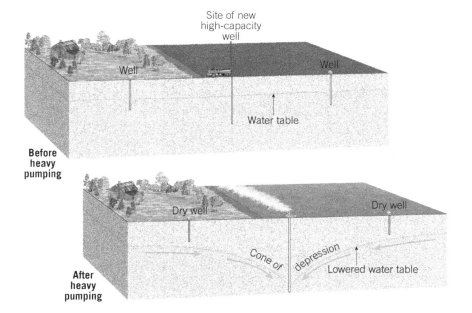

Site of new high-capacity well

Well

Well

Water table

Before heavy pumping

Dry well

Dry well

Cone of depression

Lowered water table

After heavy pumping

SMARTFIGURE 13
Cone of depression
For most small domestic wells, the cone of depression is negligible. When wells are heavily pumped, the cone of depression can be large and may lower the water table such that nearby shallower wells may be left dry.

a second example. These crystalline rocks are usually not very permeable, except where they are cut by many intersecting joints and fractures. Therefore, when a well drilled into such rock does not intersect an adequate network of fractures, it is likely to be unproductive.

6 CONCEPT CHECKS

1. Relate *drawdown* to *cone of depression*.
2. How does a heavily pumping well affect the water table?
3. In Figure 14, two wells are at the same level. Why was one successful and the other not?

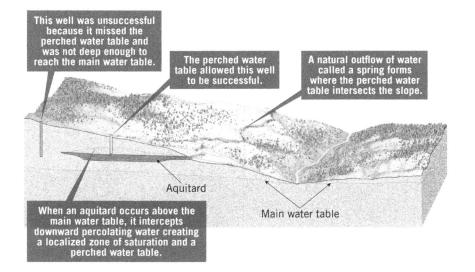

FIGURE 14 Perched water table

This well was unsuccessful because it missed the perched water table and was not deep enough to reach the main water table.

The perched water table allowed this well to be successful.

A natural outflow of water called a spring forms where the perched water table intersects the slope.

Aquitard

When an aquitard occurs above the main water table, it intercepts downward percolating water creating a localized zone of saturation and a perched water table.

Main water table

Drought Impacts the Hydrologic System

Drought is a period of abnormally dry weather that persists long enough to produce a significant hydrologic imbalance such as crop damage or water supply shortages. Drought severity depends upon the degree of moisture deficiency, its duration, and the size of the affected area.

Drought status map for July 30, 2012

During the summer of 2012, extreme or exceptional drought conditions existed over large parts of the United States. Because of the drought, more than 1000 counties in 26 states were declared disaster areas.

The drought was a result of months of meager precipitation accompanied by record-setting summer temperatures and desiccating winds. To examine current and archived drought maps go to: *http://droughtmonitor.unl.edu*

INTENSITY
D0 Abnormally Dry
D1 Drought - Moderate
D2 Drought - Severe
D3 Drought - Extreme
D4 Drought - Exceptional

The record breaking 2012 drought decimated crops and grazing lands. It was the worst since the infamous Dust Bowl era of the 1930s. In many areas soil moisture was depleted and the water table dropped significantly.

Daniel Acker/Bloomberg/Alan

DROUGHT CATEGORIES

METEOROLOGICAL DROUGHT	AGRICULTURAL DROUGHT	HYDROLOGICAL DROUGHT
PRECIPITATION DEFICIENCY (results in reduced runoff and infiltration)	**SOIL MOISTURE DEFICIENCY** (results in low crop yields)	**REDUCED STREAMFLOW, INFLOW TO RESERVOIRS LAKES, AND PONDS; REDUCED WETLANDS** (results in reduced domestic water supply and wildlife habit.

After the onset of meteorological drought, agriculture is affected first, followed by reductions in streamflow and water levels in lakes, streams, and underground. When meteorological drought ends, agricultural drought ends as soil moisture is replenished. It can take much longer for hydrological drought to end.

COMPARING AVERAGE YEARLY COSTS—DROUGHTS, FLOODS, AND HURRICANES

HURRICANES
$1.2 to $4.8 billion
NASA

FLOODS
$2 to $3 billion
AP Photo/Jeff Roberson

DROUGH
$6 to $8 billic
Daniel Acker/Bloomberg/Getty Imag

Although natural disasters such as floods and hurricanes usually generate more attention, droughts can be just as devastating and often carry a bigger price tag. Unlike other hazards which are short-lived, drought occurs in a gradual "creeping" way, making its onset and end difficult to determine.

7 Artesian Systems

In most wells, water cannot rise on its own. If water is first encountered at a depth of 30 meters it remains at that level, fluctuating perhaps 1 or 2 meters with seasonal wet and dry periods. However, in some wells, water rises, sometimes overflowing at the surface. Such wells are abundant in the Artois region of northern France, and so we call these self-rising wells *artesian*.

To many people, the term *artesian* is applied to any well drilled to great depths. This use of the term is incorrect. Others believe that an artesian well must flow freely at the surface. Although this is a more correct notion than the first, it represents too narrow a definition. The term **artesian** is applied to *any* situation in which groundwater under pressure rises above the level of the aquifer. As you will see, this does not always mean a free-flowing surface discharge.

For an artesian system to exist, two conditions usually are met (**FIGURE 15**): (1) Water is confined to an aquifer that is inclined so that one end can receive water, and (2) aquitards, both above and below the aquifer, must be present to prevent the water from escaping. Such an aquifer is called a **confined aquifer**. When such a layer is tapped, the pressure created by the weight of the water above will force the water to rise. If there were no friction, the water in the well would rise to the level of the

water at the top of the aquifer. However, friction reduces the height of the pressure surface. The greater the distance from the recharge area (where water enters the inclined aquifer), the greater the friction and the less the rise of water.

In Figure 15, well 1 is a **nonflowing artesian well** because at this location, the pressure surface is below ground level. When the pressure surface is above the ground and a well is drilled into the aquifer, a **flowing artesian well** is created (well 2 in Figure 15). Not all artesian systems are wells. *Artesian springs* also exist. Here groundwater may reach the surface by rising along a natural

SMARTFIGURE 15
Artesian systems
These groundwater systems occur where an inclined aquifer is surrounded by impermeable beds (aquitards). Such aquifers are called *confined aquifers*. The photo shows a flowing artesian well.
(Photo by James E. Patterson)

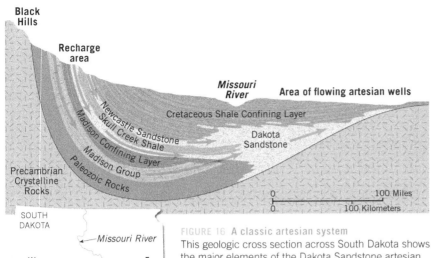

FIGURE 16 A classic artesian system
This geologic cross section across South Dakota shows the major elements of the Dakota Sandstone artesian system.

FIGURE 17 City water systems
City water systems can be considered to be artificial artesian systems.

fracture such as a fault rather than through an artificially produced hole. In deserts, artesian springs are sometimes responsible for creating oases.

Artesian systems act as conduits, often transmitting water great distances from remote areas of recharge to points of discharge. A well-known artesian system in South Dakota is a good example of this (FIGURE 16). In the western part of the state, the edges of a series of sedimentary layers have been bent up to the surface along the flanks of the Black Hills. One of these beds, the permeable Dakota Sandstone, is sandwiched between impermeable strata and gradually dips into the ground toward the east. When the aquifer was first tapped, water poured from the ground surface, creating fountains many meters high. In some places the force of the water was

sufficient to power waterwheels. Such scenes no longer occur because thousands of additional wells now tap the same aquifer. This depleted the reservoir, and the water table in the recharge area was lowered. As a consequence, the pressure dropped to the point where many wells stopped flowing altogether and had to be pumped.

On a different scale, city water systems can be considered examples of artificial artesian systems (FIGURE 17). The water tower, into which water is pumped, would represent the area of recharge, the pipes the confined aquifer, and the faucets in homes the flowing artesian wells.

7 CONCEPT CHECKS

1. Sketch a simple cross section of an artesian system with a flowing well. Label aquitards, aquifers, and the pressure surface.
2. Why do some artesian wells not flow at Earth's surface.

EYE on Earth

In 1900, when this well was drilled near Woonsocket in eastern South Dakota, a "gusher" of water was the result. The stream of water from a 3-inch pipe reached a height of nearly 30 meters (100 feet). Thousands of additional wells now tap the same aquifer. (Photo by N.H. Darton/USGS)

Question 1 Describe or sketch the subsurface geologic situation that was responsible for this fountain of water.

Question 2 What term is applied to a well such as this?

Question 3 Today wells that tap this aquifer do not flow freely at the surface but must be pumped. Suggest a likely reason.

8 Springs, Hot Springs, and Geysers

The phenomena described in this section often arouse people's curiosity and wonder. The fact that springs, hot springs, and geysers are rather mysterious phenomena is not difficult to understand, for here is water (sometimes very hot water) flowing or spewing from the ground in all kinds of weather, in seemingly inexhaustible supply, but with no obvious source.

Springs

Not until the middle of the seventeenth century did the French physicist Pierre Perrault invalidate the age-old assumption that precipitation could not adequately account for the amount of water emanating from springs and flowing in rivers. Over several years, Perrault computed the quantity of water that fell on France's Seine River basin. He then calculated the mean annual runoff by measuring the river's discharge. After allowing for the loss of water by evaporation, he showed that there was sufficient water remaining to feed the springs. Thanks to Perrault's pioneering efforts and the measurements by many afterward, we now know that the source of springs is water from the zone of saturation and that the ultimate source of this water is precipitation.

Whenever the water table intersects Earth's surface, a natural outflow of groundwater results, which we call a **spring** (FIGURE 18). Springs such as the one pictured in Figure 18 form when an aquitard blocks the downward movement of groundwater and forces it to move laterally. Where the permeable bed crops out, a spring results. Another example is illustrated in Figure 14, which shows a perched water table intersecting a slope.

Springs, however, are not confined to places where a perched water table creates a flow at the surface. Many geologic situations lead to the formation of springs because subsurface conditions vary greatly from place to place. Even in areas underlain by impermeable crystalline rocks, permeable zones may exist in the form of fractures or solution channels. If these openings fill with water and intersect the ground surface along a slope, a spring results.

Hot Springs

There is no universally accepted definition of *hot spring*. One frequently used definition is that the water in a **hot spring** is 6° to 9° C (10° to 15° F) warmer than the mean annual air temperature for the locality where it occurs (FIGURE 19). In the United States alone, there are more than 1000 such springs.

FIGURE 18 **Thousand Springs**
These well-known springs are along the Snake River in Hagerman Valley, Idaho. (Photo by David R. Frazier/Alamy Images)

FIGURE 19 **Hot springs**
These examples represent the two different ways the water in hot springs is heated. (Top photo by New York Daily News/Getty Images; bottom photo by Andre Hasson/Alamy)

The springs at Warm Springs, Georgia, the presidential retreat of Franklin Roosevelt, were heated by the geothermal gradient.

Many hot springs, including this one in Iceland, are associated with areas that have experienced recent igneous activity.

Temperatures in deep mines and oil wells usually rise with increasing depth, an average of about 25° C per kilometer, a figure known as the *geothermal gradient*. Therefore, when groundwater circulates at great depths, it becomes heated. If the hot water rises rapidly to the surface, it may emerge as a hot spring. The water of some hot springs in the eastern United States is heated in this manner. The springs at Warm Springs, Georgia, the presidential retreat of Franklin Roosevelt (Figure 19B), are one example. The temperature of these hot springs is always near 32°C (90°F). Another example is Hot Springs National Park, Arkansas, where water temperatures average about 60° C (140° F).

The great majority (more than 95 percent) of the hot springs (and geysers) in the United States are found in the West. A glance at FIGURE 20 reinforces this fact. The

reason for such a distribution is that the sources of heat for most hot springs are magma bodies and hot igneous rocks, and it is in the West that igneous activity has occurred more recently. The hot springs and geysers of the Yellowstone region are well known examples.

Geysers

Geysers are intermittent hot springs or fountains in which columns of water are ejected with great force at various intervals, often rising 30 to 60 meters (100 to 200 feet) into the air. After the jet of water ceases, a column of steam rushes out, usually with a thunderous roar. Perhaps the most famous geyser in the world is Old Faithful in Yellowstone National Park (FIGURE 21). The great abundance, diversity, and spectacular nature of Yellowstone's geysers and other thermal features undoubtedly was the primary reason for its becoming the first national park in the United States. Geysers are also found in other parts of the world, notably New Zealand and Iceland. In fact, the Icelandic word *geysa*, meaning "to gush," gives us the name *geyser*.

How Geysers Work   Geysers occur where extensive underground chambers exist within hot igneous rocks. How they operate is shown in FIGURE 22. As relatively cool groundwater enters the chambers, it is heated by the surrounding rock. At the bottom of the chambers, the water is under great pressure because of the weight of the overlying water. This great pressure prevents the water from boiling at the normal surface temperature of 100° C (212° F). For example, water at the bottom of a 300-meter (1000-foot) water-filled chamber must attain nearly 230° C (450° F) before it will boil. The heating causes the water to expand, with the result that some is forced out at the surface. This loss of water reduces the pressure on the remaining water in the chamber, which lowers the boiling point. A portion of the water deep within the chamber quickly turns to steam, and the geyser erupts (Figure 22). Following eruption, cool groundwater again seeps into the chamber, and the cycle begins anew.

Geyser Deposits   When groundwater from hot springs and geysers flows out at the surface, material in solution is often precipitated, producing an accumulation of chemical sedimentary rock. The material deposited at any given place commonly reflects the chemical makeup of the rock through which the water circulated. When the

Water near the bottom is heated to near its boiling point. The boiling point is higher at the bottom because pressure is high due to the weight of all the water above.

Higher up in the geyser the water is also heated, therefore it expands causing some to flow out at the top. This outflow reduces the pressure on the water at the bottom.

When pressure is reduced at the bottom, boiling occurs. Some of the bottom water flashes into steam. The expanding steam triggers an eruption.

Then the water flows back in and the whole process begin anew.

 SMARTFIGURE 22 How a geyser works
A geyser can form if the underground plumbing does not allow heat to be readily distributed by convection.

FIGURE 23 Yellowstone's Mammoth Hot Springs
Although most of the deposits associated with geysers and hot springs in Yellowstone National Park are silica-rich geyserite, the deposits here consist of a form of limestone called travertine. (Photo by Jamie and Judy Wild/Danita Delimont/Alamy)

water contains dissolved silica, a material called *siliceous sinter*, or *geyserite*, is deposited around the spring. When the water contains dissolved calcium carbonate, a form of limestone called *travertine*, or *calcareous tufa*, is deposited. The latter term is used if the material is spongy and porous.

The deposits at Mammoth Hot Springs in Yellowstone National Park are more spectacular than most others (FIGURE 23). As the hot water flows upward through a series of channels and then out at the surface, the reduced pressure allows carbon dioxide to separate and escape from the water. The loss of carbon dioxide causes the water to become supersaturated with calcium carbonate, which then precipitates. In addition to containing dissolved silica and calcium carbonate, some hot springs contain sulfur, which gives water a poor taste and unpleasant odor. Undoubtedly, Rotten Egg Spring, Nevada, is such a situation.

8 CONCEPT CHECKS

1. Describe some circumstances that lead to the formation of a spring.
2. What warms the waters that flow at Hot Springs National Park, Arkansas, and at Warm Springs, Georgia?
3. What is the source of heat for most hot springs and geysers? How is this reflected in the distribution of these features?
4. Describe what occurs to cause a geyser to erupt.

9 Environmental Problems

Like many of our other valuable natural resources, groundwater is being exploited at an increasing rate. In some areas, overuse threatens the groundwater supply. In other places, groundwater withdrawal has caused the ground and everything resting on it to sink. Still other localities are concerned with the possible contamination of the groundwater supply.

Mining Groundwater

Many natural systems tend to establish a condition of equilibrium. The groundwater system is no exception. The water table's height reflects a balance between the rate of recharge and the rate of discharge and withdrawal. Any imbalance will either raise or lower the water table. Long-term imbalances can lead to a significant drop in the water table if there is either a decrease in recharge due to prolonged drought or an increase in groundwater discharge or withdrawal.

Because of its high porosity, excellent permeability, and great size, the High Plains aquifer, the largest in the United States, accumulated enough freshwater to fill Lake Huron.

EXPLANATION
Water-level change, in feet
Declines
More than 150
100 to 150
50 to 100
25 to 50
10 to 25
No substantial change
+10 to –10
Rises
25 to 50
10 to 25
More than 50
Area of little or no saturated thickness

The U. S. Geological Survey estimates that during the past 60 years, water in storage in the High Plains aquifer declined by about 200 million acre feet (about 65 trillion gallons) with 62 percent of the total decline occurring in Texas.

FIGURE 24 High Plains aquifer
The map shows changes in groundwater levels from predevelopment to 2005. Extensive pumping for irrigation has led to water level declines in excess of 100 feet in parts of four states. Water level rises have occurred where surface water is used for irrigation, such as along the Platte River in Nebraska. (After U.S. Geological Survey)

Many believe that groundwater is an endlessly renewable resource because it is continually replenished by rainfall and melting snow. But in some regions, groundwater has been and continues to be treated as a *nonrenewable* resource. Where this occurs, the water available to recharge the aquifer falls significantly short of the amount being withdrawn.

The High Plains aquifer provides one example (FIGURE 24). Underlying about 111 million acres (450,000 square kilometers [174,000 square miles]) in parts of eight western states, it is one of the largest and most agriculturally significant aquifers in the United States. It accounts for about 30 percent of all groundwater withdrawn for irrigation in the country. Mean annual precipitation is modest—ranging from about 40 centimeters (16 inches) in western portions to about 71 centimeters (28 inches) in eastern parts. Evaporation rates, on the other hand, are high—ranging from about 150 centimeters (60 inches) in the cooler northern parts of the region to 265 centimeters (105 inches) in the warmer southern parts. Because evaporation rates are high relative to precipitation, there is little rainwater to recharge the aquifer. Thus, in some parts of the region, where intense irrigation has been practiced for an extended period, depletion of groundwater has been severe. Figure 24 bears this out. The U.S. Geological Survey estimates that during the past 50 to 60 years, water in storage in the High Plains aquifer declined about 200 million acre feet (about 65 trillion gallons), with 62 percent of the total decline occurring in Texas.

Subsidence

As you will see later in this chapter, surface subsidence can result from natural processes related to groundwater. However, the ground may also sink when water is pumped from wells faster than natural recharge processes can replace it. This effect is particularly pronounced in areas underlain by thick layers of unconsolidated sediments. As the water is withdrawn, the water pressure drops, and the weight of the overburden is transferred to the sediment. The greater pressure packs the sediment grains tightly together, and the ground subsides.

Many areas may be used to illustrate land subsidence caused by excessive pumping of groundwater from relatively loose sediment. A classic example in the United States occurred in the San Joaquin Valley of California, where subsidence approached 9 meters (30 feet) in some areas (FIGURE 25). Many other cases of land subsidence due to groundwater pumping exist in the United States, including Las Vegas, Nevada; New Orleans and Baton Rouge, Louisiana; portions of southern Arizona (FIGURE 26; and the Houston—Galveston area of Texas. In the low-lying coastal area between Houston and Galveston, land subsidence ranges from 1.5 to 3 meters (5 to 9 feet). The result is that about 78 square kilometers (30 square miles) are permanently flooded.

Outside the United States, one of the most spectacular examples of subsidence occurred in Mexico City, a portion of which is built on a former lake bed. In the first half of the twentieth century, thousands of wells were sunk into the water-saturated sediments beneath the city. As water was withdrawn, portions of the city subsided by as much as 6 to 7 meters (20 to 23 feet). In some places buildings have sunk to such a point that access to them from the street is located at what used to be the second-floor level!

FIGURE 25 That sinking feeling! The San Joaquin Valley, an important agricultural area, relies heavily on irrigation. Between 1925 and 1975, this part of the valley subsided almost 9 meters (30 feet) because of the withdrawal of groundwater and the resulting compaction of sediments. (Photo courtesy of U.S. Geological Survey)

Saltwater Contamination

In many coastal areas, the groundwater resource is being threatened by the encroachment of saltwater. To understand this problem, let us examine the relationship between fresh groundwater and salty groundwater. FIGURE 27 is a diagrammatic cross section that illustrates this relationship in a coastal area underlain by permeable homogeneous materials. Freshwater is less dense than saltwater, so it floats on the saltwater and forms a large lens-shaped body that may extend to considerable depths below sea level. In such a situation, if the water table is 1 meter above sea level, the base of the freshwater body will extend to a depth of about 40 meters below sea level. Stated another way, the depth of the freshwater below sea level is about 40 times greater than the elevation of the water table above sea level. Thus, when excessive pumping lowers the water table by a certain amount, the bottom of the freshwater zone will rise by 40 times that amount. Therefore, if groundwater withdrawal continues to exceed recharge, there will come a time when the elevation of the saltwater will be sufficiently high to be drawn into wells,

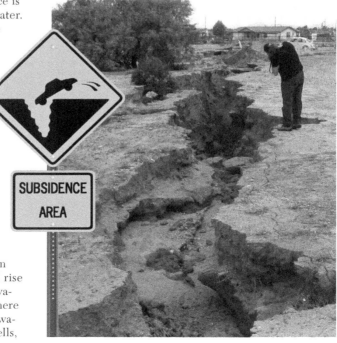

FIGURE 26 Land subsidence in south-central Arizona In southern Arizona, heavy pumping has led to water table declines of up to 180 meters (600 feet). This has triggered extensive and uneven permanent compaction of sediments and the formation of large fissures (cracks) in the ground around the margins of subsiding basins. (Photo by Todd Shipman/Arizona Geological Survey)

609

Because freshwater is less dense than saltwater, it floats on the saltwater and forms a lens-shaped body that may extend to considerable depths below sea level.

If excessive pumping lowers the water table, the base of the freshwater zone will rise 40 times that amount. The result may be saltwater contamination of wells.

thus contaminating the freshwater supply. Deep wells and wells near the shore are usually the first to be affected.

In urbanized coastal areas, the problems created by excessive pumping are compounded by a decrease in the rate of natural recharge. As more and more of the surface is covered by streets, parking lots, and buildings, infiltration into the soil is diminished.

In an attempt to correct the problem of saltwater contamination of groundwater resources, a network of recharge wells may be used. These wells allow wastewater to be pumped back into the groundwater system. A second method of correction is accomplished by building large recharge basins. These basins collect surface drainage and allow it to seep into the ground. On New York's Long Island, where the problem of saltwater contamination was recognized more than 50 years ago, both of these methods have been employed with considerable success (FIGURE 28).

Contamination of freshwater aquifers by saltwater is primarily a problem in coastal areas, but it can also threaten noncoastal locations. Many ancient sedimentary rocks of marine origin were deposited when the ocean covered places that are now far inland. In some instances, significant quantities of seawater were trapped and still remain in the rock. These strata sometimes contain quantities of freshwater that people may pump. However, if freshwater is removed more rapidly than it is replenished, saline water may encroach and render the wells unusable. Such a situation threatened users of a deep (Cambrian age) sandstone aquifer in the Chicago area. To counteract this, water from Lake Michigan was allocated to the affected communities to offset the rate of withdrawal from the aquifer.

Groundwater Contamination

The pollution of groundwater is a serious matter, particularly in areas where aquifers provide a large part of the water supply. One common source of groundwater pollution is sewage. Its sources include an ever-increasing number of septic tanks, as well as inadequate or broken sewer systems and farm wastes.

If sewage water that is contaminated with bacteria enters the groundwater system, it may become purified through natural processes. The harmful bacteria may be mechanically filtered by the sediment through which the water percolates, destroyed by chemical oxidation, and/or assimilated by other organisms. For purification to occur, however, the aquifer must be of the correct composition. For example, extremely permeable

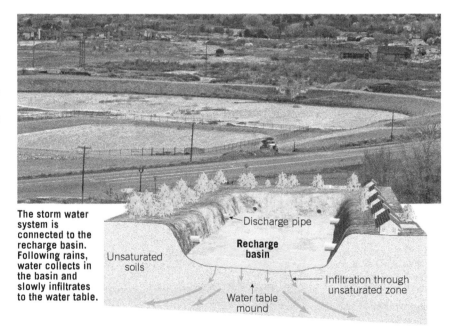

The storm water system is connected to the recharge basin. Following rains, water collects in the basin and slowly infiltrates to the water table.

aquifers (such as highly fractured crystalline rock, coarse gravel, or cavernous limestone) have such large openings that contaminated groundwater may travel long distances without being cleansed. In this case, the water flows too rapidly and is not in contact with the surrounding material long enough for purification to occur. This is the problem at well 1 in FIGURE 29A.

On the other hand, when the aquifer is composed of sand or permeable sandstone, it can sometimes be purified after traveling only a few dozen meters through it. The openings between sand grains are large enough to permit water movement, yet the movement of the water is slow enough to allow ample time for its purification (well 2, FIGURE 29B).

Although the contaminated water has traveled more than 100 meters before reaching Well 1, the water moves too rapidly through the cavernous limestone to be purified.

A.

As the discharge from the septic tank percolates through the permeable sandstone, it moves more slowly and is purified in a relatively short distance.

B.

FIGURE 29 Comparing two aquifers
In this example, the lime-stone aquifer allowed the contamination to reach a well but the sandstone aquifer did not.

EYE on Earth

These satellite images show changes over a 21-year span to a portion of the desert in northern Saudi Arabia, a region known for its sunshine, high temperatures, and meager rainfall. The green circles are agricultural fields that are about 1 kilometer (0.62 mile) in diameter. Water for irrigation is pumped from deep aquifers and distributed around a center point within each field—a technique known as center pivot irrigation. The deep aquifers contain water that dates to the Ice Age about 20,000 years ago, a time when the climate in this region was wetter and milder. (Photo by NASA)

Each circle is 1 km in diameter

1991   2012

NASA   NASA

Question 1 Is it likely that agricultural activity in this region is sustainable indefinitely? Explain.

Question 2 A significant portion of the water placed on these fields is "lost" (not available to the crops). Suggest a reason for the loss of water.

Question 3 Relate what is occurring to groundwater in the region pictured here to an example of a similar situation in the United States.

FIGURE 30 Changing direction
Drawdown at the heavily pumped well changed the slope of the water table, which led to contamination of the small well.

Originally the outflow from the septic tank moved away from the small well.

The heavily pumped well changed the slope of the water table, causing contaminated groundwater to flow toward the small well.

Sometimes sinking a well can lead to groundwater pollution problems. If the well pumps a sufficient quantity of water, the cone of depression will locally increase the slope of the water table. In some instances, the original slope may even be reversed. This could lead to the contamination of wells that yielded unpolluted water before heavy pumping began (FIGURE 30). Also recall that the rate of groundwater movement increases as the slope of the water table gets steeper. This could produce problems because a faster rate of movement allows less time for the water to be purified in the aquifer before it is pumped to the surface.

Other sources and types of contamination also threaten groundwater supplies (FIGURE 31). These include widely used substances such as highway salt, fertilizers

that are spread across the land surface, and pesticides. In addition, a wide array of chemicals and industrial materials may leak from pipelines, storage tanks, landfills, and holding ponds. Some of these pollutants are classified as *hazardous*, meaning that they are either flammable, corrosive, explosive, or toxic. In land disposal, potential contaminants are heaped onto mounds or spread directly over the ground. As rainwater oozes through the refuse, it may dissolve a variety of organic and inorganic materials. If the leached material reaches the water table, it will mix with the groundwater and contaminate the supply. Similar problems may result from leakage of shallow excavations called holding ponds into which a variety of liquid wastes are disposed.

Because groundwater movement is usually slow, polluted water can go undetected for a long time. In fact, contamination is sometimes discovered only after drinking water has been affected and people become ill. By this time, the volume of polluted water may be very large, and even if the source of contamination is removed immediately, the problem is not solved. Although the sources of groundwater contamination are numerous, there are relatively few solutions.

Once the source of the problem has been identified and eliminated, the most common practice is simply to abandon the water supply and allow the pollutants to be flushed away gradually. This is the least costly and

FIGURE 31 Potential sources of contamination
Sometimes agricultural chemicals, materials leached from landfills, and leaking gasoline storage tanks contaminate an aquifer. (Photo A by Michael Collier; photo B by Picsfive/Shutterstock; photo C by Earth Gallery Environment/Alamy)

A.

B.

C.

easiest solution, but the aquifer must remain unused for many years. To accelerate this process, polluted water is sometimes pumped out and treated. Following removal of the tainted water, the aquifer is allowed to recharge naturally, or in some cases the treated water or other freshwater is pumped back in. This process is costly, time-consuming, and may be risky because there is no way to be certain that all of the contamination has been removed. Clearly, the most effective solution to ground-water contamination is prevention.

9 CONCEPT CHECKS

1. Describe the problem associated with pumping groundwater for irrigation in the southern High Plains.
2. Explain why ground may subside after groundwater is pumped to the surface.
3. Which aquifer would be most effective in purifying polluted groundwater: coarse gravel, sand, or cavernous limestone?
4. Describe a significant problem that may arise when groundwater is heavily pumped at a coastal site.

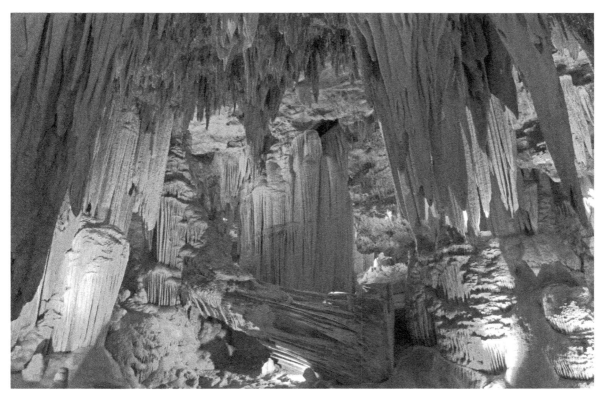

Luray Caverns are situated in Virginia's Shenandoah Valley. Groundwater is responsible for creating its chambers and decorating them. These processes are discussed beginning on the next page. (Photo by Glow Images)

10 The Geologic Work of Groundwater

Groundwater dissolves rock. This fact is key to understanding how caverns and sinkholes form. Because soluble rocks, especially limestone, underlie millions of square kilometers of Earth's surface, it is here that the groundwater carries on its important role as an erosional agent. Limestone is nearly insoluble in pure water but is quite easily dissolved by water containing small quantities of carbonic acid, and most groundwater contains this acid. It forms because rainwater readily dissolves carbon dioxide from the air and from decaying plants. Therefore, when groundwater comes in contact with limestone, the carbonic acid reacts with the calcite (calcium carbonate) in the rocks to form calcium bicarbonate, a soluble material that is then carried away in solution:

$$\underset{\text{calcite}}{CaCO_3} + \underset{\text{carbonic acid}}{(H^+ + HCO_3^-)} \rightarrow \underset{\text{calcium ion}}{Ca^{2+}} + \underset{\text{bicarbonate ion}}{2\ HCO_3^-}$$

Caverns

The most spectacular results of groundwater's erosional handiwork are limestone **caverns**. In the United States alone, about 17,000 caves have been discovered, and new ones are being found every year. Although most are relatively small, some have spectacular dimensions. Mammoth Cave in Kentucky and Carlsbad Caverns in southeastern New Mexico are famous examples. The Mammoth Cave system is the most extensive in the world, with more than 540 kilometers (335 miles) of interconnected passages. The dimensions at Carlsbad Caverns are impressive in a different way. Here we find the largest and perhaps most spectacular single chamber. The Big Room at Carlsbad Caverns has an area equivalent to 14 football fields and enough height to accommodate the U.S. Capitol building.

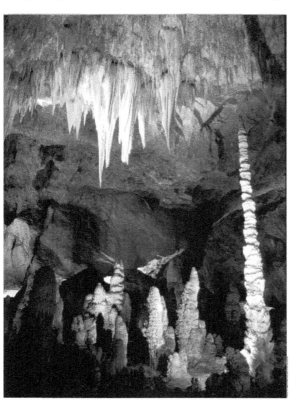

FIGURE 32 Cave decorations
Speleothems are of many types, including stalactites, stalagmites, and columns. This scene is in New Mexico's Carlsbad Caverns National Park. (Photo by Fritz Poelking/Glow Images)

Cavern Development Most caverns are created at or just below the water table, in the zone of saturation. Here acidic groundwater follows lines of weakness in the rock, such as joints and bedding planes. As time passes, the dissolving process slowly creates cavities and gradually enlarges them into caverns. Material that is dissolved by the groundwater is eventually discharged into streams and carried to the ocean.

In many caves, development has occurred at several levels, with the current cavern-forming activity occurring at the lowest elevation. This situation reflects the close relationship between the formation of major subterranean passages and the river valleys into which they drain. As streams cut their valleys deeper, the water table drops as the elevation of the river drops. Consequently, during periods when surface streams are rapidly downcutting, surrounding groundwater levels drop rapidly, and cave passages are abandoned by the water while the passages are still relatively small in cross-sectional area. Conversely, when the entrenchment of streams is slow or negligible, there is time for large cave passages to form.

How Dripstone Forms Certainly the features that arouse the greatest curiosity for most cavern visitors are the stone formations that give some caverns a wonderland appearance. These are not erosional features, like the cavern itself, but depositional features created by the seemingly endless dripping of water over great spans of time. The calcium carbonate that is left behind produces the limestone we call travertine. These cave deposits, however, are also commonly called *dripstone*, an obvious reference to their mode of origin. Although the formation of caverns takes place in the zone of saturation, the deposition of dripstone is not possible until the caverns are above the water table in the unsaturated zone. As soon as the chamber is filled with air, the stage is set for the decoration phase of cavern building to begin.

Dripstone Features—Speleothems The various dripstone features found in caverns are collectively called **speleothems** (*spelation* = cave, *them* = put), no two of which are exactly alike (FIGURE 32). Perhaps the most familiar speleothems are **stalactites** (*stalaktos* = trickling). These icicle-like pendants hang from the ceiling of the cavern and form where water seeps through cracks above. When the water reaches air in the cave, some of the dissolved carbon dioxide escapes from the drop, and calcite precipitates. Deposition occurs as a ring around the edge of the water drop. As drop after drop follows, each leaves an infinitesimal trace of calcite behind, and a hollow limestone tube is created. Water then moves through the tube, remains suspended momentarily at the end, contributes a tiny ring of calcite, and falls to the cavern floor. The stalactite just described is appropriately called a *soda straw* (FIGURE 33). Often the hollow tube of the soda straw becomes plugged or its supply of water increases. In either case, the water is forced to flow and hence deposit along the outside of the tube. As deposition continues, the stalactite takes on the more common conical shape.

Speleothems that form on the floor of a cavern and reach upward toward the ceiling are called **stalagmites** (*stalagmos* = dropping). The water supplying the calcite for stalagmite growth falls from the ceiling and splatters over the surface. As a result, stalagmites do not have a central tube and are usually more massive in appearance and rounded on their upper ends than stalactites. Given enough time, a downward-growing stalactite and an upward-growing stalagmite may join to form a *column*.

Karst Topography

Many areas of the world have landscapes that, to a large extent, have been shaped by the dissolving power of groundwater. Such areas are said to exhibit **karst topography**, named for the Krs Plateau in Slovenia, located along the northeastern shore of the Adriatic Sea, where such topography is strikingly developed. In the United States, karst landscapes occur in many areas that are underlain by limestone, including portions of Kentucky, Tennessee, Alabama, southern Indiana, and central and northern Florida (FIGURE 34). Generally, arid and semiarid areas

FIGURE 33 Soda straw
This live soda straw stalactite is in Chinn Springs Cave, Independence County, Arkansas. (Photo by Dante Fenolio/ Photo Researchers, Inc.)

FIGURE 34 Development of a karst landscape

During early stages, groundwater percolates through limestone along joints and bedding planes. Solution activity creates and enlarges caverns at and below the water table.

With time, caverns grow larger and the number and size of sinkholes increase. Surface drainage is frequently funneled below ground.

Collapse of caverns and coalescence of sinkholes form larger, flat-floored depressions. Eventually solution activity may remove most of the limestone from the area, leavin isolated remnants as in Figure 36.

FIGURE 35 Sinkholes
Karst landscapes are typically punctuated with these
depressions. (Top photo by
David Wall/Alamy Images; bottom
photo by AP Photo/The Florida
Times-Union, Jon M. Fletcher).

Groundwater was responsible for creating these sinkholes west of Timaru on New Zealand's South Island.

This small sinkhole formed suddenly when the roof of a cavern collapsed, eliminating the backyard of this house in Lake City, Florida.

are too dry to develop karst topography. When solution features exist in such regions, they are likely to be remnants of a time when rainier conditions prevailed.

Karst areas typically have irregular terrain punctuated with many depressions, called **sinkholes**, or **sinks** (FIGURE 35). In the limestone areas of Florida, Kentucky, and southern Indiana, there are tens of thousands of these depressions, varying in depth from just 1 or 2 meters to a maximum of more than 50 meters.

Sinkholes commonly form in two ways. Some develop gradually over many years, without any physical disturbance to the rock. In these situations, the limestone immediately below the soil is dissolved by downward-sweeping rainwater that is freshly charged with carbon dioxide. With time, the bedrock surface is lowered and the fractures into which the water seeps are enlarged. As the fractures grow in size, soil subsides into the widening voids, from which it is removed by groundwater flowing in the passages below. These depressions are usually shallow and have gentle slopes.

In contrast, sinkholes can also form abruptly and without warning when the roof of a cavern collapses under its own weight. Typically, the depressions created in this manner are steep-sided and deep. When they form in populous areas, they may represent a serious geologic hazard. Such a situation is shown in the lower photo of Figure 35.

In addition to a surface pockmarked by sinkholes, karst regions characteristically show a striking lack of surface drainage (streams). Following rainfall, the runoff is quickly funneled belowground through sinks. It then flows through caverns until it finally reaches the water table. Where streams do exist at the surface, their paths are usually short. The names of such streams often give a clue to their fate. In the Mammoth Cave area of Kentucky, for example, there is Sinking Creek, Little Sinking Creek, and

Sinking Branch. Some sinkholes become plugged with clay and debris, creating small lakes or ponds.

Some regions of karst development exhibit landscapes that look very different from the sinkhole-studded terrain depicted in Figure 34. One striking example is an extensive region in southern China that is described as exhibiting *tower karst*. As Figure 3 shows, the term *tower* is appropriate because the landscape consists of a maze of isolated steep-sided hills that rise abruptly from the ground. Each is riddled with interconnected caves and passageways. This type of karst topography forms in wet tropical and subtropical regions having thick beds of highly jointed limestone. Here groundwater has dissolved large volumes of limestone, leaving only these residual towers. Karst development occurs more rapidly

Groundwater

FIGURE 36 Tower karst in China
One of the best-known and most distinctive regions of tower karst development is along the Li River in the Guilin District of southeastern China. The painting "Peach Garden Land of Immortals" clearly depicts this distinctive landscape. (Landscape photo Philippe Michel/AGE Fotostock; painting photo by Qiu Ying)

in tropical climates due to the abundant rainfall and the greater availability of carbon dioxide from the decay of lush tropical vegetation. The extra carbon dioxide in the soil means there is more carbonic acid for dissolving limestone. Other tropical areas of advanced karst development include portions of Puerto Rico, western Cuba, and northern Vietnam.

10 CONCEPT CHECKS

1. How does groundwater create caves?
2. What causes cave formation to stop at one level (depth) but continue or begin at a lower level?
3. How do stalactites and stalagmites form?
4. Describe two ways in which sinkholes form.

CONCEPTS IN REVIEW: GROUNDWATER

1 The Importance of Groundwater

Describe the importance of groundwater as a source of freshwater and groundwater's roles as a geologic agent.

• Groundwater occurs below Earth's surface, mainly in tiny pore spaces between rock or sediment grains. Though it is a small fraction of all the water on Earth, groundwater makes up 94 percent of all liquid freshwater and is a critical resource for human civilization. Groundwater is important geologically, too: It dissolves rock to make caverns and supplies surface streams with additional water.

RESOURCE SOURCE From where do you get your drinking water? Does groundwater or surface water supply it?

2 The Distribution of Groundwater

Prepare a sketch with labels that summarizes the distribution of water beneath Earth's surface.

KEY WORDS zone of soil moisture, zone of saturation (phreatic zone), groundwater, water table, capillary fringe, unsaturated zone (vadose zone)

• A portion of the rain that falls on the land soaks into the ground. Typically, a hole dug into the ground penetrates the zone of soil moisture and then crosses the unsaturated zone, where pore spaces contain both water and air. The soil grows moist again just above the water table, in the capillary fringe. Crossing the water table, the hole begins to fill (to the height of the water table) with water that flows in from the zone of saturation. The water table is the boundary between the groundwater below and the unsaturated zone above.

LABEL IT Examine this profile view showing the distribution of water in unconsolidated sediments and label the various portions of the groundwater complex.

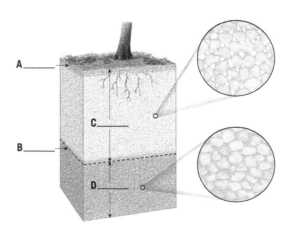

3 The Water Table

Discuss the factors that cause variations in the water table and describe the interactions between groundwater and streams.

KEY WORDS gaining stream, losing stream

• The shape of the water table is strongly influenced by surface topography. It bulges upward under hills and slopes downward into valleys. Where the water table intersects the surface of Earth, wetlands exist. If there is an extended drought, the water table will gradually drop and flatten out.

• Groundwater contributes water to some surface streams (gaining streams), while in other streams, the flow is reversed: The stream gives up water that soaks into the groundwater (losing streams). Groundwater also contributes water to lakes and wetlands.

DRAW IT Sketch a landscape and a water table that mimics the surface topography. Include at least one gaining stream and one losing stream in your sketch.

4 Factors Influencing the Storage and Movement of Groundwater

Summarize the factors that influence the storage and movement of groundwater.

KEY WORDS porosity, permeability, aquitard, aquifer

• Porosity is the percentage of total volume of rock or sediment that consists of empty space. The degree of connectivity between pores is permeability: the material's ability to transmit a fluid.

• Aquifers are geologic units with relatively high permeability. Sand is a good example. Geologic materials that retard the flow of water are aquitards. Shale is a good example.

RESOURCEFUL RESEARCH Use Table 1 to select two good aquifers and two aquitards. What rocks or geologic materials did you choose? Why?

5 How Groundwater Moves

Sketch a simple groundwater flow system and explain it. Discuss how groundwater movement is measured and the different scales of movement.

KEY WORDS recharge area, discharge area, hydraulic gradient, hydraulic conductivity, Darcy's law

- Groundwater flows slowly through underground pore spaces, moving on average only a few centimeters per day. Driven by gravity and pressure, it moves as a three-dimensional mass from areas of recharge (where water is added) to areas of discharge (where water leaves the groundwater system), such as springs, gaining streams, or even wells drilled by people.

- French engineer Henry Darcy pioneered the quantification of groundwater flow by measuring the slope of the water table (the hydraulic gradient) and the permeability of the sediment or rock (the hydraulic conductivity). These factors can be combined in the equation known as Darcy's law to arrive at an estimate of an aquifer's discharge.

- Groundwater flows both short and long distances at both shallow and deep levels. Closer to the surface, the flow is more local in scale, while at greater depths, the flow occurs over regional scales.

PLOT IT Use this figure to draw in arrows showing groundwater flow on several scales. Label both recharge and discharge areas.

6 Wells

Discuss water wells and their relationship to the water table.

KEY WORDS well, drawdown, cone of depression, perched water table

- For centuries, humans have been obtaining groundwater by drilling wells. As water is pumped out, the water table immediately adjacent to the well drops. This drawdown results in a "dimple" in the surface of the water table called the *cone of depression*. If there is sufficient drawdown, the cone of depression might encompass a large enough area that neighboring wells might go dry.

- A perched water table results from groundwater "piled up" atop an aquitard that is above the main body of groundwater. The shape of the water table is complex, which results in challenges for people trying to dig a productive well.

TROUBLESHOOTING Assume that the wells in this diagram are all pumping at full capacity, and each is producing the same amount of water at the surface. If the water table drops, which well is most likely to go dry first? Last?

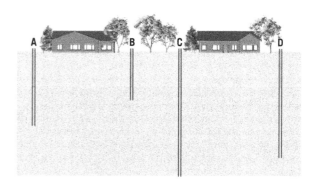

7 Artesian Systems

Sketch and label a simple artesian system.

KEY WORDS artesian, confined aquifer, nonflowing artesian well, flowing artesian well

- Artesian wells tap into inclined aquifers bounded above and below by aquitards. For the system to qualify as artesian, the water in the well must be under sufficient pressure for the water to rise above the top of confined aquifer. Artesian wells may be flowing or nonflowing, depending on whether the pressure surface is above or below the ground surface.

- The shower in your home is an artificial "artesian system." A greater vertical difference between your showerhead and the artificial pressure surface from a water tower gives better water pressure (and hence a more satisfying shower!).

MODEL IT If you were building a scale model of the geology associated with a flowing artesian well, what materials would you use, and how would you arrange them so that they accurately depicted a natural artesian system?

8 Springs, Hot Springs, and Geysers

Distinguish among springs, hot springs, and geysers.

KEY WORDS spring, hot spring, geyser

- Springs are naturally occurring spots where groundwater leaves the ground and flows out onto the surface. They may be due to the intersection of a perched water table and Earth's surface.
- Hot springs are like regular springs but hot. They transfer heat from the deeper crust to the surface. Generally, this heat comes from relatively shallow bodies of magma.
- Geysers are intermittent hot springs that "erupt" hot water periodically. They are fed by large underground chambers that fill with water that

warms past the boiling point. Once most of the water in the chamber has been sufficiently heated, it will flash to water vapor and rapidly expand, expelling some liquid water as it forces its way to the surface in an eruption. Geysers can precipitate silica or calcium carbonate around the geyser vent, producing the rocks siliceous sinter (geyserite) or travertine (tufa).

RELATE THEM Are all geysers also hot springs? Are all springs also hot springs? How are these three phenomena related to each other? Which term is most inclusive, and which is most specific?

9 Environmental Problems

List and discuss important environmental problems associated with groundwater.

- Groundwater can be "mined" by being extracted at a rate that is greater than the rate of replenishment. When groundwater is treated as a nonrenewable resource, as it is in parts of the High Plains aquifer, the water table drops, in some cases by more than 45 meters (150 feet).
- The extraction of groundwater can cause pore space to decrease in volume and the grains of loose Earth materials to pack more closely together. This overall compaction of sediment volume results in the subsidence of the land surface.

- Saltwater contamination is an environmental problem that is common near coastal areas. Fresh groundwater "floats" on salty groundwater due to its lower density. But if sufficient freshwater is pumped out to lower the water table by some amount, the base of the freshwater lens will rise about 40 times that amount. Deep wells may begin to access the deeper, salty water instead.
- Contamination of groundwater with sewage, highway salt, fertilizer, or industrial chemicals is another issue of critical concern. Once groundwater is contaminated, the problem is very difficult to solve, requiring expensive remediation or simply abandonment of the aquifer.

LOCAL EFFECTS Which of the environmental problems that affect groundwater are most likely to be major issues in your region? Why?

10 The Geologic Work of Groundwater

Explain the formation of caverns and the development of karst topography.

KEY WORDS cavern, speleothem, stalactite, stalagmite, karst topography, sinkhole (sink)

- Groundwater dissolves rock, in particular limestone, leaving behind void spaces in the rock. Caverns form at the zone of saturation, but later dropping of the water table may leave them open and dry—and available for people to explore.
- Dripstone is rock deposited by dripping of water containing dissolved calcium carbonate inside caverns. Speleothems are features made of dripstone and include stalactites, stalagmites, and columns.
- Karst topography is a distinctive type of landscape dominated by dissolution of limestone near the surface of Earth. Collapsing caverns show up as sinkholes. Streams flowing on the surface may "sink" into the subterranean cavern system, and in other places the same water may re-emerge as a spring. If enough limestone is dissolved, only isolated pinnacles of limestone will remain, towering over the landscape as "tower karst."

WHICH IS WHICH? Identify the various speleothems shown in this photograph. Would these speleothems have formed in the saturated zone or unsaturated zone? Why?

Miroslav/AGE Fotostock

GIVE IT SOME THOUGHT

1. Imagine a water molecule that is part of a groundwater system in an area of gently rolling hills in the eastern United States. Describe some possible paths the molecule might take through the hydrologic cycle if:
   a. It were pumped from the ground to irrigate a farm field.
   b. There were a long period of heavy rainfall.
   c. The water table in the vicinity of the molecule developed a steep cone of depression due to heavy pumping from a nearby well.

   Combine your understanding of the hydrologic cycle with your imagination and include possible short-term and long-term destinations and information about how the molecule gets to these places via evaporation, transpiration, condensation, precipitation, infiltration, and runoff. Remember to consider possible interactions with streams, lakes, groundwater, the ocean, and the atmosphere.

2. Identify a location in the United States where you might find a gaining stream and a location where you would expect to find a losing stream. Why did you select each location? Describe a situation that would cause a gaining stream to become a losing stream. Also describe a situation in which a losing becomes a gaining stream.

3. In the GEOgraphic feature the United States ranks third in water use, behind India and China. Refer to that feature as you answer the following questions.
   a. If the amount of water extracted worldwide each year is 4000 cubic kilometers, how much water does each of the top three countries use?
   b. The population of each of the top three countries in 2010 was as follows: China, 1.4 billion; India, 1.2 billion; United States, 309 million. Determine the per capita (per person) use of water for each country.

4. The cemetery in this photo is located in New Orleans, Louisiana. Like other cemeteries in the area, all of the burial plots are aboveground. Based on what you have learned in this chapter, suggest a reason for this rather unusual practice.

(Photo by Caitlin Mirra/Shutterstock)

5. Which one of the three basic rock types (igneous, sedimentary, or metamorphic) has the greatest likelihood of being a good aquifer? Why?

6. During a trip to a grocery store, your friend wants to buy some bottled water. Some brands promote the fact that their product is artesian. Other brands boast that their water comes from a spring. Your friend asks, "Is artesian water or spring water necessarily better than water from other sources?" How would you answer?

7. What is the likely difference between an intermittent stream (one that flows off and on) and a stream that flows all the time, even during extended dry periods?

8. Imagine that you are an environmental scientist who has been hired to solve a groundwater contamination problem. Several homeowners have noticed that their well water has a funny smell and taste. Some think the contamination is coming from a landfill, but others think it might be a nearby cattle feedlot or chemical plant. Your first step is to gather data from wells in the area and prepare the map of the water table shown here.
   a. Based on your map, can any of the three potential sources of contamination be eliminated? If so, explain.
   b. What other steps would you take to determine the source of the contamination?

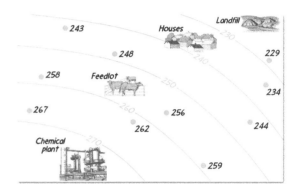

9. An acquaintance is considering purchasing a large tract of productive irrigated farmland in western Texas. His intention is to continue growing crops on the land for years to come. If he asked your opinion about the area he selected, what figure in this chapter would you consult before you responded? How would this figure help your friend evaluate his potential purchase?

10. Sinkholes commonly form in one of two ways. Examine the accompanying photo, which shows a sinkhole in Winter Park, Florida, and describe how it likely formed.

(Photo by AP Photo)

MasteringGeology™

Glossary

Aquifer Rock or sediment through which groundwater moves easily.

Aquitard An impermeable bed that hinders or prevents groundwater movement.

Artesian well A well in which the water rises above the level where it was initially encountered.

Capillary fringe A relatively narrow zone at the base of the zone of aeration. Here water rises from the water table in tiny, threadlike openings between grains of soil or sediment.

Cavern A naturally formed underground chamber or series of chambers most commonly produced by solution activity in limestone.

Cone of depression A cone-shaped depression in the water table immediately surrounding a well.

Confined aquifer An aquifer that has impermeable layers (aquitards) both above and below.

Darcy's law An equation which states that groundwater discharge depends on the hydraulic gradient, hydraulic conductivity, and cross-sectional area of an aquifer.

Discharge area A location, such as a spring or a stream, where groundwater flows back to the surface.

Drawdown The difference in height between the bottom of a cone of depression and the original height of the water table.

Flowing artesian well An artesian well in which water flows freely at Earth's surface because the pressure surface is above ground level.

Gaining stream Streams that gain water from the inflow of groundwater through the streambed.

Geyser A fountain of hot water ejected periodically from the ground.

Groundwater Water in the zone of saturation.

Hot spring A spring in which the water is 6–9° C (10–15° F) warmer than the mean annual air temperature of its locality.

Hydraulic conductivity A factor relating to groundwater flow; it is a coefficient that takes into account the permeability of the aquifer and the viscosity of the fluid.

Hydraulic gradient The slope of the water table. It is determined by finding the height difference between two points on the water table and dividing by the horizontal distance between the two points.

Karst A type of topography formed on soluble rock (especially limestone) primarily by dissolution. It is characterized by sinkholes, caves, and underground drainage.

Losing stream A stream that loses water to the groundwater system by outflow through the streambed.

Nonflowing artesian well An artesian well in which water does not rise to the surface because the pressure surface is below ground level.

Perched water table A localized zone of saturation above the main water table, created by an impermeable layer (aquiclude).

Permeability A measure of a material's ability to transmit water.

Phreatic zone See Saturated zone.

Porosity The volume of open spaces in rock or soil.

Recharge area An area where groundwater is replenished.

Sinkhole A depression produced in a region where soluble rock has been removed by groundwater.

Speleothem A collective term for the dripstone features found in caverns.

Spring A flow of groundwater that emerges naturally at the ground surface.

Stalactite An icicle-like structure that hangs from the ceiling of a cavern.

Stalagmite A columnlike form that grows upward from the floor of a cavern.

Unsaturated zone The area above the water table where openings in soil, sediment, and rock are not saturated but filled mainly with air.

Vadose zone See Unsaturated zone.

Water table The upper level of the saturated zone of groundwater.

Zone of saturation The zone where all open spaces in sediment and rock are completely filled with water.

Zone of soil moisture A zone in which water is held as a film on the surface of soil particles and may be used by plants or withdrawn by evaporation. The uppermost subdivision of the unsaturated zone.

Glaciers and Glaciation

From Chapter 18 of *Earth: An Introduction to Physical Geology*, Eleventh Edition. Edward J. Tarbuck, Frederick K. Lutgens, Dennis Tasa.

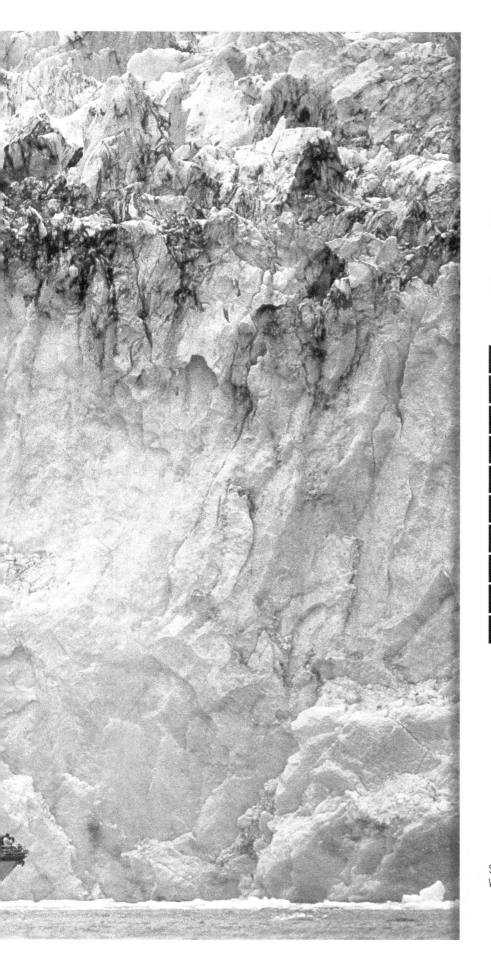

Glaciers and Glaciation

Surprise Glacier in Alaska's Prince William Sound, near the town of Whittier Glaciers are abundant in this region. (Photo by Michael Collier)

Each statement represents the primary learning objective for the corresponding major heading within the chapter. After you complete the chapter you should be able to:

1   List the different types of glaciers, summarize their characteristics, and describe the present-day location and extent of glaciers on Earth.

2   Describe how glaciers move, the rates at which they move, and the significance of the glacial budget.

3   Discuss the processes of glacial erosion.

4   Identify and describe the major features created by glacial erosion.

5   Distinguish between the two basic types of glacial drift.

6   List and describe the major features associated with till.

7   Explain the formation of landforms composed of stratified drift.

8   Describe and explain several important effects of Ice Age glaciers other than erosional and depositional landforms.

9   Briefly discuss the development of glacial theory.

10   Summarize current ideas on the causes of ice ages.

Climate has a strong influence on the nature and intensity of Earth's external processes. This fact is dramatically illustrated in this chapter because the existence and extent of glaciers is largely controlled by Earth's changing climate.

Like running water and groundwater, glaciers represent a significant erosional process. These moving masses of ice are responsible for creating many unique landforms and are part of an important link in the rock cycle in which the products of weathering are transported and deposited as sediment.

Today glaciers cover nearly 10 percent of Earth's land surface; however, in the recent geologic past, ice sheets were three times more extensive, covering vast areas with ice thousands of meters thick. Many regions still bear the marks of these glaciers. The basic character of such diverse places as the Alps, Cape Cod, and Yosemite Valley was fashioned by now-vanished masses of glacial ice. Moreover, Long Island, the Great Lakes, and the fiords of Norway and Alaska all owe their existence to glaciers. Glaciers, of course, are not just a phenomenon of the geologic past. As you will see, they are still sculpting the landscape and depositing debris in many regions today.

Wyoming's Wind River Range
Glaciers have been the most dramatic agents of erosion here during the past 2 million years.
(Photo by Michael Collier)

1   Glaciers: A Part of Two Basic Cycles

Glaciers are a part of two fundamental cycles in the Earth system—the hydrologic cycle and the rock cycle. The water of the hydrosphere is constantly cycled through the atmosphere, biosphere, and geosphere. Time and time again, water evaporates from the oceans into the atmosphere, precipitates upon the land, and flows in rivers and underground back to the sea. However, when precipitation falls at high elevations or high latitudes, the water may not immediately make its way toward the sea. Instead, it may become part of a glacier. Although the ice will eventually melt, allowing the water to continue its path to the sea, water can be stored as glacial ice for many tens, hundreds, or even thousands of years.

A **glacier** is a thick ice mass that forms over hundreds or thousands of years. It originates on land from the accumulation, compaction, and recrystallization of snow. A glacier appears to be motionless, but it is not; glaciers move very slowly. Like running water, groundwater, wind, and waves, glaciers are dynamic erosional agents that accumulate, transport, and deposit sediment. As such, glaciers are among the agents that perform a basic function in the rock cycle. Although glaciers are found in many parts of the world today, most are located in remote areas, either near Earth's poles or in high mountains.

Valley (Alpine) Glaciers

Literally thousands of relatively small glaciers exist in lofty mountain areas, where they usually follow valleys that were originally occupied by streams. Unlike the rivers that previously flowed in these valleys, the glaciers advance slowly, perhaps only a few centimeters per day. Because of their setting, these moving ice masses are termed **valley glaciers**, or **alpine glaciers** (FIGURE 1). Each glacier actually is a stream of ice, bounded by precipitous rock walls, that flows downvalley from an accumulation center near its head. Like rivers, valley glaciers can be long or short, wide or narrow, single or with branching tributaries. Generally, alpine glaciers are longer than they are wide. Some extend for just a fraction of a kilometer, whereas others go on for many tens of kilometers. The west branch of the Hubbard Glacier, for example, runs through 112 kilometers (nearly 70 miles) of mountainous terrain in Alaska and the Yukon Territory.

FIGURE 1 Valley glacier These tongues of ice are also called *alpine glaciers*. Hubbard Glacier is still eroding the Alaskan landscape. The dark stripe of sediment in the center of the glacier is a medial moraine. (Photo by Michael Collier)

Ice Sheets

In contrast to valley glaciers, **ice sheets** exist on a much larger scale. The low total annual solar radiation reaching the poles makes these regions eligible for great ice accumulations. Presently each of Earth's polar regions supports an ice sheet—Greenland in the Northern Hemisphere and Antarctica in the Southern Hemisphere (FIGURE 2).

Ice Age Ice Sheets   About 18,000 years ago glacial ice not only covered Greenland and Antarctica but also large portions of North America, Europe, and Siberia. This date in Earth history is appropriately known as the *Last Glacial Maximum*. The term implies that there were other glacial maximums, which is indeed the case. Throughout the Quaternary period, which began about 2.6 million years ago and extends to the present, ice sheets formed, advanced over broad areas, and then melted away. These alternating glacial and interglacial periods occurred over and over again.

Greenland's ice sheet occupies 1.7 million square kilometers (663,000 square miles), about 80 percent of the island.

The area of the Antarctic Ice Sheet is almost 14 million square kilometers (5,460,000 square miles). Ice shelves occupy an additional 1.4 million square kilometers (546,000 square miles).

Greenland and Antarctica   Some people mistakenly think that the North Pole is covered by glacial ice, but this is not the case. The ice that covers the Arctic Ocean is **sea ice**—frozen seawater. Sea ice floats because ice is less dense than liquid water. Although sea ice never completely disappears from the Arctic, the area covered with sea ice expands and contracts with the seasons. The thickness of sea ice ranges from a few centimeters for new ice to 4 meters (13 feet) for sea ice that has survived for years. By contrast, glaciers can be hundreds or thousands of meters thick.

Glaciers form on land, and in the Northern Hemisphere, Greenland supports an ice sheet. Greenland extends between about 60 and 80 degrees north latitude. This largest island on Earth is covered by an imposing ice sheet that occupies 1.7 million square kilometers (more than 660,000 square miles), or about 80 percent of the island. Averaging nearly 1500 meters (5000 feet) thick, the ice extends 3000 meters (10,000 feet) above the island's bedrock floor in some places.

In the Southern Hemisphere, the huge Antarctic Ice Sheet attains a maximum thickness of about 4300 meters (14,000 feet) and covers nearly the entire continent, an area of more than 13.9 million square kilometers (5.4 million square miles). Because of the proportions of these huge features, they are often called *continental ice sheets*. Indeed, the combined areas of present-day continental ice sheets represent almost 10 percent of Earth's land area.

These enormous masses flow out in all directions from one or more snow-accumulation centers and completely obscure all but the highest areas of underlying terrain. Even sharp variations in the topography beneath a glacier usually appear as relatively subdued undulations on the surface of the ice. Such topographic differences, however, do affect the behavior of the ice sheets, especially near their margins, by guiding flow in certain directions and creating zones of faster and slower movement.

Ice Shelves   Along portions of the Antarctic coast, glacial ice flows into the adjacent ocean, creating features called **ice shelves**. These large, relatively flat masses of glacial ice extend seaward from the coast but remain attached to the land along one or more sides. About 80 percent of the ice lies below the surface of the ocean, so in shallow water, the ice shelf "touches bottom" and is said to be *grounded*. In deeper water, the ice shelf floats (FIGURE 3). There are ice shelves along more than half of the Antarctic coast but very few in Greenland.

The shelves are thickest on their landward sides, and they become thinner seaward. They are sustained by ice from the adjacent ice sheet as well as being nourished by snowfall and the freezing of seawater to their bases. Antarctica's ice shelves extend over approximately 1.4 million square kilometers (0.6 million square miles). The Ross and Ronne-Filchner Ice Shelves are the largest, with the Ross Ice Shelf alone covering an area approximately

FIGURE 3 Ice shelves
An ice shelf forms when a glacier or ice sheet flows into the adjacent ocean.

Icebergs

In shallow water, the ice shelf is *grounded*.

In deeper water the ice shelf floats.

As ice melts, material transported by the glacier is released and falls to the ocean floor. The rocks are called *dropstones*.

the size of Texas (see Figure 2). In recent years, satellite monitoring has shown that some ice shelves are unstable and breaking apart. For example, during a 35-day span in February and March 2002, an ice shelf on the eastern side of the Antarctic Peninsula, known as the Larsen B Ice Shelf, broke apart and separated from the continent. Thousands of icebergs were set adrift in the adjacent Weddell Sea. The event was captured in satellite imagery (FIGURE 4). This was not an isolated happening but part of a trend. Since 1974 the extent of seven ice shelves

surrounding the Antarctic Peninsula has declined by about 13,500 square kilometers (nearly 5300 square miles). Scientists attribute the breakup of the ice shelves to strong regional climate warming.

Other Types of Glaciers

In addition to valley glaciers and ice sheets, other types of glaciers are also identified. Covering some uplands and plateaus are masses of glacial ice called **ice caps**.

January 31, 2002

50km

Before

March 7, 2002

50km

After

FIGURE 4 Collapse of an ice shelf
These satellite images document the breakup of the Larsen B Ice Shelf adjacent to the Antarctic Peninsula in 2002. (NASA)

FIGURE 5 Iceland's
Vatnajökull ice cap
In 1996 the Grimsvötn volcano erupted beneath this
ice cap, an event that triggered melting and floods.
(NASA)

Ice caps completely bury the underlying terrain but are much smaller than ice sheets.

When a valley glacier is no longer confined, it spreads out to become a piedmont glacier.

FIGURE 6 Piedmont glacier
Piedmont glaciers occur where valley glaciers exit a mountain range onto broad lowlands.

Like ice sheets, ice caps completely bury the underlying landscape but are much smaller than the continental-scale features. Ice caps occur in many places, including Iceland and several of the large islands in the Arctic Ocean (FIGURE 5).

Often ice caps and ice sheets feed **outlet glaciers**. These tongues of ice flow down valleys, extending outward from the margins of these larger ice masses. The tongues are essentially valley glaciers that are avenues for ice movement from an ice cap or ice sheet through

mountainous terrain to the sea. Where they encounter the ocean, some outlet glaciers spread out as floating ice shelves. Often large numbers of icebergs are produced.

Piedmont glaciers occupy broad lowlands at the bases of steep mountains and form when one or more alpine glaciers emerge from the confining walls of mountain valleys. Here the advancing ice spreads out to form a broad lobe (FIGURE 6). The size of individual piedmont glaciers varies greatly. Among the largest is the broad Malaspina Glacier along the coast of southern Alaska. It covers thousands of square kilometers of the flat coastal plain at the foot of the lofty St. Elias range.

1 CONCEPT CHECKS

1. Where are glaciers found today, and what percentage of Earth's land surface do they cover?
2. Describe how glaciers fit into the hydrologic cycle. What role do they play in the rock cycle?
3. List and briefly distinguish among four types of glaciers.
4. What is the difference between an ice sheet and an ice shelf? How are they related?

Sea ice in the Beaufort Sea near Barrow, Alaska. Sea ice is not part of a glacier, rather it is frozen seawater. (Photo by Michael Collier)

2 Formation and Movement of Glacial Ice

Snow is the raw material from which glacial ice originates; therefore, glaciers form in areas where more snow falls in winter than melts during the summer. Glaciers develop in the high-latitude polar realm because, even though annual snowfall totals are modest, temperatures are so low that little of the snow melts. Glaciers can form in mountains because temperatures drop with an increase in altitude. So even near the equator, glaciers may form at elevations above about 5000 meters (16,400 feet). For example, Tanzania's Mount Kilimanjaro, which is located practically astride the equator at an altitude of 5895 meters (19,336 feet), has glaciers at its summit. The elevation above which snow remains throughout the year is called the **snowline**. As you would expect, the elevation of the snowline varies with latitude. Near the equator, it occurs high in the mountains, whereas in the vicinity of the 60th parallel, it is at or near sea level. Before a glacier is created, snow must be converted into glacial ice.

Glacial Ice Formation

When temperatures remain below freezing following a snowfall, the fluffy accumulation of delicate hexagonal crystals soon changes. As air infiltrates the spaces between the crystals, the extremities of the crystals evaporate and the water vapor condenses near the centers of the crystals. In this manner, snowflakes become smaller, thicker, and more spherical, and the large pore spaces disappear. By this process air is forced out and what was once light, fluffy snow is recrystallized into a much denser mass of small grains having the consistency of coarse sand. This granular recrystallized snow is called **firn** and is commonly found making up old snow banks near the end of winter. As more snow is added, the pressure on the lower layers gradually increases, compacting the ice grains at depth. Once the thickness of ice and snow exceeds 50 meters (160 feet), the weight is sufficient to fuse firn into a solid mass of interlocking ice crystals. Glacial ice has now been formed.

The rate at which this transformation occurs varies. In regions where the annual snow accumulation is great, burial is relatively rapid and snow may turn to glacial ice in a matter of a decade or less. Where the yearly addition of snow is less abundant, burial is slow and the transformation of snow to glacial ice may take hundreds of years.

Movement of a Glacier

The movement of glacial ice is generally referred to as *flow*. The fact that glacial movement is described in this way seems paradoxical; how can a solid flow? The way in which ice moves is complex and is of two basic types. The first of these, **plastic flow**, involves movement *within* the ice. Ice behaves as a brittle solid until the pressure upon it is equivalent to the weight of about 50 meters (165 feet) of ice. Once that load is surpassed, ice behaves as a plastic material, and flow begins. Such flow occurs

because of the molecular structure of ice. Glacial ice consists of layers of molecules stacked one upon the other. The bonds between layers are weaker than those within each layer. Therefore, when a stress exceeds the strength of the bonds between the layers, the layers remain intact and slide over one another.

A second and often equally important mechanism of glacial movement consists of an entire ice mass slipping along the ground. With the exception of some glaciers located in polar regions where the ice is probably frozen to the solid bedrock floor, most glaciers are thought to move by this sliding process, called **basal slip**. In this process, meltwater probably acts as a hydraulic jack and perhaps as a lubricant that helps the ice over the rock. The source of the liquid water is related in part to the fact that the melting point of ice decreases as pressure increases. Therefore, deep within a glacier, the ice may be at the melting point even though its temperature is below 0° C (32° F).

In addition, other factors may contribute to the presence of meltwater deep within a glacier. Temperatures may be increased by plastic flow (an effect similar to frictional heating), by heat added from the Earth below, and by the refreezing of meltwater that has seeped down from above. This last process relies on the property that as water changes state from liquid to solid, heat (termed *latent heat of fusion*) is released.

FIGURE 7 illustrates the effects of these two basic types of glacial motion. This vertical profile through a glacier also shows that not all the ice flows forward at the same rate. Frictional drag with the bedrock floor causes the lower portions of the glacier to move more slowly.

In contrast to the lower portion of the glacier, the upper 50 meters (160 feet) or so are not under sufficient pressure to exhibit plastic flow. Rather, the ice in this uppermost zone is brittle, and this zone is appropriately referred to as the **zone of fracture**. The ice in the zone of fracture is carried along "piggyback" style by the ice

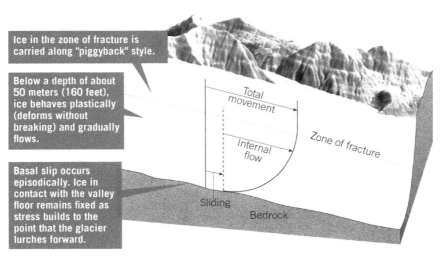

Movement of a glacier
This vertical cross section through a glacier shows that movement is divided into two components. Also notice that the rate of movement is slowest at the base of the glacier, where frictional drag is greatest.

Ice in the zone of fracture is carried along "piggyback" style.

Below a depth of about 50 meters (160 feet), ice behaves plastically (deforms without breaking) and gradually flows.

Basal slip occurs episodically. Ice in contact with the valley floor remains fixed as stress builds to the point that the glacier lurches forward.

Total movement

Internal flow

Zone of fracture

Sliding

Bedrock

Rates of Glacial Movement

Unlike streamflow, glacial movement is not obvious. If we could watch an alpine glacier move, we would see that, as with the water in a river, all the ice in the valley does not move at an equal rate. Just as friction with the valley floor slows the movement of the ice at the bottom of a glacier, the drag created by the valley walls causes the rate of flow to be greatest in the center of the glacier.

below. When the glacier moves over irregular terrain, the zone of fracture is subjected to tension, resulting in cracks called **crevasses** (FIGURE 8). These gaping cracks may extend to depths of 50 meters (160 feet) and can make travel across glaciers dangerous. Below this depth, plastic flow seals them off.

This was first demonstrated in experiments during the nineteenth century, in which markers were carefully placed in a straight line across the top of a valley glacier. Periodically, the positions of the stakes were recorded, revealing the type of movement just described.

FIGURE 8 Crevasses
As a glacier moves, internal stresses cause these large cracks to develop by brittle deformation in the upper portion of the glacier called the zone of fracture. Crevasses can extend to depths of 50 meters (160 feet) and can make travel across glaciers dangerous. (Photo on left by Michael Collier; photo on right by Wave/Glow Images)

Lambert Glacier drains about 900,000 square kilometers (500,000 square miles) of East Antarctica.

Amery Ice Shelf

Ice Velocity (m/year)
0   400   800   1200

The slowest movement occurs along divides.

Area of more rapid movement.

Ronne-Filchner Ice Shelf

Divide separating glacier basins.

Ross Ice Shelf

Divides are generally over mountains that shape the flow of ice.

0   500   1000 km

Velocity (meters per year)
<1.5   10   100   1000

FIGURE 9 Movement of Antarctic ice These maps result from thousands of satellite measurements taken over several years. Outflow from the interior is organized into a series of drainage basins separated by ice divides. Flow is concentrated into narrow, mountain-bound glaciers or into relatively fast-moving ice streams surrounded by slower-moving ice. (NASA)

How rapidly does glacial ice move? Average velocities vary considerably from one glacier to another. Some move so slowly that trees and other vegetation may become well established in the debris that has accumulated on the glacier's surface, whereas others may move at rates of up to several meters per day. Recent satellite radar imaging provided a comprehensive view of flow patterns of the Antarctic Ice Sheet. An examination of FIGURE 9 shows that portions of some outlet glaciers move at rates greater than 800 meters (2600 feet) per year, whereas ice in some interior regions creep along at less than 2 meters (6.5 feet) per year.

The advance of some glaciers is characterized by periods of extremely rapid movements called **surges**. Glaciers that exhibit such movement may flow along in an apparently normal manner and then speed up for a relatively short time before returning to the normal rate again. The flow rates during surges are as much as 100 times the normal rate. Evidence indicates that many glaciers may be of the surging type.

It is not yet clear whether the mechanism that triggers these rapid movements is the same for each surging-type glacier. However, researchers studying the Variegated Glacier shown in FIGURE 10 have determined that

the surges of this ice mass take the form of a rapid increase in basal sliding that is caused by increases in water pressure beneath the ice. The increased water pressure at the base of the glacier acts to reduce friction between the underlying bedrock and the moving ice. The pressure buildup, in turn, is related to changes in the system of passageways that conduct water along the glacier's bed and deliver it as outflow to the terminus.

Budget of a Glacier

Snow is the raw material from which glacial ice originates; therefore, glaciers form in areas where more snow falls in winter than melts during summer. Glaciers are constantly gaining and losing ice.

Glacial Zones Snow accumulation and ice formation occur in the **zone of accumulation**. Its outer limits are defined by the snowline. As noted earlier, the elevation of the snowline varies greatly, from sea level in polar regions to altitudes approaching 5000 meters (16,000 feet) near the equator. Above the snowline, in the zone of accumulation, the addition of snow thickens the glacier and promotes movement. Below the snowline is the **zone of wastage**.

FIGURE 10 Surge of the
Variegated Glacier

August 1964

August 1965

Position before surge

Position before surge

Position after surge

FIGURE 10 Surge of the
Variegated Glacier
A surge of this valley glacier near Yakutat, Alaska,
northwest of Juneau, is
captured in these two aerial
photographs taken 1 year
apart. During a surge, ice
velocities in Variegated
Glacier are 20 to 50 times
greater than during quiet
phases. (Photos by Austin Post,
U.S. Geological Survey)

Here there is a net loss to the glacier as all of the snow
from the previous winter melts, as does some of the glacial
ice (FIGURE 11).

In addition to melting, glaciers also waste as large
pieces of ice break off the front of a glacier, in a process
called **calving**. Calving creates *icebergs* in places where
the glacier has reached the sea or a lake (FIGURE 12). Because icebergs are just slightly less dense than seawater,
they float very low in the water, with more than 80 percent
of their mass submerged. Along the margins of Antarctica's
ice shelves, calving is the primary means by which these
masses lose ice. A glance back at Figure 4 illustrates this
process. The relatively flat icebergs produced here can be
several kilometers across and 600 meters (2000 feet) thick.
By comparison, thousands of irregularly shaped icebergs
are produced by outlet glaciers flowing from the margins
of the Greenland Ice Sheet. Many
drift southward and find their way
into the North Atlantic, where they
can be hazardous to navigation.

Glacial Budget Whether the margin of a glacier is advancing, retreating, or remaining stationary depends
on the budget of the glacier. The **glacial budget** is the balance, or lack
of balance, between accumulation at
the upper end of the glacier and loss
at the lower end. This loss is termed
ablation. If ice accumulation exceeds ablation, the glacial front advances until the two factors balance.
When this happens, the terminus of
the glacier becomes stationary.

If a warming trend increases
ablation and/or if a drop in snowfall
decreases accumulation, the ice
front will retreat. As the terminus of the glacier retreats,

SMARTFIGURE 11 Zones of
a glacier
The snowline separates the
zone of accumulation and the
zone of wastage. Whether the
ice front advances, retreats, or
remains stationary depends on
the balance or lack of balance
between accumulation and
wastage (ablation).

ZONE OF ACCUMULATION
More snow falls each
winter than melts
each summer

ZONE OF WASTAGE
All the snow from the
previous winter melts along
with some glacial ice

Snowline

Crevasses

Braided streams

634

In the large image, ice is calving from the terminus of Hubbard Glacier in Wrangell-St. Elias National Park, Alaska. (Photo by Bernhard Edmaier/Photo Researchers, Inc.) The smaller photo shows an iceberg in Canada's Labrador Sea. (Photo by Radius Images/Getty)

Icebergs form when large masses calve from the front of a glacier after it reaches a water body.

Only about 20 percent or less of an iceberg protrudes above the waterline.

the extent of the zone of wastage diminishes. Therefore, in time a new balance will be reached between accumulation and wastage, and the ice front will again become stationary. Whether the margin of a glacier is advancing, retreating, or stationary, the ice within the glacier continues to flow forward. In the case of a receding glacier, the ice still flows forward but not rapidly enough to offset ablation.

2 CONCEPT CHECKS

1. Briefly describe how snow becomes glacial ice.
2. Describe the two components of glacial movement.
3. How rapidly does glacial ice move? Provide some examples.
4. What are the two zones of a glacier? How does the glacial budget relate to these zones?
5. Under what circumstances will the front of a glacier advance? Retreat? Remain stationary?

EYE on Earth

The central focus of this satellite image is Byrd Glacier in Antarctica. In this region, the glacier advances at a rate of about 0.8 kilometer (0.5 mile) per year. Take note of its position in relation to other labeled features. (Photo by NASA)

Question 1 Is Byrd Glacier flowing toward the top or the bottom of the image? How did you figure this out?

Question 2 What term describes this type of glacier?

Antarctica Fact File

Earth's southernmost continent surrounds the South Pole (90° S. Latitude) and is almost entirely south of the Antarctic Circle (66.5° S. Latitude). This icy landmass is the fifth largest continent and is twice as large as Australia. It also has the distinction of being the coldest, driest, and windiest continent and also has the highest average elevation.

Larsen
Ice Shelf

Rothera (UK)

Ronne-Filchner
Ice Shelf

ANTARCTIC PENINSULA

**EAST
ANTARCTICA**
(Average thickness of ice sheet
is 2226 m/7,300 ft)

Amery
Ice Shelf

Mt. Vinson
4892 m
(16,050 ft)

TRANSANTARCTIC MOUNTAINS

South Pole
Amundsen-Scott (USA)

Shackleton
Ice Shelf

**WEST
ANTARCTICA**
(Average thickness
of ice sheet is
1306 m/4,283 ft)

Vostok (Russia)
Lowest temperature ever
recorded −89.2°C (−128.6°F)

KEY

Ice-free rock
Ice sheet
Ice shelf

Ross
Ice Shelf

McMurdo (USA)

Mt. Erebus
3794 m (12,444 ft)

Thickest ice
4776 m (15,670 ft)

| 0 | KILOMETERS | 2000 |
| 0 | MILES | 1000 |

Antarctica is 1.4 times larger than the United States and about 58 times bigger than the United Kingdom. The continent is almost completely ice covered. The ice-free area amounts to only 44,890 square kilometers (17,330 square miles) or just 0.32 percent (32/100 of 1 percent) of the continent.

ANSMET

1 CM

Meteorites are rocky or metallic particles from space that have fallen on Earth. These ancient fragments provide clues to the origin and history of our solar system. Antarctica is an especially good place to collect these dark masses from space because even small ones are relatively easy to spot. In addition, ice flow patterns tend to concentrate them in certain areas.

Practically all of the continent belongs to the same climate classification, aptly termed ice cap climate, in which the average temperature of the warmest month is 0° C (32° F) or below. Take a look at the graph and you will see that some areas are much colder than others.

ROTHERA ANNUAL MEAN −5.3°

McMURDO ANNUAL MEAN −16.9°

AMUNDSEN-SCOTT ANNUAL MEAN −49.4°

VOSTOK ANNUAL MEAN −55.1°

DATA SHOWS MONTHLY MEAN TEMPERATURES IN CELSIUS

| 10° | 0° | −10° | −20° | −30° | −40° | −50° | −60° | −70° | −80° |

JAN FEB MAR APR MAY JUN JUL AUG SEP OCT NOV DEC

What if the ice melted? The discharge at the mouth of the Mississippi River is 17,300 cubic meters (593,000 cubic feet) per second. If Antarctica's ice sheets melted at a suitable rate, they could maintain the flow of the Mississippi River for more than 50,000 years! If all of the continent's ice were to melt, sea level would rise by an estimated 56 meters (more than 180 feet). Antarctica's ice represents about 65 percent of Earth's entire supply of freshwater.

The Transantarctic Mountains are a 3300-kilometer- (2600-mile-) long range that separates the West Antarctic Ice Sheet and the East Antarctic Ice Sheet. Vinson Massif is the highest peak at 4892 meters (16,050 feet). Most of the mountains are buried beneath the continent's huge ice sheets.

About half of the continent's coastal areas are characterized by ice shelves. The Ross Ice Shelf is about the size of France, whereas the Ronne-Filchner Ice Shelf has an area similar to that of Spain.

John Goodge/NSF

Rick Price/Getty Images

McMurdo Station is the main U.S. scientific research station. It is the largest installation on the continent, capable of supporting more than 1200 residents. The total population at all research stations is about 4000 in summer and 1000 in winter. There are no permanent (indigenous) human residents on the continent.

ZUMA Wire Service/Alamy

MCMURDO STATION ANTARCTICA

Dan Leeth/Alamy

3 Glacial Erosion

Glaciers are capable of great erosion. For anyone who has observed the terminus of an alpine glacier, the evidence of its erosive force is clear (FIGURE 13). You can witness firsthand the release of rock material of various sizes from the ice as it melts. All signs lead to the conclusion that the ice has scraped, scoured, and torn rock from the floor and walls of the valley and carried it downvalley. It should be pointed out, however, that in mountainous regions, mass-wasting processes also make substantial contributions to the sediment load of a glacier.

FIGURE 13 Evidence of glacial erosion
Close-up view at the terminus of a valley glacier in Alaska. The glacier clearly acquired a significant quantity of rock debris as it advanced across the landscape. (Photo by Michael Collier)

The rock debris dropped by melting ice is a jumbled mixture of different size sediments.

Once rock debris is acquired by a glacier, the enormous competence of ice will not allow the debris to settle out like the load carried by a stream or by the wind. Indeed, as a medium of sediment transport, ice has no equal. Consequently, glaciers can carry huge blocks that no other erosional agent could possibly budge (FIGURE 14). Although today's glaciers are of limited importance as erosional agents, many landscapes that were modified by the widespread glaciers of the Ice Age still reflect, to a high degree, the work of ice.

Glaciers erode the land primarily in two ways: plucking and abrasion. First, as a glacier flows over a fractured bedrock surface, it loosens and lifts blocks of rock and incorporates them into the ice. This process, known as **plucking**, occurs when meltwater penetrates the cracks and joints of bedrock beneath a glacier and freezes. As the water expands, it exerts tremendous leverage that pries the rock loose. In this manner, sediment of all sizes becomes part of the glacier's load.

The second major erosional process is **abrasion** (FIGURE 15). As the ice and its load of rock fragments slide over bedrock, they function like sandpaper to smooth and polish the surface below. The pulverized rock produced by the glacial "grist mill" is appropriately called **rock flour**. So much rock flour may be produced that meltwater streams flowing out of a glacier often have the cloudy appearance of skim milk and offer visible evidence of the grinding power of ice. Lakes fed by such streams frequently have a distinctive turquoise color (FIGURE 16).

When the ice at the bottom of a glacier contains large rock fragments, long scratches and grooves called **glacial striations** may even be gouged into the bedrock (Figure 15A). These linear grooves provide clues to the direction of ice flow. By mapping the striations over large areas, patterns of glacial flow can often be reconstructed. On the other hand, not all abrasive action produces striations. The rock surfaces over which the glacier moves may also become highly polished by the ice and its load of finer particles. The broad expanses of smoothly polished granite in Yosemite National Park provide an excellent example (Figure 15B).

As is the case with other agents of erosion, the rate of glacial erosion is highly

FIGURE 14 Glacial erratic
A large glacially transported boulder in Denali National Park, Alaska. Such boulders are called *glacial erratics*. (Photo by Michael Collier)

Glacial erratic

Glacial erratic

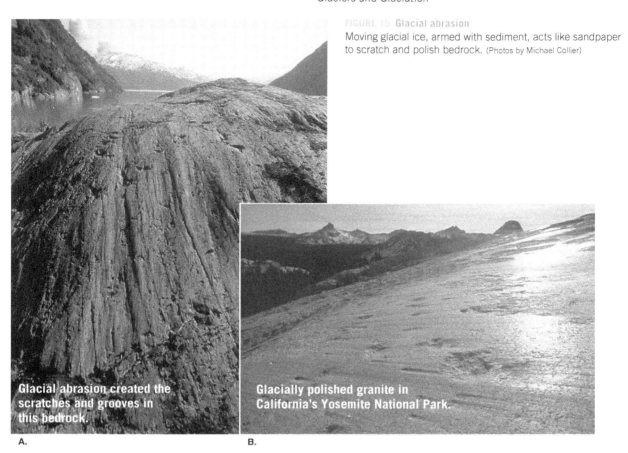

FIGURE 15 Glacial abrasion
Moving glacial ice, armed with sediment, acts like sandpaper to scratch and polish bedrock. (Photos by Michael Collier)

Glacial abrasion created the scratches and grooves in this bedrock.

A.

Glacially polished granite in California's Yosemite National Park.

B.

FIGURE 16 Distinctive color caused by rock flour
Many lakes that are fed by glaciers have a distinctive turquoise color. The distinctive color occurs because the rock flour suspended in the lake reflects different parts of the visible spectrum more strongly than others. (Photo by Grant/Shutterstock)

EYE on Earth

This photo shows an iceberg floating in the ocean near the coast of Greenland. (Photo by Andrzej Gibasiewicz/Shutterstock)

Question 1 How do icebergs form? What term applies to this process?

Question 2 Using the knowledge you have gained about these features, explain the common phrase "It's only the tip of the iceberg."

Question 3 Is an iceberg the same as sea ice? Explain.

Question 4 If this iceberg were to melt, how would sea level be affected?

Andrzej Gibasiewicz/Shutterstock

variable. This differential erosion by ice is largely controlled by four factors: (1) rate of glacial movement; (2) thickness of the ice; (3) shape, abundance, and hardness of the rock fragments contained in the ice at the base of the glacier; and (4) the erodibility of the surface beneath the glacier. Variations in any or all of these factors from time to time and/or from place to place mean that the features, effects, and degree of landscape modification in glaciated regions can vary greatly.

3 CONCEPT CHECKS

1. How do glaciers accumulate their load of sediment?
2. What are some visible effects of glacial erosion?
3. What factors influence the capacity of a glacier to erode?

Hikers in the Cordillera Blanca of Peru. Valley glaciers have sculpted this high mountain landscape. Meltwater from these glaciers is a major source for the rivers in the region. (Photo by Kristin Piljay)

4 Landforms Created by Glacial Erosion

The erosional effects of valley glaciers and ice sheets are quite different. A visitor to a glaciated mountain region is likely to see a sharp and angular topography. The reason is that as alpine glaciers move downvalley, they tend to accentuate the irregularities of the mountain landscape by creating steeper canyon walls and making bold peaks even more jagged. By contrast, continental ice sheets generally override the terrain and hence subdue rather than accentuate the irregularities they encounter. Although the erosional potential of ice sheets is enormous, landforms carved by these huge ice masses usually do not inspire the same wonderment and awe as do the erosional features created by valley glaciers. Much of the rugged mountain scenery so celebrated for its majestic beauty is the product of erosion by alpine glaciers. FIGURE 17 shows a hypothetical mountain area before, during, and after glaciation. You will refer to this figure often in the following discussion.

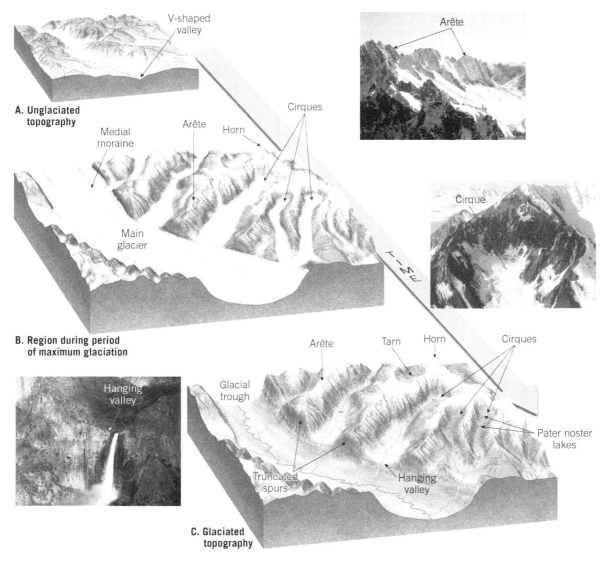

SMARTFIGURE 17
Erosional landforms created by alpine glaciers
The unglaciated landscape in part **A** is modified by valley glaciers in part **B**. After the ice recedes, in part **C**, the terrain looks very different than before glaciation. (Arête photo by James E. Patterson; cirque photo by Marli Miller; hanging valley photo by John Warden/Superstock)

Glaciated Valleys

A hike up a glaciated valley reveals a number of striking ice-created features. The valley itself is often a dramatic sight. Unlike streams, which create their own valleys, glaciers take the path of least resistance by following the course of existing stream valleys. Prior to glaciation, mountain valleys are characteristically narrow and V-shaped because streams are well above base level and are therefore downcutting. However, during glaciation these narrow valleys undergo a transformation as the glacier widens and deepens them, creating a U-shaped **glacial trough** (Figure 17 and FIGURE 18). In addition to producing a broader and deeper valley, the glacier also straightens the valley. As ice flows around sharp curves, its great erosional force removes the spurs of land that extend into the valley. The results of this activity are triangular-shaped cliffs called **truncated spurs**.

The amount of glacial erosion that takes place in different valleys in a mountainous area varies. Prior to glaciation, the mouths of tributary streams join the main (trunk) valley at the elevation of the stream in that valley. During glaciation, the amount of ice flowing through the main valley can be much greater than the amount advancing down each tributary. Consequently, the valley containing the trunk glacier is eroded deeper than the smaller valleys that feed it. Thus, when the glaciers eventually recede, the valleys of tributary glaciers are left standing above the main glacial trough and are termed **hanging valleys** (Figure 17). Rivers flowing through hanging valleys may produce spectacular waterfalls, such as those in Yosemite National Park (Figure 17).

As hikers walk up a glacial trough, they may pass a series of bedrock depressions on the valley floor that were probably created by plucking and then scoured by the abrasive force of the ice. If these depressions are filled with water, they are called **pater noster lakes** (Figure 17). The Latin name means "our Father" and is a reference to a string of rosary beads.

At the head of a glacial valley is a very characteristic and often imposing feature called a **cirque**. As the photo in Figure 17 illustrates, these bowl-shaped depressions have precipitous walls on three sides but are open on the downvalley side. The cirque is the focal point of the glacier's growth because it is the area of snow accumulation and ice formation. Cirques begin as irregularities in the mountainside that are subsequently enlarged by the frost wedging and plucking that occur along the sides and bottom of the glacier. After the glacier has melted away, the cirque basin is often occupied by a small lake called a **tarn** (Figure 17).

Sometimes, when two glaciers exist on opposite sides of a divide, each flowing away from the other, the dividing ridge between their cirques is largely eliminated as plucking and frost action enlarge each one. When this occurs, the two glacial troughs come to intersect, creating a gap or pass from one valley into the other. Such a feature is termed a **col**. Some important and well-known mountain passes that are cols include St. Gotthard Pass in the Swiss Alps, Tioga Pass in California's Sierra Nevada, and Berthoud Pass in the Colorado Rockies.

Before leaving the topic of glacial troughs and their associated features, one more rather well-known feature should be discussed: fiords. **Fiords** are deep, often spectacular steep-sided inlets of the sea that are present at high latitudes where mountains are adjacent to the ocean (FIGURE 19). They are drowned glacial troughs that became submerged as the ice left the valley and sea level rose following the Ice Age. The depths of fiords may exceed 1000 meters (3300 feet). However, the great depths of these flooded troughs are only partly explained by the post–Ice Age rise in sea level. Unlike the situation governing the downward erosional work of rivers, sea level does not act as base level for glaciers. As a consequence, glaciers are capable of eroding their beds far below the surface of the sea. For example, a 300-meter-thick

FIGURE 18 A U-shaped glacial trough
Prior to glaciation, a mountain valley is typically narrow and V-shaped. During glaciation, an alpine glacier widens, deepens, and straightens the valley, creating the classic U-shape shown here. (Photo by Michael Collier)

FIGURE 19 Fiords
The coast of Norway is known for its many fiords. Frequently these ice-sculpted inlets of the sea are hundreds of meters deep. (Satellite images courtesy of NASA; photo by Inger Helene Boasson/ AGE Fotostock)

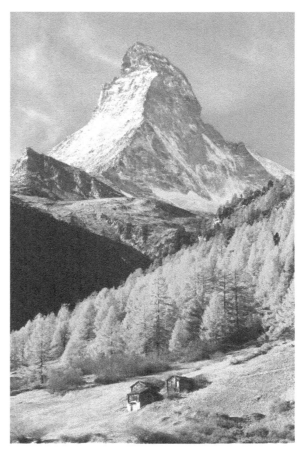

FIGURE 20 The Matterhorn
Horns are sharp, pyramid-like peaks that were shaped by alpine glaciers. The Matterhorn, in the Swiss Alps, is a famous example. (Photo by Yoshio Tomii/ SuperStock)

(1000-foot-thick) glacier can carve its valley floor more than 250 meters (820 feet) below sea level before downward erosion ceases and the ice begins to float. Norway, British Columbia, Greenland, New Zealand, Chile, and Alaska all have coastlines characterized by fiords.

Arêtes and Horns

A visit to the Alps and the Northern Rockies, or many other scenic mountain landscapes carved by valley glaciers, reveals glacial troughs, cirques, pater noster lakes, and the other related features just discussed. You also are likely to see sinuous sharp-edged ridges called **arêtes** (French for "knife-edge") and sharp pyramid-like peaks called **horns** projecting above the surroundings. Both

features can originate from the same basic process—the enlargement of cirques produced by plucking and frost action (Figure 17). In the case of the spires of rock called horns, groups of cirques around a single high mountain are responsible. As the cirques enlarge and converge, an isolated horn is produced. The most famous example is the Matterhorn in the Swiss Alps (FIGURE 20).

Arêtes can be formed in a similar manner, except that the cirques are not clustered around a point but rather exist on opposite sides of a divide. As the cirques grow, the divide separating them is reduced to a narrow knifelike partition. Arêtes may, however, also be created in another way. When two glaciers occupy parallel valleys, an arête can form when the divide separating the moving tongues of ice is progressively narrowed as the glaciers scour and widen their adjacent valleys.

Roches Moutonnées

In many glaciated landscapes, but most frequently where continental ice sheets have modified the terrain, the ice carves small streamlined hills from

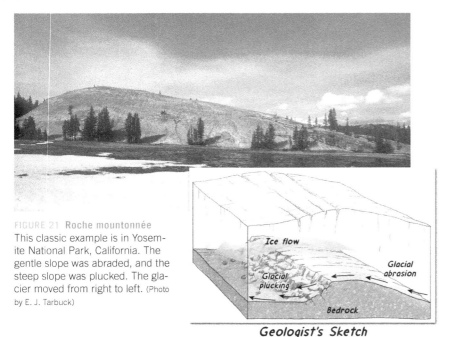

FIGURE 21 Roche mountonnée
This classic example is in Yosemite National Park, California. The gentle slope was abraded, and the steep slope was plucked. The glacier moved from right to left. (Photo by E. J. Tarbuck)

Geologist's Sketch

protruding bedrock knobs. Such an asymmetrical knob of bedrock is called a **roche moutonnée** (French for "sheep rock"). They are formed when glacial abrasion smooths the gentle slope facing the oncoming ice sheet and plucking steepens the opposite side as the ice rides over the knob (FIGURE 21). Roches moutonnées indicate the direction of glacial flow because the gentler slope is generally on the side from which the ice advanced.

4 CONCEPT CHECKS

1. How does a glaciated mountain valley differ in appearance from a mountain valley that was not glaciated?
2. Describe the features created by glacial erosion that you might expect to see in an area where valley glaciers recently existed.
3. Sketch a profile (side view) of a roche moutonnée. Include an arrow to show the direction from which the ice advanced.

Alaska's McBride Glacier widened and deepened this valley. The glacier is now shrinking and its terminus is retreating up the valley. (Photo by Michael Collier)

5 Glacial Deposits

A glacier picks up and transports a huge load of debris as it slowly advances across the land. Ultimately these materials are deposited when the ice melts. In regions where glacial sediment is deposited, it can play a significant role in forming the physical landscape. For example, in many areas once covered by the continental ice sheets of the recent Ice Age, the bedrock is rarely exposed because glacial deposits that are tens or even hundreds of meters thick completely mantle the terrain. The general effect of these deposits is to reduce the local relief and thus level the topography. Indeed, rural country scenes that are familiar to many of us—rocky pastures in New England, wheat fields in the Dakotas, rolling farmland in the Midwest—result directly from glacial deposition.

Long before the theory of an extensive Ice Age was ever proposed, much of the soil and rock debris covering portions of Europe was recognized as coming from somewhere else. At the time, these "foreign" materials were believed to have been "drifted" into their present positions by floating ice during an ancient flood. As a consequence, the term *drift* was applied to this sediment. Although rooted in an incorrect concept, this term was so well established by the time the true glacial origin of the debris became widely recognized that it remained in the basic glacial vocabulary. Today **glacial drift** is an all-embracing term for sediments of glacial origin, no matter how, where, or in what shape they were deposited.

One of the features distinguishing drift from sediments laid down by other erosional agents is that glacial deposits consist primarily of mechanically weathered rock debris that underwent little or no chemical weathering prior to deposition. Thus, minerals that are notably prone to chemical decomposition, such as hornblende and the plagioclase feldspars, are often conspicuous components in glacial sediments.

Geologists divide glacial drift into two distinct types: (1) materials deposited directly by the glacier, which are known as *till*, and (2) sediments laid down by glacial meltwater, called *stratified drift*.

Glacial Till

Till is deposited as glacial ice melts and drops its load of rock fragments. Unlike moving water and wind, ice cannot sort the sediment it carries; therefore, deposits of till are characteristically unsorted mixtures of many particle sizes (FIGURE 22). A close examination of this sediment shows that many of the pieces are scratched and polished as a result of being dragged along by the glacier. Such pieces help distinguish till from other deposits that are a mixture of different sediment sizes, such as material from a debris flow or a rockslide.

Boulders found in the till or lying free on the surface are called **glacial erratics** if they are different from the bedrock below (see Figure 14). Of course, this means

that they must have been derived from a source outside the area where they are found. Although the locality of origin for most erratics is unknown, the origin of some can be determined. In many cases, boulders were transported as far as 500 kilometers (300 miles) from their source area and, in a few instances, more than 1000 kilometers (600 miles). Therefore, by studying glacial erratics as well as the mineral composition of the remaining till,

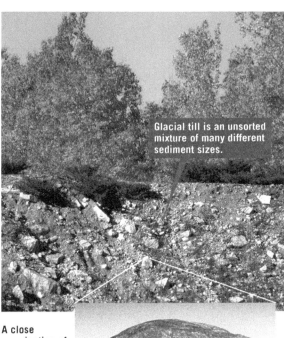

Glacial till is an unsorted mixture of many different sediment sizes.

A close examination of glacial till often reveals cobbles that have been scratched as they were dragged along by the ice.

FIGURE 22 Glacial till Unlike sediment deposited by running water and wind, material deposited directly by a glacier is not sorted. (Photos by E. J. Tarbuck)

EYE on Earth

This mountain landscape is in Montana's glacier National Park. Lake St. Mary occupies a glacial trough. (Photo by Dan Sherwood/AGE Fotostock)

Question 1 How does the current shape of the valley compare to its shape prior to glaciation? Explain.

Question 2 An arrow is pointing to a narrow ridge. What term is applied to such features?

geologists are sometimes able to trace the path of a lobe of ice.

In portions of New England and other areas, erratics dot pastures and farm fields. In fact, in some places these large rocks were cleared from fields and piled to make fences and walls. Keeping the fields clear, however, is an ongoing chore because each spring newly exposed erratics appear. Wintertime frost heaving has lifted them to the surface.

Stratified Drift

As the name implies, **stratified drift** is sorted according to the size and weight of the particles. Because ice is not capable of such sorting activity, these materials are not deposited directly by the glacier as till is but instead reflect the sorting action of glacial meltwater. Accumulations of stratified drift often consist largely of sand and gravel—that is, bed-load material—because the finer rock flour remains suspended and therefore is commonly carried far from the glacier by the meltwater streams.

5 CONCEPT CHECKS

1. What term can be applied to any glacial deposit?
2. Distinguish between till and stratified drift.
3. What is a glacial erratic?

6 Landforms Made of Till

The most common term for landforms made of glacial deposits is *moraine*. French peasants originally used the term when referring to the ridges and embankments of rock debris found near the margins of glaciers in the French Alps. Today, however, moraine has a broader meaning, because it is applied to a number of landforms, all of which are composed primarily of till.

Lateral and Medial Moraines

Alpine glaciers produce two types of moraines that occur exclusively in mountain valleys. The first of these is called a **lateral moraine**. As discussed earlier, when an alpine glacier moves down a valley, the ice erodes the sides of the valley with great efficiency. In addition, large quantities of debris are added to the glacier's surface as rubble falls or slides from higher up on the valley walls and collects on the margins of the moving ice. When the ice eventually melts, this accumulation of debris is dropped next to the valley walls. These ridges of till paralleling the sides of the valley constitute the lateral moraines.

The second type of moraine that is unique to alpine glaciers is the **medial moraine** (FIGURE 23). Medial moraines are created when two alpine glaciers coalesce to form a single ice stream. The till that was once carried along the sides of each glacier joins to form a single dark stripe of debris within the newly enlarged glacier. The sketch in Figure 23 illustrates this nicely. The creation of these dark stripes within the ice stream is one obvious proof that glacial ice moves because the moraine could not form if the ice did not flow downvalley. It is quite common to see several medial moraines within a single large alpine glacier because a streak will form whenever a tributary glacier joins the main valley.

End and Ground Moraines

Sometimes a glacier is compared to a conveyor belt. No matter whether the front of a glacier or an ice sheet is advancing, retreating, or stationary, it is constantly moving sediment forward and dropping it at its terminus. This is a useful analogy when considering end and ground moraines.

End Moraines   An **end moraine** is a ridge of till that forms at the terminus of a glacier and is characteristic of ice sheets and valley glaciers alike (FIGURE 24). These relatively common landforms are deposited when a state of equilibrium is attained between ablation and ice accumulation. That is, the end moraine forms when the ice is melting and evaporating near the end of the glacier at

FIGURE 23 Formation of a medial moraine
Kennicott Glacier is a 43-kilometer- (27-mile-) long valley glacier that is sculpting the mountains in Alaska's Wrangell-St. Elias National Park. The dark stripes of sediment are medial moraines. (Photo by Michael Collier)

Medial moraines

Lateral moraine

Lateral moraines join to form medial moraine

Lateral moraine

Medial moraine

Geologist's Sketch

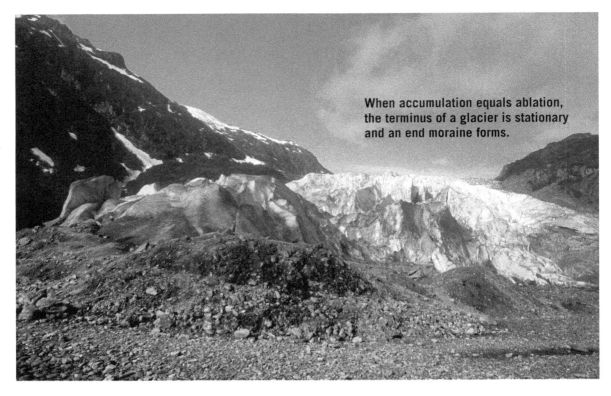

This end moraine formed at the terminus of Exit Glacier in Kenai Fiords National Park, Alaska. (Photo by Michael Collier)

When accumulation equals ablation, the terminus of a glacier is stationary and an end moraine forms.

a rate equal to the forward advance of the glacier from its region of nourishment. Although the terminus of the glacier is stationary, the ice continues to flow forward, delivering a continuous supply of sediment in the same manner a conveyor belt delivers goods to the end of a production line. As the ice melts, the till is dropped and the end moraine grows. The longer the ice front remains stable, the larger the ridge of till becomes.

Ground Moraine Eventually the time comes when ablation exceeds nourishment. At this point, the front

of the glacier begins to recede in the direction from which it originally advanced. However, as the ice front retreats, the conveyor-belt action of the glacier continues to provide fresh supplies of sediment to the terminus. In this manner, a large quantity of till is deposited as the ice melts away, creating a rock-strewn, undulating plain. This gently rolling layer of till deposited as the ice front recedes is termed **ground moraine**. Ground moraine has a leveling effect, filling in low spots and clogging old stream channels, often leading to a derangement of the existing drainage system. In areas where this layer of till is still relatively fresh, such as the northern Great Lakes region, poorly drained swampy lands are quite common.

Terminal and Recessional Moraines Periodically, a glacier will retreat to a point where ablation and nourishment once again balance. When this happens, the ice front stabilizes and a new end moraine forms. The pattern of end moraine formation and ground moraine deposition may be repeated many times before the glacier has completely vanished. Such a pattern is illustrated in FIGURE 25. It should be pointed out that the outermost end moraine marks

End moraines deposited during the most recent (Wisconsinan) stage are the most prominent.

End moraines:
Wisconsinan Age
End moraines:
Illinoian Age

0   150mi
0   150km

Driftless
area

Extent of
Wisconsinan
glaciation

Extent of
Illinoian glaciation

the limit of the glacial advance. Because of its special status, this end moraine is also called the **terminal moraine**. On the other hand, the end moraines that were created as the ice front occasionally stabilized during retreat are termed **recessional moraines**. Note that terminal and recessional moraines are essentially alike; the only difference between them is their relative positions.

End moraines deposited by the most recent major stage of Ice Age glaciation are prominent features in many parts of the Midwest and Northeast. In Wisconsin the wooded, hilly terrain of the Kettle Moraine near Milwaukee is a particularly picturesque example. A well-known example in the Northeast is Long Island. This linear strip of glacial sediment that extends northeastward from New York City is part of an end moraine complex that stretches from eastern Pennsylvania to Cape Cod, Massachusetts (FIGURE 26). The end

moraines that make up Long Island represent materials that were deposited by a continental ice sheet in the relatively shallow waters off the coast and built up many meters above sea level. Long Island Sound, the narrow body of water separating the island and the mainland, was not built up as much by glacial deposition and was therefore subsequently flooded by the rising sea following the Ice Age.

FIGURE 27 represents a hypothetical area during glaciation and following the retreat of ice sheets. It shows the moraines that were described in this section, as well

FIGURE 26 **Two significant end moraines in the Northeast** The Ronkonkoma moraine, which was deposited about 20,000 years ago, extends through central Long Island, Martha's Vineyard, and Nantucket. The Harbor Hill moraine formed about 14,000 years ago and extends along the north shore of Long Island, through southern Rhode Island and Cape Cod.

SMARTFIGURE 27 **Common depositional landforms**
This diagram depicts a hypothetical area affected by ice sheets in the recent geologic past. (Drumlin photo courtesy of Ward's Natural Science Establishment; esker photo by Richard P. Jacobs/JLM Visuals; kame photo by John Dankwardt; kettle lake photo by Carlyn Iverson/Photo Researchers, Inc.; braided river photo by Michael Collier)

FIGURE 28 Drumlin field
A portion of the drumlin field shown on the Palmyra, New York, 7.5-minute topographic map. North is at the top. The drumlins are steepest on the north side, indicating that the ice advanced from this direction.

Drumlins

Lake Ontario

Drumlins

Moraines are not the only landforms composed of till. In some areas that were once covered by continental ice sheets, a special variety of glacial landscape exists—one characterized by smooth, elongate, parallel hills called **drumlins** (Figure 27). Certainly one of the best-known drumlins is Bunker Hill in Boston, the site of the famous Revolutionary War battle in 1775.

An examination of Bunker Hill or other less famous drumlins would reveal that drumlins are streamlined, asymmetrical hills composed largely of till. They range in height from about 15 to 50 meters and may be up to 1 kilometer long. The steep side of the hill faces the direction from which the ice advanced, whereas the gentler, longer slope points in the direction the ice moved. Drumlins are not found as isolated landforms but rather occur in clusters called *drumlin fields* (FIGURE 28). One such cluster, east of Rochester, New York, is estimated to contain about 10,000 drumlins. Although drumlin formation is not fully understood, the streamlined shape of drumlins indicates that they were molded in the zone of plastic flow within an active glacier. It is believed that many drumlins originate when glaciers advance over previously deposited drift and reshape the material.

as the depositional features that are discussed in the sections that follow. This figure depicts landscape features similar to what might be encountered if you were traveling in the upper Midwest or New England. As you read upcoming sections dealing with other glacial deposits, you will be referred to this figure several times.

6 CONCEPT CHECKS

1. How are medial moraines and lateral moraines related? In what kind of setting are these features found?
2. Contrast end moraine and ground moraine. Relate their formation to the budget of a glacier.
3. Distinguish between a terminal end moraine and a recessional end moraine.
4. Sketch a profile (side view) of a drumlin. Include an arrow to indicate the direction from which the ice advanced.

EYE on Earth

This wall is located in New England and is built of diverse stones and boulders cleared from nearby fields. In 1914, Robert Frost wrote a now-famous poem titled "Mending Wall" about a feature like this one. It begins with these lines:

"Something there is that doesn't love a wall,
That sends the frozen-ground-swell under it,
And spills the upper boulders in the sun;
And makes gaps even two can pass abreast."

Question 1 What is the likely weathering process causing the wall to swell and "spill" its boulders?

Question 2 Given the wall's location in New England, did all of the rocks in the wall come from local sources? Explain.

Question 3 What term applies to the rocks composing the wall?

Photo by Jerry and Marcy Monkman/Danita Delimont/Alamy

7   Landforms Made of Stratified Drift

Much of the material acquired and transported by a glacier is ultimately deposited by streams of glacial meltwater flowing on, within, beneath, and beyond a glacier. This sediment is termed *stratified drift*. Unlike glacial till, stratified drift shows some degree of sorting. There are two basic categories of features composed of stratified drift: *Ice-contact deposits* accumulate on, within, or immediately adjacent to a glacier. *Outwash sediments* or simply *outwash*, is material deposited by meltwater streams beyond the terminus of a glacier.

Outwash Plains and Valley Trains

At the same time that an end moraine is forming, water from the melting glacier cascades over the till, sweeping some of it out in front of the growing ridge of unsorted debris. Meltwater generally emerges from the ice in rapidly moving streams that are often choked with suspended material and carry a substantial bed load as well. As the water leaves the glacier, it moves onto the relatively flat surface beyond and rapidly loses velocity. As a consequence, much of its bed load is dropped, and the meltwater begins weaving a complex pattern of braided channels (Figure 27). In this way, a broad, ramplike surface composed of stratified drift is built adjacent to the downstream edge of most end moraines. When the feature is formed in association with an ice sheet, it is termed an **outwash plain**, and when largely confined to a mountain valley, it is usually referred to as a **valley train**.

Outwash plains and valley trains often are pockmarked with basins or depressions known as **kettles** (Figure 27). Kettles also occur in deposits of till. Kettles are formed when blocks of stagnant ice become wholly or partly buried in drift and eventually melt, leaving pits in the glacial sediment. Although most kettles do not exceed 2 kilometers in diameter, some with diameters exceeding 10 kilometers occur in Minnesota. Likewise, the typical depth of most kettles is less than 10 meters, although the vertical dimensions of some approach 50 meters. In many cases water eventually fills the depression and forms a pond or lake. One well-known example is Walden Pond near Concord, Massachusetts. It is here that Henry David Thoreau lived alone for 2 years in the 1840s and about which he wrote his famous book *Walden; or, Life in the Woods*.

Ice-Contact Deposits

When the melting terminus of a glacier shrinks to a critical point, flow virtually stops, and the ice becomes stagnant. Meltwater that flows over, within, and at the base of the motionless ice lays down deposits of stratified drift. Then, as the supporting ice melts away, the stratified sediment is left behind in the form of hills, terraces, and ridges. Such accumulations are collectively termed **ice-contact deposits** and are classified according to their shapes.

When the ice-contact stratified drift is in the form of a mound or steep-sided hill, it is called a **kame** (Figure 27). Some kames represent bodies of sediment deposited by meltwater in openings within or depressions on top of the ice. Others originate as deltas or fans built outward from the ice by meltwater streams. Later, when the stagnant ice melts away, these various accumulations of sediment collapse to form isolated, irregular mounds.

When glacial ice occupies a valley, **kame terraces** may be built along the sides of the valley. These features commonly are narrow masses of stratified drift laid down between the glacier and the side of the valley by streams that drop debris along the margins of the shrinking ice mass.

A third type of ice-contact deposit is a long, narrow, sinuous ridge composed largely of sand and gravel. Some are more than 100 meters high, with lengths in excess of 100 kilometers. The dimensions of many others are far less spectacular. Known as **eskers**, these ridges are deposited by meltwater rivers flowing within, on top of, and beneath a mass of motionless, stagnant glacial ice (Figure 27). Many sediment sizes are carried by the torrents of meltwater in the ice-banked channels, but only the coarser material can settle out of the turbulent stream.

7 CONCEPT CHECKS

1. What is an outwash plain? How is it different from a valley train?
2. Describe the formation of a kettle.
3. How do kames and eskers form?

8 Other Effects of Ice Age Glaciers

In addition to the massive erosional and depositional work carried out by Ice Age glaciers, the ice sheets had other effects, sometimes profound, on the landscape. For example, as the ice advanced and retreated, animals and plants were forced to migrate. This led to stresses that some organisms could not tolerate. Hence, a number of plants and animals became extinct. Other effects of Ice Age glaciers that are described in this section involve adjustments in Earth's crust due to the addition and removal of ice and sea-level changes associated with the formation and melting of ice sheets. The advance and retreat of ice sheets also led to significant changes in the routes taken by rivers. In some regions, glaciers acted as dams that created large lakes. When these ice dams failed, the effects on the landscape were profound. In areas that today are deserts, lakes of another type, called pluvial lakes, formed.

Crustal Subsidence and Rebound

In areas that were major centers of ice accumulation, such as Scandinavia and the Canadian Shield, the land has been slowly rising over the past several thousand years. Uplifting of almost 300 meters (1000 feet) has occurred in the Hudson Bay region. This, too, is the result of the continental ice sheets. But how can glacial ice cause such vertical crustal movement? We now understand that the land is rising because the added weight of the 3-kilometer-thick (2-mile-thick) mass of ice caused downwarping of Earth's crust. Following the removal of this immense load, the crust has been adjusting by gradually rebounding upward ever since (FIGURE 29).*

---

* This concept is termed *isostatic adjustment*.

Sea-Level Changes

One of the most interesting and perhaps dramatic effects of the Ice Age was the fall and rise of sea level that accompanied the advance and retreat of the glaciers. Sea level would rise by an estimated 60 or 70 meters if the water locked up in the Antarctic Ice Sheet were to melt completely. Such an occurrence would flood many densely populated coastal areas.

Although the total volume of glacial ice today is great, exceeding 25 million cubic kilometers, during the Ice Age the volume of glacial ice amounted to about 70 million cubic kilometers, or 45 million cubic kilometers more than at present. Because we know that the snow from which glaciers are made ultimately comes from the evaporation of ocean water, the growth of ice sheets must have caused a worldwide drop in sea level (FIGURE 30). Indeed, estimates suggest that sea level was as much as 100 meters (330 feet) lower than it is today. Thus, land that is presently flooded by the oceans was dry. The Atlantic coast of the United States lay more than 100 kilometers (60 miles) to the east of New York City, France and Britain were joined where the famous English Channel is today, Alaska and Siberia were connected across the Bering Strait, and Southeast Asia was tied by dry land to the islands of Indonesia.

Changes to Rivers and Valleys

Among the effects associated with the advance and retreat of North American ice sheets were changes in the routes of many rivers and the modification in the size and shape of many valleys. If we are to understand the present pattern of rivers and lakes in the central and northeastern United States (and many other places as well), we need to be aware of glacial history. Two examples are used to illustrate these effects.

Upper Mississippi Drainage Basin   FIGURE 31A shows the familiar present-day pattern of rivers in the central United States, with the Missouri, Ohio, and Illinois Rivers as major tributaries to the Mississippi. FIGURE 31B

FIGURE 29 Crustal subsidence and rebound These simplified diagrams illustrate subsidence and rebound resulting from the addition and removal of continental ice sheets.

In northern Canada and Scandinavia, where the greatest accumulation of glacial ice occurred, the added weight caused downwarping of the crust.

Crust

Mantle

Crust

Mantle

Ever since the ice melted, there has been gradual uplift or rebound of the crust.

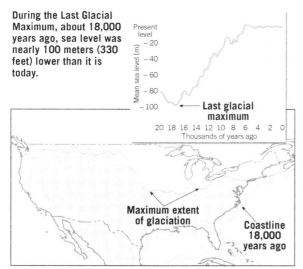

During the Last Glacial Maximum, about 18,000 years ago, sea level was nearly 100 meters (330 feet) lower than it is today.

During the Last Glacial Maximum, the shoreline extended out onto the present day continental shelf.

FIGURE 30 Changing sea level
As ice sheets form and then melt away, sea level falls and rises, causing the shoreline to shift.

depicts drainage systems in this region prior to the Ice Age. The pattern is *very* different from the present. This remarkable transformation of river systems resulted from the advance and retreat of the ice sheets.

Notice that prior to the Ice Age, a significant part of the Missouri River drained north toward Hudson Bay. Moreover, the Mississippi River did not follow the present Iowa–Illinois boundary but rather flowed across west-central Illinois, where the lower Illinois River flows today. The preglacial Ohio River barely reached to the present-day state of Ohio, and the rivers that today feed the Ohio in western Pennsylvania flowed north and drained into the North Atlantic. The Great Lakes were created by glacial erosion during the Ice Age. Prior to the Pleistocene epoch, the basins occupied by these huge lakes were lowlands with rivers that ran eastward to the Gulf of St. Lawrence.

The large Teays River was a significant feature prior to the Ice Age (Figure 31B). It flowed from West Virginia across Ohio, Indiana, and Illinois, and it discharged into the Mississippi River not far from present-day Peoria. This river valley, which would have rivaled the Mississippi in size, was completely obliterated during the Pleistocene, buried by glacial deposits hundreds of feet thick. Today the sands and gravels in the buried Teays valley make it an important aquifer.

New York's Finger Lakes
The recent geologic history of west-central New York State south of Lake Ontario was dominated by ice sheets. We have already noted the drumlins in the vicinity of Rochester (see Figure 28). Many other depositional features and erosional effects

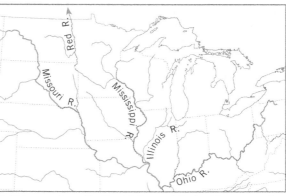

A. This map shows the Great Lakes and the familiar present-day pattern of rivers. Quaternary ice sheets played a major role in creating this pattern

B. Reconstruction of drainage systems prior to the Ice Age. The pattern was very different from today, and the Great Lakes did not exist.

FIGURE 31 Changing rivers
The advance and retreat of ice sheets caused major changes in the routes followed by rivers in the central United States.

occur in the region. Perhaps the best known are the Finger Lakes. They consist of 11 long, narrow, roughly parallel water bodies oriented north–south like fingers on a pair of outstretched hands (FIGURE 32). Prior to the Ice Age, the Finger Lakes area consisted of a series of river valleys that were oriented parallel to the direction of ice movement. Multiple episodes of glacial erosion transformed these valleys into deep, steep-walled lakes. Two of the lakes are very deep; the greatest depth of Seneca Lake is more than 180 meters (600 feet), and Cayuga Lake is nearly 135 meters (450 feet) deep, and the beds of both lakes are below sea level. The depth to which the glaciers carved these basins is much greater. There are hundreds of feet of glacial sediment in the deep rock troughs below the lake beds.

Ice Dams Create Proglacial Lakes

Ice sheets and alpine glaciers can act as dams to create lakes by trapping glacial meltwater and blocking the

With the retreat of the ice sheet came enormous volumes of meltwater. The Great Plains generally slope upward to the west. As the terminus of the ice sheet receded northeastward, meltwater was trapped between the ice on one side and the sloping land on the other, causing Lake Agassiz to deepen and spread across the landscape. It came into existence about 12,000 years ago and lasted for about 4500 years. Such water bodies are termed **proglacial lakes**, referring to their position just beyond the outer limits of a glacier or ice sheet. The history of Lake Agassiz is complicated by the dynamics of the ice sheet, which, at various times, readvanced and affected lake levels and drainage systems. Where drainage occurred depended upon the water level of the lake and the position of the ice sheet.

Lake Agassiz left marks over a broad region. Former beaches, many kilometers from any water, mark former shorelines. Several modern river valleys, including the Red River and the Minnesota River, were originally cut by water entering or leaving the lake. Present-day remnants of Lake Agassiz include Lakes Winnipeg, Manitoba, Winnipegosis, and Lake of the Woods. The sediments of the former lake basin are now fertile agricultural land.

Research shows that the shifting of glaciers and the failure of ice dams can cause the rapid release of huge volumes of water. Such events occurred during the history of Lake Agassiz. A dramatic example of such glacial outbursts occurred in the Pacific Northwest between about 15,000 and 13,000 years ago and is briefly described in FIGURE 34.

flow of rivers. Some of these lakes are relatively small, short-lived impoundments. Others can be large and exist for hundreds or thousands of years.

FIGURE 33 is a map of Lake Agassiz—the largest lake to form during the Ice Age in North America.

Pluvial Lakes

While the formation and growth of ice sheets was an obvious response to significant changes in climate, the existence of the glaciers themselves triggered important climatic changes in the regions beyond their margins. In arid and semiarid areas on all the continents, temperatures were lower and thus evaporation rates were lower, but at the same time, moderate

Cordilleran ice sheet

The Purcell lobe blocks the river creating a 600 meter- (2000-foot-) high dam.

Area of Missoula flooding

Spokane

Clark Fork River

Lake Missoula was up to 300 kilometers (185 miles) long and held more water than present-day Lake Ontario.

Lake Missoula

Missoula

Yakima

WASHINGTON

Lewiston

Columbia River

OREGON

IDAHO

MONTANA

This prehistoric proglacial lake in western Montana periodically broke through the ice dam that created it. This resulted in huge floods (megafloods) that shaped the landscape of eastern Washington State.

FIGURE 34 Lake Missoula and the Channeled Scablands During a span of 1500 years, more than 40 megafloods from Lake Missoula carved the Channeled Scablands. (Photo by John S. Shelton)

The towering mass of rushing water from each megaflood stripped away layers of sediment and soil and cut deep canyons (coulees) into the underlying layers of basalt to create the Channeled Scablands.

precipitation totals were experienced. This cooler, wetter climate formed many **pluvial lakes** (*pluvia* = rain). In North America the greatest concentration of pluvial lakes occurred in the vast Basin and Range region of Nevada and Utah (FIGURE 35). By far the largest of the lakes in this region was Lake Bonneville. With maximum depths exceeding 300 meters (1000 feet) and an area of 50,000 square kilometers (20,000 square miles), Lake Bonneville was nearly the same size as present-day Lake Michigan. As the ice sheets waned, the climate again grew more arid, and the lake levels lowered in response. Although most of the lakes completely disappeared, a few small remnants of Lake Bonneville remain, the Great Salt Lake being the largest and best known.

FIGURE 35 Pluvial lakes During the Ice Age, the Basin and Range region experienced a wetter climate than it has today. Many basins turned into large lakes.

The Great Salt Lake is a remnant of Lake Bonneville

OREGON | IDAHO

NEVADA

Lake Lahontan

Lake Bonneville was nearly the size of present-day Lake Michigan

CALIFORNIA

UTAH

ARIZONA

WA | MT

OR | ID

NV | UT

CA

AZ

0   120 mi
0   120 km

8 CONCEPT CHECKS

1. List and briefly describe five effects of Ice Age glaciers aside from the formation of major erosional and depositional features.
2. Examine Figure 30 and determine how much sea level has changed since the Last Glacial Maximum.
3. Compare the two parts of Figure 30 and identify three major changes to the flow of rivers in the central United States during the Ice Age.
4. Contrast proglacial lakes and pluvial lakes. Give an example of each.

Earth's Shrinking Glaciers

Glaciers are sensitive to changes in temperature and precipitation and therefore can provide clues about changes in climate. With few exceptions, glaciers have been retreating at unprecedented rates over the past century.

Change in Columbia Glacier between 1986 and 2011. This glacier descends from an ice field 3050 meters (10,000 feet) above sea level into a narrow inlet that leads into Prince William Sound in southeastern Alaska. It is one of the most rapidly changing glaciers in the world. Between 1986 and 2011 the terminus retreated more than 20 kilometers (12 miles). The glacier had also thinned substantially as shown by the expansion of exposed areas of brown bedrock.

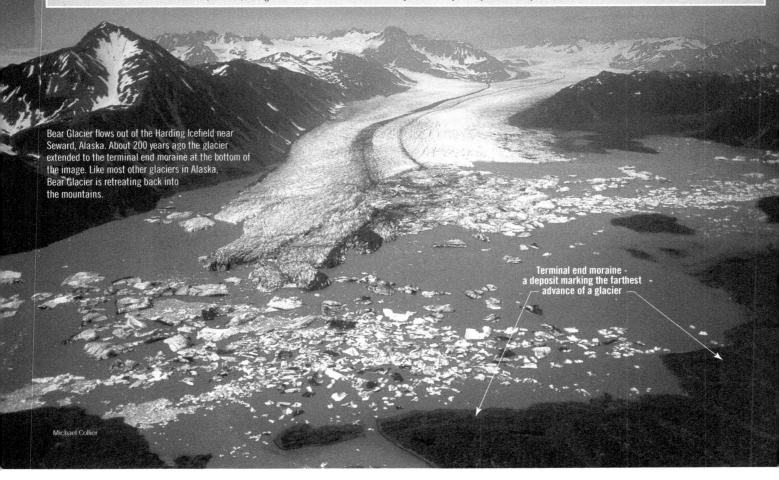

Bear Glacier flows out of the Harding Icefield near Seward, Alaska. About 200 years ago the glacier extended to the terminal end moraine at the bottom of the image. Like most other glaciers in Alaska, Bear Glacier is retreating back into the mountains.

Terminal end moraine - a deposit marking the farthest advance of a glacier

Michael Collier

656

150 years ago, there were 147 glaciers in Montana's Glacier National Park. Today only 37 remain, and these may vanish by 2030 or even sooner. This is a view of shrinking Jackson Glacier.

Ed Reschke/Getty Images

Riggs Glacier

Muir Glacier

NSIDC

NSIDC

Two images taken 63 years apart from the same spot in Alaska's Glacier Bay National Park. Muir Glacier, which is prominent in the 1941 photo, has retreated out of view in the 2004 image. Also, Riggs Glacier (upper right) has thinned and retreated significantly.

AREA OF LOSS

AREA OF LOSS

AREA OF GAIN

AREA OF LOSS

Glacial Meltwater

EQUIVALENT WATER PER YEAR (CENTIMETERS)

NET LOSS ◄ −25 −20 −15 −10 −5 0 5 10 15 20 25 ► NET GAIN

This map was compiled using observations from NASA's Gravity Recovery and Climate Experiment (GRACE) satellites. It shows where Greenland gained mass during the 2003-2005 study period and where it lost mass. Overall, Greenland lost 20 percent more mass than it gained from snowfall each year.

Robbie Shone/Photo Researchers, Inc

9 The Glacial Theory and the Ice Age

The Ice Age, was a time when ice sheets and alpine glaciers were far more extensive than they are today. There was a time when the most popular explanation for what we now know to be glacial deposits was that the materials had been drifted in by means of icebergs or perhaps simply swept across the landscape by a catastrophic flood. What convinced geologists that an extensive ice age was responsible for these deposits and many other glacial features?

In 1821 a Swiss engineer, Ignaz Venetz, presented a paper suggesting that glacial landscape features occurred at considerable distances from the existing glaciers in the Alps. This implied that the glaciers had once been larger and occupied positions farther downvalley. Another Swiss scientist, Louis Agassiz, doubted the proposal of widespread glacial activity put forth by Venetz. He set out to prove that the idea was not valid. However, his 1836 fieldwork in the Alps convinced him of the merits of his colleague's hypothesis. In fact, a year later Agassiz hypothesized a great ice age that had extensive and far-reaching effects—an idea that was to give Agassiz widespread fame.

The proof of the glacial theory proposed by Agassiz and others constitutes a classic example of applying the principle of uniformitarianism. Realizing that certain features are produced by no other known process but glacial action, they were able to begin reconstructing the extent of now-vanished ice sheets based on the presence of features and deposits found far beyond the margins of present-day glaciers and ice sheets. In this manner, the development and verification of the glacial theory continued during the nineteenth century, and through the efforts of many scientists, a knowledge of the nature and extent of former ice sheets became clear (FIGURE 36).

By the beginning of the twentieth century, geologists had largely determined the extent of the Ice Age glaciation. Further, during the course of their investigations, they discovered that many glaciated regions had not one layer of drift but several. Moreover, close examination of these older deposits showed well-developed zones of chemical weathering and soil formation, as well as the remains of plants that require warm temperatures. The evidence was clear; there had been not just one glacial advance but many, each separated by extended periods when climates were as warm as or warmer than the present. The Ice Age had not simply been a time when the ice advanced over the land, lingered for a while, and then receded. Rather, the period was a very complex event, characterized by a number of advances and withdrawals of glacial ice.

By the early twentieth century, a fourfold division of the Ice Age had been established for both North America and Europe. The divisions were based largely on studies of glacial deposits. In North America each of the four major stages was named for the midwestern state where deposits of that stage were well exposed and/or were first studied. These are, in order of occurrence, the Nebraskan, Kansan, Illinoian, and Wisconsinan. These traditional divisions remained in place for many years, until it was learned that sediment cores from the ocean floor contain a much more complete record of climate change during the Ice Age. Unlike the glacial record on land, which is punctuated by many unconformities, seafloor sediments provide an uninterrupted record of climatic cycles for this period. Studies of these seafloor sediments showed that glacial/interglacial cycles had occurred about every 100,000 years. About 20 such cycles of cooling and warming were identified for the span we call the Ice Age.

During the Ice Age, ice left its imprint on almost 30 percent of Earth's land area, including about 10 million square kilometers of North America, 5 million square kilometers of Europe, and 4 million square kilometers of Siberia (FIGURE 37). The amount of glacial ice in the Northern Hemisphere was roughly twice that of the Southern Hemisphere. The

FIGURE 36 Evidence from the seafloor
Cores of seafloor sediment provided data that led to a more complete understanding of the complexity of Ice Age climates. (Photo by Gary Braasch/ZUMA Press/ Newscom)

primary reason is that the southern polar ice could not spread far beyond the margins of Antarctica. By contrast, North America and Eurasia provided great expanses of land for the spread of ice sheets.

Today we know that the Ice Age began between 2 million and 3 million years ago. This means that most of the major glacial stages occurred during a division of the geologic time scale called the **Quaternary period**. However, this period does not encompass all of the last glacial period. The Antarctic Ice Sheet, for example, probably formed at least 30 million years ago.

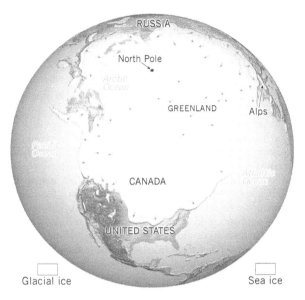

FIGURE 37 Where was the ice?
This map shows the maximum extent of ice sheets in the Northern Hemisphere during the Ice Age.

9 CONCEPT CHECKS

1. What was the best source of data showing Ice Age climate cycles?
2. About what percentage of Earth's land surface was affected by glaciers during the Quaternary period?
3. Where were ice sheets more extensive during the Ice Age: the Northern Hemisphere or the Southern Hemisphere? Why?

EYE on Earth

This aerial image is from the Alaska Range in the south-central part of the state. These mountains have been sculpted by many valley glaciers.

Question 1 Explain the origin of the numerous stripes of debris.

Question 2 Do the glaciers in this image appear to be growing or shrinking? What observations support your answer?

Question 3 The velocity of the two main ice streams must vary. Based on what you can observe, which glacier experienced a period of accelerated flow?

Question 4 What term is applied to a situation in which a glacier "speeds up" for a relatively short period of time?

Michael Collier

10 Causes of Ice Ages

A great deal is known about glaciers and glaciation. Much has been learned about glacier formation and movement, the extent of glaciers past and present, and the features created by glaciers, both erosional and depositional. However, the causes of ice ages are not completely understood.

Although widespread glaciation has been rare in Earth's history, the Ice Age that encompassed most of the Quaternary period is not the only glacial period for which records exist. Earlier glaciations are indicated by deposits called **tillite**, a sedimentary rock formed when glacial till becomes lithified (FIGURE 38). Such deposits, found in strata of several different ages, usually contain striated rock fragments, and some overlie grooved and polished bedrock surfaces or are associated with sandstones and conglomerates that show features of outwash deposits. Two Precambrian glacial episodes have been identified in the geologic record, the first approximately 2 billion years ago and the second about 600 million years ago.

Any theory that attempts to explain the causes of ice ages must successfully answer two basic questions. (1) *What causes the onset of glacial conditions?* For continental ice sheets to have formed, average temperature must have been somewhat lower than at present and perhaps substantially lower than throughout much of geologic time. Thus, a successful theory would have to account for the cooling that finally leads to glacial conditions. (2) *What caused the alternation of glacial and interglacial stages that have been documented for the Quaternary period?* The first question deals with long-term trends in temperature on a scale of millions of years, and the second question relates to much shorter-term changes.

Although the literature of science contains many hypotheses related to the possible causes of glacial periods, we will discuss only a few major ideas to summarize current thought.

Plate Tectonics

Probably the most attractive proposal for explaining the fact that extensive glaciations have occurred only a few times in the geologic past comes from the theory of plate tectonics. Because glaciers can form only on land, we know that landmasses must exist somewhere in the higher latitudes before an ice age can commence. Many scientists suggest that ice ages have occurred only when Earth's shifting crustal plates have carried the continents from tropical latitudes to more poleward positions.

Glacial features in present-day Africa, Australia, South America, and India indicate that these regions, which are now tropical or subtropical, experienced an ice age near the end of the Paleozoic era, about 250 million years ago. However, there is no evidence that ice sheets existed during this same period in what are today the higher latitudes of North America and Eurasia. For many years this puzzled scientists. Was the climate in these relatively tropical latitudes once like it is today in Greenland and Antarctica? Why did glaciers not form in North America and Eurasia? Until the plate tectonics theory was formulated, there had been no reasonable explanation.

Today scientists understand that the areas containing these ancient glacial features were joined together as a single supercontinent, called Pangaea, located at latitudes far to the south of their present positions. Later this landmass broke apart, and its pieces, each moving on a different plate, migrated toward their present locations (FIGURE 39). Now we know that during the geologic past, plate movements accounted for many dramatic climate changes as landmasses shifted in relation to one another and moved to different latitudinal positions. Changes in oceanic circulation also must have occurred, altering the transport of heat and moisture and consequently the climate as well. Because the rate of plate movement is very slow—a few centimeters annually—appreciable changes in the positions of the continents occur only over great spans of geologic time. Thus, climate changes triggered by shifting plates are extremely gradual and happen on a scale of millions of years.

Variations in Earth's Orbit

Because climatic changes brought about by moving plates are extremely gradual, the plate tectonics theory cannot be used to explain the alternation between glacial and

FIGURE 38 **Tillite**
When glacial till is lithified, it becomes the sedimentary rock known as *tillite*. Tillite strata are evidence for ice ages that occurred prior to the Quaternary period. (Photo by Brian Roman)

The supercontinent Pangaea showing the area covered by glacial ice near the end of the Paleozoic era.

The continents as they appear today. The white areas indicate where evidence of the late Paleozoic ice sheets exists.

FIGURE 39 A late Paleozoic ice age
Shifting tectonic plates sometimes move landmasses to high latitudes, where the formation of ice sheets is possible.

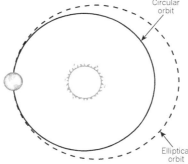

The shape of Earth's orbit changes during a cycle that spans about 100,000 years. It gradually changes from nearly circular to more elliptical and then back again. This diagram greatly exaggerates the amount of change.

SMARTFIGURE 40
Orbital variations
Periodic variations in Earth's orbit are linked to alternating glacial and interglacial conditions during the Ice Age.

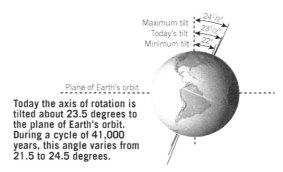

Today the axis of rotation is tilted about 23.5 degrees to the plane of Earth's orbit. During a cycle of 41,000 years, this angle varies from 21.5 to 24.5 degrees.

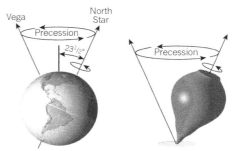

Earth's axis wobbles like a spinning top. Consequently, the axis points to different spots in the sky during a cycle of about 26,000 years.

interglacial climates that occurred during the Pleistocene epoch. Therefore, we must look to some other triggering mechanism that might cause climate change on a scale of thousands rather than millions of years. Today many scientists strongly suspect that the climate oscillations that characterized the Quaternary period are linked to variations in Earth's orbit. This hypothesis was first developed and strongly advocated by the Serbian astrophysicist Milutin Milankovitch and is based on the premise that variations in incoming solar radiation are a principal factor in controlling Earth's climate.

Milankovitch formulated a comprehensive mathematical model based on the following elements (FIGURE 40):

- Variations in the shape (*eccentricity*) of Earth's orbit about the Sun
- Changes in *obliquity*—that is, changes in the angle that the axis makes with the plane of Earth's orbit
- The wobbling of Earth's axis, called *precession*

Using these factors, Milankovitch calculated variations in the receipt of solar energy and the corresponding surface temperature of Earth back into time, in an attempt to correlate these changes with the climate fluctuations of the Quaternary. In explaining climate changes that result from these three variables, note that they cause little or no variation in the *total* solar energy reaching the ground. Instead, their impact is felt because they change the degree of contrast between the seasons.

Somewhat milder winters in the middle to high latitudes mean greater snowfall totals, whereas cooler summers would bring a reduction in snowmelt.

Among the studies that have added credibility to the astronomical hypothesis of Milankovitch is one in which deep-sea sediments containing certain climatically sensitive microorganisms were analyzed to establish a chronology of temperature changes going back nearly one-half million years.[*] This time scale of climate change was then compared to astronomical calculations of eccentricity, obliquity, and precession to determine whether a correlation existed. Although the study was very involved and mathematically complex, the conclusions were

---

[*]J. D. Hays, John Imbrie, and N. J. Shackelton, "Variations in the Earth's Orbit: Pacemaker of the Ice Ages," *Science* 194 (1976): 1121–32.

FIGURE 41 Ice cores contain clues to shifts in climate
This scientist is slicing an ice core from Antarctica for analysis. He is wearing protective clothing and a mask to minimize contamination of the sample. Chemical analyses of ice cores can provide important data about past climates. (Photo by British Antarctic Survey/Photo Researchers)

gases carbon dioxide and methane than the post–Ice Age atmosphere (FIGURE 41). Carbon dioxide and methane are important "greenhouse" gases, which means they trap radiation emitted by Earth and contribute to the heating of the atmosphere. When the amount of carbon dioxide and methane in the atmosphere increases, global temperatures rise, and when there is a reduction in these gases, as occurred during the Ice Age, temperatures fall. Therefore, reductions in the concentrations of greenhouse gases help explain the magnitude of the temperature drop that occurred during glacial times. Although scientists know that concentrations of carbon dioxide and methane dropped, they do not know what caused the drop. As often occurs in science, observations gathered during one investigation yield information and raise questions that require further analysis and explanation.

straightforward: The researchers found that major variations in climate over the past several hundred thousand years were closely associated with changes in the geometry of Earth's orbit; that is, cycles of climate change were shown to correspond closely with the periods of obliquity, precession, and orbital eccentricity. More specifically, the authors stated: "It is concluded that changes in the earth's orbital geometry are the fundamental cause of the succession of Quaternary ice ages."[*]

Let us briefly summarize the ideas just described. The theory of plate tectonics provides an explanation for the widely spaced and nonperiodic onset of glacial conditions at various times in the geologic past, whereas the theory proposed by Milankovitch and supported by the work of J. D. Hays and his colleagues furnishes an explanation for the alternating glacial and interglacial episodes of the Quaternary.

Other Factors

Variations in Earth's orbit correlate closely with the timing of glacial–interglacial cycles. However, the variations in solar energy reaching Earth's surface caused by these orbital changes do not adequately explain the magnitude of the temperature changes that occurred during the most recent Ice Age. Other factors must also have contributed. One factor involves variations in the composition of the atmosphere. Other influences involve changes in the reflectivity of Earth's surface and in ocean circulation. Let's take a brief look at these factors.

Chemical analyses of air bubbles that become trapped in glacial ice at the time of ice formation indicate that the Ice Age atmosphere contained less of the

Obviously, whenever Earth enters an ice age, extensive areas of land that were once ice free are covered with ice and snow. In addition, a colder climate causes the area covered by sea ice (frozen surface seawater) to expand. Ice and snow reflect a large portion of incoming solar energy back to space. Thus, energy that would have warmed Earth's surface and the air above is lost, and global cooling is reinforced.

Yet another factor that influences climate during glacial times relates to ocean currents. Research has shown that ocean circulation changes during ice ages. For example, studies suggest that the warm current that transports large amounts of heat from the tropics toward higher latitudes in the North Atlantic was significantly weaker during the Ice Age. This would lead to a colder climate in Europe, amplifying the cooling attributable to orbital variations.

In conclusion, we emphasize that the ideas just discussed do not represent the only possible explanations for ice ages. Although interesting and attractive, these proposals are certainly not without critics, nor are they the only possibilities currently under study. Other factors may be, and probably are, involved.

10 CONCEPT CHECKS

1. How does the theory of plate tectonics help us understand the causes of ice ages?
2. Does the theory of plate tectonics explain alternating glacial/interglacial climates during the Ice Age?
3. Briefly summarize the climate change hypothesis that involves variations in Earth's orbit.

*J. D. Hays et al., p. 1131.

CONCEPTS IN REVIEW: GLACIERS AND GLACIATION

1 Glaciers: A Part of Two Basic Cycles

List the different types of glaciers, summarize their characteristics, and describe the present-day location and extent of glaciers on Earth.

KEY WORDS glacier, valley glacier (alpine glacier), ice sheet, sea ice, ice shelf, ice cap, outlet glacier, piedmont glacier

- A glacier is a thick mass of ice originating on land from the compaction and recrystallization of snow, and it shows evidence of past or present flow. Glaciers are part of both the hydrologic cycle and the rock cycle because they store and release freshwater, and they grind away at rock, distributing the resulting sediment to other locations.
- Valley glaciers flow down mountain valleys, while ice sheets are very large masses of ice, such as those that cover Greenland and Antarctica. (The North Pole is ocean covered in sea ice, not glaciers.) During the Last Glacial Maximum, around 18,000 years ago, Earth was in an Ice Age that covered large areas of the land surface with glacial ice.
- When valley glaciers leave the confining mountains, they may spread out into broad lobes called piedmont glaciers. Similarly, ice shelves form when glaciers flow into the ocean and spread out to form a wide layer of floating ice.
- Ice caps are like smaller ice sheets. Both ice sheets and ice caps may be drained by outlet glaciers, which often resemble valley glaciers and piedmont glaciers.

ICE IDENTIFICATION What term is applied to the ice at the North Pole? What term best describes Greenland's ice? Are both considered glaciers? Explain.

North pole

Greenland

NASA

2 Formation and Movement of Glacial Ice

Describe how glaciers move, the rates at which they move, and the significance of the glacial budget.

KEY WORDS snowline, firn, plastic flow, basal slip, zone of fracture, crevasse, surge, zone of accumulation, zone of wastage, calving, glacial budget, ablation

- When snow piles up sufficiently, it recrystallizes to dense granules of firn, which can then pack together even more tightly to make glacial ice.
- When ice is put under pressure, it will flow very slowly. The uppermost 50 meters of the glacier don't have sufficient pressure to flow, so they break open in dangerous cracks called crevasses that occur in the zone of fracture. Additionally, most glaciers also move by sliding. Meltwater is thought to facilitate this basal slip.

- Glaciers move slowly, but their rate of flow is measurable. Fast glaciers may move 800 meters per year, while slow glaciers may manage only 2 meters per year. Some glaciers experience periodic surges of sudden movement—probably due to acceleration of basal slip.
- A glacier's rate of flow does not necessarily correlate to the position of the terminus. Instead, if the glacier has a positive "budget," the terminus will advance. This occurs when the glacier gains more snow in its upper zone of accumulation than it loses at its downstream zone of wastage. If calving of icebergs, melting, or other forms of ablation exceed the input of new ice, then the glacier's terminus will retreat. Even a retreating glacier is still experiencing downstream flow.

CALCULATE IT If a glacier gains 0.5 cubic kilometer of ice annually and loses 0.75 cubic kilometer through ablation, will its terminus advance or recede? Will the glacier be flowing? Why or why not?

3 Glacial Erosion

Discuss the processes of glacial erosion.

KEY WORDS plucking, abrasion, rock flour, glacial striation

- Glaciers are powerful agents of erosion, with a much higher competence than either liquid water or air. Glaciers acquire sediment through plucking from the bedrock beneath the glacier, by abrasion of the bedrock using sediment already in the ice, and when mass wasting processes drop landslides on top of the glacier. Grinding of the bedrock produces characteristic grooves called glacial striations.

COMPARE THEM How does glacial ice compare to running water in terms of its ability to erode the landscape? Describe their similarities and differences in terms of competence, capacity, and rate of flow.

4 Landforms Created by Glacial Ice

Identify and describe the major features created by glacial erosion.

KEY WORDS glacial trough, truncated spur, hanging valley, pater noster lake, cirque, tarn, col, fiord, arête, horn, roche moutonnée

- Glacial troughs have a U-shaped profile, very distinctive and different from a stream-carved mountain valley, which typically shows a V-shaped profile. Lining the edge of the valley may be triangle-shaped cliffs called truncated spurs. Higher up, hanging valleys mark the spots where tributary glaciers once flowed into the main glacier. These may sport extraordinary waterfalls.
- In coastal mountain settings, a glacial trough may be eroded below sea level and subsequently flooded by the ocean to become a fiord, a narrow steep-sided inlet.
- At the head of a valley glacier is an amphitheater-shaped cirque, which may or may not have a small lake called a tarn at the bottom of the basin. Other glacial lakes in the bottom of the valley resemble beads on a string, and are called pater noster lakes. The intersection of two cirques produced by glaciers flowing in opposite directions forms a saddle-shaped col.
- If two glaciers are flowing parallel to each other, their troughs may intersect in a knife-edge ridge called an arête. A high point with numerous cirques surrounding it indicates that multiple glaciers flowed away from a point in a radial array, leaving behind a pyramidal horn. Protrusions of bedrock may experience glacial abrasion on their upstream side and plucking on their downstream side. This produces characteristically asymmetric knobs of bedrock called roches moutonnées.

LABEL IT Examine the illustration of a mountainous landscape after glaciation. Identify and label key landforms that resulted from glacial erosion.

5 Glacial Deposits

Distinguish between the two basic types of glacial drift.

KEY WORDS glacial drift, till, glacial erratic, stratified drift

- With all the carving action that a glacier is capable of, a tremendous quantity of sediment is generated. This sediment, called glacial drift, ends up being deposited somewhere downstream of its source area. If the deposition of glacial drift occurs directly by ice, we call the sediment till. Stratified drift refers to sediment that leaves the ice, carried along by currents of meltwater.
- Till is characterized by extremely poor sorting. The larger pieces are called erratics because their rock types differ from the rock in the area where they end up. Erratics often bear glacial polish and striations. Stratified drift has experienced the sorting action of liquid water, which separates sand and gravel from larger and smaller particles.

SORT IT OUT Do you think erratics are ever found in stratified drift? Why or why not?

6 Landforms Made of Till

List and describe the major features associated with till.

KEY WORDS lateral moraine, medial moraine, end moraine, ground moraine, terminal moraine, recessional moraine, drumlin

- Along the edge of a valley glacier, lateral moraines form. If two glaciers merge, their lateral moraines blend together into a stripe of dirty ice called a medial moraine.
- At the end of the glacial "conveyer belt," more till is deposited. When the ice front is stationary, this can build up in an end moraine. The end moraine furthest from the source of the glacier is dubbed the terminal moraine, while temporary stabilizations of the glacier's terminus during an overall period of retreat will produce a series of recessional moraines. End moraines from the recent Ice Age are important landscape features in the upper Midwest and New England.
- Ground moraine creates a relatively flat, poorly drained landscape full of small hills and hummocks. Sometimes the till is organized into streamlined hills called drumlins, each roughly the shape of an upside-down spoon. Drumlins tend to occur in large numbers called drumlin fields.

7 Landforms Made of Stratified Drift

Explain the formation of landforms composed of stratified drift.

KEY WORDS outwash plain, valley train, kettle, ice-contact deposit, kame, kame terrace, esker

- Stratified drift is sorted by meltwater. It can be deposited immediately adjacent to a glacier or carried some distance away to be laid down as outwash. Rivers draining an ice sheet produce a broad outwash plain beyond the end moraine. A similar feature hemmed in by the walls of a mountain valley is called a valley train. In both cases, braided channels distribute the sediment. Blocks of ice buried by the sediment may melt to produce depressions called kettles, which are sometimes filled with water.
- Ice-contact deposits include kames, which are mounds or steep-sided hills of stratified drift. They represent the former position of sediment-filled lakes on top of (or within) the glacier. Kame terraces are narrow masses of stratified drift deposited adjacent to a stagnant glacier. Meltwater streams flowing through tunnels in the ice may leave behind the sinuous forms of eskers.

LABEL IT   Examine the illustration of depositional features formed in the wake of a retreating ice sheet. Name the features and indicate which landforms are composed of till and which are composed of stratified drift.

8 Other Effects of Ice Age Glaciers

Describe and explain several important effects of Ice Age glaciers other than erosional and depositional landforms.

KEY WORDS proglacial lake, pluvial lake

- The Ice Age was not merely a time of erosion and deposition. The presence of the huge ice sheets had other important effects. One is the phenomenon of crustal subsidence and rebound. Glaciers are heavy—so heavy that they can cause the crust to flex downward under their tremendous load. After the glaciers melt off, that weight is released, and the crust slowly rebounds vertically upward.
- Ice sheets are nourished by water that ultimately comes from the ocean, so when ice sheets grow, sea level falls, and when they melt, sea level rises. At the Last Glacial Maximum, global sea level was about 100 meters lower than it is today. At that time, the coastlines of the modern continents were vastly different, and in some cases the continents were actually connected by dry land.
- The advance and retreat of ice sheets caused significant changes to the paths followed by rivers. In addition, glaciers deepened and widened stream valleys and lowlands to create features such as the Great Lakes and New York's Finger Lakes.
- An ice sheet can act as a dam by trapping meltwater or blocking the flow of rivers to create proglacial lakes. Glacial Lakes Agassiz and Missoula both impounded tremendous quantities of water. In Lake Missoula's case, the water drained out catastrophically when the ice dam periodically broke.
- Pluvial lakes are similar to proglacial lakes in that they existed during the height of the Ice Age, but they are different in that they existed far from the actual glaciers, in a climate that was cooler and wetter than today's. Lake Bonneville is a classic example from Utah and Nevada. A shrunken remnant of it survives as the Great Salt Lake.

DEBATE IT   Of the five listed effects of Ice Age glaciers, which one seems most important to the region where you live? Explain your answer.

9 The Glacial Theory and the Ice Age

Briefly discuss the development of glacial theory.

KEY WORD Quaternary period

- The idea of a geologically recent Ice Age was born in the early 1800s in Switzerland. By applying a uniformitarian approach to field study of glacial landforms, Louis Agassiz and others established that only the former presence of tremendous quantities of glacial ice could explain the landscape of Europe (and later North America and Siberia). As additional research accumulated, especially data from the study of

seafloor sediments, it was revealed that the Quaternary period was marked by numerous advances of glacial ice.

MISSING ANALOGUE   If Earth was experiencing an especially warm period, no glacial ice would exist. On such a world, scientists like Louis Agassiz would have had a much more difficult time using the principle of uniformitarianism to deduce the existence of massive ice sheets in the geologic past. If Earth lacked any modern examples of glaciers, what evidence would you find most compelling as an indication that a major Ice Age had recently occurred?

10 Causes of Ice Ages

Summarize current ideas on the causes of ice ages.

KEY WORD tillite

- While rare, glacial episodes have occurred in Earth history prior to the recent glaciations we call the Ice Age. Lithified till, called tillite, is a major line of evidence for these ancient ice ages. There are several reasons that glacial ice might accumulate globally, including the position of the continents, which is driven by plate tectonics. Antarctica's position over the South Pole is doubtless a key reason for its massive ice sheets, for instance.

- The Quaternary period is marked by not only glacial advances but also intervening episodes of glacial retreat. One way to explain these oscillations is through variations in Earth's orbit, which lead to seasonal variations in the distribution of solar radiation. The orbit's shape varies (eccentricity), the tilt of the planet's rotational axis varies (obliquity), and the axis slowly "wobbles" over time (precession). These three Milankovitch effects, each of which occur on different time scales, collectively do a good job of accounting for colder and warmer periods during the Quaternary.

- Additional factors that may be important for initiating or ending glaciations include rising or falling levels of greenhouse gases, changes in the reflectivity of the surface of Earth, and variations in the ocean currents that redistribute heat energy from warmer to colder regions.

EFFECTS & CAUSES   In the late Paleozoic era, parts of India, Africa, and Australia were covered by ice sheets, while Greenland, Siberia, and Canada were ice free. Explain why this occurred.

GIVE IT SOME THOUGHT

1. The accompanying diagram shows the results of a classic experiment used to determine how glacial ice moves in a mountain valley. The experiment occurred over an 8-year span. Refer to the diagram and answer the following:
   a. What was the average yearly rate at which ice in the center of the glacier advanced?
   b. About how fast was the center of the glacier advancing *per day*?
   c. Calculate the average rate at which ice along the sides of the glacier moved forward.
   d. Why was the rate at the center different than along the sides?

2. Studies have shown that during the Ice Age the margins of some ice sheets advanced southward from the Hudson Bay region at rates ranging from about 50 to 320 meters per year.
   a. Determine the maximum amount of time required for an ice sheet to move from the southern end of Hudson Bay to the south shore of present day Lake Erie, a distance of 1600 kilometers.
   b. Calculate the minimum number of years required for an ice sheet to move this distance.

3. The accompanying image shows the top of a valley glacier in which the ice is fractured.
   a. What term is applied to fractures such as these?
   b. In what vertical zone do these breaks occur?
   c. Do the fractures likely extend to the base of the glacier? Explain.

Glow Images

4. If Earth were to experience another Ice Age, one hemisphere would have substantially more expansive ice sheets than the other. Would it be the Northern Hemisphere or the Southern Hemisphere? What is the reason for the large disparity?

5. While taking a break from a hike in the Northern Rockies with a fellow geology enthusiast, you notice that the boulder you are sitting on is part of a deposit that consists of a jumbled mixture of many different sediment sizes. Since you are in an area that once had extensive valley glaciers, your colleague suggests that the deposit must be glacial till. Although you know this is certainly a good possibility, you remind your companion that other processes in mountain areas also produce unsorted deposits. What might such a process be? How might you and your friend determine whether this deposit is actually glacial till?

6. Glacial ice is classified as a metamorphic rock, yet glaciers are a basic part of the hydrologic cycle. Should glaciers be considered part of the geosphere, or do they belong to the hydrosphere? Explain.

7. If the budget of a valley glacier were balanced for an extended time span, what feature would you expect to find at the terminus of the glacier? Is it composed of till or stratified drift? Now assume that the glacier's budget changes so that ablation exceeds accumulation. How would the terminus of the glacier change? Describe the deposit you would expect to form under these conditions.

8. Assume that you and a nongeologist friend are visiting Alaska's Hubbard Glacier, shown here. After studying the glacier for quite a long time, your friend asks, "Do these things really move?" How would you convince your friend that this glacier does indeed move, using evidence that is clearly visible in this image?

Michael Collier

MasteringGeology™   www.masteringgeology.com

Looking for additional review and test prep materials? Visit the Study Area in MasteringGeology to enhance your understanding of this chapter's content by accessing a variety of resources, including **Self-Study Quizzes**, **Geoscience Animations, GEODe Tutorials, RSS feeds, flashcards, web links, self-study quizzes**, and an optional **Pearson eText**.

Glossary

Ablation A general term for the loss of ice and snow from a glacier.

Abrasion The grinding and scraping of a rock surface by the friction and impact of rock particles carried by water, wind, and ice.

Alpine glacier A glacier confined to a mountain valley, which in most instances had previously been a stream valley.

Arête A narrow, knifelike ridge separating two adjacent glaciated valleys.

Basal slip A mechanism of glacial movement in which the ice mass slides over the surface below.

Calving Wastage of a glacier that occurs when large pieces of ice break into the water.

Cirque An amphitheater-shaped basin at the head of a glaciated valley produced by frost wedging and plucking.

Col A pass between mountain valleys where the headwalls of two cirques intersect.

Crevasse A deep crack in the brittle surface of a glacier.

Drumlin A streamlined symmetrical hill composed of glacial till. The steep side of the hill faces the direction from which the ice advanced.

End moraine A ridge of till marking a former position of the front of a glacier.

Esker A sinuous ridge composed largely of sand and gravel deposited by a stream flowing in a tunnel beneath a glacier near its terminus.

Fiord A steep-sided inlet of the sea formed when a glacial trough was partially submerged.

Firn Granular, recrystallized snow. A transitional stage between snow and glacial ice.

Glacial budget The balance, or lack of balance, between ice formation at the upper end of a glacier and ice loss in the zone of wastage.

Glacial drift An all-embracing term for sediments of glacial origin, no matter how, where, or in what shape they were deposited.

Glacial erratic An ice-transported boulder that was not derived from the bedrock near its present site.

Glacial striations Scratches and grooves on bedrock caused by glacial abrasion.

Glacial trough A mountain valley that has been widened, deepened, and straightened by a glacier.

Glacier A thick mass of ice originating on land from the compaction and recrystallization of snow that shows evidence of past or present flow.

Ground moraine An undulating layer of till deposited as an ice front retreats.

Hanging valley A tributary valley that enters a glacial trough at a considerable height above the floor of the trough.

Horn A pyramid-like peak formed by glacial action in three or more cirques surrounding a mountain summit.

Ice-contact deposit An accumulation of stratified drift deposited in contact with a supporting mass of ice.

Ice cap A mass of glacial ice covering a high upland or plateau and spreading out radially.

Ice sheet A very large, thick mass of glacial ice flowing outward in all directions from one or more accumulation centers.

Ice shelf A large, relatively flat mass of floating ice that forms where glacial ice flows into bays and that extends seaward from the coast but remains attached to the land along one or more sides.

Kame A steep-sided hill composed of sand and gravel, originating when sediment collected in openings in stagnant glacial ice.

Kame terrace A narrow, terracelike mass of stratified drift deposited between a glacier and an adjacent valley wall.

Kettle holes Depressions created when blocks of ice become lodged in glacial deposits and subsequently melt.

Lateral moraine A ridge of till along the sides of a valley glacier composed primarily of debris that fell to the glacier from the valley walls.

Medial moraine A ridge of till formed when lateral moraines from two coalescing alpine glaciers join.

Outlet glacier A tongue of ice normally flowing rapidly outward from an ice cap or ice sheet, usually through mountainous terrain to the sea.

Outwash plain A relatively flat, gently sloping plain consisting of materials deposited by melt-water streams in front of the margin of an ice sheet.

Pater noster lakes A chain of small lakes in a glacial trough that occupies basins created by glacial erosion.

Piedmont glacier A glacier that forms when one or more alpine glaciers emerge from the confining walls of mountain valleys and spread out to create a broad sheet in the lowlands at the base of the mountains.

Plastic flow A type of glacial movement that occurs within a glacier, below a depth of approximately 50 meters (165 feet), in which the ice is not fractured.

Plucking A process by which pieces of bedrock are lifted out of place by a glacier.

Pluvial lake A lake formed during a period of increased rainfall. For example, this occurred in many nonglaciated areas during periods of ice advance elsewhere.

Proglacial lake A lake created when a glacier acts a dam blocking the flow of a river or trapping glacial meltwater. The term refers to the position of such lakes just beyond the outer limits of a glacier.

Quaternary period The most recent period on the geologic time scale. It began about 2.6 million years ago and extends to the present.

Recessional moraine An end moraine formed as the ice front stagnated during glacial retreat.

Roche moutonnée An asymmetrical knob of bedrock that is formed when glacial abrasion smoothes the gentle slope facing the advancing ice sheet and plucking steepens the opposite side as the ice overrides the knob.

Rock flour Ground-up rock produced by the grinding effect of a glacier.

Sea ice Frozen seawater that is associated with polar regions. The area covered by sea ice expands in winter and shrinks in summer.

Snowline The lower limit of perennial snow.

Stratified drift Sediments deposited by glacial meltwater.

Surge A period of rapid glacial advance. Surges are typically sporadic and short-lived.

Tarn A small lake in a cirque.

Terminal moraine The end moraine that marks the farthest advance of a glacier.

Tillite A rock formed when glacial till is lithified.

Till Unsorted sediment deposited directly by a glacier.

Truncated spurs Triangular-shaped cliffs produced when spurs of land that extend into a valley are removed by the great erosional force of a valley glacier.

Valley glacier See *Alpine glacier*.

Valley train A relatively narrow body of stratified drift deposited on a valley floor by meltwater streams that issue from the terminus of an alpine glacier.

Zone of accumulation The part of a glacier that is characterized by snow accumulation and ice formation. The outer limit of this zone is the snowline.

Zone of fracture The upper portion of a glacier consisting of brittle ice.

Zone of wastage The part of a glacier beyond the snowline, where annually there is a net loss of ice.

Shorelines

Shorelines

Sand bar at the outermost point of Cape Hatteras, North Carolina.
(Photo by Michael Collier)

Each statement represents the primary learning objective for the corresponding major heading within the chapter. After you complete the chapter you should be able to:

1　Explain why the shoreline is considered a dynamic interface and identify the basic parts of the coastal zone.

2　List and discuss the factors that influence the height, length, and period of a wave and describe the motion of water within a wave.

3　Explain how waves erode and how waves move sediment along the shore.

4　Describe the features typically created by wave erosion and those resulting from sediment deposited by longshore transport processes.

5　Summarize the ways in which people deal with shoreline erosion problems.

6　Contrast the erosion problems faced on the Atlantic and Gulf coasts with those along the Pacific coast.

7　Describe the basic structure and characteristics of a hurricane and the three broad categories of hurricane destruction.

8　Contrast emergent and submergent coasts.

9　Explain the cause of tides, their monthly cycles, and patterns. Describe the horizontal flow of water that accompanies the rise and fall of tides.

The restless waters of the ocean are constantly in motion. Winds generate surface currents, the gravity of the Moon and Sun produces tides, and density differences create deep-ocean circulation. Further, waves carry the energy from storms to distant shores, where their impact erodes the land.

When storm waves strike this Hatteras North Carolina beach, these homes are obviously vulnerable. (Photo by Michael Collier)

Shorelines are dynamic environments. Their topography, geologic makeup, and climate vary greatly from place to place. Continental and oceanic processes converge along the shore to create landscapes that frequently undergo rapid change. When it comes to the deposition of sediment, shore areas are transition zones between marine and continental environments.

1 The Shoreline: A Dynamic Interface

Nowhere is the restless nature of the ocean's water more noticeable than along the shore—the dynamic interface among air, land, and sea. An *interface* is a common boundary where different parts of a system interact. This is certainly an appropriate designation for the coastal zone. Here we can see the rhythmic rise and fall of tides and observe waves constantly rolling in and breaking. Sometimes the waves are low and gentle. At other times they pound the shore with awesome fury.

The Coastal Zone

Although it may not be obvious, the shoreline is constantly being modified by waves. For example, along Cape Cod, Massachusetts, wave activity is eroding cliffs of poorly consolidated glacial sediment so aggressively that the cliffs are retreating inland up to 1 meter per year (FIGURE 1A). By contrast, at Point Reyes, California, the far more durable bedrock cliffs are less susceptible to wave attack and therefore are retreating much more slowly (FIGURE 1B). Along both coasts, wave activity is moving sediment along the shore and building narrow sandbars that protrude into and across some bays.

Present-Day Shorelines The nature of present-day shorelines is not just the result of the relentless attack of the land by the sea. Rather, the shore has a complex character that results from multiple geologic processes. For example, practically all coastal areas were affected by the worldwide rise in sea level that accompanied the melting of glaciers at the close of the Pleistocene epoch. As the sea encroached landward, the shoreline retreated, becoming superimposed upon existing landscapes that had resulted from such diverse processes as stream erosion, glaciation, volcanic activity, and the forces of mountain building.

Human Activity Today the coastal zone is experiencing intensive human activity. Unfortunately, people often treat the shoreline as if it were a stable platform on which structures can safely be built. This attitude inevitably leads to conflicts between people and nature. As you will see, many coastal landforms, especially beaches and barrier islands, are relatively fragile, short-lived features that are inappropriate sites for development. The aerial image of North Carolina's Hatteras Island on the facing page is a good example.

Basic Features

In general conversation, a number of terms are used when referring to the boundary between land and sea. In the preceding paragraphs, the terms *shore*, *shoreline*, *coastal zone*, and *coast* were all used. Moreover, when many think of the land–sea interface, the word *beach* comes to mind. Let's take a moment to clarify these terms and introduce some other terminology used by those who study the land–sea boundary zone.

FIGURE 1 Cape Cod and Point Reyes
A. A satellite image of Cape Cod, Martha's Vineyard (left), and Nantucket (right). Although waves constantly modify this coastal landscape, they are not responsible for creating it. Rather, the original size and shape of Cape Cod resulted from the positioning of moraines and other glacial materials deposited during the Ice Age. (Image courtesy of Earth Satellite Corporation/Science Photo Library/Photo Researchers, Inc.)
B. A high-altitude image of the Point Reyes area north of San Francisco. The 5.5-kilometer- (3.4-mile-) long south-facing cliffs are exposed to the full force of the waves from the Pacific Ocean. Nevertheless, this promontory retreats slowly because the bedrock from which it formed is very resistant. (Image courtesy of USDA-ASCS)

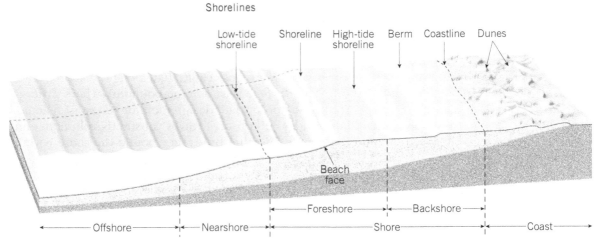

Low-tide shoreline | Shoreline | High-tide shoreline | Berm | Coastline | Dunes

Beach face

Offshore — Nearshore — Shore — Coast

Foreshore — Backshore

You will find it helpful to refer to FIGURE 2, which is an idealized profile of the coastal zone.

The **shoreline** is the line that marks the contact between land and sea. Each day, as tides rise and fall, the position of the shoreline migrates. Over longer time spans, the average position of the shoreline gradually shifts as sea level rises or falls.

The **shore** is the area that extends between the lowest tide level and the highest elevation on land that is affected by storm waves. By contrast, the **coast** extends inland from the shore as far as ocean-related features can

FIGURE 3 Beaches
A beach is an accumulation of sediment on the landward margin of an ocean or a lake, and can be thought of as material in transit along the shore. Beaches are composed of whatever material is locally available. (Photo A by David R. Frazier/Photo Library/Alamy Images; photo B by E.J. Tarbuck)

This beach on Florida's Sanibel Island consists of shells and shell fragments.

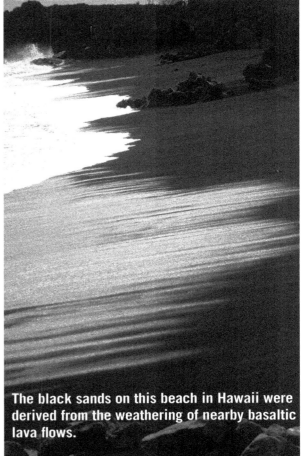

The black sands on this beach in Hawaii were derived from the weathering of nearby basaltic lava flows.

be found. The **coastline** marks the coast's seaward edge, whereas the inland boundary is not always obvious or easy to determine.

As Figure 2 illustrates, the shore is divided into the *foreshore* and the *backshore*. The **foreshore** is the area that is exposed when the tide is out (low tide) and submerged when the tide is in (high tide). The **backshore** is landward of the high-tide shoreline. It is usually dry, being affected by waves only during storms. Two other zones are commonly identified. The **nearshore zone** lies between the low-tide shoreline and the line where waves break at low tide. Seaward of the nearshore zone is the **offshore zone**.

Beaches

For many, a beach is the sandy area where people lie in the sun and walk along the water's edge. Technically, a **beach** is an accumulation of sediment found along the landward margin of an ocean or a lake. Along straight coasts, beaches may extend for tens or hundreds of kilometers. Where coasts are irregular, beach formation may be confined to the relatively quiet waters of bays.

Beaches consist of one or more **berms**, which are relatively flat platforms often composed of sand that are adjacent to coastal dunes or cliffs and marked by a change in slope at the seaward edge. Another part of the beach is the **beach face**, which is the wet, sloping surface that extends from the berm to the shoreline. Where beaches are sandy, sunbathers usually prefer the berm, whereas joggers prefer the wet, hard-packed sand of the beach face.

Beaches are composed of whatever material is locally abundant. The sediment for some beaches is derived from the erosion of adjacent cliffs or nearby coastal mountains. Other beaches are built from sediment delivered to the coast by rivers.

Although the mineral makeup of many beaches is dominated by durable quartz grains, other minerals may be dominant. For example, in areas such as southern Florida, where there are no mountains or other sources of rock-forming minerals nearby, most beaches are composed of shell fragments and the remains of organisms that live in coastal waters (FIGURE 3A). Some beaches on volcanic islands in the open ocean are composed of weathered grains of the basaltic lava that comprise the islands or of coarse debris eroded from coral reefs that develop around islands in low latitudes (FIGURE 3B).

Regardless of the composition, the material that comprises the beach does not stay in one place. Instead, crashing waves are constantly moving it. Thus, beaches can be thought of as material in transit along the shore.

1 CONCEPT CHECKS

1. Why is the shoreline described as being an interface?
2. Distinguish among *shore*, *shoreline*, *coast*, and *coastline*.
3. What is a beach? Distinguish between *beach face* and *berm*.

The material composing this beach is quartz sand.
(Photo by Shutterstock)

A Brief Tour of America's Coasts*

1 A small portion of the Cape Cod coast shows the entrance to Nauset Bay. Depending on the whims of recent storms and the strength of coastal currents, the opening into the bay may only be a few hundred feet wide. Tidal currents have created an underwater sandbar just inside the harbor.

10 Sea ice hugs Alaska's north slope near Barrow. The Arctic shore is locked in ice for much of the year.

7 This highway clings to the California Coast south of Big Sur. Uplift is occurring in this area near the boundary separating the Pacific and North American plates.

3 North Carolina's Outer Banks. Oregon Inlet Bridge connecting Bodie Island (foreground) and Hatteras Island. These narrow wisps of sand are part of an extensive barrier island system. The beach and dunes on the left face the Atlantic Ocean. On the right are the quieter waters of Pamlico Sound.

*Prepared with the assistance of Michael Collier. All photos by Michael Collier.

Coasts are among Earth's most dynamic landscapes. Waves, tides, and currents continuously shape this interface between land and sea. Coasts may also exhibit the effects of mountain building, sea level changes, rivers, glaciers, and people. Here is a very small glimpse at the diversity and beauty of America's coasts.

The delta of the Mississippi River is a major feature in the Gulf of Mexico. This low-lying coastal zone is a maze of low soggy islands that are barely above sea level with a myriad of natural distributries and artificial channels.

9 A small glacier flows down a steep mountain slope into the Cook Inlet southwest of Anchorage, Alaska. The total length of Alaska's irregular coastline is nearly 71,000 kilometers (44,000 miles).

2 Spruce and fir cover Turtle Island, part of Maine's Acadia National Park. This region was sculpted by Ice Age glaciers, then flooded when sea level rose as the ice sheets melted.

4 Mobjack Bay near Gloucester, Virginia, is part of the much larger Chesapeake Bay. These bays, called estuaries, are actually river valleys that were drowned when sea level rose at the end of the Ice Age.

6 Waves have aggressively attacked the coast north of La Push Harbor, Washington. In places, remnants of the cliff remain as sea stacks.

8 Cliffs and waterfalls along the north coast of Hawaii's Big Island. This portion of the island receives abundant rainfall. There are still active volcanoes elsewhere on the island.

11 Padre Island is a barrier island that protects the coast of southern Texas from storms. Winds off the Gulf of Mexico create dunes, which offer a temporary footing for vegetation that is occasionally stripped away by hurricanes.

2 Waves

Ocean waves are caused by energy traveling along the interface between ocean and atmosphere, often transferring energy from a storm far out at sea over distances of several thousand kilometers. That's why even on calm days, the ocean still has waves that travel across its surface. When observing waves, always remember that you are watching *energy* travel through a medium (water). If you make waves by tossing a pebble into a pond, or by splashing in a pool, or by blowing across the surface of a cup of coffee, you are imparting *energy* to the liquid, and the waves you see are the visible evidence of the energy passing through.

Wind-generated waves provide most of the energy that shapes and modifies shorelines. Where the land and sea meet, waves that may have traveled unimpeded for hundreds or thousands of kilometers suddenly encounter a barrier that will not allow them to advance farther and must absorb their energy. Stated another way, the shore is the location where a practically irresistible force confronts an almost immovable object. The conflict that results is never-ending and sometimes dramatic.

Wave Characteristics

Most ocean waves derive their energy and motion from the wind. When a breeze is less than 3 kilometers (2 miles) per hour, only small wavelets appear. At greater wind speeds, more stable waves gradually form and advance with the wind.

Characteristics of ocean waves are illustrated in FIGURE 4, which shows a simple, nonbreaking wave form. The tops of the waves are the *crests*, which are separated by *troughs*. Halfway between the crests and troughs is the *still water level*, which is the level the water would occupy if there were no waves. The vertical distance between trough and crest is called the **wave height**, and the horizontal distance between successive crests (or troughs) is the **wavelength**. The time it takes one full wave—one wavelength—to pass a fixed position is the **wave period**.

The height, length, and period that are eventually achieved by a wave depend on three factors: (1) the wind speed, (2) the length of time the wind has blown, and (3) the **fetch**, or distance that the wind has traveled across

open water. As the quantity of energy transferred from the wind to the water increases, the height and steepness of the waves increase as well. Eventually a critical point is reached where waves grow so tall that they topple over, forming ocean breakers called *whitecaps*.

For a particular wind speed, there is a maximum fetch and duration of wind beyond which waves will no longer increase in size. When the maximum fetch and duration are reached for a given wind velocity, the waves are said to be "fully developed." The reason that waves can grow no further is that they are losing as much energy through the breaking of whitecaps as they are receiving from the wind.

When wind stops or changes direction, or if waves leave the stormy area where they were created, they continue on without relation to local winds. The waves also undergo a gradual change to *swells*, which are lower and longer and may carry a storm's energy to distant shores. Because many independent wave systems exist at the same time, the sea surface acquires a complex, irregular pattern. Hence, the sea waves we watch from the shore are often a mixture of swells from faraway storms and waves created by local winds.

Circular Orbital Motion

Waves can travel great distances across ocean basins. In one study, waves generated near Antarctica were tracked as they traveled through the Pacific Ocean basin. After more than 10,000 kilometers (over 6000 miles), the waves finally expended their energy a week later, along the shoreline of the Aleutian Islands of Alaska. The water itself doesn't travel this distance, but the wave form does. As the wave travels, the water passes the energy along by moving in a circle. This movement is called *circular orbital motion*.

Observation of an object floating in waves reveals that it moves not only up and down but also

FIGURE 4 Wave basics
An idealized nonbreaking wave showing its basic parts and the movement of water with increasing depth.

slightly forward and backward with each successive wave. FIGURE 5 shows that a floating object moves up and backward as the crest approaches, up and forward as the crest passes, down and forward after the crest, and down and backward as the trough approaches; it rises and moves backward again as the next crest advances. When the movement of the toy boat shown in Figure 5 is traced as a wave passes, it can be seen that the boat moves in a circle and returns to essentially the same place. Circular orbital motion allows a wave form (the wave's shape) to move forward *through the water* while the individual water particles that transmit the wave move in a circle. Wind moving across a field of wheat causes a similar phenomenon: The wheat itself doesn't travel across the field, but the waves do.

The energy contributed by the wind to the water is transmitted not only along the surface of the sea but also downward. However, beneath the surface, the circular motion rapidly diminishes until, at a depth equal to one-half the wavelength measured from the still water level, the movement of water particles becomes negligible. This depth is known as the *wave base*. The dramatic decrease of wave energy with depth is shown by the rapidly diminishing diameters of water-particle orbits in Figure 4.

Waves in the Surf Zone

As long as a wave is in deep water, it is unaffected by water depth (FIGURE 6, *left*). However, when a wave approaches the shore, the water becomes shallower and influences wave behavior. The wave begins to "feel bottom" at a water depth equal to its wave base. Such depths interfere with water movement at the base of the wave and slow its advance (Figure 6, *center*).

As a wave advances toward the shore, the slightly faster waves farther out to sea catch up, decreasing the wavelength. As the speed and length of the wave

SMARTFIGURE 5
Passage of a wave
The movements of the toy boat show that the wave form advances, but the water does not advance appreciably from the original position. In this sequence, the wave moves from left to right as the boat (and the water in which it is floating) rotates in an imaginary circle.

diminish, the wave steadily grows higher. Finally, a critical point is reached when the wave is too steep to support itself and the wave front collapses, or *breaks* (Figure 6, *right*), causing water to advance up the shore.

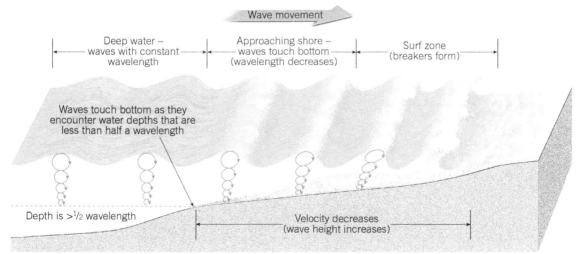

FIGURE 6 Waves approaching the shore
Waves touch bottom as they encounter water depths that are less than half a wavelength. As a result, the wave speed decreases, and the faster-moving waves farther from shore begin to catch up, which causes the distance between waves (the wavelength) to decrease. This causes an increase in wave height to the point where the waves finally pitch forward and break in the surf zone.

The turbulent water created by breaking waves is called **surf**. On the landward margin of the surf zone the turbulent sheet of water from collapsing breakers, called *swash*, moves up the slope of the beach. When the energy of the swash has been expended, the water flows back down the beach toward the surf zone as *backwash*.

2 CONCEPT CHECKS

1. List three factors that determine the height, length, and period of a wave.
2. Describe the motion of a floating object as a wave passes.
3. How do a wave's speed, wavelength, and height change as it moves into shallow water and breaks?

EYE on Earth

This surfer is enjoying a ride on a large wave along the coast of Maui. (Photo by Getty Images)

Question 1 What was the source of energy that created this wave?

Question 2 How was the wavelength changing just prior to the time when this photo was taken?

Question 3 Why was the wavelength changing?

Question 4 Many waves exhibit circular orbital motion. Is that true of the wave in this photo? Explain.

Ron Dahlquist/Getty Images

3 The Work of Waves

During calm weather, wave action is minimal. However, just as streams do most of their work during floods, so too do waves accomplish most of their work during storms. The impact of high, storm-induced waves against the shore can be awesome in its violence (FIGURE 7).

Wave Erosion

Each breaking wave may hurl thousands of tons of water against the land, sometimes causing the ground to literally tremble. The pressures exerted by Atlantic waves in wintertime, for example, average nearly 10,000 kilograms per square meter (more than 2000 pounds per square foot). The force during storms is even greater. It is no wonder that cracks and crevices are quickly opened in cliffs, seawalls, breakwaters, and anything else that is subjected to these enormous shocks. Water is forced into every opening, causing air in the cracks to become highly compressed by the thrust of crashing waves. When the wave subsides, the air expands rapidly, dislodging rock fragments and enlarging and extending fractures.

In addition to the erosion caused by wave impact and pressure, **abrasion**—the sawing and grinding action of the water armed with rock fragments—is also important. In fact, abrasion is probably more intense in the surf zone than in any other environment. Smooth, rounded stones and pebbles along the shore are obvious reminders of the relentless grinding action of rock against rock in the surf zone (FIGURE 8A). Further, the waves use such fragments as "tools" as they cut horizontally into the land (FIGURE 8B).

Sand Movement on the Beach

Beaches are sometimes called "rivers of sand." The reason is that the energy from breaking waves often causes large quantities of sand to move along the beach face and in the surf zone roughly parallel to the shoreline. Wave energy also causes sand to move perpendicular to (toward and away from) the shoreline.

Movement Perpendicular to the Shoreline   If you stand ankle deep in water at the beach, you will see that swash and backwash move sand toward and away from the shoreline. Whether there is a net loss or addition of

FIGURE 7 Storm waves
When large waves break against the shore, the force of the water can be powerful and the erosional work that is accomplished can be great. These storm waves are breaking along the coast of Wales. (The Photo Library/Alamy Images)

681

A.

B.

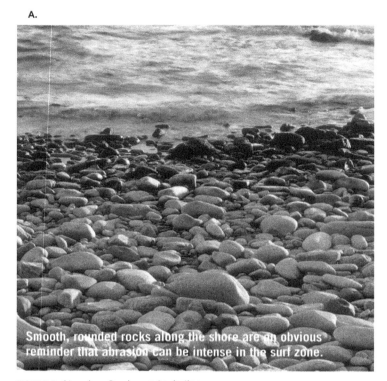

Smooth, rounded rocks along the shore are an obvious reminder that abrasion can be intense in the surf zone.

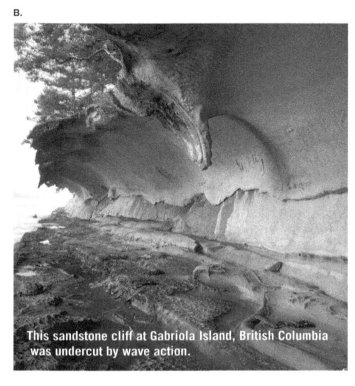

This sandstone cliff at Gabriola Island, British Columbia was undercut by wave action.

FIGURE 8 Abrasion: Sawing and grinding
Breaking waves armed with rock debris can do a great deal of erosional work. (Photo A by Michael Collier; photo B by Fletcher and Baylis/Photo Researchers, Inc.)

sand depends on the level of wave activity. When wave activity is relatively light (less energetic waves), much of the swash soaks into the beach, which reduces the backwash. Consequently, the swash dominates and causes a net movement of sand up the beach face toward the berm.

When high-energy waves prevail, the beach is saturated from previous waves, so much less of the swash soaks in. As a result, the berm erodes because backwash is strong and causes a net movement of sand down the beach face.

Along many beaches, light wave activity is the rule during the summer. Therefore, a wide sand berm gradually develops. During winter, when storms are frequent and more powerful, strong wave activity erodes and narrows the berm. A wide berm that may have taken months to build can be dramatically narrowed in just a few hours by the high-energy waves created by a strong winter storm.

Wave Refraction The bending of waves, called **wave refraction**, plays an important part in shoreline processes (FIGURE 9). It affects the distribution of energy along the shore and thus strongly influences where and to what degree erosion, sediment transport, and deposition will take place.

Waves seldom approach the shore straight on. Rather, most waves move toward the shore at an angle. However, when they reach the shallow water of a smoothly sloping bottom, they are bent and tend to become parallel to the shore. Such bending occurs because the part of the wave nearest the shore reaches shallow water and slows first, whereas the end that is still in deep water continues forward at its full speed. The net result is a wave front that may approach nearly parallel to the shore, regardless of the original direction of the wave.

Because of refraction, wave impact is concentrated against the sides and ends of headlands that project into the water, whereas wave attack is weakened in bays. This differential wave attack along irregular coastlines is illustrated in Figure 9. As the waves reach the shallow water in front of the headland sooner than they do in adjacent bays, they are bent more nearly parallel to the protruding land and strike it from all three sides. By contrast, refraction in the bays causes waves to diverge and expend less energy. In these zones of weakened wave activity, sediments can accumulate and form sandy beaches. Over a long period, erosion of the headlands and deposition in the bays will straighten an irregular shoreline.

As these waves approach nearly straight on, refraction causes the wave energy to be concentrated at headlands (resulting in erosion) and dispersed in bays (resulting in deposition).

Beach deposits

Headland

Waves travel at original speed in deep water

Waves "feel bottom" and slow down in surf zone

Shoreline

Result: waves bend so that they strike the shore more directly

Wave refraction at Rincon Point, California

SMARTFIGURE 9 **Wave refraction**
As waves first touch bottom in the shallows along an irregular coast, they are slowed; they then bend (refract) and align nearly parallel to the shoreline. (Photo by Rich Reid/National Geographic/Getty Images)

Longshore Transport Although waves are refracted, most still reach the shore at some angle, however slight. Consequently, the uprush of water from each breaking wave (the *swash*) is at an oblique angle to the shoreline. However, the backwash is straight down the slope of the beach. The effect of this pattern of water movement is to transport sediment in a zigzag pattern along the beach face (FIGURE 10). This movement is called **beach drift**, and it can transport sand and pebbles hundreds or even thousands of meters each day. However, a more typical rate is 5 to 10 meters per day.

Waves that approach the shore at an angle also produce currents within the surf zone that flow parallel to the shore and move substantially more sediment than beach drift. Because the water here is turbulent, these **longshore currents** easily move the fine suspended sand and roll larger sand and gravel along the bottom. When the sediment transported by longshore currents is added to the quantity moved by beach drift, the total amount can be very large. At Sandy Hook, New Jersey, for example, the quantity of sand transported

along the shore over a 48-year period averaged almost 750,000 tons annually. For a 10-year period in Oxnard, California, more than 1.5 million tons of sediment moved along the shore each year.

Both rivers and coastal zones move water and sediment from one area (*upstream*) to another (*downstream*). As a result, the beach has often been characterized as

Path of sand particles

Beach drift

Net movement of sand grains

Longshore current

Beach drift occurs as incoming waves carry sand at an angle up the beach, while the water from spent waves carries it directly down the slope of the beach. Similar movements occur offshore in the surf zone to create the longshore current.

Longshore current

These waves approaching the beach at a slight angle near Oceanside, California, produce a longshore current moving from left to right.

SMARTFIGURE 10
The longshore transport system
The two components of the transport system, beach drift and longshore currents, are created by breaking waves that approach the beach at an angle. These processes transport large quantities of material along the beach and in the surf zone. (Photo by John S. Shelton)

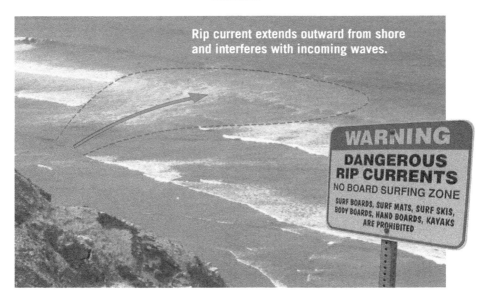

FIGURE 11 Rip current **FIGURE 11 Rip current** These concentrated movements of water flow opposite the direction of breaking waves. (Photo by A. P. Trujillo/APT Photos)

Wave refraction along the California coast south of Shelter Cove. (Photo by Michael Collier)

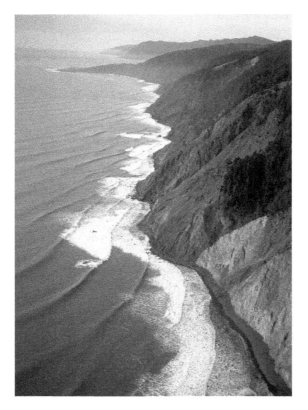

a "river of sand." Beach drift and longshore currents, however, move in a zigzag pattern, whereas rivers flow mostly in a turbulent, swirling fashion. In addition, the direction of flow of longshore currents along a shoreline can change, whereas rivers flow in the same direction (downhill). Longshore currents change direction because the direction that waves approach the beach changes seasonally. Nevertheless, longshore currents generally flow southward along both the Atlantic and Pacific shores of the United States.

Rip Currents **Rip currents** are concentrated movements of water that flow in the *opposite* direction of breaking waves. (Sometimes rip currents are incorrectly called *rip tides*, although they are unrelated to tidal phenomena.) Most of the backwash from spent waves finds its way back to the open ocean as an unconfined flow across the ocean bottom called *sheet flow.* However, sometimes a portion of the returning water moves seaward in the form of surface rip currents. These currents do not travel far beyond the surf zone before breaking up and can be recognized by the way they interfere with incoming waves or by the sediment that is often suspended within the rip current (FIGURE 11). They can be hazardous to swimmers, who, if caught in them, can be carried out away from shore. The best strategy for exiting a rip current is to swim *parallel* to the shore for a few tens of meters.

3 CONCEPT CHECKS

1. Why do waves approaching the shoreline often bend?
2. What is the effect of wave refraction along an irregular coastline?
3. Describe the two processes that contribute to longshore transport.

4 Shoreline Features

A fascinating assortment of shoreline features can be observed along the world's coastal regions. Although the same processes cause change along every coast, not all coasts respond in the same way. Interactions among different processes and the relative importance of each process depend on local factors. The factors include (1) the proximity of a coast to sediment-laden rivers, (2) the degree of tectonic activity, (3) the topography and composition of the land, (4) prevailing winds and weather patterns, and (5) the configuration of the coastline and nearshore areas. Features that originate primarily because of erosion are called *erosional features*, whereas accumulations of sediment produce *depositional features*.

Erosional Features

Many coastal landforms owe their origin to erosional processes. Such erosional features are common along the rugged and irregular New England coast and along the steep shorelines of the West Coast of the United States.

Wave-cut Cliffs, Wave-cut Platforms, and Marine Terraces

As the name implies, **wave-cut cliffs** originate in the cutting action of the surf against the base of coastal land. As erosion progresses, rocks overhanging the notch at the base of the cliff crumble into the surf, and the cliff retreats. A relatively flat, benchlike surface, called a **wave-cut platform**, is left behind by the receding cliff (FIGURE 12, *left*). The platform broadens as wave attack continues. Some debris produced by the breaking waves remains along the water's edge as sediment on the beach, and the remainder is transported farther seaward. If a wave-cut platform is uplifted above sea level by tectonic forces, it becomes a **marine terrace** (Figure 12, *right*). Marine terraces are easily recognized by their gentle seaward-sloping shape and are often desirable sites for coastal roads, buildings, or agriculture.

Sea Arches and Sea Stacks Waves vigorously attack headlands that extend into the sea because of refraction. The surf erodes the rock selectively, wearing away the softer or more highly fractured rock at the fastest rate. At first, sea caves may form. When two caves on opposite sides of a headland unite, a **sea arch** results (FIGURE 13). Eventually the arch falls in, leaving an isolated remnant, or **sea stack**, on the wave-cut platform (Figure 13). In time, it too will be consumed by the action of the waves.

Depositional Features

Sediment eroded from the beach is transported along the shore and deposited in areas where wave energy is low. Such processes produce a variety of depositional features.

Spits, Bars, and Tombolos

Where beach drift and longshore currents are active, several features related to the movement of sediment along the shore may develop.

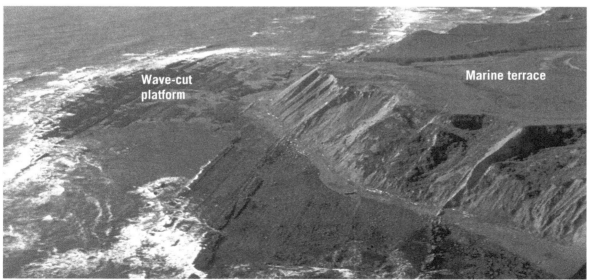

FIGURE 12 Wave-cut platform and marine terrace
This wave-cut platform is exposed at low tide along the California coast at Bolinas Point near San Francisco. A wave-cut platform was uplifted to create the marine terrace. (Photo by John S. Shelton)

Wave-cut platform

Marine terrace

FIGURE 13 Sea stack and sea arch
FIGURE 13 Sea stack and sea arch
These features at the tip of Mexico's Baja Peninsula resulted from the vigorous wave attack of a headland. (Photo by Lew Robertson/Getty Images)

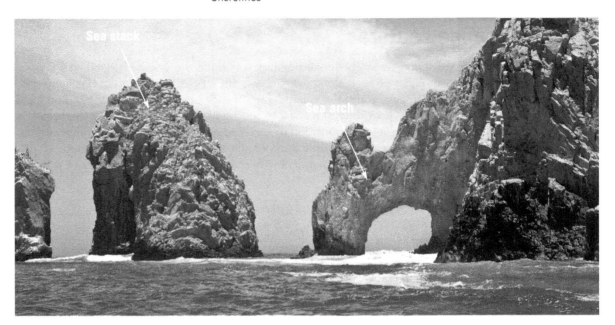

FIGURE 14 Some depositional features
A. High-altitude image of a well-developed spit and baymouth bar along the coast of Martha's Vineyard, Massachusetts. (Image courtesy of USDA-ASCS)
B. This photograph, taken from the International Space Station, shows Provincetown Spit at the tip of Cape Cod. Can you pick out this feature on the satellite image in Figure 1A? (NASA image)

A.

B.

A **spit** (*spit* = spine) is an elongated ridge of sand that projects from the land into the mouth of an adjacent bay. Often the end of a spit that is in the water hooks landward in response to the dominant direction of the longshore current (FIGURE 14). The term **baymouth bar** is applied to a sandbar that completely crosses a bay, sealing it off from the open ocean (Figure 14). Such a feature tends to form across bays where currents are weak, allowing a spit to extend to the other side. A **tombolo** (*tombolo* = mound), a ridge of sand that connects an island to the mainland or to another island, forms in much the same manner as a spit.

Barrier Islands The Atlantic and Gulf coastal plains are relatively flat and slope gently seaward. The shore zone is characterized by **barrier islands**. These low ridges of land parallel the coast at distances from 3 to 30 kilometers offshore. From Cape Cod, Massachusetts, to Padre Island, Texas, nearly 300 barrier islands rim the coast (FIGURE 15).

Most barrier islands are 1 to 5 kilometers wide and 15 to 30 kilometers long. The tallest features are sand dunes, which usually reach heights of 5 to 10 meters; in a few areas, unvegetated dunes are more than 30 meters high. The lagoons separating these narrow islands from the shore represent zones of relatively quiet water that allow small craft traveling between New York and northern Florida to avoid the rough waters of the North Atlantic.

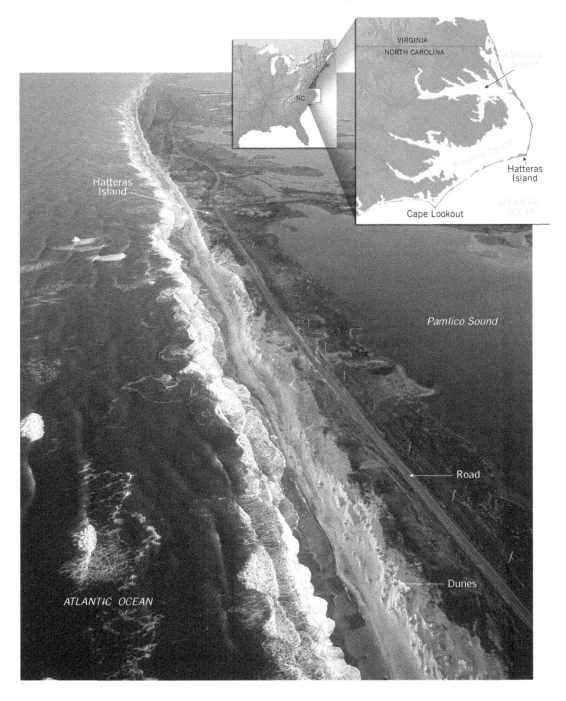

FIGURE 15 Barrier islands Nearly 300 barrier islands rim the Gulf and Atlantic coasts. The islands along the coast of North Carolina are excellent examples. (Photo by Michael Collier)

Barrier islands form in several ways. Some originated as spits that were severed from the mainland by wave erosion or by the general rise in sea level after the last episode of glaciation. Others are created when turbulent waters in the line of breakers heap up sand scoured from the bottom. Because these sand barriers rise above normal sea level, the sand likely piles up as a result of the work of storm waves at high tide. Finally, some barrier islands may be former sand-dune ridges that originated along the shore during the last glacial period, when sea level was lower. When the ice sheets melted, sea level rose and flooded the area behind the beach–dune complex.

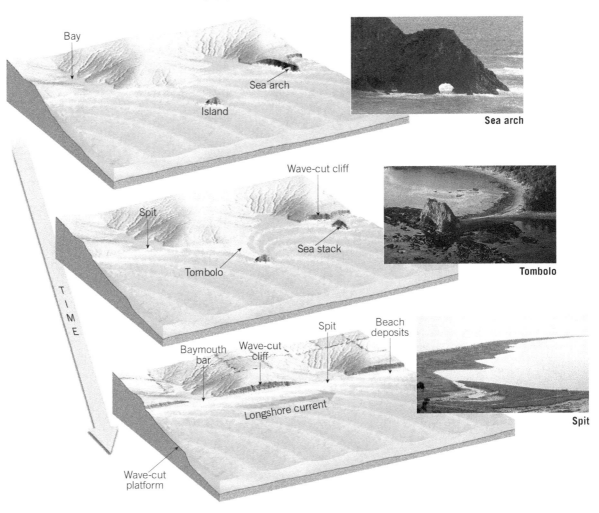

FIGURE 16 **The evolving shore**
These diagrams illustrate changes that can take place through time along an initially irregular coastline that remains relatively stable. The diagrams also illustrate many of the features described in the section on shoreline features. (Top and bottom photos by E. J. Tarbuck; middle photo by Michael Collier)

The Evolving Shore

A shoreline continually undergoes modification, regardless of its initial configuration. At first, most coastlines are irregular, although the degree of and reason for the irregularity may vary considerably from place to place. Along a coastline that is characterized by varied geology, the pounding surf may at first increase its irregularity because the waves will erode the weaker rocks more easily than the stronger ones. However, if a shoreline remains tectonically stable, marine erosion and deposition will eventually produce a straighter, more regular coast. FIGURE 16 illustrates the evolution of an initially

irregular coast. As waves erode the headlands, creating cliffs and a wave-cut platform, sediment is carried along the shore. Some material is deposited in the bays, while other debris is formed into spits and baymouth bars. At the same time, rivers fill the bays with sediment. Ultimately, a generally straight, smooth coast results.

4 CONCEPT CHECKS

1. Describe the formation of each labeled feature in Figure 16.
2. List three ways that barrier islands may form.

5 Stabilizing the Shore

Today the coastal zone teems with human activity. Unfortunately, people often treat the shoreline as if it were a stable platform on which structures can be built safely. This approach jeopardizes both people and the shoreline because many coastal landforms are relatively fragile, short-lived features that are easily damaged by development. And as anyone who has endured a tropical storm knows, the shoreline is not always a safe place to live. We will examine this latter idea more closely in the section "Hurricanes: The Ultimate Coastal Hazard."

Compared with natural hazards such as earthquakes, volcanic eruptions, and landslides, shoreline erosion is often perceived to be a more continuous and predictable process that appears to cause relatively modest damage to limited areas. In reality, the shoreline is a dynamic place that can change rapidly in response to natural forces. Exceptional storms are capable of eroding beaches and cliffs at rates that greatly exceed the long-term average. Such bursts of accelerated erosion not only have a significant impact on the natural evolution of a coast but also can have a profound impact on people who reside in the coastal zone. Erosion along our coasts causes significant property damage. Huge sums are spent annually not only to repair damage but also to prevent or control erosion. Already a problem at many sites, shoreline erosion is certain to become an increasingly serious problem as extensive coastal development continues.

During the past 100 years, growing affluence and increasing demands for recreation have brought unprecedented development to many coastal areas. As both the number and the value of buildings have increased, so too have efforts to protect property from storm waves by stabilizing the shore. Also, controlling the natural migration of sand is an ongoing struggle in many coastal areas. Such interference can result in unwanted changes that are difficult and expensive to correct.

Hard Stabilization

Structures built to protect a coast from erosion or to prevent the movement of sand along a beach are known as **hard stabilization**. Hard stabilization can take many forms and often results in predictable yet unwanted outcomes. Hard stabilization includes jetties, groins, breakwaters, and seawalls.

Jetties Since relatively early in America's history, a principal goal in coastal areas has been the development and maintenance of harbors. In many cases, this has involved the construction of jetty systems. **Jetties** are usually built in pairs and extend into the ocean at the entrances to rivers and harbors. With the flow of water confined to a narrow zone, the ebb and flow caused by the rise and fall of the tides keep the sand in motion and prevent deposition in the channel. However, as illustrated in FIGURE 17, a jetty may act as a dam against which the longshore current and beach drift deposit sand. At the same time, wave activity removes sand on the other side. Because the other side is not receiving any new sand, there is soon no beach at all.

Groins To maintain or widen beaches that are losing sand, groins are sometimes constructed. A **groin** (*groin* = ground) is a barrier built at a right angle to the beach to trap sand that is moving parallel to the shore. Groins are usually constructed of large rocks but may also be composed of wood. These structures often do their job so effectively that the longshore current beyond the groin becomes sand starved. As a result, the current erodes sand from the beach on the downstream side of the groin.

To offset this effect, property owners downstream from the structure may erect a groin on their property. In this manner, the number of groins multiplies,

Jetties interrupt the movement of sand causing deposition on the upcurrent side.

Erosion by sand-starved currents occurs downcurrent from these structures.

Jetties

Longshore current

Jetties

FIGURE 17 Jetties These structures are built at the entrances to rivers and harbors and are intended to prevent deposition in the navigation channel. The photo is an aerial view at Santa Cruz Harbor, California. (Photo by U.S. Army Corps of Engineers)

FIGURE 18 Groins
These wall-like structures trap sand that is moving parallel to the shore. This series of groins is along the shoreline near Chichester, Sussex, England. (Photo by Sandy Stockwell/London Aerial Photo Library/CORBIS)

resulting in a *groin field* (FIGURE 18). An example of such proliferation is the shoreline of New Jersey, where hundreds of these structures have been built. Because it has been shown that groins often do not provide a satisfactory solution, they are no longer the preferred method of keeping beach erosion in check.

Breakwaters and Seawalls Hard stabilization can be built parallel to the shoreline. One such structure is a **breakwater**, the purpose of which is to protect boats from the force of large breaking waves by creating a quiet water zone near the shoreline. However, when this is done, the reduced wave activity along the shore behind the structure may allow sand to accumulate. If this happens, the marina will eventually fill with sand, while the downstream beach erodes and retreats. At Santa Monica, California, where the building of a breakwater has created such a problem, the city uses a dredge to remove sand from the protected quiet water zone and deposit it downstream, where longshore currents and beach drift continue to move the sand down the coast (FIGURE 19).

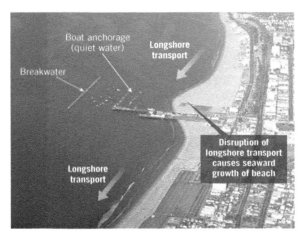

FIGURE 19 Breakwater
Aerial view of a breakwater at Santa Monica, California. The structure appears as a line in the water behind which many boats are anchored. The construction of the breakwater disrupted longshore transport and caused the seaward growth of the beach. (Photo by John S. Shelton)

Boat anchorage (quiet water)
Longshore transport
Breakwater
Disruption of longshore transport causes seaward growth of beach
Longshore transport

Another type of hard stabilization built parallel to the shoreline is a **seawall**, which is designed to armor the coast and defend property from the force of breaking waves. Waves expend much of their energy as they move across an open beach. Seawalls cut this process short by reflecting the force of unspent waves seaward. As a consequence, the beach to the seaward side of the seawall experiences significant erosion and may in some instances be eliminated entirely (FIGURE 20). Once the width of the beach is reduced, the seawall is subjected to even greater pounding by the waves. Eventually this battering will cause the wall to fail, and a larger, more expensive wall must be built to take its place.

The wisdom of building temporary protective structures along shorelines is increasingly questioned. The opinions of many coastal scientists and engineers is that halting an eroding shoreline with protective structures benefits only a few and seriously degrades or destroys the natural beach and the value it holds for the majority. Protective structures divert the ocean's energy temporarily from private properties but usually refocus that energy on the adjacent beaches. Many structures interrupt the natural sand flow in coastal currents, robbing affected beaches of vital sand replacement.

Alternatives to Hard Stabilization

Armoring the coast with hard stabilization has several potential drawbacks, including the cost of the structure and the loss of sand on the beach. Alternatives to hard stabilization include beach nourishment and relocation.

Beach Nourishment One approach to stabilizing shoreline sands without hard stabilization is **beach nourishment**. As the term implies, this practice involves adding large quantities of sand to the beach system (FIGURE 21). Extending beaches seaward makes buildings along the shoreline less vulnerable to destruction by storm waves and enhances recreational uses.

The process of beach nourishment is straightforward. Sand is pumped by dredges from offshore or trucked from inland locations. The "new" beach, however, will not be the same as the former beach. Because replenishment sand is from somewhere else, typically not another beach, it is new to the beach environment. The new sand is usually different in size, shape, sorting, and composition. These differences pose problems in terms of erodibility and the kinds of life the new sand will support.

FIGURE 20 Seawall
Seabright in northern New Jersey once had a broad, sandy beach. A seawall 5 to 6 meters (16 to 18 feet) high and 8 kilometers (5 miles) long was built to protect the town and the railroad that brought tourists to the beach. After the wall was built, the beach narrowed dramatically. (Photo by Rafael Macia/Photo Researchers, Inc.)

Seawall

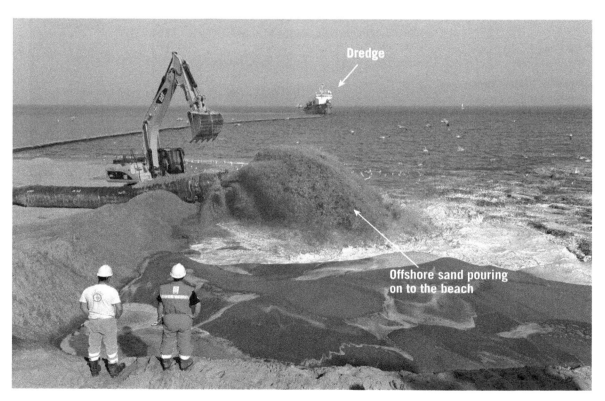

Dredge

Offshore sand pouring on to the beach

FIGURE 21 Beach nourishment
If you visit a beach along the Atlantic coast, it is more and more likely that you will walk into the surf zone atop an artificial beach. (Photo by Michael Weber/imagebroker/Alamy Images)

Beach nourishment is not a permanent solution to the problem of shrinking beaches. The same processes that removed the sand in the first place will eventually remove the replacement sand as well. Nevertheless, the number of nourishment projects has increased in recent years, and many beaches, especially along the Atlantic coast, have had their sand replenished many times. Virginia Beach, Virginia, has been nourished more than 50 times.

Beach nourishment is costly. For example, a modest project might involve 50,000 cubic yards of sand distributed across a half mile of shoreline. A good sized dump truck holds about 10 cubic yards of sand. So this small project would require about 5000 dump-truck loads. Many projects extend for many miles. Nourishing beaches typically costs millions of dollars per mile.

Relocation   Instead of building structures such as groins and seawalls to hold the beach in place or adding sand to replenish eroding beaches, another option is available. Many coastal scientists and planners are calling for a policy shift from defending and rebuilding beaches and coastal property in high-hazard areas to *relocating* storm-damaged buildings in those places and letting nature reclaim the beach. This approach is similar to an approach the federal government adopted for river floodplains following the devastating 1993 Mississippi River floods, in which vulnerable structures are abandoned and relocated on higher, safer ground.

Such proposals, of course, are controversial. People with significant near-shore investments want to rebuild and defend coastal developments from the erosional wrath of the sea. Others, however, argue that with sea level rising, the impact of coastal storms will get worse in the decades to come, and oft-damaged structures should be abandoned or relocated to improve personal safety and reduce costs. Such ideas will no doubt be the focus of much study and debate as states and communities evaluate and revise coastal land-use policies.

5 CONCEPT CHECKS

1. List at least three examples of hard stabilization and describe what each is intended to do. How does each affect distribution of sand on a beach?
2. What are two alternatives to hard stabilization, and what are the potential problems associated with each?

EYE on Earth

This structure along the eastern shore of Lake Michigan was built at the entrance to Port Shelton, Michigan.

Question 1 What is the purpose of the artificial structure pictured here?

Question 2 What term is applied to structures such as this?

Question 3 Suggest a reason there is a greater accumulation of sand on one side of the structure than the other.

Michael Collier

6 Erosion Problems Along U.S. Coasts

The shoreline along the Pacific coast of the United States is strikingly different from that of the Atlantic and Gulf coast regions. Some of the differences are related to plate tectonics. The West Coast represents the leading edge of the North American plate, and because of this, it experiences active uplift and deformation. By contrast, the East Coast is far from any active plate boundary and relatively quiet tectonically. Because of this basic geologic difference, the nature of shoreline erosion problems along America's opposite coasts is different.

Atlantic and Gulf Coasts

Much of the coastal development along the Atlantic and Gulf coasts has occurred on barrier islands. Typically, a barrier island, also termed a *barrier beach* or *coastal barrier*, consists of a wide beach that is backed by dunes and separated from the mainland by marshy lagoons. The broad expanses of sand and exposure to the ocean have made barrier islands exceedingly attractive sites for development. Unfortunately, development has taken place more rapidly than increases in our understanding of barrier island dynamics.

Because barrier islands face the open ocean, they receive the full force of major storms that strike the coast. When a storm occurs, the barriers absorb the energy of the waves primarily through the movement of sand. FIGURE 22, which shows changes at Cape Hatteras National Seashore, reinforces this point. The process and the dilemma that results have been accurately described as follows:

> Waves may move sand from the beach to offshore areas or, conversely, into the dunes; they may erode the dunes, depositing sand onto the beach or carrying it out

to sea; or they may carry sand from the beach and the dunes into the marshes behind the barrier, a process known as overwash. The common factor is movement. Just as a flexible reed may survive a wind that destroys an oak tree, so the barriers survive hurricanes and nor' easters not through unyielding strength but by giving before the storm.

This picture changes when a barrier is developed for homes or as a resort. Storm waves that previously

Various attempts to protect the lighthouse failed. They included building groins and beach nourishment. By 1999, when this photo was taken, the lighthouse was only 36 meters (120 ft.) from the water.

FIGURE 22 Relocating the Cape Hatteras lighthouse
Despite a number of efforts to protect this 21-story lighthouse, the nation's tallest lighthouse, from being destroyed due to a receding shoreline, the structure finally had to be moved. (Top photo by Don Smetzer/PhotoEdit Inc.; bottom photo by Drew C. Wilson)

Former location of lighthouse

884 meters (2900 ft.)

To save the famous candy-striped landmark, the National Park Service authorized moving the structure. After the $12 million move, it is expected to be safe for 50 years or more.

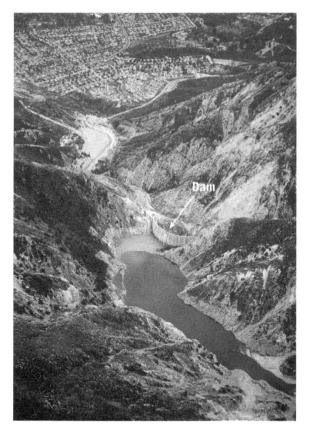

Dams such as this one in the San Gabriel Mountains near Los Angeles trap sediment that otherwise would have nourished beaches along the nearby coast. (Photo by Michael Collier)

rushed harmlessly through gaps between the dunes now encounter buildings and roadways. Moreover, since the dynamic nature of the barriers is readily perceived only during storms, homeowners tend to attribute damage to a particular storm, rather than to the basic mobility of coastal barriers. With their homes or investments at stake, local residents are more likely to seek to hold the sand in place and the waves at bay than to admit that development was improperly placed to begin with.[*]

Pacific Coast

In contrast to the broad, gently sloping coastal plains of the Atlantic and Gulf coasts, much of the Pacific coast is characterized by relatively narrow beaches that are backed by steep cliffs and mountain ranges. Recall that America's western margin is a more rugged and tectonically active region than the eastern margin. Because uplift continues, a rise in sea level in the West is not so readily apparent. Nevertheless, like the shoreline erosion

[*]Frank Lowenstein, "Beaches or Bedrooms—The Choice as Sea Level Rises," *Oceanus* 28 (No. 3, Fall 1985): p. 22 © Woods Hole Oceanographic Institute.

problems facing the East's barrier islands, West Coast difficulties also stem largely from the alteration of a natural system by people.

A major problem facing the Pacific shoreline, and especially portions of southern California, is a significant narrowing of many beaches. The bulk of the sand on many of these beaches is supplied by rivers that transport it from the mountains to the coast. Over the years, this natural flow of material to the coast has been interrupted by dams built for irrigation and flood control. The reservoirs effectively trap the sand that would otherwise nourish the beach environment (FIGURE 23). When the beaches were wider, they protected the cliffs behind them from the force of storm waves. Now, however, the waves move across the narrowed beaches without losing much energy and cause more rapid erosion of the sea cliffs.

Although the retreat of the cliffs provides material to replace some of the sand impounded behind dams, it also endangers homes and roads built on the bluffs. In addition, development atop the cliffs aggravates the problem. Urbanization increases runoff, which, if not carefully controlled, can result in serious bluff erosion. Watering lawns and gardens adds significant quantities of water to the slope. This water percolates downward toward the base of the cliff, where it may emerge in small seeps. This action reduces the slope's stability and facilitates mass wasting.

Shoreline erosion along the Pacific coast varies considerably from one year to the next, largely because of the sporadic occurrence of storms. As a consequence, when the infrequent but serious episodes of erosion occur, the damage is often blamed on the unusual storms and not on coastal development or the sediment-trapping dams that may be great distances away. If, as predicted, sea level rises at an increasing rate in the years to come, increased shoreline erosion and sea-cliff retreat should be expected along many parts of the Pacific coast.

6 CONCEPT CHECKS

1. Briefly describe what happens when storm waves strike an undeveloped barrier island.
2. How might building a dam on a river that flows to the sea affect a coastal beach?

7 | Hurricanes: The Ultimate Coastal Hazard

Whirling tropical cyclones—the greatest storms on Earth (FIGURE 24)—occasionally have wind speeds exceeding 300 kilometers (185 miles) per hour. In the United States they are known as *hurricanes*, in the Western Pacific they are called *typhoons*, and in the Indian Ocean they are simply called *cyclones*. No matter which name is used, these storms are among the most destructive of natural disasters.

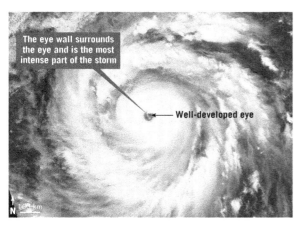

FIGURE 24 **Super Typhoon Jangmi**
In the Western Pacific, hurricanes are called typhoons. This storm struck portions of Taiwan, China, and Japan in late September 2008. It was the strongest storm worldwide that year, with sustained winds that reached 270 kilometers (165 miles) per hour. The counterclockwise spiral of the clouds indicates that it is a Northern Hemisphere storm. In the Southern Hemisphere, the spiral is clockwise. (NASA)

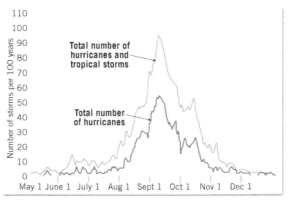

FIGURE 25 **When do Atlantic hurricanes occur?** Frequency of tropical storms and hurricanes from May 1 through December 31 in the Atlantic basin. The graph shows the number of storms to be expected over a span of 100 years. The period from late August through October is clearly the most active. (Data from National Hurricane Center/NOAA)

The vast majority of hurricane-related deaths and damage are caused by relatively infrequent yet powerful storms. Of course, the deadliest and most costly storm in recent memory occurred in August 2005, when Hurricane Katrina devastated the Gulf coast of Louisiana, Mississippi, and Alabama. Although hundreds of thousands of people fled before the storm made landfall, thousands of others were caught by the storm. In addition to the human suffering and tragic loss of life that were left in the wake of Hurricane Katrina, the financial losses caused by the storm are practically incalculable.

Our coasts are vulnerable. People are flocking to live near the ocean. The proportion of the U.S. population residing within 75 kilometers (45 miles) of a coast is well in excess of 50 percent. The concentration of such large numbers of people near the shoreline means that hurricanes place millions at risk. Moreover, the potential costs of property damage are incredible.

Profile of a Hurricane

A hurricane is a heat engine that is fueled by the energy liberated when huge quantities of water vapor condense.

The amount of energy produced by a typical hurricane in just a single day is truly immense. To get the engine started, a large quantity of warm, moist air is required, and a continuous supply is needed to keep it going.

Hurricane Formation As the graph in FIGURE 25 illustrates, hurricanes most often form in late summer and early fall. It is during this span that sea-surface temperatures reach 27° C (80° F) or higher and are thus able to provide the necessary heat and moisture to the air (FIGURE 26). This ocean-water temperature requirement accounts for the fact that hurricane formation over the relatively cool waters of the South Atlantic and eastern South Pacific is extremely rare. For the

Sea Surface Temperature (°C)

| −2 | 16.5 | 27.8 | 35 |

FIGURE 26 **Sea-surface temperatures** Among the necessary ingredients for a hurricane is warm ocean temperatures above 27° C (80° F). This color-coded satellite image from June 1, 2010, shows sea-surface temperatures at the beginning of hurricane season. (NASA)

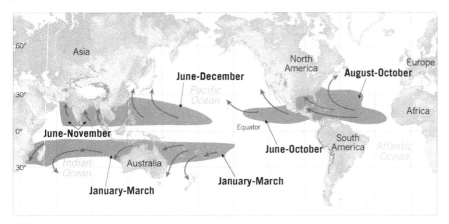

SMARTFIGURE 27 Hurricane source regions and paths
The map shows the regions where most hurricanes form as well as their principal months of occurrence and the most common tracks they follow. Hurricanes do not develop within about 5 degrees of the equator because the Coriolis effect (a force related to Earth's rotation that gives storms their "spin") there is too weak. Because warm ocean-surface temperatures are necessary for hurricane formation, hurricanes seldom form poleward of 20 degrees latitude or over the cool waters of the South Atlantic and the eastern South Pacific.

same reason, few hurricanes form poleward of 20 degrees latitude. Although water temperatures are sufficiently high, hurricanes do not develop within about 5 degrees of the equator because the Coriolis effect (a force related to Earth's rotation that gives storms their "spin") is too weak there. FIGURE 27 shows the regions where most hurricanes form.

Pressure Gradient   Hurricanes are intense low-pressure centers, which means that as you move toward the center of the storm, air pressure gets lower and lower. Such storms are said to have a very steep pressure gradient. *Pressure gradient* refers to how rapidly the pressure changes and is shown on a map with *isobars*, lines of equal pressure. Just as the spacing of contour lines on a topographic map indicates how steep or gentle a slope is, the spacing of isobars on a weather chart shows how rapidly air pressure is changing. Closely spaced isobars indicate a steep pressure gradient. The steeper the pressure gradient, the stronger the winds. A steep pressure gradient generates the rapid, inward-spiraling winds of a hurricane. As the air rushes toward the center of the storm, its velocity increases. This is similar to skaters with their arms extended spinning faster as they pull their arms in close to their bodies.

Storm Structure   As the inward rush of warm, moist surface air approaches the core of the storm, it turns upward and ascends in a ring of cumulonimbus towers (FIGURE 28). This doughnut-shaped wall of intense convective activity surrounding the center of the storm

is called the **eye wall**. It is here that the greatest wind speeds and heaviest rainfall occur. Surrounding the eye wall are curved bands of clouds that trail away in a spiral fashion. Near the top of the hurricane, the airflow is outward, carrying the rising air away from the storm center, thereby providing room for more inward flow at the surface.

At the very center of the storm is the **eye** of the hurricane (Figure 28). This well-known feature is a zone about 20 kilometers (12.5 miles) in diameter where precipitation ceases and winds subside. It offers a brief but deceptive break from the extreme weather in the enormous curving wall clouds that surround it. The air within the eye gradually descends and heats by compression, making it the warmest part of the storm. Although many people believe that the eye is characterized by clear blue skies, this is usually not the case because the subsidence in the eye is seldom strong enough to produce cloudless conditions. Although the sky appears much brighter in this region, scattered clouds at various levels are common.

Hurricane Destruction

The amount of damage caused by a hurricane depends on several factors, including the size and population density of the area affected and the shape of the ocean bottom near the shore. The most significant factor, of course, is the strength of the storm itself. By studying past storms, a scale called the *Saffir–Simpson hurricane scale* has been established to rank the relative intensities of hurricanes. As TABLE 1 indicates, a *category 5* storm is the worst possible, whereas a *category 1* hurricane is least severe.

During the hurricane season, it is common to hear scientists and reporters alike use the numbers from the Saffir–Simpson scale. When Hurricane Katrina made landfall, sustained winds were 225 kilometers (140 miles) per hour, making it a strong category 4 storm. Storms that fall into category 5 are rare. Hurricane Camille, a 1969 storm that caused catastrophic damage along the coast of Mississippi, is one well-known example.

Damage caused by hurricanes can be divided into three categories: (1) storm surge, (2) wind damage, and (3) inland flooding.

Storm Surge   Without question, the most devastating damage in the coastal zone is caused by storm surge. It not only accounts for a large share of coastal property losses but is also responsible for a high percentage of all hurricane-caused deaths. A **storm surge** is a dome of water 65 to 80 kilometers (40 to 50 miles) wide that sweeps across the coast near the point where the eye makes landfall. If all wave activity were smoothed out, the storm surge would be the height of the water above normal tide level. In addition, tremendous wave activity is superimposed on the surge. This surge of water can

Outflow of air at the top of the hurricane is important because it prevents the convergent flow at lower levels from "filling in" the storm.

Eye

Sinking air in the eye warms by compression.

Eye wall, the zone where winds and rain are most intense.

Tropical moisture spiraling inward creates rain bands that pinwheel around the storm center.

FIGURE 28 Cross section of a hurricane
(Data from World Meteorological Organization)

Cross Section of a Hurricane. Note that the vertical dimension is greatly exaggerated. (After NOAA)

Measurements of surface pressure and wind speed during the passage of Cyclone Monty at Mardie Station, Western Australia, between February 29 and March 2, 2004. (Hurricanes are called "cyclones" in this part of the world.)

Minimum pressure 964 on 3 March

inflict immense damage on low-lying coastal areas (FIGURE 29). The worst surges occur in places like the Gulf of Mexico, where the continental shelf is very shallow and gently sloping. In addition, local features such as bays and rivers can cause the surge to double in height and increase in speed.

As a hurricane advances toward the coast in the Northern Hemisphere, storm surge is always most intense on the right side of the eye, where winds are blowing *toward* the shore. In addition, on this side of the storm, the forward movement of the hurricane also contributes to the storm surge. In FIGURE 30, assume that a hurricane with peak winds of 175 kilometers (109 miles) per hour is moving toward the shore at 50 kilometers (31 miles) per hour. In this case, the net wind speed on the right side of the advancing storm is 225 kilometers (140 miles) per hour. On the left side, the hurricane's winds are blowing opposite the direction of storm movement, so the net winds are *away* from the coast at 125 kilometers (78 miles) per hour. Along the shore facing the left side of the oncoming hurricane, the water level may actually decrease as the storm makes landfall.

Wind Damage Destruction caused by wind is perhaps the most obvious of the classes of hurricane damage. Debris such as signs, roofing materials, and small items left outside become dangerous flying missiles in hurricanes. For some structures, the force of the wind is sufficient to cause total ruin. Mobile homes are

TABLE 1	Saffir–Simpson Hurricane Scale					
Scale Number (category)	Central Pressure (millibars)	Wind Speed (kph)	Wind Speed (mph)	Storm Surge (meters)	Storm Surge (feet)	Damage
1	≥980	119–153	74–95	1.2–1.5	4–5	*Minimal*
2	965–979	154–177	96–110	1.6–2.4	6–8	*Moderate*
3	945–964	178–209	111–130	2.5–3.6	9–12	*Extensive*
4	920–944	210–250	131–155	3.7–5.4	13–18	*Extreme*
5	<920	>250	>155	>5.4	>18	*Catastrophic*

particularly vulnerable. High-rise buildings are also susceptible to hurricane-force winds. Upper floors are most vulnerable because wind speeds usually increase with height. Recent research suggests that people should stay below the 10th floor but remain above any floors at risk for flooding. In regions with good building codes, wind damage is usually not as catastrophic as storm-surge damage. However, hurricane-force winds affect a much larger area than storm surge and can cause huge economic losses. For example, in 1992 it was largely the winds associated with Hurricane Andrew that produced more than $25 billion of damage in southern Florida and Louisiana.

Hurricanes sometimes produce tornadoes that contribute to the storm's destructive power. Studies have shown that more than half of the hurricanes that make landfall produce at least one tornado. In 2004 the number of tornadoes associated with tropical storms and hurricanes was extraordinary. Tropical Storm Bonnie and five landfalling hurricanes—Charley, Frances, Gaston, Ivan, and Jeanne—produced nearly 300 tornadoes that affected the southeast and mid-Atlantic states.

Heavy Rains and Inland Flooding

The torrential rains that accompany most hurricanes bring a third significant threat: flooding. Whereas the effects of storm surge and strong winds are concentrated in coastal areas, heavy rains may affect places hundreds of kilometers from the coast for up to several days after the storm has lost its hurricane-force winds.

In September 1999, Hurricane Floyd brought flooding rains, high winds, and rough seas to a large portion of the Atlantic seaboard. More than 2.5 million people evacuated their homes from Florida north to the Carolinas and beyond. It was the largest peacetime evacuation in U.S. history up to that time. Torrential rains falling on already saturated ground created devastating inland flooding. Altogether Floyd dumped more than 48 centimeters (19 inches) of rain on Wilmington, North Carolina, with 33.98 centimeters (13.38 inches) falling in a single 24-hour span.

Another well-known example is Hurricane Camille (1969). Although this storm is best known for its exceptional storm surge and the devastation it brought to coastal areas, the greatest number of deaths associated with this storm occurred in the Blue Ridge Mountains of Virginia 2 days after Camille's landfall. Many places received more than 25 centimeters (10 inches) of rain.

Detecting and Tracking Hurricanes

A location only a few hundred kilometers from a hurricane—just a day's striking distance away—may experience clear skies and virtually no wind. Before the age of weather satellites, such a situation made it difficult to warn people of impending storms. The worst natural disaster in U.S. history came as a result of a hurricane that struck an unprepared Galveston, Texas, on September 8, 1900. The strength of the storm, together with the lack of adequate warning, caught the population by surprise and took the lives of 8000 people (FIGURE 31).

In the United States, early warning systems have greatly reduced the number of deaths caused by hurricanes. At the same time, however, an astronomical rise has occurred in the amount of property damage. The primary reason for this

FIGURE 30 An approaching hurricane
Winds associated with a Northern Hemisphere hurricane that is advancing toward the coast. This hypothetical storm, with peak winds of 175 kilometers (109 miles) per hour, is moving toward the coast at 50 kilometers (31 miles) per hour. On the right side of the advancing storm, the 175-kilometer-per-hour winds are in the same direction as the movement of the storm (50 kilometers per hour). Therefore the *net* wind speed on the right side of the storm is 225 kilometers (140 miles) per hour *toward* the coast. On the left side, the hurricane's winds are blowing opposite the direction of storm movement, so the *net* winds of 125 kilometers (78 miles) per hour are *away* from the coast. Storm surge will be greatest along the part of the coast hit by the right side of the advancing hurricane.

latter trend is the rapid population growth and accompanying development in coastal areas.

Satellites The greatest single advancement in tools used for observing hurricanes has been the development of meteorological satellites. In order to detect a hurricane, it is necessary to monitor vast areas of open ocean. Before satellites, this was an impossible task. Today instruments aboard satellites can detect a potential storm even before it develops its characteristic circular cloud pattern.

Aircraft Reconnaissance When a hurricane is within range, specially instrumented aircraft can fly directly into a threatening storm and accurately measure details of its position and current state of development. Data transmission can be made directly from an aircraft in the midst of a storm to the forecast center. The data collected are critical in analyzing the current characteristics needed to forecast the future behavior of a storm.

Radar A third basic tool in the observation and study of hurricanes is radar. When a hurricane nears the coast, it is monitored by land-based Doppler weather radar. This tool provides detailed information on hurricane wind fields, rainfall intensity, and storm movement. As a result, local forecast centers are able to provide short-term warnings for floods, tornadoes, and high winds for specific areas.

FIGURE 31 Aftermath of the historic Galveston hurricane
The storm struck an unsuspecting and unprepared city on September 8, 1900. It was the worst natural disaster in U.S. history. Entire blocks were swept clean, and mountains of debris accumulated around the few remaining buildings. (AP Photo)

7 CONCEPT CHECKS

1. What factors influence where and when hurricane formation takes place?
2. Distinguish between the eye and eye wall of a hurricane.
3. Why does hurricane intensity diminish rapidly when the storm moves onto land?
4. What are the three broad categories of hurricane damage? Which one is responsible for the greatest number of hurricane-related deaths?
5. Which side of an advancing hurricane in the Northern Hemisphere has the strongest winds and highest storm surge—right or left? Explain.
6. List three tools that provide data used to track and analyze hurricanes.

EYE on Earth

This satellite image shows Cyclone Favio as it came ashore along the coast of Mozambique, Africa, on February 22, 2007. This powerful storm was moving from east to west. Since it is a Southern Hemisphere storm, the cloud pattern shows that the winds circulate in a clockwise spiral instead of the counterclockwise pattern typical of storms in the Northern Hemisphere. Portions of the cyclone had sustained winds of 203 kilometers (126 miles) per hour as it made landfall.

Question 1 Identify the eye and eye wall of the storm.

Question 2 Based on wind speed, classify the storm using the Saffir–Simpson scale.

Question 3 Which one of the lettered sites should experience the strongest storm surge? Explain.

8 Coastal Classification

The great variety of shorelines demonstrates their complexity. Indeed, to understand any particular coastal area, many factors must be considered, including rock types, size and direction of waves, frequency of storms, tidal range, and offshore topography. In addition, practically all coastal areas were affected by the worldwide rise in sea level that accompanied the melting of Ice Age glaciers at the close of the Pleistocene epoch. Finally, tectonic events that elevate or drop the land or change the volume of ocean basins must be taken into account. The large number of factors that influence coastal areas make shoreline classification difficult.

FIGURE 32 **East Coast estuaries**
The lower portions of many river valleys were flooded by the rise in sea level that followed the end of the Quaternary Ice Age, creating large estuaries such as Chesapeake and Delaware bays.

Many geologists classify coasts based on the changes that have occurred with respect to sea level. This commonly used classification divides coasts into two general categories: emergent and submergent. **Emergent coasts** develop either because an area experiences uplift or as a result of a drop in sea level. Conversely, **submergent coasts** are created when sea level rises or the land adjacent to the sea subsides.

Emergent Coasts

In some areas, the coast is clearly emergent because rising land or a falling water level exposes wave-cut cliffs and platforms above sea level. Excellent examples include portions of coastal California, where uplift has occurred in the recent geologic past. The marine terrace shown in Figure 12 illustrates this situation. In the case of the Palos Verdes Hills, south of Los Angeles, seven different terrace levels exist, indicating seven episodes of uplift. The ever-persistent sea is now cutting a new platform at the base of the cliff. If uplift follows, it too will become an elevated marine terrace.

Other examples of emergent coasts include regions that were once buried beneath great ice sheets. When glaciers were present, their weight depressed the crust, and when the ice melted, the crust began gradually to spring back. Consequently, prehistoric shoreline features may now be found high above sea level. The Hudson Bay region of Canada is such an area; portions of it are still rising at a rate of more than 1 centimeter per year.

Submergent Coasts

In contrast to the preceding examples, other coastal areas show definite signs of submergence. Shorelines that have been submerged in the relatively recent past are often highly irregular because the sea typically floods the lower reaches of river valleys flowing into the ocean. The ridges separating the valleys, however, remain above sea level and project into the sea as headlands. These drowned river mouths, which are called **estuaries** (*aestus* = tide), characterize many coasts today. Along the Atlantic coastline, the Chesapeake and Delaware bays are examples of large estuaries created by submergence (FIGURE 32). The picturesque coast of Maine, particularly in the vicinity of Acadia National Park, is another excellent example of an area that was flooded by the postglacial rise in sea level and transformed into a highly irregular coastline.

Keep in mind that most coasts have complicated geologic histories. With respect to sea level, many have, at various times, emerged and then submerged. Each time, they may retain some of the features created during the previous situation.

8 CONCEPT CHECKS

1. What observable features would lead you to classify a coastal area as emergent?
2. Are estuaries associated with submergent or emergent coasts? Explain.

Hurricane Katrina from Space

Satellites allow us to track the formation, movement, and growth of hurricanes. In addition, their specialized instruments provide data that can be transformed into images that allow scientists to analyze the internal structure and workings of these huge destructive storms.

KEY TO SYMBOLS
+ Location of storm center (at 8 A.M. EDT)
o Tropical depression
6 Tropical storm
6 Hurricane

TOTAL RAINFALL
8 16 24 32 cm
3.2 6.4 9.6 12.8 in

Storm track and rainfall values for Hurricane Katrina for the period August 23 to 31, 2005. The highest totals (dark red) exceeded 30 centimeters (12 inches) over parts of Cuba and the Florida Keys. Because the storm moved rapidly, rainfall totals (green to blue) in many areas were generally less than 13 centimeters (5 inches). Data is from the Tropical Rainfall Measuring Mission (TRMM) satellite.

A color-enhanced infrared image from the GOES-East satellite. Infrared wavelengths are invisible but can be detected as heat. Wavelengths of radiation emitted by an object depend on temperature. Longer infrared wavelengths indicate colder temperatures and shorter wavelengths are associated with warmer temperatures. The high tops of towering storm clouds are colder than the tops of clouds that produce less intense weather. The highest (coldest) cloud tops and thus the most intense storms are easily seen.

This image from NASA's QuikSCAT satellite provides a detailed look at Katrina's surface winds shortly before the storm made landfall. The image depicts relative wind speeds. The strongest winds, shown in shades of purple, circle a well-defined eye. The barbs fly with the wind and show the strong counterclockwise flow of the storm.

WIND SPEED
Wind speed increases

This eye wall tower rises 16 kilometers (10 miles) above the ocean surface. Towers this tall near the storm's center are often an indication that a storm is intensifying. Katrina grew from a category 3 to a category 4 storm soon after this image was received.

HEIGHT (km)
20
10
0

RAIN RATE (mm/hr)
0 10 20 30 40 50
NASA

Tropical Rainfall Measuring Mission (TRMM) satellite image of Katrina early on August 28, 2005. The cutaway view of the inner portion of the storm shows cloud height (vertical scale) and rainfall rates (horizontal scale). Two isolated towers (in red) are visible: one in an outer rain band and the other in the eye wall.

This relatively "traditional" image shows Katrina on August 28, 2005 as the massive storm approached the Gulf Coast. After passing over Florida as a category 1 hurricane, Katrina entered the Gulf and intensified to a category 5 storm with winds of 257 kilometers (160 miles) per hour, and even stronger gusts. When Katrina came ashore the next day it was a slightly less vigorous category 4 storm.

9 Tides

Tides are daily changes in the elevation of the ocean surface caused by gravitational interactions of Earth with the Moon and Sun. Their rhythmic rise and fall along coastlines have been known since antiquity. Other than waves, they are the easiest ocean movements to observe (FIGURE 33).

Although known for centuries, tides were not explained satisfactorily until Sir Isaac Newton applied the law of gravitation to them. Newton showed that there is a mutual attractive force between two bodies and that because oceans are free to move, they are deformed by this force. Hence, ocean tides result from the gravitational attraction exerted upon Earth by the Moon and, to a lesser extent, by the Sun.

Causes of Tides

It is easy to see how the Moon's gravitational force can cause the water to bulge on the side of Earth nearest the Moon. In addition, however, an equally large tidal bulge is produced on the side of Earth directly opposite the Moon (FIGURE 34).

Both tidal bulges are caused, as Newton discovered, by the pull of gravity. Gravity is inversely proportional to the square of the distance between two objects, meaning simply that it quickly weakens with distance. In this case, the two objects are the Moon and Earth. Because the force of gravity decreases with distance, the Moon's gravitational pull on Earth is slightly greater on the near side of Earth than on the far side. The result of this differential pulling is to stretch (elongate) the "solid" Earth very slightly. In contrast, the world ocean, which is mobile, is deformed

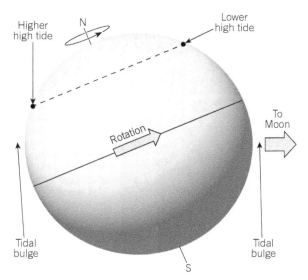

FIGURE 34 **Idealized tidal bulges caused by the Moon** If Earth were covered to a uniform depth with water, there would be two tidal bulges: one on the side of Earth facing the Moon (right) and the other on the opposite side of Earth (left). Depending on the Moon's position, tidal bulges may be inclined relative to Earth's equator. In this situation, Earth's rotation causes an observer to experience two unequal high tides during a day.

quite dramatically by this effect, producing the two opposing tidal bulges.

Because the position of the Moon changes only moderately in a single day, the tidal bulges remain in place while Earth rotates "through" them. For this reason, if you stand on the seashore for 24 hours, Earth will rotate you through alternating areas of deeper and shallower water. As you are carried into each tidal bulge, the tide rises, and as you are carried into the intervening troughs between the tidal bulges, the tide falls. Therefore, most places on Earth experience two high tides and two low tides each day.

Further, the tidal bulges migrate as the Moon revolves around Earth about every 29 days. As a result, the tides, like the time of moonrise, shift about 50 minutes later each day. After 29 days the cycle is complete, and a new one begins.

In many locations, there may be an inequality between the high tides during a given day. Depending on the position of the Moon, the tidal bulges may be inclined to the equator, as in Figure 34. This figure

FIGURE 33 **Bay of Fundy tides** High tide and low tide on Nova Scotia's Minas Basin in the Bay of Fundy. Tidal flats are exposed during low tide. (Photos courtesy of Nova Scotia Department of Tourism)

High tide

Low tide

Tidal flat

illustrates that one high tide experienced by an observer in the Northern Hemisphere is considerably higher than the high tide half a day later. In contrast, a Southern Hemisphere observer would experience the opposite effect.

Monthly Tidal Cycle

The primary body that influences the tides is the Moon, which makes one complete revolution around Earth every 29.5 days. The Sun, however, also influences the tides. It is far larger than the Moon, but because it is much farther away, its effect is considerably less. In fact, the Sun's tide-generating effect is only about 46 percent that of the Moon.

Near the times of new and full moons, the Sun and Moon are aligned, and their forces on tides are added together (FIGURE 35A). The combined gravity of these two tide-producing bodies causes larger tidal bulges (higher high tides) and deeper tidal troughs (lower low tides), producing a large tidal range. These are called the **spring tides** (*springen* = to rise up), which have no connection with the spring season but occur twice a month, during the time when the Earth–Moon–Sun system is aligned. Conversely, at about the time of the first and third quarters of the Moon, the gravitational forces of the Moon and Sun act on Earth at right angles, and each partially offsets the influence of the other (FIGURE 35B). As a result, the daily tidal range is less. These are called **neap tides** (*nep* = scarcely or barely touching), and they also occur twice each month. Each month, then, there are two spring tides and two neap tides, each about 1 week apart.

Tidal Patterns

The basic causes and types of tides have been explained. Keep in mind, however, that these theoretical considerations cannot be used to predict either the height or the time of actual tides at a particular place. This is because many factors—including the shape of the coastline, the configuration of ocean basins, and water depth—greatly influence the tides. Consequently, tides at various locations respond differently to tide-producing forces. This being the case, the nature of the tide at any coastal location can be determined most accurately by actual observation. The predictions in tidal tables and tidal data on nautical charts are based on such observations.

Three main tidal patterns exist worldwide (FIGURE 36). A **diurnal tidal pattern** (*diurnal* = daily) is characterized by a single high tide and a single low tide each tidal day. Tides of this type occur along the northern shore of the Gulf of Mexico, among other locations. A **semidiurnal tidal pattern** (*semi* = twice, *diurnal* = daily) exhibits two high tides and two low tides each tidal day, with the two highs about the same height and the two lows about the same height. This type of tidal

A. Spring Tide When the Moon is in the full or new position, the tidal bulges created by the Sun and Moon are aligned and there is a large tidal range.

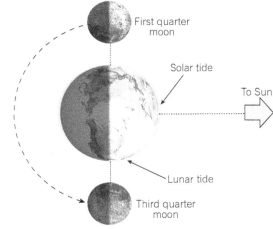

B. Neap Tide When the Moon is in the first-or third-quarter position, the tidal bulges produced by the Moon are at right angles to the bulges created by the Sun and the tidal range is smaller.

FIGURE 35 Spring and neap tides Earth–Moon–Sun positions influence the tides.

pattern is common along the Atlantic coast of the United States. A **mixed tidal pattern** is similar to a semidiurnal pattern except that it is characterized by a large inequality in high water heights, low water heights, or both. In this case, there are usually two high and two low tides each day, with high tides of different heights and low tides of different heights. Such tides are prevalent along the Pacific coast of the United States and in many other parts of the world.

Tidal Currents

Tidal current is the term used to describe the *horizontal* flow of water accompanying the rise and fall of the tide. These water movements induced by tidal forces can be important in some coastal areas. Tidal currents flow in one direction during a portion of the tidal cycle and reverse their flow during the remainder. Tidal currents that advance into the coastal zone as the tide rises are called **flood currents**. As the tide falls, seaward-moving water generates **ebb currents**. Periods of little or no current, called *slack water*, separate flood and ebb. The areas affected by these

Tidal patterns
A diurnal tidal pattern (lower right) features one high tide and one low tide each tidal day. A semidiurnal pattern (upper right) features two high tides and two low tides of approximately equal heights during each tidal day. A mixed tidal pattern (left) features two high tides and two low tides of unequal heights during each tidal day.

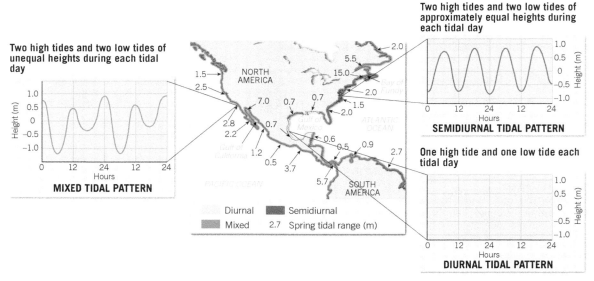

Two high tides and two low tides of unequal heights during each tidal day

MIXED TIDAL PATTERN

Two high tides and two low tides of approximately equal heights during each tidal day

SEMIDIURNAL TIDAL PATTERN

One high tide and one low tide each tidal day

DIURNAL TIDAL PATTERN

Diurnal Semidiurnal
Mixed 2.7 Spring tidal range (m)

alternating tidal currents are **tidal flats** (see Figure 33). Depending on the nature of the coastal zone, tidal flats vary from narrow strips seaward of the beach to extensive zones that may extend for several kilometers.

Although tidal currents are generally not important in the open sea, they can be rapid in bays, river estuaries, straits, and other narrow places. Off the coast of Brittany in France, for example, tidal currents that accompany a high tide of 12 meters (40 feet) may attain a speed of 20 kilometers (12 miles) per hour. While tidal currents are not generally major agents of erosion and sediment transport, notable exceptions occur where tides move through narrow inlets. Here they constantly scour the small entrances to many good harbors that would otherwise be blocked.

Sometimes deposits called **tidal deltas** are created by tidal currents (FIGURE 37). They may develop either as *flood deltas* landward of an inlet or as *ebb deltas* on the seaward side of an inlet. Because wave activity and longshore currents are reduced on the sheltered landward side, flood deltas are more common and more prominent (see Figure 14A). They form after the tidal current moves rapidly through an inlet. As the current emerges from the narrow passage into more open waters, it slows and deposits its load of sediment.

Tides and Earth's Rotation

The tides, by friction against the floor of the ocean basins, act as weak brakes that are steadily slowing Earth's rotation. The rate of slowing, however, is not great. Astronomers, who have precisely measured the length of the day over the past 300 years, have found that the day is increasing by 0.002 second per century. Although this

may seem inconsequential, over millions of years, this small effect will become very large.

If Earth's rotation is slowing, the length of each day must have been shorter and the number of days per year must have been greater in the geologic past. One method used to investigate this phenomenon involves the microscopic examination of shells of certain invertebrates. Clams and corals, as well as other organisms, grow a microscopically thin layer of new shell material each day. By studying the daily growth rings of some well-preserved fossil specimens, we can determine the number of days in a year. Studies using this ingenious technique indicate that early

FIGURE 37 **Tidal deltas**
As a rapidly moving tidal current (flood current) moves through a barrier island's inlet into the quiet waters of the lagoon, the current slows and deposits sediment, creating a tidal delta. Because this tidal delta has developed on the landward side of the inlet, it is called a *flood delta*. Such a tidal delta is shown in Figure 14A.

in the Cambrian period, about 540 million years ago, the length of the day was only 21 hours. Because the length of the year, which is determined by Earth's revolution about the Sun, does not change, the Cambrian year contained 424 of these 21-hour days. By late Devonian time, about 365 million years ago, a year consisted of about 410 days, and as the Permian period opened, about 290 million years ago, there were 390 days in a year.

9 CONCEPT CHECKS

1. Explain why an observer can experience two unequal high tides during a single day.
2. Distinguish between *neap tides* and *ebb tides*.
3. Contrast *flood current* and *ebb current*.
4. How have tides affected Earth's rotation?

EYE on Earth

An aerial view of a small portion of a coastal area.

Question 1 Is this an emergent coast or a submergent coast?

Question 2 Provide an easily seen line of evidence to support your answer to Question 1.

Question 3 Is the location more likely along the coast of North Carolina or California? Explain.

Michael Collier

CONCEPTS IN REVIEW: SHORELINES

1 The Shoreline: A Dynamic Interface

Explain why the shoreline is considered a dynamic interface and identify the basic parts of the coastal zone.

KEY WORDS shoreline, shore, coast, coastline, foreshore, backshore, nearshore zone, offshore zone, beach, berm, beach face

- The line of contact between land and ocean is a dynamic interface. Beaches sometimes occur along shorelines: They are accumulations of sediment such as sand. The sediment that makes up a beach may vary in size and composition.

- If you were to walk downhill through the coastal zone of a beach, you would cross out of a dune field and onto the backshore, which is submerged only during storms. Your path would take you past the berm to the high-tide shoreline. Seaward of that is the foreshore, which extends all the way to the low-tide shoreline and includes the wet sand of the beach face. As you swam out to sea, you would cross the nearshore's breaking waves and finally enter the offshore zone.

LIFE'S A BEACH Examine Figure 2, which shows the "anatomy" of a beach. Which beach feature is an ideal place for a recreational beach visitor to set up a towel and chair? Explain.

2 Waves

List and discuss the factors that influence the height, length, and period of a wave and describe the motion of water within a wave.

KEY WORDS wave height, wavelength, wave period, fetch, surf

- Oceans waves move energy (derived from wind) across the surface of the ocean and to the shoreline, where their energy is dissipated. How fast the wind blows, for how long, and over what distance (the fetch) determine the height, wavelength, and period of the resulting waves. Waves can grow until they break and produce whitecaps; these can dissipate as much energy as the waves gain from the wind.

- As wave energy passes through water, it causes the individual particles of water to travel along a short path shaped like a circle. An object floating on the water helps visualize this circular orbital motion: After the wave has passed, the object returns to its original position. Similar circles are being traced out by the water molecules immediately below the object, though they get smaller and smaller with increasing depth. At a depth equal to one-half the wavelength, the motion effectively diminishes to zero.

- When a wave enters water that is shallower than the wave base, it slows down, which allows waves farther from shore to catch up. As a result, wavelength decreases and wave height increases. Eventually the wave breaks, creating turbulent surf in which water rushes toward the shore.

PERSONAL GEOLOGY If you're swimming in the ocean and you see that you're about to be clobbered by a big wave, you may dive underneath it. Use your newfound knowledge of waves to explain why this method enables you to escape the full force of the wave.

3 The Work of Waves

Explain how waves erode and how waves move sediment along the shore.

KEY WORDS abrasion, wave refraction, beach drift, longshore current, rip current

- Wind-generated waves provide most of the energy that modifies shorelines. Each time a wave hits, it can impart tremendous force. The impact of waves, coupled with abrasion from the grinding action of rock particles, erodes material exposed along the shoreline.

- Wave refraction is a consequence of a wave encountering shallower water as it approaches shore. The shallowest part of the wave (closest to shore) slows the most, allowing the faster part (still in deeper water) to catch up. This modifies a wave's trajectory so that the wave front becomes almost parallel to the shore by the time it hits. Wave refraction concentrates impacting energy on headlands and dissipates that energy in bays, which become sites of sediment accumulation.

- Beach drift describes the movement of sediment in a zigzag pattern along a beach face. The swash of incoming waves pushes the sediment up the beach at an oblique angle, but the backwash transports it directly downhill. Net movement along the beach can be many meters per day. Longshore currents are a similar phenomenon in the surf zone, capable of transporting very large quantities of sediment parallel to a shoreline.

DRAW IT Sketch two other shorelines onto the shoreline photo here: one showing roughly what the shoreline would have looked like in the past and a second to show what you predict it will look like in the future.

Michael Collier

4 Shoreline Features

Describe the features typically created by wave erosion and those resulting from sediment deposited by longshore transport processes.

KEY WORDS wave-cut cliff, wave-cut platform, marine terrace, sea arch, sea stack, spit, baymouth bar, tombolo, barrier island

- Erosional features predominate in areas where bedrock is exposed at the shore. Wave-cut cliffs and wave-cut platforms form in the same setting, as waves attack coastal exposures of rock. Marine terraces are wave-cut platforms that have been vertically lifted out of the sea. If wave refraction produces more erosion along the sides of a headland than its "nose," a hole may form through the headland. This is a sea arch. Sea arches are inherently unstable and will eventually crumble. Isolated pillars of rock that remain are sea stacks.

- Depositional features are common in many coastal environments. Spits build out from the land into the open water of a bay. If this process seals off the bay entirely by connecting to the other side, a baymouth bar forms. Tombolos are similar to baymouth bars, but these sedimentary deposits occur in low-energy water between an island and another landmass. Barrier islands are offshore depositional features that parallel the shoreline.

- Over time, irregular, rocky shorelines are modified by erosion and deposition to become smoother and straighter.

THINK ABOUT IT Would you expect to find wave-cut cliffs, sea stacks, sea arches, and marine terraces along the shore of the Gulf of Mexico? Explain.

5 Stabilizing the Shore

Summarize the ways in which people deal with shoreline erosion problems.

KEY WORDS hard stabilization, jetty, groin, breakwater, seawall, beach nourishment

- *Hard stabilization* is the term that refers to any structures built along the coastline to prevent movement of sand. Jetties project out from the coast with the goal of keeping inlets open. Groins are also oriented perpendicular to the coast, but with the goal of slowing beach erosion by longshore currents. Breakwaters are parallel to the coast but located some distance offshore. Their goal is to blunt the force of incoming ocean waves, often to protect boats. Like breakwaters, seawalls are parallel to the coast, but they are built on the shoreline itself. Often the installation of hard stabilization results in increased erosion elsewhere.

- Beach nourishment is an expensive alternative to hard stabilization. Sand is pumped onto a beach from some other area, temporarily replenishing the sediment supply. Another possibility is relocating buildings away from high-risk areas and leaving the beach to be shaped by natural processes.

IDENTIFY IT Based on their position and orientation, identify the four kinds of hard stabilization illustrated in this bird's-eye view of a shoreline.

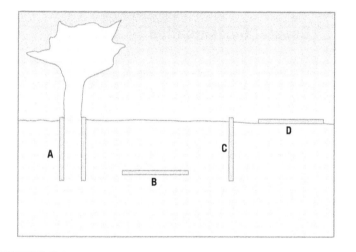

6 Erosion Problems Along U.S. Coasts

Contrast the erosion problems faced on the Atlantic and Gulf coasts with those along the Pacific coast.

- The Atlantic and Gulf coasts of the United States are markedly different from the Pacific coast. The Atlantic and Gulf coasts are lined in many places by barrier islands, which are dynamic expanses of sand that see a lot of change during storm events. Many of these low and narrow islands have also been prime sites for real estate development.

- The Pacific coast's big issue is the thinning of beaches due to sediment starvation. Rivers that drain to the coast (bringing it sand) have been dammed, resulting in reservoirs that trap sand and keep it from reaching the coast. Thinner beaches offer less resistance to incoming waves, often leading to erosion of bluffs behind the beach.

RISKY BUSINESS Your parents suggest that they are thinking of moving to a house on a bluff above a thinning Pacific beach. What advice would you give them?

7   Hurricanes: The Ultimate Coastal Hazard

Describe the basic structure and characteristics of a hurricane and the three broad categories of hurricane destruction.

KEY WORDS eye wall, eye, storm surge

- Cyclones are spiral-shaped storms called *cyclones* in the Indian Ocean, *typhoons* in the Western Pacific, and *hurricanes* in the United States. They are fueled by warm, moist air and usually form in the late summer when sea-surface temperatures are highest. Water vapor in rising warm air condenses, releasing heat and rain. Because of a steep pressure gradient, air rushes into the center of the storm. The Coriolis effect and ocean water temperatures strongly influence where hurricanes form.
- The eye at the center of a hurricane has the lowest pressure, is relatively calm, and lacks rain. The surrounding eye wall has the strongest winds and most intense rainfall. The Saffir–Simpson scale classifies storms based on their air pressure and wind speed.
- Most hurricane damage comes from one or a combination of three causes: storm surge, wind damage, or inland flooding due to heavy rains. Storm surge is ocean water that gets pushed up above the normal water level by the strong winds. In the Northern Hemisphere hurricanes

rotate counterclockwise, and storm surge is greatest on the right side of an advancing hurricane. This is due to the combination of the storm's forward movement and strong winds blowing toward the shore. (On the left side of the storm, wind is blowing out to sea, partly counteracting the force of the storm moving toward land.)

STORMY WEATHER   Examine the accompanying photo, which shows destruction caused by a strong category 4 hurricane. Which one of the three basic classes of damage was most likely responsible for this destruction? What is your reasoning?

Barry Williams/Newscom

8   Coastal Classification

Contrast emergent and submergent coasts.

KEY WORDS emergent coast, submergent coast, estuary

- Coasts may be classified by their changes relative to sea level. Emergent coasts are sites of either land uplift or sea-level fall. Marine terraces are an indication of emergent coasts. Submergent coasts are sites of land

subsidence or sea level rise. One characteristic of submergent coasts is drowned river valleys called estuaries.

INTERPRET IT   Would you expect northern Canada to be an emergent or submergent coast, considering that Ice Age glaciers have recently melted off its land?

9   Tides

Explain the cause of tides, their monthly cycles, and patterns. Describe the horizontal flow of water that accompanies the rise and fall of tides.

KEY WORDS tide, spring tide, neap tide, diurnal tidal pattern, semidiurnal tidal pattern, mixed tidal pattern, tidal current, flood current, ebb current, tidal flat, tidal delta

- Tides are daily changes in ocean-surface elevation. They are caused by gravitational pull on ocean water by the Moon and, to a lesser extent, the Sun. When the Sun, Earth, and Moon all line up about every 2 weeks (full moon or new moon), the tides are most exaggerated. When a quarter Moon is in the sky, it indicates that the Moon is pulling on Earth's water at a right angle relative to the Sun, and the daily tidal range is minimized, as the two forces partially counteract one another.

- Tides are very strongly influenced by local conditions, including the shape of the local coastline and the depth of the ocean basin. Tidal patterns may be diurnal (one high tide per day), semidiurnal (two high tides per day), or mixed (similar to semidiurnal but with significant inequality between high tides).
- A flood current is the landward movement of water during the shift between low tide and high tide. When high tide transitions to low tide again, the movement of water away from the land is an ebb current. Ebb currents may expose tidal flats to the air. If a tide passes through an inlet, the current may carry sediment that gets deposited as a tidal delta.
- The sloshing action of tides acts as a weak brake system, gradually slowing Earth's rotation over geologic time. Fossil organisms with daily growth rings in their shells have recorded the changing speed of the planet's rotation over the past 540 million years.

POSSIBLE PLANET   Would spring tides and neap tides exist on a planet that has no moons? Explain.

GIVE IT SOME THOUGHT

1. During a visit to the beach, you and a friend get in a rubber raft and paddle out into deep water *beyond* the surf zone. Tiring, you stop and take a rest. Describe the movement of the raft during your rest. How does this movement differ, if at all, from what you would have experienced if you had stopped paddling while *in* the surf zone?

2. You and a friend set up an umbrella and chairs at a beach. Your friend then goes into the surf zone to play Frisbee with another person.

Several minutes later, your friend looks back toward the beach and is surprised to see that she is no longer near where the umbrella and chairs were set up. Although she is still in the surf zone, she is 30 yards away from where she started. How would you explain to your friend why she moved along the shore?

3. Assume that it is late September 2016, and Hurricane Gaston, a category 5 storm, is projected to follow the path shown on the

John S. Shelton/University of Washington Libraries

accompanying map. The path of the arrow represents the path of the hurricane's eye. Answer the following questions:

a. Should the city of Houston expect to experience Gaston's fastest winds and greatest storm surge? Explain why or why not.

b. What is the greatest threat to life and property if this storm approaches the Dallas–Fort Worth area? Explain your reasoning.

4. A friend wants to purchase a vacation home on a barrier island. If consulted, what advice would you give your friend?

5. Hurricane Rita was a major storm that struck the Gulf coast in late September 2005, less than a month after Hurricane Katrina. The accompanying graph shows changes in air pressure and wind speed from the storm's beginning as an unnamed tropical disturbance north of the Dominican Republic on September 18 until its last remnants faded away in Illinois on September 26. Use the graph to answer these questions:

a. Which line represents air pressure, and which line represents wind speed? How did you figure this out?

b. What was the storm's maximum wind speed, in knots? Convert this answer to kilometers per hour by multiplying by 1.85.

c. What was the lowest pressure attained by Hurricane Rita?

d. Using wind speed as your guide, what was the highest category reached on the Saffir–Simpson scale? On what day was this status reached?

e. When landfall occurred, what was the category of Hurricane Rita?

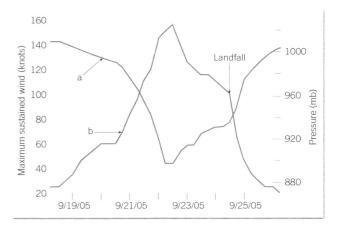

6. The force of gravity plays a critical role in creating ocean tides. The more massive an object, the stronger its pull of gravity. Explain why the Sun's influence is only about half that of the Moon, even though the Sun is much more massive than the Moon.

7. This photo shows a portion of the Maine coast. The brown muddy area in the foreground is influenced by tidal currents. What term is applied to this muddy area? Name the type of tidal current this area will experience in the hours to come.

(Photo by Marli Miller)

Glossary

Abrasion The grinding and scraping of a rock surface by the friction and impact of rock particles carried by water, wind, and ice.

Backshore The inner portion of the shore, lying landward of the high-tide shoreline. It is usually dry, being affected by waves only during storms.

Barrier island A low, elongate ridge of sand that parallels the coast.

Baymouth bar A sandbar that completely crosses a bay, sealing it off from the main body of water.

Beach An accumulation of sediment found along the landward margin of the ocean or a lake.

Beach drift The transport of sediment in a zigzag pattern along a beach, caused by the uprush of water from obliquely breaking waves.

Beach face The wet, sloping surface that extends from the berm to the shoreline.

Beach nourishment A process in which large quantities of sand are added to the beach system to offset losses caused by wave erosion. Building beaches seaward improves beach quality and storm protection.

Berm The dry, gently sloping zone on the backshore of a beach at the foot of coastal cliffs or dunes.

Breakwater A structure that protects a near-shore area from breaking waves.

Coast A strip of land that extends inland from the coastline as far as ocean-related features can be found.

Coastline The coast's seaward edge. The landward limit of the effect of the highest storm waves on the shore.

Ebb current The movement of tidal current away from the shore.

Emergent coast A coast where land formerly below sea level has been exposed by crustal uplift or a drop in sea level or both.

Estuary A funnel-shaped inlet of the sea that formed when a rise in sea level or subsidence of land caused the mouth of a river to be flooded.

Fetch The distance that the wind has traveled across the open water.

Flood current The tidal current associated with the increase in the height of the tide.

Foreshore The portion of the shore that lies between the normal high and low water marks; the intertidal zone.

Groin A short wall built at a right angle to the seashore to trap moving sand.

Jetties A pair of structures extending into the ocean at the entrance to a harbor or river that are built for the purpose of protecting against storm waves and sediment deposition.

Longshore current A near-shore current that flows parallel to the shore.

Neap tide The lowest tidal range, occurring near the times of the first and third quarters of the Moon.

Near-shore The zone of a beach that extends from the low-tide shoreline seaward to where waves break at low tide.

Offshore The relatively flat submerged zone that extends from the breaker line to the edge of the continental shelf.

Rip current A strong, narrow surface or near-surface current of short duration and high speed that moves seaward through the breaker zone at nearly a right angle to the shore.

Sea arch An arch formed by wave erosion when caves on opposite sides of a headland unite.

Sea stack An isolated mass of rock standing just offshore, produced by wave erosion of a headland.

Seawall A barrier constructed to prevent waves from reaching the area behind the wall. Its purpose is to defend property from the force of breaking waves.

Shoreline The line that marks the contact between land and sea. It migrates up and down as the tide rises and falls.

Shore Seaward of the coast, a zone that extends from the highest level of wave action during storms to the lowest tide level.

Spit An elongate ridge of sand that projects from the land into the mouth of an adjacent bay.

Spring tide The highest tidal range. Occurs near the times of the new and full moons.

Storm surge The abnormal rise of the sea along a shore as a result of strong winds.

Submergent coast A coast whose form is largely a result of the partial drowning of a former land surface due to a rise of sea level or subsidence of the crust, or both.

Surf A collective term for breakers; also the wave activity in the area between the shoreline and the outer limit of breakers.

Tidal current The alternating horizontal movement of water associated with the rise and fall of the tide.

Tidal delta A deltalike feature created when a rapidly moving tidal current emerges from a narrow inlet and slows, depositing its load of sediment.

Tidal flat A marshy or muddy area that is alternately covered and uncovered by the rise and fall of the tide.

Tide The periodic change in the elevation of the ocean surface.

Tombolo A ridge of sand that connects an island to the mainland or to another island.

Wave-cut cliff A seaward-facing cliff along a steep shoreline formed by wave erosion at its base and mass wasting.

Wave-cut platform A bench or shelf along a shore at sea level, cut by wave erosion.

Wave height The vertical distance between the trough and crest of a wave.

Wavelength The horizontal distance separating successive crests or troughs.

Wave period The time interval between the passage of successive crests at a stationary point.

Wave refraction A change in direction of waves as they enter shallow water. The portion of the wave in shallow water is slowed, which causes the waves to bend and align with the underwater contours.

Deserts and Winds

From Chapter 19 of *Earth: An Introduction to Physical Geology*, Eleventh Edition. Edward J. Tarbuck, Frederick K. Lutgens, Dennis Tasa.
Copyright © 2014 by Pearson Education, Inc. All rights reserved.

Deserts and Winds

Mount Uluru (formerly Ayers Rock) rises conspicuously above the desert plains of central Australia. (Photo by Oliver Goujon/AGE Fotostock)

Each statement represents the primary learning objective for the corresponding major heading within the chapter. After you complete the chapter you should be able to:

1   Describe the general distribution of Earth's dry lands and explain the causes for the formation of deserts in the subtropics and middle latitudes.

2   Summarize the geologic roles of weathering, running water, and wind in arid and semiarid climates.

3   Discuss the stages of landscape evolution in the Basin and Range region of the western United States.

4   List and describe the ways in which wind transports sediment.

5   Describe the processes and features associated with wind erosion.

6   Discuss the formation and movement of dunes and distinguish among different dune types. Explain how loess deposits differ from deposits of sand.

C limate has a strong influence on the nature and intensity of Earth's external processes. Another excellent example of the strong link between climate and geology is seen when we examine the development of arid landscapes. The word *desert* literally means "deserted" or "unoccupied." For many dry regions this is an appropriate description, although where water is available in deserts, plants and animals thrive. Nevertheless, the world's dry regions are probably the least familiar land areas on Earth outside the polar realm.

As you will see, arid regions are not dominated by a single geologic process. Rather, the effects of tectonic forces, running water, and wind are all apparent. Because these processes combine in different ways from place to place, the appearance of desert landscapes varies a great deal as well.

California's Death Valley is a desert in the rain shadow of the Sierra Nevada, exhibits many classic features associated with a mountainous desert landscape. (Photo by Russ Bishop/Photolibrary)

1 Distribution and Causes of Dry Lands

Desert landscapes frequently appear stark. Their profiles are not softened by a continuous carpet of soil and abundant plant life. Instead, barren rocky outcrops with steep, angular slopes are common. At some places the rocks are tinted orange and red. At others they are gray and brown and streaked with black. For many visitors, desert scenery exhibits a striking beauty; to others, the terrain seems bleak. No matter which feeling is elicited, it is clear that deserts are very different from the more humid places where most people live.

What Is Meant by *Dry*?

We all recognize that deserts are dry places, but just what is meant by the term *dry*? That is, how much rain defines the boundary between humid and dry regions? Sometimes it is arbitrarily defined by a single rainfall figure, such as 25 centimeters (10 inches) per year of precipitation. However, the concept of dryness is a relative one that refers to any situation in which an ongoing water deficiency exists. Hence, climatologists define *dry climate* as one in which yearly precipitation is not as great as the potential loss of water by evaporation.

Dryness, then, not only is related to annual rainfall totals but is also a function of evaporation, which in turn is closely dependent upon temperature. As temperatures climb, potential evaporation also increases. Fifteen to 25 centimeters of precipitation may be sufficient to support coniferous forests in northern Scandinavia or Siberia, where evaporation into the cool, humid air is

slight and a surplus of water remains in the soil. However, the same amount of rain falling on New Mexico or Iran supports only a sparse vegetative cover because evaporation into the hot, dry air is great. So, clearly, no specific amount of precipitation can serve as a universal boundary for dry climates.

The dry regions of the world encompass about 42 million square kilometers (16 million square miles), a surprising 30 percent of Earth's land surface. No other climate category covers so large a land area. Within these water-deficient regions, two climatic types are commonly recognized: **desert**, or arid, and **steppe**, or semiarid. The two share many features; their differences are primarily a matter of degree. The steppe is a marginal and more humid variant of the desert and is a transition zone that surrounds the desert and separates it from bordering humid climates. The world map showing the distribution of desert and steppe regions shows that dry lands are concentrated in the subtropics and in the middle latitudes (FIGURE 1).

Dry climates
Arid and semiarid climates cover about 30 percent of Earth's land surface. The dry region of the American West is commonly divided into four deserts. Two of these extend into Mexico.

FIGURE 2 Subtropical deserts

The distribution of subtropical deserts and steppes is closely related to the global distribution of air pressure.

A. Subtropical deserts and steppes are centered between 20° and 30° north and south latitude in association with the subtropical high-pressure belts. Dry subsiding air inhibits cloud formation and precipitation.

Subpolar low
Polar high
Polar easterlies
60°
Polar front
30°
Subtropical high
Westerlies
NE trade winds
0°
Equatorial low
SE trade winds

B. In this view from space, the Sahara Desert, the adjacent Arabian Desert and the Kalahari and Namib deserts are clearly visible as tan-colored, cloud-free zones. The band of clouds across central Africa and the adjacent oceans coincides with the equatorial low-pressure belt.

to the development of clouds and precipitation. For this reason, the areas under the influence of the equatorial low are among the rainiest on Earth. Just the opposite is true for the regions in the vicinity of 30 degrees north and south latitude, where high pressure predominates. Here, in the zones known as the *subtropical highs*, air is subsiding. When air sinks, it is compressed and warmed. Such conditions are just opposite of what is needed to produce clouds and precipitation. Consequently, these regions are known for their clear skies, sunshine, and ongoing drought (FIGURE 2B).

Subtropical Deserts and Steppes

The heart of the subtropical dry climates lies in the vicinities of the Tropics of Cancer and Capricorn. Figure 1 shows a virtually unbroken desert environment stretching for more than 9300 kilometers (5800 miles) from the Atlantic coast of North Africa to the dry lands of northwestern India. In addition to this single great expanse, the Northern Hemisphere contains another, much smaller area of subtropical desert and steppe in northern Mexico and the southwestern United States.

In the Southern Hemisphere, dry climates dominate Australia. Almost 40 percent of the continent is desert, and much of the remainder is steppe. In addition, arid and semiarid areas occur in southern Africa and make a limited appearance in coastal Chile and Peru.

The Basic Cause What causes these bands of low-latitude desert? The answer is the global distribution of air pressure and winds. FIGURE 2A, an idealized diagram of Earth's general circulation, helps visualize the relationship. Heated air in the pressure belt known as the *equatorial low* rises to great heights (usually between 15 and 20 kilometers) and then spreads out. As the upper-level flow reaches 20 to 30 degrees latitude, north or south, it sinks toward the surface. Air that rises through the atmosphere expands and cools, a process that leads

West Coast Subtropical Deserts Where subtropical deserts are found along the west coasts of continents, cold currents have a dramatic influence on the climate. The principal examples are the Atacama in South America, which is adjacent to the cold Peru Current, and the Namib in southwestern Africa, which parallels the cold Benguela Current (see Figure 1). These deserts deviate considerably from the general image we have of subtropical deserts.

The most obvious effect of the cold current is reduced temperatures. In addition, although these deserts are adjacent to the ocean, their yearly rainfall totals are among the lowest in the world. The aridity of these coastal areas is intensified because the lower air is chilled by the cold offshore waters. When air is cooled from below, it resists the upward movement needed for cloud formation and precipitation. In addition, the cold current often chills the air enough to cause fog to form. Thus, not all subtropical deserts are sunny and hot. Cold offshore currents cause west coast subtropical deserts to be relatively cool places that sometimes are foggy.

The Atacama Desert along the west coast of South America has the distinction of being the world's driest desert. The average rainfall at the Atacama's wettest locations is not more than 3 millimeters (0.12 inch) per year. At Arica, a coastal town near Chile's border with Peru, the average annual rainfall is a mere 0.5 millimeter (0.02 inch). Further inland, some stations have *never* recorded rainfall.

Middle-Latitude Deserts and Steppes

Unlike their low-latitude counterparts, middle-latitude deserts and steppes are not controlled by the subsiding air masses associated with high pressure. Instead, many of these dry lands exist because they are sheltered in the deep interiors of large land-masses. They are far removed from the ocean, which is the ultimate source of moisture for cloud formation and precipitation. One well-known example is the Gobi Desert of central Asia, shown in Figure 1 north of India.

The presence of high mountains across the paths of prevailing winds is another factor that separates middle-latitude arid and semiarid areas from water-bearing, maritime air masses. In addition, mountains force the air to lose much of its water. The mechanism is straightforward: As prevailing winds meet mountain barriers, the air is forced to ascend. When air rises, it expands and cools, a process that can produce clouds and precipitation. The windward sides of mountains, therefore, often have high precipitation. By contrast, the leeward sides of mountains are usually much drier (FIGURE 3). This situation exists because air reaching the leeward side has lost much of its moisture, and if the air descends, it is compressed and warmed, making cloud formation even less likely. The dry region that results is often referred to as a **rainshadow**. FIGURE 4, which shows the distribution of precipitation in western Washington State, is a good example. When prevailing winds from the Pacific Ocean to the west (left) meet the mountains, rainfall totals are high. By comparison, precipitation on the leeward (eastern) side of the mountains is relatively meager. In North America, the foremost mountain barriers to moisture from the Pacific are the Coast Ranges, Sierra Nevada, and Cascades. In Asia, the great Himalayan chain prevents the summertime monsoon flow of moist Indian Ocean air from reaching the interior of the continent.

Because the Southern Hemisphere lacks extensive land areas in the middle latitudes, only small areas of desert and steppe occur in this latitude range, existing primarily near the southern tip of South America in the rainshadow of the towering Andes.

The middle-latitude deserts provide an example of how tectonic processes affect climate. Rainshadow deserts exist by virtue of the mountains produced when plates collide. Without such mountain-building episodes, wetter climates would prevail where many dry regions exist today.

When moving air meets a mountain barrier, it is forced to rise. Clouds and precipitation on the windward side often result.

Air descending the leeward side is much drier.

Coast Range

Sierra Nevada Range

Rain shadow

Windward (wet)

Leeward (dry)

Great Basin

Wind

FIGURE 3 Rainshadow deserts
Mountains frequently contribute to the aridity of middle-latitude deserts and steppes by creating a rainshadow. The Great Basin Desert is a rainshadow desert that covers nearly all of Nevada and portions of adjacent states. (Photo on left by Dean Pennala/Shutterstock; photo on right by Dennis Tasa)

1 CONCEPT CHECKS

1. Explain why the boundary between humid and dry climates cannot be defined by a single rainfall amount.
2. How extensive are the desert and steppe regions of Earth?
3. What is the primary cause of subtropical deserts and steppes?
4. How do cold ocean currents influence some subtropical deserts?
5. Why do middle-latitude dry regions exist? What role do mountains play?
6. In which hemisphere (Northern or Southern) are middle-latitude deserts most common? Explain.

ANNUAL PRECIPITATION

cm		in.
>500		>200
405–499		160–199
250–404		100–159
150–249		60–99
50–149		20–59
25–49		10–19
<25		<10

250   150   50

250

50

Olympic Mountains 50   405

500

150

405

25

Cascade Mountains

250

150

50

150

250

150

150

250

50

150

250 150

150

250

50

50

150

25

50

150

50

FIGURE 4 Distribution of precipitation in western Washington State
The Olympic and Cascade Mountains receive abundant rainfall. The semiarid eastern portion of the area shown here is in a rainshadow.

2 Geologic Processes in Arid Climates

The angular hills, the sheer canyon walls, and the desert surface of pebbles or sand contrast sharply with the rounded hills and curving slopes of more humid places. To a visitor from a humid region, a desert landscape may seem to have been shaped by forces different from those operating in well-watered areas. However, although the contrasts may be striking, they do not reflect different processes. They merely disclose the differing effects of the same processes that operate under contrasting climatic conditions.

Weathering

In humid regions, relatively fine-textured soils support an almost continuous cover of vegetation that mantles the surface. The slopes and rock edges are rounded, reflecting the strong influence of chemical weathering in a humid climate. By contrast, much of the weathered debris in deserts consists of unaltered rock and mineral fragments—the result of mechanical weathering processes. In dry lands, rock weathering of any type is greatly reduced because of the lack of moisture and the scarcity of organic acids from decaying plants. However, chemical weathering is not completely lacking in deserts. Over long spans of time, clays and thin soils do form, and many iron-bearing silicate minerals oxidize, producing the rust-colored stain that tints some desert landscapes.

The Role of Water

Deserts have scant precipitation and few major rivers. Nevertheless, water plays an important role in shaping landscapes in dry regions. Permanent streams are normal in humid regions, but practically all desert streambeds are dry most of the time. Deserts have

ephemeral streams (*ephemero* = short-lived), which means they carry water only in response to specific episodes of rainfall (FIGURE 5). A typical ephemeral stream might flow only a few days or perhaps just a few hours during the year. In some years the channel might carry no water at all.

This fact is obvious even to the casual traveler who notices numerous bridges with no streams beneath them or numerous dips in the road where dry channels cross. However, when the rare heavy showers do come, so much rain falls in such a short time that all of it cannot soak in (FIGURE 6). Because desert vegetative cover is sparse, runoff is largely unhindered and consequently rapid, often creating flash floods along valley floors. These floods are quite unlike floods in humid regions. A flood on a river like the Mississippi may take several days to reach its crest and then subside. But desert floods arrive suddenly and subside quickly. Because much surface material in a desert is not anchored by vegetation, the amount of erosional work that occurs during a single short-lived rain event is impressive.

In the dry western United States, different names are used for ephemeral streams, including *wash* and *arroyo*. In other parts of the world, a dry desert stream may be

FIGURE 5 Ephemeral stream
This example is near Arches National Park in southern Utah. (Photos by E. J. Tarbuck)

An ephemeral stream shortly after a heavy shower. Although such floods are short-lived, they cause large amounts of erosion.

Most of the time desert stream channels are dry.

A familiar sign in desert areas. Roads dip into washes which can rapidly fill with water following a heavy rain.

POTENTIAL FLASH FLOOD AREAS

NEXT 21 MILES

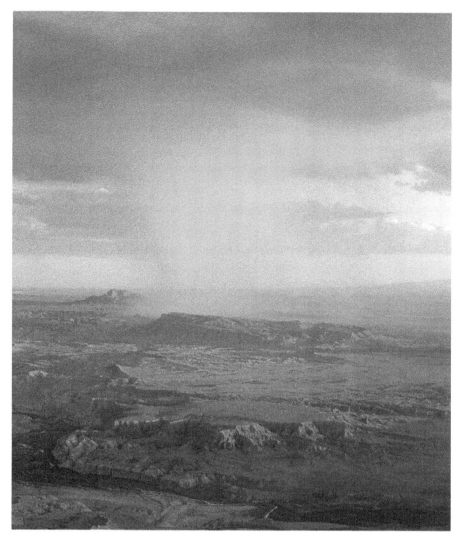

FIGURE 6 Desert storm
When rains occur, they are often heavy and of relatively short duration. Because rainfall intensity is high, not all of the water can soak in, and rapid runoff and erosion result. (Photo by Michael Collier)

a *wadi* (Arabia and North Africa), a *donga* (South America), or a *nullah* (India). The satellite images in FIGURE 7 show a wadi in the Sahara Desert.

Humid regions are notable for their integrated drainage systems. But in arid regions, streams usually lack an extensive system of tributaries. In fact, a basic characteristic of desert streams is that they are small and die out before reaching the sea. Because the water table is usually far below the surface, few desert streams can draw upon it as streams do in humid regions. Without a steady supply of water, the combination of evaporation and infiltration soon depletes the stream.

The few permanent streams that do cross arid regions, such as the Colorado and Nile Rivers, originate *outside* the desert, often in well-watered mountains. Here the water supply must be great to compensate for the losses occurring as the stream crosses the desert. For example, after the Nile leaves its headwaters in the lakes and mountains of central Africa, it traverses almost 3000 kilometers (2000 miles)

The wadi in its usual dry state.

Following a rainy period, freshly sprouted vegetation turns the wadi green.

FIGURE 7 Wadi in North Africa
These two satellite images show how rain transformed a wadi in Niger. (NASA)

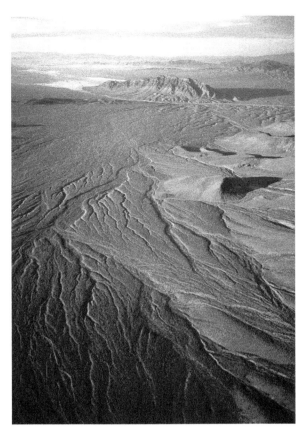

Desert rains are infrequent, but when they occur, erosion can be significant. The dry channels of ephemeral streams are conspicuous in this aerial view of a parched desert surface. (Photo by Michael Collier)

of the Sahara without a single tributary. By contrast, in humid regions the discharge of a river grows as it flows downstream because tributaries and groundwater contribute additional water along the way.

It should be emphasized that *running water, although infrequent, nevertheless does most of the erosional work in deserts* (FIGURE 8). This is contrary to the common belief that wind is the most important erosional agent sculpturing desert landscapes. Although wind erosion is indeed more significant in dry areas than elsewhere, most desert landforms are carved by running water. As you will see shortly, the main role of wind is in the transportation and deposition of sediment, which creates and shapes the ridges and mounds we call dunes.

2 CONCEPT CHECKS

1. How does the rate of rock weathering in dry climates compare to the rate in humid regions?
2. What is an ephemeral stream?
3. When a permanent stream such as the Nile River crosses a desert, does the river's discharge increase or decrease? How does this compare to a river in a humid area?
4. What is the most important erosional agent in deserts?

EYE on Earth

This classic view of Earth from space was taken in December 1968 by an *Apollo 8* astronaut. The image shows the Western Hemisphere. Dense clouds cover much of North America. A large portion of South America is also cloud covered. However, the western margin of South America is cloud free.

Question 1 What is the name of the desert that occupies the cloudless area along the western margin of South America?

Question 2 An ocean current flows just offshore of this desert area. Is it warm or cold? Toward what direction must

the current flow—toward or away from the equator?

Question 3 How does this desert's close proximity to the Pacific Ocean influence its aridity?

Question 4 In what ways is this desert different from subtropical deserts such as the Sahara and Arabian? Name a desert that has characteristics that are similar to this one.

NASA

3 Basin and Range: The Evolution of a Desert Landscape

Arid regions typically lack permanent streams and often have **interior drainage**. This means that they exhibit a discontinuous pattern of intermittent streams that do not flow out of the desert to the ocean. In the United States, the dry Basin and Range region provides an excellent example. The region includes southern Oregon, all of Nevada, western Utah, southeastern California, southern Arizona, and southern New Mexico. The name *Basin and Range* is an apt description for this almost 800,000-square-kilometer (300,000 square-mile) region because it is characterized by more than 200 relatively small mountain ranges that rise 900 to 1500 meters (3000 to 5000 feet) above the basins that separate them. In this discussion we look at how surface processes change the landscape.

In this region, as in others like it around the world, erosion mostly occurs without reference to the ocean (ultimate base level) because the interior drainage never reaches the sea. Even where permanent streams flow to the ocean, few tributaries exist, and thus only a narrow strip of land adjacent to the stream has sea level as its ultimate level of land reduction.

The block models in FIGURE 9 depict how the landscape has evolved in the Basin and Range region. During and following the uplift of the mountains, running water begins carving the elevated mass and depositing large quantities of debris in the basin. During this early stage,

relief is greatest because as erosion lowers the mountains and sediment fills the basins, elevation differences gradually diminish.

When the occasional torrents of water produced by sporadic rains move down the mountain canyons, they are heavily loaded with sediment. Emerging from the confines of the canyon, the runoff spreads over the gentler slopes at the base of the mountains and quickly loses velocity. Consequently, most of its load is dumped within a short distance. The result is a cone of debris at the mouth of a canyon known as an **alluvial fan**. Because the coarsest material is dropped first, the head of the fan

 SMARTFIGURE 9
Landscape evolution in the Basin and Range
As erosion of the mountains and deposition in the basins continue, relief diminishes.

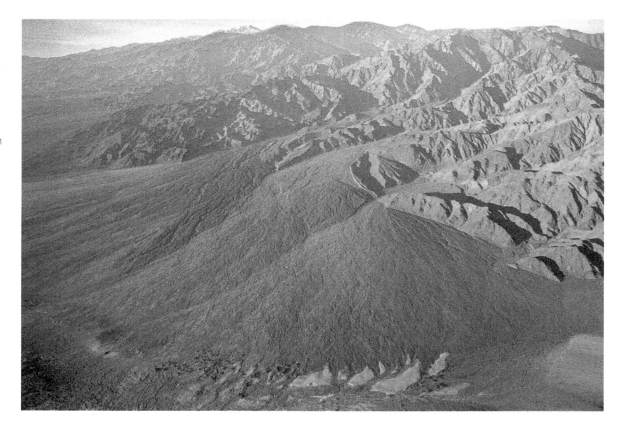

FIGURE 10 Bajada
As neighboring canyons keep depositing sediment, their alluvial fans grow and coalesce to form a bajada—a continuous apron across the base of the mountain. (Photo by Michael Collier)

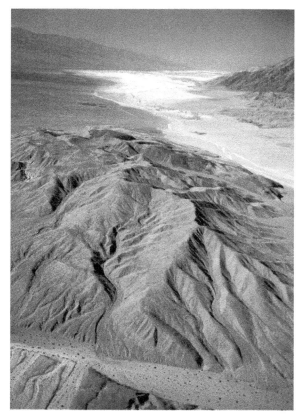

FIGURE 11 Playa in Death Valley
These dry, flat lake beds on the floor of the basin are typically composed of silt and clay. Sometimes, as in this example, they are encrusted with salt. (Photo by Michael Collier)

is steepest, having a slope of perhaps 10 to 15 degrees. Moving down the fan, the size of the sediment and the steepness of the slope decrease, and the fan merges imperceptibly with the basin floor. An examination of the fan's surface would likely reveal a braided channel pattern because of the water shifting its course as successive channels became choked with sediment. Over the years a fan enlarges, eventually coalescing with fans from adjacent canyons to produce an apron of sediment called a **bajada** along the mountain front (FIGURE 10).

On the rare occasions of abundant rainfall, streams may flow across the bajada to the center of the basin, converting the basin floor into a shallow **playa lake**. Playa lakes are temporary features that last only a few days or at best a few weeks before evaporation and infiltration remove the water. The dry, flat lake bed that remains is called a **playa**. Playas are typically composed of fine silts and clays and are occasionally encrusted with salts precipitated during evaporation (FIGURE 11). These precipitated salts may be unusual. A case in point is the sodium borate (better known as borax) mined from ancient playa lake deposits in Death Valley, California.

With the ongoing erosion of the mountain mass and the accompanying sedimentation, the local relief continues to diminish. Eventually, nearly the entire mountain mass is gone. Thus, by the late stages of erosion, the mountain areas are reduced to a few large bedrock knobs projecting above the surrounding sediment-filled basin. These isolated erosional remnants on a late-stage desert landscape are called **inselbergs**, a German word meaning "island mountains."

Each of the stages of landscape evolution in an arid climate depicted in Figure 9 can be observed in the Basin and Range region. Recently uplifted mountains in an early stage of erosion are found in southern Oregon and northern Nevada. Death Valley, California, and southern Nevada fit into the more advanced middle stage, whereas the late stage, with its inselbergs, can be seen in southern Arizona.

FIGURE 12 is a satellite image of a portion of Death Valley. Many of the features that were just described are visible. This February 2005 image shows the area shortly after a rare heavy rain. As has occurred many times over thousands of years, a wide, shallow playa lake formed in the lowest spot. By May 2005, only three months after the storm, the valley floor had returned to being a dry, salt-encrusted playa.

3 CONCEPT CHECKS

1. What is meant by *interior drainage*?
2. Describe the features and characteristics associated with each stage in the evolution of a mountainous desert.
3. Where in the United States can each stage of desert landscape evolution be observed?

FIGURE 12 Satellite image of Death Valley
Shortly before this image was taken in February 2005, heavy rains led to the formation of a small playa lake—the pool of greenish water on the basin floor. By May 2005, the lake had reverted to a salt-covered playa. (NASA)

A close-up view of a salt flat in Death Valley. The layer of salt is an evaporite deposit. (Photo by Michael Collier)

Common Misconceptions About Deserts

Deserts are hot, lifeless, sand-covered landscapes shaped largely by the forces of wind. The preceding statement summarizes the image of arid regions that many people hold, especially those living in more humid places. Is it an accurate view? The answer is no. Although there are clearly elements of reality in such an impression, it is a generalization that contains several misconceptions.

George Mongol/Alamy

In addition to record-setting heat, cold temperatures are also experienced in deserts. At Ulan Bator in Mongolia's Gobi Desert, the average high temperature in January is only -19°C (-2° F)! The average daily minimum in January at Phoenix, Arizona, is 17° C (35° F), just barely above freezing.

Jo Ann Snover/Shutterstock

Rick and Nora Bowers/Alamy

Rick and Nora Bowers/Alamy

Jack Goldfarb/AGE Fotostock

Although reduced in amount and different in character, both plant and animal life are usually present. All forms of desert life have developed adaptations that make them highly tolerant of drought. Plants are widely dispersed and provide little ground cover, but many kinds flourish in the desert.

Another mistaken assumption is the seemingly logical idea that wind is the most important agent of erosion in deserts. However, the greatest erosional work in deserts is done by running water. The infrequent rains often take the form of thunderstorms. Because the heavy rains cannot all soak in, rapid runoff results. Without a thick vegetative cover to protect the ground, erosion is great.

A mistaken assumption is that deserts consist of mile after mile of drifting sand such as these giant dunes along the southwest coast of Africa in the Namib Desert. These huge dunes reach heights of 300 to 350 meters (1000 to 1167 feet). Although sand accumulations may be striking features in some areas, they represent only a small percentage of the total desert area. For example, in the Sahara accumulations of sand cover only one-tenth of its area. The sandiest of all deserts is the Arabian, one-third of which is sand covered.

4 Transportation of Sediment by Wind

Moving air, like moving water, is turbulent and able to pick up loose debris and transport it to other locations. Just as in a stream, the velocity of wind increases with height above the surface. Also as with a stream, wind transports fine particles in suspension, while heavier ones are carried as bed load. However, the transport of sediment by wind differs from that of running water in two significant ways. First, wind's lower density compared to water renders it less capable of picking up and transporting coarse materials. Second, because wind is not confined to channels, it can spread sediment over large areas, as well as high into the atmosphere.

FIGURE 13 Transporting sand
The bed load that wind carries consists of sand grains that move by bouncing along the surface. Sand never travels far from the surface, even when winds are very strong. (Photo by Bernd Zoller/ Photolibrary)

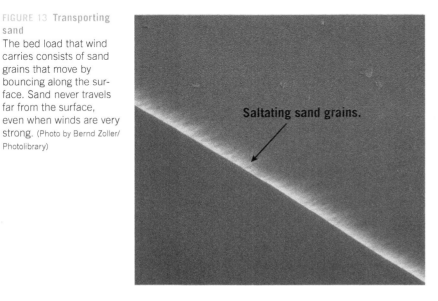

Saltating sand grains.

Bed Load

The **bed load** that wind carries consists of sand grains. Observations in the field and experiments using wind tunnels indicate that windblown sand moves mainly by skipping and bouncing along the surface—a process termed **saltation**. The term is not a reference to salt but instead derives from the Latin word meaning "to jump."

The movement of sand grains begins when wind reaches a velocity sufficient to overcome the inertia of the resting particles. At first the sand rolls along the surface. When a moving sand grain strikes another grain, one or both of them may jump into the air. Once in the air, the grains are carried forward by the wind until gravity pulls them back toward the surface. When the sand hits the surface, it either bounces back into the air or dislodges other grains, which then jump upward. In this manner, a chain reaction is established, filling the air near the ground with saltating sand grains in a short period of time (FIGURE 13).

EYE on Earth

This satellite image shows a small portion of the Zagros Mountains in dry southern Iran. Streams in this region flow only occasionally. The green tones on the image identify productive agricultural areas.

Question 1 Identify the large feature that is labeled with a question mark.

Question 2 Explain how the feature named in Question 1 formed.

Question 3 What term is used to describe streams like the ones that occur in this region?

Question 4 Speculate on the likely source of water for the agricultural areas in this image.

Basin at foot of mountains

?

Zagros Mountains

Dry river bed

N 2.5 km

NASA

Bouncing sand grains never travel far from the surface. Even when winds are very strong, the height of the saltating sand seldom exceeds 1 meter and usually is no greater than 0.5 meter. Some sand grains are too large to be thrown into the air by impact from other particles. When this is the case, the energy provided by the impact of the smaller saltating grains drives the larger grains forward. Estimates indicate that between 20 and 25 percent of the sand transported in a sandstorm is moved in this way.

Suspended Load

Unlike sand, finer particles of dust can be swept high into the atmosphere by the wind. Because dust is often composed of rather flat particles that have large surface areas compared to their weight, it is relatively easy for turbulent air to counterbalance the pull of gravity and keep these fine particles airborne for hours or even days. Although both silt and clay can be carried in suspension, silt commonly makes up the bulk of the **suspended load** because the reduced level of chemical weathering in deserts provides only small amounts of clay.

Fine particles are easily carried by the wind, but they are not so easily picked up to begin with. The reason is that the wind velocity is practically zero within a very thin layer close to the ground. Thus, the wind cannot lift the sediment by itself. Instead, the dust must be ejected or spattered into the moving air by bouncing sand grains or other disturbances. This idea is illustrated nicely by a dry, unpaved country road on a windy day. When the road is undisturbed, the wind raises little dust. However, as a car or truck moves over the road, the layer of silt is kicked up, creating a thick cloud of dust.

Although the suspended load is usually deposited relatively near its source, high winds are capable of carrying large quantities of dust great distances (FIGURE 14).

A dust storm blackens the Colorado sky in this historic image from the Dust Bowl of the 1930's.

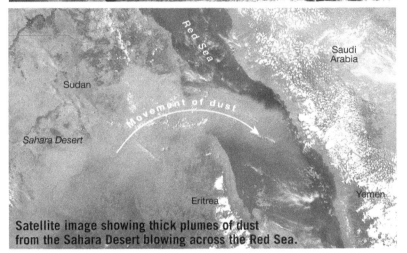

Satellite image showing thick plumes of dust from the Sahara Desert blowing across the Red Sea.

FIGURE 14 Wind's suspended load Two dramatic examples of suspended load. Dust storms can cover huge areas, and dust can be transported great distances. (Black-and-white image courtesy of U.S.D.A./Natural Resources Conservation Service; satellite image courtesy of NASA)

In the 1930s, silt that was picked up in Kansas was transported to New England and beyond, into the North Atlantic. Similarly, dust blown from the Sahara has been traced as far as the Caribbean.

4 CONCEPT CHECKS

1. Describe the way in which wind transports sand. When winds are strong, how high above the surface can sand be carried?
2. How does wind's suspended load differ from its bed load?

5 Wind Erosion

Compared to running water and glaciers, wind is a relatively insignificant erosional agent. Recall that even in deserts, most erosion is performed by intermittent running water, not by wind. Wind erosion is more effective in arid lands than in humid areas because in humid places moisture binds particles together, and vegetation anchors the soil. For wind to be an effective erosional force, dryness and scant vegetation are important prerequisites. When such circumstances exist, wind may pick up, transport, and deposit great quantities of fine sediment. During the 1930s, parts of the Great Plains experienced vast dust storms. The plowing under of the natural vegetative cover for farming, followed by severe drought, exposed the land to wind erosion and led to the area's being labeled the Dust Bowl.

Deflation and Blowouts

One way that wind erodes is by **deflation** (*de* = out, *flat* = blow), the lifting and removal of loose material. Deflation sometimes is difficult to notice because the entire surface is being lowered at the same time, but it can be significant. In portions of the 1930s Dust Bowl, vast areas of land were lowered by as much as 1 meter in only a few years.

The most noticeable results of deflation in some places are shallow depressions appropriately called **blowouts** (FIGURE 15). In the Great Plains region, from Texas north to Montana, thousands of blowouts are visible on the landscape. They range from small dimples less than 1 meter deep and 3 meters wide to depressions that approach 50 meters deep and several kilometers across. The factor that controls the depths of these basins (that is, acts as base level) is the local water table. When blowouts are lowered to the water table, damp ground and vegetation prevent further deflation.

Desert Pavement

In portions of many deserts, the surface consists of a closely packed layer of coarse particles. This veneer of pebbles and cobbles, called **desert pavement**, is only one or two stones thick (FIGURE 16). Beneath is a layer containing a significant proportion of silt and sand. When desert pavement is present, it is an important control on wind erosion because pavement stones are too large for deflation to remove. When this armor is disturbed, wind can easily erode the exposed fine silt.

For many years, the most common explanation for the formation of desert pavement was that it develops when wind removes sand and silt from poorly sorted surface deposits. As FIGURE 17A illustrates, the concentration of larger particles at the surface gradually increases as the finer particles are blown away. Eventually the surface is completely covered with pebbles and cobbles too large to be moved by the wind.

FIGURE 15 **Blowouts** Deflation is especially effective in creating these depressions when the land is dry and largely unprotected by anchoring vegetation. (Photo courtesy of U.S.D.A./ Natural Resources Conservation Service)

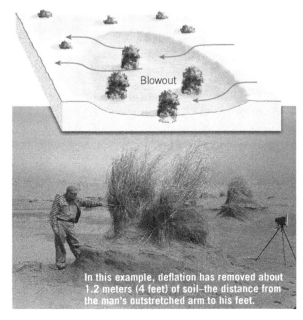

In this example, deflation has removed about 1.2 meters (4 feet) of soil—the distance from the man's outstretched arm to his feet.

Lens cap for scale.

FIGURE 16 **Desert pavement** This closely packed veneer of pebbles and cobbles is only one or two stones thick. It is underlain by material containing a significant proportion of finer particles. (Photo by Bobbé Christopherson)

Studies have shown that the process depicted in Figure 17A is not an adequate explanation for all environments in which desert pavement exists. For example, in many places, desert pavement is underlain by a relatively thick layer of silt that contains few if any pebbles and cobbles. In such a setting, deflation of fine sediment could not leave behind a layer of coarse particles. Studies have also shown that in some areas, the pebbles and cobbles composing desert pavement have all been exposed at the surface for about the same length of time. This would not be the case for the process shown in Figure 17A. Here, the coarse particles that make up the pavement reach the surface over an extended time span, as deflation gradually removes the fine material.

As a result, an alternate explanation for desert pavement was formulated (FIGURE 17B). This hypothesis suggests that pavement develops on a surface that initially consists of coarse particles. Over time, protruding cobbles trap fine, windblown grains that settle and sift downward through the spaces between the larger surface stones. The process is aided by infiltrating rainwater. In this model, the cobbles composing the pavement were never buried. Moreover, it successfully explains the lack of coarse particles beneath the desert pavement.

Ventifacts and Yardangs

Like glaciers and streams, wind also erodes by **abrasion** (*ab* = away, *radere* = to scrape). In dry regions as well as

SMARTFIGURE 17
Formation of desert pavement
A. This model shows an area with poorly sorted surface deposits. Over time, deflation lowers the surface, and coarse particles become concentrated. **B.** In this model, the surface is initially covered with cobles and pebbles. Over time, windblown dust accumulates at the surface and gradually sifts downward.

along some beaches, windblown sand cuts and polishes exposed rock surfaces. Abrasion sometimes creates interestingly shaped stones called **ventifacts** (FIGURE 18A). The side of such a stone that is exposed to the prevailing wind is abraded, leaving it polished, pitted, and with sharp edges. If the wind is not consistently from one direction, or if the pebble becomes reoriented, it may have several faceted surfaces.

Unfortunately, abrasion is often given credit for accomplishments beyond its capabilities. Such features as balanced rocks that stand high atop narrow pedestals and intricate detailing on tall pinnacles are not the results of abrasion. Sand seldom travels more than 1 meter above the surface, so the wind's sandblasting effect is obviously limited in vertical extent.

In addition to creating ventifacts, wind erosion is responsible for creating much larger features, called yardangs (from the Turkistani word *yar*, meaning "steep bank"). A

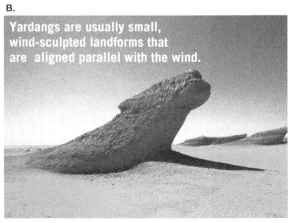

A. Ventifacts are stones that are shaped and polished by sandblasting

B. Yardangs are usually small, wind-sculpted landforms that are aligned parallel with the wind.

FIGURE 18 **Shaped by the wind**
The sandblasting effect of the wind creates ventifacts (**A**) and yardangs (**B**). (Photo A by Richard M. Busch; photo B by Mike P. Shepherd/Alamy Images)

yardang is a streamlined, wind-sculpted landform that is oriented parallel to the prevailing wind (FIGURE 18B). Individual yardangs are generally small features that stand less than 5 meters (16 feet) high and no more than about 10 meters (32 feet) long. Because the sand-blasting effect of wind is greatest near the ground, these abraded bedrock remnants are usually narrower at their base. Sometimes yardangs are large features. Peru's Ica Valley contains yardangs that approach 100 meters (330 feet) in height and several kilometers in length. Some in the desert of Iran reach 150 meters (nearly 500 feet) in height.

5 CONCEPT CHECKS

1. Why is wind erosion relatively more important in dry regions than in humid areas?
2. What factor limits the depths of blowouts?
3. Briefly describe two hypotheses used to explain the formation of desert pavement.
4. What are yardangs and ventifacts?

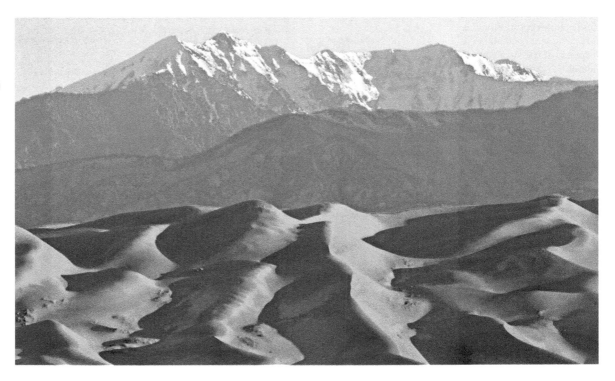

Great Sand Dunes National Park in southern Colorado with the Sangre de Cristo Mountains in the background. These are the tallest dunes in North America with some rising more than 210 meters (700 feet) above the surrounding terrain. (Photo by SuperStock)

6 Wind Deposits

Although wind is relatively unimportant in producing *erosional* landforms, significant *depositional* landforms are created by the wind in some regions. Accumulations of windblown sediment are particularly conspicuous in the world's dry lands and along many sandy coasts. Wind deposits are of two distinctive types: (1) mounds and ridges of sand from the wind's bed load, which we call dunes, and (2) extensive blankets of silt, called loess, that once were carried in suspension.

Sand Deposits

As is the case with running water, wind drops its load of sediment when velocity falls and the energy available for transport diminishes. Thus, sand begins to accumulate wherever an obstruction across the path of the wind slows its movement. Unlike many deposits of silt, which form blanketlike layers over large areas, winds commonly deposit sand in mounds or ridges called **dunes** (FIGURE 19).

As moving air encounters an object, such as a clump of vegetation or a rock, the wind sweeps around and over it, leaving a shadow of slower-moving air behind the obstacle, as well as a smaller zone of quieter air just in front of the obstacle. Some of the saltating sand grains moving with the wind come to rest in these wind shadows. As the accumulation of sand continues, it becomes a more imposing barrier to the wind and thus a more efficient trap for even more sand. If there is a sufficient supply of sand and the wind blows steadily for a long enough time, the mound of sand grows into a dune.

Many dunes have an asymmetrical profile, with the leeward (sheltered) slope being steep and the windward slope more gently inclined. The dunes in Figure 19 are a good example. Sand moves up the gentler slope on the windward side by saltation. Just beyond the crest of the dune, where the wind velocity is reduced, the sand accumulates. As more sand collects, the slope steepens, and eventually some of it slides under the pull of gravity. In this way, the leeward slope of the dune, called the **slip face**, maintains an angle of about 34 degrees, the angle of repose for loose dry sand. (The angle of repose is the steepest angle at which loose material remains stable.) Continued sand accumulation, coupled with periodic slides down the slip face, results in the slow migration of the dune in the direction of air movement.

As sand is deposited on the slip face, layers form that are inclined in the direction the wind is blowing.

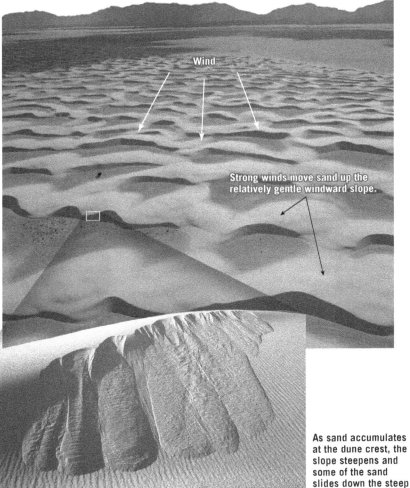

Wind

Strong winds move sand up the relatively gentle windward slope.

As sand accumulates at the dune crest, the slope steepens and some of the sand slides down the steep *slip face*.

FIGURE 19 White Sands National Monument
The dunes at this landmark in southeastern New Mexico are composed of gypsum. The dunes slowly migrate with the wind.
(Photos by Michael Collier)

Dunes commonly have an asymmetrical shape and migrate with the wind.

Sand grains deposited on the slip face at the angle of repose create the cross-bedding of dunes.

When dunes are buried and become part of the sedimentary rock record, the cross bedding is preserved.

SMARTFIGURE 20
Cross-bedding
As sand is deposited on the slip face, layers form that are inclined in the direction the wind is blowing. With time, complex patterns develop in response to changes in wind direction.
(Photo by Dennis Tasa)

Cross beds are an obvious characteristic of the Navajo Sandstone in Zion National Park, Utah.

These sloping layers are called **cross-beds** (FIGURE 20). When the dunes are eventually buried under other layers of sediment and become part of the sedimentary rock record, their asymmetrical shape is destroyed, but the cross-beds remain as testimony to their origin. Nowhere is cross-bedding more prominent than in the sandstone walls of Zion Canyon in southern Utah (Figure 20).

For some areas, moving sand is troublesome. In FIGURE 21, dunes are advancing across irrigated fields in Egypt. In portions of the Middle East, valuable oil rigs must be protected from encroaching dunes. In some cases, fences are built sufficiently upwind of the dunes to stop their migration. As sand continues to collect, however, the fences must be built higher. In Kuwait protective fences extend for almost 10 kilometers (6 miles) around one important oil field. Migrating dunes can also pose a problem to the construction and maintenance of highways and railroads that cross sandy desert regions. For example, to keep a portion of Highway 95 near Winnemucca, Nevada, open to traffic, sand must be taken away about three times a year. Each time, between 1500 and 4000 cubic meters of sand are removed. Attempts at stabilizing the dunes by planting different varieties of grasses have been unsuccessful because the meager rainfall cannot support the plants.

Types of Sand Dunes

Dunes are not just random heaps of windblown sediment. Rather, they are accumulations that usually assume patterns that are surprisingly consistent. Addressing this point, a leading early investigator of dunes, the British engineer R. A. Bagnold, observed: "Instead of finding chaos and disorder, the observer never fails to be amazed at a simplicity of form, an exactitude of repetition, and a geometric order." A broad assortment of dune forms exists, generally simplified to a few major types for discussion.

Of course, gradations exist among different forms, as well as irregularly shaped dunes that do not fit easily into any category. Several factors influence the form

FIGURE 21 **Migrating dunes** These desert dunes in Egypt are encroaching on irrigated farm fields. (Photo by George Gerster/Photo Researchers, Inc.)

Factors that influence the form and size of dunes include wind direction and velocity, the availability of sand, and the amount of vegetation.

and size that dunes ultimately assume. These include wind direction and velocity, availability of sand, and the amount of vegetation present. Six basic dune types are shown in FIGURE 22, with arrows indicating wind directions.

Barchan Dunes Solitary sand dunes shaped like crescents and with their tips pointing downwind are called **barchan dunes** (Figure 22A). These dunes form where supplies of sand are limited and the surface is relatively flat, hard, and lacking vegetation. They migrate slowly with the wind at a rate of up to 15 meters (50 feet) per year. Their size is usually modest, with the largest barchans reaching heights of about 30 meters (100 feet), while the maximum spread between their horns approaches 300 meters (1000 feet). When the wind direction is nearly constant, the crescent form of these dunes is nearly symmetrical. However, when the wind direction is not perfectly fixed, one tip becomes larger than the other.

Transverse Dunes In regions where the prevailing winds are steady, sand is plentiful, and vegetation is sparse or absent, the dunes form a series of long ridges that are separated by troughs and oriented at right angles to the prevailing wind. Because of this orientation, they are termed **transverse dunes** (Figure 22B). Many coastal dunes are of this type. In addition, transverse dunes are common in many arid regions where the extensive surface of wavy sand is sometimes called a *sand*

sea. In some parts of the Sahara and Arabian Deserts, transverse dunes reach heights of 200 meters, are 1 to 3 kilometers across, and can extend for distances of 100 kilometers or more.

There is a relatively common dune form that is intermediate between isolated barchans and extensive waves of transverse dunes. Such dunes called **barchanoid dunes** form scalloped rows of sand oriented at right angles to the wind (Figure 19C). The rows resemble a series of barchans that have been positioned side by side.

Longitudinal Dunes Long ridges of sand that form more or less parallel to the prevailing wind where sand supplies are moderate are called **longitudinal dunes** (Figure 22D). Apparently the prevailing wind direction must vary somewhat but still remain in the same quadrant of the compass. Although the smaller types are only 3 or 4 meters high and several dozens of meters long, in some large deserts, longitudinal dunes can reach great size. For example, in portions of North Africa, Arabia, and central Australia, these dunes may approach a height of 100 meters (300 feet) and extend for distances of more than 100 kilometers (62 miles).

Parabolic Dunes Unlike the other dunes that have been described thus far, **parabolic dunes** form where vegetation partially covers the sand. The shape of these dunes resembles the shape of barchans except that their tips point into the wind rather than downwind (Figure 22E). Parabolic dunes often form along coasts where

EYE on Earth

This satellite image shows a large plume of windblown sediment covering large portions of Iran, Afghanistan, and Pakistan in March 2012. The airborne material is thick enough to completely hide the area beneath it. On either side of the plume, skies are mostly clear.

Question 1 What term is applied to the erosional process that was responsible for producing this plume?

Question 2 Is the wind-transported material in the image more likely bed load or suspended load?

Question 3 People sometimes refer to events like the one pictured here as "sandstorms." Is that an appropriate description? Why or why not?

there are strong onshore winds and abundant sand. If the sand's sparse vegetative cover is disturbed at some spot, deflation creates a blowout. Sand is then transported out of the depression and deposited as a curved rim, which grows higher as deflation enlarges the blowout.

Star Dunes Confined largely to parts of the Sahara and Arabian Deserts, **star dunes** are isolated hills of sand that exhibit a complex form (Figure 22F). Their name is derived from the fact that the bases of these dunes resemble multipointed stars. Usually three or four sharp-crested ridges diverge from a central high point that in some cases may approach a height of 90 meters. As their form suggests, star dunes develop where wind directions are variable.

Loess (Silt) Deposits

In some parts of the world, the surface topography is mantled with deposits of windblown silt, called **loess**.

Over periods of perhaps thousands of years, dust storms deposited this material. When loess is breached by streams or road cuts, it tends to maintain vertical cliffs and lacks any visible layers, as you can see in FIGURE 23.

The distribution of loess worldwide indicates that there are two primary sources for this sediment: deserts and glacial outwash deposits. The thickest and most extensive deposits of loess on Earth occur in western and northern China. They were blown there from the extensive desert basins of central Asia. Accumulations of 30 meters (100 feet) are common, and thicknesses of more than 100 meters have been measured. It is this fine, buff-colored sediment that gives the Yellow River (Huang Ho) its name.

In the United States, deposits of loess are significant in many areas, including South Dakota, Nebraska, Iowa, Missouri, and Illinois, as well as portions of the Columbia Plateau in the Pacific Northwest. The correlation between the distribution of loess and important farming regions in the Midwest and eastern Washington State is not just a coincidence because soils derived from this wind-deposited sediment are among the most fertile in the world.

Unlike the deposits in China, which originated in deserts, the loess in the United States (and Europe) is an indirect product of glaciation. Its source is deposits of stratified drift. During the retreat of the ice sheets, many river valleys were choked with sediment deposited by meltwater. Strong westerly winds sweeping across the barren floodplains picked up the finer sediment and dropped it as a blanket on the eastern sides of the valleys. Such an origin is confirmed by the fact that loess deposits are thickest and coarsest on the lee side of such major glacial drainage outlets as the Mississippi and Illinois rivers and rapidly thin with increasing distance from the valleys. Furthermore, the angular, mechanically weathered particles composing the loess are essentially the same as the rock flour produced by the grinding action of glaciers.

FIGURE 23 **Loess** In some regions, the surface is mantled with deposits of windblown silt. (Top photo by James E. Patterson; bottom photo by Ashley Cooper/ Alamy)

In parts of China, loess has sufficient structural strength to permit excavation of cave-like dwellings.

6 CONCEPT CHECKS

1. How do sand dunes migrate?
2. List and briefly distinguish among basic dune types.
3. How is loess different from sand?
4. How are some loess deposits related to glaciers?

EYE on Earth

This is an aerial view of the Preston Mesa dunes in northern Arizona.

Question 1 Which one of the basic dune types is shown here?

Question 2 Sketch a simple profile (side view) of one of these dunes. Add an arrow to show the prevailing wind direction and label the dune's slip face.

Question 3 These dunes gradually migrate across the surface. Describe this process.

Michael Collier

CONCEPTS IN REVIEW: DESERTS AND WINDS

1 Distribution and Causes of Dry Lands

Describe the general distribution of Earth's dry lands and explain the causes for the formation of deserts in the subtropics and middle latitudes.

KEY WORDS desert, steppe, rainshadow

- Dry climates cover about 30 percent of Earth's land area. These regions have yearly precipitation totals that are less than the potential loss of water through evaporation. Evaporation depends on temperature, and deserts may occur in hot or cold climates. Deserts are drier than steppes, but both climatic types are considered water deficient.
- Dry climates in subtropical latitudes are associated with the global distribution of air pressure and winds. In the vicinity of the equator, warm, moist air rises (causing lots of rain) and then moves to 20 or 30 degrees latitude before sinking back toward Earth's surface. The subsiding air brings clear skies, copious sunshine, and dry conditions to these zones of subtropical high pressure.
- On the west coasts of continents, cold ocean currents accentuate the dryness associated with the subtropical highs by chilling the air. Cooling the air from below retards upward movement, so very little rain is produced (though fog may be common). These are among the driest deserts on Earth.
- Deserts also occur in continental interiors of the middle latitudes. Most are subject to the rainshadow effect, in which moist air moving inland from oceans is intercepted by mountainous obstacles. As the air is forced to rise, it cools, producing clouds and precipitation on the windward slopes. By contrast, the leeward side, called the rainshadow, tends to by quite dry.

CAUSES & EFFECTS This map shows annual precipitation across the continent of Africa. At which latitudes is the atmosphere rising? At which latitudes is it sinking? How does this atmospheric circulation influence in the continent's climates?

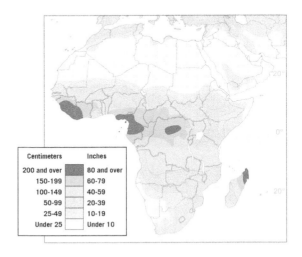

Centimeters	Inches
200 and over	80 and over
150-199	60-79
100-149	40-59
50-99	20-39
25-49	10-19
Under 25	Under 10

2 Geologic Processes in Arid Climates

Summarize the geologic roles of weathering, running water, and wind in arid and semiarid climates.

KEY WORD ephemeral stream

- In dry lands rock weathering of any type is greatly reduced because of the lack of water and the scarcity of organic acids from decaying plants.
- Practically all desert streams are dry most of the time and are said to be ephemeral. Their channels are carved out largely by flash floods that occur during sporadic storm events.
- Permanent desert streams originate in wetter climates. They must carry a great volume of water to compensate for the water they lose as they cross the desert.
- Running water is responsible for most of the erosional work in a desert. Although wind erosion is more significant in dry areas than elsewhere, the main role of wind in a desert is the transportation and deposition of sediment.

APPROXIMATE ANALOGY Develop an analogy that expresses the role of running water in sculpting the desert: infrequent but most important. Running water is to desert landscapes as _____ is to _____. (Hint: Consider analogies in the fields of personal finance, history, or health.)

When storms occur in the desert, there is little vegetation to anchor the surface so a great deal of erosion can occur in a short time.
(Photo by Alamy Images)

3 Basin and Range: The Evolution of a Desert Landscape

Discuss the stages of landscape evolution in the Basin and Range region of the western United States.

KEY WORDS interior drainage, alluvial fan, bajada, playa lake, playa, inselberg

- The Basin and Range region is a distinctive area of western North America that demonstrates some key principles of mountainous desert landscapes. The mountain ranges and intervening valleys were produced through normal faulting, but then the rock mass of the mountain ranges was redistributed by weathering, erosion, transportation, and deposition. With sufficient time, the overall effect is to reduce topographic relief by grinding down the mountains and depositing the sedimentary debris in the low-lying basins.

- Alluvial fans form during the early stage of landscape development, when the relief is highest. Over time, these fans grow and merge, so that by the middle stage, continuous bajadas of sediment cover the line where the ranges meet the basins. On the basin floor, playa lakes may form during wet periods and then dry up to produce salty playas.

- When almost all of the mountains have been worn down and almost all the low-lying basins have been filled in with sediment, the landscape has reached the late stage of development. It will be marked by isolated inselbergs of bedrock poking up through a sea of sediment.

I.D. IT (1) Identify the feature in the foreground of this photo. (2) How did this feature form? (3) With which part of Figure 9 does this photo fit best?

Michael Collier

4 Transportation of Sediment by Wind

List and describe the ways in which wind transports sediment.

KEY WORDS bed load, saltation, suspended load

- A current of air can pick up and transport sediment, though with a lower competence than a current of water or glacial ice. Wind cannot pick up the coarser particles that water can, but it is capable of transporting sediment over vast areas and even high into the atmosphere.

- A portion of the sediment transported by wind is bed load that bounces along Earth's surface. Generally, these saltating particles of sand never get more than 0.5 meter above the ground.

- Other sediment is fine grained enough to stay suspended in the air. Clay and silt are both small enough particles that they can be carried as suspended load. Once aloft, they can be carried tremendous distances, across entire continents and ocean basins.

RIGHT TOOL FOR THE JOB Imagine that you were given the job of moving a pile of sand. Would a firehose or a leafblower be more effective at moving the most sediment in the shortest time? Why?

5 Wind Erosion

Describe the processes and features associated with wind erosion.

KEY WORDS deflation, blowout, desert pavement, abrasion, ventifact, yardang

- Wind is capable of erosion, though it should be emphasized that water is the most important agent of erosion in desert regions. The incident known as the Dust Bowl is a classic example of a massive episode of soil erosion by wind during the 1930s. Localized deflation may produce shallow depressions known as blowouts.
- Desert pavement is a thin layer of coarse pebbles and cobbles that covers some desert surfaces. Two models have been proposed to explain the formation of desert pavement: (1) a model in which deflation strips the finer grains from a deposit of poorly sorted sediments and (2) an additive model in which pebbles and cobbles trap smaller windblown grains in the spaces between them.
- Ventifacts are produced when individual rocks become abraded by windblown sediment, giving the rocks a polished, pitted surface. This effect is most pronounced on the side that faces the prevailing wind. Similar "sand-blasting" of the land surface may sculpt rock outcrops into streamlined yardangs that are longest parallel to the prevailing wind direction.

KNOW IT WHEN YOU SEE IT   Suggest a reason why it might be useful for a geologist to be able to recognize ventifacts and yardangs.

6 Wind Deposits

Discuss the formation and movement of dunes and distinguish among different dune types. Explain how loess deposits differ from deposits of sand.

KEY WORDS dune, slip face, cross-bed, barchan dune, transverse dune, barchanoid dune, longitudinal dune, parabolic dune, star dune, loess

- Windblown sediments can be immense in arid areas and along sandy coasts. Dunes (sand) and loess (silt) are the two types of wind deposits.
- Dunes accumulate due to the difference in wind energy on the upwind and downwind sides of some obstacle. The wind causes sand to saltate up the gently sloped upwind side, cross the crest of the dune, and then settle out in the calmer air on the downwind side of the dune, the steeply sloped slip face. When the sand on the slip face is piled up past the angle of repose, it will spontaneously collapse in small "avalanches" of sand. Over time, this will cause a dune to slowly move in the direction of the prevailing wind, with the slip face "leading the way." If human roadways or farms are downwind, they may be overrun by the migrating dunes. Inside the dune, the buried slip faces may be preserved as cross-beds.
- There are six major kinds of dunes. Their shapes result from the pattern of prevailing winds, the amount of available sand, and the presence of vegetation. (1) Barchan dunes are crescent shaped, with the concave portion of the dune facing downwind. (2) Transverse dunes are linear in form, with the crest of the dune perpendicular to the prevailing wind direction. (3) Barchanoid dunes are intermediate in form between transverse and barchan dunes: They are shaped like the serrated edge of a bread knife. (4) Longitudinal dunes are linear but oriented parallel to the average wind direction. (5) Parabolic dunes are crescent shaped, but their orientation to the wind is opposite that of barchan dunes. (6) Star dunes have three or four ridges that radiate out from a central high point.
- Loess is windblown silt, deposited over large areas sometimes in thick blankets. Most loess is derived from either (1) deserts or (2) areas that have recently been glaciated. Winds blow over stratified drift and pick up only the finest grains, carrying them in suspension to the site of deposition.

COMPARE & CONTRAST   What do barchan dunes and parabolic dunes have in common? How are they different? What do longitudinal and transverse dunes have in common? How are they different?

Slip face

Barchan dunes are crescent shaped, and move towards the concave slip face.

GIVE IT SOME THOUGHT

1. Albuquerque, New Mexico, receives an average of 20.7 centimeters (8.07 inches) of rainfall annually. Albuquerque is considered a desert when the commonly used Köppen climate classification is applied. The Russian city of Verkhoyansk is located near the Arctic Circle in Siberia. Yearly precipitation at Verkhoyansk averages 15.5 centimeters (6.05 inches), about 5 centimeters (2 inches) less than Albuquerque, yet it is classified as a humid climate. Explain why this is the case.

2. Name three deserts that are visible on the classic view of Earth from space. Briefly explain why these regions are so dry. Can you also explain the cause of the band of clouds in the region of the equator?

NASA

3. Compare and contrast the sediment deposited by a stream, the wind, and a glacier. Which deposit should have the most uniform grain size? Which one would exhibit the poorest sorting? Explain your choices.

4. Is either of the following statements true? Are they both true? Explain your answer.
   a. Wind is more effective as an agent of erosion in dry places than in humid places.
   b. Wind is the most important agent of erosion in deserts.

5. Bryce Canyon National Park, shown in the accompanying photo, is in dry southern Utah. It is carved into the eastern edge of the Paunsaugunt Plateau. Erosion has sculpted the colorful limestone into bizarre shapes, including spires called "hoodoos." As you and a companion (who has not studied geology) are viewing the scenery in Bryce Canyon, your friend says, "It's amazing how wind has created this incredible scenery!" Now that you have studied arid landscapes, how would you respond to your companion's statement?

©zoptimist/Shutterstock

6. Examine Figure 21, which shows sand dunes encroaching on irrigated fields. What type of dunes are these? From what direction (left or right) is the prevailing wind? How were you able to determine the wind direction?

7. This close-up photo shows a small portion of one side of a barchan dune. What term is applied to this side of the dune? Is the prevailing wind direction "coming out" of the photo or "going into" the photo? Explain. Why did some of the sand break away and slide?

Michael Collier

Glossary

Abrasion The grinding and scraping of a rock surface by the friction and impact of rock particles carried by water, wind, and ice.

Alluvial fan A fan-shaped deposit of sediment formed when a stream's slope is abruptly reduced.

Bajada An apron of sediment along a mountain front created by the coalescence of alluvial fans.

Barchan dune A solitary sand dune shaped like a crescent, with its tips pointing downwind.

Barchanoid dune A type of dune that forms scalloped rows of sand oriented at right angles to the wind. This form is intermediate between isolated barchans and extensive waves of transverse dunes.

Bed load Sediment moved along the bottom of a stream by moving water, or particles moved along the ground surface by wind.

Blowout A depression excavated by wind in easily eroded materials.

Cross-bedding A structure in which relatively thin layers are inclined at an angle to the main bedding. Cross-bedding is formed by currents of wind or water.

Deflation The lifting and removal of loose material by wind.

Desert One of the two types of dry climate; the driest of the dry climates.

Desert pavement A layer of closely spaced coarse pebbles and gravel that cover barren, rocky deserts to form a relatively smooth surface.

Dune A hill or ridge of wind-deposited sand.

Ephemeral stream A stream that is usually dry because it carries water only in response to specific episodes of rainfall. Most desert streams are of this type.

Inselberg An isolated mountain remnant characteristic of the late stage of erosion in a mountainous arid region.

Interior drainage A discontinuous pattern of intermittent streams that do not flow to the ocean.

Loess Deposits of windblown silt, lacking visible layers, generally buff-colored, and capable of maintaining a nearly vertical cliff.

Longitudinal dunes Long ridges of sand oriented parallel to the prevailing wind; these dunes form where sand supplies are limited.

Parabolic dune A sand dune that is similar in shape to a barchan dune except that its tips point into the wind. These dunes often form along coasts that have strong onshore winds, abundant sand, and vegetation that partly covers the sand.

Playa The flat central area of an undrained desert basin.

Playa lake A temporary lake in a playa.

Rainshadow desert A dry area on the lee side of a mountain range. Many middle-latitude deserts are of this type.

Saltation Transportation of sediment through a series of leaps or bounces.

Slip face The steep, leeward surface of a sand dune that maintains a slope of about 34 degrees.

Star dune An isolated hill of sand that exhibits a complex form and develops where wind directions are variable.

Steppe One of the two types of dry climate. A marginal and more humid variant of the desert that separates it from bordering humid climates.

Suspended load Fine sediment carried within the body of flowing water or air.

Transverse dunes A series of long ridges oriented at right angles to the prevailing wind; these dunes form where vegetation is sparse and sand is very plentiful.

Ventifact A cobble or pebble polished and shaped by the sandblasting effect of wind.

Yardang A streamlined, wind-sculpted ridge that has the appearance of an inverted ship's hull that is oriented parallel to the prevailing wind.

Global Climate Change

From Chapter 21 of *Earth: An Introduction to Physical Geology*, Eleventh Edition. Edward J. Tarbuck, Frederick K. Lutgens, Dennis Tasa.

Global Climate Change

Mauna Loa Observatory is an important atmospheric research facility on Hawaii's Big Island. It has been collecting data and monitoring atmospheric change since the 1950s. (Photo by Forrest M. Mimms III)

Each statement represents the primary learning objective for the corresponding major heading within the chapter. After you complete the chapter you should be able to:

1   List the major parts of the climate system and some connections between climate and geology.

2   Explain why unraveling past climate changes is important and discuss several ways in which such changes are detected.

3   Discuss the composition of the atmosphere and describe the atmosphere's vertical changes in pressure and temperature.

4   Outline the basic processes involved in heating the atmosphere.

5   Discuss hypotheses that relate to natural causes of climate change.

6   Summarize the nature and cause of the atmosphere's changing composition since about 1750. Describe the climate's response.

7   Contrast positive- and negative-feedback mechanisms and provide examples of each.

8   Discuss the possible impacts of aerosols on climate change.

9   Summarize some of the possible consequences of global warming.

C limate varies from place to place. Anyone who has the opportunity to travel around the world finds such an incredible variety of climates that it is hard to believe they could all occur on the same planet. Climate is also variable over time. During the great expanse of Earth history, and long before humans were roaming the planet, there were many shifts—from warm to cold and wet to dry and back again. The geologic record is a storehouse of data that confirm this fact. Unlike changes in the geologic past, which represented natural variations, modern climate change is dominated by human influences that are sufficiently large that they exceed the bounds of natural variability. These changes are likely to continue for many centuries. The effects of humanity's venture into the unknown with climate could be very disruptive not only to humans but to many other life-forms as well.

Ancient bristlecone pines in California's White Mountains. The study of tree-growth rings is one way that scientists reconstruct past climates. Some of these trees are more than 4000 years old. (Photo by Bill Stevenson/Photolibrary)

1 Climate and Geology

The term *weather* refers to the state of the atmosphere at a given time and place. Changes in the weather are frequent and sometimes seemingly erratic. In contrast, *climate* is a description of aggregate weather conditions, based on observations over many decades. Climate is often defined simply as "average weather," but this definition is inadequate because variations and extremes are also part of a climate description.

The Climate System

Throughout this book, you have been reminded that Earth is a multidimensional system that consists of many interacting parts. A change in any one part can produce changes in any or all of the other parts—often in ways that are neither obvious nor immediately apparent. This fact is certainly true when it comes to the study of climate and climate change.

To understand and appreciate climate, it is important to realize that climate involves more than just the atmosphere (FIGURE 1). Indeed, we must recognize that there is a **climate system** that includes the atmosphere, hydrosphere, geosphere, biosphere, and cryosphere. (The *cryosphere* refers to the ice and snow that exist at Earth's surface.) The climate system *involves the exchanges of energy and moisture that occur among the five spheres.* These exchanges link the atmosphere to the other spheres so that the whole functions as an extremely complex, interactive unit. Changes to the climate system do not occur in isolation. Rather, when one part of it changes, the other components also react. The major components of the climate system are shown in FIGURE 2.

Climate–Geology Connections

Climate has a profound impact on many geologic processes. When climate changes, these processes respond. Of course, rock weathering has an obvious climate connection, as do processes that operate in arid, tropical, and glacial landscapes. Phenomena such as debris flows and river flooding are often triggered by atmospheric events such as periods of extraordinary rainfall. Clearly, the atmosphere is a basic link in the hydrologic cycle. Other climate–geology connections involve the impact of internal processes on the atmosphere. For example, the particles and gases emitted by volcanoes can change the composition of the atmosphere, and mountain building can have a significant impact on regional temperature, precipitation, and wind patterns.

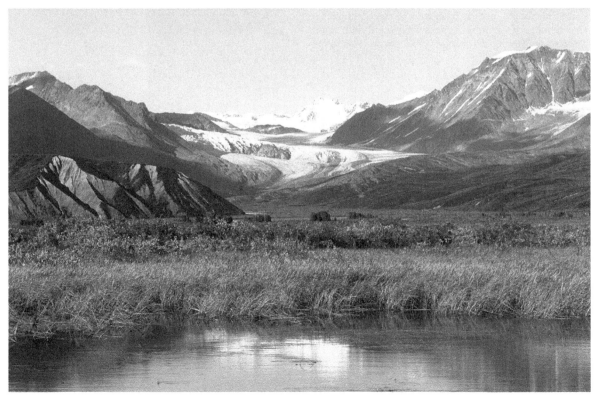

FIGURE 1 Gulkana Glacier in Alaska's Delta Range The five major parts of the climate system are represented in this image of mountains southeast of Fairbanks, Alaska. (Photo by Michael Collier)

FIGURE 2 Earth's climate system
Schematic view showing several components of Earth's climate system. Many interactions occur among the various components on a wide range of space and time scales, making the system extremely complex.

The study of sediments, sedimentary rocks, and fossils clearly demonstrates that, through the ages, practically every place on our planet has experienced wide swings in climate, such as from ice ages to conditions associated with subtropical coal swamps or desert dunes. Time scales for climate change vary from decades to millions of years.

---

1 CONCEPT CHECKS

1. What are the five major parts of the climate system?
2. List at least five connections between climate and geology.

Gases emitted by volcanoes can change the composition of the atmosphere. The dense haze shown here was created when sulfur dioxide from Hawaii's Kilauea volcano combined with oxygen and water vapor in the air to produce volcanic smog termed *vog*. Strong sunlight is an important trigger for this reaction. (Photo by Michael Collier)

2 How Is Climate Change Detected?

High-technology and precision instrumentation are now available to study the composition and dynamics of the atmosphere. But such tools are recent inventions and, therefore, have been providing data for only a short time span. To understand fully the behavior of the atmosphere and to anticipate future climate change, we must somehow discover how climate has changed over broad expanses of time.

Instrumental records go back only a couple centuries at best, and the further back we go, the less complete and more unreliable the data become. To overcome this lack of direct measurements, scientists must decipher and reconstruct past climates by using indirect evidence. Such **proxy data** come from natural recorders of climate variability, such as seafloor sediments, glacial ice, fossil pollen, and tree-growth rings, as well as from historical documents. Scientists who analyze proxy data and reconstruct past climates are engaged in **paleoclimatology**. The main goal of such work is to understand the climate of the past in order to assess the current and potential future climate in the context of natural climate variability. In the following discussion, we will briefly examine some of the important sources of proxy data.

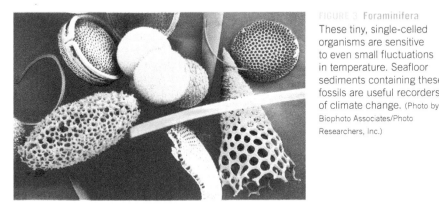

FIGURE 3 Foraminifera These tiny, single-celled organisms are sensitive to even small fluctuations in temperature. Seafloor sediments containing these fossils are useful recorders of climate change. (Photo by Biophoto Associates/Photo Researchers, Inc.)

Seafloor Sediment—A Storehouse of Climate Data

We know that the parts of the Earth system are linked so that a change in one part can produce changes in any or all of the other parts. In this section, you will see how changes in atmospheric and oceanic temperatures are reflected in the nature of life in the sea.

Most seafloor sediments contain the remains of organisms that once lived near the sea surface (the ocean–atmosphere interface). When such near-surface organisms die, their shells slowly settle to the floor of the ocean, where they become part of the sedimentary record (FIGURE 3). These seafloor sediments are useful recorders of worldwide climate change because the numbers and types of organisms living near the sea surface change with the climate.

Thus, in seeking to understand climate change as well as other environmental transformations, scientists are tapping the huge reservoir of data in seafloor sediments. The sediment cores gathered by drilling ships and other research vessels have provided invaluable data that have significantly expanded our knowledge and understanding of past climates (FIGURE 4).

FIGURE 4 Drilling for seafloor sediment The *Chikyu* (meaning "Earth" in Japanese) is a state-of-the-art scientific drilling vessel. It can drill as deep as 7000 meters (nearly 23,000 feet) below the seabed in water as deep as 2500 meters (8200 feet). It is part of the Integrated Ocean Drilling Program. (AP Photo/Itsuo Inouye)

One notable example of the importance of seafloor sediments to our understanding of climate change relates to unraveling the fluctuating atmospheric conditions of the Ice Age. The records of temperature changes contained in cores of sediment from the ocean floor have proven critical to our present understanding of this recent span of Earth history.

Oxygen Isotope Analysis

The isotopes of oxygen in water molecules or the shells of marine organisms are an important source of proxy data on past climate conditions. **Oxygen isotope analysis** is based on precise measurement of the ratio between two isotopes of oxygen: ^{16}O, which is the most common, and the heavier ^{18}O. A molecule of H_2O can form from either ^{16}O or ^{18}O. But the lighter isotope, ^{16}O, evaporates more readily from the oceans. Because of this, precipitation (and hence the glacial ice that it may form) is enriched in ^{16}O. This leaves a greater concentration of the heavier isotope, ^{18}O, in the ocean water. Thus, during periods when glaciers are extensive, more of the lighter ^{16}O is tied up in ice, so the concentration of ^{18}O in seawater increases. Conversely, during warmer interglacial periods, when the amount of glacial ice decreases dramatically, more ^{16}O is returned to the sea, so the proportion of ^{18}O relative to ^{16}O in ocean water also drops. Now, if we had some ancient recording of the changes of the $^{18}O/^{16}O$ ratio, we could determine when there were glacial periods and, therefore, when the climate grew cooler.

Fortunately, we do have such a recording. Certain marine microorganisms secrete their shells of calcium carbonate ($CaCO_3$), and the prevailing oceanic $^{18}O/^{16}O$ ratio is reflected in the composition of these hard parts. When the organisms die, their hard parts settle to the ocean floor, becoming part of the sediment layers there. Consequently, periods of glacial activity can be determined from variations in the oxygen isotope ratio found in shells of certain microorganisms buried in deep-sea sediments. A higher ratio of ^{18}O to ^{16}O in shells indicates a time when ice sheets were growing larger.

The $^{18}O/^{16}O$ ratio also varies with temperature. More ^{18}O is evaporated from the oceans when temperatures are high, and less is evaporated when temperatures are low. Therefore, the heavy isotope is more abundant in the precipitation of warm eras and less abundant during colder periods. Using this principle, scientists studying the layers of ice and snow in glaciers have been able to produce a record of past temperature changes.

Climate Change Recorded in Glacial Ice

Ice cores are an indispensable source of data for reconstructing past climates. Research based on vertical cores taken from the Greenland and Antarctic Ice Sheets has changed our basic understanding of how the climate system works.

Scientists collect samples by using a drilling rig, like a small version of an oil drill. A hollow shaft follows the drill head into the ice, and an ice core is extracted. In this way, cores that sometimes exceed 2000 meters (6500 feet) in length, and may represent more than 200,000 years of climate history, are acquired for study (FIGURE 5A).

The ice provides a detailed record of changing air temperatures and snowfall. Past temperatures are determined by *oxygen isotope analysis*. Using this technique, scientists are able to produce a record of past temperature changes. A portion of such a record is shown in FIGURE 5B.

Air bubbles trapped in the ice record variations in atmospheric composition. Changes in carbon dioxide and methane are linked to fluctuating temperatures. The cores also include atmospheric fallout such as wind-blown dust, volcanic ash, pollen, and modern-day pollution.

 SMARTFIGURE 5
Ice cores: Important sources of climate data
A. The National Ice Core Laboratory is a physical plant for storing and studying cores of ice taken from glaciers around the world. These cores represent a long-term record of material deposited from the atmosphere. The lab enables scientists to conduct examinations of ice cores, and it preserves the integrity of these samples in a repository for the study of global climate change and past environmental conditions. (Photo by USGS/National Ice Core Laboratory) **B.** This graph, showing temperature variations over the past 40,000 years, is derived from oxygen-isotope analysis of ice cores recovered from the Greenland Ice Sheet. (U.S. Geological Survey)

A.

B.

Tree Rings—Archives of Environmental History

If you look at the end of a log, you will see that it is composed of a series of concentric rings (FIGURE 6A). Tree rings can be a very useful source of proxy data on past climates. Every year, in temperate regions, trees add a layer of new wood under the bark. Characteristics of each tree ring, such as thickness and density, reflect the environmental conditions (especially climate) that prevailed during the year when the ring formed. Favorable growth conditions produce a wide ring; unfavorable ones produce a narrow ring. Trees growing at the same time in the same region show similar tree-ring patterns.

Because a single growth ring is usually added each year, the age of the tree when it was cut can be determined by counting the rings. If the year of cutting is known, the age of the tree and the year in which each ring formed can be determined by counting back from the outside ring. Scientists are not limited to working with trees that have been cut down. Small, nondestructive core samples can be taken from living trees (FIGURE 6B).

To make the most effective use of tree rings, extended patterns known as *ring chronologies* are established. They are produced by comparing the patterns of rings among trees in an area. If the same pattern can be identified in two samples, one of which has been dated, the second sample can be dated from the first by matching the ring patterns common to both. Tree-ring chronologies extending back thousands of years have been established for some regions. To date a timber sample of unknown age, its ring pattern is matched against the reference chronology.

Tree-ring chronologies are unique archives of environmental history and have important applications in such disciplines as climate, geology, ecology, and archaeology. For example, tree rings are used to reconstruct climate variations within a region for spans of thousands of years prior to human historical records. Knowledge of such long-term variations is of great value in making judgments regarding the recent record of climate change.

Other Types of Proxy Data

In addition to the sources already discussed, other sources of proxy data that are used to gain insight into past climates include fossil pollen, corals, and historical documents.

Fossil Pollen Climate is a major factor influencing the distribution of vegetation, so knowing the nature of the plant community occupying an area is a reflection of the climate. Pollen and spores are parts of the life cycles of many plants, and because they have resistant

A.

B.

FIGURE 6 Tree rings
A. Each year a growing tree produces a layer of new cells beneath the bark. If the tree is cut down and the trunk is examined, each year's growth can be seen as a ring. Because the amount of growth (the thickness of a ring) depends on precipitation and temperature, tree rings are useful records of past climate. (Photo by Daniele Taurino/ Dreamstime) **B.** Scientists are not limited to working with trees that have been cut down. Small, nondestructive core samples can be taken from living trees. (Photo by Gregory K. Scott/Photo Researchers, Inc.)

walls, they are often the most abundant, easily identifiable, and best-preserved plant remains in sediments (FIGURE 7). By analyzing pollen from accurately dated sediments, it is possible to obtain high-resolution records of vegetation changes in an area. From such information, scientists can reconstruct past climates.

Corals Coral reefs consist of colonies of corals that live in warm, shallow waters and form atop the hard material left behind by past corals. Corals build their hard skeletons from calcium carbonate ($CaCO_3$) extracted from seawater. The carbonate contains isotopes of oxygen that

FIGURE 7 Pollen
This false-color image from an electron microscope shows an assortment of pollen grains. Note how the size, shape, and surface characteristics differ from one species to another. Analysis of the types and abundance of pollen in lake sediments and peat deposits provides information about how climate has changed over time. (Photo by David Scharf/Science Photo Library)

FIGURE 8 Corals record sea-surface temperatures
Coral colonies thrive in warm, shallow tropical waters. The tiny invertebrates extract calcium carbonate from seawater to build hard parts. They live atop the solid foundation left by past coral. Chemical analysis of the changing composition of coral reefs with depth can provide useful data on past near-surface temperatures. This graph shows a 350-year record of sea-surface temperatures obtained through oxygen-isotope analysis of coral from the Galapagos Islands. (National Climatic Data Center)

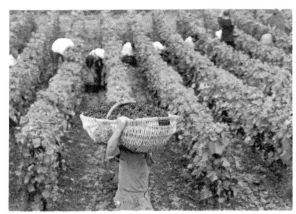

FIGURE 9 Harvest dates as climate clues
Historical records can sometimes be helpful in the analysis of past climates. The date for the beginning of the grape harvest in the fall is an integrated measure of temperature and precipitation during the growing season. These dates have been recorded for centuries in Europe and provide a useful record of year-to-year climate variations. (Photo by SGM/AGE Fotostock)

can be used to determine the temperature of the water in which the coral grew.

The portion of the skeleton that forms in winter has a density that is different from that formed in summer because of variations in growth rates related to temperature and other environmental factors. Thus, corals exhibit seasonal growth bands very much like those observed in trees. The accuracy and reliability of the climate data extracted from corals has been established by comparing recent instrumental records to coral records for the same period. Oxygen isotope analysis of coral growth rings can also serve as a proxy measurement for precipitation, particularly in areas where large variations in annual rainfall occur.

Think of coral as a paleothermometer that enables us to answer important questions about climate variability in the world's oceans. The graph in FIGURE 8 is a 350-year sea-surface temperature record based on oxygen isotope analysis of a core from the Galapagos Islands.

Historical Data   Historical documents sometimes contain helpful information. Although it might seem that

such records should readily lend themselves to climate analysis, this is not the case. Most manuscripts were written for purposes other than climate description. Furthermore, writers understandably neglected periods of relatively stable atmospheric conditions and mention only droughts, severe storms, memorable blizzards, and other extremes. Nevertheless, records of crops, floods, and the migration of people have furnished useful evidence of the possible influences of changing climate (FIGURE 9).

2 CONCEPT CHECKS

1. What are proxy data, and why are they necessary in the study of climate change?
2. Why are seafloor sediments useful in the study of past climates?
3. Explain how past temperatures are determined using oxygen-isotope analysis.
4. Aside from seafloor sediments, list four sources of proxy data.

3 Some Atmospheric Basics

In order to better understand climate change, it is helpful to possess some knowledge about the composition and structure of the atmosphere and the process by which it is heated—the *greenhouse effect*.

Composition of the Atmosphere

Air is *not* a unique element or compound. Rather, air is a *mixture* of many discrete gases, each with its own physical properties, in which varying quantities of tiny solid and liquid particles are suspended.

Clean, Dry Air As you can see in FIGURE 10, clean, dry air is composed almost entirely of two gases—78 percent nitrogen and 21 percent oxygen. Although these gases are the most plentiful components of air and are of great significance to life on Earth, they are of little or no importance in affecting weather phenomena. The remaining 1 percent of dry air is mostly the inert gas argon (0.93 percent) plus tiny quantities of a number of other gases. Carbon dioxide, although present in only minute amounts (0.0395 percent, or 395 parts per million), is nevertheless an important constituent of air because it has the ability to absorb heat energy radiated by Earth and thus influences the heating of the atmosphere.

Air includes many gases and particles that vary significantly from time to time and from place to place. Important examples include water vapor, ozone, and tiny solid and liquid particles.

Water Vapor The amount of water vapor in the air varies considerably, from practically none at all up to about 4 percent by volume. Why is such a small fraction of the atmosphere so significant? Certainly the fact that water vapor is the source of all clouds and precipitation would be enough to explain its importance. However, water vapor has other roles. Like carbon dioxide, it has the ability to absorb heat energy given off by Earth as well as some solar energy. It is, therefore, important when we examine the heating of the atmosphere.

Ozone Another important component of the atmosphere is *ozone*. It is a form of oxygen that combines three oxygen atoms into each molecule (O_3). Ozone is not the same as the oxygen we breathe, which has two atoms per molecule (O_2). There is very little ozone in the atmosphere, and its distribution is not uniform. It is concentrated well above Earth's surface in a layer called the *stratosphere*, at an altitude of between 10 and 50 kilometers (6 and 31 miles). The presence of the ozone layer in our atmosphere is crucial to those who dwell on Earth.

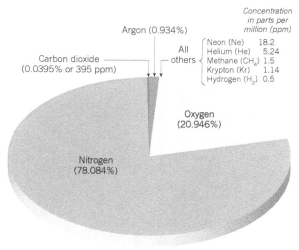

FIGURE 10 Composition of the atmosphere Proportional volume of gases composing dry air. Nitrogen and oxygen obviously dominate.

The reason is that ozone absorbs the potentially harmful ultraviolet (UV) radiation from the Sun. If ozone did not filter a great deal of the ultraviolet radiation, and if the Sun's UV rays reached the surface of Earth undiminished, our planet would be uninhabitable for most life as we know it.

Aerosols The movements of the atmosphere are sufficient to keep a large quantity of solid and liquid particles suspended within it. Although visible dust sometimes clouds the sky, these relatively large particles are too heavy to stay in the air for very long. Still, many particles are microscopic and remain suspended for considerable periods of time. They may originate from many sources, both natural and human made, and include sea salts from breaking waves, fine soil blown into the air, smoke and soot from fires, pollen and microorganisms lifted by the wind, ash and dust from volcanic eruptions, and more. Collectively, these tiny solid and liquid particles are called **aerosols**.

From a meteorological standpoint, these tiny, often invisible particles can be significant. First, many act as surfaces on which water vapor can condense, an important function in the formation of clouds and fog. Second, aerosols can absorb or reflect incoming solar radiation. Thus, when an air pollution episode is occurring, or when ash fills the sky following a volcanic eruption, the amount of sunlight reaching Earth's surface can be measurably reduced (FIGURE 11).

FIGURE 11 Aerosols
FIGURE 11 **Aerosols**
This satellite image shows two examples of aerosols. First, a dust storm is blowing across northeastern China toward the Korean Peninsula. Second, a dense haze toward the south (bottom center) is human-generated air pollution. (NASA)

Extent and Structure of the Atmosphere

To say that the atmosphere begins at Earth's surface and extends upward is obvious. However, where does the atmosphere end, and where does outer space begin? There is no sharp boundary; the atmosphere rapidly thins as

FIGURE 12 **Vertical changes in air pressure** Pressure decreases rapidly near Earth's surface and more gradually at greater heights.

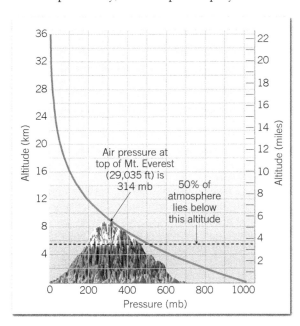

you travel away from Earth, until there are too few gas molecules to detect.

Pressure Changes with Height To understand the vertical extent of the atmosphere, let us examine changes in atmospheric pressure with height. Atmospheric pressure is simply the weight of the air above. At sea level, the average pressure is slightly more than 1000 millibars. This corresponds to a weight of slightly more than 1 kilogram per square centimeter (14.7 pounds per square inch). Obviously, the pressure at higher altitudes is less (FIGURE 12).

One-half of the atmosphere lies below an altitude of 5.6 kilometers (3.5 miles). At about 16 kilometers (10 miles), 90 percent of the atmosphere has been traversed, and above 100 kilometers (62 miles), only 0.00003 percent of all the gases making up the atmosphere remains. Even so, traces of our atmosphere extend far beyond this altitude, gradually merging with the emptiness of space.

Temperature Changes In addition to vertical changes in air pressure, there are also changes in air temperature as we ascend through the atmosphere. Earth's atmosphere is divided vertically into four layers, on the basis of temperature (FIGURE 13):

- **Troposphere.** The bottom layer in which we live is characterized by a decrease in temperature with an increase in altitude and is called the *troposphere*.

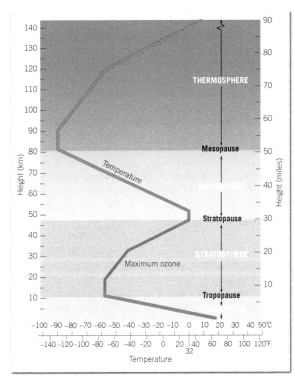

FIGURE 13 Thermal structure of the atmosphere

The term literally means the region where air "turns over," a reference to the appreciable vertical mixing of air in this lowermost zone. The troposphere is the chief focus of meteorologists because it is in this layer that essentially all important weather phenomena occur. The temperature decrease in the troposphere is called the *environmental lapse rate.* Its average value is 6.5° C per kilometer (3.5° F per 1000 feet), a figure known as the *normal lapse rate.* It should be emphasized, however, that the environmental lapse rate is not a constant but rather can be highly variable and must be regularly measured. To determine the actual environmental lapse rate as well as to gather information about vertical changes in pressure, wind, and humidity, radiosondes are used. A *radiosonde* is an instrument package that is attached to a balloon and transmits data by radio as it ascends through the atmosphere (FIGURE 14). The thickness of the troposphere is not the same everywhere; it varies with latitude and the season. On the average, the temperature drop continues to a height of about 12 kilometers (7.4 miles). The outer boundary of the troposphere is the *tropopause.*

- **Stratosphere.** Beyond the tropopause is the *stratosphere.* In the stratosphere, the temperature remains constant to a height of about 20 kilometers (12 miles) and then begins a gradual increase that continues until the *stratopause,* at a height of nearly 50 kilometers (30 miles) above Earth's surface. Below the tropopause, atmospheric properties such as temperature and humidity are readily transferred by large-scale turbulence and mixing. Above the tropopause, in the stratosphere, they are not. Temperatures increase in the stratosphere because it is in this layer that the atmosphere's ozone is concentrated. Recall that ozone absorbs ultraviolet radiation from the Sun. As a consequence, the stratosphere is heated.
- **Mesosphere.** In the third layer, the *mesosphere,* temperatures again decrease with height until, at the *mesopause,* more than 80 kilometers (50 miles) above the surface, the temperature approaches −90° C (−130° F). The coldest temperatures anywhere in the atmosphere occur at the mesopause.
- **Thermosphere.** The fourth layer extends outward from the mesopause and has no well-defined upper limit. This is the *thermosphere,* a layer that contains only a tiny fraction of the atmosphere's mass. In the extremely rarefied air of this outermost layer, temperatures again increase, due to the absorption of very short-wave, high-energy solar radiation by atoms of oxygen and nitrogen. Temperatures rise to

FIGURE 14 Radiosonde
A radiosonde is a light-weight package of instruments that is carried aloft by a small weather balloon. It transmits data on vertical changes in temperature, pressure, and humidity in the troposphere. The troposphere is where practically all weather phenomena occur, therefore it is very important to have frequent measurements.
(Photo by David R. Frazier/DanitaDelimont.com)

extremely high values of more than 1000° C (1800° F) in the thermosphere. But such temperatures are not comparable to those experienced near Earth's surface. Temperature is defined in terms of the average speed at which molecules move. Because the gases of the thermosphere are moving at very high speeds, the temperature is very high. But the gases are so sparse that, collectively, they process only an insignificant amount of heat.

3 CONCEPT CHECKS

1. What are the major components of clean, dry air? List two significant variable components.
2. Describe how air pressure changes with an increase in altitude. Does it change at a constant rate?
3. The atmosphere is divided vertically into four layers, on the basis of temperature. Name the layers from bottom to top and indicate how temperatures change in each.

4 Heating the Atmosphere

Nearly all the energy that drives Earth's variable weather and climate comes from the Sun. Before we can adequately describe how Earth's atmosphere is heated, it is helpful to know something about solar energy and what happens to this energy once it is intercepted by Earth.

Energy from the Sun

From our everyday experience, we know that the Sun emits light and heat as well as the ultraviolet rays that cause suntan. Although these forms of energy comprise a major portion of the total energy that radiates from the Sun, they are only part of a large array of energy called *radiation*, or *electromagnetic radiation*. This array, or spectrum, of electromagnetic energy is shown in FIGURE 15. All radiation—whether X-rays, microwaves, or radio waves—transmits energy through the vacuum of space at 300,000 kilometers (186,000 miles) per second and only slightly slower through our atmosphere. When an object absorbs any form of radiant energy, the result is an increase in molecular motion, which causes a corresponding increase in temperature.

To better understand how the atmosphere is heated, it is useful to have a general understanding of the basic laws governing radiation:

- **All objects, at whatever temperature, emit radiant energy.** Hence, not only hot objects like the Sun but also Earth, including its polar ice caps, continually emit energy.
- **Hotter objects radiate more total energy per unit area than do colder objects.**
- **The hotter the radiating body, the shorter the wavelength of maximum radiation.** The Sun, with a surface temperature of about 5700° C, radiates maximum energy at 0.5 micrometer, which is in the visible range. The maximum radiation for Earth occurs at a wavelength of 10 micrometers, well within the infrared (heat) range. Because the maximum Earth radiation is roughly 20 times longer than the maximum solar radiation, Earth radiation is often called *long-wave radiation*, and solar radiation is called *short-wave radiation*.
- **Objects that are good absorbers of radiation are good emitters as well.** Earth's surface and the Sun approach being perfect radiators because they absorb and radiate with nearly 100 percent efficiency for their respective temperatures. On the other hand, *gases are selective absorbers and emitters of radiation*. For some wavelengths, the atmosphere is nearly transparent (that is, little radiation is absorbed). For other wavelengths, however, the atmosphere is nearly opaque (that is, it is a good absorber). Experience tells us that the atmosphere is transparent to visible light; hence, these wavelengths readily reach Earth's surface. This is not the case for the longer-wavelength radiation emitted by Earth.

FIGURE 15 **The electromagnetic spectrum** This diagram illustrates the wavelengths and names of various types of radiation. Visible light consists of an array of colors we commonly call the "colors of the rainbow." (Photo by Michael Giannechini/Photo researchers, Inc.)

The Paths of Incoming Solar Energy

FIGURE 16 shows the paths taken by incoming solar radiation averaged for the entire globe. Notice that the atmosphere is quite transparent to incoming solar radiation. On average, about 50 percent of the solar energy reaching the top of the atmosphere passes through the atmosphere and is absorbed

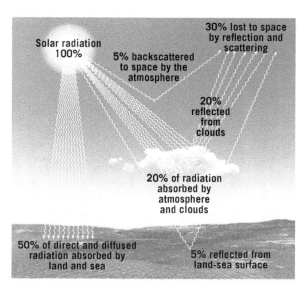

SMARTFIGURE 16 Paths taken by solar radiation

This diagram shows the average distribution of incoming solar radiation by percentage. More solar radiation is absorbed by Earth's surface than by the atmosphere.

at Earth's surface. Another 20 percent is absorbed directly by clouds and certain atmospheric gases (including oxygen and ozone) before reaching the surface. The remaining 30 percent is reflected back to space by the atmosphere, clouds, and reflective surfaces such as snow and ice. The

FIGURE 17 Albedo (reflectivity) of various surfaces
In general, light-colored surfaces tend to be more reflective than dark-colored surfaces and thus have higher albedos.

fraction of the total radiation that is reflected by a surface is called its *albedo* (FIGURE 17). Thus, the albedo for Earth as a whole (the *planetary* albedo) is 30 percent.

What determines whether solar radiation will be transmitted to the surface, scattered, or reflected outward? It depends greatly on the wavelength of the energy being transmitted, as well as on the nature of the intervening material.

The numbers shown in Figure 16 represent global averages. The actual percentages can vary greatly. An important reason for much of this variation has to do with changes in the percentage of light reflected and scattered

EYE on Earth

When this weather balloon was launched, the surface temperature was 17° C. The balloon is now at an altitude of 1 kilometer. (Photo by David R. Frazier/Photo Researchers, Inc.)

Question 1 What term is applied to the instrument package being carried aloft by the balloon?

Question 2 In what layer of the atmosphere is the balloon?

Question 3 If average conditions prevail, what is the air temperature at this altitude? How did you figure this out?

Question 4 How will the size of the balloon change, if at all, as it rises through the atmosphere? Explain.

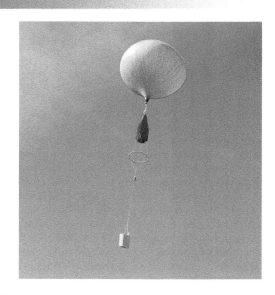

Airless bodies like the Moon All incoming solar radiation reaches the surface. Some is reflected back to space. The rest is absorbed by the surface and radiated directly back to space. As a result the lunar surface has a much lower average surface temperature than Earth.

Bodies with modest amounts of greenhouse gases like Earth The atmosphere absorbs some of the longwave radiation emitted by the surface. A portion of this energy is radiated back to the surface and is responsible for keeping Earth's surface 33°C (59°F) warmer than it would otherwise be.

Bodies with abundant greenhouse gases like Venus Venus experiences extraordinary greenhouse warming, which is estimated to raise its surface temperature by 523°C (941°F).

All outgoing longwave energy is reradiated directly back to space

Incoming shortwave solar radiation

David Cole/Alamy

Some outgoing longwave radiation absorbed by greenhouse gases

Greenhouse gases reradiate some energy Earthward

Incoming shortwave solar radiation

NASA

Most outgoing longwave radiation absorbed by greenhouse gases

Greenhouse gases reradiate considerable energy toward the Venusian surface

Incoming shortwave solar radiation

NASA

SMARTFIGURE 18 The greenhouse effect
The greenhouse effect of Earth compared with two of our close solar system neighbors.

back to space (Figure 16). For example, if the sky is overcast, a higher percentage of light is reflected back to space than when the sky is clear.

Heating the Atmosphere: The Greenhouse Effect

If Earth had no atmosphere, it would experience an average surface temperature far below freezing. But the atmosphere warms the planet and makes Earth livable. The extremely important role the atmosphere plays in heating Earth's surface has been named the **greenhouse effect**.

As discussed earlier, cloudless air is largely transparent to incoming short-wave solar radiation and, hence, transmits it to Earth's surface. By contrast, a significant fraction of the long-wave radiation emitted by Earth's land–sea surface is absorbed by water vapor, carbon dioxide, and other trace gases in the atmosphere. This energy heats the air and increases the rate at which it radiates energy, both out to space and back toward Earth's surface. Without this complicated game of "pass the hot potato," Earth's average temperature would be –18° C (0° F) rather than the current average temperature of 15° C (59° F) (FIGURE 18).

These absorptive gases in our atmosphere make Earth habitable for humans and other life-forms.

This natural phenomenon was named the greenhouse effect because it was once thought that greenhouses were heated in a similar manner. The glass in a greenhouse allows short-wave solar radiation to enter and be absorbed by the objects inside. These objects, in turn, radiate energy but at longer wavelengths, to which glass is nearly opaque. The heat, therefore, is "trapped" in the greenhouse. It has been shown, however, that air inside greenhouses attains higher temperatures than outside air mainly because greenhouses restrict the exchange of air between the inside and outside. Nevertheless, the term *greenhouse effect* remains.

4 CONCEPT CHECKS

1. What are the three paths that incoming solar radiation takes? What might cause the percentage taking each path to vary?
2. Explain why the atmosphere is heated chiefly by radiation from Earth's surface.
3. Prepare a sketch with labels that explains the greenhouse effect.

5 Natural Causes of Climate Change

A great variety of hypotheses have been proposed to explain climate change. Several have gained wide support, only to lose it and then sometimes to regain it again. Some explanations of naturally caused climate change are controversial. This is to be expected because planetary atmospheric processes are so large-scale and complex that they cannot be reproduced physically in laboratory experiments. Rather, climate and its changes must be simulated mathematically (modeled) using powerful computers.

As you read this section, you will find that more than one hypothesis may explain the same climate change. In fact, several mechanisms may interact to shift climate. Also, no single hypothesis can explain climate change on all time scales. A proposal that explains variations over millions of years generally cannot explain fluctuations over hundreds of years. If our atmosphere and its changes ever become fully understood, we will probably see that climate change is caused by many of the mechanisms discussed here, plus new ones yet to be proposed.

Plate Movements and Orbital Variations

The movement of lithospheric plates gradually moves Earth's continents closer to or farther from the equator. Although these shifts in latitude are very slow, they can have a dramatic impact on climate over spans of millions of years. Moving landmasses can also lead to significant shifts in ocean circulation, which influences heat transport around the globe.

A second natural mechanism of climate change related to the causes of ice ages involves variations in Earth's orbit. Changes in the shape of the orbit (*eccentricity*), variations in the angle that Earth's axis makes with the plane of its orbit (*obliquity*), and the wobbling of the axis (*precession*) cause fluctuations in the seasonal and latitudinal distribution of solar radiation. These variations, in turn, contributed to the alternating glacial–interglacial episodes of the Ice Age.

Volcanic Activity and Climate Change

The idea that explosive volcanic eruptions might alter Earth's climate was first proposed many years ago. It is still regarded as a plausible explanation for some aspects of climatic variability. Explosive eruptions emit huge quantities of gases and fine-grained debris into the atmosphere (FIGURE 19). The greatest eruptions are sufficiently powerful to inject material high into the atmosphere, where it spreads around the globe and remains for many months or even years.

The Effect of Volcanic Aerosols on Climate
Suspended volcanic material filters out a portion of the

This satellite image shows the sulfur dioxide (SO₂) plume in shades of purple and black. Climate may be affected when large quantities of SO_2 are injected into the atmosphere.

This image was taken from the International Space Station and shows a plume of volcanic ash streaming southeastward from the volcano.

FIGURE 19 **Mount Etna erupting in October 2002** This volcano on the island of Sicily is Europe's largest and most active volcano.

incoming solar radiation, which in turn lowers temperatures in the troposphere. More than 200 years ago, Benjamin Franklin used this idea to argue that material from the eruption of a large Icelandic volcano could have reflected sunlight back to space and therefore might have been responsible for the unusually cold winter of 1783–1784.

Perhaps the most notable cool period linked to a volcanic event is the "year without a summer" that followed the 1815 eruption of Mount Tambora in Indonesia. The eruption of Tambora is the largest of modern times. During April 7–12, 1815, this nearly 4000-meter-high (13,000-foot-high) volcano violently expelled an estimated 100 cubic kilometers (24 cubic miles) of volcanic debris. The impact of the volcanic aerosols on climate is believed to have been widespread in the Northern Hemisphere. From May through September 1816, an unprecedented series of cold spells affected the northeastern United States and adjacent portions of Canada. There was heavy snow in June and frost in July and August. Abnormal cold was also experienced in much of Western Europe. Similar, although apparently less dramatic, effects have been associated with other great explosive volcanoes, including Indonesia's Krakatoa in 1883.

Three major volcanic events have provided considerable data and insight regarding the impact of volcanoes on global temperatures. The eruptions of Washington State's Mount St. Helens in 1980, the Mexican volcano El Chichón in 1982, and Mount Pinatubo in the Philippines in 1991 have given scientists opportunities to study the atmospheric effects of volcanic eruptions with the aid of more sophisticated technology than was previously available. Satellite images and remote-sensing instruments allowed scientists to closely monitor the effects of the clouds of gases and ash that these volcanoes emitted.

Volcanic Ash and Dust When Mount St. Helens erupted, there was immediate speculation about the possible effects on climate. Could such an eruption cause our climate to change? There is no doubt that the large quantity of volcanic ash emitted by the explosive eruption had significant local and regional effects for a short period. Still, studies indicated that any longer-term lowering of hemispheric temperatures was negligible. The cooling was so slight—probably less than 0.1° C (0.2° F)—that it could not be distinguished from other natural temperature fluctuations.

Sulfuric Acid Droplets Two years of monitoring and studies following the 1982 El Chichón eruption indicated that its cooling effect on global mean temperature was greater than that of Mount St. Helens—on the order of 0.3° to 0.5° C (0.5° to 0.9° F). The eruption of El Chichón was *less explosive* than the Mount St. Helens blast, yet it had a greater impact on global temperatures. Why was that so? The reason is that the material emitted by Mount St. Helens was largely fine ash that settled out in a relatively short time. El Chichón, on the other hand, emitted far greater quantities of sulfur dioxide gas (an estimated 40 times more) than Mount St. Helens. This gas combines with water vapor in the stratosphere to produce a dense cloud of tiny sulfuric acid particles (FIGURE 20A). The particles take several years to settle out completely. They lower the troposphere's mean temperature because they reflect solar radiation back to space (FIGURE 20B).

We now understand that volcanic clouds that remain in the stratosphere for a year or more are composed largely of sulfuric-acid droplets and not of dust, as was once thought. Thus, the volume of fine debris

FIGURE 20 Volcanic haze reducing sunlight at Earth's surface The reflective haze produced by some volcanic eruptions is not volcanic ash but tiny sulfuric acid aerosols.

A plume of white haze from Anatahan Volcano blankets a portion of the Philippine Sea in April 2005. The haze consisted of tiny droplets of sulfuric acid formed when sulfur dioxide from the volcano combined with water in the atmosphere. The plume is bright and reflects sunlight back to space.

A.

Net solar radiation at Hawaii's Mauna Loa Observatory relative to 1970 (zero on the graph). The eruptions of El Chichón and Mt. Pinatubo clearly caused temporary drops in solar radiation reaching the surface.

B.

emitted during an explosive event is not an accurate criterion for predicting the global atmospheric effects of an eruption.

The Mount Pinatubo in the Philippines erupted explosively in June 1991, injecting 25 to 30 million tons of sulfur dioxide into the stratosphere. The event provided scientists with an opportunity to study the climatic impact of a major explosive volcanic eruption using NASA's spaceborne Earth Radiation Budget Experiment. During the next year, the haze of tiny aerosols increased reflectivity and lowered global temperatures by 0.5° C (0.9° F).

The impact on global temperature of eruptions like El Chichón and Mount Pinatubo is relatively minor, but many scientists agree that the cooling produced could alter the general pattern of atmospheric circulation for a limited period. Such a change, in turn, could influence the weather in some regions. Predicting, or even identifying, specific regional effects still presents a considerable challenge to atmospheric scientists.

The preceding examples illustrate that the impact on climate of a single volcanic eruption, no matter how great, is relatively small and short-lived. The graph in Figure 20B reinforces this point. Therefore, if the processes discussed in this section are to have a pronounced impact over an extended period, many great eruptions, closely spaced in time, need to occur. Because no such period of explosive volcanism is known to have occurred in historic times, it is most often mentioned as a possible contributor to prehistoric climatic shifts.

Volcanism and Global Warming   The Cretaceous period is the last period of the Mesozoic era, the era of *middle life* that is often called the "age of dinosaurs." It began about 145.5 million years ago and ended about 65.5 million years ago, with the extinction of the dinosaurs (and many other life-forms as well).

The Cretaceous climate was among the warmest in Earth's long history. Dinosaurs, which are associated with mild temperatures, ranged north of the Arctic Circle. Tropical forests existed in Greenland and Antarctica, and coral reefs grew as much as 15 degrees latitude closer to the poles than at present. Deposits of peat that would eventually form widespread coal beds accumulated at high latitudes. Sea level was as much as 200 meters (650 feet) higher than it is today, consistent with a lack of polar ice sheets.

What was the cause of the unusually warm climates of the Cretaceous period? Among the significant factors that may have contributed was an enhancement of the greenhouse effect due to an increase in the amount of carbon dioxide in the atmosphere.

Where did the additional CO_2 that contributed to the Cretaceous warming come from? Many geologists suggest that the probable source was volcanic activity. Carbon dioxide is one of the gases emitted during volcanism, and there is now considerable geologic evidence that the Middle Cretaceous was a time when there was an unusually high rate of volcanic activity. Several huge oceanic lava plateaus were produced on the floor of the western Pacific during this span. These vast features were associated with hot spots that may have been produced by large mantle plumes. Massive outpourings of lava over millions of years would have been accompanied by the release of huge quantities of CO_2, which in turn would have enhanced the atmospheric greenhouse effect. *Thus, the warmth that characterized the Cretaceous may have had its origins deep in Earth's mantle.*

This example serves to illustrate the interrelationships among parts of the Earth system. Materials and processes that at first might seem to be completely unrelated turn out to be linked. Here you have seen how processes originating deep in Earth's interior are connected directly or indirectly to the atmosphere, the oceans, and the biosphere.

Solar Variability and Climate

Among the most persistent hypotheses of climate change have been those based on the idea that the Sun is a variable star and that its output of energy varies through time. The effect of such changes would seem direct and easily understood: Increases in solar output would cause the atmosphere to warm, and reductions would result in cooling. This notion is appealing because it can be used to explain climate change of any length or intensity. However, no major *long-term* variations in the total intensity of solar radiation have yet been measured outside the atmosphere. Such measurements were not even possible until satellite technology became available. Now that such measurements are being made, we will need many decades of records before we begin to sense how variable (or invariable) energy from the Sun really is.

Over the years, some hypotheses for climate change have related to sunspot cycles. The most conspicuous and best-known features on the surface of the Sun are the dark blemishes called **sunspots** (FIGURE 21). Sunspots are huge magnetic storms that extend from the Sun's surface deep into the interior. Moreover, these spots are associated with the Sun's ejection of huge masses of particles that, on reaching Earth's upper atmosphere, interact with gases to produce displays known as the *aurora borealis*, or Northern Lights, in the Northern Hemisphere.

Sunspots occur in cycles, with the number of sunspots reaching a maximum about every 11 years (FIGURE 22). During periods of maximum sunspot activity, the Sun emits slightly more energy than during sunspot minimums. Based on measurements from space that began in 1978, the variation during an 11-year cycle is about 0.1 percent. Although sunspots are dark, they are surrounded by brighter areas, which apparently offsets the effect of the dark spots. It appears that this change in solar output is too small and the cycles are too short

This view shows an approximation of the Sun's surface. The black spots surrounded by deep orange is a sunspot region where magnetic activity is extremely intense.

The instrument that produced this image used ultraviolet, radio, and other parts of the electromagnetic spectrum. Looping lines show solar plasma following magnetic field lines.

to have any appreciable effect on global temperatures. However, there is a possibility that longer-term variations in solar output may affect climates on Earth.

For example, the span between 1645 and 1715 was a period, known as the *Maunder minimum*, during which sunspots were largely absent. This period of missing sunspots closely corresponds with a period in climate history known as the *Little Ice Age*, an especially cold period in Europe. For some scientists, this correlation suggests that a reduction in the Sun's output was likely responsible at least in part for this cold episode.

FIGURE 22 Mean annual sunspot numbers
The number of sunspots reaches a maximum about every 11 years.

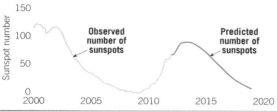

Other scientists seriously question this notion. Their hesitation stems, in part, from subsequent investigations using different climate records from around the world that failed to find a significant correlation between sunspot activity and climate.

5 CONCEPT CHECKS

1. Describe and briefly explain the effect on global temperatures of the eruptions of El Chichón and Mount Pinatubo.
2. How might volcanism lead to global warming?
3. What are sunspots? How does solar output change as sunspot numbers change? Is there a solid connection between sunspot numbers and climate change on Earth?

EYE on Earth

This volcanic eruption from Japan's Mount Kirishima began on January 26, 2011. In this view, the volcano is spewing ash 1500 meters (5000 feet) into the atmosphere. It was the largest eruption at this site since 1959. Scientists familiar with this volcanic area predicted that this eruptive phase could last for a year or more. (Photo by Kyodo/AP Images)

Question 1 How might the volcanic ash from this eruption influence air temperatures?

Question 2 Would this effect likely be long-lasting—perhaps for years? Explain.

Question 3 What "invisible" volcanic emission might have a greater effect than the volcanic ash?

6 Human Impact on Global Climate

So far we have examined potential causes of climate change that are natural. In this section, we examine how humans contribute to global climate change. One impact largely results from the addition of carbon dioxide and other greenhouse gases to the atmosphere. A second impact is related to the addition of human-generated aerosols to the atmosphere.

Human influence on regional and global climate did not just begin with the onset of the modern industrial period. There is good evidence that people have been modifying the environment over extensive areas for thousands of years. The use of fire and the overgrazing of marginal lands by domesticated animals have both reduced the abundance and distribution of vegetation. By altering ground cover, humans have modified such important climate factors as surface albedo, evaporation rates, and surface winds.

FIGURE 23 U.S. energy consumption
The graph shows energy consumption in 2011. The total was 97.5 quadrillion Btu. A quadrillion is 10 raised to the 12th power, or a million million. The burning of fossil fuels represents slightly more than 82 percent of the total.
(Data from U.S. Energy Information Administration)

Rising CO_2 Levels

Earlier you learned that carbon dioxide (CO_2) represents only about 0.0395 percent (395 parts per million) of the gases that make up clean, dry air. Nevertheless, it is a very significant component meteorologically. Carbon dioxide is influential because it is transparent to incoming short-wavelength solar radiation, but it is not transparent to some of the longer-wavelength outgoing Earth radiation. A portion of the energy leaving the ground is absorbed by atmospheric CO_2. This energy is subsequently re-emitted, part of it back toward the surface, thereby keeping the air near the ground warmer than it would be without CO_2. Thus, along with water vapor, carbon dioxide is largely responsible for the *greenhouse effect* of the atmosphere. Carbon dioxide is an important heat absorber, and it follows logically that any change in the air's CO_2 content could alter temperatures in the lower atmosphere.

Earth's tremendous industrialization of the past two centuries has been fueled—and still is fueled—by burning fossil fuels: coal, natural gas, and petroleum (FIGURE 23). Combustion of these fuels has added great quantities of carbon dioxide to the atmosphere. FIGURE 24 shows changes in CO_2 concentrations at Hawaii's Mauna Loa Observatory, where measurements have been made since 1958 (see the chapter-opening

photo). The graph shows an annual seasonal cycle and a steady upward trend over the years. The up-and-down of the seasonal cycle is due to the vast land area of the Northern Hemisphere, which contains the majority of land-based vegetation. During spring and summer in the Northern Hemisphere, when plants are absorbing CO_2 as part of photosynthesis, concentrations decrease. The annual increase in CO_2 during the cold months occurs as vegetation dies and leaves fall and decompose, which releases CO_2 back into the air.

The use of coal and other fuels is the most prominent means by which humans add CO_2 to the atmosphere, but it is not the only way. The clearing of forests also contributes substantially because CO_2 is released as vegetation is burned or decays. Deforestation is particularly pronounced in the tropics, where vast tracts are cleared for

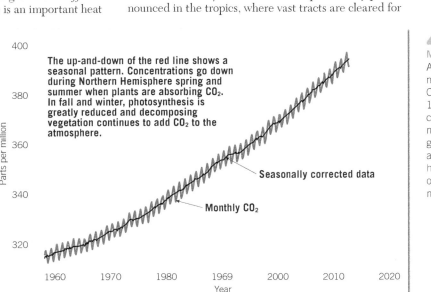

The up-and-down of the red line shows a seasonal pattern. Concentrations go down during Northern Hemisphere spring and summer when plants are absorbing CO_2. In fall and winter, photosynthesis is greatly reduced and decomposing vegetation continues to add CO_2 to the atmosphere.

Seasonally corrected data

Monthly CO_2

SMARTFIGURE 24
Monthly CO_2 concentrations
Atmospheric CO_2 has been measured at Mauna Loa Observatory, Hawaii, since 1958. There has been a consistent increase since monitoring began. This graphic portrayal is known as the *Keeling Curve* in honor of the scientist who originated the measurements. (NOAA)

EYE on Earth

The Amundsen-Scott South Pole Station is an American research facility. Among the phenomena that are monitored here are variations in atmospheric composition. The accompanying graph shows changes in the air's CO_2 content at South Pole Station (90 degrees south latitude) and at a similar facility at Barrow, Alaska (71 degrees north latitude) (Photo by Scot Jackson, National Science Foundation/ZUMA/Newscom)

Question 1 Describe how the two lines on the graph differ.

Question 2 Which line on the graph represents the South Pole, and which represents Barrow, Alaska?

Question 3 Explain how you were able to determine which line is which.

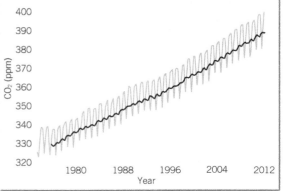

ranching and agriculture or are subjected to inefficient commercial logging operations (FIGURE 25). According to United Nations estimates, nearly 10.2 million hectares (25.1 million acres) of tropical forest were permanently destroyed each year during the 1990s. Between the years 2000 and 2005, the average figure increased to 10.4 million hectares (25.7 million acres) per year.

Some of the excess CO_2 is taken up by plants or is dissolved in the ocean. It is estimated that about 45 percent remains in the atmosphere. FIGURE 26 is a graphic record of changes in atmospheric CO_2 extending back more than 400,000 years. Over this long span, natural fluctuations have varied from about 180 to 300 ppm. As a result of human activities, the present CO_2 level is about 30 percent higher than its highest level over at least the past 650,000 years. The rapid increase in CO_2 concentrations since the onset of industrialization is obvious. The annual rate at which atmospheric CO_2 concentrations are growing has been increasing over the past several decades.

The Atmosphere's Response

Given the increase in the atmosphere's carbon dioxide content, have global temperatures actually increased? The answer is "yes." According to a 2007 report by the Intergovernmental Panel on Climate Change (IPCC), "Warming of the climate system is unequivocal, as is now evident from observations of increases in global average air and ocean temperatures, widespread

FIGURE 25 Tropical deforestation
Clearing the tropical rain forest is a serious environmental issue. In addition to causing a loss of biodiversity, it is a significant source of carbon dioxide. Fires are frequently used to clear the land. This scene is in Brazil's Amazon basin. (Photo by Pete Oxford/Nature Picture Library)

melting of snow and ice, and rising global sea level."* Most of the observed increase in global average temperatures since the mid-twentieth century is *very likely* due to the observed increase in human-generated greenhouse gas concentrations. (As used by the IPCC, *very likely* indicates a probability of 90–99 percent.) Global warming since the mid-1970s is now about 0.6° C (1° F), and total warming in the past century is about 0.8° C (1.4° F). The upward trend in surface temperatures is shown in FIGURE 27A. The world map in FIGURE 27B compares surface temperatures for 2011 to the base period (1951–1980). You can see that the greatest warming has been in the Arctic and neighboring high-latitude regions. Here are some related facts:

- When we consider the time span for which there are instrumental records (since 1850), the warmest 16 years have all been in the past 17 years (1995–2011).
- Global mean temperature is now higher than at any time in at least the past 500 to 1000 years.
- The average temperature of the global ocean has increased to depths of at least 3000 meters (10,000 feet).

Are these temperature trends caused by human activities, or would they have occurred anyway? The scientific consensus of the IPCC is that human activities were *very likely* responsible for most of the temperature increase since 1950.

What about the future? Projections for the years ahead depend in part on the quantities of greenhouse gases that are emitted. FIGURE 28 shows the best estimates of global warming for several different scenarios. The 2007 IPCC report also states that if there is a doubling of the preindustrial level of carbon dioxide (280 ppm) to 560 ppm, the "likely" temperature increase will be in the range of 2° to 4.5° C (3.5° to 8.1° F). The increase is "very unlikely" (1 to 10 percent probability) to be less than 1.5° C (2.7° F), and values higher than 4.5° C (8.1° F) are possible.

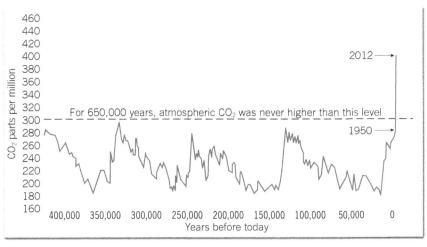

FIGURE 26 CO₂ concentrations over the past 400,000 years Most of these data come from the analysis of air bubbles trapped in ice cores. The record since 1958 comes from direct measurements at Mauna Loa Observatory, Hawaii. The rapid increase in CO_2 concentrations since the onset of the Industrial Revolution is obvious. (NOAA)

The Role of Trace Gases

Carbon dioxide is not the only gas that contributes to the global increase in temperature. In recent years, atmospheric scientists have come to realize that the industrial and agricultural activities of people are causing a buildup of several trace gases that also play a significant role. The substances are called *trace gases* because their concentrations are so much lower than the concentration of carbon dioxide. The trace gases that are most important are methane (CH_4), nitrous oxide (N_2O), and

A.

FIGURE 27 Global temperatures The year 2011 was 1 of the 10 warmest years on record. **A.** The graph depicts global temperature change in degrees Celsius since the year 1880. **B.** The world map shows how temperatures in 2011 deviated from the mean for the 1951–1980 base period. The high latitudes in the Northern Hemisphere clearly stand out. (NASA/Goddard Institute for Space Studies)

Temperature difference (°C) compared to 1951-80 mean

B.

---

*IPCC, "Summary for Policy Makers." In *Climate Change 2007: The Physical Science Basis* (Cambridge, UK: Cambridge University Press), p. 4. The Intergovernmental Panel on Climate Change is an authoritative group that provides advice to the world community through periodic reports that assess the state of knowledge of causes of climate change. More than 1250 authors and 2500 scientific reviewers from more than 130 countries contributed to the 2007 report. The next major assessment report is expected to be published in several parts between September 2013 and October 2014.

FIGURE 28 Temperature projections to 2100
The right half of the graph shows projected global warming based on different emissions scenarios. The shaded zone adjacent to each colored line shows the uncertainty range for each scenario. The basis for comparison (0.0 on the vertical axis) is the global average for the period 1980 to 1999. The orange line represents the scenario in which CO_2 concentrations were held constant at values for the year 2000. (NOAA)

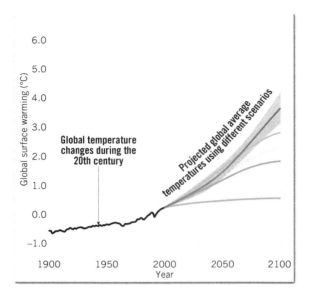

chlorofluorocarbons (CFCs). These gases absorb wavelengths of outgoing radiation from Earth that would otherwise escape into space. Although individually their impact is modest, taken together, these trace gases play a significant role in warming the troposphere.

Methane Although present in much smaller amounts than CO_2, methane's significance is greater than its relatively small concentration would indicate (FIGURE 29). The reason is that methane is about 20 times more effective than CO_2 at absorbing infrared radiation emitted by Earth.

Methane is produced by *anaerobic* bacteria in wet places where oxygen is scarce (*anaerobic* means "without air," specifically oxygen). Such places include swamps, bogs, wetlands, and the guts of termites and grazing animals such as cattle and sheep. Methane is also generated

in flooded paddy fields ("artificial swamps") used for growing rice (FIGURE 30). Mining of coal and drilling for oil and natural gas are other sources because methane is a product of the formation of these fuels.

The concentration of methane in the atmosphere has risen rapidly since 1800, an increase that has been in step with the growth in human population. This relationship reflects the close link between methane formation and agriculture. As population has risen, so have the number of cattle and rice paddies.

Nitrous Oxide Sometimes called "laughing gas," nitrous oxide is also building in the atmosphere, although not as rapidly as methane (see Figure 29). The increase results primarily from agricultural activity. When farmers use nitrogen fertilizers to boost crop yields, some of the nitrogen enters the air as nitrous oxide. This gas is also produced by high-temperature combustion of fossil fuels. Although the annual release into the atmosphere is small, the lifetime of a nitrous oxide molecule is about 150 years! If the use of nitrogen fertilizers and fossil fuels grows at projected rates, nitrous oxide may make a contribution to greenhouse warming that approaches half that of methane.

CFCs Unlike methane and nitrous oxide, chlorofluorocarbons (CFCs) are not naturally present in the atmosphere. CFCs are manufactured chemicals with many uses that have gained notoriety because they are responsible for ozone depletion in the stratosphere. The role of CFCs in global warming is less well known. CFCs are very effective greenhouse gases. They were not developed until the 1920s and were not used in great quantities until the 1950s. Although corrective action has been taken, CFC levels will *not* drop rapidly. CFCs remain in the atmosphere for decades, so even if all CFC emissions were to stop immediately, the atmosphere would not be free of them for many years.

FIGURE 29 Methane and nitrous oxide
Although CO_2 is most important, these trace gases also contribute to global warming. Over the 2000-year span shown here, there were relatively minor fluctuations until the industrial era. The graph on the right shows recent trends. (U.S. Global Change Research Program and NOAA)

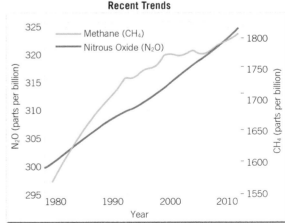

A Combined Effect Carbon dioxide is clearly the most important single cause of the projected global greenhouse warming. However, it is not the only contributor. When the effects of all human-generated greenhouse gases other than CO_2 are added together and projected into the future, their collective impact significantly increases the impact of CO_2 alone.

Sophisticated computer models show that the warming of the lower atmosphere caused by CO_2 and trace gases will not be the same everywhere. Rather, the temperature response in polar regions could be two to three times greater than the global average. One reason is that the polar troposphere is very stable, which suppresses vertical mixing and thus limits the amount of surface heat that is transferred upward. In addition, the expected reduction in sea ice will also contribute to the greater temperature increase. This topic will be explored more fully in the next section.

6 CONCEPT CHECKS

1. Why has the CO_2 level of the atmosphere been increasing over the past 200 years?
2. How has the atmosphere responded to the growing CO_2 levels?
3. How are temperatures in the lower atmosphere likely to change as CO_2 levels continue to increase?
4. Aside from CO_2, what trace gases are contributing to global temperature change?

FIGURE 30 Methane Methane is produced by anaerobic bacteria in wet places, where oxygen is scarce. (*Anaerobic* means "without air," specifically oxygen.) Such places include swamps, bogs, wetlands, and the guts of termites and grazing animals such as cattle and sheep. Methane is also generated in flooded paddy fields ("artificial swamps") used for growing rice. Coal mining and drilling for oil and natural gas are other sources of methane. (Photo by Robert Harding Picture Library/SuperStock)

Grazing animals are one source of methane, which is a significant greenhouse gas. (Photo by Glow Images)

Greenhouse Gas (GHG) Emissions

GLOBAL GREENHOUSE GAS EMISSIONS
BY GAS

How can we compare different GHGs when some are more effective at warming the atmosphere than others? To make comparisons it is necessary to use a unit that takes into account these differing impacts. The preferred unit, called CO_2 equivalent, expresses the impact of a GHG in terms of the impact of an equivalent amount of CO_2.

1%
CFCs

8%
NITROUS OXIDE

14%
METHANE

17%
CARBON DIOXIDE
(deforestation, decay of biomass, etc.)

57%
CARBON DIOXIDE
(fossil fuel use)

3%
CARBON DIOXIDE
(other)

UNITED STATES GREENHOUSE GAS EMISSIONS
BY SOURCE

Compare the sources of United States emissions with the global figures and you will see some significant differences. Can you explain the difference in the transportation category? Forests and land use are a source for global emissions but are not listed for the U.S. Why? Land areas can act as a sink (absorbing CO_2 from the air) or a source of GHG emissions. In the U.S. since 1990, managed forests and other lands have absorbed more CO_2 from the atmosphere than they emit.

7%
AGRICULTURE

11%
COMMERCIAL & RESIDENTIAL

35%
ELECTRICITY

20%
INDUSTRY

27%
TRANSPORTATION

Usually when you see power lines like these, the electricity they are transmitting was generated by burning fossil fuels.

Kodda/Shutterstock

13.5 Climate Change: Accelerating

The ever-escalating emissions of greenhouse gases (GHG) can be traced to all parts of the planet and to all sections of society and the economy.

GLOBAL GREENHOUSE GAS EMISSIONS
BY SOURCE

The burning of fossil fuels is a major part of emissions from energy supply, industry, transport, and residential and commercial buildings.

3% WASTE MANAGEMENT
17% FORESTRY
26% ENERGY SUPPLY
14% AGRICULTURE
13% TRANSPORT
19% INDUSTRY
8% RESIDENTIAL & COMMERCIAL BUILDINGS

GLOBAL CO$_2$ EMISSIONS FROM
FOSSIL FUEL COMBUSTION

Notice that the U.S. is responsible for 19 percent of global emissions. The U.S. population represents about 4.5 percent of the world total.

23% CHINA
28% OTHER
2% CANADA
4% JAPAN
6% RUSSIAN FEDERATION
6% INDIA
13% EU-27 (excluding Estonia, Latvia and Lithuania)
19% USA

HOW MUCH CO$_2$ DOES AN
AVERAGE AMERICAN PRODUCE?

17,000 POUNDS OF CO$_2$
by using **1,100 kilowatt-hours of electricity**
per month

8,800 POUNDS OF CO$_2$
by using **6,300 cubic feet of natural gas**
per month

1,000 POUNDS OF CO$_2$
by creating **4.5 pounds of trash**
per day

1,000 POUNDS OF CO$_2$
by **driving 160 miles**
per week

8,900 POUNDS OF CO$_2$
by **flying 1,900 miles**
per year

RelaXimages/SuperStock

7 Climate-Feedback Mechanisms

Climate is a very complex interactive physical system. Thus, when any component of the climate system is altered, scientists must consider many possible outcomes, some of which amplify the initial effect and some of which balance it out. These possible outcomes are called **climate-feedback mechanisms**. They complicate climate-modeling efforts and add greater uncertainty to climate predictions.

Types of Feedback Mechanisms

What climate-feedback mechanisms are related to carbon dioxide and other greenhouse gases? One important mechanism is that warmer surface temperatures increase evaporation rates. This in turn increases the atmosphere's water vapor content. Remember that water vapor is an even more powerful absorber of radiation emitted by Earth than is carbon dioxide. Therefore, with more water vapor in the air, the temperature increase caused by carbon dioxide and the trace gases is reinforced.

Recall that the temperature increase at high latitudes may be two to three times greater than the global average. This projection is based in part on the likelihood that the area covered by sea ice will decrease as surface temperatures rise. Because ice reflects a much larger percentage of incoming solar radiation than does open water, the melting of the sea ice causes a surface having a high albedo to be replaced by a surface with a much lower albedo (FIGURE 31). The result is a substantial increase in the solar energy absorbed at the surface. This in turn feeds back to the atmosphere and magnifies the initial temperature increase created by higher levels of greenhouse gases.

So far, the climate-feedback mechanisms discussed have magnified the temperature rise caused by the buildup of carbon dioxide. Because these effects reinforce the initial change, they are called **positive-feedback mechanisms**. However, other effects must be classified as **negative-feedback mechanisms** because they produce results that are just the opposite of the initial change and tend to offset it.

One probable result of a global temperature rise would be an accompanying increase in cloud cover due to the higher moisture content of the atmosphere. Most clouds are good reflectors of solar radiation. At the same time, however, they are also good absorbers and emitters of radiation emitted by Earth. Consequently, clouds produce two opposite effects. They are a negative-feedback mechanism because they increase the reflection of solar radiation and thus diminish the amount of solar energy available to heat the atmosphere. On the other hand, clouds act as a positive-feedback mechanism by absorbing and emitting radiation that would otherwise be lost from the troposphere.

Which effect, if either, is stronger? Scientists still are not sure whether clouds will produce net positive or negative feedback. Although recent studies have not settled the question, they seem to lean toward the idea that clouds do not dampen global warming but rather produce a small positive feedback overall.*

Global warming caused by human-induced changes in atmospheric composition continues to be one of the most-studied aspects of climate change. Although no models yet incorporate the full range of potential factors and feedbacks, there is strong scientific consensus that the increasing levels of atmospheric carbon dioxide and trace gases have already warmed the planet and will continue to do so into the foreseeable future.

Computer Models of Climate: Important Yet Imperfect Tools

Earth's climate system is amazingly complex. Comprehensive state-of-the-science climate simulation models are among the basic tools used to develop possible climate-change scenarios. Called *general circulation models (GCMs)*, they are based on fundamental laws of physics and chemistry and incorporate human and biological interactions. The models simulate many variables, including temperature, rainfall, snow cover, soil moisture,

FIGURE 31 Sea ice as a feedback mechanism The image shows the springtime breakup of sea ice near Antarctica. The diagram shows a likely feedback loop. A reduction in sea ice acts as a positive-feedback mechanism because surface albedo decreases, and the amount of energy absorbed at the surface increases. (Photo by Radius Images/Alamy Images)

Decline in the perennial ice cover

Longer melt period

Reduced reflectivity

Warmer ocean

Increased absorption of solar radiation

*A. E. Dessler, "A Determination of the Cloud Feedback from Climate Variations over the Past Decade," *Science* 330: 1523–1526, December 10, 2010.

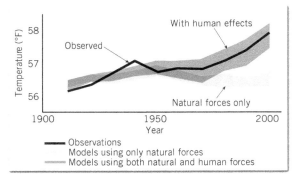

FIGURE 32 Computer models
The blue band shows how global average temperatures would have changed due to natural forces only, as simulated by climate models. The red band shows model projections of the effects of human and natural forces combined. The black line shows actual observed global average temperatures. As the blue band indicates, without human influences, temperatures over the past century would actually have first warmed and then cooled slightly over recent decades. Bands of color are used to express the range of uncertainty. (U.S. Global Change Research Program)

winds, clouds, sea ice, and ocean circulation over the entire globe through the seasons and over spans of decades.

In many other fields of study, hypotheses can be tested by direct experimentation in the laboratory or by observations and measurements in the field. However, this is often not possible in the study of climate. Rather, scientists must construct computer models of how our

planet's climate system works. If we understand the climate system correctly and construct a model appropriately, then the behavior of the model climate system should mimic the behavior of Earth's climate system (FIGURE 32).

What factors influence the accuracy of climate models? Clearly, mathematical models are *simplified* versions of the real Earth and cannot capture its full complexity, especially at smaller geographic scales. Moreover, when computer models are used to simulate future climate change, many assumptions have to be made that significantly influence the outcome. They must consider a wide range of possibilities for future changes in population, economic growth, consumption of fossil fuels, technological development, improvements in energy efficiency, and more.

Despite many obstacles, our ability to use supercomputers to simulate climate continues to improve. Although today's models are far from infallible, they are powerful tools for understanding what Earth's future climate might be like.

7 CONCEPT CHECKS

1. Distinguish between positive and negative climate-feedback mechanisms.
2. Provide at least one example of each type of feedback mechanism.
3. What factors influence the accuracy of computer models of climate?

The role of clouds as climate feedback mechanisms is complex and still a focus of research. This image, taken from the International Space Station, shows bands of high clouds that were created when condensation trails (contrails) from jet aircraft remained in the sky and spread out. In some places, such layers of "artificial clouds" are common. (NASA)

8 How Aerosols Influence Climate

Increasing the levels of carbon dioxide and other greenhouse gases in the atmosphere is the most direct human influence on global climate. But it is not the only impact. Global climate is also affected by human activities that contribute to the atmosphere's aerosol content. Recall that *aerosols* are the tiny, often microscopic, liquid and solid particles that are suspended in the air. Unlike cloud droplets, aerosols are present even in relatively dry air. Atmospheric aerosols are composed of many different materials, including soil, smoke, sea salt, and sulfuric acid. Natural sources are numerous and include such phenomena as dust storms and volcanoes.

Most human-generated aerosols come from the sulfur dioxide emitted during the combustion of fossil fuels and as a consequence of burning vegetation to clear agricultural land. Chemical reactions in the atmosphere convert the sulfur dioxide into sulfate aerosols, the same material that produces acid precipitation. The satellite images in FIGURE 33 provide an example.

How do aerosols affect climate? Aerosols act directly by reflecting sunlight back to space and indirectly by making clouds "brighter" reflectors. The second effect relates to the fact that many aerosols (such as those composed of salt or sulfuric acid) attract water and thus are especially effective as cloud condensation nuclei. The large quantity of aerosols produced by human activities (especially industrial emissions) trigger an increase in the number of cloud droplets that form within a cloud. A greater number of small droplets increases the cloud's brightness, causing more sunlight to be reflected back to space.

One category of aerosols, called *black carbon*, is soot generated by combustion processes and fires. Unlike most other aerosols, black carbon warms the atmosphere because it is an effective absorber of incoming solar radiation. In addition, when deposited on snow and ice, black carbon reduces surface albedo, thus increasing the amount of light absorbed. Nevertheless, despite the warming effect of black carbon, the overall effect of atmospheric aerosols is to cool Earth.

Studies indicate that the cooling effect of human-generated aerosols offsets a portion of the global warming caused by the growing quantities of greenhouse gases in the atmosphere. The magnitude and extent of the cooling effect of aerosols is uncertain. This uncertainty is a significant hurdle in advancing our understanding of how humans alter Earth's climate.

FIGURE 33 Human-generated aerosols These satellite images show a serious air pollution episode that plagued China on October 8, 2010. (NASA)

This satellite image shows the extremely high levels of aerosols associated with this air pollution episode. At an index value of 4, aerosols are so dense that you would have difficulty seeing the midday sun.

It is important to point out some significant differences between global warming by greenhouse gases and aerosol cooling. After being emitted, greenhouse gases, such as carbon dioxide, remain in the atmosphere for many decades. By contrast, aerosols released into the troposphere remain there for only a few days or, at most, a few weeks before they are "washed out" by precipitation. Because of their short lifetime in the troposphere, aerosols are distributed unevenly over the globe. As expected, human-generated aerosols are concentrated near the areas that produce them—namely industrialized regions that burn fossil fuels and land areas where vegetation is burned.

The lifetime of aerosols in the atmosphere is short. Therefore, the effect of aerosols on today's climate is determined by the amount emitted during the preceding couple weeks. By contrast, the carbon dioxide and trace gases released into the atmosphere remain for much longer spans and thus influence climate for many decades.

8 CONCEPT CHECKS

1. What are the main sources of human-generated aerosols?
2. What effect does black carbon have on atmospheric temperatures?
3. What is the net effect of aerosols on temperatures in the troposphere?
4. How long do aerosols remain in the atmosphere before they are removed?
5. How does the residence time of aerosols compare to that of CO_2?

EYE on Earth

This satellite image from August 2007 shows the effects of tropical deforestation in a portion of the Amazon basin in western Brazil. Intact forest is dark green, whereas cleared areas are tan (bare ground) or light green (crops and pasture). Notice the relatively dense smoke in the left center of the image. (NASA)

Question 1 How does the destruction of tropical forests change the composition of the atmosphere?

Question 2 Describe the effect that tropical deforestation has on global warming.

9   Some Possible Consequences of Global Warming

What consequences can be expected if the carbon dioxide content of the atmosphere reaches a level that is twice what it was early in the twentieth century? Because the climate system is complex, predicting the distribution of particular regional changes can be speculative. It is not yet possible to pinpoint specifics, such as where or when it will become drier or wetter. Nevertheless, plausible scenarios can be given for larger scales of space and time.

As noted, the magnitude of the temperature increase will not be the same everywhere. The temperature rise will probably be smallest in the tropics and increase toward the poles. As for precipitation, the models indicate that some regions will experience significantly more precipitation and runoff, whereas others will experience a decrease in runoff due to reduced precipitation or greater evaporation caused by higher temperatures.

TABLE 1 summarizes some of the most likely effects and their possible consequences. The table also provides the IPCC's estimate of the probability of each effect. Levels of confidence for these projections vary from "likely" (67 to 90 percent probability) to "very likely" (90 to 99 percent probability) to "virtually certain" (greater than 99 percent probability).

Sea-Level Rise

A significant impact of a human-induced global warming is a rise in sea level. As this occurs, coastal cities, wetlands, and low-lying islands could be threatened with more frequent flooding, increased shoreline erosion, and saltwater encroachment into coastal rivers and aquifers.

Research indicates that sea level has risen about 25 centimeters (9.75 inches) since 1870. As FIGURE 34 indicates, the rate of sea-level rise has been greater in recent years. Some models indicate that additional rise may approach or even exceed 50 centimeters (20 inches) by the end of the twenty-first century. Such a change may seem modest, but scientists realize that any rise in sea level along a *gently* sloping shoreline, such as the Atlantic and Gulf coasts of the United States, will lead to significant erosion and severe and permanent inland flooding (FIGURE 35). If this happens, many beaches and wetlands will be eliminated, and coastal civilization would be severely disrupted. Low-lying and densely populated places such as Bangladesh and the small island nation of the Maldives are especially vulnerable. The average elevation in the Maldives is 1.5 meters (less than 5 feet), and its highest point is just 2.4 meters (less than 8 feet) above sea level.

TABLE 1 Projected Changes and Effects of Global Warming in the Twenty-First Century

Projected Changes and Estimated Probability*	Examples of Projected Impacts
Higher maximum temperatures; more hot days and heat waves over nearly all land areas (*virtually certain*).	Increased incidence of death and serious illness in older age groups and urban poor. Increased heat stress in livestock and wildlife. Shift in tourist destinations. Increased risk of damage to a number of crops. Increased electric cooling demand and reduced energy supply reliability.
Higher minimum temperatures; fewer cold days, frost days, and cold waves over nearly all land areas (*virtually certain*)	Decreased cold-related human morbidity and mortality. Decreased risk of damage to a number of crops, and increased risk to others. Extended range and activity of some pest and disease vectors. Reduced heating energy demand.
Increases in frequency of heavy precipitation events over most areas (*very likely*)	Increased flood, landslide, avalanche, and debris flow damage. Increased soil erosion. Increased flood runoff could increase recharge of some floodplain aquifers. Increased pressure on government and private flood insurance systems and disaster relief.
Increases in area affected by drought (*likely*)	Decreased crop yields. Increased damage to building foundations caused by ground shrinkage. Decreased water-resource quantity and quality. Increased risk of wildfires.
Increases in intense tropical cyclone activity (*likely*)	Increased risks to human life, risk of infectious-disease epidemics, and many other risks. Increased coastal erosion and damage to coastal buildings and infrastructure. Increased damage to coastal ecosystems, such as coral reefs and mangroves.

Virtually certain indicates a probability greater than 99 percent, *very likely* indicates a probability of 90–99 percent, and *likely* indicates a probability of 67–90 percent.

Source: Adapted from Climate Change 2007: Synthesis Report. Contribution of Working Groups I, II and III to the Fourth Assessment Report of the Intergovernmental Panel on Climate Change, Figure SPM.3. IPCC, Geneva, Switzerland.

How is a warmer atmosphere related to a rise in sea level? One significant factor is thermal expansion. Higher air temperatures warm the adjacent upper layers of the ocean, which in turn causes the water to expand and sea level to rise.

Perhaps a more easily visualized contributor to global sea-level rise is melting glaciers. With few exceptions, glaciers around the world have been retreating at unprecedented rates over the past century. Some mountain glaciers have disappeared altogether. A recent 18-year satellite study showed that the mass of the Greenland and Antarctic Ice Sheets dropped an average of 475 gigatons per year. (A gigaton is 1 billion metric tons.) That is enough water to raise sea level 1.5 millimeters (0.05 inch) per year. The loss of ice was not steady but was occurring at an accelerating rate during the study period. Each year over the course of the study period, the two ice sheets lost a combined average of 36.3 gigatons more than they did the year before. During the same span, mountain glaciers and ice caps lost an average of slightly more than 400 gigatons per year.

Because rising sea level is a gradual phenomenon, coastal residents may overlook it as an important contributor to shoreline erosion problems. Rather, the blame may be assigned to other forces, especially storm activity. Although a given storm may be the immediate cause, the magnitude of its destruction may result from the relatively small sea level rise that allowed the storm's power to cross a much greater land area.

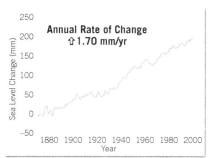

Annual Rate of Change
⇧ 1.70 mm/yr

A. Sea Level Change 1870 to 2000

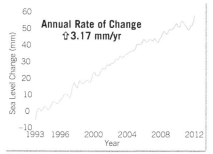

Annual Rate of Change
⇧ 3.17 mm/yr

B. Sea Level Change 1993 to 2012

FIGURE 34 Rising sea level
These graphs show sea-level change from 1870 until 2012. Note the difference in the rate of change between the two graphs. **A.** This graph shows historical sea-level data derived from coastal tide gauges. **B.** This graph shows the average sea level since 1993, derived from global satellite measurements. (NASA)

Arctic Sea Ice Climate models are in general agreement that one of the strongest signals of global warming should be a loss of sea ice in the Arctic. This is indeed occurring. The area covered by sea ice naturally grows during the frigid Arctic winters and shrinks when temperatures climb in the spring and summer. Since 1979, satellites have observed a 13 percent decline per decade in the minimum summertime extent of sea ice in the Arctic. The thickness of the ice has also been declining.

The map in FIGURE 36A compares the average sea ice extent for early September 2012 to the long-term average for the period 1979–2000. The extent of sea ice in September 2012 set a record. On that date the extent was less than 4 million square kilometers (1.54 million square miles)—70,000 square kilometers (27,000 square miles) less than the previous record low set in September 2007. The trend is also clear when you examine the graph in FIGURE 36B. Is it possible that this trend may be part of a natural cycle? Yes, but it is more likely that the sea ice decline represents a combination of natural variability and human-induced global warming, with the latter becoming increasingly evident in coming decades. As was noted in the section "Climate-Feedback Mechanisms," a

The Changing Arctic

A 2005 study of climate change in the Arctic began with the following statement:

> For nearly 30 years, Arctic sea ice extent and thickness have been falling dramatically. Permafrost temperatures are rising and coverage is decreasing. Mountain glaciers and the Greenland ice sheet are shrinking. Evidence suggests we are witnessing the early stage of an anthropogenically induced global warming superimposed on natural cycles, reinforced by reductions in Arctic ice.*

Where the slope is gentle a small rise in sea level causes a substantial shift

Shoreline shift

Original shoreline

Sea level rise

Where the slope is steep the same sea level rise causes a small shift

Original shoreline

Shoreline shift

Sea level rise

FIGURE 35 Slope of the shoreline
The slope of the shoreline is critical to determining the degree to which sea-level changes will affect it. As sea level gradually rises, the shoreline retreats, and structures that were once thought to be safe from wave attack become vulnerable.

*J. T. Overpeck, et al., "Arctic System on Trajectory to New, Seasonally Ice-Free States," *EOS, Transactions, American Geophysical Union,* 86 (34): 309, August 23, 2005.

A. Sea ice is frozen sea-water. In winter the Arctic Ocean is completely ice covered. In summer, a portion of the ice melts. This map shows the extent of sea ice in early September 2012 compared to the average extent of the period 1979 to 2000. The extent in 2012 was the lowest on record. **B.** The graph clearly depicts the trend in the area covered by Arctic sea ice at the end of the summer melt period. (NASA)

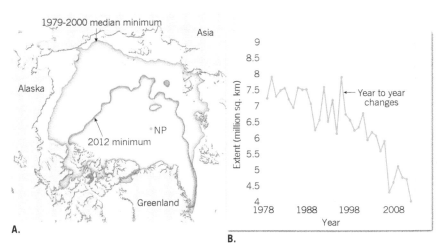

A.

B.

reduction in sea ice represents a positive-feedback mechanism that reinforces global warming.

Permafrost   During the past decade, mounting evidence has indicated that the extent of permafrost in

the Northern Hemisphere has decreased, as would be expected under long-term warming conditions. FIGURE 37 presents one example which shows that such a decline is occurring.

In the Arctic, short summers thaw only the top layer of frozen ground. The permafrost beneath this *active layer* is like the cement bottom of a swimming pool. In summer, water cannot percolate downward, so it saturates the soil above the permafrost and collects on the surface in thousands of lakes. However, as Arctic temperatures climb, the bottom of the "pool" seems to be "cracking." Satellite imagery shows that over a 20-year span, a significant number of lakes have shrunk or disappeared altogether. As the permafrost thaws, lake water drains deeper into the ground.

Thawing permafrost represents a potentially significant positive-feedback mechanism that may reinforce global warming. When vegetation dies in the Arctic, cold temperatures inhibit its total decomposition. As a consequence, over thousands of years, a great deal of organic matter has become stored in the permafrost. When the permafrost thaws, organic matter that may have been frozen for millennia comes out of "cold storage" and decomposes. The result is the release of carbon dioxide and methane—greenhouse gases that contribute to global warming.

Increasing Ocean Acidity

The human-induced increase in the amount of carbon dioxide in the atmosphere has some serious implications for ocean chemistry and for marine life. Recent studies show that about one-third of the human-generated carbon dioxide currently ends up in the oceans. As a result, the ocean's pH becomes lowered, making seawater more acidic.

When atmospheric CO_2 dissolves in seawater (H_2O), it forms carbonic acid (H_2CO_3). This lowers the ocean's pH and changes the balance of certain chemicals found naturally in seawater. In fact, the oceans have already absorbed enough carbon dioxide for surface waters to have experienced a pH decrease of 0.1 pH units since preindustrial times, with an additional pH decrease likely in the future. Moreover, if the current trend in carbon dioxide emissions continues, by the year 2100, the ocean will experience a pH decrease of at least 0.2 pH units, which represents a change in ocean chemistry that has not occurred

This false-color image pair shows lakes dotting the tundra in 1973 and 2002. The tundra vegetation is colored a faded red, whereas lakes appear blue or blue-green. Many lakes disappeared or shrunk considerably between 1973 and 2002. After studying satellite imagery of about 10,000 large lakes in a 500,000-square-kilometer (195,000-square-mile) area in northern Siberia, scientists documented an 11 percent decline in the number of lakes, at least 125 of which disappeared completely. (NASA)

A. June 27, 1973

B. July 2, 2002

for millions of years. This shift toward acidity and the changes in ocean chemistry that result make it more difficult for certain marine creatures to build hard parts out of calcium carbonate. The decline in pH thus threatens a variety of calcite-secreting organisms as diverse as microbes and corals, which concerns marine scientists because of the potential consequences for other sea life that depend on the health and availability of these organisms.

The Potential for "Surprises"

In summary, you have seen that climate in the twenty-first century, unlike the preceding 1000 years, is not expected to be stable. Rather, a constant state of change is very likely. Many of the changes will probably be gradual environmental shifts, imperceptible from year to year. Nevertheless, the effects, accumulated over decades, will have powerful economic, social, and political consequences.

Despite our best efforts to understand future climate shifts, there is also the potential for "surprises." This simply means that, due to the complexity of Earth's climate system, we might experience relatively sudden, unexpected changes or see some aspects of climate shift in an unexpected manner. The report *Climate Change Impacts on the United States* describes the situation like this:

> Surprises challenge humans' ability to adapt, because of how quickly and unexpectedly they occur. For example, what if the Pacific Ocean warms in such a way that El Niño events become much more extreme? This could reduce the frequency, but perhaps not the strength, of hurricanes along the East Coast, while on the West Coast, more severe winter storms, extreme precipitation events, and damaging winds could become common. What if large quantities of methane, a potent greenhouse gas currently frozen in icy Arctic tundra and sediments, began to be released to the atmosphere

by warming, potentially creating an amplifying "feedback loop" that would cause even more warming? We simply do not know how far the climate system or other systems it affects can be pushed before they respond in unexpected ways.

> There are many examples of potential surprises, each of which would have large consequences. Most of these potential outcomes are rarely reported, in this study or elsewhere. Even if the chance of any particular surprise happening is small, the chance that at least one such surprise will occur is much greater. In other words, while we can't know which of these events will occur, it is likely that one or more will eventually occur.*

The impact on climate of an increase in atmospheric carbon dioxide and trace gases is obscured by some uncertainties. Yet climate scientists continue to improve our understanding of the climate system and the potential impacts and effects of global climate change. Policymakers are confronted with responding to the risks posed by emissions of greenhouse gases, knowing that our understanding is imperfect. However, they are also faced with the fact that climate-induced environmental changes cannot be reversed quickly, if at all, due to the lengthy time scales associated with the climate system.

---

*National Assessment Synthesis Team, *Climate Change Impacts on the United States: The Potential Consequences of Climate Variability and Change* (Washington, DC: U.S. Global Research Program, 2000), p. 19.

9 CONCEPT CHECKS

1. List and describe the factors that are causing sea level to rise.
2. Is global warming greater near the equator or near the poles? Explain.
3. Based on Table 1, what projected changes relate to something other than temperature?

CONCEPTS IN REVIEW: GLOBAL CLIMATE CHANGE

1   Climate and Geology

List the major parts of the climate system and some connections between climate and geology.

KEY WORD climate system

- *Climate* is a description of aggregate weather conditions in an area. Over time, if those conditions shift toward a new situation with hotter or cooler temperatures and/or more or less precipitation, the climate is said to have changed.

- Earth's climate system is a complex interchange of energy and moisture that occurs between the atmosphere, hydrosphere, geosphere, biosphere, and cryosphere. When the climate changes, geologic processes such as weathering, mass wasting, and erosion may change as well.

WHAT'S THE DIFFERENCE? There is an old saying that "Climate is what you expect; weather is what you get." Explain this saying in terms of the definitions of climate and weather.

2   How Is Climate Change Detected?

Explain why unraveling past climate changes is important and discuss several ways in which such changes are detected.

KEY WORDS proxy data, paleoclimatology, oxygen isotope analysis

- The geologic record yields multiple kinds of indirect evidence about past climate. These proxy data are the focus of paleoclimatology. Proxy data can come from seafloor sediment, oxygen isotopes, tree rings, coral growth bands, fossil pollen, and even historical documents.
- Trees grow thicker rings in warmer, wetter years and thinner rings in colder, drier years. The pattern of ring thickness can be matched up between trees of overlapping ages for a long-term record of a region's climate.
- Oxygen isotope analysis is based on the difference between heavier ^{18}O and lighter ^{16}O and their relative amounts in water molecules (H_2O). The $^{18}O/^{16}O$ ratio of ocean water rises during cold times because it's easier to evaporate water that contains lightweight oxygen. During warmer times, more energy is available to evaporate water containing ^{18}O, plus glacial ice melts, and sends some of its ^{16}O back to the sea. This makes the marine $^{18}O/^{16}O$ ratio drop. Oxygen isotopes can also be measured in the shells of fossil marine organisms or the water molecules that make up glacial ice. Glacial ice also traps small samples of the atmosphere in air bubbles.

INTERPRET IT Examine the graph, which shows how the marine oxygen isotope ratio has varied in the past 70 million years. Make a general statement about the trend in Earth surface temperatures over the time span covered by this data. Explain.

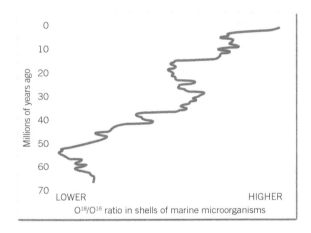

O^{18}/O^{16} ratio in shells of marine microorganisms

3   Some Atmospheric Basics

Discuss the composition of the atmosphere and describe the atmosphere's vertical changes in pressure and temperature.

KEY WORD aerosol

- Air is a mixture of gases, some of which are active in absorbing heat energy. Some important gases for the climate are carbon dioxide, water vapor, and ozone.
- Aerosols are tiny solid and liquid particles that are suspended in the air. They help trigger the condensation of water vapor to form clouds. Aerosols can also act like an atmospheric "sun screen," filtering incoming sunlight.

- The atmosphere is densest closest to the surface of Earth. It thins rapidly with increasing altitude and gradually fades off into space. Temperature varies through a vertical section of the atmosphere. Generally, temperatures drop in the troposphere, warm in the stratosphere, cool in the mesosphere, and increase through the thermosphere.

UPPER LIMITS Virgin Galactic is a new "space tourism" company that will take travelers (for $200,000) up to an altitude of 21 kilometers in a special craft called *SpaceShipTwo*. What layer of the atmosphere will those rich passengers see when they look out the window? Which layers will still be above them? (*Hint: See* Figure 13.)

4 Heating the Atmosphere

Outline the basic processes involved in heating the atmosphere.

KEY WORD greenhouse effect

- The Sun provides the short-wave energy that runs Earth's weather and climate. A portion of incoming sunlight is reflected and absorbed before reaching Earth's surface.
- The energy that reaches the surface can be absorbed and then radiated upward as long-wave radiation. Some of this energy gets absorbed by gases such as water vapor and carbon dioxide, heating the air and raising the planet's temperature. This atmospheric "greenhouse effect" is responsible for Earth's surface having a moderate temperature that is habitable for life.

POSSIBLE PLANETS The atmosphere of Mars is more than 95 percent carbon dioxide, but its average temperature is $-55°$ C $(-67°$ F). Suggest some reasons why a planet with an atmosphere made mostly of a greenhouse gas can be so cold.

5 Natural Causes of Climate Change

Discuss hypotheses that relate to natural causes of climate change.

KEY WORD sunspot

- The natural functions of the Earth system produce climate change. The position of lithospheric plates can influence the climate of the continents as well as oceanic circulation. Variations in the shape of Earth's orbit, angle of axial tilt, and orientation of the axis all cause changes in the distribution of solar energy.
- Volcanic aerosols act like a sun shade, screening out a portion of incoming solar radiation. Volcanic sulfur dioxide emissions that reach the stratosphere are particularly important. Combined with water to form tiny droplets of sulfuric acid, these aerosols can remain aloft for several years.
- Volcanoes emit carbon dioxide. During times of especially large eruptions, such as those that produced oceanic lava plateaus during the Cretaceous period, volcanic emissions of carbon dioxide may contribute to the greenhouse effect sufficiently to cause global warming.
- Since Earth's climate is fueled by solar energy, it matters if the Sun varies in its energy output. The Sun's level of variability remains unknown, as satellite-based measuring of its output has been active for only a few decades. Sunspots are dark features on the surface of the Sun associated with periods of increased solar energy output. The number of sunspots rises and drops throughout an 11-year cycle. During the peak of the cycle, the Sun puts out about 0.1 percent more energy than during the lowest part of the cycle, but this small cyclical effect is not correlated with the current episode of global warming.

DOUBLE-EDGED SWORD Some volcanic emissions are thought to trigger global cooling, while others are thought to contribute to global warming. List, compare, and contrast these emissions and their effects.

6 Human Impact on Global Climate

Summarize the nature and cause of the atmosphere's changing composition since about 1750. Describe the climate's response.

- Human activities produce climate change through the release of carbon dioxide (CO_2) and trace gases. Humans release CO_2 when they cut down forests or when they burn fossil fuels such as coal, oil, and natural gas. A steady rise in atmospheric CO_2 levels has been documented at Mauna Loa, Hawaii, and other locations around the world.
- More than half of the carbon released by humans is absorbed by new plant matter or dissolved in the oceans. About 45 percent remains in the atmosphere, where it can influence climate. Air bubbles trapped in glacial ice reveal that there is currently about 30 percent more CO_2 than the atmosphere has contained in the past 650,000 years.
- As a result of the extra heat retention from the extra CO_2, Earth's atmosphere has warmed by about $0.8°$ C in the past 100 years, most of it since the 1970s. Temperatures are projected to increase by another $2°$ to $4.5°$ C in the future.
- Trace gases such as methane, nitrous oxide, and CFCs also play a significant role in increasing global temperature.

CALCULATE IT In total, all of Earth's volcanoes are estimated to release about 0.26 gigatons of CO_2 to the atmosphere per year. When land-use changes, cement production, waste gas flaring, and the burning of fossil fuel are tallied up, human activities produce a total of about 35 gigatons per year. How much more CO_2 is released by human activities than volcanic emissions?

7 Climate-Feedback Mechanisms

Contrast positive- and negative-feedback mechanisms and provide examples of each.

KEY WORDS climate-feedback mechanism, positive-feedback mechanism, negative-feedback mechanism

- A change in one part of the climate system may trigger in other parts of the climate system changes that amplify or diminish the initial effect. These climate-feedback mechanisms are called positive-feedback mechanisms if they reinforce the initial change and negative-feedback mechanisms if they counteract the initial effect. The melting of sea ice due to global warming (decreasing albedo and increasing the initial effect of warming) is one example of a positive-feedback mechanism. The production of more clouds (blotting out incoming solar radiation, leading to cooling) is an example of a negative-feedback mechanism.
- Computer models of climate give scientists a tool for testing hypotheses about climate change. Although these models are far simpler than the real climate system, they are useful tools for predicting the future climate.

HOT STUFF Changes in precipitation and temperature due to climate change can increase the risk of forest fires. Describe two ways that the event shown in this photo could contribute to global warming.

John McColgan, BLM, Alaska Fire Service

8 How Aerosols Influence Climate

Discuss the possible impacts of aerosols on climate change.

- Most aerosols (tiny suspended solid and liquid particles) act to cool the climate by reflecting a portion of incoming solar radiation before it reaches Earth's surface. Other aerosols, such as black carbon, absorb incoming solar radiation and act to warm the climate. Humans produce both kinds of aerosols through the burning of fossil fuels and deforestation.

- Aerosols remain in the troposphere for a relatively brief time (a few weeks at the longest), unlike long-lived greenhouse gases such as CO_2, which persist for decades.

TIME TO WORK Why do sulfate aerosols spend less time in the atmosphere than greenhouse gases such as carbon dioxide? Explain and suggest natural ways that both substances can be removed from the atmosphere.

9 Some Possible Consequences of Global Warming

Summarize some of the possible consequences of global warming.

- In the future, Earth's surface temperature is likely to continue to rise. The heating will likely be greatest in the polar regions and least in the tropics. Some areas will get drier, and other areas will get wetter.
- Sea level is predicted to rise for several reasons, including the melting of glacial ice and thermal expansion (a given mass of seawater takes up more volume when it is warm than when it is cool). Low-lying, gently sloped, highly populated coastal areas are most at risk.
- Sea ice cover and thickness in the Arctic have been declining since satellite observations began in 1979.
- Because of the warming of the Arctic, permafrost is melting, releasing CO_2 and methane to the atmosphere in a positive-feedback mechanism.
- The extra CO_2 absorbed by oceans is making their water more acidic. This change in ocean chemistry threatens many calcite-secreting organisms, including reef-building corals.
- Because the climate system is complicated, dynamic, and imperfectly understood, it could produce sudden, big changes with little warning.

BREAK OUT THE TREND This ice breaker is plowing through sea ice in the Arctic Ocean. What parts (spheres) of the climate system are represented in this photograph? How has summer sea ice minimum in the Arctic Ocean been changing since 1979? (Hint: See Figure 36.)

Wolfgang Bechtold/imagebroker/Alamy

GIVE IT SOME THOUGHT

1. The five major parts (spheres) of the climate system are represented in Figure 1. List an example of each that is apparent in the image.

2. Refer to Figure 2, which illustrates various components of Earth's climate system. Boxes represent interactions or changes that occur in the climate system. Select three boxes and provide an example of an interaction or change associated with each. Explain how these interactions may influence temperature.

3. Describe one way in which changes in the biosphere can cause changes in the climate system. Next, suggest one way in which the biosphere is affected by changes in some other part of the climate system. Finally, indicate one way in which the biosphere records changes in the climate system.

4. Figure 16 shows that about 30 percent of the Sun's energy intercepted by Earth is reflected or scattered back to space. If Earth's albedo were to increase to 50 percent, how would you expect Earth's average surface temperature to change? Explain.

5. Volcanic events, such as the eruptions of El Chichón and Mount Pinatubo, have been associated with drops in global temperatures. During the Cretaceous period, volcanic activity was associated with global warming. Explain the apparent paradox.

6. The accompanying photo is a 2005 view of Athabasca Glacier in the Canadian Rockies. A line of boulders in the foreground marks the outer limit of the glacier in 1992. Is the behavior of Athabasca Glacier shown in this image typical of other glaciers around the world? Describe a significant impact of such behavior.

Hughrocks

7. It has been suggested that global warming over the past several decades likely would have been greater were it not for the effect of certain types of air pollution. Explain how this could be true.

8. Motor vehicles are a significant source of CO_2. Using electric cars, such as the one pictured here, is one way to reduce emissions from this source. Although these vehicles emit little or no CO_2 or other air pollutants directly into the air, can they still be connected to such emissions? If so, explain.

David Pearson/Alamy

9. During a conversation, an acquaintance indicates that he is skeptical about global warming. When you ask him why he feels that way, he says, "The past couple of years in this area have been among the coolest I can remember." While you assure this person that it is useful to question scientific findings, you suggest to him that his reasoning in this case may be flawed. Use your understanding of the definition of *climate* along with one or more graphs in the chapter to persuade this person to reevaluate his reasoning.

MasteringGeology™

www.masteringgeology.com

Looking for additional review and test prep materials? Visit the Study Area in MasteringGeology to enhance your understanding of this chapter's content by accessing a variety of resources, including **Self-Study Quizzes,** **Geoscience Animations, GEODe Tutorials, RSS feeds, flashcards, web links, self-study quizzes,** and an optional **Pearson eText.**

Glossary

Aerosols Tiny solid and liquid particles suspended in the atmosphere.

Climate-feedback mechanism Various outcomes that may result when one of this complex interactive physical system's elements is altered.

Climate system Exchanges of energy and moisture occurring among the atmosphere, hydrosphere, lithosphere, biosphere, and cryosphere.

Greenhouse effect The transmission of short-wave solar radiation by the atmosphere coupled with the selective absorption of longer-wavelength terrestrial radiation, especially by water vapor and carbon dioxide, resulting in warming of the atmosphere.

Negative-feedback mechanism As used in climatic change, any effect that is opposite the initial change and tends to offset it.

Oxygen isotope analysis A method of deciphering past temperatures based on the precise measurement of the ratio between two isotopes of oxygen, 16O and 18O. Analysis is commonly made of seafloor sediments and cores from ice sheets.

Paleoclimatology The study of ancient climates; the study of climate and climate change prior to the period of instrumental records using proxy data.

Positive-feedback mechanism As used in climatic change, any effect that acts to reinforce the initial change.

Proxy data Data gathered from natural recorders of climate variability such as tree rings, ice cores, and ocean-floor sediments.

Sunspot A dark area on the Sun that is associated with powerful magnetic storms that extend from the Sun's surface deep into the interior.

Earth's Evolution Through Geologic Time

From Chapter 22 of *Earth: An Introduction to Physical Geology*, Eleventh Edition. Edward J. Tarbuck, Frederick K. Lutgens, Dennis Tasa.

Earth's
Evolution
Through
Geologic Time

Grand Prismatic Pool in Yellowstone National Park. This hot-water pool gets its blue color from several species of heat-tolerant cyanobacteria. Microscopic fossils of organisms similar to modern cyanobacteria are among Earth's oldest fossils. (Photo by Michael Collier)

Each statement represents the primary learning objective for the corresponding major heading within the chapter. After you complete the chapter you should be able to:

1 List the principle characteristics that make Earth unique among the planets.
2 Outline the major stages in the evolution of Earth, from the Big Bang to the formation of our planet's layered internal structure.
3 Describe how Earth's atmosphere and oceans have formed and evolved through time.
4 Explain the formation of continental crust, how continental crust becomes assembled into continents, and the role that the supercontinent cycle has played in this process.
5 List and discuss the major geologic events in the Paleozoic, Mesozoic, and Cenozoic eras.
6 Describe some of the hypotheses on the origin of life and the characteristics of early prokaryotes, eukaryotes, and multicelled organisms.
7 Discuss the major developments in the history of life during the Paleozoic era.
8 Discuss the major developments in the history of life during the Mesozoic era.
9 Discuss the major developments in the history of life during the Cenozoic era.

The Galapagos, a chain of tropical volcanic islands located about 900 kilometers (560 miles) west of South America During his historic voyage, Charles Darwin observed several species of finches that varied mainly in their beaks, which are adapted for specific diets of cactus, flowers, insects, or seeds. He concluded that a common ancestor gave rise to these new species, some of which are found on only one island. (Photo by AGE Fotostock)

E arth has a long and complex history. Time and again, the splitting and collision of continents has resulted in the formation of new ocean basins and the creation of great mountain ranges. Furthermore, the nature of life on our planet has experienced dramatic changes through time.

1   Is Earth Unique?

There is only one place in the universe, as far as we know, that can support life—a modest-sized planet called Earth that orbits an average-sized star, the Sun. Life on Earth is ubiquitous; it is found in boiling mudpots and hot springs, in the deep abyss of the ocean, and even under the Antarctic Ice Sheet. Living space on our planet, however, is significantly limited when we consider the needs of individual organisms, particularly humans. The global ocean covers 71 percent of Earth's surface, but only a few hundred meters below the water's surface, pressures are so intense that humans cannot survive without an atmospheric diving suit. In addition, many continental areas are too steep, too high, or too cold for us to inhabit (FIGURE 1). Nevertheless, based on what we know about other bodies in the solar system—and the hundreds of planets recently discovered orbiting around other stars—Earth is still by far the most accommodating.

What fortuitous events produced a planet so hospitable to life? Earth was not always as we find it today. During its formative years, our planet became hot enough to support a magma ocean. It also survived a several-hundred-million-year period of extreme bombardment by asteroids, to which the heavily cratered surfaces of Mars and the Moon testify. The oxygen-rich atmosphere that makes higher life-forms possible developed relatively recently. Serendipitously, Earth seems to be the right planet, in the right location, at the right time.

The Right Planet

What are some of the characteristics that make Earth unique among the planets? Consider the following:

- If Earth were considerably larger (more massive), its force of gravity would be proportionately greater. Like the giant planets, Earth would have retained a thick, hostile atmosphere consisting of ammonia and methane, and possibly hydrogen and helium.
- If Earth were much smaller, oxygen, water vapor, and other volatiles would escape into space and be lost forever. Thus, like the Moon and Mercury, both of which lack atmospheres, Earth would be void of life.
- If Earth did not have a rigid lithosphere overlaying a weak asthenosphere, plate tectonics would not operate. The continental crust (Earth's "highlands") would not have formed without the recycling of plates. Consequently, the entire planet would likely be covered by an ocean a few kilometers deep. As author Bill Bryson so aptly stated, "There might be life in that lonesome ocean, but there certainly wouldn't be baseball."[*]
- Most surprisingly, perhaps, is the fact that if our planet did not have a molten metallic core, most of the life-forms on Earth would not exist. Fundamentally, without the flow of iron in the core,

FIGURE 1 Much of Earth's surface is uninhabitable Climbers near the top of Mount Everest. At this altitude, the level of oxygen is only one-third the amount available at sea level. (Photo courtesy of Woodfin Camp and Associates)

Earth could not support a magnetic field. It is the magnetic field that prevents lethal cosmic rays from showering Earth's surface and from stripping away our atmosphere.

The Right Location

One of the primary factors that determine whether a planet is suitable for higher life-forms is its location in the solar system. The following scenarios substantiate Earth's advantageous position:

- If Earth were about 10 percent closer to the Sun, our atmosphere would be more like that of Venus and consist mainly of the greenhouse gas carbon dioxide. As a result, Earth's surface temperature would be too hot to support higher life-forms.
- If Earth were about 10 percent farther from the Sun, the problem would be reversed—it would be too cold. The oceans would freeze over, and Earth's active water cycle would not exist. Without liquid water, all life would perish.
- Earth is near a star of modest size. Stars like the Sun have a life span of roughly 10 billion years. During most of this time, radiant energy is emitted at a fairly constant level. Giant stars, on the other hand,

*A Short History of Nearly Everything (Broadway Books, 2003).

FIGURE 2
Paleontologist and technicians excavating a dinosaur known as *Titanosaurus* in southern Argentina. (Photo by Bernardo Gonzalez/ RIGA/EPA/Newscom)

consume their nuclear fuel at very high rates and "burn out" in a few hundred million years. Therefore, Earth's proximity to a modest-sized star allowed enough time for the evolution of humans, who first appeared on this planet only a few million years ago.

The Right Time

The last, but certainly not the least, fortuitous factor for Earth is timing. The first organisms to inhabit Earth were extremely primitive and came into existence roughly 3.8 billion years ago. From that point in Earth's history, innumerable changes occurred—life-forms came and went, and there were many changes in the physical environment of our planet. Consider two of the many timely Earth-altering events:

- Earth's atmosphere has developed over time. Earth's primitive atmosphere is thought to have been composed mostly of methane, water vapor, ammonia, and carbon dioxide—but no free oxygen. Fortunately, microorganisms evolved that released oxygen into the atmosphere through the process of *photosynthesis*. About 2.5 billion years ago, an atmosphere with free oxygen came into existence. The result was the evolution of the ancestors of the vast array of organisms that occupy Earth today.
- About 65 million years ago, our planet was struck by an asteroid 10 kilometers (6 miles) in diameter. This

impact likely caused a mass extinction during which nearly three-quarters of all plant and animal species were obliterated—including dinosaurs (FIGURE 2). Although this may not seem fortuitous, the extinction of dinosaurs opened new habitats for small mammals that survived the impact. These habitats, along with evolutionary forces, led to the development of many large mammals that occupy our modern world. Without this event, mammals may not have evolved beyond the small rodent-like creatures that live in burrows.

As various observers have noted, Earth developed under "just right" conditions to support higher life-forms. Astronomers refer to this as the *Goldilocks scenario*. Like the classic "Goldilocks and the Three Bears" fable, Venus is too hot (Papa Bear's porridge), Mars is too cold (Mama Bear's porridge), but Earth is just right (Baby Bear's porridge).

Viewing Earth's History

The remainder of this chapter focuses on the origin and evolution of planet Earth—the one place in the Universe we know fosters life. Researchers utilize many tools to interpret clues about Earth's past. Using these tools, as well as clues contained in the rock record, scientists continue to unravel many complex events of the geologic past. The goal of this chapter is to provide a brief overview of the history of our planet and its life-forms—a journey that takes us back about 4.6 billion years, to the formation of Earth. Later, we will consider how our physical world assumed its present state and how Earth's inhabitants changed through time. We suggest that you reacquaint yourself with the *geologic time scale* presented in FIGURE 3 and refer to it throughout the chapter.

1 CONCEPT CHECKS

1. In what way is Earth unique among the planets of our solar system?
2. Explain why Earth is just the right size as a planet.
3. Why is Earth's molten, metallic core important to humans living today?
4. Why is Earth's location in the solar system ideal for the development of higher life-forms?

Earth's Evolution Through Geologic Time

Eon	Era	Period		Epoch	Development of Plants and Animals
Phanerozoic	Cenozoic	Quaternary		Holocene —0.01	Humans develop
				Pleistocene —2.6	
			Neogene	Pliocene —5.3	"Age of Mammals"
		Tertiary		Miocene —23.0	
			Paleogene	Oligocene —33.9	
				Eocene —55.8	Extinction of dinosaurs and many other species
				Paleocene —65.5	
	Mesozoic	Cretaceous		"Age of Reptiles"	First flowering plants
		—145.5			
		Jurassic			First birds
		—199.6			
		Triassic			Dinosaurs dominant
		—251			
	Paleozoic	Permian		"Age of Amphibians"	Extinction of trilobites and many other marine animals
		—299			
		Carboniferous	Pennsylvanian		First reptiles
			—318		Large coal swamps
			Mississippian		Amphibians abundant
		—359			
		Devonian		"Age of Fishes"	First insect fossils
					Fishes dominant
		—416			
		Silurian			First land plants
		—444			
		Ordovician		"Age of Invertebrates"	First fishes
					Cephalopods dominant
		—488			
		Cambrian			Trilobites dominant
					First organisms with shells
		—542			
Precambrian	Proterozoic				First multicelled organisms
	—2500		The Precambrian comprises about 88% of the geologic time scale		
	Archean				First one-celled organisms
	~4000				
	Hadean*				
	~4600				Origin of Earth

Relative Time Span

Phanerozoic: Cenozoic / Mesozoic / Paleozoic

Precambrian: Proterozoic / Archean / Hadean*

* Hadean is the informal name for the span that begins at Earth's formation and ends with Earth's earliest-known rocks.

FIGURE 3 The geologic time scale
Numbers represent time in millions of years before the present. The Precambrian accounts for about 88 percent of geologic time.

Birth of a Planet

The universe had been evolving for several billion years before our solar system and Earth began to from. The universe began about 13.7 billion years ago with the Big Bang, when all matter and space came into existence. Shortly thereafter, the two simplest elements, hydrogen and helium, formed. These basic elements were the ingredients for the first star systems. Several billion years later, our home galaxy, the Milky Way, came into existence. It was within a band of stars and nebular debris in an arm of this spiral galaxy that the Sun and planets took form nearly 4.6 billion years ago.

From the Big Bang to Heavy Elements

According to the Big Bang theory, the formation of our planet began about 13.7 billion years ago, with a cataclysmic explosion that created all matter and space (FIGURE 4). Initially, subatomic particles (protons, neutrons, and electrons) formed. Later, as this debris cooled, atoms of hydrogen and helium, the two lightest elements, began to form. Within a few hundred million years, clouds of these gases condensed and coalesced into stars that compose the galactic systems we now observe.

As these gases contracted to become the first stars, heating triggered the process of *nuclear fusion*. Within the interiors of stars, hydrogen nuclei convert to helium nuclei, releasing enormous amounts of radiant energy (heat, light, cosmic rays). Astronomers have determined that in stars more massive than our Sun, other thermonuclear reactions occur that generate all the elements on the periodic table up to number 26, iron. The heaviest elements (beyond number 26) are created only at extreme temperatures during the explosive death of a star eight or more times as massive as the Sun. During these cataclysmic **supernova** events, exploding stars produce all the elements heavier than iron and spew them into interstellar space. It is from such debris that our Sun and solar system formed. According to the Big Bang scenario, atoms in your body were produced billions of years ago, in the hot interior of now-defunct stars, and the gold in your jewelry was produced during a supernova explosion that occurred in some distant place.

From Planetesimals to Protoplanets

Recall that the solar system, including Earth, formed about 4.6 billion years ago, from the **solar nebula**, a large rotating cloud of interstellar dust and gas (Figure 4E).. As the solar nebula contracted, most of the matter collected in the center to create the hot *protosun*. The remaining materials formed a thick, flattened, rotating disk, within which matter gradually cooled and condensed into grains and clumps of icy, rocky, and metallic material. Repeated collisions resulted in most of the material eventually collecting into asteroid-sized objects called **planetesimals**.

The composition of planetesimals was largely determined by their proximity to the protosun. As you might expect, temperatures were highest in the inner solar system and decreased toward the outer edge of the disk. Therefore, between the present orbits of Mercury and Mars, the planetesimals were composed mainly of materials with high melting temperatures—metals and rocky substances. The planetesimals that formed beyond the orbit of Mars, where temperatures are low, contained high percentages of ices—water, carbon dioxide, ammonia, and methane—as well as smaller amounts of rocky and metallic debris.

Through repeated collisions and accretion (sticking together), these planetesimals grew into eight **protoplanets** and their moons (Figure 4G). During this process, the same amount of matter was concentrated into fewer and fewer bodies, each having greater and greater masses.

At some point in Earth's evolution, a giant impact occurred between a Mars-sized object and a young, semimolten Earth. This collision ejected huge amounts of debris into space, some of which coalesced to form the Moon (Figure 4 J,K,L).

Earth's Early Evolution

As material continued to accumulate, the high-velocity impact of interplanetary debris (planetesimals) and the decay of radioactive elements caused the temperature of our planet to steadily increase. This early period of heating resulted in a magma ocean, perhaps several hundred kilometers deep. Within the magma ocean, buoyant masses of molten rock rose toward the surface and eventually solidified to produce thin rafts of crustal rocks. Geologists call this early period of Earth's history the **Hadean**, which began with the formation of Earth about 4.6 billion years ago and ended roughly 3.8 billion years ago (FIGURE 5). The name *Hadean* is derived from the Greek word *Hades*, meaning "the underworld," referring to the "hellish" conditions on Earth at the time.

During this period of intense heating, Earth became hot enough that iron and nickel began to melt.

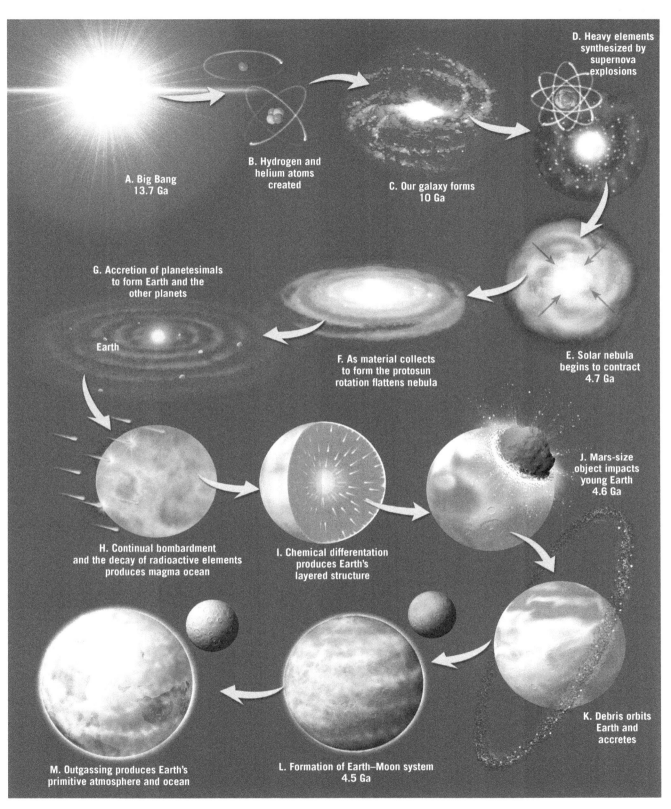

SMARTFIGURE 4 Major events that led to the formation of early Earth

FIGURE 5 Artistic depiction of Earth during the Hadean The Hadean is an unofficial eon of geologic time that occurred before the Archean. Its name refers to the "hellish" conditions on Earth. During the Hadean, Earth had a magma ocean and experienced intense bombardment by nebular debris.

Melting produced liquid blobs of heavy metal that sank under their own weight. This process occurred rapidly on the scale of geologic time and produced Earth's dense iron-rich core. The formation of a molten iron core was the first of many stages of chemical differentiation in which Earth converted from a homogeneous body, with roughly the same matter at all depths, to a layered planet with material sorted by density (Figure 4I).

This period of chemical differentiation established the three major divisions of Earth's interior—the iron-rich *core*; the thin *primitive crust*; and Earth's thickest layer, the *mantle*, located between the core and the crust. In addition, the lightest materials—including water vapor, carbon dioxide, and other gases—escaped to form a primitive atmosphere and, shortly thereafter, the oceans.

2 CONCEPT CHECKS

1. What two elements made up most of the very early universe?
2. What is the name of the cataclysmic event in which an exploding star produces all the elements heavier than iron?
3. Briefly describe the formation of the planets from the solar nebula.
4. Describe the conditions on Earth during the Hadean.

3 | Origin and Evolution of the Atmosphere and Oceans

We can be thankful for our atmosphere; without it, there would be no greenhouse effect, and Earth would be nearly 60° F colder. Earth's water bodies would be frozen over, and the hydrologic cycle would be nonexistent.

The air we breathe is a stable mixture of 78 percent nitrogen, 21 percent oxygen, about 1 percent argon (an inert gas), and small amounts of gases such as carbon dioxide and water vapor. However, our planet's original atmosphere 4.6 billion years ago was substantially different.

Earth's Primitive Atmosphere

Early in Earth's formation, its atmosphere likely consisted of gases most common in the early solar system: hydrogen, helium, methane, ammonia, carbon dioxide, and water vapor. The lightest of these gases—hydrogen and helium—most likely escaped into space because Earth's gravity was too weak to hold them. The remaining gases—methane, ammonia, carbon dioxide, and water vapor—contain the basic ingredients of life: carbon, hydrogen, oxygen, and nitrogen. This early atmosphere was enhanced by a process called **outgassing**, through which gases trapped in the planet's interior are released. Outgassing from hundreds of active volcanoes still remains an important planetary function worldwide (FIGURE 6). However, early in Earth's history, when massive heating and fluidlike motion occurred in the mantle, the gas output would likely have been immense. These early eruptions probably released mainly water vapor, carbon dioxide, and sulfur dioxide, with minor amounts of other gases. Most importantly, free oxygen was not present in Earth's primitive atmosphere.

Oxygen in the Atmosphere

As Earth cooled, water vapor condensed to form clouds, and torrential rains began to fill low-lying areas, which became the oceans. In those oceans, nearly 3.5 billion years ago, photosynthesizing bacteria began to release oxygen into the water. During *photosynthesis*, organisms use the Sun's energy to produce organic material (energetic molecules of sugar containing hydrogen and carbon) from carbon dioxide (CO_2) and water (H_2O). The first bacteria probably used hydrogen sulfide (H_2S) rather than water as the source of hydrogen. One of the earliest known bacteria, *cyanobacteria* (once called blue-green algae), began to produce oxygen as a by-product of photosynthesis.

Initially, the newly released free oxygen was readily captured by chemical reactions with organic matter and dissolved iron in the ocean. It seems that large quantities of iron were released into the early ocean through

FIGURE 6 Outgassing produced Earth's first enduring atmosphere Outgassing continues today from hundreds of active volcanoes worldwide. (Photo by Lee Frost/Robert Harding)

submarine volcanism and associated hydrothermal vents. Iron has tremendous affinity for oxygen. When these two elements join, they become iron oxide (rust). As it accumulated on the seafloor, these early iron oxide deposits created alternating layers of iron-rich rocks and chert, called **banded iron formations** (FIGURE 7). Most banded iron deposits accumulated in the Precambrian, between 3.5 and 2 billion years ago, and represent the world's most important reservoir of iron ore.

As the number of oxygen-generating organisms increased, oxygen began to build in the atmosphere. Chemical analysis of rock suggests that a significant amount of

FIGURE 7 Layered iron-rich rocks called banded iron formations These banded iron formations were deposited from seawater during the Precambrian. Much of the oxygen generated as a by-product of photosynthesis was readily consumed by chemical reactions with iron to produce these rocks. (Courtesy Spencer R. Titley)

oxygen appeared in the atmosphere around 2.5 billion years ago, in a phenomenon called the **Great Oxygenation Event**. Thereafter, oxygen levels in the atmosphere gradually climbed, with one apparent spike that occurred at the end of the Pennsylvanian period. The availability of free oxygen had a positive impact on the development of aerobic life-forms (oxygen-consuming organisms). On the other hand, it likely wiped out huge portions of Earth's anaerobic organisms (organisms that do not require oxygen), for which oxygen is poisonous.

Another possible consequence of the Great Oxygenation Event was that the free oxygen combined with methane, a strong greenhouse gas that helped keep the surface of our planet warm. One hypothesis proposes that the removal of methane from the atmosphere resulted in a period of global glaciation, referred to as **Snowball Earth**. Although it is a controversial idea, there is mounting evidence for at least one other period of global glaciation, during which Earth's surface froze over and later thawed.

A positive benefit of having molecular oxygen in the atmosphere is that oxygen molecules (O_2) readily absorb ultraviolet radiation and rearrange themselves to form *ozone* (O_3). Ozone is concentrated in the *stratosphere*, where it absorbs much of the harmful ultraviolet radiation before it reaches the surface. For the first time, Earth's landmasses were protected from this form of solar radiation, which is particularly harmful to DNA—the stuff of which living organisms are made. Marine organisms had always been shielded from harmful ultraviolet radiation by seawater, but with the development of the atmosphere's protective ozone layer, the continents also became more hospitable.

Evolution of the Oceans

When Earth cooled sufficiently to allow water vapor to condense, rainwater fell and collected in low-lying areas. By 4 billion years ago, it is estimated that as much as 90 percent of the current volume of seawater was contained in the developing ocean basins. Because volcanic eruptions released into the atmosphere large quantities of sulfur dioxide, which readily combines with water to form hydrochloric acid, the earliest rainwater was highly acidic. The level of acidity was even greater than the acid rain that damaged lakes and streams in eastern North America during the latter part of the twentieth century. Consequently, Earth's rocky surface weathered at an accelerated rate. The products released by chemical weathering included atoms and molecules of various substances—including sodium, calcium, potassium, and silica—that were carried into the newly formed oceans. Some of these dissolved substances precipitated to become chemical sediment that mantled the ocean floor. Other substances formed soluble salts, which increased the salinity of seawater. Research suggests that the salinity of the oceans increased rapidly at first but has remained constant over the past 2 billion years.

Earth's oceans also serve as a repository for tremendous volumes of carbon dioxide, a major constituent in the primitive atmosphere. This is significant because carbon dioxide is a greenhouse gas that strongly influences the heating of the atmosphere. Venus, once thought to be very similar to Earth, has an atmosphere composed of 97 percent carbon dioxide that produced a "runaway" greenhouse effect. As a result, its surface temperature is 475° C (900° F).

Carbon dioxide is readily soluble in seawater, where it often joins other atoms or molecules to produce various chemical precipitates. The most common compound generated by this process is calcium carbonate ($CaCO_3$) which makes up limestone, the most abundant chemical sedimentary rock. About 542 million years ago, marine organisms began to extract calcium carbonate from seawater to make their shells and other hard parts. Included were trillions of tiny marine organisms, such as foraminifera, whose shells were deposited on the seafloor at the end of their life cycle. Today, some of these deposits can be observed in the chalk beds exposed along the White Cliffs of Dover, England, shown in FIGURE 8. By "locking up" carbon dioxide, these limestone deposits store this greenhouse gas so it cannot easily reenter the atmosphere.

FIGURE 8 White Chalk Cliffs, England
Similar deposits are also found in northern France.
(Photo by David Wall/AGE Fotostock)

These prominent chalk cliffs are composed largely of tiny shells of marine organisms, such as foraminifera.

3 CONCEPT CHECKS

1. What is meant by *outgassing*, and what modern phenomenon serves that role today?
2. Identify the most abundant gases that were added to Earth's early atmosphere through the process of outgassing.
3. Why is the evolution of a type of bacteria that used photosynthesis to produce food important to most modern organisms?
4. Why was rainwater highly acidic early in Earth's history?
5. How does the ocean remove carbon dioxide from the atmosphere? What role do tiny marine organisms, such as foraminifera, play?

4 Precambrian History: The Formation of Earth's Continents

Earth's first 4 billion years are encompassed in the time span called the *Precambrian*. Representing nearly 90 percent of Earth's history, the Precambrian is divided into the *Archean eon* ("ancient age") and the *Proterozoic eon* ("early life"). Our knowledge of this ancient time is limited because much of the early rock record has been obscured by the very Earth processes you have been studying, especially plate tectonics, erosion, and deposition. Most Precambrian rocks lack fossils, which hinders correlation of rock units. In addition, rocks this old are often metamorphosed and deformed, extensively eroded, and frequently concealed by younger strata. Indeed, Precambrian history is written in scattered, speculative episodes, like a long book with many missing chapters.

Earth's First Continents

Geologists have discovered tiny crystals of the mineral zircon that formed 4.4 billion years ago—evidence that crustal rocks began to form early in Earth's history. What differentiates continental crust from oceanic crust? Recall that oceanic crust is a relatively dense (3.0 g/cm³) homogeneous layer of basaltic rocks derived from partial melting of the rocky upper mantle. In addition, oceanic crust is thin, averaging only 7 kilometers (4.3 miles) thick. Continental crust, on the other hand, is composed of a variety of rock types, has an average thickness of nearly 40 kilometers (25 miles), and contains a large percentage of low-density (2.7 g/cm³), silica-rich rocks such as granite.

The significance of the differences between continental crust and oceanic crust cannot be overstated in a review of Earth's geologic evolution. Oceanic crust, because it is relatively thin and dense, is found several kilometers below sea level—unless of course it has been pushed onto a landmass by tectonic forces. Continental crust, because of its great thickness and lower density, may extend well above sea level. Also, recall that oceanic crust of normal thickness readily subducts, whereas thick, buoyant blocks of continental crust resist being recycled into the mantle.

Making Continental Crust
Earth's first crust was probably ultramafic in composition, but because physical evidence no longer exists, we are not certain. The hot, turbulent mantle that most likely existed during the Archean eon recycled most of this material back into the mantle. In fact, it may have been continuously recycled, in much the same way that the "crust" that forms on a lava lake is repeatedly replaced with fresh lava from below (FIGURE 9).

The oldest preserved continental rocks occur as small, highly deformed terranes, which are incorporated within somewhat younger blocks of continental crust (FIGURE 10). One of the oldest of these is the 4-billion-year-old Acasta gneiss, located in Canada's Northwest Territories. Older crustal rocks may exist in the Nuvvuagittuq Greenstone Belt in Quebec, but the technique used to date them is controversial.

The formation of continental crust is a continuation of the gravitational segregation of Earth materials that began during the final stage of our planet's formation. Dense metallic material, mainly iron and nickel, sank to form Earth's core, leaving behind the less dense rocky material of which the mantle is composed. It is from Earth's rocky mantle that low-density, silica-rich minerals were gradually distilled to form continental crust.

The crust covering this lava lake is continually being replaced with fresh lava from below, much like Earth's crust was recycled early in its history.

FIGURE 9 Earth's early crust was continually recycled

(Photo by Juerg Alean/www.stromboli.net)

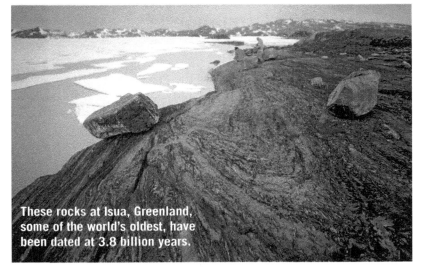

These rocks at Isua, Greenland, some of the world's oldest, have been dated at 3.8 billion years.

This process is analogous to making sour mash whiskeys. In the production of whiskeys, various grains, such as corn, are fermented to generate alcohol, with sour mash being the byproduct. This mixture is then heated or distilled, which drives off the lighter material (alcohol) and leaves behind the sour mash. In a similar manner, partial melting of mantle rocks generates low-density, silica-rich materials that buoyantly rise to the surface to form Earth's crust, leaving behind the dense mantle rocks. However, little is known about the details of the mechanisms that generated these silica-rich melts during the Archean.

Some geologists think that some type of plate-like motion operated early in Earth's history. In addition, hot-spot volcanism was likely active during this time. However, because the mantle was hotter in the

Archean than it is today, both of these phenomena would have progressed at higher rates than their modern counterparts. Hot-spot volcanism is thought to have created immense shield volcanoes as well as oceanic plateaus. Simultaneously, subduction of oceanic crust generated volcanic island arcs. Collectively, these relatively small crustal fragments represent the first phase in creating stable, continent-size landmasses.

From Continental Crust to Continents The growth of larger continental masses was accomplished through collision and accretion of various types of crustal fragments, as illustrated in FIGURE 11. This type of collision tectonics deformed and metamorphosed sediments caught between converging crustal fragments, thereby shortening and thickening the developing crust. In the deepest regions of these collision zones, partial melting of the thickened crust generated silica-rich magmas that ascended and intruded the rocks above. The result was the formation of large crustal provinces that, in turn, accreted with others to form even larger crustal blocks called **cratons**.

The portion of a modern craton that is exposed at the surface is referred to as a **shield**. The assembly of a large craton involves the accretion of several crustal blocks that cause major mountain-building episodes similar to India's collision with Asia. FIGURE 12 shows the extent of crustal material that was produced during the Archean and Proterozoic eons. This was accomplished by the collision and accretion of many thin, highly mobile terranes into nearly recognizable continental masses.

Although the Precambrian was a time when much of Earth's continental crust was generated, a substantial amount of crustal material was destroyed as well. Crust can be lost either by weathering and erosion or by direct reincorporation into the mantle through subduction. Evidence suggests that during much of the Archean, thin slabs of continental crust

Volcanic island arc   Volcanic island arc   Oceanic plateau   Volcanic island arc

Sediments   Sediments   Sediments

Melting in lower crust to form felsic magmas   Mantle plume

A. Scattered crustal fragments separated by ocean basins

Melting in lower crust to form felsic magmas

B. Collision of volcanic island arc and oceanic plateau to form a larger crustal block

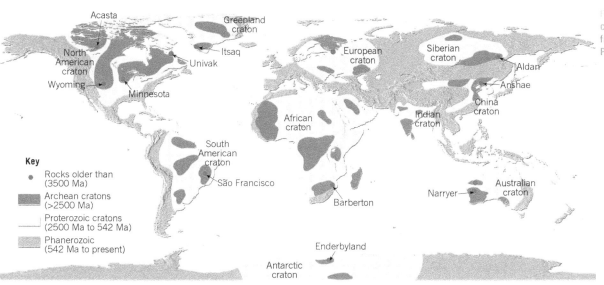

FIGURE 12 Distribution of crustal material remaining from the Archean and Proterozoic eons

Key

- Rocks older than (3500 Ma)
- Archean cratons (>2500 Ma)
- Proterozoic cratons (2500 Ma to 542 Ma)
- Phanerozoic (542 Ma to present)

were eliminated, mainly by subduction into the mantle. However, by about 3 billion years ago, cratons grew sufficiently large and thick to resist subduction. After that time, weathering and erosion became the primary processes of crustal destruction. By the close of the Precambrian, an estimated 85 percent of the modern continental crust had formed.

The Making of North America

North America provides an excellent example of the development of continental crust and its piecemeal assembly into a continent. Notice in FIGURE 13 that very little continental crust older than 3.5 billion years remains. In the late Archean, between 3 and 2.5 billion years ago, there was a period of major continental growth. During this span, the accretion of numerous island arcs and other fragments generated several large crustal provinces. North America contains some of these crustal units, including the Superior and Hearne/Rae cratons shown in Figure 13. It remains unknown where these ancient continental blocks formed.

About 1.9 billion years ago, these crustal provinces collided to produce the Trans-Hudson mountain belt (Figure 13). (Such mountain-building episodes were not restricted to North America because ancient deformed strata of similar age are also found on other continents.) This event built the North American craton, around which several large and numerous small crustal fragments were later added. One of these late arrivals is the Piedmont province of the Appalachians. In addition, several terranes were added to the western margin of North America during the Mesozoic and Cenozoic eras to generate the mountainous North American Cordillera.

Supercontinents of the Precambrian

At different times, parts of what is now North America have combined with other continental landmasses to form a supercontinent. **Supercontinents** are large landmasses that contain all, or nearly all, the existing continents. Pangaea was the most recent, but certainly not the

North America was assembled from crustal blocks that were joined by processes very similar to modern plate tectonics. These ancient collisions produced mountainous belts that include remnant volcanic island arcs, trapped by the colliding continental fragments.

Age (Ga)
- <1.0
- 1.0–1.2
- 1.6–1.7
- 1.7–1.8
- 1.8–2.0
- 2.5–3.0
- >3.5

SMARTFIGURE 13 The major geologic provinces of North America and their ages in billions of years (Ga)

Supercontinent Cycle

The idea that rifting and dispersal of one supercontinent is followed by a long period during which the fragments are gradually reassembled into a new supercontinent with a different configuration is called the **supercontinent cycle**. The assembly and dispersal of supercontinents had a profound impact on the evolution of Earth's continents. In addition, this phenomenon greatly influenced global climates and contributed to periodic episodes of rising and falling sea level.

Supercontinents, Mountain Building, and Climate

As continents move, the patterns of ocean currents and global winds change, which influences the global distribution of temperature and precipitation. One example of how a supercontinent's dispersal influenced climate is the formation of the Antarctic Ice Sheet. Although eastern Antarctica remained over the South Pole for more than 100 million years, it was not glaciated until about 25 million years ago. Prior to this period of glaciation, South America was connected to the Antarctic Peninsula. This arrangement of landmasses helped maintain a circulation pattern in which warm ocean currents reached the coast of Antarctica, as shown in FIGURE 16A. This is similar to the way in which the modern Gulf Stream keeps Iceland mostly ice free, despite its name. However, as South America separated from Antarctica, it moved northward, permitting ocean circulation to flow from west to east around the entire continent of Antarctica (FIGURE 16B). This cold current, called the West Wind Drift, effectively isolated the entire Antarctic coast from the warm, poleward-directed currents in the southern oceans. As a result, most of the Antarctic landmass became covered with glacial ice.

Local and regional climates have also been impacted by large mountain systems created by the collision of large cratons. Because of their high elevations, mountains exhibit markedly lower average temperatures than surrounding lowlands. In addition, when air rises over these lofty structures, lifting "squeezes" moisture from the air, leaving the region downwind relatively dry. A modern analogy is the wet, heavily forested western slopes of the Sierra Nevada compared to the dry climate of the Great Basin Desert that lies directly to the east.

only, supercontinent to exist in the geologic past. The earliest well-documented supercontinent, *Rodinia*, formed during the Proterozoic eon, about 1.1 billion years ago. Although its reconstruction is still being researched, it is clear that Rodinia's configuration was quite different from Pangaea's (FIGURE 14). One obvious distinction is that North America was located near the center of this ancient landmass.

Between 800 and 600 million years ago, Rodinia gradually split apart. By the end of the Precambrian, many of the fragments reassembled, producing a large landmass in the Southern Hemisphere called *Gondwana*, comprised mainly of present-day South America, Africa, India, Australia, and Antarctica (FIGURE 15). Other continental fragments also developed—North America, Siberia, and Northern Europe. We consider the fate of these Precambrian landmasses later in the chapter.

A. Continent of Gondwana

B. Continents not a part of Gondwana

Supercontinents and Sea-Level Changes

Significant and numerous sea-level changes have been documented in geologic history, a many of them appear to be related to the assembly and dispersal of supercontinents. If sea level rises, shallow seas advance onto the continents. Evidence for periods when the seas advanced onto the continents include thick sequences of ancient marine sedimentary rocks that blanket large areas of modern landmasses—including much of the eastern two-thirds of the United States.

The supercontinent cycle and sea-level changes are directly related to rates of *seafloor spreading*. When the rate of spreading is rapid, as it is along the East Pacific Rise today, the production of warm oceanic crust is also high. Because warm oceanic crust is less dense (takes up more space) than cold crust, fast-spreading ridges occupy more volume in the ocean basins than do slow-spreading centers. (Think of getting into a tub filled with water.) As a result, when the rates of seafloor spreading increase, more seawater is displaced, which results in the sea level rising. This, in turn, causes shallow seas to advance onto the low-lying portions of the continents.

Oceanic circulation 50 million years ago brought warm seawater to the coastal areas of Antarctica, keeping this continent nearly ice-free.

A. Non-glaciated

As South America separated from Antarctica, the West Wind Drift developed. This newly formed ocean circulation effectively cut-off Antarctica from warm currents and contributed to the formation of its vast ice sheets.

B. Glaciated

SMARTFIGURE 16
Connection between ocean circulation and the climate in Antarctica

4 CONCEPT CHECKS

1. Briefly explain how low-density continental crust was produced from Earth's rocky mantle.
2. Describe how cratons came into being.
3. How can the movement of continents trigger climate change?
4. What is the supercontinent cycle? What supercontinent proceeded Pangaea?
5. Explain how seafloor spreading rates are related to sea-level changes.

EYE on Earth

The oldest-known sample of Earth is a 4.4-billion-year-old zircon crystal found in a metaconglomerate in the Jack Hills area of western Australia. Zircon is a silicate mineral that commonly occurs in trace amounts in most granitic rocks. (Photo by John W. Valley/NSF)

Question 1 What is the parent rock of a metaconglomerate?

Question 2 Assuming that this zircon crystal originated as part of a granite intrusion, briefly describe its journey from the time of its formation until it was discovered in Jack Hill.

Question 3 Is this zircon crystal younger or older than the metaconglomerate in which it was found? Explain.

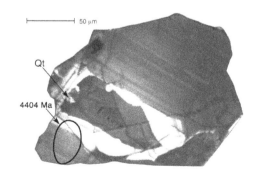

5 Geologic History of the Phanerozoic: The Formation of Earth's Modern Continents

The time span since the close of the Precambrian, called the *Phanerozoic eon*, encompasses 542 million years and is divided into three eras: *Paleozoic*, *Mesozoic*, and *Cenozoic*. The beginning of the Phanerozoic is marked by the appearance of the first life-forms with hard parts such as shells, scales, bones, or teeth—all of which greatly enhance the chances for an organism to be preserved in the fossil record. Thus, the study of Phanerozoic crustal history was aided by the availability of fossils, which improved our ability to date and correlate geologic events. Moreover, because every organism is associated with its own particular niche, the greatly improved fossil record provided invaluable information for deciphering ancient environments.

Paleozoic History

As the Paleozoic era opened, North America hosted no living things, neither plant nor animal. There were no Appalachian or Rocky Mountains; the continent was largely a barren lowland. Several times during the early Paleozoic, shallow seas moved inland and then receded from the continental interior and left behind the thick deposits of limestone, shale, and clean sandstone that mark the shorelines of these previously midcontinent shallow seas.

Formation of Pangaea One of the major events of the Paleozoic was the formation of the supercontinent Pangaea, which began with a series of collisions that gradually joined North America, Europe, Siberia, and other smaller crustal fragments (FIGURE 17). These events eventually generated a large northern continent called *Laurasia*. This tropical landmass supported warm wet conditions that led to the formation of vast swamps that eventually converted to coal.

Simultaneously, the vast southern continent of *Gondwana* encompassed five continents—South America, Africa, Australia, Antarctica, and India—and perhaps portions of China. Evidence of extensive continental glaciation places this landmass near the South Pole. By the end of the Paleozoic, Gondwana had migrated northward and collided with Laurasia,

FIGURE 17 Formation of Pangaea During the late Paleozoic, Earth's major landmasses joined to produce the supercontinent of Pangaea. (After P. Hoffman, J. Rogers, and others)

A. Cambrian (500 Ma)

B. Silurian (425 Ma)

C. Mississippian (340 Ma)

D. Triassic (250 Ma)

culminating in the formation of the supercontinent *Pangaea*.

The accretion of Pangaea spans more than 300 million years and resulted in the formation of several mountain belts. The collision of northern Europe (mainly Norway) with Greenland produced the Caledonian Mountains, whereas the joining of northern Asia (Siberia) and Europe created the Ural Mountains. Northern China is also thought to have accreted to Asia by the end of the Paleozoic, whereas southern China may not have become part of Asia until after Pangaea had begun to rift. (Recall that India did not begin to accrete to Asia until about 50 million years ago.)

Pangaea reached its maximum size about 250 million years ago, as Africa collided with North America (Figure 17D). This event marked the final and most intense period of mountain building in the long history of the Appalachian Mountains (FIGURE 18).

Mesozoic History

Spanning about 186 million years, the Mesozoic era is divided into three periods: the *Triassic*, *Jurassic*, and *Cretaceous*. Major geologic events of the Mesozoic include the breakup of Pangaea and the evolution of our modern ocean basins.

Changes in Sea Levels The Mesozoic era began with much of the world's continents above sea level. The exposed Triassic strata are primarily red sandstones and mudstones that lack marine fossils, features that indicate a terrestrial environment. (The red color in sandstone comes from the oxidation of iron.)

As the Jurassic period opened, the sea invaded western North America. Adjacent to this shallow sea, extensive continental sediments were deposited on what is now the Colorado Plateau. The most prominent is the Navajo Sandstone, a cross-bedded, quartz-rich layer, that in some places approaches 300 meters (1000 feet) thick. These remnants of massive dunes indicate that an enormous desert occupied much of the American Southwest during early Jurassic times (FIGURE 19). Another well-known Jurassic deposit is the Morrison Formation—the world's richest storehouse of dinosaur fossils. Included are the fossilized bones of massive dinosaurs such as *Apatosaurus* (formerly *Brontosaurus*), *Brachiosaurus*, and *Stegosaurus*.

FIGURE 18 The Appalachian Mountains, a product of a continental collision (Photo by Jerry Whaley/AGE Fotostock)

FIGURE 19 Massive, cross-bedded sandstone cliffs in Zion National Park These sandstone cliffs are the remnants of ancient sand dunes that were part of an enormous desert during the Jurassic period. (Photo by Ruth Tomlinson/Robert Harding)

Coal Formation in Western North America   As the Jurassic period gave way to the Cretaceous, shallow seas again encroached upon much of western North America, as well as the Atlantic and Gulf coastal regions. This led to the formation of "coal swamps" similar to those of the Paleozoic era. Today, the Cretaceous coal deposits in the western United States and Canada are economically important. For example, on the Crow Native American reservation in Montana, there are nearly 20 billion tons of high-quality, Cretaceous-age coal.

The Breakup of Pangaea   Another major event of the Mesozoic era was the breakup of Pangaea. About 185 million years ago, a rift developed between what is now North America and western Africa, which marked the birth of the Atlantic Ocean. As Pangaea gradually broke apart, the westward-moving North American plate began to override the Pacific basin. This tectonic event triggered a continuous wave of deformation that moved inland along the entire western margin of North America.

Formation of the North American Cordillera   By Jurassic times, subduction of the Farallon plate had begun to produce the chaotic mixture of rocks that exist today in the Coast Ranges of California. Further inland, igneous activity was widespread, and for more than 100 million years volcanism was rampant as huge masses of magma rose within a few miles of Earth's surface. The remnants of this activity include the granitic plutons of the Sierra Nevada, as well as the Idaho batholith and British Columbia's Coast Range batholith.

The subduction of the Farallon plate under the western margin of North America also resulted in the piecemeal addition of crustal fragments to the entire Pacific margin of the continent—from Mexico's Baja Peninsula to northern Alaska. Each collision displaces earlier accreted terranes further inland, adding to the zone of deformation as well as to the thickness and lateral extent of the continental margin.

Compressional forces moved huge rock units in a shingle-like fashion toward the east. Across much of North America's western margin, older rocks were thrust eastward over younger strata, for distances exceeding 150 kilometers (90 miles). Ultimately, this activity was responsible for generating a vast portion of the North American Cordillera that extends from Wyoming to Alaska.

Toward the end of the Mesozoic, the southern portions of the Rocky Mountains developed. This mountain-building event, called the *Laramide Orogeny*, occurred when large blocks of deeply buried Precambrian rocks were lifted nearly vertically along steeply dipping faults, upwarping the overlying younger sedimentary strata. The mountain ranges produced by the Laramide Orogeny include Colorado's Front Range, the Sangre de Cristo of New Mexico and Colorado, and the Bighorns of Wyoming.

Cenozoic History

The Cenozoic era, or "era of recent life," encompasses the past 65.5 million years of Earth history. It was during this span that the physical landscapes and life-forms of our modern world came into existence. The Cenozoic era represents a considerably smaller fraction of geologic time than either the Paleozoic or the Mesozoic. Nevertheless, much more is known about this time span because the rock formations are more widespread and less disturbed than those of any preceding era.

Most of North America was above sea level during the Cenozoic era. However, the eastern and western margins of the continent experienced markedly contrasting events because of their different plate boundary relationships. The Atlantic and Gulf coastal regions, far removed from an active plate boundary, were tectonically stable. By contrast, western North America was the leading edge of the North American plate. As a result, plate interactions during the Cenozoic account for many events of mountain building, volcanism, and earthquakes.

Eastern North America   The stable continental margin of eastern North America was the site of abundant marine sedimentation. The most extensive deposition surrounded the Gulf of Mexico, from the Yucatan Peninsula to Florida, where a massive buildup of sediment caused the crust to downwarp. In many instances, faulting created structures in which oil and natural gas accumulated. Today, these and other petroleum traps are

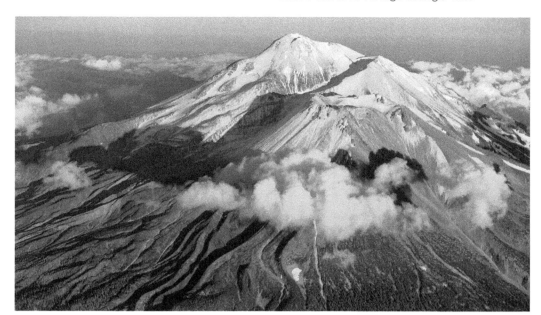

FIGURE 20 Mount Shasta, California
This volcano is one of several large composite cones that comprise the Cascade Range. (Photo by Michael Collier)

the Gulf Coast's most economically important resource, evidenced by numerous offshore drilling platforms.

By early Cenozoic time, the Appalachians had eroded to create a low plain. Later, isostatic adjustments again raised the region and rejuvenated its rivers. Streams eroded with renewed vigor, gradually sculpting the surface into its present-day topography. Sediments from this erosion were deposited along the eastern continental margin, where they accumulated to a thickness of many kilometers. Today, portions of the strata deposited during the Cenozoic are exposed as the gently sloping Atlantic and Gulf coastal plains, where a large percentage of the eastern and southeastern United States population resides.

Western North America In the West, the Laramide Orogeny responsible for building the southern Rocky Mountains was coming to an end. As erosional forces lowered the mountains, the basins between uplifted ranges began to fill with sediment. East of the Rockies, a large wedge of sediment from the eroding mountains created the gently sloping Great Plains.

Beginning in the Miocene epoch, about 20 million years ago, a broad region from northern Nevada into Mexico experienced crustal extension that created more than 100 fault-block mountain ranges. Today, they rise abruptly above the adjacent basins, forming the Basin and Range province.

During the development of the Basin and Range province, the entire western interior of the continent gradually uplifted. This event reelevated the Rockies and rejuvenated many of the West's major rivers. As the rivers became incised, many spectacular gorges were created, including the Grand Canyon of the Colorado River, the Grand Canyon of the Snake River, and the Black Canyon of the Gunnison River.

Volcanic activity was also common in the West during much of the Cenozoic. Beginning in the Miocene epoch, great volumes of fluid basaltic lava flowed from fissures in portions of present-day Washington, Oregon, and Idaho. These eruptions built the extensive (3.4-million-square-kilometer [1.3-million-square–mile]) Columbia Plateau. Immediately west of the Columbia Plateau, volcanic activity was different in character. Here, more viscous magmas with higher silica content erupted explosively, creating the Cascades, a chain of stratovolcanoes extending from northern California into Canada, some of which are still active (**FIGURE 20**).

As the Cenozoic was drawing to a close, the effects of mountain building, volcanic activity, isostatic adjustments, and extensive erosion and sedimentation created the physical landscape we know today. All that remained of Cenozoic time was the final 2.6-million-year episode called the Quaternary period. During this most recent, and ongoing, phase of Earth's history, humans evolved and the action of glacial ice, wind, and running water added to our planet's long, complex geologic history.

5 CONCEPT CHECKS

1. During which period of geologic history did the supercontinent Pangaea come into existence?
2. Where is most Cretaceous age coal found today in the United States?
3. During which period of geologic history did Pangaea begin to break apart?
4. Describe the climate during the early Jurassic period.
5. Compare and contrast eastern and western North America during the Cenozoic era.

6 Earth's First Life

The oldest fossils provide evidence that life on Earth was established at least 3.5 billion years ago. Microscopic fossils similar to modern cyanobacteria have been found in silica-rich chert deposits worldwide. Notable examples include southern Africa, where rocks date to more than 3.1 billion years, and the Lake Superior region of western Ontario and northern Minnesota, where the Gunflint Chert contains some fossils that are older than 2 billion years. Chemical traces of organic matter in rocks of greater age have led paleontologists to strongly suggest that life may have existed as early as 3.8 billion years ago.

Origin of Life

How did life begin? This question sparks considerable debate, and hypotheses abound. Requirements for life, assuming the presence of a hospitable environment, include the chemical raw materials that are found in essential molecules such as proteins. Proteins are made from organic compounds called *amino acids*. The first amino acids may have been synthesized from methane and ammonia, both of which were plentiful in Earth's primitive atmosphere. Some scientists suggest that these gases could have been easily reorganized into useful organic molecules by ultraviolet light. Others consider lightning to have been the impetus, as the well-known experiments conducted by Stanley Miller and Harold Urey attempted to demonstrate.

Still other researchers suggest that amino acids arrived "ready-made," delivered by asteroids or comets that collided with a young Earth. A group of meteorites (debris from asteroids and comets that strike Earth) called *carbonaceous chrondrites*, known to contain amino acid–like organic compounds, led to a hypothesis which concludes that early life had an extraterrestrial beginning.

Yet another hypothesis proposes that the organic material needed for life came from the methane and hydrogen sulfide that spews from deep-sea hydrothermal vents (black smokers). It is also possible that life originated in hot springs similar to those found in Yellowstone National Park.

Earth's First Life: Prokaryotes

Regardless of where or how life originated, it is clear that the journey from "then" to "now" involved change. The first known organisms were simple single-cell bacteria called **prokaryotes**, which means their genetic material (DNA) is *not separated* from the rest of the cell by a nucleus. Because oxygen was largely absent from Earth's early atmosphere and oceans, the first organisms employed anaerobic (without oxygen) metabolism to extract energy from "food." Their food source was likely organic molecules in their surroundings, but that supply was very limited. Later, bacteria evolved that used solar energy to synthesize organic compounds (sugars). This event was an important turning point in biological evolution: For the first time, organisms had the capability of producing food for themselves as well as for other life-forms.

Recall that photosynthesis by ancient cyanobacteria, a type of prokaryote, contributed to the gradual rise in the level of oxygen, first in the ocean and later in the atmosphere. It was these early organisms, which began to inhabit Earth 3.5 billion years ago, that dramatically transformed our planet. Fossil evidence for the existence of these microscopic bacteria includes distinctively layered mats, called **stromatolites**, composed of slimy material secreted by these organisms, along with trapped sediments (FIGURE 21A). What is known about

FIGURE 21
Stromatolites are among the most common Precambrian fossils
A. Cross-section though fossil stromatolites deposited by cyanobacteria. (Photo by Sinclair Stammers/Photo Researchers, Inc.) **B.** Modern stromatolites exposed at low tide in western Australia. (Photo by Bill Bachman/Photo Researchers, Inc.)

A.

B.

these ancient fossils comes mainly from the study of modern stromatolites like those found in Shark Bay, Australia (FIGURE 21B). Today's stromatolites look like stubby pillars built as microbes slowly move upward to avoid being buried by sediment that is continually being deposited upon them.

Evolution of Eukaryotes   The oldest fossils of more advanced organisms, called **eukaryotes**, are about 2.1 billion years old. The first eukaryotes were microscopic, single-cell organisms, but unlike prokaryotes, the cellular structures of eukaryotes contain nuclei. This distinctive structure is what all multicellular organisms that now inhabit our planet—trees, birds, fish, reptiles, and humans—have in common.

During much of the Precambrian, life consisted exclusively of single-celled organisms. It wasn't until perhaps 1.2 billion years ago that multicelled eukaryotes evolved. Green algae, one of the first multicelled organisms, contained chloroplasts (used in photosynthesis) and were the likely ancestors of modern plants. The first primitive marine animals did not appear until somewhat later, perhaps 600 million years ago (FIGURE 22).

Fossil evidence suggests that organic evolution progressed at an excruciatingly slow pace until the end of the Precambrian. At that time, Earth's continents were largely barren, and the oceans were populated primarily by organisms, many too small to be seen with the naked eye. Nevertheless, the stage was set for the evolution of larger and more complex plants and animals.

FIGURE 22 **Ediacaran fossil** The Ediacarans are a group of sea-dwelling animals that may have come into existence about 600 million years ago. These soft-bodied organisms were up to 1 meter in length and are the oldest animal fossils so far discovered. (Photo courtesy of the South Australian Museum)

6 CONCEPT CHECKS

1. What group of organic compounds are essential for the formation of DNA and RNA and therefore necessary for life as we know it?
2. Why do some researchers think that a type of asteroid, called *carbonaceous chrondrites*, played an important role in the development of life on Earth?
3. What are stromatolites? What group of organisms is thought to have produced them?
4. Compare *prokaryotes* with *eukaryotes*. Within which of these two groups do all multicelled organisms belong?

EYE on Earth

The rocks shown here are Cambrian-age stromatolites of the Hoyt Limestone, exposed at Lester Park, near Saratoga Springs, New York.

Question 1 Using Figure 3, determine approximately how many years ago these rocks were deposited.

Question 2 What is the name of the group of organisms that likely produced these limestone deposits?

Question 3 What was the environment like in this part of New York when these rocks were deposited?

M. C. Rygel

Evolution of Life Through Geologic Time

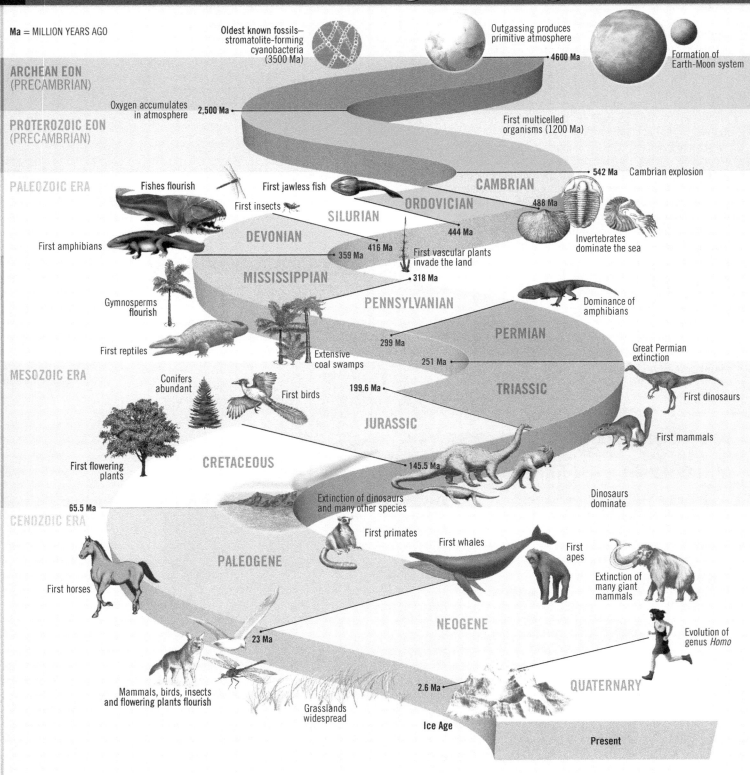

Ma = MILLION YEARS AGO

Oldest known fossils—stromatolite-forming cyanobacteria (3500 Ma)

Outgassing produces primitive atmosphere

4600 Ma

Formation of Earth-Moon system

ARCHEAN EON (PRECAMBRIAN)

Oxygen accumulates in atmosphere   2,500 Ma

PROTEROZOIC EON (PRECAMBRIAN)

First multicelled organisms (1200 Ma)

542 Ma   Cambrian explosion

PALEOZOIC ERA

Fishes flourish

First jawless fish

CAMBRIAN

ORDOVICIAN   488 Ma

First insects

SILURIAN

444 Ma

DEVONIAN   416 Ma

First amphibians   359 Ma

First vascular plants invade the land

Invertebrates dominate the sea

MISSISSIPPIAN   318 Ma

Gymnosperms flourish

PENNSYLVANIAN

Dominance of amphibians

First reptiles

299 Ma

PERMIAN

251 Ma

Great Permian extinction

MESOZOIC ERA

Extensive coal swamps

Conifers abundant

First birds   199.6 Ma

TRIASSIC

First dinosaurs

JURASSIC

First mammals

First flowering plants

CRETACEOUS   145.5 Ma

Dinosaurs dominate

65.5 Ma

Extinction of dinosaurs and many other species

CENOZOIC ERA

First primates

First whales

First apes

First horses

PALEOGENE

Extinction of many giant mammals

Evolution of genus *Homo*

NEOGENE

23 Ma

Mammals, birds, insects and flowering plants flourish

Grasslands widespread

2.6 Ma

QUATERNARY

Ice Age

Present

7 Paleozoic Era: Life Explodes

The Cambrian period marks the beginning of the Paleozoic era, a time span that saw the emergence of a spectacular variety of new life-forms. All major invertebrate (animals lacking backbones) groups made their appearance, including jellyfish, sponges, worms, mollusks (clams and snails), and arthropods (insects and crabs). This huge expansion in biodiversity is often referred to as the **Cambrian explosion**.

Early Paleozoic Life-Forms

The Cambrian period was the golden age of *trilobites* (FIGURE 23). Trilobites developed a flexible exoskeleton of a protein called chitin (similar to a lobster shell), which permitted them to be mobile and search for food by burrowing through soft sediment. More than 600 genera of these mud-burrowing scavengers flourished worldwide.

The Ordovician marked the appearance of abundant cephalopods—mobile, highly developed mollusks that became the major predators of their time (FIGURE 24). Descendants of these cephalopods include the squid, octopus, and chambered nautilus that inhabit our modern oceans. Cephalopods were the first truly large organisms on Earth, including one species that reached a length of nearly 10 meters (30 feet).

The early diversification of animals was driven, in part, by the emergence of predatory lifestyles. The larger mobile cephalopods preyed on trilobites that were typically smaller than a child's hand. The

FIGURE 23 Fossil of a trilobite
Trilobites dominated the early Paleozoic ocean, scavenging food from the bottom. (Photo by Ed Reschke/ Peter Arnold, Inc.)

evolution of efficient movement was often associated with the development of greater sensory capabilities and more complex nervous systems. These early animals developed sensory devices for detecting light, odor, and touch.

FIGURE 24 Artistic depiction of a shallow Ordovician sea
During the Ordovician period (488–444 million years ago), the shallow waters of an inland sea over central North America contained an abundance of marine invertebrates. Shown in this reconstruction are corals, trilobites, snails, brachiopods, and straight-shelled cephalopods. (© The Field Museum, Neg. # GEO80820c, Chicago)

FIGURE 25 Land plants of the Paleozoic
The Silurian saw the first upright-growing (vascular) plants. Plant fossils became increasingly common from the Devonian onward.

Small upright-growing, vascular plants begin to invade the land

SILURIAN PERIOD

First tree-size plants become common

DEVONIAN PERIOD

Extensive forests covered vast areas of the continents

MISSISSIPPIAN PERIOD

primitive sharks with cartilage skeletons and bony fish—the groups in which many modern fish are classified. Fish, the first large vertebrates, proved to be faster swimmers than invertebrates and possessed more acute senses and larger brains. They became the dominant predators of the sea, which is why the Devonian period is often referred to as the "Age of the Fishes."

Vertebrates Move to Land

During the Devonian, a group of fish called the *lobe-finned fish* began to adapt to terrestrial environments (FIGURE 26). Lobe-finned fish had internal sacks that could be filled with air to supplement their "breathing" through gills. One group of lobe-finned fish probably occupied freshwater tidal flats or small ponds. Some began to use their fins to move from one pond to another in search of food or to evacuate deteriorating ponds. This favored the evolution of a group of animals able to stay out of water longer and move on land more efficiently. By the late Devonian, lobe-finned fish had evolved into air-breathing amphibians with strong legs yet retained a fishlike head and tail (Figure 26).

Modern amphibians, such as frogs, toads, and salamanders, are small and occupy limited biological niches. However, conditions during the late Paleozoic were ideal for these newcomers to land. Large tropical swamps that were teeming with large insects and millipedes extended across North America, Europe, and Siberia (see FIGURE 27). With virtually no predatory risks, amphibians diversified rapidly. Some even took on lifestyles and forms similar to modern reptiles such as crocodiles.

Despite their success, amphibians were not fully adapted to life out of water. In fact, amphibian means "double life" because these animals need both the water from where they came and the land to which they moved. Amphibians are born in water, as exemplified by tadpoles, complete with gills and tails. These features disappear during the maturation process, resulting in air-breathing adults with legs.

Approximately 400 million years ago, green algae that had adapted to survive at the water's edge gave rise to the first multicellular land plants. The primary difficulty in sustaining plant life on land was obtaining water and staying upright, despite gravity and winds. These earliest land plants were leafless, vertical spikes about the size of a human index finger (FIGURE 25). However, the fossil record indicates that by the beginning of the Mississippian period, there were forests with trees tens of meters tall (Figure 25).

In the ocean, fish perfected an internal skeleton as a new form of support, and they were the first creatures to have jaws. Armor-plated fish that evolved during the Ordovician continued to adapt. Their armor plates thinned to lightweight scales that increased their speed and mobility. Other fish evolved during the Devonian, including

Reptiles: The First True Terrestrial Vertebrates

Reptiles were the first true terrestrial animals with improved lungs for active lifestyles and "waterproof" skin that helped prevent the loss of body fluids. Most importantly, reptiles developed shell-covered eggs laid on land. The elimination of a water-dwelling stage (like the tadpole stage in frogs) was an important evolutionary step. Vertebrates advance from water dwelling lobefin

FIGURE 26 Comparison of the anatomical features of the lobe-finned fish and early amphibians
A. The fins on the lobe-finned fish contained the same basic elements (*h*, humerus, or upper arm; *r*, radius; and *u*, ulna, or lower arm) as those of the amphibians. **B.** This amphibian is shown with the standard five toes, but early amphibians had as many as eight toes. Eventually the amphibians evolved to have a standard toe count of five.

A. Lobe-finned fish

B. Early amphibian

FIGURE 27 Artistic depiction of a Pennsylvanian-age coal swamp Shown are scale trees (left), seed ferns (lower left), and scouring rushes (right). Also note the large dragonfly. (© The Field Museum, Neg. # GEO85637c, Chicago. Photographer John Weinstein)

fish, to amphibians, to reptiles—the first true terrestrial vertebrates (FIGURE 28).

Of interest is the fact that the watery fluid within the reptilian egg closely resembles seawater in chemical composition. Because the reptile embryo develops in this watery environment, the shelled egg has been characterized as a "private aquarium" in which the embryos of these land vertebrates spend their water-dwelling stage of life. With this "sturdy egg," the remaining ties to the water were broken, and reptiles moved inland.

SMARTFIGURE 28 Relationships of vertebrate groups and their divergence from lobefin fish

The Great Permian Extinction

By the close of the Permian period, a **mass extinction** occurred in which a large number of Earth's species became extinct. During this mass extinction, 70 percent of all land-dwelling vertebrate species and perhaps 95 percent of all marine organisms were obliterated; it was the most significant of five mass extinctions that occurred over the past 500 million years. Each extinction wreaked havoc with the existing biosphere, wiping out large numbers of species. In each case, however, survivors entered new biological communities that were ultimately more diverse. Therefore, mass extinctions actually invigorated life on Earth, as the few hardy survivors eventually filled more environmental niches than those left behind by the victims.

Several mechanisms have been proposed to explain these ancient mass extinctions. Initially, paleontologists believed they were gradual events caused by a combination of climate change and biological forces, such as predation and competition. Other research groups have attempted to link certain mass extinctions to the explosive impact of a large asteroid striking Earth's surface.

The most widely held view is that the Permian mass extinction was driven mainly by volcanic activity because it coincided with a period of voluminous eruptions of flood basalts that blanketed about 1.6 million square kilometers (624,000 square miles), an area nearly the size of Alaska. This event, which lasted roughly 1 million years, occurred in northern Russia, in an area called the Siberian Traps. It was the largest volcanic eruption in the past 500 million years. The release of huge amounts of carbon dioxide likely generated a period of accelerated greenhouse warming, while the emissions of sulfur dioxide is credited with producing copious amounts of acid rain. These drastic changes in the environment likely put excessive stress on many of Earth's life-forms.

The Permian extinction may be linked to a relatively brief period during which there were voluminous eruptions of flood basalts. These eruptions were much larger than the one shown here in Iceland. The release of massive quantities of carbon dioxide may have contributed to a significant period of global warming. In addition, the emission of sulfur dioxide produced copious amounts of acid rain.

Together, these changes to the environment likely triggered the demise of many life forms. (Photo by Rangnar Sigurdsson/AGE Fotostock)

7 CONCEPT CHECKS

1. What is the Cambrian explosion?
2. What animal group was dominant in Cambrian seas?
3. What did plants have to overcome in order to move onto land?
4. What group of animals is thought to have left the ocean to become the first amphibians?
5. Why are amphibians not considered "true" land animals?
6. What major development allowed reptiles to move inland?

8   Mesozoic Era: Age of the Dinosaurs

As the Mesozoic era dawned, its life-forms were the survivors of the great Permian extinction. These organisms diversified in many ways to fill the biological voids created at the close of the Paleozoic.

Gymnosperms: The Dominant Mesozoic Trees

On land, conditions favored organisms that could adapt to drier climates. One such group of plants, **gymnosperms**, produced "naked" seeds that are exposed on modified leaves that usually form cones. The seeds are not enclosed in fruits as, for example, are apple seeds. Unlike the first plants to invade the land, seed-bearing gymnosperms did not depend on free-standing water for fertilization. Consequently, these plants were not restricted to a life near the water's edge.

The gymnosperms quickly became the dominant trees of the Mesozoic. Examples of this group include cycads that resembled large pineapple plants; ginkgo plants that had fan-shaped leaves, much like their modern relatives; and the largest plants, the conifers, whose modern descendants include the pines, firs, and junipers (FIGURE 29). The best-known fossil occurrence of these ancient trees is in northern Arizona's Petrified Forest National Park. Here, huge petrified logs lie exposed at the surface, having been weathered from rocks of the Triassic Chinle Formation (FIGURE 30).

Reptiles: Dominating the Land, Sea, and Sky

Among the animals, reptiles readily adapted to the drier Mesozoic environment, thereby relegating amphibians to the swamps and wetlands where most remain today.

The first reptiles were small, but larger forms evolved rapidly, particularly the dinosaurs. One of the largest was *Apatosaurus*, which weighed more than 30 tons and measured over 25 meters (80 feet) from head to tail. Some of the largest dinosaurs were carnivorous (*Tyrannosaurus*), whereas others were herbivorous (like ponderous *Apatosaurus*).

Some reptiles evolved specialized characteristics that enabled them to occupy drastically different environments. One group, the pterosaurs, became airborne. These "dragons of the sky" possessed huge membranous wings that allowed them rudimentary flight. How the largest pterosaurs (some had wing spans of 8 meters [26 feet] and weighed 90 kilograms [200 pounds]) took flight is still unknown. Another group, exemplified

FIGURE 29 Cycads, a type of gymnosperm that was very common in the Mesozoic These plants have palm-like leaves and large cones.(Photo by Jiri Loun/Photo Reseachers Inc.)

FIGURE 30 Petrified logs of Triassic age, Arizona's Petrified Forest National Park (Photo by Bernd Siering/AGE Fotostock)

FIGURE 31 Flying reptiles like *Archaeopteryx* are the ancestors of modern birds
Fossil evidence indicates that *Archaeopteryx* had feathers like modern birds but retained many characteristics of reptiles. The sketch shows an artist's reconstruction of *Archaeopteryx*. (Photo by Michael Collier)

Archaeopteryx

Toothed beak (reptilian feature)

Wing claws (reptilian feature)

Airfoil wings with feathers (bird feature)

Long tail with vertebrae (reptilian feature)

Tail feathers (bird feature)

by the fossil *Archaeopteryx*, led to more successful flyers—birds (FIGURE 31). These ancestors of modern birds had feathered wings but retained reptilian characteristics, such as sharp teeth, clawed digits in its wings, and a long tail with many vertebrae. A recent study concluded that *Archaeopteryx* were unable to use flapping flight. Rather, by running and leaping into the air, these bird-like reptiles escaped predators with glides and downstrokes. Other researchers disagree and see them as climbing animals that glided down to the ground, following the idea that birds evolved from tree-dwelling gliders. Whether birds took to the air from the ground

up or from the trees *down* is a question scientists continue to debate.

Other reptiles returned to the sea, including fish-eating plesiosaurs and ichthyosaurs (FIGURE 32). These reptiles became proficient swimmers but retained their reptilian teeth and breathed by means of lungs rather than gills.

For nearly 160 million years, dinosaurs reigned supreme. However, by the close of the Mesozoic, like many reptiles they became extinct. Select reptile groups survived to recent times, including turtles, snakes, crocodiles, and lizards. The huge, land-dwelling dinosaurs, the marine plesiosaurs, and the flying pterosaurs are known only through the fossil record. What caused this great extinction?

8 CONCEPT CHECKS

1. What group of plants became the dominant trees during the Mesozoic era? Name a modern descendant of this group.
2. What group of reptiles led to the evolution of modern birds?
3. What was the dominant reptile group on land during the Mesozoic?
4. Name two reptiles that returned to life in the sea.

FIGURE 32 During the Mesozoic, some reptiles returned to the sea
Reptiles, including *Ichthyosaur*, became the dominant marine animals. (Photo by Chip Clark)

9 Cenozoic Era: Age of Mammals

During the Cenozoic, mammals replaced reptiles as the dominant land animals. At nearly the same time, **angiosperms** (flowering plants with covered seeds) replaced gymnosperms as the dominant plants. The Cenozoic is often called the "Age of Mammals" but can also be considered the "Age of Flowering Plants" because, in the plant world, angiosperms enjoy a status similar to that of mammals in the animal world.

The development of flowering plants strongly influenced the evolution of both birds and mammals that feed on seeds and fruits as well as many insect groups. During the middle of the Cenozoic, another type of angiosperm, grasses, developed and spread rapidly over the plains (FIGURE 33). This fostered the emergence of herbivorous (plant-eating) mammals, which, in turn, provided the evolutionary foundation for large predatory mammals.

During the Cenozoic, the ocean was teeming with modern fish such as tuna, swordfish, and barracuda. In addition, some mammals, including seals, whales, and walruses, took up life in the sea.

From Reptiles to Mammals

The earliest mammals coexisted with dinosaurs for nearly 100 million years but were small rodent-like creatures that gathered food at night, when dinosaurs were probably less active. Then, about 65 million years ago, fate intervened when a large asteroid collided with Earth and dealt a crashing blow to the reign of the dinosaurs. This transition, during which one dominant group is replaced by another, is clearly visible in the fossil record.

Mammals are distinct from reptiles in that they give birth to live young that suckle on milk and are warm blooded. This latter adaptation allowed mammals to lead more active lives and to occupy more diverse habitats than reptiles because they could survive in cold regions. (Modern reptiles are cold blooded and dormant during cold weather. However, recent studies suggest that dinosaurs may have been warm blooded.) Other mammalian adaptations included the development of insulating body hair and more efficient organs such as hearts and lungs.

With the demise of the large Mesozoic reptiles, Cenozoic mammals diversified rapidly. The many forms that exist today evolved from small primitive mammals that were characterized by short legs; flat, five-toed feet; and small brains. Their development and specialization took four principal directions: (1) increase in size, (2) increase in brain capacity, (3) specialization of teeth to better accommodate their diet, and (4) specialization of limbs to be better equipped for a particular lifestyle or environment.

Marsupial and Placental Mammals

Two groups of mammals, the marsupials and the placentals, evolved and diversified during the Cenozoic. The groups differ principally in their modes of reproduction. Young marsupials are born live at a very early stage of development. At birth, the tiny and immature young enter the mother's pouch to suckle and complete their

B.

A.

FIGURE 33 Angiosperms became the dominant plants during the Cenozoic This plant group, commonly known as flowering plants, are seed-plants that have reproductive structures called flowers and fruits. **A.** The most diverse and widespread of modern plants, many angiosperms display easily recognizable flowers. **B.** Some angiosperms, including grasses, have very tiny flowers. The expansion of the grasslands during the Cenozoic era greatly increased the diversity of grazing mammals and the predators that feed on them. (Photo A by Mike Potts/Nature Picture Library; photo B by Torleif/CORBIS)

FIGURE 34 Kangaroos, examples of marsupial mammals
After the breakup of Pangaea, the Australian marsupials evolved differently than their relatives in the Americas. (Photo by Martin Harvey/Peter Arnold Inc.)

development. Today, marsupials are found primarily in Australia, where they underwent a separate evolutionary expansion largely isolated from placental mammals. Modern marsupials include kangaroos, opossums, and koalas (FIGURE 34).

Placental mammals (eutherians), conversely, develop within the mother's body for a much longer period, so birth occurs when the young are comparatively mature. Members of this group include wolves, elephants, bats, manatees, and monkeys. Most modern mammals, including humans, are placental.

Humans: Mammals with Large Brains and Bipedal Locomotion

Both fossil and genetic evidence suggest that around 7 or 8 million years ago in Africa, several populations of anthropoids (informally called apes) diverged. One line would eventually produce modern apes such as gorillas, orangutans, and chimpanzees, while the other population would produce several varieties of human ancestors. We have a good record of this evolution in fossils found in several sedimentary basins in Africa, in particular the rift valley system in East Africa.

The genus *Australopithecus*, which came into existence about 4.2 million years ago, showed skeletal characteristics that were intermediate between our ape-like ancestors and modern humans. Over time, these human ancestors evolved features that suggest an upright posture and therefore a habit of walking around on two legs, rather than four. Evidence for this bipedal stride includes, footprints preserved in 3.2-million-year-old ash deposits at Laetoli, Tanzania (FIGURE 35). This new way of

moving around is correlated with our human ancestors leaving forest habitat in Africa and moving to open grass-lands for hunting and gathering food.

The earliest fossils of our genus *Homo* include *Homo habilis*, nicknamed "handy man" because their remains were often found with sharp stone tools in sedimentary deposits from 2.4 to 1.5 million years ago. *Homo habilis* had a shorter jaw and a larger brain than its ancestors. The development of a larger brain size is thought to be correlated with an increase in tool use.

During the next 1.3 million years of evolution, our ancestors developed substantially larger brains and long slender legs with hip joints adapted for long-distance walking. These species (including *Homo erectus*) ultimately gave rise to our species, *Homo sapiens*, as well as some extinct species, including the Neanderthals (*Homo neanderthalis*). Despite having the same-sized brain as present-day humans and being able to fashion hunting tools from wood and stone, Neanderthals became extinct about 28,000 years ago. At one time, Neanderthals were

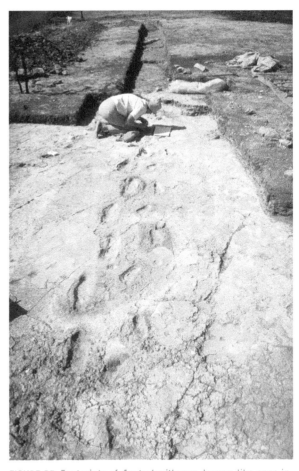

FIGURE 35 Footprints of *Australopithecus*, human-like apes in ash deposits at Laetoli, Tanzania
(Photo by John Reader/Photo Researchers Inc.)

considered a stage in the evolution of *Homo sapiens*, but that view has largely been abandoned.

Humans (*Homo sapiens*) originated in Africa about 200,000 years ago and began to spread around the globe. The oldest-known fossils of *Homo sapiens* outside of Africa, were found in the Middle East and date back to 115,000 years ago. Humans are known to have co-existed with Neanderthals, but whether the two groups interbred is still being debated. By 36,000 years ago, humans were producing spectacular cave paintings in Europe (FIGURE 36).

FIGURE 36 **Cave painting of animals by early humans** (Photo courtesy of Sisse Brimberg/ National Geographic Society)

Large Mammals and Extinction

During the rapid mammal diversification of the Cenozoic era, some groups became very large. For example, by the Oligocene epoch, a hornless rhinoceros evolved that stood nearly 5 meters (16 feet) high. It is the largest land mammal known to have existed. As time passed, many other mammals evolved to larger forms—more, in fact, than now exist. Many of these large forms were common as recently as 11,000 years ago. However, a wave of late Pleistocene extinctions rapidly eliminated these animals from the landscape.

North America experienced the extinction of mastodons and mammoths, both huge relatives of the modern elephant (FIGURE 37). In addition, saber-toothed cats, giant beavers, large ground sloths, horses, giant bison, and others died out. In Europe, late Pleistocene extinctions included woolly rhinos, large cave bears, and Irish elk. Scientists remain puzzled about the reasons for this recent wave of extinctions that targeted large animals. Because these large animals survived several major glacial advances and interglacial periods, it is difficult to ascribe extinctions of these animals to climate change. Some scientists hypothesize that early humans hastened the decline of these mammals by selectively hunting large forms.

CONCEPT CHECKS

1. What animal group became the dominant land animals of the Cenozoic era?
2. Explain how the demise of the large Mesozoic reptiles impacted the development of mammals.
3. Where has most of the evidence for the early evolution of our ancestors been discovered?
4. What two characteristics best separate humans from other mammals?
5. Describe one hypothesis that explains the extinction of large mammals in the late Pleistocene.

FIGURE 37 **Mammoths** These relatives of modern elephants were among the large mammals that became extinct at the close of the Ice Age (Image courtesy of Jonathan Blair/Woodfin Camp)

© leonello calvetti / Shutterstock

Demise of the Dinosaurs

The geologic time scale marks the transitions, or boundaries, of significant periods of geological and/or biological change. Of special interest to geoscientists is the boundary between the Mesozoic Era and the Cenozoic Era, about 65.5 million years ago, when roughly 70 percent of all plant and animal species died out in a mass extinction

Gulf of Mexico

CHICXULUB CRATER

MEXICO

Yucatán

The most widely accepted hypothesis on the demise of the dinosaurs proposes that about 65.5 million years ago, Earth was struck by an asteroid—a relict from the formation of the solar system. The errant mass of rock was approximately 10 kilometers in diameter and struck Earth with 100 million megatons of force.

This asteroid struck a shallow tropical sea in the area of Mexico's Yucatan Peninsula and generated Chicxulub crater which is about 180 kilometers in diameter and 10 kilometers deep. Much of the plant and animal life that survived the initial impact likely fell victim to firestorms triggered by atmospheric heating. Following the impact, the huge amount of debris ejected into the atmosphere greatly reduced the amount of sunlight reaching Earth's surface. This resulted in an extended period of global cooling that inhibited photosynthesis, which ultimately caused the demise of the dinosaurs.

Artistic recreation of Chicxulub crater

VikOl/Shutterstock

Oleg Znamenskiy/Shutterstock

Wesley Aston/Shutterstock

Photri Inc./AGE Fotostock

Nationalparks

The mass extinction of the dinosaurs opened habitats for the small mammals that survived the impact. These new habitats, along with evolutionary forces, led to the development of the large mammals that occupy our modern world.

The transition from the Mesozoic to the Cenozoic era marks the end of the dinosaurs, a group that had dominated the landscape for more than 100 million years, and the beginning of the era when mammals became the most prominent land animals.

What evidence supports a massive, catastrophic impact more than 65 million years ago? A thin layer of sediment has been discovered worldwide at Earth's physical boundary separating the Mesozoic and Cenozoic eras. This sediment contains a high level of iridium, an element that is rare in Earth's crust but is found in much higher proportions in stony meteorites. Scientists believe this layer contains debris from the impact.

IRIDIUM LAYER

CONCEPTS IN REVIEW: EARTH'S EVOLUTION THROUGH GEOLOGIC TIME

1   Is Earth Unique?

List the principle characteristics that make Earth unique among the planets.

- As far as we know, Earth is unique among planets in the fact that it hosts life. The planet's size, composition, location, and age all contribute to conditions that life (or at least our kind of life) finds congenial.

POSSIBLE PLANET   If you worked for NASA as an astrobiologist, what characteristics would you look for in a newly discovered planet as you consider whether it is possible that it might host living organisms?

2   Birth of a Planet

Outline the major stages in the evolution of Earth, from the Big Bang to the formation of our planet's layered internal structure.

KEY WORDS supernova, solar nebula, planetesimal, protoplanet, Hadean

- The universe is thought to have formed around 13.7 billion years ago, with the Big Bang, which generated space, time, energy, and matter. Early stars grew and generated lightweight elements through nuclear fusion of smaller atoms. Some large stars exploded in supernovae, generating heavier atoms and spewing them into space.
- The story of Earth and the solar system begins around 4.6 billion years ago, with the contraction of a solar nebula under the influence of gravity. Collisions between clumps of matter in this spinning disc resulted in the growth of planetesimals and then protoplanets. Over time, the matter of the solar nebula was concentrated into a smaller number of larger bodies: the Sun, the rocky inner planets, the icy outer planets, moons, comets, and asteroids.
- Heat production on the early Earth was much higher than it is today, thanks to the kinetic energy of impacting asteroids and planetesimals, as well as decay of radioactive isotopes. On the hot young Earth, temperatures quickly climbed high enough that rock and iron melted, and the planet differentiated by density into layers of core, mantle, and crust. This began the "hellish" first span of geologic time, the Hadean.

SAME AS IT EVER WAS   The photo shows Comet Shoemaker-Levy 9 impacting Jupiter in 1994. After this event, what happened to Jupiter's total mass? What happened to the number of objects in the solar system? Relate this example to the nebular theory and evolution of the solar system.

Comet Shoemaker-Levy 9 impacted planet Jupiter in 1994.

NASA

3 Origin and Evolution of the Atmosphere and Oceans

Describe how Earth's atmosphere and oceans have formed and evolved through time.

KEY WORDS outgassing, banded iron formation, Great Oxygenation Event, Snowball Earth

- Earth's atmosphere is essential for life. It originated when volcanic outgassing added to the primordial atmosphere of gases common in the early solar system: methane, ammonia, carbon dioxide, and water vapor.
- Free oxygen began to accumulate partly through photosynthesis by cyanobacteria, which released oxygen as a waste product. Much of this early oxygen immediately reacted with iron dissolved in seawater and settled to the ocean floor as chemical sediments called banded iron formations. The Great Oxygenation Event of 2.5 billion years ago marks the first evidence of significant amounts of free oxygen in the atmosphere. This glut of oxygen may be responsible for reacting with atmospheric methane and thereby cutting out its beneficial greenhouse effect, a change that pushed the planet into a global ice age called the Snowball Earth.
- Earth's oceans formed after the planet's surface had cooled. Soluble ions weathered from the crust were carried to the ocean, making it salty. The oceans also absorbed tremendous amounts of carbon dioxide from the atmosphere.

INTERPRET IT In Antoine de Saint-Exupéry's classic children's story *The Little Prince*, the title character visits a chunk of space rock similar to a planetesimal. In this drawing, what processes are illustrated that also could have occurred on the early Earth?

4 Precambrian History: The Formation of Earth's Continents

Explain the formation of continental crust, how continental crust becomes assembled into continents, and the role that the supercontinent cycle has played in this process.

KEY WORDS craton, shield, supercontinent, supercontinent cycle

- The Precambrian includes the Archean and Proterozoic eons. Both of these eons have a rather patchy record because the processes of the rock cycle operating over billions of years have destroyed much of the evidence.
- Continental crust was produced over time through the recycling of ultramafic and mafic crust in an early version of plate tectonics. Small crustal fragments formed and accreted to one another, amalgamating over time into large crustal provinces called cratons. Over time, North

America and other continents grew through the accretion of new terranes around the edges of this central "nucleus" of crust.
- Early cratons not only merged but sometimes rifted apart, too. The supercontinent Rodinia formed around 1.1 billion years ago and then rifted apart, opening up new ocean basins. In time, these too would close, forming a new supercontinent called Pangaea around 300 million years ago. Like Rodinia before it, Pangaea broke up as part of the ongoing supercontinent cycle.
- Seafloor spreading upon the breakup of a supercontinent may displace enough water that sea level rises and shallow seas flood low-lying portions of the continents. The breakup of continents can also influence the direction of ocean currents, with important consequences for climate.

MORE THAN THE SUM OF ITS PARTS Consult Figure 13 and use it to give a history of the North American continent's assembly over the past 3.5 billion years. Which pieces of the continent were added at what times?

5 Geologic History of the Phanerozoic: The Formation of Earth's Modern Continents

List and discuss the major geologic events in the Paleozoic, Mesozoic, and Cenozoic eras.

- The Phanerozoic eon encompasses the most recent 542 million years of geologic time.
- In the Paleozoic era, North America experienced a series of collisions that resulted in the rise of the young Appalachian mountain belt and the assembly of Pangaea. High sea levels caused the ocean to cover vast areas of the continent and resulted in a thick sequence of sedimentary strata.
- In the Mesozoic, Pangaea broke up, and the Atlantic Ocean began to form. As the continent moved westward, the Cordillera began to rise due to subduction and the accretion of terranes along the west coast. Vast deserts saw the deposition of thick layers of dune sand, while other environments were right for the burial of coal swamps.
- In the Cenozoic era, a thick sequence of sediments was deposited along the Atlantic margin and the Gulf of Mexico. Meanwhile, western North America experienced an extraordinary episode of crustal extension; the Basin and Range province resulted.

COMPARE THEM Contrast the tectonics of eastern and western North America during the Mesozoic era. Relate the two situations to each other.

6 Earth's First Life

Describe some of the hypotheses on the origin of life and the characteristics of early prokaryotes, eukaryotes, and multicelled organisms.

KEY WORDS prokaryote, stromatolite, eukaryote

- Life began from nonlife. Whether the genetic code of life (DNA and RNA) or biologically active molecules (proteins) came first is a matter of some controversy. Amino acids are a necessary building block for proteins. They may have been assembled with energy from ultraviolet light or lightning, or in a hot spring, or on another planet, only to be delivered later to Earth on meteorites.
- The first organisms were relatively simple single-celled prokaryotes that thrived in low-oxygen environments. They formed around 3.8 billion years ago. The advent of photosynthesis allowed microbial mats to build up (domed toward the Sun) and form stromatolites.
- Eukaryotes have larger, more complex cells than prokaryotes. The oldest eukaryotic cells formed around 2.1 billion years ago. Eventually, some eukaryotic cells linked together and differentiated their structures and functions, producing the earliest multicellular organisms.

INTERPRET IT Are these stromatolites right-side up, or have they been flipped upside down by folding of the crust? Explain.

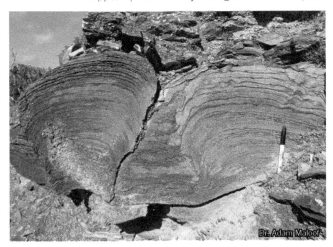
Dr. Adam Maloof

7 Paleozoic Era: Life Explodes

Discuss the major developments in the history of life during the Paleozoic era.

KEY WORDS Cambrian explosion, mass extinction

- At the beginning of the Cambrian period, abundant fossil hard parts appear in sedimentary rocks. The source of these shells and other skeletal material were a profusion of new animals, including trilobites and cephalopods.
- Plants colonized the land around 400 million years ago and soon diversified into forests.

- In the Devonian, some lobe-finned fish began to spend time out of water and gradually evolved into the first amphibians. A subset of the amphibian population evolved waterproof skin and eggs and split off to become the reptile line.
- The Paleozoic era ended with the largest mass extinction in the geologic record. It is not certain what caused this deadly event, but it may have been related to the eruption of the Siberian Traps flood basalts.

ONE UP What advantages do reptiles have over amphibians? What advantages do amphibians have over fish? Suggest a reason that fish would still exist in a world that has also evolved reptiles.

8 Mesozoic Era: Age of the Dinosaurs

Discuss the major developments in the history of life during the Mesozoic era.

KEY WORD gymnosperm

- Plants diversified during the Mesozoic. The flora of that time was dominated by gymnosperms, the first plants with "naked" seeds that allowed them to grow beyond the edge of water bodies.
- Reptiles diversified, too. The dinosaurs came to dominate the land, the pterosaurs dominated the air, and a suite of several different marine

reptiles swam the seas. The first birds evolved during the Mesozoic, exemplified by *Archaeopteryx*, a transitional fossil.
- As with the Paleozoic, the Mesozoic ended with a mass extinction, probably due to a massive meteorite impact in what is now Chicxulub, Mexico.

MAKE A PREDICTION Would a paleontologist be likely to announce that some dinosaurs ate apples? Explain.

9 Cenozoic Era: Age of Mammals

Discuss the major developments in the history of life during the Cenozoic era.

KEY WORD angiosperm

- Once the giant Mesozoic reptiles were extinct, mammals were able to diversify on the land, in the air, and in the oceans. Mammals are warm blooded, have hair on their bodies, and nurse their young with milk. Marsupial mammals are born very young and then move to a pouch on the mother, while placental mammals spend a longer time *in utero* and are born in a relatively mature state compared to marsupials.

- Flowering plants, called angiosperms, diversified and spread around the world through the Cenozoic era.
- Humans evolved from primate ancestors in Africa over a period of 8 million years. They are distinguished from their ape ancestors by an upright, bipedal posture, large brains, and tool use. The oldest anatomically modern human fossils are 200,000 years old. These "cavemen" coexisted with Neanderthals, produced the earliest art, and may have been responsible for the widespread Pleistocene extinctions of many large mammals.

THE RIGHT PLACE Suggest a geologic reason why the rift valley system of East Africa is so rich in human ancestor fossils.

GIVE IT SOME THOUGHT

1. Refer to the geologic time scale in Figure 3. The Precambrian accounts for nearly 90 percent of geologic time. Why do you think it has fewer divisions than the rest of the time scale?

2. Referring to Figure 4, write a brief summary of the events that led to the formation of Earth.

3. What does the existence of iron-rich rocks during the Precambrian indicate about the evolution of Earth's atmosphere?

4. Describe two ways in which the sudden appearance of oxygen in the atmosphere about 2.5 billion years ago influenced the development of modern life-forms.

5. Five mass extinctions, in which 50 percent or more of Earth's marine species became extinct, are documented in the fossil record. Use the accompanying graph, which depicts the time and extent of each mass extinction, to answer the following:
   a. Which of the five mass extinctions was the *most extreme*? Identify this extinction by name and when it occurred.
   b. What group of animals was most affected by the extinction referred to in Question a?
   c. When did the *most recent* mass extinction occur?
   d. During the most recent mass extinction, what prominent animal group was eliminated?
   e. What animal group experienced a major period of diversification following the most recent mass extinction?

6. Currently, oceans cover about 71 percent of Earth's surface. This percentage was much higher early in Earth history. Explain.

7. Contrast the eastern and western margins of North America during the Cenozoic era in terms of their relationships to plate boundaries.

8. Suggest at least one reason why plants moved onto land before animals.

9. Some scientists have proposed that the environments around black smokers may be similar to the extreme conditions that existed early in Earth history. Therefore, these scientists look to the unusual life that exists around black smokers for clues about how earliest life may have survived. Compare and contrast the environment of a black smoker to the environment on Earth approximately 3 to 4 billion years ago. Do you think there are parallels between the two, and if so, do you think black smokers are good examples of the environment that earliest life may have experienced? Explain.

10. About 250 million years ago, plate movement assembled all the previously separated landmasses together to form the supercontinent Pangaea. The formation of Pangaea resulted in deeper ocean basins, which caused a drop in sea level and caused shallow coastal areas to dry up. Thus, in addition to rearranging the geography of our planet, continental drift has had a major impact on life on Earth. Use the accompanying diagrams to answer the following:
   a. Which of the following types of habitats would likely diminish in size during the formation of a supercontinent: deep-ocean habitats, wetlands, shallow marine environments, or terrestrial (land) habitats? Explain.
   b. During the breakup of a supercontinent, what would happen to sea level—would it remain the same, rise, or fall?
   c. Explain how and why the development of an extensive oceanic ridge system that forms during the breakup of a supercontinent affects sea level.

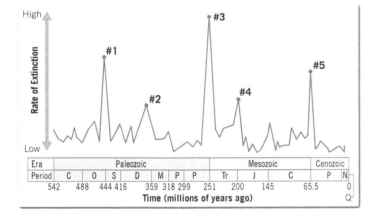

Four hypothetical continents   **Newly formed supercontinent**

TIME

MasteringGeology™   www.masteringgeology.com

Looking for additional review and test prep materials? Visit the Study Area in MasteringGeology to enhance your understanding of this chapter's content by accessing a variety of resources, including **Self-Study Quizzes,** **Geoscience Animations, GEODe Tutorials, RSS feeds, flashcards, web links, self-study quizzes,** and an optional **Pearson eText.**

Glossary

Angiosperm A flowering plant in which fruits contain the seeds.
Banded iron formations A finely layered iron and silica-rich (chert) layer deposited mainly during the Precambrian.
Cambrian explosion The huge expansion in biodiversity that occurred at the beginning of the Paleozoic era.

Craton The part of the continental crust that has attained stability; that is, it has not been affected by significant tectonic activity during the Phanerozoic eon. It consists of the shield and the stable platform.
Eukaryotes An organism whose genetic material is enclosed in a nucleus; plants, animals, and fungi are eukaryotes.
Great Oxygenation Event A time about 2.5 billion years ago, when a significant amount of oxygen appeared in the atmosphere.

Gymnosperm A group of seed-bearing plants that includes conifers and Ginkgo. The term means "naked seed," a reference to the unenclosed condition of the seeds.

Hadean The earliest time interval (eon) of Earth history. The time before the planet's first rocks.

Mass extinction An event in which a large percentage of species become extinct.

Outgassing The escape of dissolved gases from molten rocks.

Planetesimal A solid celestial body that accumulated during the first stages of planetary formation. Planetesimals aggregated into increasingly larger bodies, ultimately forming the planets.

Prokaryotes Refers to the cells or organisms such as bacteria whose genetic material is not enclosed in a nucleus.

Protoplanets A developing planetary body that grows by the accumulation of planetesimals.

Shield A large, relatively flat expanse of ancient igneous and metamorphic rocks within the craton.

Snowball Earth A hypothesis that relates a period of global glaciation to the Great Oxygenation Event.

Solar nebula The cloud of interstellar gas and/or dust from which the bodies of our solar system formed.

Stromatolites Distinctively layered mounds of calcium carbonate, which are fossil evidence for the existence of ancient microscopic bacteria.

Supercontinent A large landmass that contains all, or nearly all, of the existing continents.

Supercontinent cycle The idea that the rifting and dispersal of one supercontinent is followed by a long period during which the fragments gradually reassemble into a new supercontinent.

Supernova An exploding star that increases its brightness many thousands of times.

Energy and Mineral Resources

From Chapter 23 of *Earth: An Introduction to Physical Geology*, Eleventh Edition. Edward J. Tarbuck, Frederick K. Lutgens, Dennis Tasa.

Energy and Mineral Resources

The Bingham Canyon copper mine, southwest of Salt Lake City, Utah, is one of the largest open-pit mines in the world. The rim is nearly 4 kilometers (2.5 miles) across and 900 meters (3000 feet) deep. (Photo by Michael Collier)

Each statement represents the primary learning objective for the corresponding major heading within the chapter. After you complete the chapter you should be able to:

1   Distinguish between renewable and nonrenewable resources.
2   Compare and contrast the traditional fossil fuels and describe how each contributes to U.S. energy consumption.
3   Contrast oil sands, oil shale, and gas hydrates as potential sources of energy.
4   Describe the importance of nuclear energy and discuss its pros and cons.
5   List and discuss the major sources of renewable energy. Describe the contribution of renewable energy to the overall U.S. energy supply.
6   Distinguish among resource, reserve, and ore.
7   Explain how different igneous and metamorphic processes produce economically significant mineral deposits.
8   Discuss ways in which surface processes produce ore deposits.
9   Distinguish between two broad categories of nonmetallic mineral resources and list examples of each.

aterials that we extract from Earth are the basis of modern civilization. A high percentage of the products and substances we use every day were mined from Earth's crust and/or manufactured using energy extracted from the crust. We humans consume huge quantities of energy and mineral resources, and demand continues to grow. In 1960, the world population was 3 billion. In 2011, Earth was home to 7 billion people. By 2025, the planet's population is expected to approach 8 billion people. Improving living standards in many parts of the world add to demand as well.

How long can our remaining resources sustain the rising standard of living in today's industrialized countries and still provide for the growing needs of developing regions? How much environmental deterioration are we willing to accept in pursuit of resources? Can alternatives be found? If we are to cope with an increasing per capita demand and a growing world population, we must understand our resources and their limits.

The San Juan power plant near Farmington, New Mexico, is fueled by coal. (Photo by Michael Collier)

1 Renewable and Nonrenewable Resources

Resources are commonly divided into two broad categories—renewable and nonrenewable. **Renewable resources** can be replenished over relatively short time spans such as months, years, or decades. Common examples are plants and animals for food, natural fibers for clothing, and trees for lumber and paper. Energy from flowing water, wind, and the Sun are also considered renewable.

By contrast, **nonrenewable resources** continue to be formed in Earth, but the processes that create them are so slow that significant deposits take millions of years to accumulate. For human purposes, Earth contains fixed quantities of these substances. When the present supplies are mined or pumped from the ground, there will be no more. Examples are fossil fuels (for example, coal, oil, natural gas) and many important metals (for example, iron, copper, uranium, gold). Some of these nonrenewable resources, such as aluminum, can be used over and over again; others, such as oil, cannot be recycled.

Occasionally some resources can be placed in either category, depending on how they are used. Groundwater is one such example. Where it is pumped from the ground at a rate that can be replenished, groundwater can be classified as a renewable resource. However, in places where groundwater is withdrawn faster than it is replenished, the water table drops steadily. In this case, the groundwater is being "mined" just like other nonrenewable resources.

Most of the energy and mineral resources we use are nonrenewable. How much of these does the average person in the United States use each year? FIGURE 1 shows the annual per capita consumption of several important mineral and energy resources. This is each person's prorated share of the materials required by industry to provide the vast array of homes, cars, electronics, cosmetics, packaging, and so on that modern society requires. Figures for other highly industrialized countries, such as Canada, Australia, and several nations in Western Europe are comparable.

Nonmetallic Resources

5713 kg (12695 lbs)
Stone

4025 kg (8945 lbs)
Sand and gravel

360 kg (790 lbs)
Cement

137 kg (304 lbs)
Clays

178 kg (395 lbs)
Salt

162 kg (361 lbs)
Phosphate rock

302 kg (672 lbs)
Other nonmetals

Metallic Resources

249 kg (553 lbs)
Iron

35 kg (77 lbs)
Aluminum

6 kg (14 lbs)
Lead

6 kg (13 lbs)
Manganese

11 kg (25 lbs)
Copper

5 kg (11 lbs)
Zinc

9 kg (20 lbs)
Other metals

Energy Resources

3500 kg (7700 lbs)
Petroleum

3700 kg (8140 lbs)
Coal

3850 kg (8470 lbs)
Natural gas

FIGURE 1 How much do each of us use? The annual per capita consumption of nonmetallic and metallic resources for the United States is about 11,000 kilograms (12 tons). About 97 percent of the materials used are nonmetallic. The per capita use of oil, coal, and natural gas exceeds 11,000 kilograms. (U.S. Geological Survey)

1 CONCEPT CHECKS

1. Distinguish between renewable and nonrenewable resources.
2. Are resources such as aluminum, that can be recycled, considered renewable?
3. Do we use a greater quantity of metallic or nonmetallic resources?

2 | Energy Resources: Traditional Fossil Fuels

Coal, petroleum, and natural gas are the primary fuels of our modern industrial economy (FIGURE 2). About 82 percent of the energy consumed in the United States today comes from these basic fossil fuels. Although major shortages of oil and gas will not occur for many years, proven reserves are declining. Despite new exploration, even in very remote regions and severe environments, new sources are not keeping pace with consumption.

Unless large new petroleum reserves are discovered (which is possible but not likely), a greater share of our future needs will have to come from coal and from alternative energy sources, such as nuclear, geothermal, solar, wind, tidal, and hydroelectric power. Two fossil-fuel alternatives—oil sands and oil shale—are also mentioned as promising sources of liquid fuels. In the following sections, we will briefly examine the fuels that have traditionally supplied our energy needs, as well as sources that will provide an increasing share of our future requirements.

Coal

Along with oil and natural gas, coal is commonly called a **fossil fuel**. Such a designation is appropriate because each time we burn coal, we are using energy from the Sun that was stored by plants many millions of years ago. We are indeed burning a "fossil."

Coal has been an important fuel for centuries. In the nineteenth and early twentieth centuries, cheap and plentiful coal powered the Industrial Revolution. By 1900 coal was providing 90 percent of the energy used in the

SMARTFIGURE 2
U.S. energy consumption, 2011
The total was 97.5 quadrillion Btu. A quadrillion is 10 raised to the 12th power, or a million million. A quadrillion Btu is a convenient unit for referring to U.S. energy use as a whole.
(U.S. Department of Energy/Energy Information Agency)

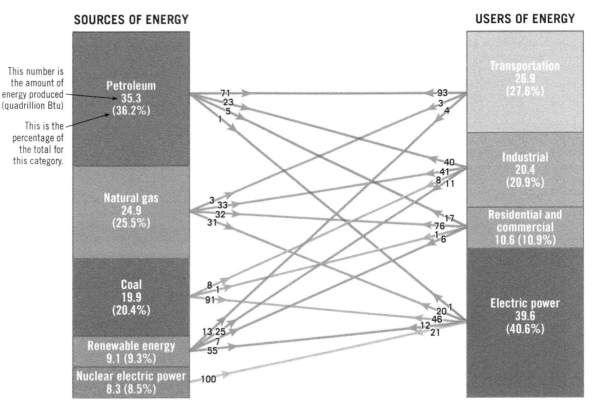

Reading this double graph:
The left side indicates what energy sources we use. The right side shows where we use the energy.
The lines with numbers that connect the graphs provide more details. Use the top line as an example. It shows that 71% of the petroleum is used by the transportation sector. It also indicates that 93% of the energy used by the transportation sector is petroleum.

United States. Although still important, coal currently accounts for a much smaller proportion of the nation's energy needs: about 20 percent.

Until the 1950s, coal was an important domestic heating fuel as well as a power source for industry. However, its direct use in the home has been largely replaced by oil, natural gas, and electricity. These fuels are preferred because they are more readily available (delivered via pipes, tanks, or wiring) and cleaner to use.

Nevertheless, coal remains the major fuel used in power plants to generate electricity, and it is therefore indirectly an important source of energy for our homes. An examination of Figure 2 shows that in 2011, 91 percent of the coal use in the United States was for generating electricity. It also shows that coal was the fuel used to generate 46 percent of U.S. electrical power.

In the decades to come, it is estimated that the percentage of our electricity generated from coal will decrease because of greater use of natural gas and renewable technologies. However, this does not mean that we will use less coal. Because overall demand for electricity will increase, the actual amount of coal used may increase as well. Expanded coal production is possible because the world has enormous reserves and the technology to mine coal efficiently. In the United States, coal fields are widespread and contain supplies that should last for hundreds of years (FIGURE 3).

Although coal is plentiful, its recovery and use present a number of challenges. Surface mining can turn the countryside into a scarred wasteland if careful (and costly) reclamation is not carried out to restore the land. Today all U.S. surface mines must reclaim the land. Although underground mining does not scar the landscape to the same degree, it has been costly in terms of human life and health. Strong federal safety regulations have made U.S. mining quite safe. However, the hazards of collapsing roofs, gas explosions, and the heavy equipment required remain. Over the years, the share of coal produced from surface mines has increased significantly: from 51 percent in 1949 to nearly 70 percent in 2011 (FIGURE 4).

Air pollution is a significant problem associated with the burning of coal. Much coal contains significant quantities of sulfur. Despite efforts to remove sulfur before the coal is burned, some remains; when the coal is burned, the sulfur is converted into noxious sulfur oxide gases. Through a series of complex chemical

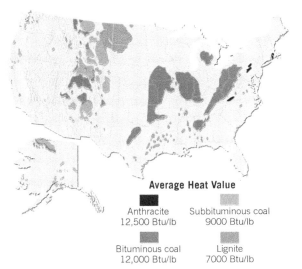

FIGURE 3 Coal fields of the United States Most of the coal mined is subbituminous and bituminous. Wyoming and West Virginia are the leading producers. (Data from the U.S. Geological Survey)

Average Heat Value

Anthracite 12,500 Btu/lb

Subbituminous coal 9000 Btu/lb

Bituminous coal 12,000 Btu/lb

Lignite 7000 Btu/lb

reactions in the atmosphere, the sulfur oxides are converted to sulfuric acid, which then falls to Earth's surface in rain or snow. This acid precipitation can have adverse ecological effects over widespread areas.

As is the case when other fossil fuels are burned, the combustion of coal produces carbon dioxide. This major greenhouse gas plays a significant role in the heating of our atmosphere.

Oil and Natural Gas

Together, oil and natural gas provided more than 60 percent of the energy consumed in the United States in 2011. By examining Figure 2, you can see

FIGURE 4 Surface coal mine Nearly 70 percent of U.S. coal production is from surface mines. Wyoming is by far the largest producer, accounting for about 40 percent of the coal mined in the United States in 2011. This mine is in Campbell County, Wyoming. (Photo by David R. Frazier photography, Inc./ Alamy Images)

that the transportation sector of the U.S. economy relies almost totally on petroleum as an energy source. In 2011 natural gas production exceeded coal production for the first time in more than 30 years. An important reason is the use of new technologies that have increased production from shale formations. Users of natural gas are almost evenly divided among the three categories other than transportation in Figure 2.

Petroleum Formation

Petroleum and natural gas are found in similar environments and frequently occur together. Both consist of various hydrocarbon compounds (compounds consisting of hydrogen and carbon mixed together). They may also contain relatively small quantities of other elements, such as sulfur, nitrogen, and oxygen. Like coal, petroleum and natural gas are biological products derived from the remains of organisms. However, the environments in which they form are very different, as are the organisms. Coal is formed mostly from plant material that accumulated in a swampy environment above sea level. Oil and gas are derived from the remains of both plants and animals having a marine origin.

The formation of oil and natural gas begins with the accumulation of sediment in ocean areas that are rich in plant and animal remains. These accumulations must occur where biological activity is high, such as in nearshore areas. However, most marine environments are oxygen rich, which leads to the decay of organic remains before they can be buried by other sediments. Therefore,

accumulations of oil and gas are not as widespread as are the marine environments that support abundant biological activity. This limiting factor notwithstanding, large quantities of organic matter are buried and protected from oxidation in many offshore sedimentary basins. With increasing burial over millions of years, chemical reactions gradually transform some of the original organic matter into the liquid and gaseous hydrocarbons we call petroleum and natural gas.

Unlike the organic matter from which they formed, the newly created petroleum and natural gas are mobile. These fluids are gradually squeezed from the compacting, mud-rich layers where they originate into adjacent permeable beds such as sandstone, where openings between sediment grains are larger. Because this occurs under water, the rock layers containing the oil and gas are saturated with water. Because oil and gas are less dense than water, they migrate upward through the water-filled pore spaces of the enclosing rocks. Unless something halts this upward migration, the fluids will eventually reach the surface, at which point the volatile components will evaporate.

Traps for Oil and Gas

Sometimes the upward migration of oil and natural gas is halted. A geologic environment that allows for economically significant amounts of oil and gas to accumulate underground is termed an **oil trap**. Several geologic structures may act as oil traps, but all have two basic conditions in common: a porous, permeable **reservoir rock** that will yield petroleum and natural gas in sufficient

FIGURE 5 Drilling for oil Oil accumulates in oil traps that consist of porous, permeable *reservoir rock* overlain by an impermeable *cap rock*. (North Sea photo by Peter Bowater/Photo Researchers, Inc.; historic photo by Hulton Archive/Getty Images)

Modern offshore oil production platform in the North Sea.

The first successful oil well was completed by Edwin Drake (right) on August 27, 1859, near Titusville, PA. The oil-bearing reservoir rock was encountered at a depth of 21 meters (69 feet).

A. Anticline

B. Fault trap

SMARTFIGURE 6
Common oil traps

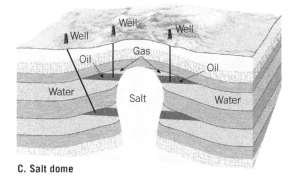

C. Salt dome

D. Stratigraphic (pinchout) trap

quantities to make drilling worthwhile and a **cap rock**, such as shale, that is virtually impermeable to oil and gas. The cap rock halts the upwardly mobile oil and gas and keeps the oil and gas from escaping at the surface (FIGURE 5). FIGURE 6 illustrates some common oil and natural-gas traps, which are described in the following list:

- **Anticline.** One of the simplest traps is an *anticline*, an uparched series of sedimentary strata (Figure 6A). As the strata are bent, the rising oil and gas collect at the apex (top) of the fold. Because of its lower density, the natural gas collects above the oil. Both rest upon the denser water that saturates the reservoir rock. One of the world's largest oil fields, El Nala in Saudi Arabia, is the result of an anticlinal trap, as is the famous Teapot Dome in Wyoming.
- **Fault trap.** This type of trap forms when strata are displaced in such a manner as to bring a dipping reservoir rock into position opposite an impermeable bed, as shown in Figure 6B. In this case, the upward migration of the oil and gas is halted where it encounters the fault.
- **Salt dome.** In the Gulf coastal plain region of the United States, important accumulations of oil occur in association with *salt domes.* Such areas have thick accumulations of sedimentary strata, including layers of rock salt. Salt occurring at great depths has been

forced to rise in columns by the pressure of overlying beds. These rising salt columns gradually deform the overlying strata. Because oil and gas migrate to the highest level possible, they accumulate in the upturned sandstone beds adjacent to the salt column (Figure 6C).
- **Stratigraphic (pinchout) trap.** Yet another important geologic circumstance that may lead to significant accumulations of oil and gas is termed a *stratigraphic trap.* These oil-bearing structures result primarily from the original pattern of sedimentation rather than structural deformation. The stratigraphic trap illustrated in Figure 6D exists because a sloping bed of sandstone thins to the point of disappearance.

How do geologists locate oil traps? Changes in the composition or structure of rock cause seismic waves to reflect off boundaries between layers. This characteristic of waves is especially useful in the exploration for oil and natural gas, as artificially generated seismic waves can be used to probe the crust (FIGURE 7). Oil and natural gas would be much more difficult and expensive to find without seismic imaging because a huge number of wells would have to be randomly drilled to locate oil traps.

When the lid created by the cap rock is punctured by drilling, the oil and natural gas, which are under pressure, migrate from the pore spaces of the reservoir

FIGURE 7 Seismic search for oil and natural gas Reflected seismic waves are used to search for underground reservoirs of oil and natural gas. The seismic waves from explosions reflect off the boundaries between layers of different composition. Using computer programs, the data show the geometry of the strata, including folds and faults. Using this information, geologists map potential petroleum reservoirs in Earth's crust.

rock to the drill hole. On rare occasions, when fluid pressure is great, it may force oil up the drill hole to the surface, causing a "gusher" or oil fountain at the surface. Usually, however, a pump is required to lift out the oil.

A drill hole is not the only means by which oil and gas can escape from a trap. Traps can be broken by natural forces. For example, Earth movements may create fractures that allow the hydrocarbon fluids to escape. Surface erosion may breach a trap with similar results. The older the rock strata, the greater the chance that deformation or erosion has affected a trap. Indeed, not all ages of rock yield oil and gas in the same proportions. The greatest production comes from the youngest rocks, those of Cenozoic age. Older Mesozoic rocks produce considerably less, followed by even smaller yields from the still older Paleozoic strata. There is virtually no oil produced from the most ancient rocks, those of Precambrian age.

Hydraulic Fracturing In some shale deposits, there are significant reserves of natural gas that cannot naturally leave because of the rock's low permeability. The practice of *hydraulic fracturing* (often called "fracking") shatters the shale, opening up cracks through which the natural gas can flow into wells and then be brought to the surface. The fracturing of the shale is initiated by pumping fluids into the rock at very high pressures. The fluid is mostly water but also includes other chemicals that aid in the fracturing process. Some of these chemicals may be toxic, and there are concerns about fracking fluids leaking into aquifers that supply people with freshwater. The injection fluid also includes sand, so once fractures open up in the shale, the sand grains can keep them propped open and permit the gas to continue to flow. Once the fracturing has been accomplished, the fracking fluid is brought back to the surface. This wastewater is then injected into deep disposal wells. In some locations, these injections appear to trigger numerous minor earthquakes. Because of concerns about potential groundwater contamination and induced seismicity, hydraulic fracturing remains a controversial practice. Its environmental effects remain a focus of continuing research.

2 CONCEPT CHECKS

1. Why are coal, oil, and natural gas called *fossil fuels*? Do all three form under the same circumstances?
2. What part of U.S. energy consumption does each of the fossil fuels represent? Where is most coal used? How about petroleum?
3. List some advantages and disadvantages of coal.
4. What is an oil trap? Sketch two examples. What do all oil traps have in common?

In 2011, 71 percent of the petroleum consumed in the United States was used for transportation. Petroleum represented 93 percent of the energy used for transportation. (Photo by Burwell and Burwell Photography/Getty Images)

3 | Oil Sands, Oil Shale, and Gas Hydrates

In years to come, world oil supplies will dwindle. When this occurs, a lower grade of hydrocarbon may have to be substituted. Are the fuels derived from oil sands and oil shale good candidates? Some areas of the ocean floor are covered with sediments that contain huge quantities of natural gas. Might these deposits provide energy in the future?

Oil Sands

Oil sands are usually mixtures of clay and sand combined with water and varying amounts of a black, highly viscous tar known as *bitumen*. The use of the term *sand* can be misleading because not all deposits are associated with sands and sandstones. Some occur in other materials, including shales and limestones. The oil in these deposits is very similar to heavy crude oils pumped from wells. The major difference between conventional oil reservoirs and oil sand deposits is in the viscosity (resistance to flow) of the oil they contain. In oil sands, the oil is much more viscous and cannot simply be pumped out (FIGURE 8).

Substantial oil sand deposits occur in several locations around the world. By far the largest are in the Canadian province of Alberta.

Some oil sands are mined at the surface in a manner similar to the strip mining of coal. The excavated material is then heated with pressurized steam until the bitumen softens and rises. Once collected, the oily material is treated to remove impurities, and then hydrogen is added. This last step upgrades the material to a synthetic crude, which can then be refined. Extracting and refining oil sands requires a great deal of energy— nearly half as much as the end product yields! Nevertheless, oil sands from Alberta's vast deposits are the source of about 50 percent of Canada's oil production. In 2012, about 1.6 million barrels of crude bitumen were produced per day. It is estimated that this amount will double by 2022.

Obtaining oil from oil sand has environmental drawbacks. Substantial land disturbance is associated with mining huge quantities of rock and sediment. Moreover, large quantities of water are required for processing, and when processing is completed, contaminated water and sediment accumulate in toxic disposal ponds.

About 80 percent of the oil sands in Alberta are buried too deeply for surface mining. Oil from these deep deposits must be recovered by using *in situ* (Latin for "in place") techniques. Using drilling technology, steam is injected into the deposit to heat the oil sand, reducing the viscosity of the bitumen. The hot, mobile bitumen migrates toward producing wells, which pump it to the surface, while the sand is left in place. Production using *in situ* techniques already rivals open-pit mining and in the

FIGURE 8 A close up of oil sand
Notice how solid the material is. Sometimes the term "tar sand" is used to describe bitumen deposits, but it is inaccurate because tar is a human-made substance produced by distilling organic matter. Bitumen looks like tar but is a naturally occurring substance. (Petter Essick/Aurora Photos/Alamy Images)

future will replace mining as the main source of bitumen production from the oil sands.

Challenges facing *in situ* processes include increasing the efficiency of oil recovery, managing the water used to make steam, and reducing the costs of energy required for the process.

Oil Shale

Oil shale contains enormous amounts of untapped oil. Worldwide, the U.S. Geological Survey estimates that there are more than 3000 billion barrels of oil contained in shales that would yield more than 38 liters (10 gallons) of oil per ton of shale. But this figure is misleading because fewer than 200 billion barrels are known to be recoverable with present technology. Still, estimated U.S. resources are about 14 times as great as those of conventionally recoverable oil, and estimates will probably increase as more geologic information is gathered.

Roughly half of the world supply of oil shale is in the Green River Formation in Colorado, Utah, and Wyoming (FIGURE 9). In this region the oil shale is part of sedimentary layers that accumulated at the bottoms of two vast, shallow lakes during the Eocene epoch (57 million to 36 million years ago).

Oil shale has been suggested as a potential source of oil as conventional sources dwindle and prices rise. However, the heat energy in oil shale is about one-eighth that in crude oil, due to the large proportion of mineral matter in the shale. This mineral matter adds cost to mining, processing, and waste disposal. Producing oil

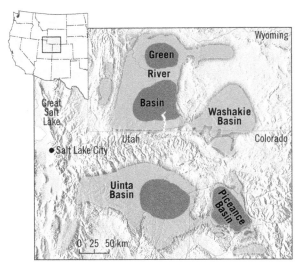

Green River Formation
Distribution of oil shale in the Green River Formation of Colorado, Utah, and Wyoming. The areas shaded with the darker color represent the richest deposits. Oil shale is a potential source of oil that is not yet economical to exploit. (U.S. Geological Survey)

from oil shale has some of the same problems as producing oil from oil sands. Surface mining causes widespread land disturbance and presents significant waste-disposal problems. Moreover, processing requires large amounts of water, which is in short supply in the semiarid region of the Green River Formation.

At present, oil is plentiful on world markets. Therefore, with current technologies, most oil shale is not worth mining. In the 1980s industry largely abandoned

oil shale research-and-development efforts. In 2005, however, a U.S. Department of Energy study suggested that the large amount of oil that potentially can be extracted from oil shale in the United States probably ensures its eventual inclusion in the national energy mix.

Gas Hydrates: A Fuel from Ocean-Floor Sediments

Gas hydrates are unusually compact chemical structures made of water and natural gas. The most common type of natural gas is methane, which produces *methane hydrate*. Gas hydrates occur beneath permafrost areas on land and under the ocean floor at depths below 525 meters (1720 feet).

Most oceanic gas hydrates are created when bacteria break down organic matter trapped in seafloor sediments, producing methane gas with minor amounts of ethane and propane. These gases combine with water in deep-ocean sediments (where pressures are high and temperatures are low) in such a way that the gas is trapped inside a lattice-like cage of water molecules.

Vessels that have drilled into gas hydrates have retrieved cores of mud mixed with chunks or layers of gas hydrates (FIGURE 10A) that fizzle and evaporate quickly when they are exposed to the relatively warm, low-pressure conditions at the ocean surface. Gas hydrates resemble chunks of ice but ignite when lit by a flame because methane and other flammable gases are released as gas hydrates vaporize (FIGURE 10B).

Some estimates indicate that as much as 20 quadrillion cubic meters (700 quadrillion cubic feet) of methane are locked up in sediments containing gas hydrates. This is equivalent to about *twice* as much carbon as Earth's coal, oil, and conventional gas reserves combined, so gas hydrates have great potential. A major drawback in exploiting reserves of gas hydrate is that they rapidly decompose at surface temperatures and pressures. In the future, however, these vast seafloor reserves of energy may help power modern society.

A.

FIGURE 10 Gas hydrates
A. This sample was retrieved from the ocean floor and shows layers of white, ice-like gas hydrate mixed with mud. **B.** Gas hydrates evaporate when exposed to surface conditions and release natural gas, which can be ignited. (Photos courtesy of GEOMAR Research Center, Kiel, Germany)

B.

3 CONCEPT CHECKS

1. What are oil sands, and where are they most plentiful?
2. What is the significance of the Green River Formation in Colorado, Utah, and Wyoming?
3. What are gas hydrates?
4. Which of the energy sources discussed in this section currently contributes to our energy supply?
5. Describe some obstacles or problems associated with each of the energy sources discussed in this section.

4 Nuclear Energy

Nuclear energy meets an important part of U.S. energy needs. A glance back at Figure 2 shows that nuclear power was the source of about 8 percent of U.S. energy consumption in 2011. Figure 2 also shows that 100 percent of that energy was used to produce electricity. The right side of Figure 2 also shows that 21 percent of U.S. electricity is from nuclear energy.

The fuel for these nuclear power plants comes from radioactive materials that release energy by the process of **nuclear fission**. Fission is accomplished by bombarding the nuclei of heavy atoms, commonly uranium-235, with neutrons. This causes the uranium nuclei to split into smaller nuclei and to emit neutrons and heat energy. The ejected neutrons, in turn, bombard the nuclei of adjacent uranium atoms, producing a *chain reaction.* If the supply of fissionable material is sufficient and if the reaction is allowed to proceed in an uncontrolled manner, an enormous amount of energy would be released, in the form of an atomic explosion.

In a nuclear power plant, the fission reaction is controlled by moving neutron-absorbing rods into or out of the nuclear reactor. The result is a controlled nuclear chain reaction that releases great amounts of heat. The energy produced is transported from the reactor and used to drive steam turbines that turn electrical generators, which is similar to what occurs in most conventional power plants.

Uranium

Uranium-235 is the only naturally occurring isotope that is readily fissionable, and it is therefore the primary fuel used in nuclear power plants.* Although large quantities of uranium ore have been discovered, most contain less than 0.05 percent uranium. Of this small amount, 99.3 percent is the nonfissionable isotope uranium-238, and just 0.7 percent consists of the fissionable isotope uranium-235. Because most nuclear reactors operate with fuels that are at least 3 percent uranium-235, the two isotopes must be separated in order to concentrate the fissionable uranium-235. The process of separating the uranium isotopes is difficult and substantially increases the cost of nuclear power.

Although uranium is a rare element in Earth's crust, it does occur in enriched deposits. Some of the most important occurrences are associated with what are believed to be ancient placer deposits in streambeds.**

*Thorium, although not capable by itself of sustaining a chain reaction, can be used with uranium-235 as a nuclear fuel.

For example, in Witwatersrand, South Africa, grains of uranium ore (as well as rich gold deposits) were concentrated by virtue of their high density in rocks made largely of quartz pebbles. In the United States, the richest uranium deposits are found in Jurassic and Triassic sandstones in the Colorado Plateau and in younger rocks in Wyoming. Most of these deposits have formed through the precipitation of uranium compounds from groundwater. Here, precipitation of uranium occurs as a result of a chemical reaction with organic matter, as evidenced by the concentration of uranium in fossil logs and organic-rich black shales.

Obstacles to Development

At one time, nuclear power was heralded as the clean, cheap source of energy that would replace fossil fuels. However, several obstacles have emerged to hinder the development of nuclear power as a major energy source. Not the least of these is the skyrocketing costs of building nuclear facilities that contain numerous safety features. More important, perhaps, is the concern over the possibility of a serious accident at one of the nearly 200 nuclear plants in existence worldwide.

The March 2011 emergency at Japan's Fukushima nuclear power plant is a recent example (FIGURE 11). A

**Placer deposits are discussed later in the chapter.

FIGURE 11 Tsunami destroys nuclear power plant In March 2011, an earthquake and massive tsunami destroyed Japan's Fukushima nuclear power plant. The event triggered a reevaluation of nuclear power in many countries. (Photo by SSEI KATO/AFP/Getty Images)

powerful earthquake generated a tsunami that devastated the coastal zone where the plant was situated. A series of equipment failures, nuclear meltdowns, and releases of radioactive materials followed.

It should be emphasized that the concentrations of fissionable uranium-235 and the design of reactors are such that nuclear power plants cannot explode like atomic bombs. The dangers arise from the possible escape of radioactive debris during a meltdown of the core or other malfunction. In addition, hazards such as the disposal of nuclear waste and the relationship that exists between nuclear energy programs and the proliferation of nuclear weapons must be considered as we evaluate the pros and cons of employing nuclear power.

Among the "pros" for nuclear energy is the fact that nuclear power plants do not emit carbon dioxide—the greenhouse gas that contributes significantly to global warming. By contrast, the generation of electricity from fossil fuels produces large quantities of carbon dioxide. Thus, substituting nuclear power for power generated by fossil fuels represents one option for reducing carbon emissions.

4 CONCEPT CHECKS

1. What portion of U.S. energy consumption is provided by nuclear power?
2. What is the primary fuel used in nuclear power plants?
3. List some pros and cons of nuclear energy.

All of the nuclear energy and more than 50 percent of the renewable energy produced in the United States is used for generating electricity. (Photo by Shutterstock)

5 Renewable Energy

Unlike fossils fuels, which are exhaustible, renewable energy sources regenerate and can be sustained indefinitely. The use of renewable energy is not new. More than 150 years ago, wood supplied a high percentage of our energy needs. Today coal, oil, and natural gas dominate, but the use of renewable forms of energy is on the rise. In 2011 consumption of renewable energy in the United States represented about 9 percent of all energy used (FIGURE 12A). About 13 percent of U.S. electricity is generated from renewable sources. The use of renewable fuels has been increasing during the past 40 years and is expected to continue growing during the next 30 years (FIGURE 12B). Nevertheless, the U.S. Department of Energy projects that we will still rely on nonrenewable fuels to meet most of our needs.

Solar Energy

The term *solar energy* generally refers to the direct use of the Sun's rays to supply energy for the needs of people. The simplest and perhaps most widely used *passive solar collectors* are south-facing windows. As sunlight passes through the glass, its energy is absorbed by objects in the room. These objects in turn radiate heat that warms the air.

More elaborate systems used for home heating involve *active solar collectors*. These roof-mounted devices are usually large, blackened boxes that are covered with a transparent material. The heat they collect can be transferred to where it is needed by circulating air or fluids through pipes. In Israel, for example, about 80 percent of all homes are equipped with solar collectors that provide hot water.

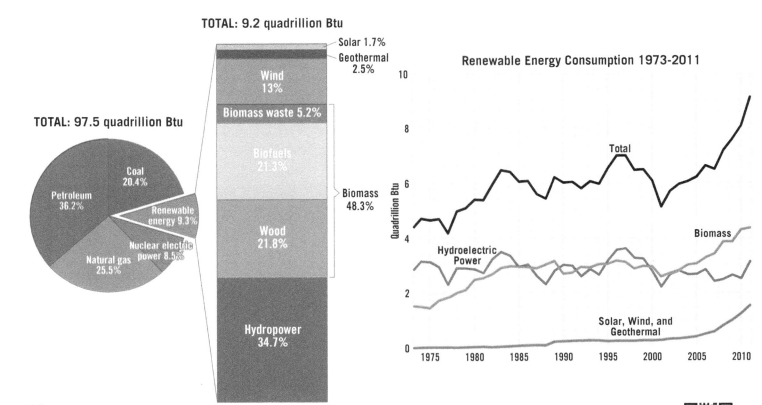

SMARTFIGURE 12 Renewable energy

In 2011 renewable energy represented about 9 percent of U.S. energy consumption. The graph on the right shows that renewable energy consumption more than doubled between 1973 and 2011. Notice the sharp increase in solar, wind, and geothermal since 2005. (U.S. Energy Information Administration)

Research is currently under way to improve the technologies for concentrating sunlight. One method uses parabolic troughs as solar energy collectors. Each collector resembles a large tube that has been cut in half. Their highly polished surfaces reflect sunlight onto a collection pipe (FIGURE 13). A fluid (usually oil) runs through the pipe and absorbs the concentrated sunlight. The fluid is heated to over 200° C (400° F) and is typically used to make steam that drives a turbine to produce electricity. Parabolic troughs usually have a north–south alignment and gradually rotate to track the Sun.

Another type of collector uses photovoltaic (solar) cells that convert the Sun's energy directly into electricity (FIGURE 14). Photovoltaic cells are usually connected together to create solar panels in which sunlight knocks electrons into higher energy states, to produce electricity.

For many years solar cells were used mainly to power calculators and novelty devices. Today, however, large photovoltaic power stations are connected to electric grids to supplement other power generating facilities. The cost of solar cells makes generating electricity from this source more costly than that from conventional sources. However, as the cost of fossil fuels increases, advances in photovoltaic technology should narrow the price difference.

Another technology that is being developed, called the *Stirling dish*, converts thermal energy to electricity by using a mirror array to focus the Sun's rays on the receiver end of a Stirling engine. The internal side of a receiver then heats hydrogen gas, causing it to expand. The pressure created by the expanding gas drives a piston, which turns a small electric generator.

Wind Energy

Air has mass, and when it moves (that is, when the wind blows), it contains the energy of that motion—kinetic energy. A portion of that energy can be converted into other forms—mechanical force or electricity—that we can use to perform work (FIGURE 15).

Mechanical energy from wind is commonly used for pumping water in rural or remote places. The "farm

Photovoltaic Solar Resource Potential of the United States

kWh/m²/Day
<6.8 6.0 5.0 4.0 3.0 >2.2

FIGURE 15 **Wind power**
Wind power development has been expanding rapidly. (Farm windmill photo by Mehmet Dilsiz/Shutterstock; wind turbine photo by John Mead/Science Photo Library/Photo Researchers, Inc.)

windmill," still a familiar sight in many rural areas, is an example. Mechanical energy converted from wind can also be used for other purposes, such as sawing logs, grinding grain, and propelling sailboats. In addition, wind-powered electric turbines generate electricity for homes, businesses, and for sale to utilities.

Today, modern wind turbines are being installed at breakneck speed. In fact, worldwide, in 2011 the installed wind power capacity exceeded 237,000 megawatts, an increase of 20 percent over 2010.* China has the greatest installed capacity (nearly 63,000 megawatts in 2011), followed by the United States (about 47,000 megawatts in 2011). According to the World Wind Energy Association, wind turbines were capable of supplying 3 percent of worldwide electricity demand at the beginning of 2012.

Wind speed is a crucial element in determining whether a place is a suitable site for installing a wind-energy facility. Generally a minimum average wind speed of 21 kilometers (13 miles) per hour is necessary for a large-scale wind-power plant to be profitable. A small difference in wind speed results in a large difference in energy production and, therefore, a large difference in the cost of the electricity generated. For example, a turbine operating on a site with an average wind speed of 19.3 kilometers (12 miles) per hour would generate about 33 percent more electricity than one operating at 17.7 kilometers (11 miles) per hour. Also, there is little energy to be harvested at low wind speeds; 9.6-kilometer

(6-mile) per-hour winds contain less than one-eighth the energy of 19.3-kilometer (12-mile) per-hour winds.

The United States has tremendous wind energy resources. Currently 34 states have commercial facilities that produce electricity from wind power. In early 2009, the leading state in installed capacity was Texas, followed by Iowa, California, and Minnesota. Despite the fact that California gave birth to the modern U.S. wind industry, 16 states have greater wind potential. As shown in TABLE 1, the top five states for wind energy potential are North Dakota, Texas, Kansas, South Dakota, and Montana. Although only a small fraction of U.S. electrical generation currently comes from wind

TABLE 1	The Leading States for Wind Energy Potential	
Rank	State	Potential*
1	North Dakota	1210
2	Texas	1190
3	Kansas	1070
4	South Dakota	1030
5	Montana	1020
6	Nebraska	868
7	Wyoming	747
8	Oklahoma	725
9	Minnesota	657
10	Iowa	551

*The total amount of electricity that could potentially be generated each year, measured in *billions* of kilowatt hours. A typical American home would use several hundred kilowatt hours per month.

Source: U.S. Department of Energy.

*One megawatt is enough electricity to supply 250–300 average American households.

FIGURE 16 Wind energy
potential for the United
States
Large wind systems require
average wind speeds of
about 6 meters per second
(13 miles per hour). (Map
data from National Renewable Energy Laboratory)

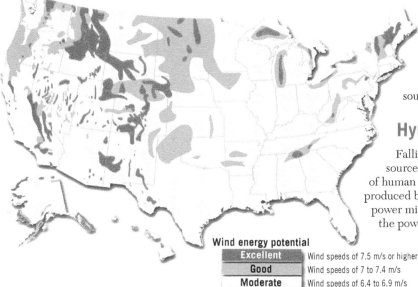

Wind energy potential

Excellent	Wind speeds of 7.5 m/s or higher
Good	Wind speeds of 7 to 7.4 m/s
Moderate	Wind speeds of 6.4 to 6.9 m/s

electricity from wind. Iowa (15.4 percent) and North Dakota (12 percent) were the leaders. Thus wind-generated electricity appears to be shifting from being an "alternative" to a "mainstream" energy source.

Hydroelectric Power

Falling water has been an energy source for centuries. Through much of human history, the mechanical energy produced by waterwheels has been used to power mills and other machinery. Today, the power generated by falling water is used to drive turbines that produce electricity, hence the term **hydroelectric power**. In the United States, hydroelectric power plants contributed about 8 percent of the country's demand in 2011. Most of this energy is produced at large dams, which allow for a controlled flow of water (FIGURE 17). The water impounded in a reservoir is a form of stored energy that can be released at any time to produce electricity.

Although water power is considered a renewable resource, the dams built to provide hydroelectricity have finite lifetimes. All rivers carry suspended

energy, it has been estimated that wind energy potential equals more than twice the total electricity currently consumed (FIGURE 16).

The U.S. Department of Energy has announced a goal of obtaining 5 percent of U.S. electricity from wind by the year 2020—a goal that seems consistent with the current growth rate of wind energy nationwide. In 2011, five states produced more than 5 percent of their

FIGURE 17 Grand Coulee
Dam
More than one-half of U.S.
hydroelectric capacity is
concentrated in Washing-
ton, Oregon, and California.
In 2011 about 29 percent
of the total hydropower was
generated in Washington,
the location of the nation's
largest hydroelectric
facility—Grand Coulee
Dam. (Photo by Photo
Researchers, Inc.)

Because the entire country consists of geologically young volcanic rocks, warm water can be encountered in holes drilled almost anywhere.

Key
• Hydrothermal system greater than 150° C
▢ Zone of rifting and volcanism

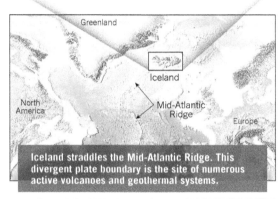

Iceland straddles the Mid-Atlantic Ridge. This divergent plate boundary is the site of numerous active volcanoes and geothermal systems.

The steam at this power station in southwestern Iceland is used to generate electricity. Hot (83 °C) water from the plant is sent via an insulated pipeline to Reykjavik for space heating.

FIGURE 18 Geothermal development in Iceland
More than 45 percent of Iceland's energy comes from geothermal sources. (Photo by Simon Fraser/Science Photo Library/Photo Researchers, Inc.)

sediment that is deposited behind the dam as soon as it is built. Eventually sediment may completely fill the reservoir. This takes 50 to 300 years, depending on the quantity of suspended material transported by the river.

An example is Egypt's huge Aswan High Dam, which was completed in the 1960s. It is estimated that half of the reservoir will be filled with sediment from the Nile River by the year 2025.

The availability of appropriate sites is an important limiting factor in the development of large-scale hydroelectric power plants. A good site provides a significant height for the water to fall and a high rate of flow. Hydroelectric dams exist in many parts of the United States, with the greatest concentrations occurring in the Southeast and the Pacific Northwest. Most of the best U.S. sites have already been developed, limiting the future expansion of hydroelectric power. The total power produced by hydroelectric sources might still increase, but the relative share provided by this source will likely decline because other alternate energy sources will increase at a faster rate.

In recent years, a different type of hydroelectric power production has come into use. Called a *pumped water-storage system*, it is actually a type of energy management. During times when demand for electricity is low, unneeded power produced by nonhydroelectric sources is used to pump water from a lower reservoir to a storage area at a higher elevation. Then, when demand for electricity is great, the water stored in the higher reservoir is available to drive turbines and produce electricity to supplement the power supply.

Geothermal Energy

Geothermal energy is harnessed by tapping natural underground reservoirs of steam and hot water. These occur where subsurface temperatures are high, due to relatively recent volcanic activity or nearby magma chambers. Geothermal energy is put to use in two ways: The steam and hot water are used for heating and to generate electricity.

Iceland is a large volcanic island with current volcanic activity (FIGURE 18). In Iceland's capital, Reykjavik, steam and hot water are pumped into buildings throughout the city for space heating. They also warm greenhouses, where fruits and vegetables are grown all year. In the United States, localities in several western states use hot water from geothermal sources for space heating.

The Italians began generating electricity geothermally in 1904, so the idea is not new. In 2011, 24 countries produced more than 64 million megawatt hours (million watts). The United States was responsible for more than 25 percent of the total and was the leading producer. Nevertheless, geothermal power represented just 0.4 percent (four-tenths of 1 percent) of U.S. electric power.

The first commercial geothermal power plant in the United States was built in 1960 at The Geysers, north of San Francisco (FIGURE 19). The Geysers remains the world's largest geothermal power plant, generating nearly 1000 megawatts of U.S. geothermal power. In addition to The Geysers, geothermal development is occurring elsewhere in the western United States, including

FIGURE 19 The Geysers This facility, near the city of Santa Rosa in northern California, is the world's largest electricity-generating geothermal development. Most of the steam wells are about 3000 meters (10,000 feet) deep. California's 35 geothermal power plants were responsible for 80 percent of U.S. geothermal power production in 2011. (AP Photo/Calpine)

Nevada, Utah, and the Imperial Valley in southern California. The U.S. geothermal generating capacity of about 3000 megawatts is enough to supply more than 3 million homes. This is an amount of electricity comparable to burning about 60 million barrels of oil each year.

The following geologic factors favor a geothermal reservoir of commercial value:

1. *A potent source of heat*, such as a large magma chamber deep enough to ensure adequate pressure and slow cooling but not so deep that the natural water circulation is inhibited. Such magma chambers are most likely in regions of recent volcanic activity.
2. *Large and porous reservoirs with channels connected to the heat source*, near which water can circulate and then be stored in the reservoir.
3. *A cap of low-permeability rocks* that inhibits the flow of water and heat to the surface. A deep, well-insulated reservoir contains much more stored energy than a similar but uninsulated reservoir.

As with other alternative methods of power production, geothermal sources are not expected to provide a high percentage of the world's growing energy needs. Nevertheless, in regions where its potential can be developed, the use of geothermal energy will continue to grow.

Biomass: Renewable Energy from Plants and Animals

Biomass is organic material made from plants and animals. It is a renewable energy source because we can always grow more trees and crops, and waste will always exist. Some examples of biomass fuels are wood, crops, manure, and some garbage. When burned, the chemical energy in biomass is released as heat. A common example

is burning a log in a wood stove or fireplace. Wood and garbage can be burned to produce steam for making electricity or to provide heat to industries and homes.

Burning biomass is not the only way to release its energy. Biomass can be converted to other usable forms of energy, such as methane gas, or transportation fuels, such as ethanol and biodiesel. In 2011, biomass fuels provided about 4 percent of the energy used in the United States. The following list summarizes the main sources of biomass energy.

- Wood biomass includes wood chips from forestry operations, residues from lumber, pulp/paper, and furniture mills, and fuel wood for space heating. The largest single source of wood energy is "black liquor," a residue of pulp, paper, and paperboard production.
- Biofuels include alcohol fuels such as ethanol, and "biodiesel," a fuel from grain oils and animal fats. Most biofuel used in the United States is ethanol produced from corn.
- Municipal waste contains biomass such as paper, cardboard, food scraps, grass clippings, and leaves. Waste can be recycled, composted, sent to landfills, or used in waste-to-energy plants. There are hundreds of landfills in the United States that recover *biogas*, which is methane that forms as waste decomposes in low-oxygen (anaerobic) conditions. The methane is burned to produce electricity and heat.

Tidal Power

Several methods of generating electrical energy from the oceans have been proposed, but the ocean's energy potential remains largely untapped. The development of tidal power is the principal example of energy production from the ocean.

Tides have been used as a source of power for centuries. Beginning in the twelfth century, waterwheels driven by the tides were used to power gristmills and sawmills. During the seventeenth and eighteenth centuries, much of Boston's flour was produced at a tidal mill. Today far greater energy demands must be satisfied, and more sophisticated ways of using the force created by the perpetual rise and fall of the ocean must be employed.

Tidal power is harnessed by constructing a dam across the mouth of a bay or an estuary in a coastal area having a large tidal range (FIGURE 20A). The narrow opening between the bay and the open ocean magnifies the variations in water level that occur as the tides rise and fall. The strong in-and-out flow that results at such a site is then used to drive turbines and electrical generators.

Tidal energy utilization is exemplified by the tidal power plant at the mouth of the Rance River in France. By far the largest yet constructed, this plant went into operation in 1966 and produces enough power to satisfy the needs of Brittany and also contribute to the demands of other regions. Much smaller experimental facilities have been built near Murmansk in Russia and near Taliang in China, and on the Annapolis River estuary, an arm of the

A.

B.

FIGURE 20 Tidal power
A. Simplified diagram showing the principle of the tidal dam. Electricity is generated only when a sufficient water-height difference exists between the bay and the ocean. **B.** Tidal power plant at Annapolis Royal, Nova Scotia, on the Bay of Fundy. (Photo by James P. Blair/National Geographic Image Collection)

Bay of Fundy in the Canadian province of Nova Scotia (FIGURE 20B).

Along most of the world's coasts, it is not possible to harness tidal energy. If the tidal range is less than 8 meters (25 feet), or if narrow, enclosed bays are absent, tidal power development is uneconomical. For this reason, the tides will never provide a very high portion of our ever-increasing electrical energy requirements. Nevertheless, the development of tidal power may be worth pursuing at feasible sites because electricity produced by the tides consumes no exhaustible fuels and creates no noxious wastes.

5 CONCEPT CHECKS

1. How important is renewable energy to the overall U.S. energy supply?
2. What is the greatest use of renewable energy?
3. Describe two ways in which solar energy is used to produce electricity.
4. Which has had the more rapid rate of growth rate in the United States in recent years: wind power or hydroelectric power?
5. What is biomass? List four examples.
6. Where in the United States is hydroelectric power development most concentrated? How about geothermal power development?

EYE on Earth

Lake Powell is the reservoir that was created when Glen Canyon Dam was built across the Colorado River. As water in the lake is released, it drives turbines and produces electricity. (Photo by Michael Collier)

Question 1 What term is applied to the energy generated at Glen Canyon Dam?

Question 2 Is this energy considered renewable or nonrenewable?

Question 3 Explain why most dams and reservoirs do not last indefinitely.

6 Mineral Resources

Earth's crust is the source of a wide variety of useful and essential substances. In fact, practically every manufactured product contains substances derived from minerals. TABLE 2 lists some important examples.

Mineral resources are the endowment of useful minerals ultimately available commercially. Resources include already identified deposits from which minerals can be extracted profitably, called **reserves**, as well as known deposits that are not yet economically or technologically recoverable. Deposits inferred to exist but not yet discovered are also considered as mineral resources. In addition, the term **ore** is used to denote useful metallic minerals that can be mined at a profit. In common usage, the term *ore* is also applied to some nonmetallic minerals, such as fluorite and sulfur. However, materials used for such purposes as building stone, road aggregate,

abrasives, ceramics, and fertilizers are not usually called ores; rather, they are classified as industrial rocks and minerals.

Recall that more than 98 percent of the continental crust is composed of only eight elements. Except for oxygen and silicon, all other elements make up a relatively small fraction of common crustal rocks (FIGURE 21). Indeed, the natural concentrations of many elements are exceedingly small. A deposit containing the average percentage of a valuable element is worthless if the cost of extracting it exceeds the value of the material recovered. To be considered valuable, an element must be concentrated above the level of its average crustal abundance. Generally, the lower the crustal abundance, the greater the concentration.

For example, copper makes up about 0.0135 percent of the crust. However, for a material to be considered a copper ore, it must contain a concentration that is about 50 times this amount. Aluminum, in contrast, represents 8.13 percent of the crust and must be concentrated to only about four times its average crustal percentage before it can be extracted profitably.

It is important to realize that a deposit may become profitable to extract or lose its profitability because of economic changes. If demand for a metal increases and

TABLE 2	Occurrence of Metallic Minerals	
Metal	Principal Ores	Geologic Occurrences
Aluminum	Bauxite	Residual product of weathering
Chromium	Chromite	Magmatic segregation
Copper	Chalcopyrite Bornite Chalcocite	Hydrothermal deposits; contact metamorphism; enrichment by weathering processes
Gold	Native gold	Hydrothermal deposits; placers
Iron	Hematite Magnetite Limonite	Banded sedimentary formations; magmatic segregation
Lead	Galena	Hydrothermal deposits
Magnesium	Magnesite Dolomite	Hydrothermal deposits
Manganese	Pyrolusite	Residual product of weathering
Mercury	Cinnabar	Hydrothermal deposits
Molybdenum	Molybdenite	Hydrothermal deposits
Nickel	Pentlandite	Magmatic segregation
Platinum	Native platinum	Magmatic segregation; placers
Silver	Native silver Argentite	Hydrothermal deposits; enrichment by weathering processes
Tin	Cassiterite	Hydrothermal deposits; placers
Titanium	Ilmenite Rutile	Magmatic segregation; placers
Tungsten	Wolframite Scheelite	Pegmatites; contact metamorphic deposits; placers
Uranium	Uraninite (pitchblende)	Pegmatites; sedimentary deposits
Zinc	Sphalerite	Hydrothermal deposits

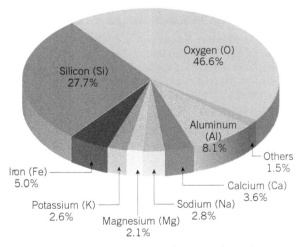

FIGURE 21 Most abundant elements in the continental crust More than 98 percent of the continental crust is composed of just eight elements. The concentration of many elements that are important mineral resources is part of the "others" category on the graph.

prices rise, the status of a previously unprofitable deposit changes, and it becomes an ore. The status of unprofitable deposits may also change if a technological advance allows the useful element to be extracted at a lower cost than before. This occurred at the copper-mining operation located at Bingham Canyon, Utah, one of the largest open-pit mines on Earth (see the chapter-opening photo). Mining was halted here in 1985 because outmoded equipment had driven the cost of extracting the copper beyond the selling price. The owners responded by replacing an antiquated 1000-car railroad with conveyor belts and pipelines for transporting the ore and waste. These devices achieved a cost reduction of nearly 30 percent and returned this mining operation to profitability.

Over the years, geologists have been keenly interested in learning how natural processes produce localized concentrations of essential metallic minerals. One well-established fact is that occurrences of valuable mineral resources are closely related to the rock cycle. That is, the mechanisms that generate igneous, sedimentary, and metamorphic rocks, including the processes of weathering and erosion, play a major role in producing concentrated accumulations of useful elements. Moreover, with the development of the plate tectonics theory, geologists added yet another tool for understanding the processes by which one rock is transformed into another.

6 CONCEPT CHECKS

1. Contrast *resource* and *reserve*.
2. What is an ore?

EYE on Earth

The image on the left shows an active landfill where tons of trash and garbage are dumped every day. Eventually this site will be reclaimed to resemble the area shown on the right and become a source of energy. (Left Photo by NHPA/SuperStock; Right Photo by Jim West/Alamy Images)

Question 1 Explain how an area filled with trash and waste could become a source of energy. What form of energy will it be? How might it be used?

Question 2 Will this energy be considered renewable or nonrenewable? Explain.

Alberta's Oil Sands*

With its insatiable appetite for energy, the world is turning toward unconventional sources as the most accessible supplies are exhausted. Huge oil reserves, spread across more than 140,000 square kilometers (54,000 square miles) of northern Alberta, are the third-largest proven crude oil reserves in the world next to Saudi Arabia and Venezuela. The oil is in the form of bitumen, a solid substance that must be heated or chemically diluted before it flows through pipelines. Extraction involves environmental challenges—protection of surface water, disposal of waste water, reclamation of what once was boreal forest, as well as increased discharge of carbon dioxide into the atmosphere.

Bitumen can be strip mined as in this photo, but most will be removed after softening when steam is injected underground.

ALBERTA

Canada

United States

Fort McMurray

Edmonton

Calgary

* Prepared with the assistance of Michael Collier. All images by Michael Collier.

Tailings ponds hold wastewater after bitumen has been separated from sand. The ponds are continuously maintained because decades may pass before sediments and associated heavy metals will settle out and a pond can be drained.

The Athabasca River flows past tailings ponds and refineries. The oil industry is trying very hard to keep contaminants out of the river.

After bitumen has been removed, mines are recontoured and topsoil is replaced in an effort to reclaim what had been a boreal forest.

An overview of a portion of the surface mining operation.

This refinery converts bitumen into products such as gasoline and diesel fuel.

7   Igneous and Metamorphic Processes

Some of the most important accumulations of metals, such as gold, silver, copper, mercury, lead, platinum, and nickel, are produced by igneous and metamorphic processes (see Table 2). These mineral resources, like most others, result from processes that concentrate desirable materials to the extent that extraction is economically feasible.

Magmatic Segregation

The igneous processes that generate some of these metal deposits are quite straightforward. For example, as a large magma body cools, the heavy minerals that crystallize early tend to settle to the lower portion of the magma chamber. This type of magmatic segregation is particularly active in large basaltic magmas where chromite (ore of chromium), magnetite, and platinum are occasionally generated. Layers of chromite, interbedded with other heavy minerals, are mined from such deposits in the Stillwater Complex of Montana. Another example is the Bushveld Complex in South Africa, which contains over 70 percent of the world's known reserves of platinum.

Magmatic segregation is also important in the late stages of the magmatic process. This is particularly true of granitic magmas, in which the residual melt can become enriched in rare elements and heavy metals. Further, because water and other volatile substances do not crystallize along with the bulk of the magma body, these fluids make up a high percentage of the melt during the final phase of solidification. Crystallization in a fluid-rich environment, where ion migration is enhanced, results in the formation of crystals several centimeters, or even a few meters, in length. The resulting rocks, called **pegmatites**, are composed of these unusually large crystals.

Most pegmatites are granitic in composition and consist of unusually large crystals of quartz, feldspar, and muscovite. Feldspar is used in the production of ceramics, and muscovite is used for electrical insulation and glitter. Further, pegmatites often contain some of the least abundant elements. Thus, in addition to the common silicates, some pegmatites include semiprecious gems such as beryl, topaz, and tourmaline. Moreover, minerals containing the elements lithium, cesium, uranium, and the rare earths[*] are occasionally found (FIGURE 22). Most pegmatites are located within large igneous masses or as dikes or veins that cut into the host rock surrounding the magma chamber (FIGURE 23).

Not all late-stage magmas produce pegmatites, nor do all have a granitic composition. Rather, some magmas become enriched in iron or occasionally copper. For example, at Kiruna, Sweden, magma composed of more than 60 percent magnetite solidified to produce one of the largest iron deposits in the world.

---

[*]The rare earths are a group of 15 elements (atomic numbers 57 through 71) that possess similar properties. They are useful catalysts in petroleum refining and are used to improve color retention in television picture tubes.

Diamonds

Another economically important mineral with an igneous origin is diamond. Although best known as gems, diamonds are used extensively as abrasives. Diamonds originate at depths of nearly 200 kilometers (125 miles), where the confining pressure is great enough to generate this high-pressure form of carbon. Once crystallized, the diamonds are carried upward through pipe-shaped conduits that increase in diameter toward the surface. In diamond-bearing pipes, nearly the entire pipe contains diamond crystals that are disseminated throughout an ultramafic rock called *kimberlite*. The most productive kimberlite pipes are those found in South Africa. The only equivalent source of diamonds in the United States is located near Murfreesboro, Arkansas, but this deposit is exhausted and today serves merely as a tourist attraction.

Hydrothermal Solutions

Among the best-known and most important ore deposits are those generated from **hydrothermal** (hot-water) **solutions**. Included in this group are the gold deposits of the Homestake Mine in South Dakota; the lead, zinc,

FIGURE 22 **Pegmatites**
This pegmatite in the Black Hills of South Dakota was mined for its large crystals of spodumene, an important source of lithium. Arrows are pointing to impressions left by crystals. Note the person in the upper center of the photo for scale.
(Photo by James G. Kirchner)

and silver ores near Coeur d'Alene, Idaho; the silver deposits of the Comstock Lode in Nevada; and the copper ores of the Keweenaw Peninsula in Michigan (FIGURE 24).

Vein Deposits The majority of hydrothermal deposits originate from hot, metal-rich fluids that are remnants of late-stage magmatic processes. During solidification, liquids plus various metallic ions accumulate near the top of the magma chamber. Because of their mobility, these ion-rich solutions can migrate great distances through the surrounding rock before they are eventually deposited, usually as sulfides of various metals (see Figure 23). Some of this fluid moves along openings such as fractures or bedding planes, where it cools and precipitates the metallic ions to produce **vein deposits**. Many of the most productive deposits of gold, silver, and mercury occur as hydrothermal vein deposits.

Disseminated Deposits Another important type of accumulation generated by hydrothermal activity is called a **disseminated deposit**. Rather than being concentrated in narrow veins and dikes, these ores are distributed as minute masses throughout the entire rock mass. Much of the world's copper is extracted from disseminated deposits, including those at Chuquicamata, Chile, and the huge Bingham Canyon copper mine in Utah. Because these accumulations contain only 0.4 to 0.8 percent copper, between 125 and 250 kilograms of ore must be mined for every 1 kilogram of metal recovered. The environmental impact of these large excavations, including the problem of waste disposal, is significant.

Some hydrothermal deposits have been generated by the circulation of ordinary groundwater in regions where magma was emplaced near the surface. The Yellowstone National Park area is a modern example of such a situation (see Figure 23). When groundwater invades a zone of recent igneous activity, its temperature rises, greatly enhancing its ability to dissolve minerals. These migrating hot waters remove metallic ions from intrusive igneous rocks and carry them upward, where they may be deposited as an ore body. Depending on the conditions, the resulting accumulations may occur as vein deposits, as disseminated deposits, or, where hydrothermal solutions reach the surface in the form of hot springs or geysers, as surface deposits.

Hydrothermal Activity at Oceanic Ridges With the development of the plate tectonics theory, it became clear that some hydrothermal deposits originated along

Hydrothermal metamorphism can occur at shallow crustal depths in regions where geysers and hot springs are active.

Hydrothermal vein deposits

Geyser

Pegmatite deposits

Fault

Igneous body (pluton)

Magma chamber

SMARTFIGURE 23 Pegmatites and hydrothermal deposits Illustration of the relationship between an igneous body and associated pegmatites and hydrothermal mineral deposits. (Photo by Pavel Svoboda/Fotolia)

ancient oceanic ridges. A well-known example is found on the island of Cyprus, where copper has been mined for more than 4000 years. Apparently, these deposits represent ores that formed on the seafloor at an ancient oceanic spreading center.

Since the mid-1970s, active hot springs and metal-rich sulfide deposits have been detected at several sites, including study areas along the East Pacific Rise and the Juan de Fuca Ridge. The deposits form where heated seawater, rich in dissolved metals and sulfur, gushes from the seafloor as particle-filled clouds called *black smokers*. As shown in FIGURE 25, seawater infiltrates the hot

FIGURE 24 **Native copper** This nearly pure metal from northern Michigan's Keweenaw Peninsula is an excellent example of a hydrothermal deposit. At one time this area was an important source of copper, but it is now largely depleted. (Photo by E. J. Tarbuck)

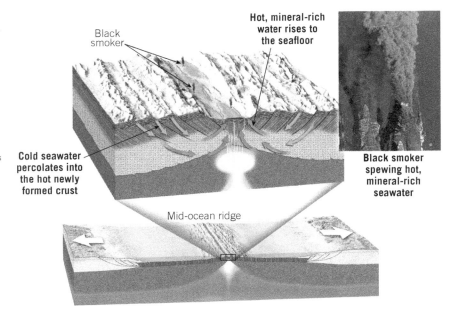

FIGURE 25 Sulfide deposits along a mid-ocean ridge
Massive sulfide deposits can result from the circulation of seawater through the oceanic crust along active spreading centers. As seawater infiltrates the hot basaltic crust, it leaches sulfur, iron, copper, and other metals. The hot, enriched fluid returns to the seafloor near the ridge axis along faults and fractures. Some metal sulfides may be precipitated in these channels as the rising fluid begins to cool. When the hot liquid emerges from the seafloor and mixes with cold seawater, the sulfides precipitate to form massive deposits. Photo shows a close-up view of a black smoker spewing hot, mineral-rich seawater along the East Pacific Rise. (Photo by Fisheries and Oceans Canada/Uvic-Verena Tunnicliffe/Newscom)

oceanic crust along the flanks of the ridge. As the water moves through the newly formed material, it is heated and chemically interacts with the basalt, extracting and transporting sulfur, iron, copper, and other metals. Near the ridge axis, the hot, metal-rich fluid rises along faults. Upon reaching the seafloor, the spewing liquid mixes with the cold seawater, and the sulfides precipitate to form massive sulfide deposits.

Metamorphic Processes

The role of metamorphism in producing mineral deposits is frequently tied to igneous processes. For example, many of the most important metamorphic ore deposits are produced by contact metamorphism. Here the host rock is recrystallized and chemically altered by heat, pressure, and hydrothermal solutions emanating from an intruding igneous body. The extent to which the host rock is altered depends on the nature of the intruding igneous mass as well as the nature of the host rock.

Some resistant materials, such as quartz sandstone, may show very little alteration, whereas others, including limestone, might exhibit the effects of metamorphism for several kilometers from the igneous pluton. As hot, ion-rich fluids move through limestone, chemical reactions take place, producing useful minerals such as garnet and corundum. Further, these reactions release carbon dioxide, which greatly facilitates the outward migration

of metallic ions. Thus, extensive aureoles of metal-rich deposits commonly surround igneous plutons that have invaded limestone strata.

The most common metallic minerals associated with contact metamorphism are sphalerite (zinc), galena (lead), chalcopyrite (copper), magnetite (iron), and bornite (copper). The hydrothermal ore deposits may be disseminated throughout the altered zone or exist as concentrated masses that are located either next to the intrusive body or along the margins of the metamorphic zone.

Regional metamorphism can also generate useful mineral deposits. Recall that at convergent plate boundaries, the oceanic crust and sediments that have accumulated at the continental margins are carried to great depths. In these high-temperature, high-pressure environments, the mineralogy and texture of the subducted materials are altered, producing deposits of nonmetallic minerals such as talc and graphite.

7 CONCEPT CHECKS

1. Describe two examples of mineral resources associated with magmatic segregation.
2. What are hydrothermal deposits? List two general types.
3. Describe the process at oceanic ridges that produces sulfide ore deposits.
4. Relate ore deposits to contact metamorphism.

8 Mineral Resources Related to Surface Processes

The preceding discussion focused on mineral resources that are closely linked to igneous activity and metamorphism. In this section, we look at examples of metallic mineral resources that accumulate as a result of surface processes.

Weathering and Ore Deposits

Weathering creates many important mineral deposits by concentrating minor amounts of metals that are scattered through unweathered rock into economically valuable concentrations. Such a transformation is often termed **secondary enrichment**, and it takes place in one of two ways. In one situation, chemical weathering coupled with downward-percolating water removes undesirable materials from decomposing rock, leaving the desirable elements enriched in the upper zones of the soil. The second way is basically the reverse of the first. That is, the desirable elements that are found in low concentrations near the surface are removed and carried to lower zones, where they are redeposited and become more concentrated.

FIGURE 26 Bauxite
This ore of aluminum forms as a result of weathering processes under tropical conditions. Its color varies from red or brown to nearly white. (Photo by E. J. Tarbuck)

Bauxite   The formation of *bauxite*, the principal ore of aluminum, is one important example of an ore created as a result of enrichment by weathering processes (FIGURE 26). Although aluminum is the third-most-abundant element in Earth's crust, economically valuable concentrations of this important metal are not common because most aluminum is tied up in silicate minerals from which it is extremely difficult to extract.

Bauxite forms in rainy tropical climates, in association with the deeply weathered soils known as laterites. (In fact, bauxite is sometimes referred to as *aluminum laterite*.) When aluminum-rich source rocks are subjected to the intense and prolonged chemical weathering of the tropics, most of the common elements, including calcium, sodium, and silicon, are removed by leaching. Because aluminum is extremely insoluble, it becomes concentrated in the soil as bauxite, a hydrated aluminum oxide. Thus, the formation of bauxite depends both on climatic conditions in which chemical weathering and leaching are pronounced and on the presence of an aluminum-rich source rock. Important deposits of nickel and cobalt are also found in laterite soils that develop from igneous rocks rich in ferromagnesian silicate minerals.

Other Deposits   Many copper and silver deposits result when weathering processes concentrate metals that are deposited through a low-grade primary ore. Usually such enrichment occurs in deposits containing pyrite (FeS_2), the most common and widespread sulfide mineral. Pyrite is important because when it chemically weathers, sulfuric acid forms, which enables percolating waters to dissolve the ore metals. Once dissolved, the metals gradually migrate downward through the primary ore body until they are precipitated. Deposition takes place because of changes that occur in the chemistry of the solution when it reaches the saturated zone (the zone beneath the surface where all pore spaces are filled with groundwater). In this manner, the small percentage of dispersed metal can be removed from a large volume of rock and redeposited as a higher-grade ore in a smaller volume of rock.

This enrichment process is responsible for the economic success of many copper deposits, including one located in Miami, Arizona. Here the ore was upgraded from less than 1 percent copper in the primary deposit to as much as 5 percent copper in some localized zones of enrichment. When pyrite weathers (oxidizes) near the surface, residues of iron oxide remain. The presence of these rusty-colored caps at the surface indicates the possibility of an enriched copper ore below, and this represents a visible sign for prospectors.

Placer Deposits

The sorting of sediments usually results in like-sized grains being deposited together. However, sorting according to the specific gravity of particles also occurs. This latter type of sorting is responsible for the creation of **placers**, which are deposits formed when heavy minerals are mechanically concentrated by currents. Placers associated with streams are among the most common and best known, but the sorting action of waves can also create placers along the shore. Placer deposits usually involve minerals that are not only heavy but also durable

FIGURE 27 **Placers**
These deposits form when heavy minerals are mechanically concentrated by currents. (Photo on left by Underwood Archives/Getty Images; photo on right from the Library of Congress)

(to withstand physical destruction during transportation) and chemically resistant (to endure weathering processes). Placers form because heavy minerals settle quickly from a current, whereas less-dense particles remain suspended and are carried onward. Common sites of accumulation include point bars on the insides of meanders as well as cracks, depressions, and other irregularities on streambeds.

Many economically important placer deposits exist, with accumulations of gold the best known. Indeed, it was the placer deposits discovered in 1848 that led to the famous California Gold Rush. Years later, similar deposits created a gold rush to Alaska as well (FIGURE 27). Panning for gold by washing sand and gravel from a flat pan to concentrate the fine "dust" at the bottom was a common method early prospectors used to recover the precious metal, and it is a process similar to that which created the placer in the first place.

In addition to gold, other heavy and durable minerals form placers. These include platinum, diamonds, and tin. The Ural Mountains contain placers rich in platinum, and placers are important sources of diamonds in southern Africa. Significant portions of the world's supply of cassiterite, the principal ore of tin, have come from placer deposits in Malaysia and Indonesia. Cassiterite is often widely disseminated through granitic igneous rocks. In this state, the mineral is not sufficiently concentrated to be extracted profitably.

However, as the enclosing rock dissolves and disintegrates, the heavy and durable cassiterite grains are set free. Eventually the freed particles are washed to a stream, where they are deposited in placers that are significantly more concentrated than the original deposit. Similar circumstances and events are common to many minerals mined from placers.

In some cases, if the source rock for a placer deposit can be located, it too may become an important ore body. By following placer deposits upstream, one can sometimes locate the original ore body. This is how the gold-bearing veins of the mother lode in California's Sierra Nevada batholith were found, as well as the famous Kimberley diamond mine of South Africa. The placers were discovered first, and their source was found at a later time.

8 CONCEPT CHECKS

1. What is secondary enrichment?
2. Name the primary ore of aluminum and describe its formation.
3. How might the mineral pyrite play a role in creating an ore deposit?
4. Describe the way in which minerals accumulate in placers. List four minerals that are mined from such deposits.

9 Nonmetallic Mineral Resources

Earth materials that are not used as fuels or processed for the metals they contain are referred to as **nonmetallic mineral resources**. Realize that use of the word *mineral* is very broad in this economic context and is quite different from the geologist's strict definition of *mineral* (any naturally occurring inorganic solid that possesses an orderly crystalline structure and a definite chemical composition that allows for some variation). Nonmetallic mineral resources are extracted and processed either for the nonmetallic elements they contain or for the physical and chemical properties they possess.

People often do not realize the importance of non-metallic minerals because they see only the products that result from their use and not the minerals themselves. That is, many nonmetallics are used up in the process of creating other products. Examples include the fluorite and limestone that are part of the steelmaking process, the abrasives required to make a piece of machinery, and the fertilizers needed to grow a food crop (see TABLE 3).

The quantities of nonmetallic minerals used each year are enormous. A glance back at Figure 1 reminds us that the per capita consumption of nonfuel resources in the United States totals more than 11 metric tons, of which about 94 percent are nonmetallics. Nonmetallic

FIGURE 28 Limestone quarry
Limestone is considered both a building material and an industrial mineral. This quarry is near Amsterdam, Indiana.
(Photo by Daniel Dempster/Alamy Images)

mineral resources are commonly divided into two broad groups: *building materials* and *industrial minerals*. Because some substances have many different uses, they are found in both categories. Limestone, perhaps the most versatile and widely used rock of all, is the best example (FIGURE 28). As a building material, it is used not only as crushed rock and building stone but also in the making of cement. Moreover, as an industrial mineral, limestone is an ingredient in the manufacture of steel and is used in agriculture to reduce the acidity of soils.

Building Materials

Natural aggregate consists of crushed stone, sand, and gravel. From the standpoint of quantity and value, aggregate is a very important building material. The United States produces nearly 2 billion tons of aggregate per year, which represents about one-half of the entire nonenergy mining volume in the country. It is produced commercially in every state and is used in nearly all building construction and in most public works projects (FIGURE 29).

Besides aggregate, other important building materials include gypsum for plaster and wallboard, clay for tile and bricks, and limestone and shale, which combine to form cement. Cement and aggregate go into the making of concrete, a material that is essential to practically all construction. Aggregate gives concrete its strength and volume, and cement binds the mixture into a rock-hard substance. Building just 2 kilometers of four-lane highway requires more than 85 tons of aggregate. Building an average six-room house requires 90 tons of aggregate.

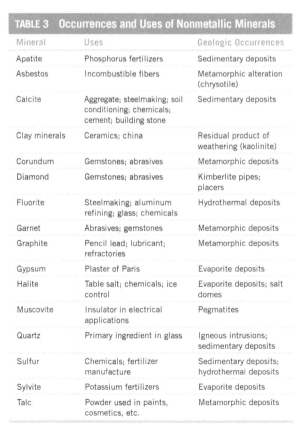

TABLE 3	Occurrences and Uses of Nonmetallic Minerals	
Mineral	Uses	Geologic Occurrences
Apatite	Phosphorus fertilizers	Sedimentary deposits
Asbestos	Incombustible fibers	Metamorphic alteration (chrysotile)
Calcite	Aggregate; steelmaking; soil conditioning; chemicals; cement; building stone	Sedimentary deposits
Clay minerals	Ceramics; china	Residual product of weathering (kaolinite)
Corundum	Gemstones; abrasives	Metamorphic deposits
Diamond	Gemstones; abrasives	Kimberlite pipes; placers
Fluorite	Steelmaking; aluminum refining; glass; chemicals	Hydrothermal deposits
Garnet	Abrasives; gemstones	Metamorphic deposits
Graphite	Pencil lead; lubricant; refractories	Metamorphic deposits
Gypsum	Plaster of Paris	Evaporite deposits
Halite	Table salt; chemicals; ice control	Evaporite deposits; salt domes
Muscovite	Insulator in electrical applications	Pegmatites
Quartz	Primary ingredient in glass	Igneous intrusions; sedimentary deposits
Sulfur	Chemicals; fertilizer manufacture	Sedimentary deposits; hydrothermal deposits
Sylvite	Potassium fertilizers	Evaporite deposits
Talc	Powder used in paints, cosmetics, etc.	Metamorphic deposits

FIGURE 29 Aggregate is a building material
Crushed stone, sand, and gravel are primarily used for aggregate in the construction industry, especially in cement concrete for residential and commercial buildings, bridges, and airports, and as cement concrete or bituminous concrete (asphalt) for highway construction. A large percentage is used without a binder as road base, for road surfacing, and as railroad ballast. (Photo by Robert Ginn/PhotoEdit)

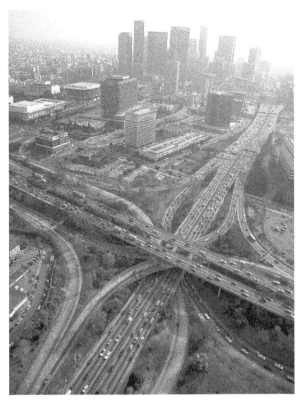

Because most building materials are widely distributed and present in almost unlimited quantities, they have little intrinsic value. Their economic worth comes only after the materials are removed from the ground and processed. Since their per-ton value compared with those of metals and industrial minerals is low, mining and

quarrying operations are usually undertaken to satisfy local needs. Except for special types of cut stone used for building and monuments, transportation costs greatly limit the distance most building materials can be moved.

Industrial Minerals

Many nonmetallic resources are classified as industrial minerals. In some instances, these materials are important because they are sources of specific chemical elements or compounds. Such minerals are used in the manufacture of chemicals and the production of fertilizers. In other cases, their importance is related to the physical properties they exhibit. Examples include minerals such as corundum and garnet, which are used as abrasives. Although supplies of industrial minerals are generally plentiful, most of these minerals are not nearly as abundant as building materials. Moreover, deposits are far more restricted in distribution and extent. As a result, many of these nonmetallic resources must be transported considerable distances, which of course adds to their cost. Unlike most building materials, which need a minimum of processing before they are ready to use, many industrial minerals require considerable processing to extract the desired substance at the proper degree of purity for its ultimate use.

Fertilizers The growth in world population beyond 7 billion requires that the production of basic food crops continue to expand. Therefore, fertilizers—primarily nitrate, phosphate, and potassium compounds—are extremely important to agriculture. The synthetic nitrate industry, which derives nitrogen from the atmosphere, is the source of practically all the world's

FIGURE 30 Potash mine evaporation ponds west of Moab, Utah
Potash (potassium chloride) at this site is obtained using a system that combines solution mining and solar evaporation. Water from the nearby Colorado River is injected into deposits that are 900 meters (3000 feet) below the surface. The mineral-rich water is brought to the surface and piped to 400 acres of shallow ponds. The water evaporates, leaving behind deposits of potash and common salt (sodium chloride). A blue dye is added to assist the evaporation process. The crystals are harvested and sent to a mill, where the potash is separated from the salt by using a flotation process. (Photo by Michael Collier)

nitrogen fertilizers. The primary source of phosphorus and potassium, however, remains Earth's crust. The mineral apatite is the primary source of phosphate. In the United States, most production comes from marine sedimentary deposits in Florida and North Carolina. Although potassium is an abundant element in many minerals, the primary commercial sources are evaporite deposits containing the mineral sylvite. In the United States, deposits near Carlsbad, New Mexico, have been especially important. FIGURE 30 shows a mining operation in southern Utah that produces sylvite (commonly called potash).

Sulfur   Because it has many uses, sulfur is an important nonmetallic resource. In fact, the quantity of sulfur used is considered one index of a country's level of industrialization. More than 80 percent is used to produce sulfuric acid. Although its principal use is in the manufacture of phosphate fertilizer, sulfuric acid has a large number of other applications as well. Sources include deposits of native sulfur associated with salt domes and volcanic areas, as well as common iron sulfides such as pyrite. In recent years an increasingly important source has been the sulfur removed from coal, oil, and natural gas in order to make these fuels less polluting.

Salt   Common salt, known by the mineral name *halite*, is another important and versatile resource. It is among the most prominent nonmetallic minerals used as a raw material in the chemical industry. In addition, large quantities are used to "soften" water and to keep streets and highways free of ice. Of course, most people are aware that it is also a basic nutrient and a part of many food products.

Salt is a common evaporite, and thick deposits are exploited using conventional underground mining techniques. Subsurface deposits are also tapped, using brine wells in which a pipe is introduced into a salt deposit and water is pumped down the pipe. The salt dissolved by the water is brought to the surface through a second pipe. This is also the process used to obtain the potassium chloride (potash) in Figure 30. In addition, seawater continues to serve as a source of salt, as it has for centuries. The salt is harvested after the Sun evaporates the water.

9 CONCEPT CHECKS

1. Which is greater, the per capita consumption of metallic resources or of nonmetallic mineral resources?
2. Distinguish between *building materials* and *industrial minerals*.
3. List two examples of building materials. What are three examples of industrial minerals?
4. What is an example of a substance that may be either a building material or an industrial mineral?

This large granite quarry is in Barre, Vermont. (Photo by David Lyons/Alamy)

CONCEPTS IN REVIEW: ENERGY AND MINERAL RESOURCES

1 Renewable and Nonrenewable Resources

Distinguish between renewable and nonrenewable resources.

KEY WORDS renewable resources, nonrenewable resources

- *Renewable resources* can be replenished over relatively short time spans. An example is trees used for lumber and paper pulp.

Nonrenewable resources form so slowly that, from a human standpoint, Earth contains fixed supplies. Examples include fuels such as oil and coal and metals such as copper and gold.

RECYCLE Some resources can be recycled. Does that mean they can be classified as renewable? Explain.

2 Energy Resources: Traditional Fossil Fuels

Compare and contrast the traditional fossil fuels and describe how each contributes to U.S. energy consumption.

KEY WORDS fossil fuel, oil trap, reservoir rock, cap rock

- Coal, oil, and natural gas are all fossil fuels. In each, the energy of ancient sunlight, captured by photosynthesis, is stored in the hydrocarbons that made up plants or other living things and that were then buried by sediments.
- Coal is formed from compressed plant fragments, originally deposited in ancient swamps. Burning it supplies about 20 percent of U.S. energy use. Coal mining can be risky and environmentally damaging, and burning coal generates several kinds of pollution.
- Oil and natural gas are formed from the heated remains of marine plankton. Together, they account for about 60 percent of U.S. energy use. Both oil and natural gas leave their source rock (typically shale) and migrate to an oil trap made up of other, more porous rocks, called reservoir rocks, covered by a suitable impermeable cap rock.

- Hydraulic fracturing (or "fracking") is a method of opening up pore space in otherwise impermeable rocks, permitting natural gas to flow out into wells.

LOGO MOJO As you can see here, the Sinclair Oil Company's logo speaks directly to the "fossil" nature of the fuel it sells. However, is it likely that any *dinosaur* carbon has ended up in Sinclair's oil? Explain.

Vespasian/Alamy

3 Oil Sands, Oil Shale, and Gas Hydrates

Contrast oil sands, oil shale, and gas hydrates as potential sources of energy.

KEY WORDS oil shale, oil sands, gas hydrates

- Oil sands are sedimentary deposits that contain bitumen in their pore spaces. Because of its high viscosity, the bitumen cannot be pumped out of the rock and must be processed with steam (a significant energy input).
- The United States has a tremendous amount of oil shale in the Eocene-age Green River Formation. Extracting it is energy intensive and consumes large quantities of water.

- Gas hydrates are complex molecules made of natural gas and water. Some form under high pressure and low temperature in marine sediments. Gas hydrates also form in permafrost environments. When brought to Earth's surface, they rapidly decompose into methane and water.

ENGINEER IT What technical or economic issues will likely have to be resolved before gas hydrates become a useful addition to U.S. energy supplies?

4 Nuclear Energy

Describe the importance of nuclear energy and discuss its pros and cons.

KEY WORD nuclear fission

Uraninite is a major ore of uranium. (Photo by Harry Taylor/Dorling Kindersley)

- Nuclear power plants use a controlled nuclear fission chain reaction, in which heavy atoms such as uranium are bombarded with neutrons to cause atoms to split. This releases heat that boils water and drives steam turbines that generate electricity.
- Uranium ore is mined from old placer deposits or sites of groundwater precipitation. The proportion of uranium-235 must be concentrated before it is capable of supporting a fission reaction.
- Nuclear power plants carry significant risks, and building a safe plant is a very expensive proposition.

CALCULATE IT In 2011, U.S. uranium reserves were estimated at about 1,227 million pounds of uraninite. At current rates of usage, this represents about 23 years' worth of demand. If the United States were to raise its nuclear power generation capacity to 17 percent (compare to Figure 2), how long would the U.S. uranium reserves last?

5 Renewable Energy

List and discuss the major sources of renewable energy. Describe the contribution of renewable energy to the overall U.S. energy supply.

KEY WORDS hydroelectric power, geothermal energy, biomass

- Renewable energy resources are replenished rapidly, and their use can be sustained for an indefinite period of time. Free solar energy, which will last as long as the Sun shines, can be captured through passive solar design, active solar collectors (to heat liquids), and photovoltaic cells (for electricity).
- Wind energy is harvested with windmills or turbines. Wind speed is an important variable when considering a site to erect a turbine.
- When running water is dammed, its energy may be harvested as hydroelectric power. At suitable natural sites for damming, pumped water-storage systems are sometimes used to produce "artificial" hydroelectric power.

- Geothermal energy uses heat in Earth's subsurface to produce hot water or electricity. A geothermal site requires (1) a potent source of heat, (2) large subsurface reservoirs, and (3) a cap of low-permeability rock.
- Biomass is animal or plant matter than may be burned directly or converted into a fuel. Campfires, corn ethanol additives to gasoline, and methane capture at landfills are all examples of biomass energy.
- Tidal energy works by impounding the waters of the high tide and then releasing them at low tide through a dam, much like hydroelectric power. It requires a suitable coastline and tidal range, so it's not applicable in most areas.

SOME LIKE IT HOT Which locations in the United States appear to be most suitable for geothermal energy development? Which locations are likely the least suitable?

6 Mineral Resources

Distinguish among resource, reserve, and ore.

KEY WORDS mineral resources, reserves, ore

- Ores are metallic mineral resources that can be economically mined. We refer to the "stockpile" of as-yet-unmined but economically recoverable mineral resources as *reserves*. To be considered valuable, a mineral resource must have the element of interest concentrated above the level of its average crustal abundance.

REVISED RESERVES Give two examples of events that would cause estimates of U.S. platinum reserves to be revised.

7 Igneous and Metamorphic Processes

Explain how different igneous and metamorphic processes produce economically significant mineral deposits.

KEY WORDS pegmatite, hydrothermal solution, vein deposit, disseminated deposit

- Igneous processes concentrate some elements through magmatic segregation, emplacement of pegmatites, and eruption of kimberlites.
- Magmas may give off hydrothermal (hot-water) solutions that penetrate surrounding rock, carrying dissolved metals in them. The metal ores may be precipitated as fracture-filling deposits (veins) or may "soak" into surrounding strata, producing a great many tiny deposits disseminated through the host rock. Black smokers at deep-sea vents are another example of metal-rich hydrothermal deposits.
- Contact and regional metamorphism may both produce concentrations of nonmetallic and metallic mineral resources, particularly where igneous plutons intrude limestone.

COMPARE THEM Compare and contrast pegmatites and vein deposits.

8 Mineral Resources Related to Surface Processes

Discuss ways in which surface processes produce ore deposits.

KEY WORDS secondary enrichment, placer

• Weathering creates ore deposits by concentrating minor amounts of metals into economically valuable deposits. The process, called secondary enrichment, is accomplished either by removing undesirable materials and leaving the desired elements enriched in the upper zones of the soil or removing and carrying the desirable elements to lower zones, where they are redeposited and become more concentrated. Bauxite, the principle ore of aluminum, is associated with the first of these processes.

• Placer deposits form when tough, dense minerals such as gold are sorted by water currents and separated from lower-density sediments.

THE RIGHT SPOT   Would Jamaica, New Zealand, or Sweden be most likely to have bauxite deposits forming at the present time? Explain.

9 Nonmetallic Mineral Resources

Distinguish between two broad categories of nonmetallic mineral resources and list examples of each.

KEY WORD nonmetallic mineral resources

• Earth materials that are not used as fuels or processes for the metals they contain are referred to as nonmetallic resources. Many are sediments or sedimentary rocks. The two broad groups of nonmetallic resources are building materials and industrial minerals.

WHICH IS IT?   Is limestone considered an industrial mineral or a building material? Include examples as part of your explanation.

GIVE IT SOME THOUGHT

1. At one time, most of the energy used in the United States was renewable. Subsequently, things changed, and most of our energy began to come from nonrenewable sources. What was the renewable energy that was once dominant? What replaced it?

2. While in the car with a friend, a radio news story mentions a coal mine accident in which some miners have been injured. After hearing this, your friend says, "I thought coal was sort of an old-fashioned fuel that wasn't used much anymore." How would you convince your friend that he's mistaken?

3. The scene in this photo seems an unlikely source of renewable energy, but it is. Describe how this could be the case.

JoeFox/Alamy

4. In the years to come, coal will likely represent a smaller percentage of U.S. energy consumption than it does at present. However, it is also predicted that coal production will increase. Explain this apparent paradox.

5. As you and a companion are taking a walk, you mention that you have been reading about renewable and nonrenewable resources. Shortly after mentioning this fact, the two of you pass a refuse container that has a sign that says "Aluminum cans only." Upon seeing this, your companion says, "They sure recycle lots of aluminum these days. That makes it a renewable resource, right?" How would you reply?

Texas Stock Photo/Alamy

6. This chapter includes a discussion of industrial minerals. Are these substances actually minerals? That is, do they meet the geologist's strict definition of *mineral*? Explain.

7. Assume that you just read a magazine article about a copper mine that is closing. In the article, a mining geologist states that there was plenty of copper-bearing rock remaining and that the concentration of copper was uniform and of equal quality to what had been mined in the past. Later in the article, a spokesperson for the mine owner states, "No ore remains." Assume that both the geologist and the spokesperson are correct and suggest an explanation for the apparently contradicting statements.

Glossary

Biomass Organic material that is renewable energy derived from trees, crops, and waste. Examples include biofuels such as ethanol and biodiesel, as well as biogas, which is methane recovered from landfills.

Cap rock A necessary part of an oil trap. The cap rock is impermeable and hence keeps upwardly mobile oil and gas from escaping at the surface.

Disseminated deposit Any economic mineral deposit in which the desired mineral occurs as scattered particles in the rock but in sufficient quantity to make the deposit an ore.

Fossil fuel General term for any hydrocarbon that may be used as a fuel, including coal, oil, natural gas, bitumen from tar sands, and shale oil.

Gas hydrates Compact chemical structures made of water and natural gas (usually methane) that occur in permafrost and under the ocean floor at depths greater than 525 meters (1720 feet).

Geothermal energy Natural steam used for power generation.

Hydroelectric power Electricity generated by falling water that is used to drive turbines.

Hydrothermal solution The hot, watery solution that escapes from a mass of magma during the latter stages of crystallization. Such solutions may alter the surrounding country rock and are frequently the source of significant ore deposits.

Mineral resource All discovered and undiscovered deposits of a useful mineral that can be extracted now or at some time in the future.

Nonmetallic mineral resource A mineral resource that is not a fuel or processed for the metals it contains.

Nonrenewable resource A resource that forms or accumulates over such long time spans that it must be considered as fixed in total quantity.

Nuclear fission The splitting of atomic nuclei into smaller nuclei, causing neutrons to be emitted and heat energy to be released.

Oil sands Mixtures of clay, sand, water, and a black viscous form of petroleum known as bitumen.

Oil shale A fine-grained sedimentary rock that contains a solid mixture of organic compounds from which liquid hydrocarbons called shale oil can be produced.

Oil trap A geologic structure that allows for significant amounts of oil and gas to accumulate.

Ore Usually a useful metallic mineral that can be mined at a profit. The term is also applied to certain nonmetallic minerals such as fluorite and sulfur.

Pegmatite A very coarse-grained igneous rock (typically granite) commonly found as a dike associated with a large mass of plutonic rock that has smaller crystals. Crystallization in a water-rich environment is believed to be responsible for the very large crystals.

Placer A deposit formed when heavy minerals are mechanically concentrated by currents, most commonly streams and waves.

Placers are sources of gold, tin, platinum, diamonds, and other valuable minerals.

Renewable resource A resource that is virtually inexhaustible or that can be replenished over relatively short time spans.

Reserve Already identified deposits from which minerals can be extracted profitably.

Reservoir rock The porous, permeable portion of an oil trap that yields oil and gas.

Secondary enrichment The concentration of minor amounts of metals that are scattered through unweathered rock into economically valuable concentrations by weathering processes.

Vein deposit A mineral that fills a fracture or fault in a host rock. Such deposits have a sheetlike, or tabular, form.

Metric and English Units Compared

Units

1 kilometer (km) = 1000 meters (m)
1 meter (m) = 100 centimeters (cm)
1 centimeter (cm) = 0.39 inch (in.)
1 mile (mi) = 5280 feet (ft)
1 foot (ft) = 12 inches (in.)
1 inch (in.) = 2.54 centimeters (cm)
1 square mile (mi^2) = 640 acres (a)
1 kilogram (kg) = 1000 grams (g)
1 pound (lb) = 16 ounces (oz)
1 fathom = 6 feet (ft)

Conversions

When you want
to convert: multiply by: to find:

Length

inches	2.54	centimeters
centimeters	0.39	inches
feet	0.30	meters
meters	3.28	feet
yards	0.91	meters
meters	1.09	yards
miles	1.61	kilometers
kilometers	0.62	miles

Area

square inches	6.45	square centimeters
square centimeters	0.15	square inches
square feet	0.09	square meters
square meters	10.76	square feet
square miles	2.59	square kilometers
square kilometers	0.39	square miles

Volume

cubic inches	16.38	cubic centimeters
cubic centimeters	0.06	cubic inches
cubic feet	0.028	cubic meters
cubic meters	35.3	cubic feet
cubic miles	4.17	cubic kilometers
cubic kilometers	0.24	cubic miles
liters	1.06	quarts
liters	0.26	gallons
gallons	3.78	liters

Masses and Weights

ounces	28.35	grams
grams	0.035	ounces
pounds	0.45	kilograms
kilograms	2.205	pounds

Temperature

When you want to convert degrees Fahrenheit (°F) to degrees Celsius (°C), subtract 32 degrees and divide by 1.8.

When you want to convert degrees Celsius (°C) to degrees Fahrenheit (°F), multiply by 1.8 and add 32 degrees.

When you want to convert degrees Celsius (°C) to Kelvins (K), delete the degree symbol and add 273. When you want to convert Kelvins (K) to degrees Celsius (°C), add the degree symbol and subtract 273.

FIGURE 1 A comparison of Fahrenheit and Celsius temperature scales.

Index

864

868